D1198868

HOW THINGS WORK

HOW THINGS WORK

IV

ILLUSTRATIONS RESEARCHED BY
ROGER JEAN SÉGALAT

Edito-Service S.A., Geneva, Publishers

13 047 04 R

CONTENTS

HOW THINGS WORK

COLOR TELEVISION

Color television, like color printing and some systems of color photography, is based on the mixing of three primary colors (red, green and blue) on the additive principle. So-called complementary colors are produced by mixing the primary colors in pairs: yellow or ocher (by mixing red and green), magenta (red and blue) and cyan (green and blue). When all three primary colors are mixed, the resulting color is white.

The terms "hue" and "saturation" are employed with reference to colors: "hue" denotes the essential color, while "saturation" signifies its dilution with white light. Fig. 1 represents the so-called color triangle in a form known as the CIE chromaticity diagram. The three corners of the triangle correspond to the three primaries—supersaturated green (top), supersaturated blue (bottom left), and supersaturated red (bottom right). The colored area of the diagram comprises all colors actually occurring in nature, including the colors of the spectrum. At *R* all the light is red and is therefore said to be saturated. On moving toward *W* in the diagram, white light is added to the red, and its color is said to be desaturated (but its hue remains unchanged); at *W* there is full desaturation—i.e., the color is white. Desaturated colors are called pastel colors or pale shades.

Applying the additive color-mixing principle, the simplest form of color television is represented by what is known as the simultaneous system, in which three pictures (red, green and blue) are transmitted simultaneously, as distinct from the sequential system, in which the pictures are transmitted one color at a time in rapid sequence.

(more)

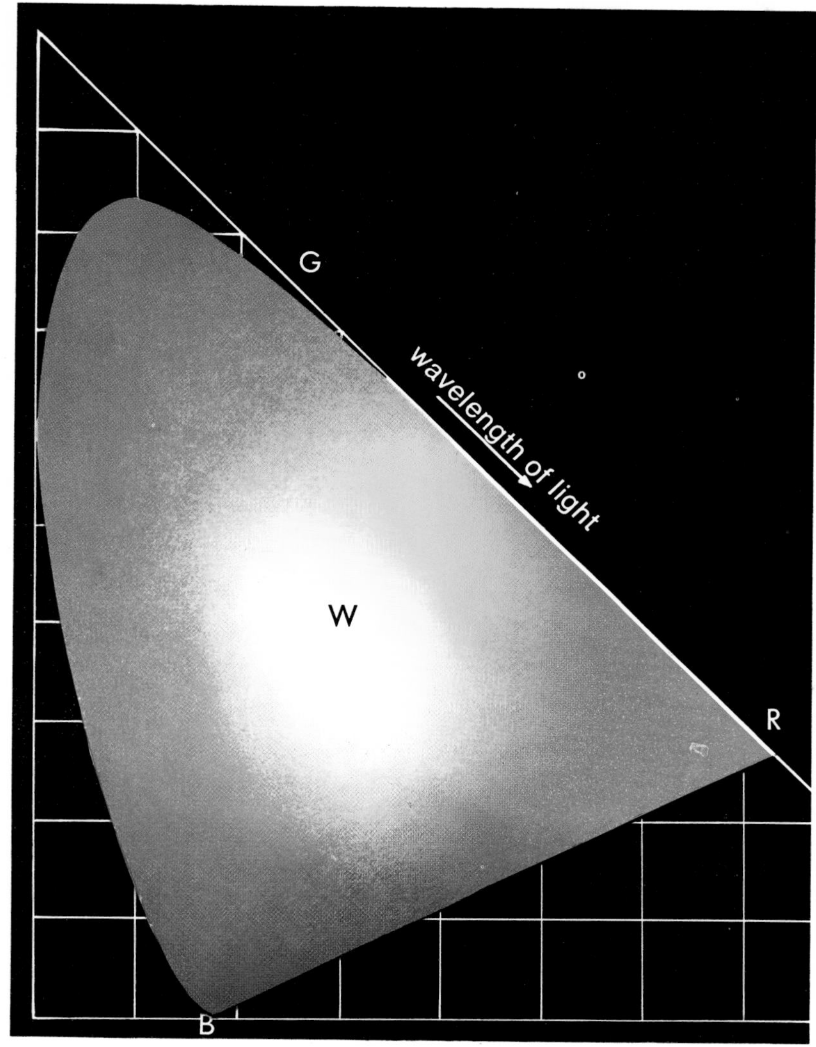

FIG. 1

In the simultaneous arrangement shown schematically in Fig. 2 the camera comprises three tubes (e.g., image orthicon tubes; see Vol. I, page 146). By means of a beam-splitting device (a system of mirrors and color filters), the first tube forms a red image (*R*), the second forms a green image (*G*), and the third forms a blue image (*B*). The three camera tubes have identical scanning patterns, so that the picture signals they produce are identical, except that they differ in color. In the receiver the primary color signals E_R, E_G and E_B are simultaneously fed to three color picture tubes and thus converted back into three separate color images (red, green and blue). These are superimposed optically by means of mirrors, so that the viewer sees them as one composite picture in which the correct colors are obtained by addition of the three primary colors. The great drawback of this system is the large band-width required for the simultaneous transmission of the three color signals.

The three main color television systems in present-day regular use are the NTSC system (developed in the U.S.A. by the National Television System Committee and first demonstrated in 1953), the SECAM system (developed in France, 1958), and the PAL system (a German development of the NTSC system, 1961, now used also in Britain). The basic principles are shared by all three systems, the only major difference being in the manner in which the chrominance signals are transmitted.

In the NTSC system the primary color signals E_R, E_G and E_B are converted by a device called a color coder into a "luminance" (i.e., brightness or brilliance) signal E_Y and two "chrominance" signals. Chrominance comprises hue and saturation as its two component characteristics. The luminance signal gives no information about the color of the picture; it is a monochrome signal which can be received by an ordinary monochrome (black and white) receiver. It is this separation of the color information from the luminance information that is essential to a so-called "compatible" color television system, i.e., one which transmits signals that can also be satisfactorily received by existing monochrome receivers.

The luminance signal is subtracted from the primary color signals, and the color-difference signals thus obtained are further combined, in the transmitter, to produce two signals *I* and *Q* which serve to modulate the chrominance subcarrier signal. This signal is amplitude-modulated in accordance with the saturation values and phase-modulated in accordance with the hues. The luminance and chrominance components are combined to form the overall color picture signal, which is transmitted. The picture signal wave is a composite wave in which the chrominance wave is superimposed upon part of the luminance wave.

(more)

FIG. 2
SIMULTANEOUS SYSTEM OF COLOR TELEVISION

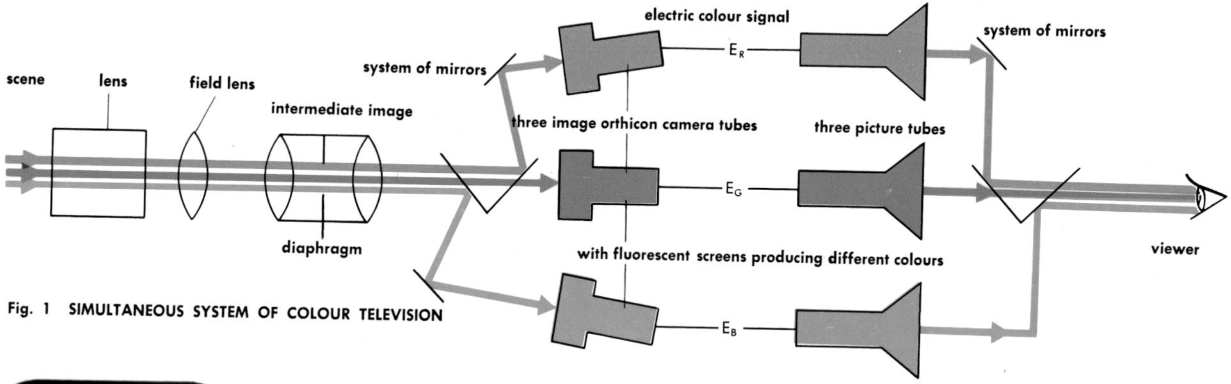

scene
lens
field lens
intermediate image
diaphragm
system of mirrors
electric colour signal
three image orthicon camera tubes
with fluorescent screens producing different colours
E_R
E_G
E_B
three picture tubes
system of mirrors
viewer

Fig. 1 SIMULTANEOUS SYSTEM OF COLOUR TELEVISION

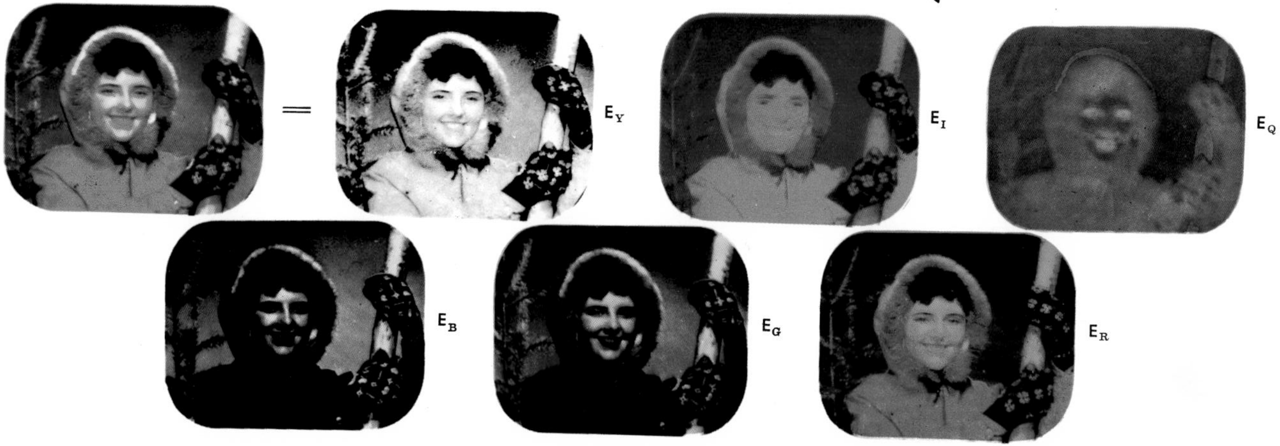

=
E_Y
E_I
E_Q
E_B
E_G
E_R

The primary color signals, which have been converted into luminance and chrominance components at the transmitter, have to be reconverted into primary color signals before they can be applied to the color picture tube. Instead of using three separate picture tubes, as envisaged in the simultaneous system, the NTSC and the other two modern systems use only one tube, called a shadow-mask tube or tricolor tube. This contains three electron guns; these guns produce three separate electron beams, which move simultaneously in the scanning pattern over the viewing screen and produce a red, a green and a blue image respectively. The screen is covered with three separate sets of uniformly distributed tiny phosphor dots. The dots of each of these three sets glow in a different color when struck by an electron beam. Electrons discharged by the "red" gun, i.e., the gun controlled by the red primary color signal, impinge only on the red-glowing phosphor dots and are prevented from impinging on the green- and blue-glowing dots by the shadow mask, which is a metal sheet containing a large number of tiny holes, each of which is accurately aligned with the different colored phosphor dots on the screen. Similarly, the electrons from the other two guns fall only on the blue and the green dots respectively. In this way three separate color images are formed simultaneously on the screen. The dots producing the three colors are so small and so close together that the eye does not see them as separate points of light, but forms an overall impression of continuous color. See Fig. 3.

The color receiver contains a tuner and intermediate frequency amplifiers Color reproduction is divided into luminance and chrominance functions. A video detector applies the luminance component, after amplification, to all three electron guns of the picture tube. The inverse operations of the addition and subtraction circuits at the transmitter are performed by appropriate circuits in the receiver. In this way three color-difference signals are obtained (the difference between the luminance signal and the primary color signals), which are applied to the respective electron guns in addition to the luminance signal. The net control signal applied to each gun conforms to the primary color signal coming from the corresponding tube in the camera.

The modern shadow-mask tube in the color television receiver has the phosphor dots applied directly to the curved glass front of the tube (in the earlier tubes the dots were on a flat glass plate inside the tube, as in Fig. 3). The shadow mask of a 25-inch tube has about 440,000 holes, and three times that number of dots on the screen. The principle of the tube is simple, but its actual operation is complex. Various adjustments are necessary to compensate for inevitable inaccuracies and distortions, particularly convergence adjustments and purity adjustments.

(more)

Fig. 3 SHADOW-MASK COLOUR TELEVISION TUBE

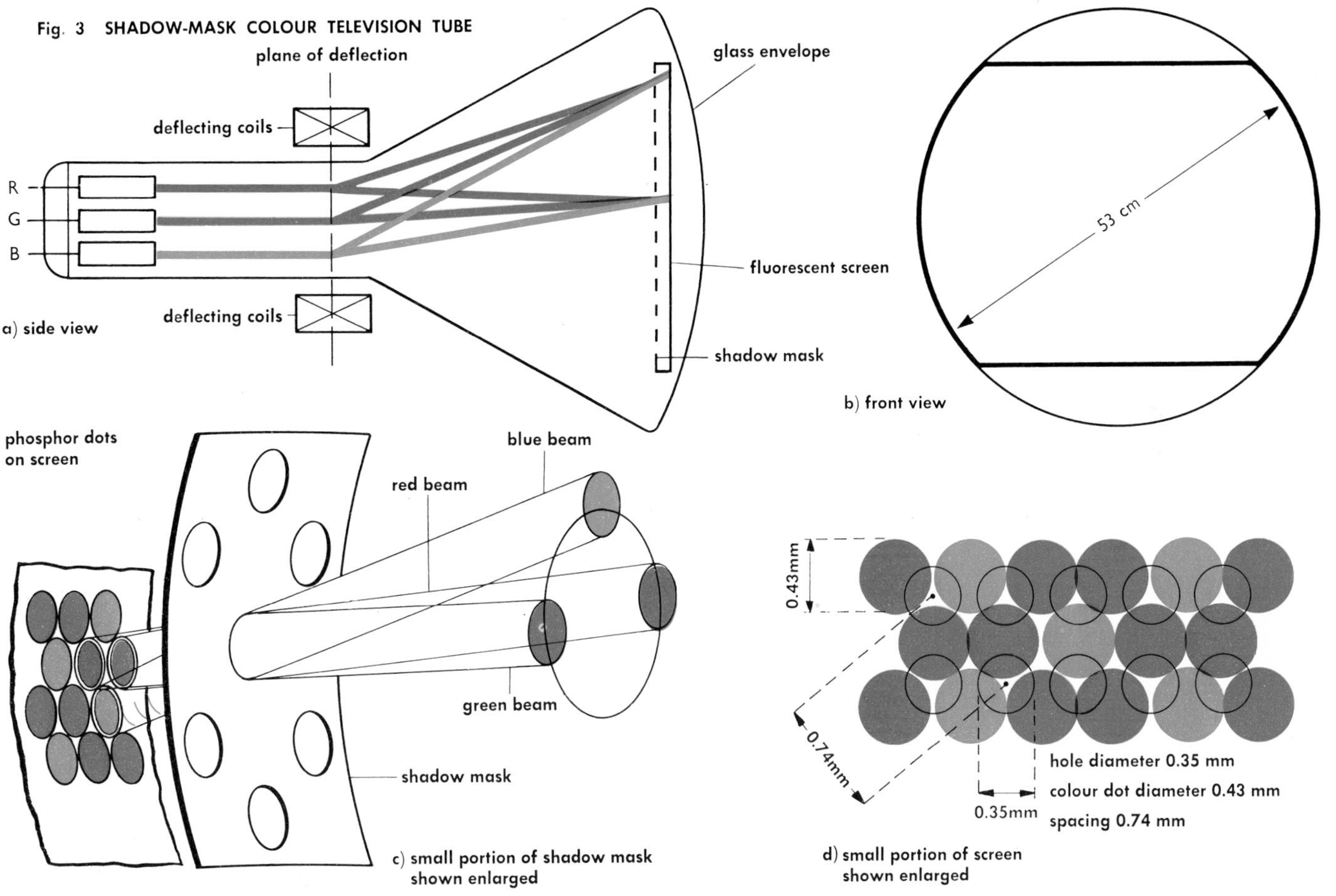

The type of color television camera at present in extensive use has three image orthicon tubes, the scene being split up by means of special mirrors (dichroic mirrors) into red, green and blue components (see Fig. 2). Other three-tube cameras have so-called plumbicon tubes; vidicon tubes are sometimes also used for the purpose (see Vol. I, page 146).

As already mentioned, the three main modern color systems differ in the manner in which the two chrominance signals are transmitted on a single subcarrier (i.e., a carrier wave which is applied as a modulating wave to another carrier). In the NTSC system the two signals are transmitted on the subcarrier by using a special modulating system (quadrature modulation). In the PAL system the same principle is applied, except that one of the chrominance signals is reversed on alternate lines (hence the name "phase alternation, line"). On the other hand, in the SECAM system the chrominance signals are transmitted sequentially, one at a time.

The subcarrier in the NTSC system is modulated by the I and Q chrominance signals, these being respectively situated 33 degrees ahead of the $E_R - E_Y$ axis and the $E_B - E_Y$ axis in the vector diagram. In the PAL system this modulation is performed by the so-called V and U signals, whose vectors correspond in direction to the two above-mentioned axes respectively. These are shown in Fig. 4, where the colors of the color triangle are represented in a circular diagram, together with subcarrier vectors for various colors; "burst" denotes the burst signal, which is the transmitted synchronizing signal which controls the phase and frequency of the color oscillator in the receiver. The V and U chrominance signals are used to modulate two subcarriers of the same frequency, but 90 degrees out of phase, i.e., quadrature modulation, just as in the NTSC system, except that the V signal is reversed on alternate lines. The basic reason for adopting this complication is that it reduces certain errors and improves the performance.

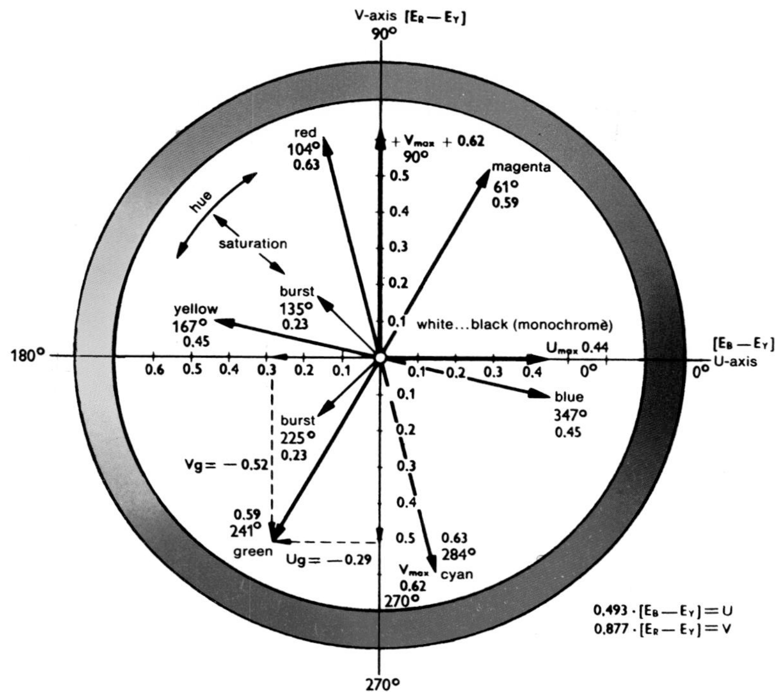

FIG. 4 COLOR VECTORS FOR PAL SYSTEM

CARTOGRAPHY

Cartography, the art and science of map making, had its origins in ancient times. Maps are an important means of communicating information concerning angles, distances, areas and directions. They are used for a wide range of purposes: as aids for sea or air navigation (charts); for military, scientific, technical, agricultural, educational, commercial and administrative purposes (e.g., cadastral maps of land-holdings, etc.); for local and regional planning and development; for motoring and tourism; etc. A very important requirement, besides accuracy, is that the map should be clearly legible. To help achieve this, colors are generally used. Present-day methods of cartographic design and reproduction enable modern maps to be given a high degree of clarity and precision.

The first consideration in the compilation of any map is the purpose for which

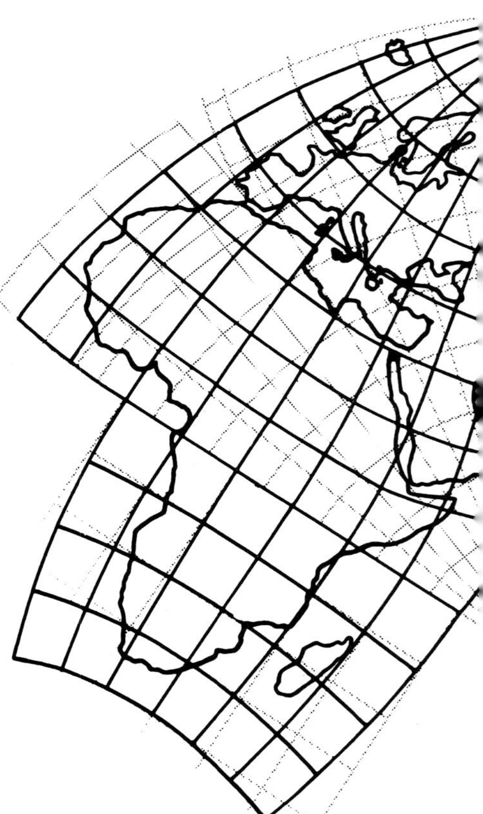

Europe, Africa, Asia and Australia represented on a so-called interrupted projection (a compromise projection)

it is to be used. A suitable map projection must be chosen, depending on whether the map will have to show only a small part of the earth's surface, a relatively large area such as a country or indeed a continent, or the whole surface of the earth. It will to some extent depend also on whether the map must fulfill geographical, navigational or traffic engineering requirements. Many different projections and variants thereof have been developed. The basic problem arises from the need for mapping the features of a spherically curved surface (the terrestrial sphere) upon a plane (a flat map). It is impossible to make this transformation without modifying the geometric relationships in some manner. However, there are a great many possibilities of transformation that can retain one or more of the spherical relationships. The actual process of transformation is called "projection."

(more)

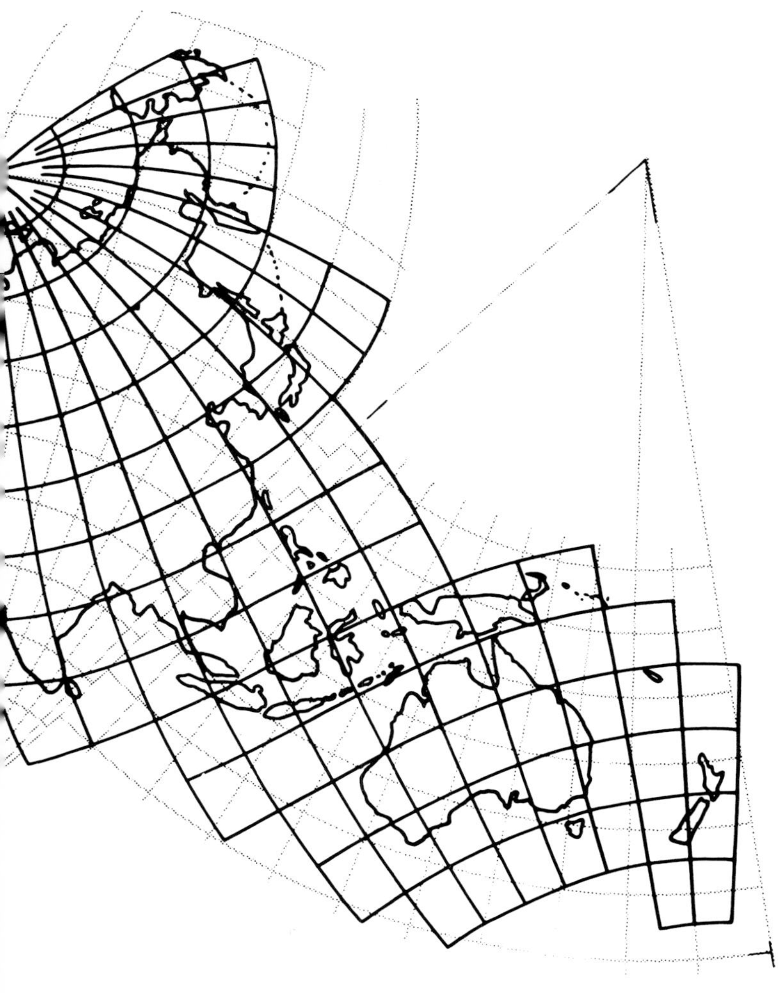

Cartography (continued)

When the projection has been decided, the meridians and parallels of latitude are constructed (this system of lines is called the map graticule). A small-scale map has to be compiled from data given on large-scale survey maps of the region concerned. These basic data are coastlines, rivers, lakes and political boundaries, which have to be transferred to the map which is being compiled. When these data have been drawn in, the cartographer has, as it were, a skeleton on which to hang the other

Contour lines of a mountainous region

details. Clear representation of relief features (mountains, valleys, etc.) is important on certain maps. The most important method is by contouring, i.e., by drawing contour lines (or contours), which each have a constant elevation above sea level. If the vertical contour interval is small enough, so that the contours are sufficiently close together, they will express the relief character of the terrain (slopes, mountain peaks, plateaus, plains, etc.). When sufficient contours and information concerning the terrain features are available, the technique known as shading may be applied. This gives a kind of "plastic" (three-dimensional) effect, so that the map gives the

The same region as above, with shading

impression of a topographic model of the landscape. Oblique shading of hills and mountains is usually based on the assumption that the incident light is inclined at 45 degrees and comes from the northwesterly direction. Features of the sea or ocean bed can similarly be represented by depth contour lines.

Depth-contour lines of the ocean bed

Another commonly employed method of relief representation is by means of hypsometric coloring (also known as altitude tinting or layer tinting): a range of different colors is used to represent different zones of elevation, which can thus be easily visualized. Conventionally, low land is colored green, followed by shades of buff or yellow, and ranging to dark brown (and sometimes red or purple) for high altitudes.

Before a map can be reproduced for publication, it must be redrawn in finished form. Freehand lettering has now largely been superseded by other techniques, especially stick-up (or preprinted) lettering: the names are printed, cut out, and stuck in position on the map. Another and more recent method which is coming into wider use is photolettering. In multicolor map reproduction the problem of register (precise fit of individual drawings which have to be superimposed) has largely been solved by the introduction of synthetic plastics which are free from shrinkage effects and generally retain their shape better than does paper.

Most maps are printed by either letterpress or lithography (cf. Vol. II, pp. 124 and 130), the latter process being used more particularly for large maps. The basic steps are: photographing the original drawing; processing the negative; making the plate; presswork. Printing plates for lithography and letterpress printing are made of various metals or of plastics. Presswork involves placing the completed plate on the press, inking, and feeding the paper through the press. The reproduction of maps in color differs from black reproduction only in that different colored inks are used. Each separate ink requires a separate printing plate, so that all the steps in the process have to be repeated each time, thus greatly increasing the cost. This is more particularly true of the "flat color" reproduction process, which is most often employed. Alternatively, "process color" may be used in which the map is reproduced from a single color drawing by the four-color process in essentially the same way as color photographs and painted art work are reproduced in popular magazines (see Vol. I, page 196). On the other hand, the flat color process requires a number of separate drawings: a number of line copies of the map are made. On these copies

(more)

the cartographer makes separate finished drawings in black for each solid printing color to be used. A color guide for background tints is provided by him for the printer's information. A wide variety of tints can be produced in the plate-making and printing processes. The accompanying illustrations show the eight successive

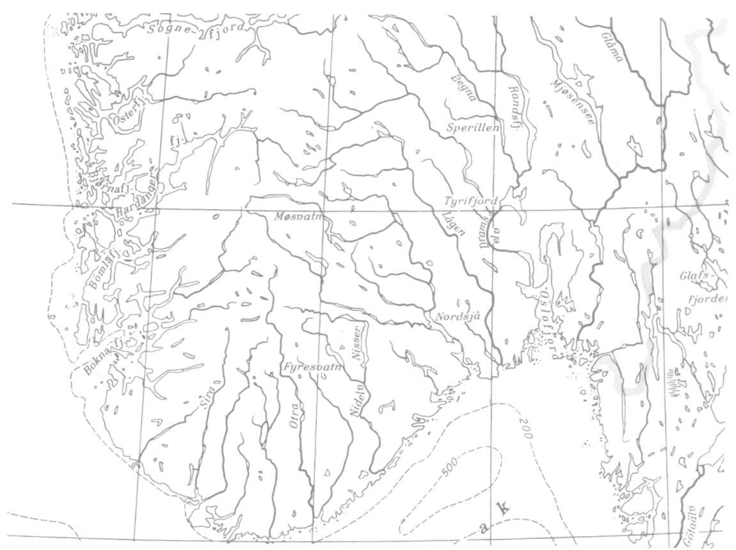

Coastline, rivers and lakes

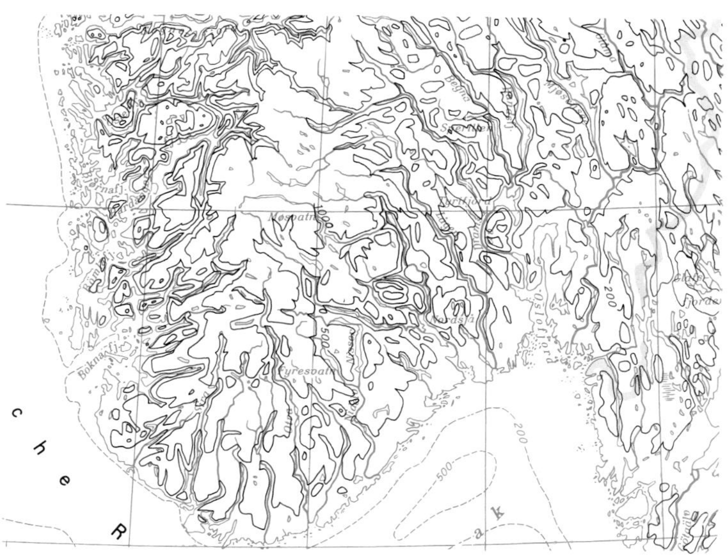

Contour lines added

printing stages in the reproduction of a modern map on the scale of 1:5,000,000. Each stage (a separate printing plate) registers accurately on the preceding one, the finished map being produced in one continuous operation on a multiple-color press.

On small-scale maps much topographical and physical detail has to be omitted.

(more)

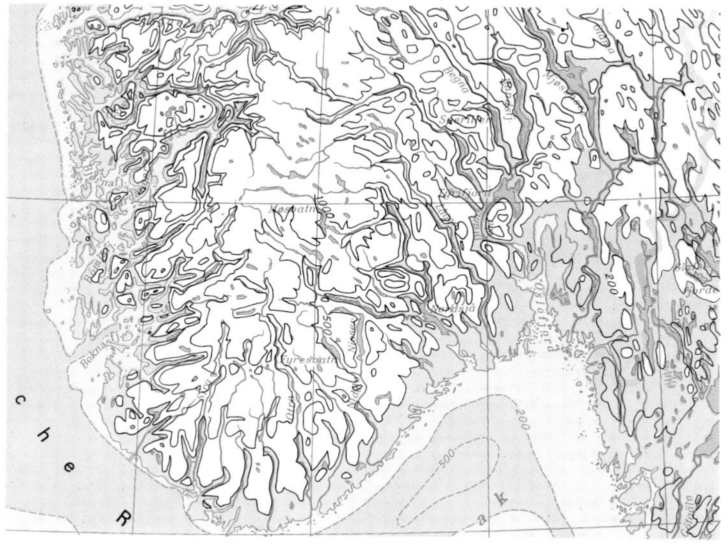

Light-blue tints are printed first

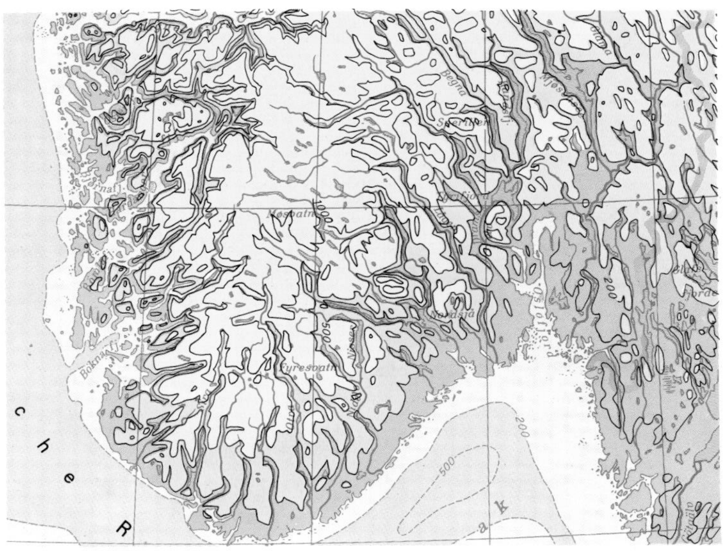

Next, yellow (where superimposed on blue it produces green)

Cartography (continued)

Those details which are retained must be suitably generalized. For instance, cities and towns are represented by artificial symbols (conventional signs, e.g., dots, circles, etc.). Different styles and sizes of lettering used for the names of towns may serve

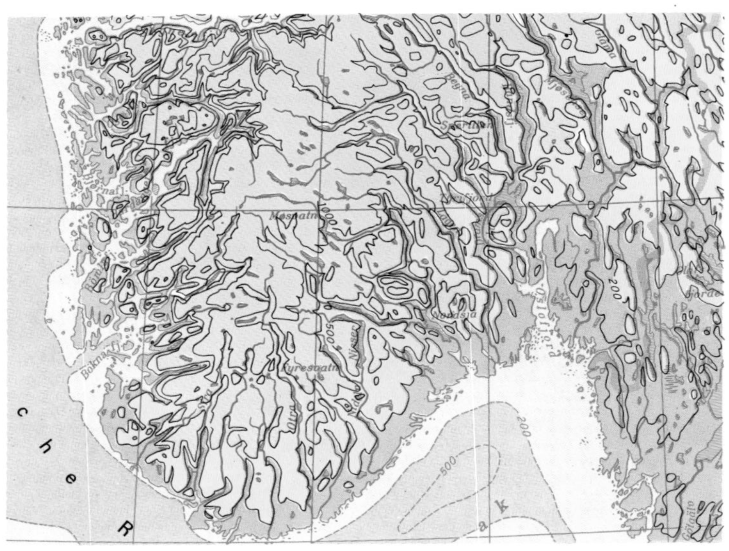

Brown altitude tinting is obtained by superimposing light red on yellow

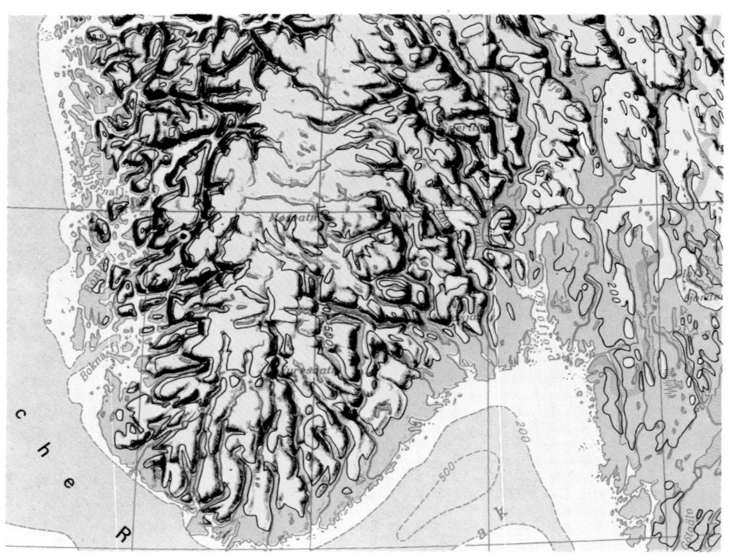

Shading of mountains added

as indications of size (number of inhabitants). An explanation of the symbols is usually given in the margins of the map or in the so-called map legend, together with the title and indication of scale.

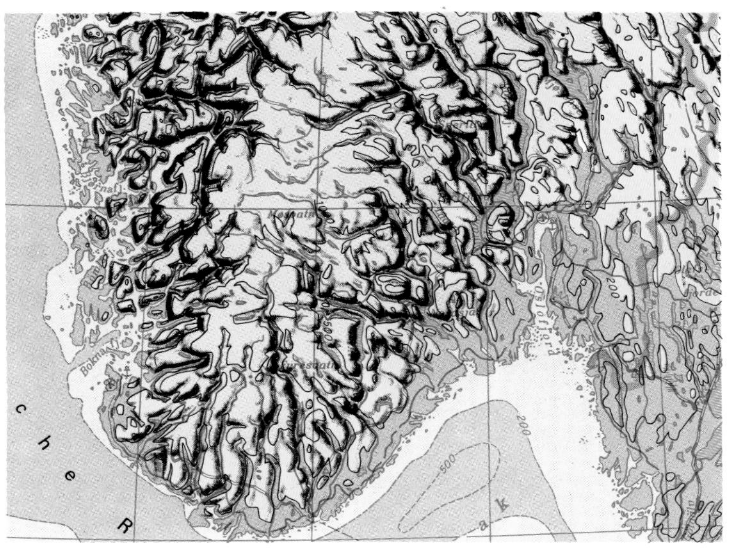

Railways and roads added in dark red

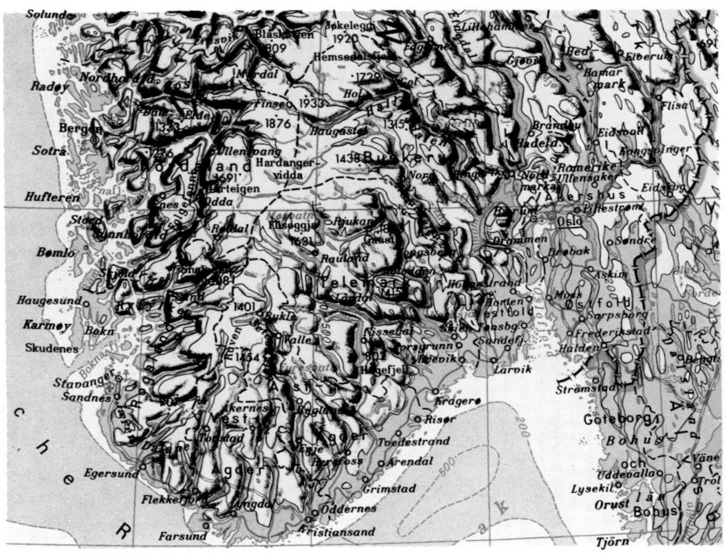

Finally, lettering and certain other details are printed in black

ENGINE TUNING

The term "tuning" applied to automobile engines refers to a number of measures all aimed at getting better performance, particularly in the case of standard production engines. Because of mass-production requirements, some of these measures requiring individual operations on the engines cannot be applied in the factory. Other measures consist in partly or wholly removing certain limitations on the engine speed and power output which have deliberately been embodied in the engine by the manufacturer with a view to obtaining longer service life. The enhanced performance is attended with severer working conditions of the components, so that engine life is shortened. However, it is possible partly to offset this by suitable modifications to the cooling system and lubrication.

Increasing the cubic capacity:
Within limits, an increase in the cubic capacity of the cylinders is a fairly simple technical matter (cf. Vol. III, p. 280). There are two ways of doing this:

1. Increasing the cylinder bore. This procedure, known as "overboring," is practicable only if pistons of appropriately larger diameter are obtainable. If the cylinder wall is thick enough to permit overboring beyond the maximum piston diameter available from the engine manufacturer, it will be necessary to obtain or make pistons specially. Many automobile manufacturers can, however, supply suitably larger pistons, which are normally used in a higher-powered type of engine than the one whose capacity is to be increased by overboring.
2. Increasing the piston stroke. This, on the other hand, is not always a technically easy modification. It will in any case be necessary to fit a new crankshaft with a larger crank radius. As a rule such a crankshaft is not readily obtainable. However, the Volkswagen 1200 cc engine, for example, can be fairly easily modified to near 1300 cc by fitting it with the crankshaft normally employed in the 1500 cc engine. For some types of engine it is indeed possible to obtain from components dealers the appropriate crankshaft for increasing the piston stroke. If such a crankshaft is not obtainable, however, it is still possible to achieve the desired result by obtaining a crankshaft forging and eccentrically grinding the crankpins, bearing in mind that the increase in stroke is equal to twice the eccentricity e (Figs. 1a and 1b).

(more)

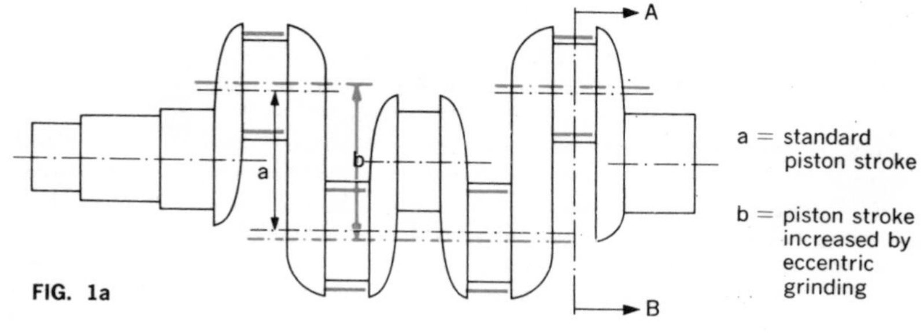

FIG. 1a

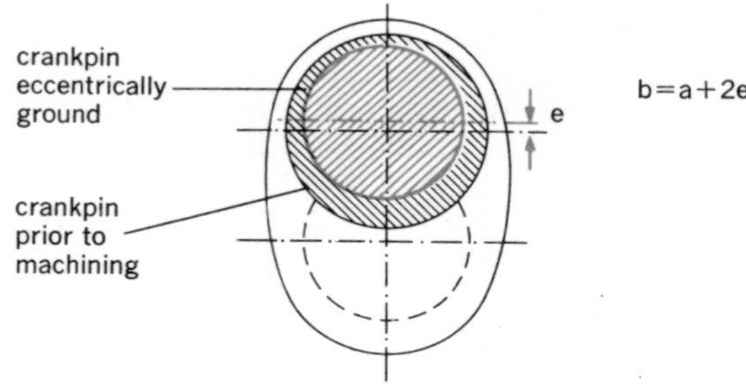

FIG. 1b section A–B

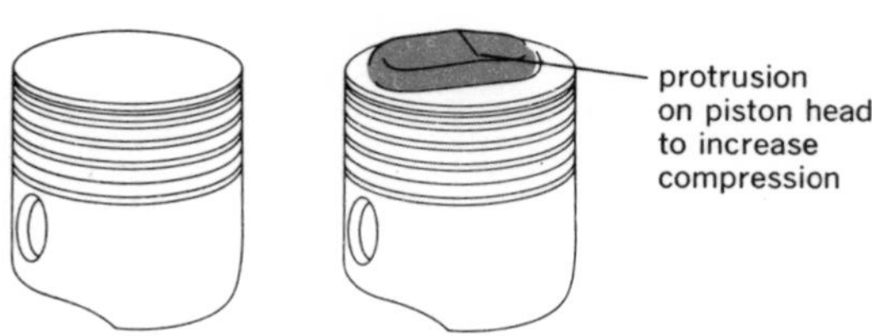

FIG. 2b

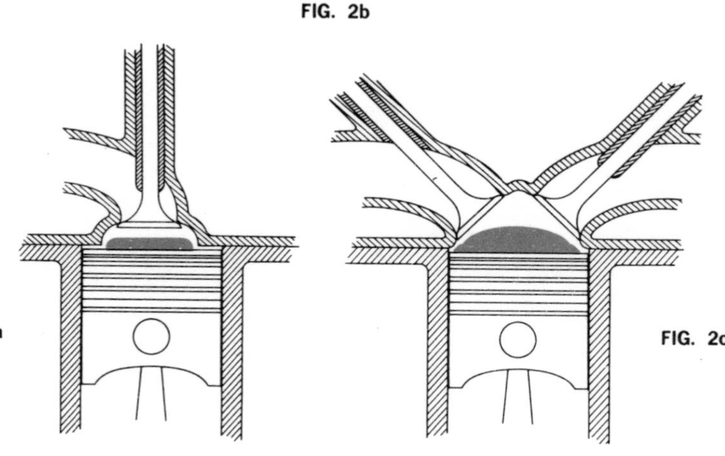
FIG. 2a

FIG. 2c

Increasing the mean effective pressure:

1. Increasing the compression. An increase in the compression ratio of an engine results in better fuel utilization and a higher mean effective pressure. A drawback is that the firing pressure is considerably increased as well, so that all the main moving parts of the engine are more severely loaded. Besides, detonation phenomena, associated with self-ignition of the combustion mixture, impose limits on the attainable increase in compression ratio, as explained on p. 282, Vol. III. According to formula (9) on that page, the compression ratio can be increased in two ways. In the first place, the piston-swept working volume of the cylinder (V_H) can be increased by either of the methods described on the preceding page. Secondly, the volume of the combustion chamber (V_B) may be reduced. Of course, these two measures can be applied in combination with each other. The most reliable method of reducing the volume of the combustion chamber is to employ pistons of special design of which the head protrudes into the combustion chamber at top dead center (see Figs. 2a and 2c, page 27). Many engine manufacturers and components dealers can supply pistons with specially shaped heads (Fig. 2b) for various makes of engines. Another possibility of reducing the combustion chamber consists in removing metal from the cylinder head at its contact surface with the cylinder block. However, care must be taken not to remove too much metal, as this could result in piercing of the water jacket, undue loss of structural rigidity, and excessive increase in compression (Fig. 1). Alternatively, the individual cylinder or the whole cylinder block can be reduced in height, for which purpose the cylinder head must be suitably grooved to receive the top of the cylinder (Fig. 2). Finally, another way to reduce combustion-chamber volume is by means of buildup welding on the inside.

(more)

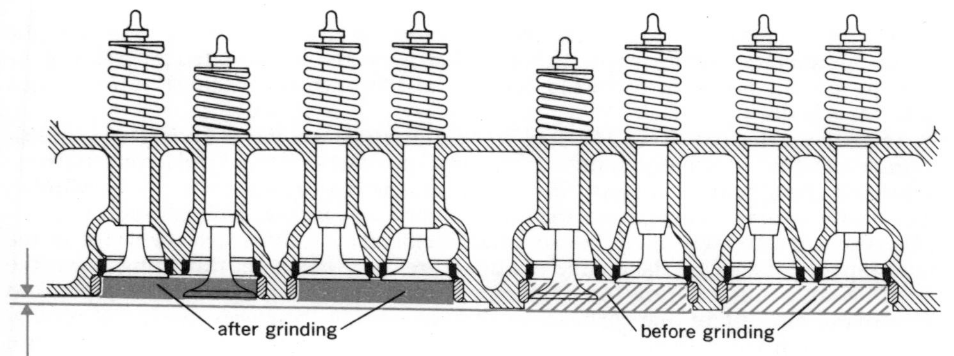
after grinding
before grinding

FIG. 1

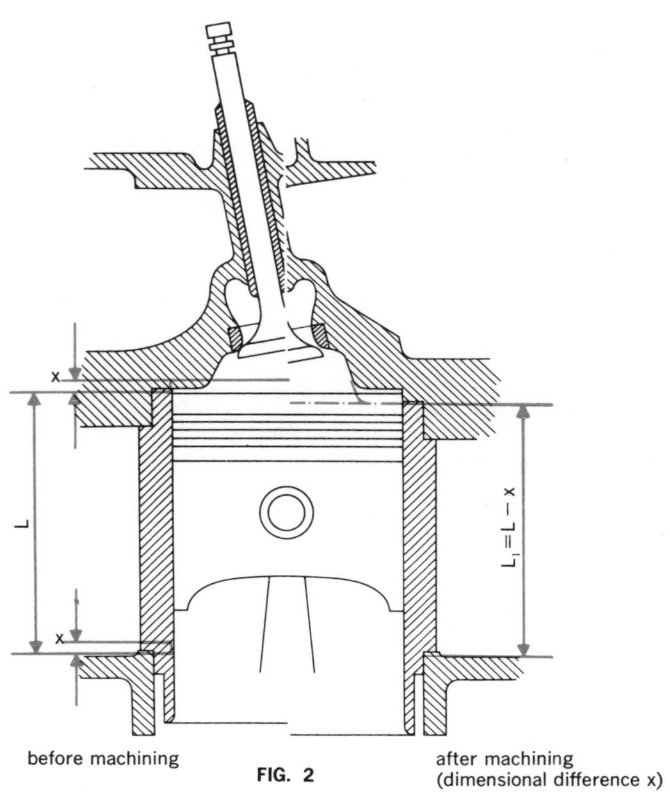
x
L
x
$L_1 = L - x$
before machining
after machining
(dimensional difference x)

FIG. 2

With all the measures so far described it is essential to determine the actual volume of the combustion chamber with the aid of kerosene and a graduated pipette (Fig. 1). The piston should be at top dead center and the inlet and exhaust valves closed when this is done.

2. Improving the gas flow. The fuel-and-air mixture for the cylinders of a multi-cylinder engine is usually supplied by only one carburetor. A relatively narrow, long and often bent or curved inlet pipe connects the carburetor to each cylinder. This shape is unfavorable, from the point of view of gas flow, as it causes throttling effects which adversely affect the volumetric efficiency. Quite often the shape of the inlet pipe is utilized by the engine manufacturer as a means of throttling down the gas flow and thus limiting the engine performance. Changing the inlet pipes and employing more than one carburetor often constitute the easiest means of tuning. It does not involve dismantling the engine. Multiple-carburetor assemblies are available for many engines from components dealers, so that in most cases the owner of the vehicle is spared the effort and cost of developing such a system for his engine. The greatest gain in performance is achieved when each cylinder is provided with its own individual carburetor. However, if the inlet duct is cast integrally with the cylinder head, it is not possible to do more than merely enlarge the opening to which the carburetor is connected. For this purpose, the cylinder head must be removed. The inlet opening can be enlarged as much as the wall thickness of the water passages will permit. Fig. 2 shows the increased inlet cross section in the cylinder head of a Fiat engine. The connection to the carburetor is formed by means of an adapter.

Fitting of the inlet pipes and carburetors should be done with care. The transitions from carburetor to inlet pipe and from the latter to the cylinder must not comprise any projecting edges or constrictions (e.g., the edges of gaskets) that will reduce the cross-sectional area of flow.

In a Volkswagen engine the inlet ducts of the two rows of cylinders are located far apart, with the carburetor midway between them. The gas-flow passages comprise bends and are quite long (Figs. 3a and 3b), besides being narrow (in order to throttle down the engine and thus limit its performance). To prevent condensation of gas vapor, the inlet pipe is heated (Fig. 3b). This heating lowers the volumetric efficiency of the engine, however, because the density of the combustion mixture is thereby reduced, so that the actual quantity (in terms of weight) drawn into the cylinders is reduced. Measures to improve the gas flow to the cylinders of a Volkswagen engine are therefore particularly rewarding in that they result in a marked increase in performance. Each pair of cylinders shares one inlet opening in the cylinder head, giving access to a forked inlet duct. For this reason it is not possible to fit more than two carburetors to such an engine (Fig. 4).

(more)

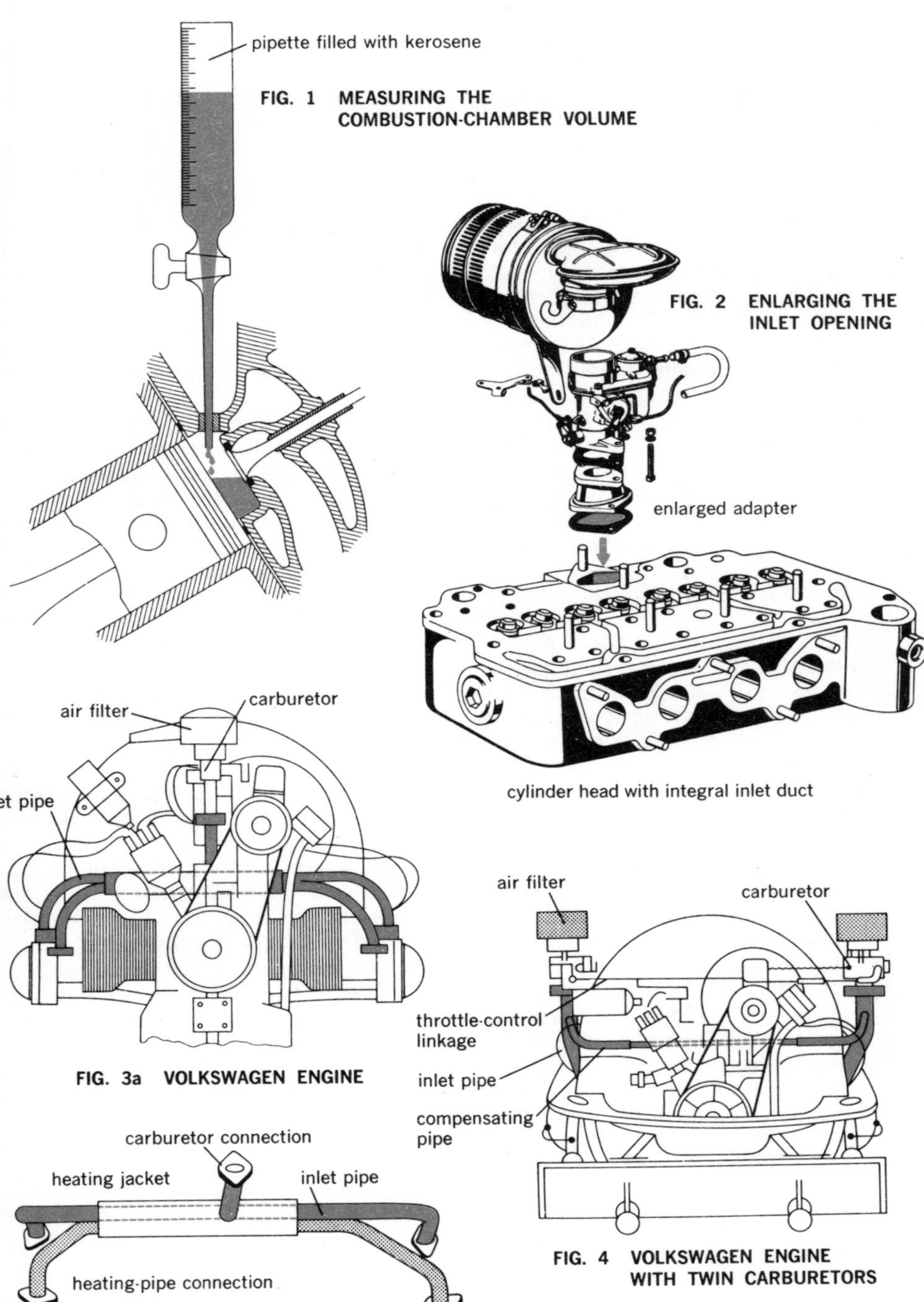

FIG. 1 MEASURING THE COMBUSTION-CHAMBER VOLUME

FIG. 2 ENLARGING THE INLET OPENING

FIG. 3a VOLKSWAGEN ENGINE

FIG. 3b INLET MANIFOLD OF VOLKSWAGEN ENGINE WITH INLET-PIPE HEATING SYSTEM

FIG. 4 VOLKSWAGEN ENGINE WITH TWIN CARBURETORS

Modifying the cylinder head constitutes a further important measure for improving the gas intake and exhaust and thus obtaining better engine performance. In particular, the use of larger valves and seatings and enlargement of the ports are important tuning operations.

First of all, the desired larger valve size must be decided. If the inlet valve and the exhaust valve are of equal or nearly equal size, then only the inlet valve need be enlarged. For equal valve lift, the diameter of the outlet valve can be up to 15% smaller than that of the inlet valve (p. 288, Vol. III). The maximum size of the inlet valve will depend on the available space for accommodating the valve in the cylinder head (Figs. 1a and 1b). The wall thickness of the cylinder head around the valve seat should be sufficient to ensure that the valve-seat rings will not work loose in operation. A further limiting factor with regard to valve size arises if it is desired that the engine have adequate flexibility of performance in the middle speed range (p. 292, Vol. III). When new larger valve-seat rings have been shrink-fitted at the inlet ports, the work of shaping and enlarging the ports and ducts can start from there (these operations are known as "porting"). The tools required for this work are a flexible-shaft grinding machine and a selection of rotary files and grinding wheels. The inlet ports must be given very careful treatment. All constrictions and projections should be removed as far as possible (see Fig. 1a). It is often possible to enlarge the ducts accurately for a distance of a few centimeters from the carburetor with the aid of a drill fitted with a face-milling cutter or a reamer. The inlet-valve guide may be cut off level with the wall of the port, provided that accurate centering of the valve is still ensured. On the other hand, the outlet-valve guide should not be cut down (Fig. 1b), as that would impair heat conduction away from this valve, which becomes red-hot in operation. When the ducts and ports have been suitably shaped and enlarged by rough machining or grinding, they must be given a fine internal finish, preferably to a shining polish. Gas flow is improved by opening out the inlet port to a size only slightly smaller than the valve head (Fig. 2a as compared with Fig. 2b). This can be done by the use of a milling cutter with an angle of 75 degrees to enlarge the port, followed up with a cutter of 45 degrees to form the actual seat. The seat of the inlet valve should be made about 1.5 mm (0.06 in.) wide, while the outlet-valve seat should be 2 mm (0.08 in.) wide, this greater width being desirable to provide better dissipation of heat. Quite often the transition from valve stem to valve head can be machined to a more favorable shape from the viewpoint of gas flow. The edges should be rounded. Finally, the head should be polished in order to obviate any harmful notch effects (Fig. 3). This treatment is not to be recommended for exhaust valves, however; instead, valves faced with hard metal (stellite) should be fitted on the exhaust side (Fig. 4). For highly tuned engines it may be essential to employ sodium-filled hollow-stem exhaust valves (p. 302, Vol. III) to obtain satisfactory valve service life. The exhaust port should be shaped and enlarged to a gradual divergent shape from the valve seat (Fig. 5a). Abrupt increases in cross section of the duct must be avoided. If the duct is not correctly shaped, turbulence which impairs the gas flow will occur in it. It is not necessary to give the wall of the port and duct a very fine finish, however.

(more)

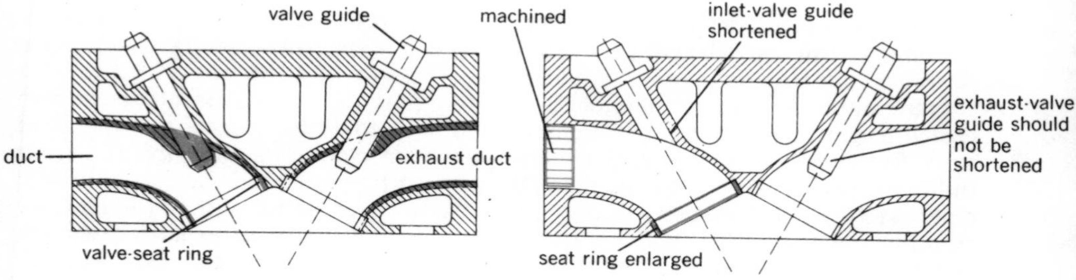

FIG. 1a CYLINDER HEAD BEFORE MACHINING

FIG. 1b CYLINDER HEAD AFTER ENLARGEMENT OF THE PORTS

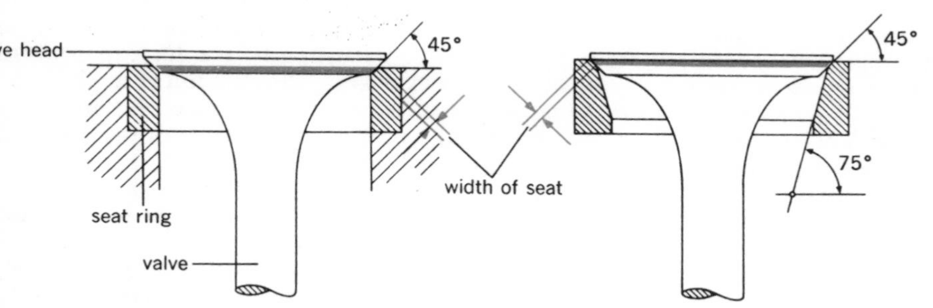

FIG. 2a VALVE SEAT IN A STANDARD ENGINE

FIG. 2b VALVE SEAT MODIFIED BY MACHINING

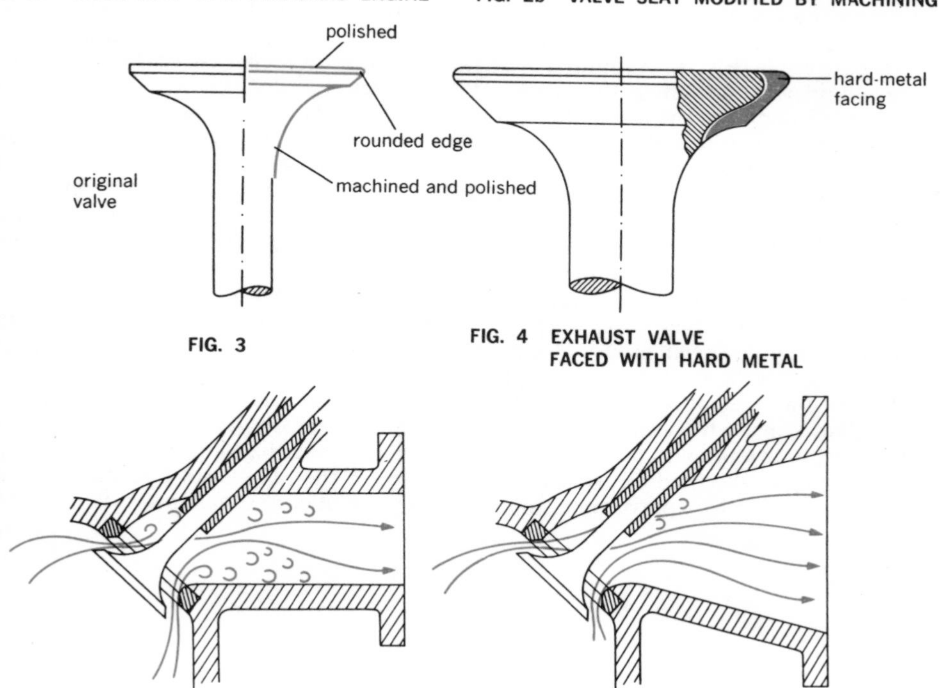

FIG. 3

FIG. 4 EXHAUST VALVE FACED WITH HARD METAL

FIG. 5a TURBULENCE IN EXHAUST DUCT

FIG. 5b EXHAUST DUCT ENLARGED TO GIVE GOOD FLOW CONDITIONS

Engine Tuning (continued)

The pipe connections to the inlet and to the exhaust side of the engine should be modified to suit the enlarged gas-flow passages. It is specially essential to achieve a clean, smooth transition at such connections (Figs. 1a and 1b).

Quite often the exhaust manifold is a casting that has an unfavorable shape with regard to gas flow. To improve the situation, it is advisable to fit a new manifold made from steel pipes, with each exhaust port connected to its own pipe. If there is sufficient space to accommodate them, the exhaust pipes should be left as individual pipes. Merging of the pipes will depend on the firing sequence of the cylinders: for example, the pipes from cylinders 1 and 4 are combined into one exhaust manifold, and those from cylinders 2 and 3 are combined into a second exhaust manifold. The two manifolds are continued separately to the exhaust muffler. For various cars the components industry supplies complete high-performance exhaust systems with special manifolds.

In addition to the measures already referred to, changing the valve lift and valve timing (p. 293, Vol. III) are further important means of improving the gas flow.

In engines whose valves are actuated through push rods, the lift can, within limits, be increased by modification of the rocker-arm transmission (Fig. 2). It is necessary to fit new rocker arms. A higher transmission ratio is obtained, for instance, when the Volkswagen 1200 cc engine is fitted with the rocker arms of the 1500 cc engine. When different rocker arms are used, it is important to check that there is still sufficient clearance between the valves and the piston head at top dead center. Increasing the valve lift is a worthwhile modification in a case where the lift is equal to less than a quarter of the inlet diameter.

An increase in the valve lift results in an increased cross-sectional area of the opening, so that the corresponding curve in the diagram is higher (red curve in Fig. 3). The valve timing is not thereby changed, however. It is hardly possible to change the timing effectively without fitting a different camshaft, though it is possible, for example, to increase the lift and increase the valve-opening period by grinding down the base circle (Fig. 4). Without any change in timing, a higher curve (Fig. 3) can also be obtained by flattening the profile of the tappet or the rocker arm. This measure is easy to apply, but is not suitable for flat mushroom-type tappets. Both measures have the disadvantage that they impose an additional load upon the valve mechanism because of the larger acceleration forces. For this reason it is better not to adopt such measures and, instead, to fit a special camshaft that gives a different valve timing and has larger cams producing a larger lift (Fig. 5). Such camshafts may be obtainable from engine manufacturers, who often supply sports and racing camshafts in addition to standard camshafts. The camshaft should be carefully selected for the desired purpose. The choice will always have to be a compromise between maximum obtainable power output and flexibility of performance in the lower and medium engine-speed ranges. A camshaft that improves the output at high speeds of rotation will, because of the greater valve overlap, give a lower volumetric efficiency and therefore a poorer power output at low and medium speeds than a standard camshaft. It thus reduces the operational flexibility of the engine; more frequent gear changing becomes necessary. On the other hand, measures to increase the output in the medium speed range will lower the maximum output. Extremes can be avoided by appropriate adjustment of the inlet-and-exhaust system.

(more)

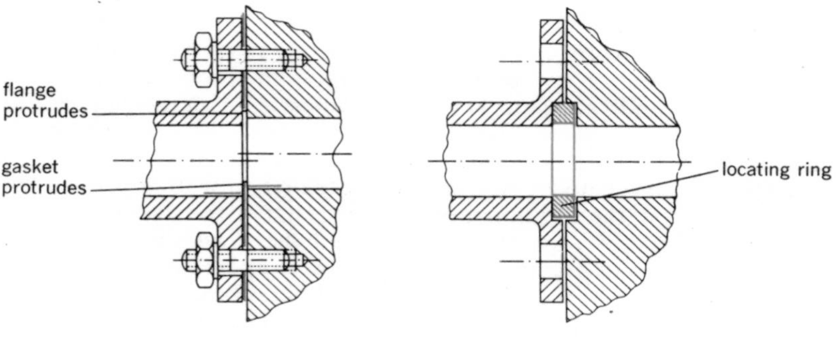

FIG. 1a POOR TRANSITION   FIG. 1b GOOD TRANSITION

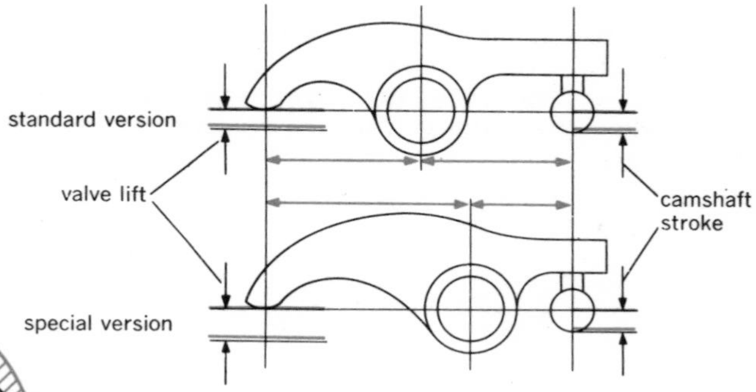

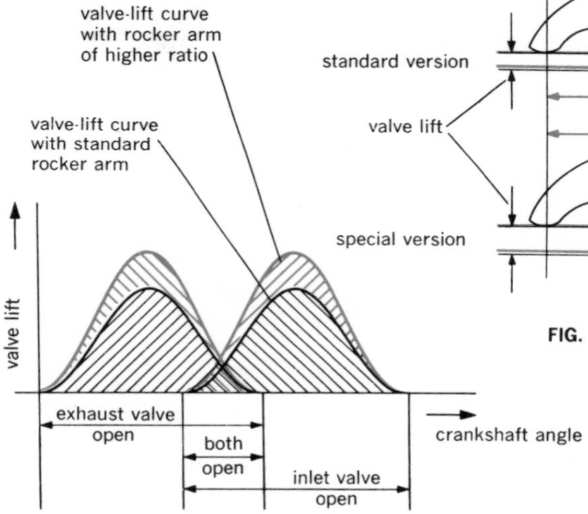

FIG. 3 VALVE-LIFT CURVE

FIG. 2 ROCKER ARMS WITH DIFFERENT RATIOS

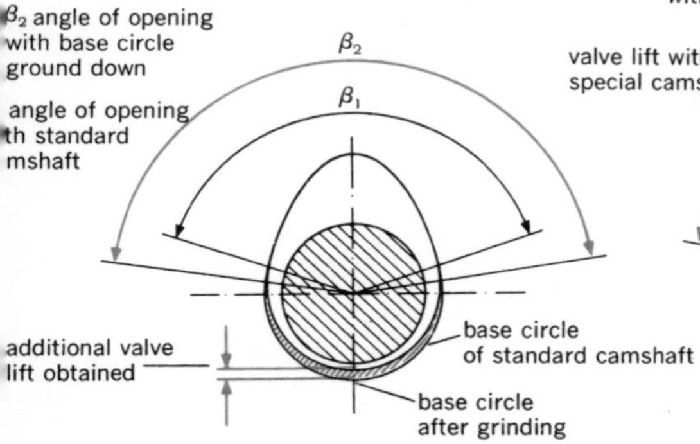

FIG. 4 CAMSHAFT MODIFIED TO INCREASE VALVE-OPENING PERIOD

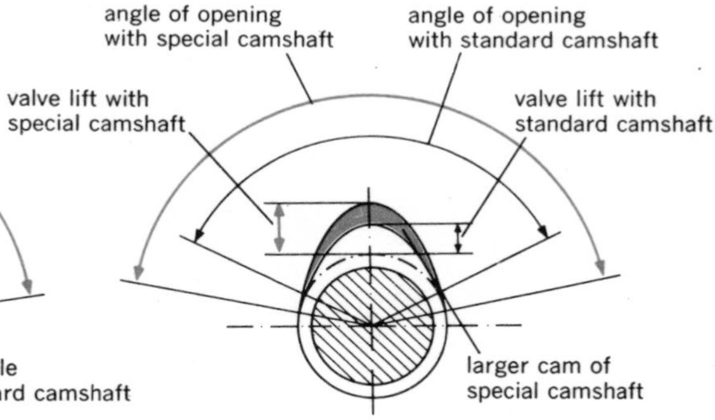

FIG. 5 SPECIAL CAMSHAFT

Engine Tuning (continued)

Increasing the speed of rotation:

In the internal-combustion engine, all reciprocating parts have to be accelerated from a momentarily stationary condition to maximum speed and then at once to be decelerated to a standstill again. The forces associated with this acceleration and deceleration exert quite severe loads upon the piston, the connecting rod, the camshaft and the bearings concerned and may cause damage to these parts.

1. Work on the valve mechanism. Acceleration of the reciprocating parts of the valve mechanism results from the rotational speed of the engine, the shape of the valve-lift curve (determined by the shape of the cams), and the magnitude of the valve lift (see page 35). In a new engine model with push-rod-operated valves, the mass of the valve mechanism can be reduced by suitable choice of materials for the moving parts concerned and by appropriate design. This can be achieved by the use of lighter materials (e.g., titanium, Fig. 1). On the other hand, reducing the weight of these severely stressed components in an existing engine by grinding or machining them down to smaller dimensions is inadmissible because of the increased risk of fracture and failure. It is possible to fit an existing engine with an overhead camshaft and thus dispense with tappets and push rods, so that the reciprocating masses are reduced (Fig. 2b as compared with Fig. 2a). This is a laborious and expensive modification, however, since it involves making a new cylinder head of appropriate design.

(more)

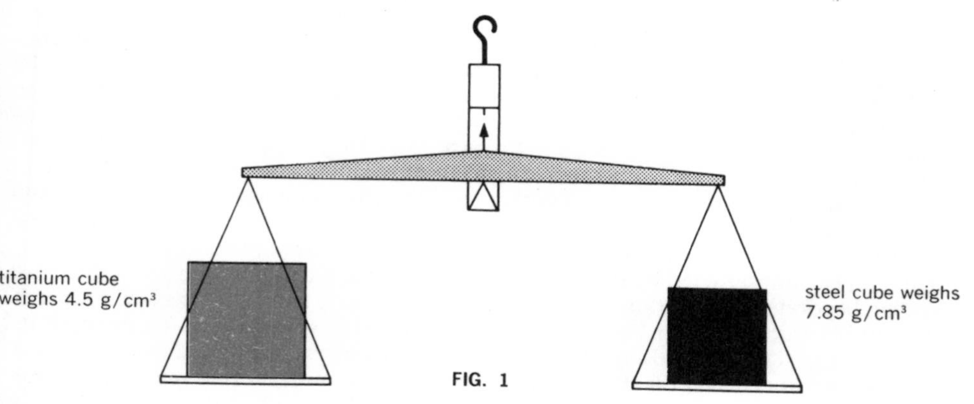

FIG. 1

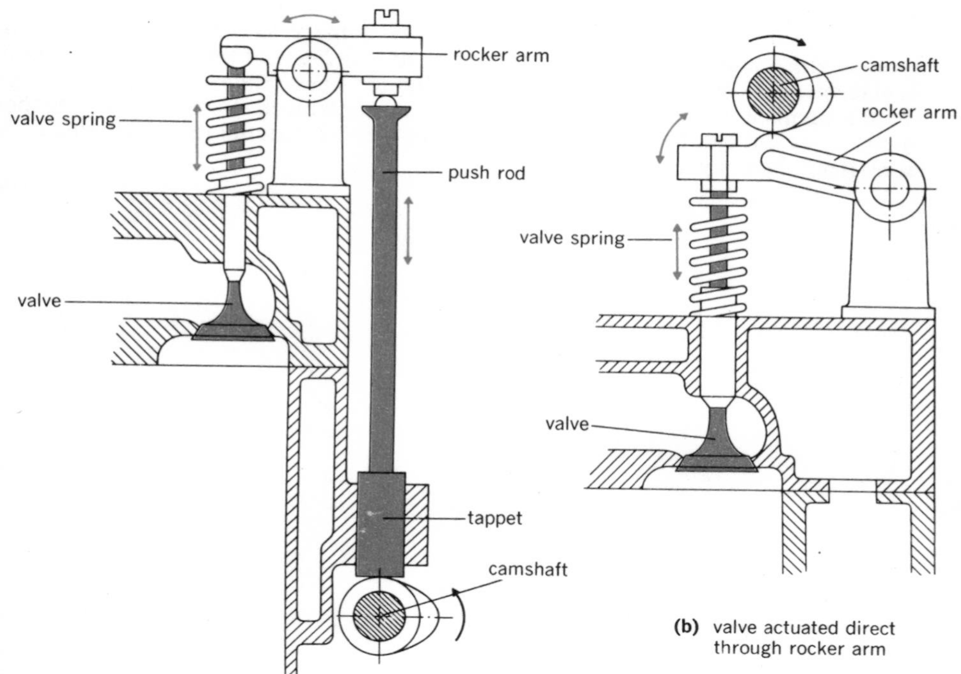

(a) valve actuated through tappet, push rod and rocker arm

(b) valve actuated direct through rocker arm

FIG. 2 VALVE AND CAMSHAFT ARRANGEMENTS

The maximum speed of rotation of an engine is limited by the throttling effect of the inlet-and-exhaust system (Vol. III, p. 288 et seq.) and by valve flutter due to the natural oscillation of the valves. A valve and its spring together constitute an oscillating system with a particular frequency of its own (its so-called natural frequency). When the engine is run up to high speeds, it may happen that the reciprocating movements of the valve come within the natural frequency range of this system. When this happens, the valve and spring tend to move independently of the motion imparted to them by the camshaft. The opening and closure of the valve now no longer conform to the correct timing, so that the power output of the engine decreases. This can be counteracted by steps taken to increase the natural frequency of the valve system beyond the speed range of the engine. This is fairly simple to achieve. A washer of suitable thickness can be inserted under the valve spring so as to increase its stiffness (Fig. 1). It should be checked that the coils of the spring are not in contact with one another when the maximum valve lift is attained. Another method consists in fitting a stiffer spring; or the natural frequency behavior may be improved by use of two or even three springs of different stiffness telescoped together (Fig. 2).

2. Work on the crank mechanism. The acceleration developed in the crank mechanism depends on the engine speed and the piston stroke. The total reciprocating mass is determined by the weight of the pistons, gudgeon pins and connecting rods. In order to reduce the forces that they exert upon the crankpins, it is necessary to reduce the weight of these reciprocating parts as far as possible. This must not be done by removing metal from the pistons and connecting rods, however, as this could result in fracture of the parts and serious damage to the engine. Very-high-speed engines should be fitted with forged pistons because of their greater strength. Replacement of steel connecting rods by lighter ones made of titanium brings about a significant reduction of the weight of the crank mechanism (Fig. 3). A further saving in weight can be effected by removal of surplus material (by machining on a lathe) from the gudgeon pin (Fig. 4).

(more)

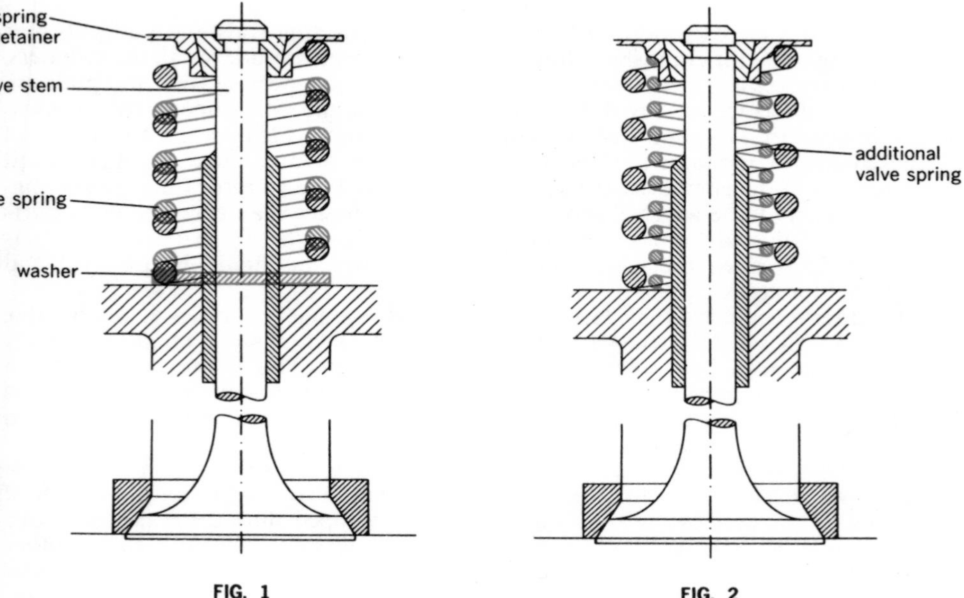

FIG. 1

FIG. 2

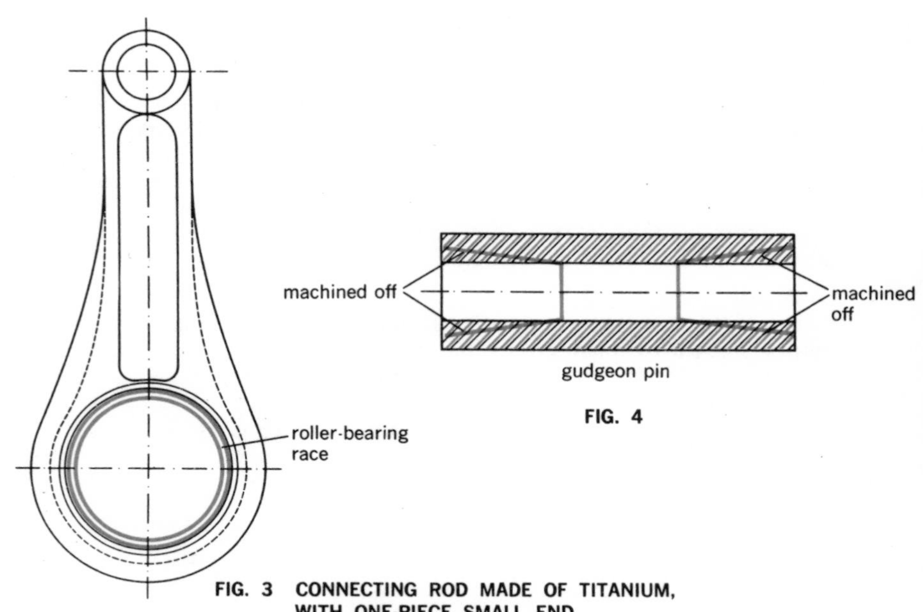

FIG. 4

FIG. 3 CONNECTING ROD MADE OF TITANIUM, WITH ONE-PIECE SMALL END

Engine Tuning (continued)

The inertia forces produced by the pistons, connecting rods and gudgeon pins and acting upon the crankshaft should be of the same magnitude for all the cylinders. For this reason it is necessary to weigh the pistons, connecting rods and gudgeon pins carefully (Fig. 1). Any differences in weight should be compensated, so as to ensure smooth, vibration-free running of the engine at high speeds and to avoid uneven stress conditions in the crankshaft. Where very large increases in the speed of rotation of the engine are desired, the rotating and the reciprocating connecting-rod parts should be weighed separately, and the weights of all corresponding parts should be adjusted to make them equal (Figs. 2a and 2b). To avoid notch effects that would weaken the connecting rods, their surfaces should be polished and inspected for cracks.

In order to improve their fatigue strength and running properties, it is advisable to subject all severely stressed components such as crankshaft, connecting rods, rockers, etc., to a heat treatment in a nitriding bath. This treatment consists in keeping the components immersed for about one hour in a bath of molten salts which give off nitrogen. After undergoing this treatment, the components require no further finishing operations before being fitted.

The flywheel mounted on the crankshaft accommodates the clutch mechanism and serves to absorb fluctuations in speed and thus even out the torque output of the engine. It receives the rotational impulse developed during the power stroke and ensures that the crankshaft continues to rotate smoothly through the other strokes. Obviously, this function of the flywheel is especially important in a single-cylinder engine. Accordingly, as there is a larger number of cylinders driving the shaft, the flywheel becomes relatively less important and its weight can be correspondingly reduced. A heavy flywheel prevents a rapid increase in rotational speed when the throttle is open, as its large mass also has to be accelerated. Faster acceleration can be obtained by removal of metal from the flywheel (by machining) to reduce its weight (Fig. 3). There will, however, be some sacrifice of smooth running in the low speed range.

After the foregoing operations have been carried out, the crankshaft—with the flywheel and clutch mounted on it—should be dynamically and statically balanced. Correction is made by addition or subtraction of weight at suitable points. When the shaft runs steadily, it is said to be in dynamic balance; it is then automatically in static balance also. Dynamic balancing is done with the aid of electronic machines. The engine can then be reassembled. Care should be taken to check and ensure that all moving parts rotate or slide easily and smoothly.

Other measures:
With a highly tuned engine, it is necessary to adapt the clutch to the increased power output. The thrust springs of the pressure plate should be replaced by more powerful ones (Fig. 4). If obtainable, it is advisable to fit a spring plate clutch, which has the advantage over the conventional clutch with coil springs that it develops a higher thrust pressure and embodies less rotating mass (Fig. 5).

(more)

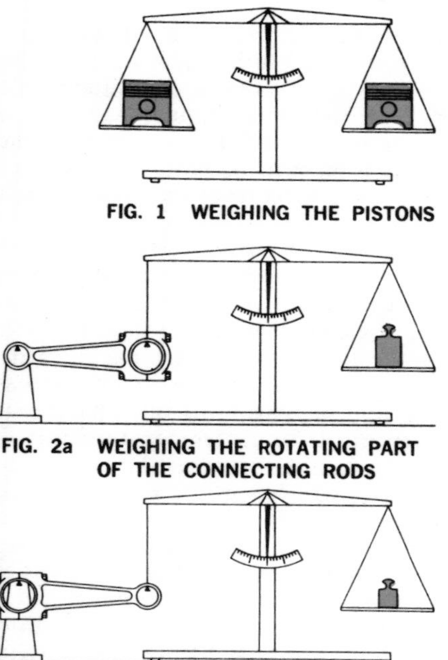

FIG. 1 WEIGHING THE PISTONS

FIG. 2a WEIGHING THE ROTATING PART OF THE CONNECTING RODS

G. 2b WEIGHING THE RECIPROCATING PART OF THE CONNECTING RODS

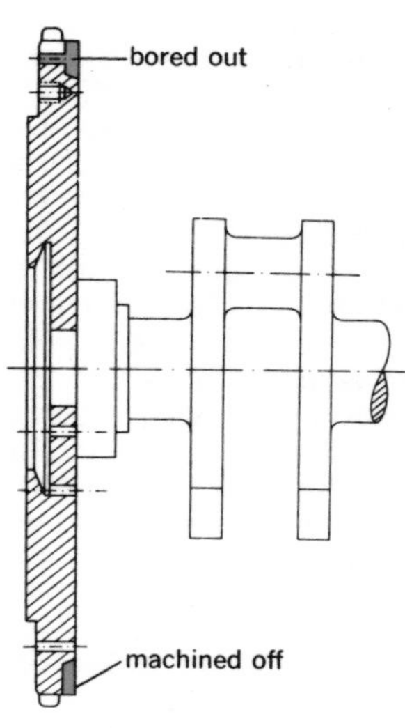

FIG. 3 REDUCING THE WEIGHT OF THE FLYWHEEL

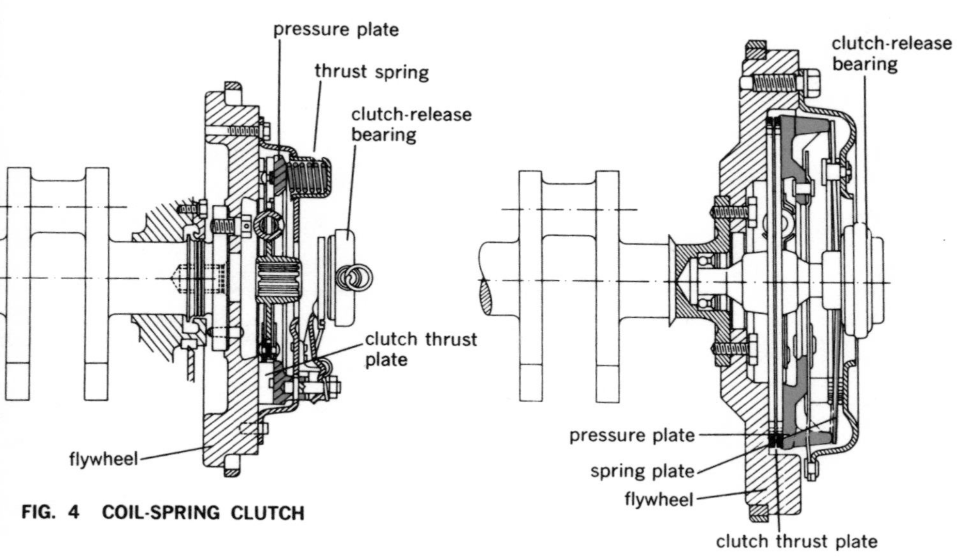

FIG. 4 COIL-SPRING CLUTCH

FIG. 5 SPRING-PLATE CLUTCH

Engine Tuning (continued)

Since the object of tuning is to improve the gas flow in the engine, it results in a higher fuel consumption and correspondingly greater evolution of heat, which has to be dissipated so as to prevent overheating. The existing radiator of a water-cooled rear-mounted engine is liable to be inadequate for the tuned engine. If there is no room to fit a large radiator, the effective cooling surface will have to be increased by installation of an auxiliary radiator, which will have to be mounted under the vehicle (Fig. 1). In some cases it is possible to install a radiator of sufficient capacity at the front of the vehicle instead.

The cooling-air flow rate for an air-cooled engine can, within certain limits, be increased by modification of the V-belt drive. It must be ensured that sufficient air can flow into the engine compartment. With a rear-mounted engine this can nearly always be achieved by opening the cover of the engine compartment (Fig. 1).

In addition, attention must be paid to the cooling of the lubricating oil. If the engine is already equipped with an oil cooler, it will usually be possible to increase its capacity. By fixing cooling fins to the sump and increasing its oil capacity it is likewise possible to achieve a substantial lowering of the oil temperature (Fig. 2). For better cooling of the bearings, the oil flow rate should be increased by increasing the capacity of the oil pump (Fig. 3). Contaminants consisting of abraded particles remain in suspension in the oil and thus enter the engine. To prevent premature wear of the bearings, the oil must be continually filtered. Most modern engines are equipped with a full-flow or a bypass filter. If no filter is already fitted, it is possible to install one in the bypass oil flow (Fig. 4).

Finally, there remains some work to be done on the ignition system. The ignition wire may be of the resistance type having a graphite core, which is liable to fracture easily. It is advisable to fit a copper-core wire instead, in which case it is necessary also to fit a radio-shielded connector for the spark plug. To obtain a stronger ignition spark at higher speeds of rotation, the standard ignition coil should be replaced by a high-output coil. It is also necessary to fit spark plugs with a higher thermal value.

Of course, the brakes, spring suspension, shock absorbers and tires must be properly suited to the enhanced performance of the tuned engine.

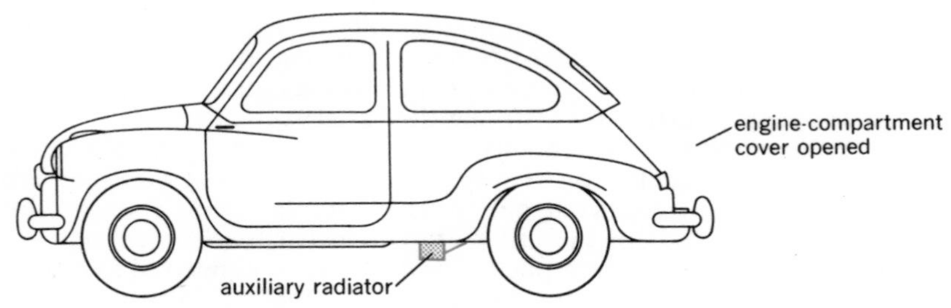

FIG. 1

FIG. 2 CAST-ALUMINUM SUMP WITH COOLING FINS

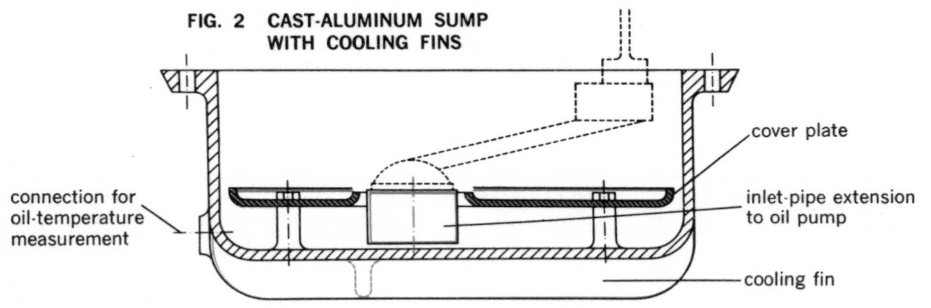

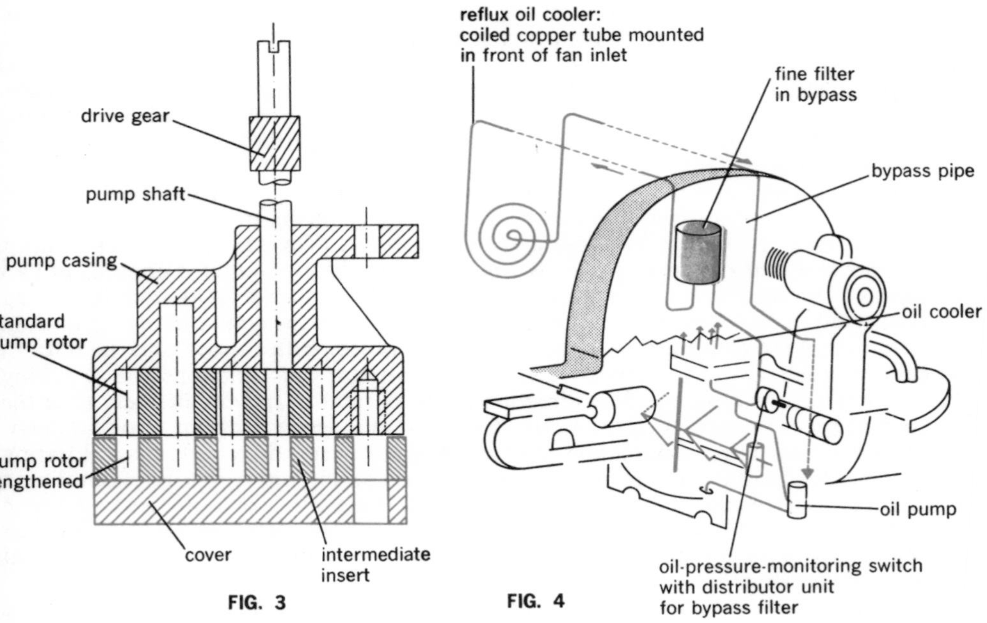

FIG. 3

FIG. 4

GENERATOR (DYNAMO)

Principles: The car generator is usually driven by a V-belt from the engine. It generates electricity when the engine is running. Its capacity is sufficient to supply current to all consumer equipment such as the ignition system, headlights, etc., and also to supply current for charging the battery.

The functioning of a dynamo—or, to use the more general term, a generator—is based on the phenomenon of induction: When a coil of wire is moved in a magnetic field so that it intersects magnetic lines of force, an electric current flows through the coil when the ends of the latter are connected to electrical equipment to form a circuit. For the sake of simplicity the coil may be conceived as consisting of a single loop of wire (Fig. 1) which is rotated in a magnetic field between the poles of a permanent magnet. Each of the two ends of the loop is connected to a slip ring. A carbon brush is in contact with each ring, and the two brushes are connected to a sensitive current-measuring instrument. When the loop of wire, which is assumed to be initially in the horizontal position, is rotated clockwise (Fig. 2), the loop will progressively—as its angle of rotation increases—intersect more and more lines of force. As a result, the current generated in the circuit increases in intensity, so that the needle of the measuring instrument shows a correspondingly larger deflection. The current increases until the loop reaches the vertical position—i.e., when its plane is parallel to the magnetic lines of force. With further clockwise rotation of the loop, the current flowing through the circuit decreases until it becomes zero when the rotating loop reaches the horizontal position—i.e., when its plane is perpendicular to the lines of force. According to the so-called "right-hand rule" (Fig. 3), the current flows in the direction indicated by the red arrows in Fig. 1. When the clockwise rotation of the loop is continued through the horizontal position, the current once again increases, but now flows in the opposite direction to that in the first half revolution of the loop. The measuring instrument now shows a deflection in the opposite direction. It is thus seen that in the course of one complete revolution of the loop (or the coil) the current undergoes a complete reversal of direction. As appears from the lower diagram in Fig. 2, it increases to a maximum, then decreases, momentarily becomes zero, then increases again to a maximum (but of opposite sign to the first maximum), and finally decreases again to zero, when the coil has returned to its initial position. This sequence of a current flowing first in one direction and then in the other is called the "cycle" and is accomplished in a length of time and called the "period." A current presenting such a pattern of variation is called an alternating current.

Direct-current generator: An alternating current may not be suitable, however, since the battery needs a direct current—a current flowing in one direction only—for charging. To obtain this result, the generator is provided with a commutator instead of a pair of slip rings. In its simplest form the commutator consists of two halves of a metal ring which are insulated from each other (Fig. 4), each half being connected to one of the two ends of the rotating loop. In the course of one revolution each half of the commutator is successively in contact with the top and the bottom carbon brush (C and D) respectively. The commutator thus functions as a switching device which reverses the flow direction of the current in the circuit every time the current becomes zero. As a result, the current does indeed vary from zero to a maximum and back to zero, but it now always flows in the same direction: it is a pulsating current. The pulsations can be evened out to something more nearly resembling a direct current of constant magnitude by the use of a number of loops, each of whose ends is connected to one segment of the commutator, which in this case is composed of as many pairs of segments as there are loops: the segments are all insulated from one another (Fig. 5).

In an actual generator the loops are in fact coils consisting of a winding of wire around an iron core. The whole rotating assembly comprising the windings, core

(more)

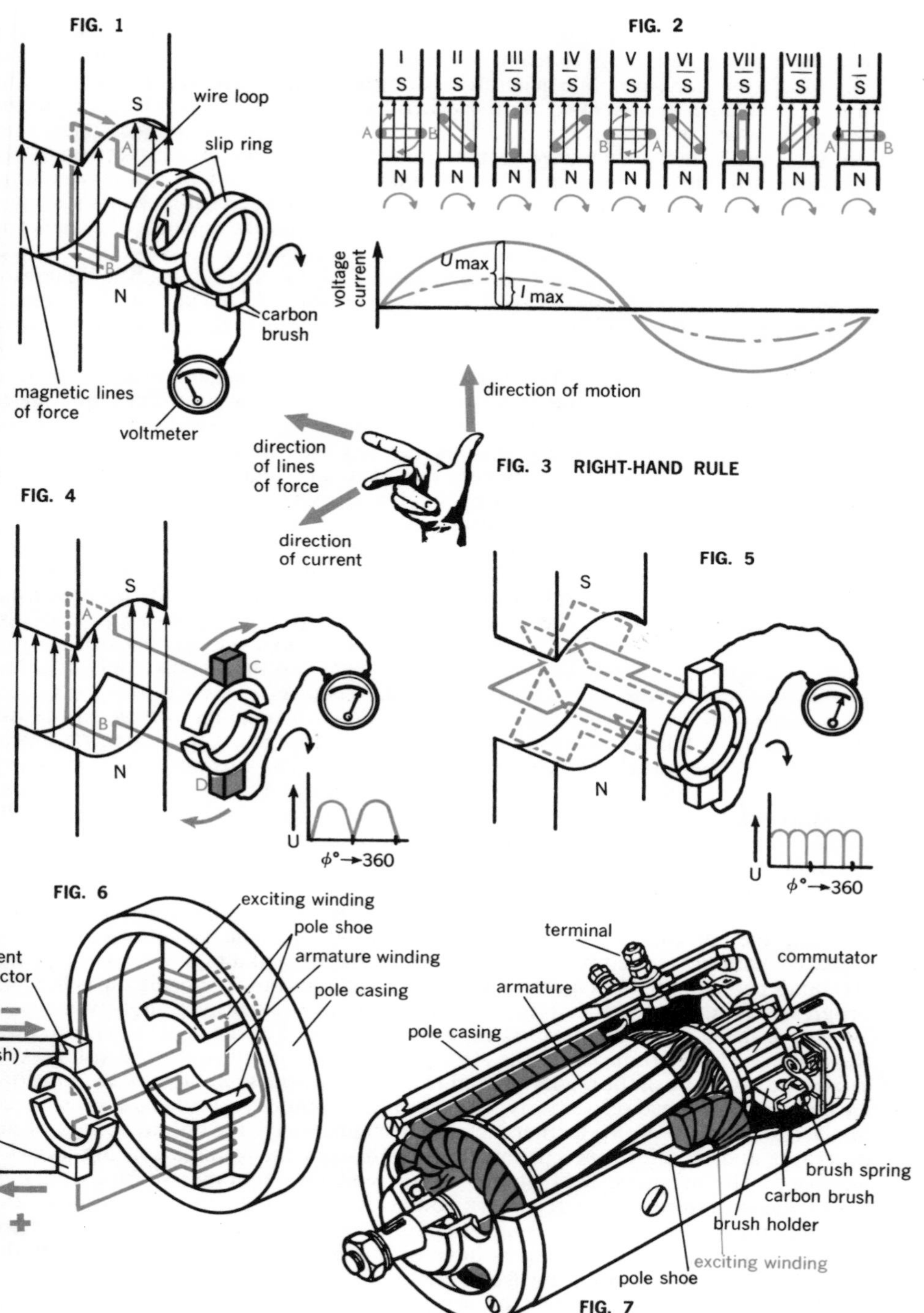
FIG. 1
S
wire loop
slip ring
A
B
N
carbon brush
magnetic lines of force
voltmeter
FIG. 2
I II III IV V VI VII VIII I
S
N
A B
voltage current
Umax
I max
direction of motion
direction of lines of force
direction of current
FIG. 3 RIGHT-HAND RULE
FIG. 4
S
A
B
C
D
N
U
φ°→360
FIG. 5
S
N
U
φ°→360
FIG. 6
exciting winding
pole shoe
armature winding
pole casing
rrent llector
ush)
terminal
commutator
armature
pole casing
brush spring
carbon brush
brush holder
exciting winding
pole shoe
FIG. 7

and commutator is called armature. It rotates between the poles of a magnet, which may be a permanent magnet made of special steel (only in very small generators), but which, for an automobile generator, is normally an electromagnet energized by some of the current generated by the generator itself (Fig. 6). When the armature begins to rotate, a weak current is at first generated because the magnetic field is as yet very weak, being due only to the residual magnetism of the electromagnet. However, this field rapidly increases in intensity as a result of the current that energizes the electromagnet, so that in turn the generated current becomes stronger, and so on until the magnetic field reaches saturation and the generator is operating at full power (Fig. 7). This process is known as self-excitation.

Regulator: The voltage and current generated by an automobile generator depend on the speed of rotation at which the generator is driven and on the intensity of the magnetic field. As the engine speed varies considerably during normal driving, the voltage and therefore the strength of the current supplied by the generator would fluctuate continually. Yet it is essential to have a constant voltage and thus ensure effective charging of the battery at all times, despite variations in engine speed and in load on the generator. To achieve this, a regulating device is employed whereby the current that energizes the electromagnet is varied in such a manner that the output voltage of the generator is kept constant. The regulator comprises several switch contacts which are actuated by small electromagnets. Between the positive and the negative terminal of the generator is connected an electromagnet, called the voltage coil. When the generator is running at low speed and thus generates only a low voltage, the current flowing through the voltage coil is not strong enough to produce a magnetic field of sufficient strength to attract the armature of the spring-loaded regulator contact. The current then flows from the positive pole of the generator through the spring-loaded contact and through the exciting coil—which helps to produce the magnetic field of the generator—to the negative pole (Fig. 8a), so that the field magnet is strongly energized. When, as a result of this excitation, the voltage rises, the stronger current that now flows through the voltage coil causes the armature of the regulator contact to be attracted against the restraining force developed by the spring. The contact is thus opened. The current from the positive pole of the generator now no longer flows only through the exciting coil but also goes through the resistance *B* (Fig. 8b). Because of this resistance interposed into the circuit, the current through the exciting coil is weakened, and the voltage output of the generator decreases in consequence. This in turn reduces the strength of the current that energizes the voltage coil, with the result that the contact armature is released and springs back to its initial position, thus closing the contact again and enabling the current to flow direct to the exciting coil. The sequence of events is repeated, with the regulator contact opening and closing at a rate of between 50 and 200 times per second. With increasing engine speed the contact closing times become progressively shorter, so that the exciting current is correspondingly weakened. When the speed of the engine (and thus the drive speed of the generator) increases, the magnetic field produced by the strong current flowing through the voltage coil causes the armature of the regulator contact to oscillate between the contact positions for high and low speed respectively. The exciting current is then constantly weakened by the resistance *B*. With a further increase in engine speed, the output voltage of the generator and therefore the current flowing through the voltage coil are likewise increased. The magnetic field of the voltage coil now becomes so strong that it draws the armature of the regulator contact to the "high speed" position; the exciting coil of the generator is short-circuited and therefore receives no current (Fig. 8c). As a result, the output voltage of the generator goes down, so that the spring pulls back the armature from the "high speed" position and the exciting current can again flow (through the resistance *B*, Fig. 8b). This sequence of events is repeated in rapid succession.

(more)

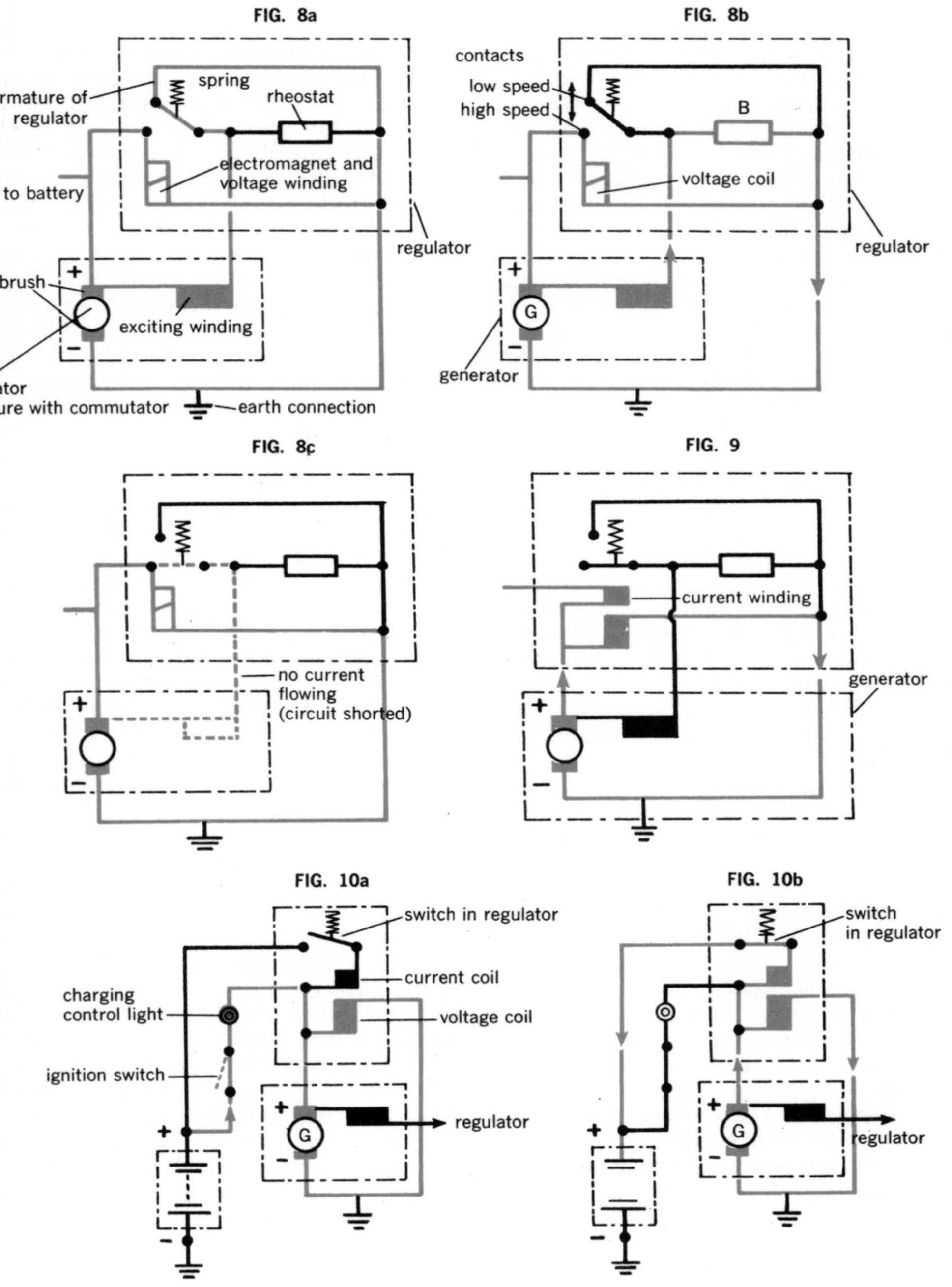
FIG. 8a
spring
armature of regulator
rheostat
electromagnet and voltage winding
to battery
regulator
brush
exciting winding
erator
nature with commutator
earth connection
FIG. 8b
contacts
low speed
high speed
B
voltage coil
regulator
G
generator
FIG. 8c
no current flowing (circuit shorted)
FIG. 9
current winding
generator
FIG. 10a
switch in regulator
current coil
charging control light
voltage coil
ignition switch
regulator
G
FIG. 10b
switch in regulator
G
regulator

Generator (continued)

The power output of the generator is measured in terms of the product of voltage and current strength. The voltage is regulated in the manner described in the foregoing. It is still necessary to limit the maximum current. The iron core of the voltage coil is provided with a second winding (the current coil) through which the whole current output of the generator flows (Fig. 9). The magnetic field produced by this coil intensifies the field produced by the voltage coil. When a high current flows through the current coil, this too brings about a sequence of events, as already described, whereby the energizing current of the exciting coil is weakened. The output voltage of the generator, and therefore also the current it yields, are thus reduced.

When the generator is not rotating, or is being driven only at very low speed, there exists a difference in voltage between the battery and the generator. If the engine is not then switched off, the battery will discharge itself through the generator. To prevent this, the regulator is provided with an additional magnetic switch, whose iron core is likewise provided with a voltage coil and a current coil (Figs. 10a and 10b). The voltage coil is connected to the positive and the negative pole of the generator. It is so adjusted that the armature of the switch contact, attracted by the magnetic field produced by the voltage coil, closes the contact to the battery only when the voltage of the generator is higher than that of the battery. The current flowing to the battery energizes the current coil, whose magnetic field augments that of the voltage coil (Fig. 10b). If the battery voltage is higher than the generator voltage, the current flows in the opposite direction through the current coil; its magnetic field weakens that of the voltage coil, so that the spring-loaded switch contact automatically opens (Fig. 10a). The charging control light on the instrument panel is connected between the positive pole of the battery and that of the generator. If—when the ignition is switched on—the battery voltage is higher than the generator voltage, current will flow through the control light when the switch contact of the regulator is open. The light glows and thus indicates that the ignition has been switched on. When the switch contact of the regulator closes, the control light is short-circuited and is extinguished, thus indicating that the generator is working and the consumer-equipment circuits are connected. Figs. 11a to 11d show the electrical connections and functioning of a widely used type of two-element regulator (contact 1 for low speeds, contact 2 for high speeds).

Three-phase generator: In principle, every generator produces an alternating current. In the case of the direct-current generator this is "rectified" by the commutator, which reverses the direction of the current just as it is about to change its direction naturally, so that a one-way flow of current is obtained. The three-phase alternating-current generator, which is sometimes used in automobiles instead of the direct-current generator, has no commutator. Rectification of the alternating current is, instead, effected by means of semiconductor diodes (see Vol. I, page 96) which prevent the flow of current in one direction and permit it in the other direction. These diodes are accommodated in the generator. The latter differs in construction from the direct-current generator in that the exciting current is here fed—through bushes and slip rings—to the exciting coil which is in the rotor of the machine and establishes a rotating magnetic field (Fig. 12). The magnetic lines of force intersect the fixed coils in the stator, the current thus being generated by induction in these coils. The residual magnetism of the rotor core is not sufficient for self-excitation, and for this reason the magnetic field initially has to be built up by an energizing current supplied by the battery. The three-phase generator has the advantage that it is of lighter and more compact construction than a direct-current generator of comparable output and that it supplies electricity even when the engine is idling.

It is regulated by appropriate control of the exciting current, just as in the case of the direct-current generator.

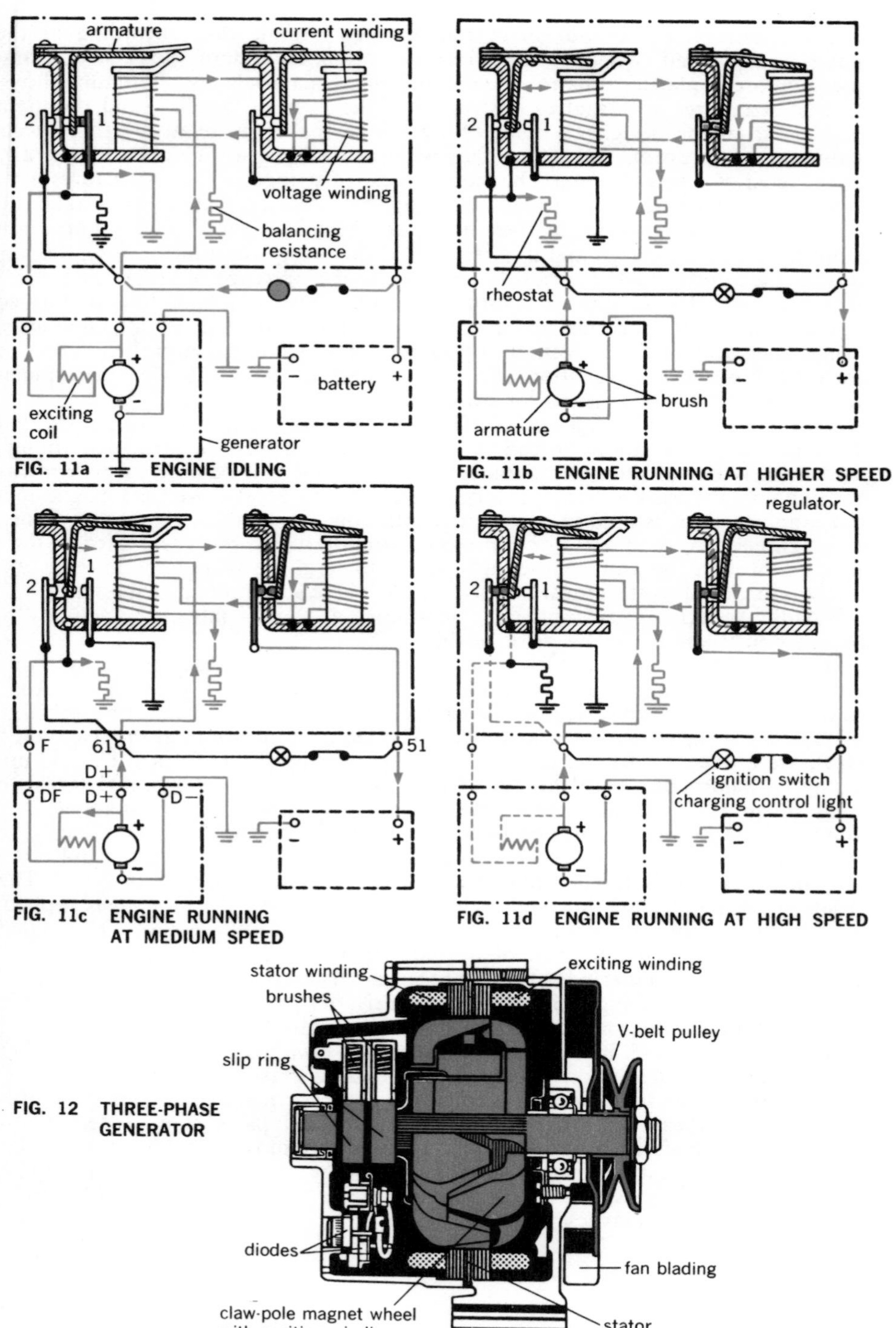

FIG. 11a ENGINE IDLING

FIG. 11b ENGINE RUNNING AT HIGHER SPEED

FIG. 11c ENGINE RUNNING AT MEDIUM SPEED

FIG. 11d ENGINE RUNNING AT HIGH SPEED

FIG. 12 THREE-PHASE GENERATOR

PRESENT-DAY METHODS OF AIRCRAFT CONSTRUCTION

The construction methods in current use for aircraft vary according to the materials employed: wood, composite construction, aluminum alloys, steel, glass-fiber-reinforced plastics. The most commonly used materials are aluminum alloys. Aircraft structures are usually constructed in the form of "shells," and the main problem from the designer's point of view is to make the relatively thin sheets withstand compression and shear loads without buckling. Fuselages are generally constructed of sheets reinforced by members called stringers. These structures have to withstand bending, shear, torsion, and internal pressure. Care must be taken to avoid stress concentrations at rivet holes, etc. Metal fatigue is a very important problem in aircraft design and it is recognized that every component has a definite fatigue life, which may be seriously reduced by the presence of cracks and stress concentrations. The fatigue life is estimated on the basis of fatigue tests performed on the components concerned and in test flights of the completed aircraft. Obviously, stringent inspection and detection of possible cracks while the aircraft is in service are further essential precautions. In this connection, the "fail-safe" principle is nowadays applied. It consists, for example, in deliberately introducing a joint to prevent the spread of a fatigue crack. Thus, in a fail-safe wing structure a crack that starts in one panel cannot spread to the next. In this way the structure, though weakened, is not at once dangerously weakened and will be able to perform its function until the crack is detected at the next inspection. Steel, as well as a magnesium and titanium alloy, is used in parts where additional strength or rigidity combined with lightness are required. For supersonic aircraft, which become heated in their passage through the atmosphere, light alloys undergo an unacceptable reduction in strength. Stainless steel must be used for the whole structure of such aircraft.

Broadly speaking, "differential," "semi-integral" and "integral" methods of aircraft construction can be distinguished.

"Differential" construction is characterized by the fact that each major assembly comprises a fairly large number of units which are connected together by riveting, bolting or spot welding, riveting being the most important connecting method. A drawback is the ever-present possibility of stress concentrations at the rivet holes, which are formed by drilling or punching. The rivet heads are formed by cold upsetting or hammering with the aid of various kinds of power-operated tools. In "semi-integral" construction, the numerous units of which the assemblies are composed are joined together by bonding with high-strength resin adhesives. The advantage over riveting is that with bonded connections there is better and more uniform stress distribution, so that stress concentrations are largely obviated. The surfaces to be bonded are thoroughly cleaned and degreased, the adhesive is applied, and the components are held pressed together under uniform pressure. The bonded joints are cured at a temperature of around 150° C. Typical of this method of construction, more particularly for wings, are so-called sandwich structures, characterized by low weight and high strength. They consist of two skin plates (e.g., aluminum sheeting) with an intermediate core of sheet-aluminum "honeycombs," foamed plastics, or balsa wood. In "integral" construction each major assembly is in effect a single unit, fabricated in one piece—e.g., by casting, extruding, stamping, etching. or machining from a solid block. It is employed more particularly for wing structures and tail units, these being the most severely stressed parts of a modern high-performance aircraft. Etching techniques are used to remove metal from particular areas and thus produce "integral" components of the desired shape. A nonmetallic form of "integral" construction consists in the use of components molded from glass-fiber-reinforced plastics.

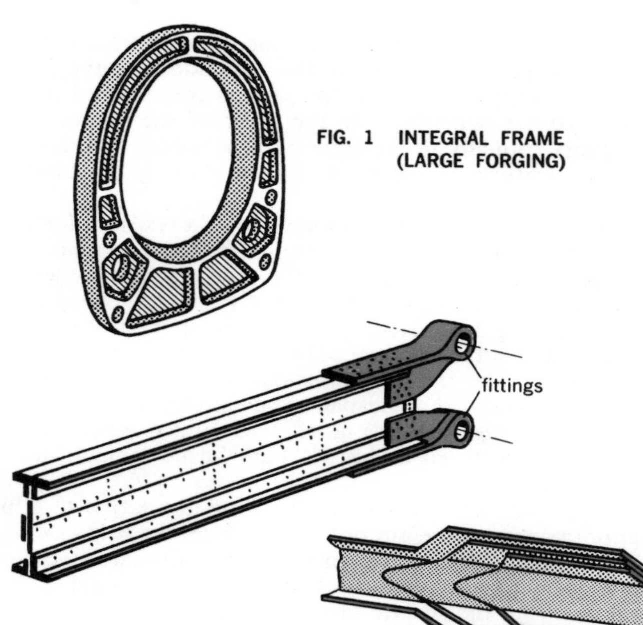

FIG. 1 INTEGRAL FRAME (LARGE FORGING)

G. 2 SPAR COMPOSED OF INDIVIDUAL SECTIONS AND PLATES

FIG. 3 GLUED NOSE SPAR ROOT

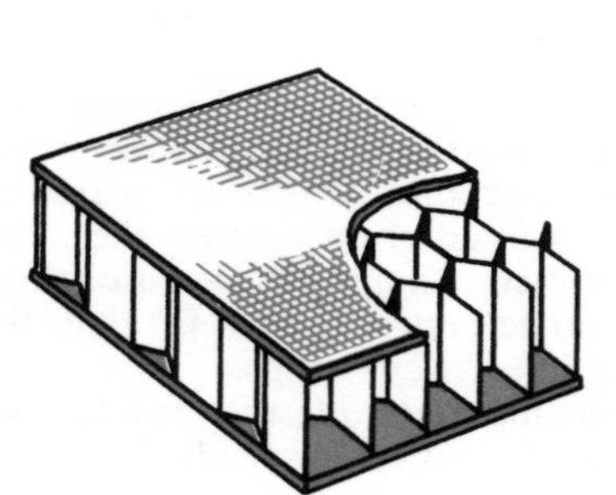

FIG. 4 SANDWICH CONSTRUCTION COMPRIZING HONEYCOMB CORE WITH GLUED-ON SKIN PLATES

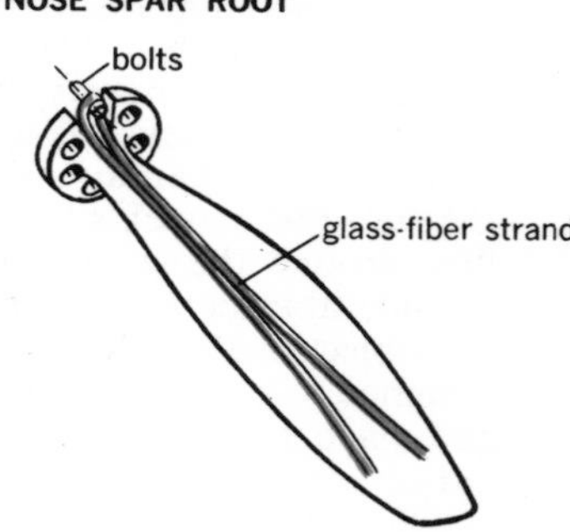

FIG. 5 COMPONENT MADE FROM GLASS-FIBER-REINFORCED PLASTIC

WING GEOMETRY

An airfoil (or aerofoil), such as the wing of an aircraft, develops a resultant force acting upwards, i.e., transversely to the direction of flight. How this upward force, the "lift," is developed by the airfoil section is explained in Vol. II, page 284. The forces involved are dependent on the speed of the aircraft (the dynamic pressure increases proportionally to the square of the speed) and more particularly also on the geometric features of the wing—i.e., its cross-sectional shape and its shape in plan.

The term "drag" in a general sense denotes a resistant force acting in a direction opposite to the direction of motion and parallel to the relative airstream. The wing of an aircraft flying at less than half the speed of sound encounters, in addition to surface-friction drag and pressure drag, a resistance called induced drag, which is the part of the drag associated with the development of lift and is proportional to the square of the lift coefficient. This coefficient represents the relative lift of a particular airfoil. The induced resistance can be kept down to a low value by providing a large ratio of wingspan to mean chord—i.e., the ratio of the length of the wing to its average width (Fig. 1). This ratio is especially important in aircraft whose wings are required to have a high lift coefficient and therefore develop a large lift—e.g., gliders.

The "sweep" denotes the slant of the wing in relation to a line perpendicular to the longitudinal axis of the aircraft. It influences the behavior of the flow conditions in the so-called boundary layer immediately adjacent to the wing surface. In the case of a swept-wing aircraft with sweepback of the wing (Fig. 2), the streamline flow first separates from the surface of the wing in the region of the wing tips when the angle of attack is very large (cf. Vol. II, page 284). Since the ailerons are located in that part of the wing they are liable to become ineffective under such conditions, so that any minor disturbance may cause stalling and uncontrolled rolling motion ("roll-off"). On the other hand, with a forward sweep of the wing (Fig. 3), separation of the flow starts nearer the wing root, so that the ailerons continue to be effective and the aircraft remains under control.

In the case of an aircraft flying at more than half the speed of sound (but still in the subsonic range), supersonic speeds will occur in certain parts of the streamline flow around the wing, which are associated with shock waves that give rise to a considerable increase in drag. If the wing is given a sweep, the critical speed at which this objectionable effect occurs is shifted to a higher value. For this reason all aircraft designed to operate in the speed range between mach 0.5 (half the speed of sound) and mach 1.0 (the speed of sound) have swept wings.

For supersonic speeds, i.e., exceeding mach 1.0, the optimum wing shape in plan is different from the optimum shape for subsonic speeds. The ratio of span to mean chord is now of less importance; on the other hand, a more pronounced sweep is desirable. These considerations led to the development of the delta-wing aircraft (Fig. 4). Such aircraft develop a large lift only at high angles of attack as compared with straight-wing aircraft. This is especially important in connection with takeoff and landing. Landing speeds are very high. At supersonic speeds above mach 1.5 the nonswept short-span wing (Fig. 5) is, in terms of drag, more favorable than any other shape. However, though important, this is not the only consideration that governs the geometry of aircraft wings. In modern military aircraft the "variable-geometry" wing has been introduced in order to obtain relatively favorable conditions for takeoff and landing (long wingspan, position "a" in Fig. 6) and for supersonic flight (position "b"). The changeover is effected by swinging the wings back when the aircraft is in flight ("swing-wing" aircraft).

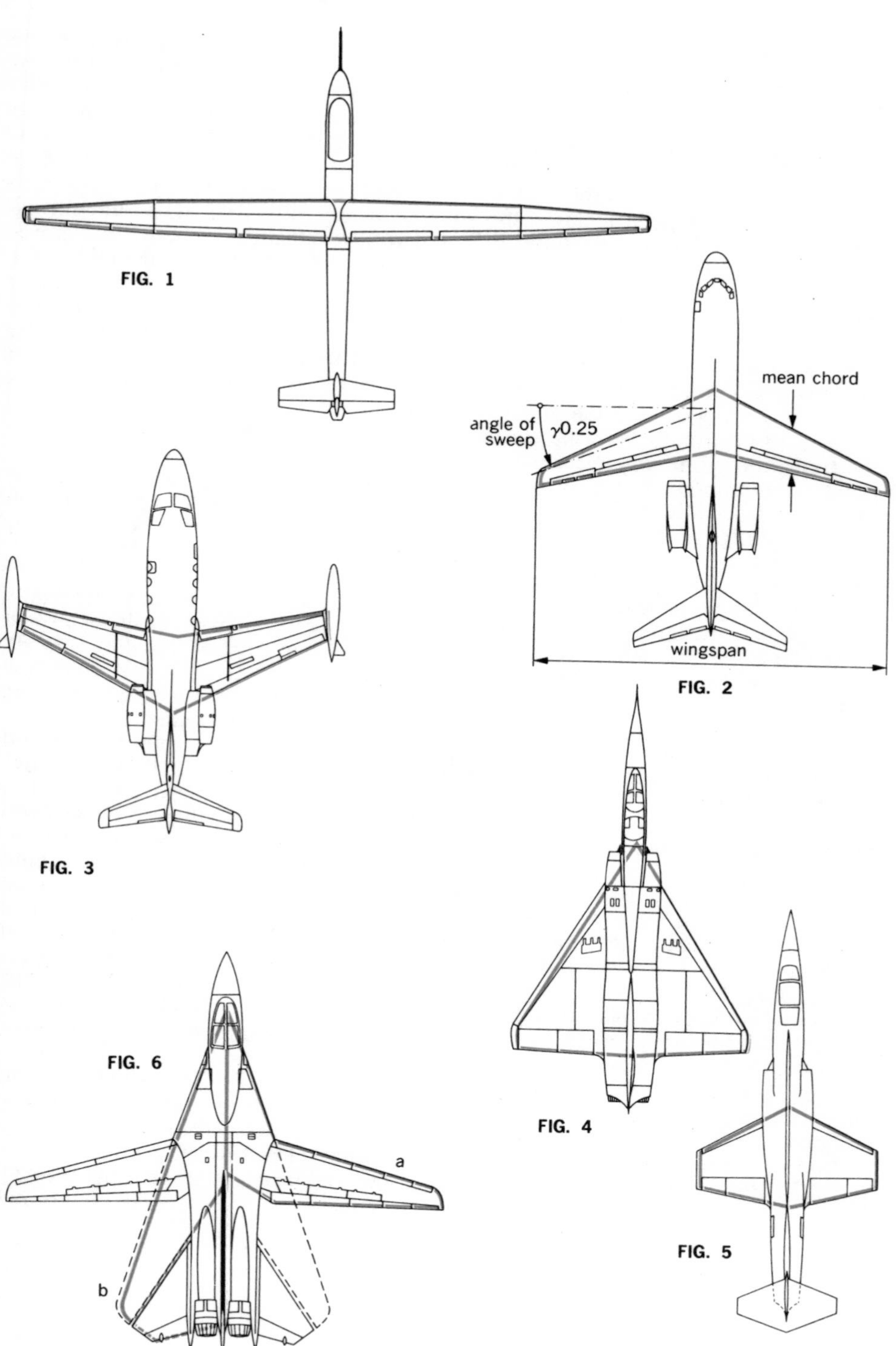
FIG. 1
mean chord
angle of sweep
γ0.25
wingspan
FIG. 2
FIG. 3
FIG. 4
FIG. 5
FIG. 6
a
b

AIRFOILS AND AIRFLOW PHENOMENA

The airflow behavior depends on the shape of the airfoil section and on the phenomena occurring at the *boundary layer*, which is the thin layer of air adjacent to a solid surface—such as an airfoil—over which air is flowing and which is distinguished from the main airflow by distinctive flow characteristics of its own set up by friction. The flow in the boundary layer (see Fig. 1, where the thickness of this layer is shown greatly exaggerated) may be *laminar* or *turbulent*. In laminar flow the velocity distribution in the layer shows a steady increase from zero at the surface of the airfoil—more particularly, the wing of an aircraft—to a maximum corresponding to the velocity of the main airflow. The flow is relatively smooth and moves in layers parallel to the surface; hence the term "laminar." In turbulent flow, the fairly regular motion of the laminar boundary layer is destroyed: the boundary layer undergoes transition: it becomes thicker and is characterized by large random motions (turbulence). These effects may give rise to *separation*, a term which denotes that the flow in the boundary layer detaches itself from the surface of the wing (at the separation point) and that immediately adjacent to the surface, flow even occurs in a direction opposite to the direction of the main flow (Fig. 2).

The airflow around the wing starts at the stagnation point and is laminar up to the transition point, where turbulence sets in. The latter point is located near the point of minimum pressure, approximately where the wing has its greatest thickness. Normally the turbulent boundary layer detaches itself (separates) from the trailing edge of the wing, where eddies develop. If this separation occurs too far forward toward the leading edge, there is serious loss of lift and an increase in drag. This is liable to happen when the angle of attack exceeds the critical value called the stalling angle or when the airspeed becomes too low. Some aircraft, especially sports planes, are equipped with a stall-warning device which may consist of a short triangular plate or a length of wire fitted to the leading edge of the wing (Fig. 3). When the angle of attack becomes dangerously large, separation of the airflow commences at this plate or wire. There is an immediate (but not yet dangerous) loss of lift, which warns the pilot that he is approaching the stalling angle.

Regions of the wing where laminar separation is liable to occur may be provided with devices for producing turbulence (Fig. 4). The resulting turbulent flow "adheres" better to the surface than the laminar flow and premature separation is thus prevented. Such devices may, for example, take the form of small projecting plates which break up the laminar flow. "Swept" wings are provided with so-called fences, which are plates or vanes placed parallel to the main airflow and prevent flow (and separation) in the direction from wing root to tip, this subsidiary flow being promoted by the sweep of the wing. A similar effect is obtained by forming the leading edge of the wings with "sawtooth" notches (Fig. 6). At the tail of the aircraft, interference of the boundary layers of the horizontal and the vertical stabilizers produces interference drag. To diminish this, the so-called T tail has been developed, in which the horizontal surfaces are placed at the top of the vertical fin (Fig. 7), while the junction of these components is provided with a fairing—i.e., a streamlined casing designed to reduce drag.

Steering an aircraft in three directions is effected by means of the rudder (which guides the aircraft in the horizontal plane), the elevator (which controls the pitch—i.e., makes the tail go up or down), and the ailerons (which control the rolling motion of the aircraft by their differential rotation). The rudder is attached to a vertical stabilizer, while the ailerons are set at the trailing edges of the wings (Fig. 5).

(more)

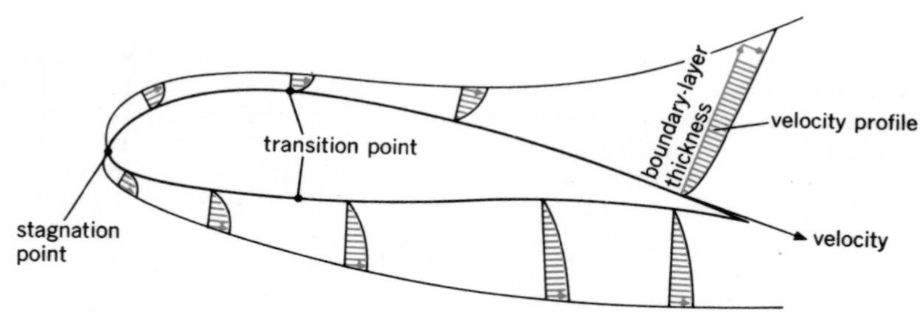

FIG. 1

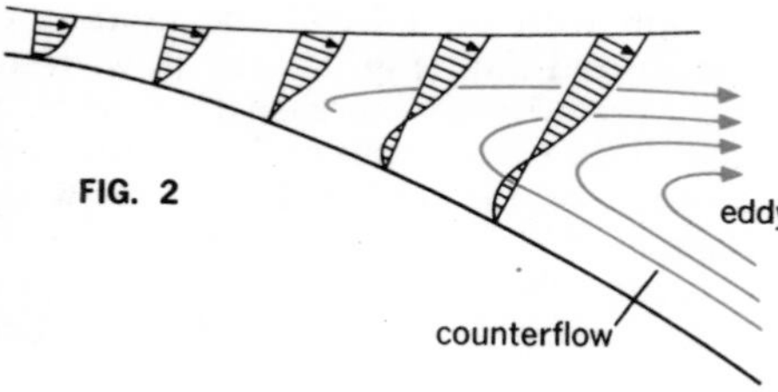

eddy

counterflow

FIG. 2

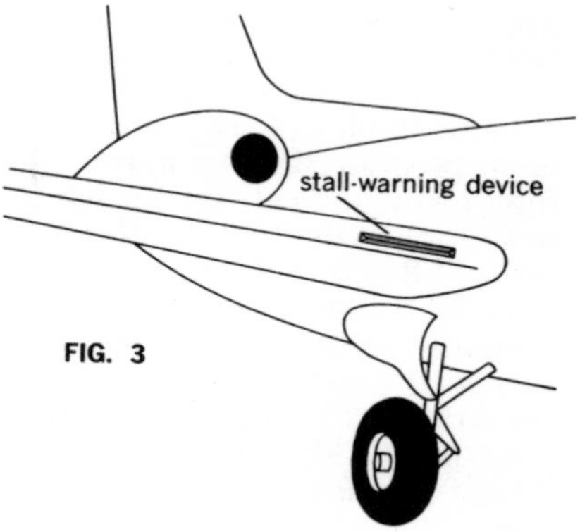

stall-warning device

FIG. 3

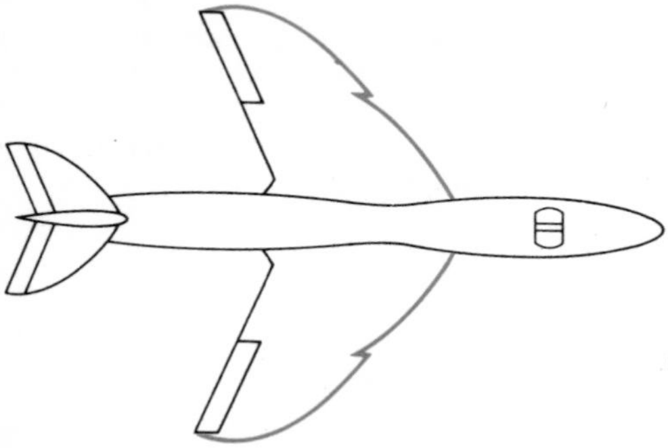

FIG. 6

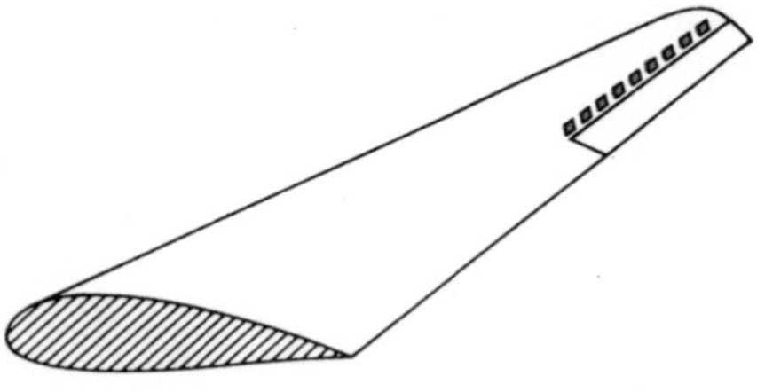

FIG. 4

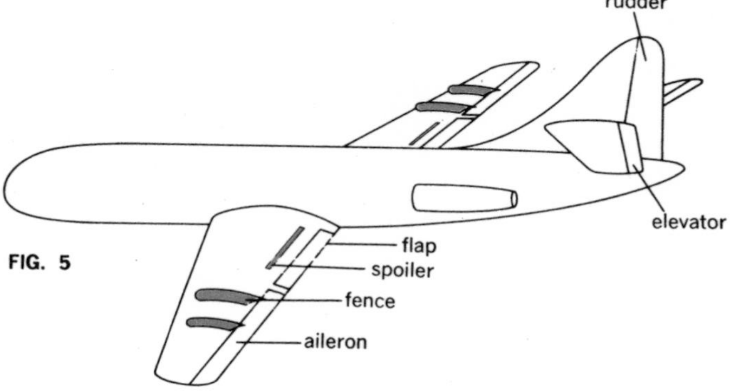

FIG. 5

Sometimes the horizontal and vertical stabilizers are not provided with separately movable attachments (elevator and rudder), but can each be moved as a whole so as to alter the angle of attack. The trailing edge of the rudder may be provided with a small subsidiary rudder called a trimming tab (Fig. 7) by means of which the pilot adjusts the trim of the aircraft—i.e., the condition of static balance in pitch during rectilinear flight, with the main control surfaces seeking their neutral positions.

Further adjustments are achieved by means of flaps, these being control surfaces which serve to control the speed by increasing the drag and thus acting as a brake or to increase the lift or aid in recovery from a dive. The slat (Fig. 8) is a movable auxiliary airfoil running along the leading edge of a wing; in normal flight it is in contact with the latter, but it can be lifted away to form a slot at certain angles of attack, so that air flows through the slot and reenergizes the boundary layer on the low-pressure upper surface of the wing. The plain wing flap (Fig. 9) increases the camber (curvature) of the wing, with the result that the lift is improved and the angle of attack at which separation occurs is increased, so that the airspeed can be reduced without stalling. This is important in connection with the takeoff and landing of high-speed aircraft. An improved form is the slotted flap (Fig. 8); the flow of air through the slot between the flap and the wing gives a further increase in lift without separation of the boundary layer. In contrast with the other types of flap mentioned, the split flap (Fig. 10) serves to reduce the pressure on the suction face of the wing. whereby an increase in the lift is likewise achieved. Landing flaps (Fig. 9) serve primarily to slow down the aircraft for landing; they break down the airflow around the aircraft and thus function as brakes. Such flaps are sometimes called spoilers, more particularly when installed on the underside of the wing.

A special "dynamic" device for boundary-layer control is the jet flap which consists of a flat jet of air expelled at high velocity from a narrow slot at the trailing edge of the wing and which exercises an action similar to that of an ordinary flap. The same principle is embodied in the blown flap (Fig. 11), an ordinary trailing-edge flap in which separation from the upper surface is delayed by blowing. This principle is also successfully applied to elevators (Fig. 12). Another modern control method, still in the experimental stage, consists in keeping the airflow laminar by sucking in air from the boundary layer through numerous small holes.

fairing
trimming tab
trimming tab

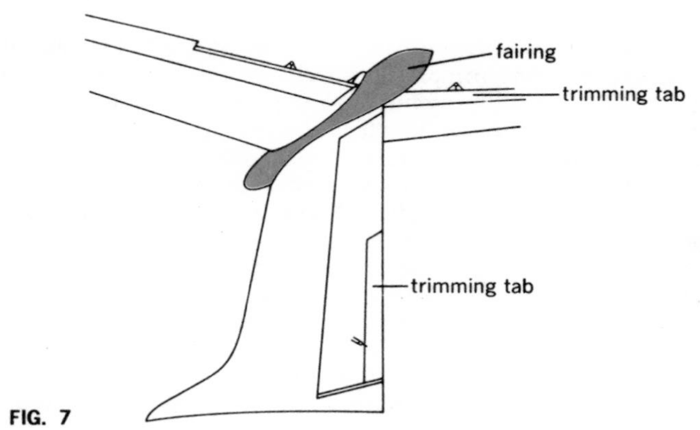

FIG. 7

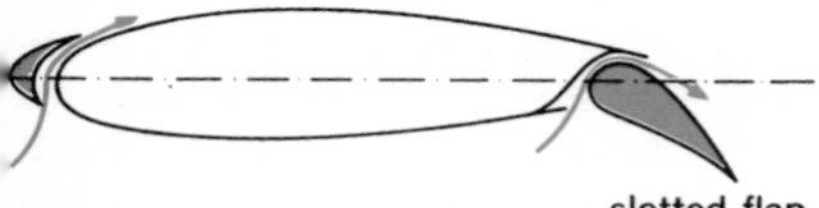

slat
slotted flap

G. 8

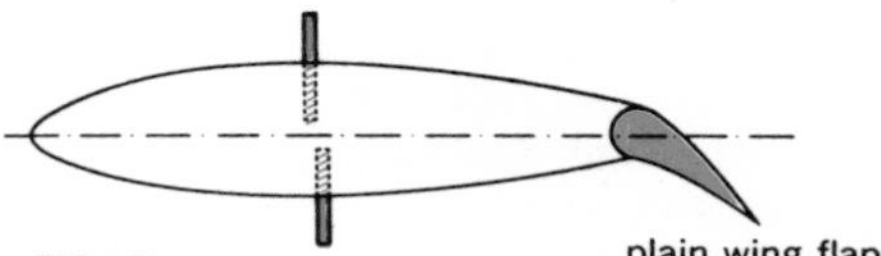

landing brake
plain wing flap

FIG. 9

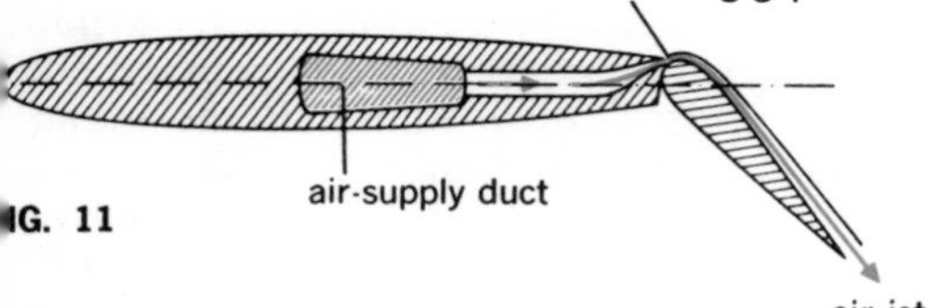

blowing gap
air-supply duct
air jet

IG. 11

split flap

FIG. 10

FIG. 12

Lockheed "Hercules"
air-supply duct
blowing gap
turbojets for supplying air

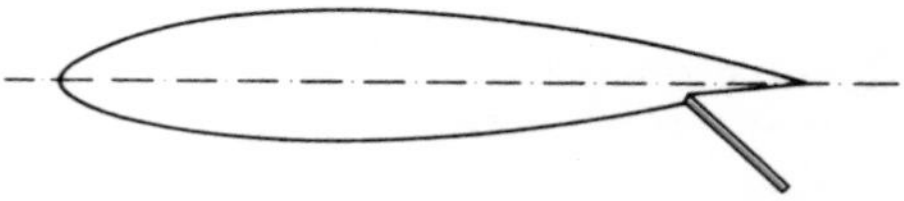

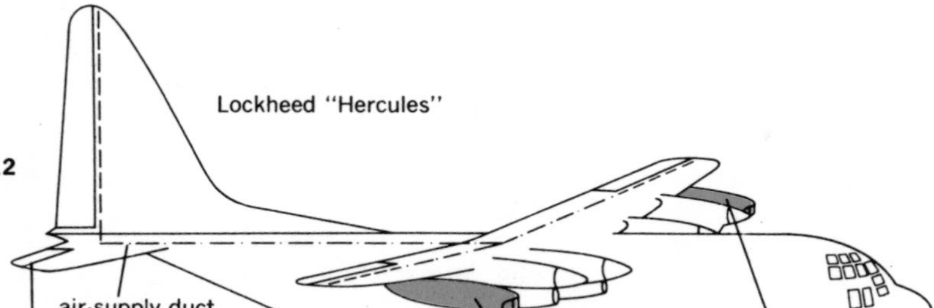

WIND TUNNEL

Many of the forces and moments to which an aircraft is subjected by the airflow cannot be accurately determined by purely theoretical calculations. The aircraft designer must therefore have recourse to experimental aerodynamics, which from the earliest days has contributed much to the progress made in aeronautical science. One of the most important experimental aids is the wind tunnel, a device whereby the reactions of a carefully controlled airstream on scale models of airplanes or their component parts can be studied. The first condition that a model for testing in the wind tunnel must satisfy is that of geometric similarity with the full-scale prototype. In addition, certain other important conditions relating to flow conditions and velocity must be satisfied (Reynolds number; mach number; see page 52) to enable valid measurements to be performed on the model. The Reynolds number is a correction factor applied to the analysis of the flow around the model; it corrects for the scale effect resulting from the difference in size between model and prototype. When the fluid flow around the model is the same as that around the prototype, there is said to be dynamic similarity. For complete similarity between the full-scale airplane and a model that is, say, one-tenth its linear size, the air velocity in the wind tunnel would have to be ten times as high as the speed for which the airplane is to be designed. For high-speed aircraft this would require impracticably high wind velocities in the tunnel and impracticably strong models to withstand the high pressures associated with such velocities. For these reasons, the tests are usually made on models at Reynolds numbers well below those for the full-scale conditions; in the interpretation of the results, due allowance is made for this difference in dynamic conditions. Various methods and devices are employed for performing the measurements of the forces, moments, torques and pressures to which the models, attached to special balances or rigidly supported, are subjected in the wind tunnel (Fig. 1). The airflow pattern can be made visible by a number of methods.

There are several categories of wind tunnels: low-speed tunnels, high-speed subsonic tunnels, and transonic tunnels (for speeds around the speed of sound), supersonic tunnels (up to about mach 5—i.e., five times the speed of sound), hypersonic tunnels (for higher speeds). A distinction is further to be made between the open-circuit tunnel (Eiffel type, Fig. 2) and the closed-circuit tunnel (Prandtl type, Fig. 3). In the open-circuit tunnel the duct is large at its entrance, but reduces to a much smaller area at the test section (or working section), in which the desired wind velocities are produced and the measurements on the model are performed. Beyond the test section, the duct expands gradually. The airflow is produced by a powerful fan. The closed-circuit tunnel enables much better control to be maintained over the pressure, temperature and humidity of the air. After passing the model and the fan, the air returns to the test section through a return-flow duct with banks of guide vanes to lead it smoothly round the bends. Modern wind tunnels are usually of the closed-circuit type. The test section may be of the closed-jet type (in which the tunnel walls are continuous and enclose the test section) or of the open-jet type (in which the model is tested in a free jet of air, as shown in Fig. 3).

Up to the late 1920s, wind tunnels were all of the low-speed type, producing maximum air speeds of about 120 mph. High-speed subsonic tunnels and supersonic tunnels were developed in the following decade. For a time there was a gap between the subsonic and the supersonic speed ranges, which was bridged by the transonic wind tunnel, a postwar development, enabling tests to be made right through the transonic range (approximately between mach 0.8 and mach 1.2). The hypersonic

(more)

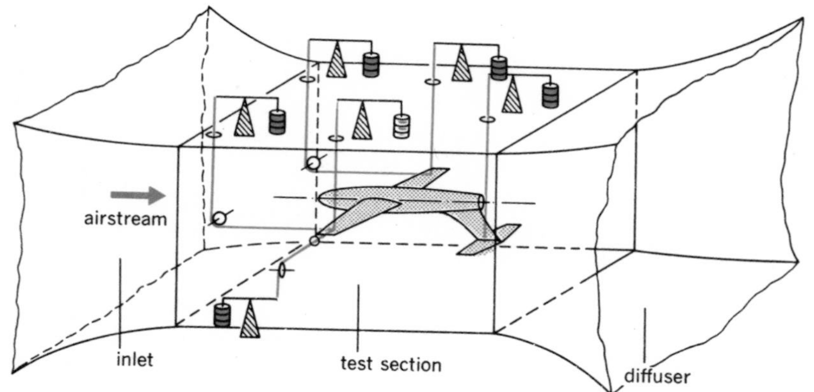

FIG. 1 MODEL SUSPENDED IN WIND TUNNEL

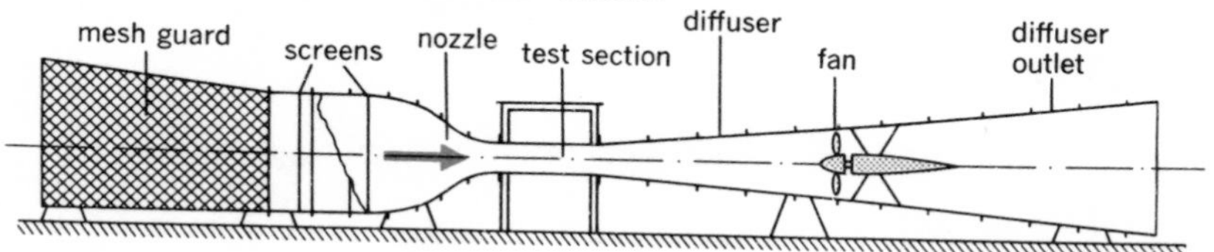

FIG. 2 OPEN-CIRCUIT SUBSONIC WIND TUNNEL (EIFFEL TYPE)

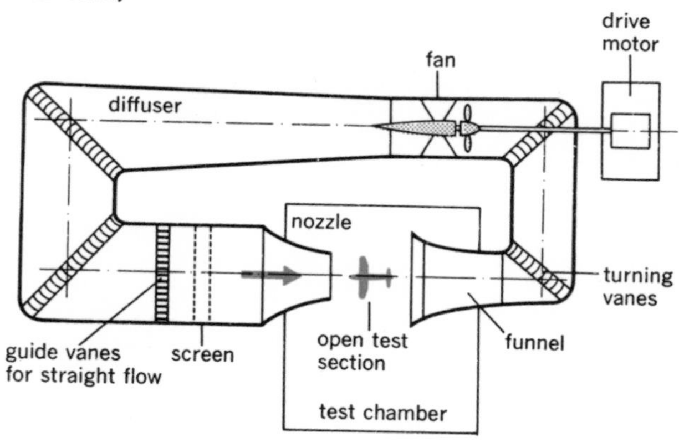

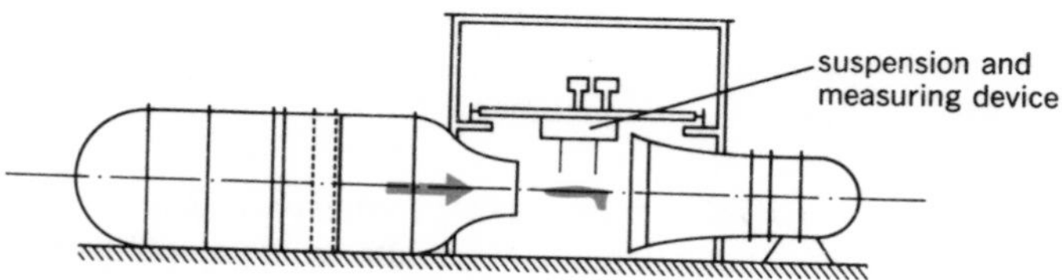

FIG. 3 CLOSED-CIRCUIT SUBSONIC WIND TUNNEL (PRANDTL TYPE)

A VTOL jet aircraft is perched atop struts as workmen prepare it for tests in the world's largest wind tunnel at the Ames Research Center in California, USA
Photo USIS

wind tunnel, the most recent development, is used for studying the conditions associated with the launching and flight of rocket-propelled missiles and earth satellites.

In the subsonic wind tunnel, as described in the foregoing, the test section is located at the narrowest part of the duct, where the highest speeds—below the speed of sound—are produced. In the supersonic wind tunnel (Fig. 4), the test section is preceded by a constriction, a so-called convergent-divergent nozzle, in which the very high speeds are attained. Each different supersonic speed requires the use of a differently shaped nozzle; in some tunnels the nozzle has a flexible wall so that it can be varied in shape by hydraulic adjusting equipment instead of having to be exchanged for another. Beyond the test section is a second constriction, in which the ultrasonic speed diminishes to subsonic values. The wind is produced by a multi-stage axial-flow compressor or by the high-speed jet from a set of gas turbines. The friction of the wind against the tunnel walls generates heat, which is removed by a cooler incorporated into the circuit, so as to maintain a constant temperature in the test section. The power requirement to maintain a continuous flow of air at supersonic speeds is very high. For very high speeds this becomes a very uneconomical method of operation, and to overcome this problem intermittently operated wind tunnels have been developed. Power is stored in the form of compressed air or vacuum, the wind being produced in short blasts, whereby a considerable saving in power input for operating the tunnel is effected. Broadly speaking, there are two types of intermittent wind tunnel. In one type the measurements are performed during the time when a valve between the test section and the pressure storage vessel (e.g., vacuum vessel, Fig. 5) is open. This vessel is connected to the wind tunnel through a quick-closing valve; the actual tunnel comprises a convergent-divergent nozzle, the test section, and a second constriction (the diffuser). Before the test commences, the vacuum vessel is evacuated; when the valve is opened, air rushes into the vessel so that a supersonic speed is attained in the test section, depending on the shape of the nozzle and the degree of vacuum in the vessel. So long as this vacuum is sufficient to maintain sonic speed in the throat of the nozzle, the supersonic speed in the test section remains constant. An air drier is installed at the intake to intercept any moisture that might condense into droplets in the test section, where they could disturb the flow conditions. The second type of intermittent wind tunnel (Fig. 6) is a tube along which gas is driven by various means for a very short time (a fraction of a second) during which the force acting on the model is measured by special techniques. The tube, which is of constant cross section and closed at both ends, is divided into a high-pressure and a low-pressure part by a gastight diaphragm. The test section, located behind a convergent-divergent nozzle, is in the high-pressure part. Before the test is started, the appropriate pressures are produced in the two parts of the tube by pumping in and pumping out air respectively. When the diaphragm is ruptured, a constant airflow speed will very briefly exist in the test section.

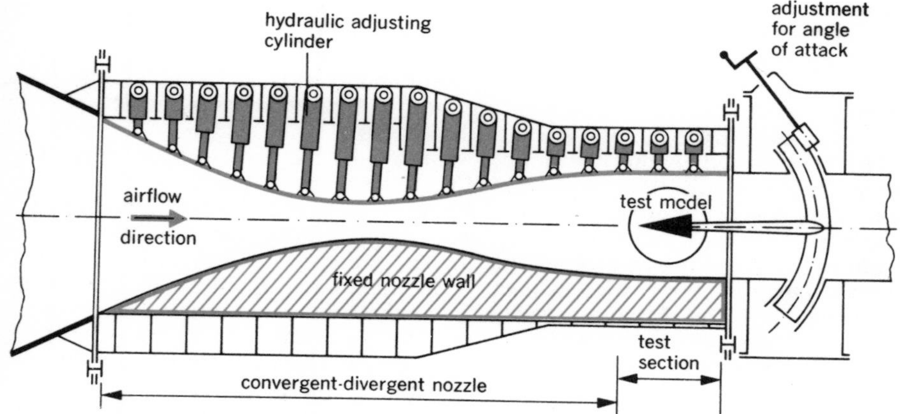

FIG. 4 CONVERGENT-DIVERGENT NOZZLE AND TEST-MODEL SUSPENSION IN SUPERSONIC WIND TUNNEL

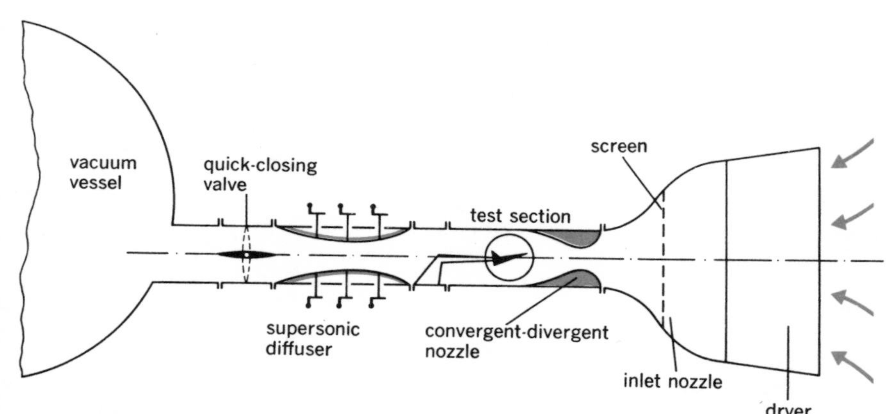

FIG. 5 INTERMITTENT WIND TUNNEL

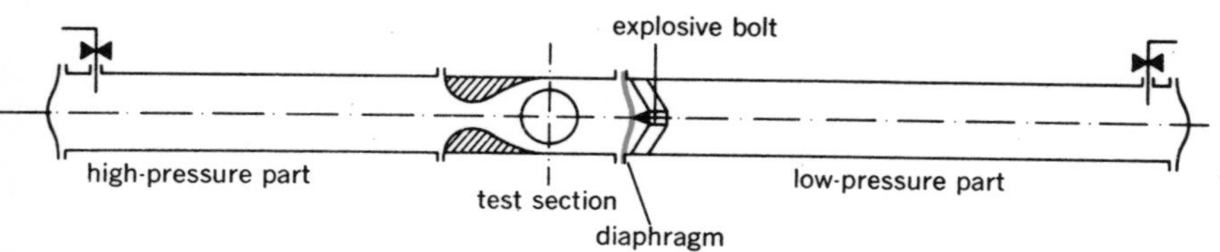

FIG. 6 INTERMITTENT WIND TUNNEL, SHOCK-WAVE TYPE

HYDRAULIC POWER SYSTEMS IN AIRCRAFT

In most aircraft, actuation of control surfaces (rudder, elevator, ailerons, flaps) and retractable landing gear is performed by hydraulic power transmission. One important reason why hydraulic systems have come to be widely used in aeronautical engineering is that they can transmit and exert large forces without taking up much space. The hydraulic working fluid is high-pressure oil, which also acts as a lubricant for the moving parts of the system.

The *pumps* used in the hydraulic system are of the displacement type. These pumps deliver a pulsating output which is, however, quite satisfactory for the purpose. They are of the rotary type (vane pumps; gear pumps) or the reciprocating type (plunger pumps); see Fig. 1. The plunger pump is the type most widely employed in aircraft because it can produce the highest pressures, mainly, up to about 350 kg/cm^2, which is about twice as high as the maximum attainable by gear pumps. Plunger pumps are of the radial-cylinder or the axial-cylinder type and comprise more than one cylinder, in order to equalize the pulsations in the output. The axial-cylinder pump is driven by a swash plate which drives the plungers by performing a wobbling rotary motion. The stroke of the plungers and therefore the output flow rate can be varied by tilting the swash plate (variable-stroke pump).

The hydraulic power supplied by the pumps is converted back into rotary motion by *hydraulic motors*. They are similar to pumps in construction in that they may be of the gear, vane or plunger type. In the last-mentioned type the plungers drive the swash plates, to which the power output is connected. *Hydraulic cylinders* convert hydraulic power into linear reciprocating motion by the admission of oil to one or the other side of the piston (Fig. 2). *Valves* serve to control the direction and rate of flow of the hydraulic oil, and to regulate the pressure. A relief valve bypasses the oil flow back to the tank as soon as the oil pressure exceeds a certain preset value. When it falls below this value, the valve automatically closes again. A pressure-reducing valve reduces the oil pressure of the system to a lower value which may be required for operating a second hydraulic system. Control valves are of various kinds, more particularly rotary valves and piston valves. Fig. 3 shows a section through a four-way/three-way piston valve: depending on the position to which the piston is moved, certain ports in the cylinder are opened and closed, causing the oil to flow as selected. Such selector valves may be operated manually, mechanically, electrically or hydraulically. Nonreturn valves (Fig. 4) cut off the oil flow in one direction, but allow it to pass in the other direction. Throttle valves are used to establish a particular oil-flow rate, which is dependent on the pressure, however. A flow-control valve, on the other hand, maintains the flow constant, regardless of the pressure. It comprises an adjustable throttle and a differential-pressure piston installed before or after it. Hydraulic accumulators in which oil is stored under constant pressure are employed in cases where oil-flow rates exceeding the delivery rate of the pump are required for short periods—e.g., when a number of controls in the aircraft have to be simultaneously actuated. Accumulators may be of the spring-loaded or the gas-pressure-operated type. In the former a spring-loaded piston keeps the oil under pressure in a cylinder; in the latter the same result is achieved by gas pressure on a diaphragm which transmits the pressure to the oil.

(more)

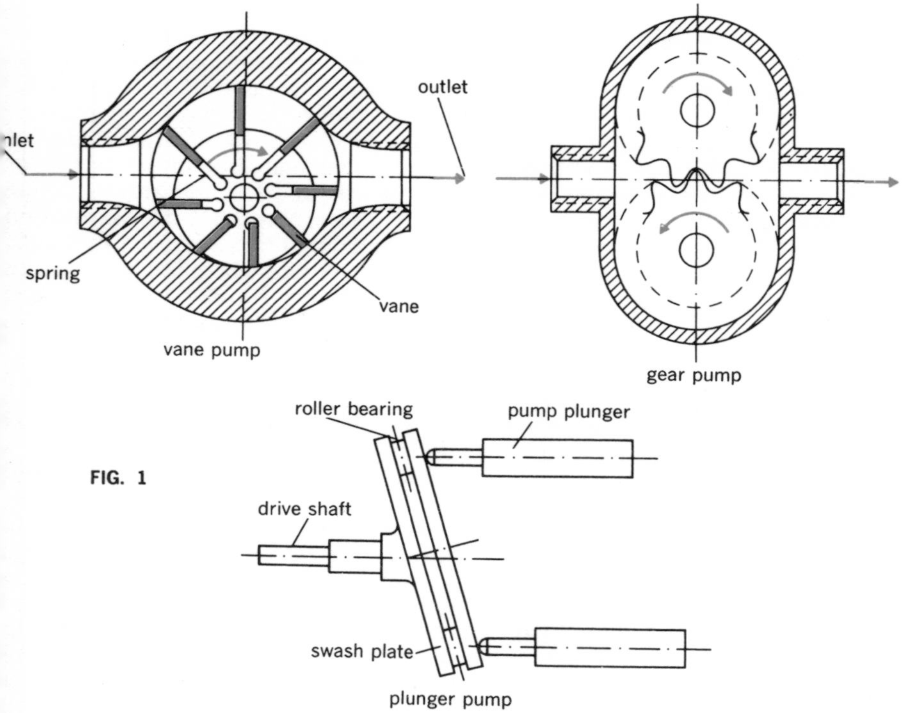

nlet
outlet
spring
vane
vane pump
gear pump
roller bearing
pump plunger
drive shaft
swash plate
plunger pump

FIG. 1

piston rod
connection A
connection B

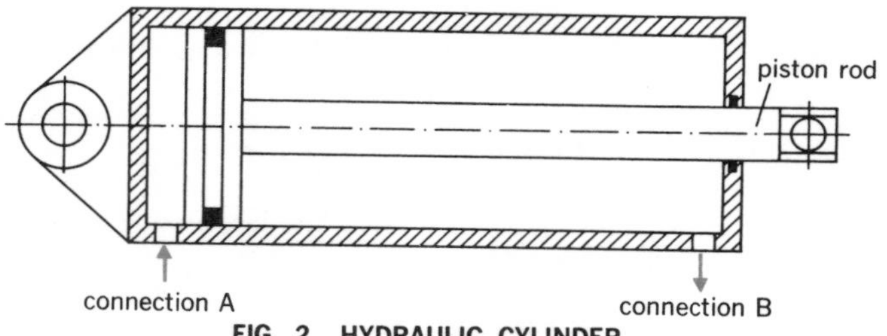

FIG. 2 HYDRAULIC CYLINDER

tank
cyl. A
pump
cyl. B

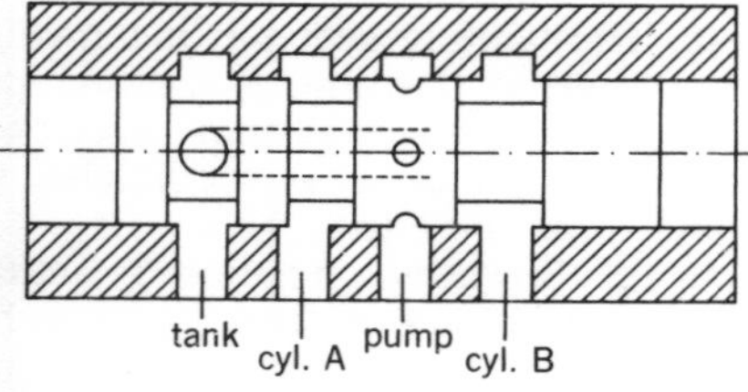

FIG. 3 FOUR-WAY/THREE-WAY PISTON VALVE

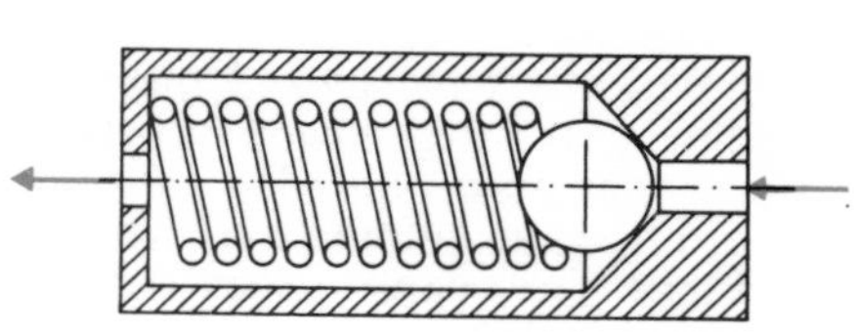

FIG. 4 NONRETURN VALVE

Hydraulic Power Systems in Aircraft (continued)

The hydraulic installation in a modern aircraft comprises the equipment fo supplying the oil under pressure (pumps), the pipeline system for distributing th oil, and the equipment for utilizing the hydraulic power (cylinders, hydrauli motors). In addition, there are devices for controlling the airflow and pressur (valves of various kinds); a monitoring system may also be incorporated. Th control surfaces of airliners and military aircraft are actuated by means of two o three systems which are entirely independent of one another and are also quit separate from the systems for operating the landing gear, brakes, etc. This separatio of the systems is a safeguard to obtain maximum functional reliability. The hydrauli working fluid is usually a mineral oil. However, for systems where fire hazard is a important consideration, a solution of glycol in water may be used, while syntheti fluids or silicic acid esters are used for systems in which high working temperature occur.

The accompanying diagram represents the hydraulic system operating the landin gear and flaps of a six-seater passenger aircraft.

1. Landing gear. Lowering the landing gear is initiated by means of a hand-operate control lever, whereby the following operations are set in motion:
(a) the "landing gear" selector valve is mechanically shifted from the locked neutra position to the "lowering" position;
(b) the loading valve cuts in the pump (closes the bypass), so that the pressure i the system builds up;
(c) by means of a limit switch, the energizing current of an electromagnet actuatin the "doors" selector valve is interrupted; the piston moves to its spring-controlle central position, in which the oil passages for opening the doors are connected t one another. While the aircraft is in flight, the electromagnet is constantly energize in order to keep the piston in its end position, against the action of the centerin springs. The reason for this arrangement is that it enables the doors to be opene in the event of a fault in the electric-power supply, because when that happens, th piston of the selector valve automatically moves to the central position, as alread described.

The flow of hydraulic oil passes through the "landing gear" selector valve an nonreturn valve to the "doors" selector valve, from where it flows to the door actuating cylinders. The oil first releases the mechanical locking devices of thes cylinders, so that the doors open and uncover the hatches through which the landin gear is lowered. When the doors are fully opened, the pressure in the hydrauli system rises. When a certain pressure has been reached, the connector valve allows oil to flow to the cylinders for releasing the landing gear. The pistons of thes cylinders are thus set in motion and at the same time, by means of a mechanica tripping device, cause the nonreturn valves to open, while the locking device securing the landing gear are released. The oil flows through the nonreturn valve into the actuating cylinders which lower the landing gear. A further buildup i pressure now occurs; the "landing gear" selector valve moves to its central positio and thereby relieves the pressure in the system. The landing gear has meanwhil automatically been locked mechanically in the lowered position. Retracting th landing gear after takeoff proceeds in the opposite sequence to that described except that now a time-lag valve delays the closing of the doors of the hatches t ensure that the landing gear has had ample time to be retracted and locked.

2. Flaps. The "flaps" selector valve is moved to the "lowering" position by actua tion of a hand-operated lever. Now again the loading valve cuts in the pump, thereb causing pressure to build up in the system. Interposed between the flap-actuatin cylinders and "flaps" selector valves is a throttle which prevents too-rapid lowerin of the flaps after the locking devices have been released.

Hydraulic system of a passenger aircraft in flight (piston in "doors" valve is in left-hand position)

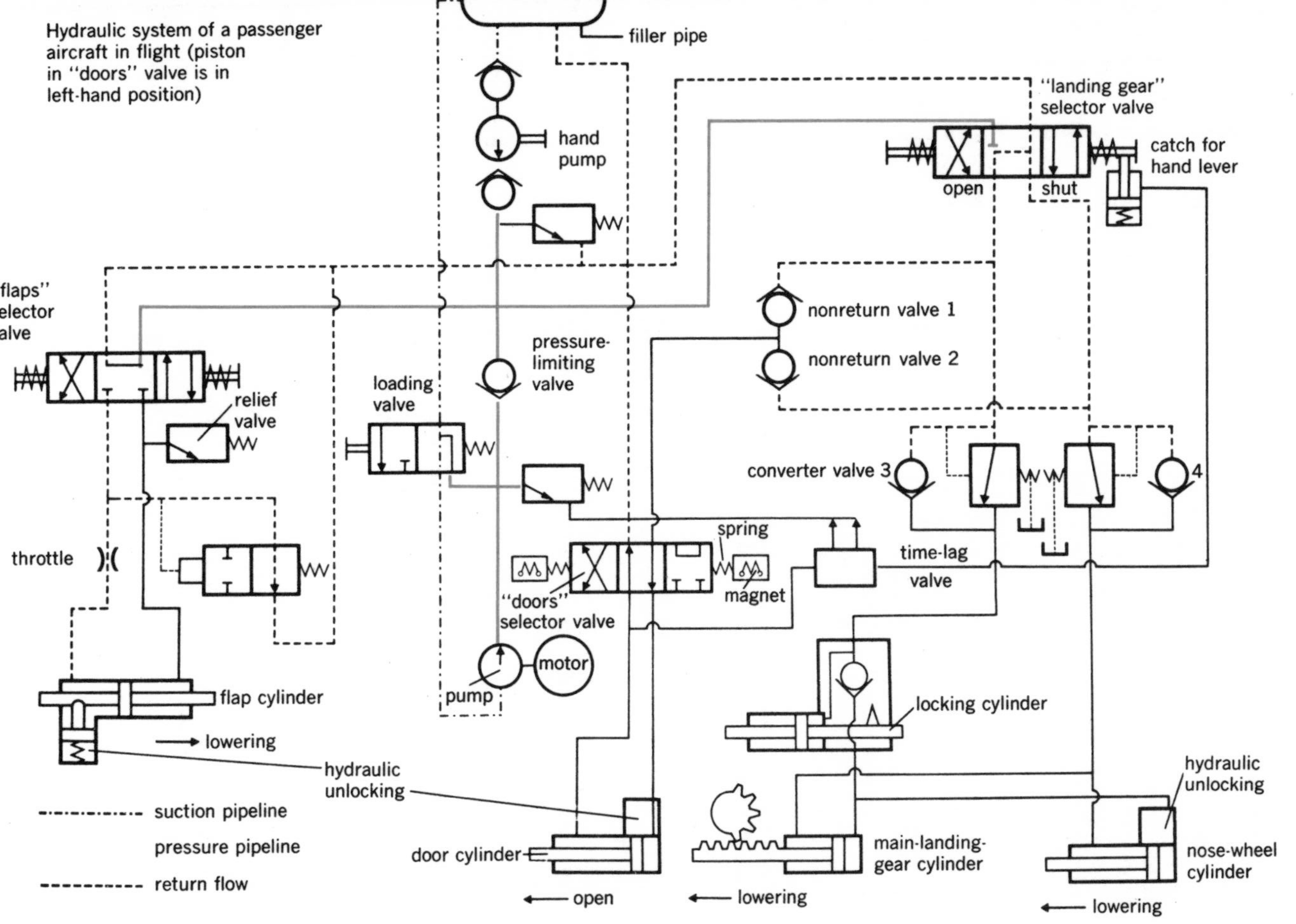

RAMJET PROPULSION

The ramjet engine (cf. Vol. II, page 292) began to compete with the turbojet when aircraft speeds increased beyond mach 2, thus entering a range where the compression produced by the airspeed becomes sufficient to perform the function of the compressor of the turbojet. For this reason the development of the ramjet—also known as the "athodyd," a contraction of "aerothermodynamic duct"—has come into prominence in recent years. The air rushes into the inlet at supersonic speed and enters the combustion chamber, where it is heated by the combustion of fuel injected into the chamber. The heated air and the gases of combustion are discharged from a nozzle, thus producing the thrust (Fig. 1). The main technical problem presented by the ramjet is to ensure steady combustion. For this it is generally necessary to have airflow speeds of less than about 100 m/sec (330 ft/sec) in the combustion chamber. This is a requirement difficult to fulfill at high airspeeds. For increasingly high speeds the ramjet evolves into something more resembling a rocket-propulsion unit (Fig. 2). In such engines the pressure developed in the combustion chamber is of the order of 100 atm. (about 1500 lb/in.^{2}), and the nozzle from which the jet emerges has to be made larger and larger. For very high speeds, in excess of mach 6, the engine evolves into the kind of system shown schematically in Fig. 3, where the inlet cone has become a specially shaped central body surrounded by an annular combustion chamber. As a result of allowing the gases of combustion to expand around the circumference of the conically tapering "tail" of the central body, a saving in overall construction weight of the engine is effected. From this example it is apparent how future high-speed ramjet engines are likely to become increasingly incorporated into the structure of the aircraft and thus become an integral feature thereof. The logical further development of the athodyd would consist in external combustion of fuel behind a shock wave. The shock wave is formed at the nose of the aircraft and is associated with an abrupt increase in pressure. It could therefore serve theoretically as the "front wall" of a combustion chamber, fuel being injected into the air behind the shock wave. The fuel would ignite spontaneously in consequence of the high temperature that always develops behind the shock wave. External expansion of the gases of combustion at the rear part of the aircraft provides the propelling thrust. The appropriately shaped surfaces represented in Fig. 4 may be conceived as part of the aircraft's fuselage or combination of fuselage and wing. This form of propulsion is in turn a transition to the athodyd with ultrasonic combustion. The main problem encountered here is that of stability of the flame. This may be achieved by enclosing it within a recirculation zone close to the surface of the aircraft (Fig. 5). Alternatively, the propulsion system may take the form of a rocket motor which emits a stream of fuel-enriched gas into which air is injected and which is then brought to combustion. The main difference in relation to the conventional ramjet with subsonic combustion is that, instead of having to reduce the supersonic speed of the intake air to a subsonic value low enough to permit flame stability in the combustion chamber, the greater part of the kinetic energy of the intake air is now not converted into potential energy by adiabatic compression. This compression prior to combustion in the conventional ramjet reduces the efficiency of the ramjet at high mach numbers.

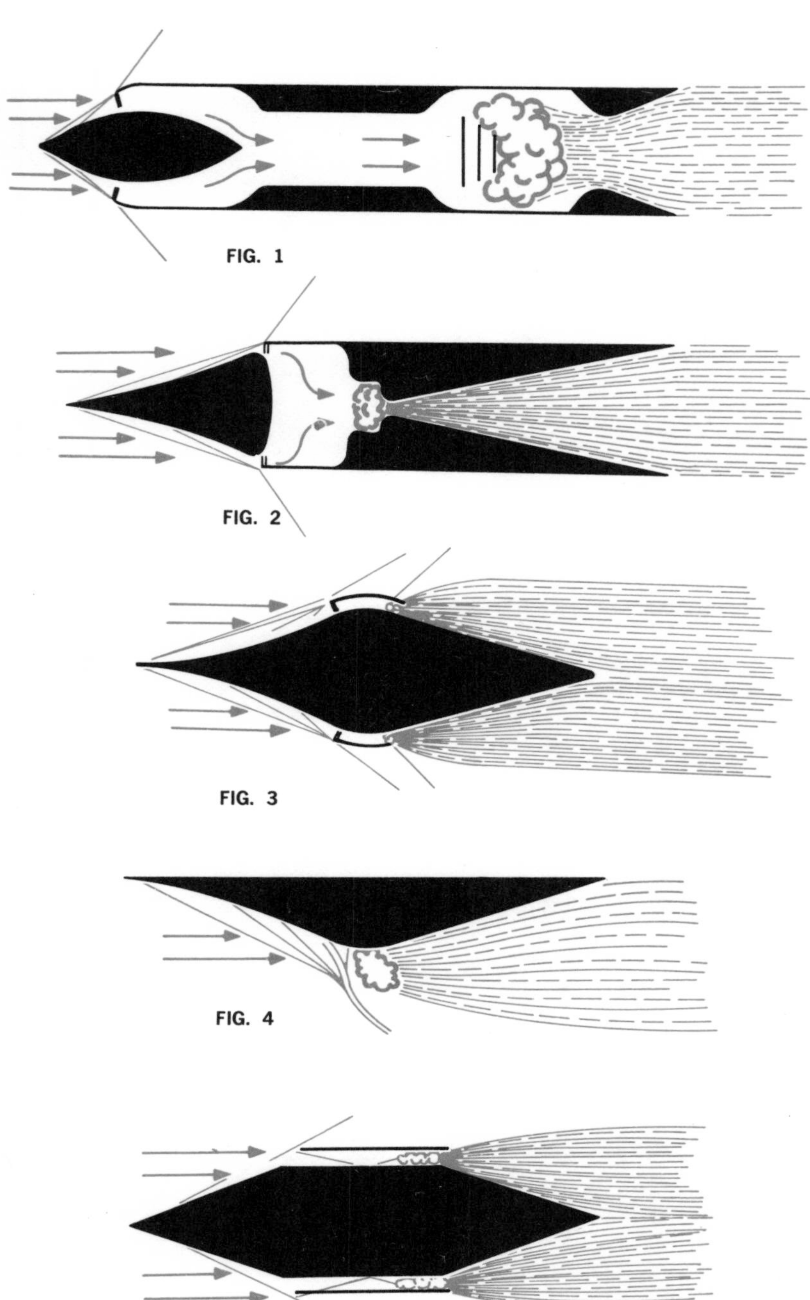
FIG. 1
FIG. 2
FIG. 3
FIG. 4
FIG. 5

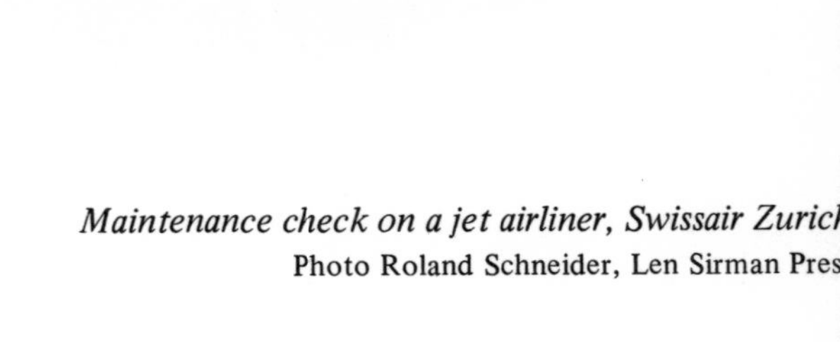

Maintenance check on a jet airliner, Swissair Zurich
Photo Roland Schneider, Len Sirman Press

VERTICAL-TAKEOFF-AND-LANDING AIRCRAFT (VTOL)

Aircraft capable of vertical takeoff and landing (usually abbreviated as VTOL have important military and civil potentialities and are under active developmen by aircraft firms in a number of countries. One general advantage claimed for thes aircraft is their greater safety in that the hazards associated with conventional takeof and landing are eliminated. A further advantage is that they do not require airfield with long and expensive runways (see Fig. 1), so that, despite the higher direc operating costs of VTOL aircraft, an overall saving is effected in comparison wit conventional aircraft.

Of course, the helicopter (cf. Vol. II, page 290) has essentially solved the problem of vertical takeoff and landing, but its applications are limited by its relatively low speed. In recent years a large number of new VTOL aircraft types have emerged Vertical takeoff without the use of large rotors became practicable with the advent of the gas-turbine engine because it could generate much more thrust for a give weight than the piston engine. Many new problems have had to be solved: e.g., in connection with stability and control during hovering and the transition from vertical to forward flight, and vice versa, since conventional control surfaces ar ineffective at low forward speeds.

Depending on the position of the aircraft during the takeoff, a distinction is mad between "tail sitters" and "flat risers." In the first-mentioned category the whol aircraft rests with its tail on the ground and its nose pointing vertically upwards After takeoff, it is gradually brought into the normal flying position by operatio of the controls. The "flat riser" takes off in the normal position, i.e., with the fuselag parallel to the ground. In this last-mentioned category of VTOL aircraft, th propulsion engines may be swiveled from the vertical position for takeoff and landing to horizontal for forward propulsion. This principle is illustrated for a propeller engine in Fig. 2. With turbojet propulsion, the propulsion engines can b used for takeoff and landing by suitably directing the jets downwards. In additio to the propeller VTOL aircraft and the turbojet VTOL aircraft, a third type is based on the ducted fan, this being a propeller or fan within a duct or shroud, which in some types can be tilted in the same manner as the propeller engine in Fig. 2. In Fig. 3 a ducted-fan propulsion unit of the dual-propulsion type is illustrated. It is a combination of a ducted fan and a jet engine. Each of the two wings of the aircraft may be provided with such a fan, "buried" in the thickness of the wing. The jet engine provides the propulsion in the normal way when the aircraft is in forward flight. For takeoff and landing, the jet exhaust is deflected to drive the fan, which thus develops a powerful vertical thrust.

The present trend of development is toward the direct utilization of the thrust developed by turbojet (cf. Vol. II, page 296). In a case where separate lift engines are provided in addition to the propulsion engine there is of course the problem of extra weight due to having two sets of engines, only one of which is in use at any particular time. In this respect the arrangement where only one set of engines is provided, which can be swiveled from vertical to horizontal, and vice versa, or where the jets themselves can be deflected to produce a thrust in the desired direction (Fig. 4) is advantageous. This is especially true in high-speed fighter aircraft, whose engines produce a large thrust which can be utilized for vertical takeoff. On the other hand, separate lift engines (as in Fig. 5) or a combination of swiveling jet engines and a set of auxiliary lift engines (as in Fig. 6) may be more advantageous for other types of aircraft, such as civil aircraft, with lower cruising speeds.

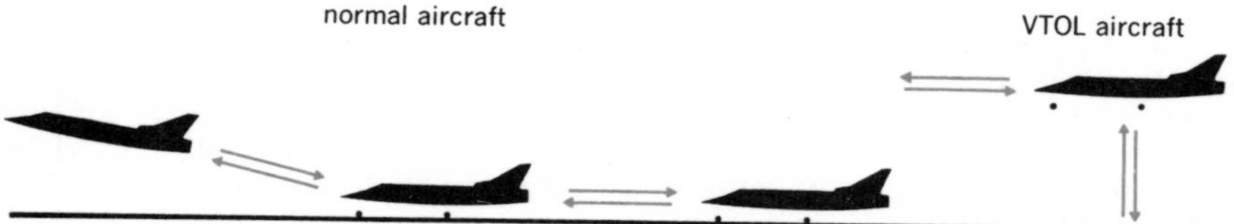

FIG. 1

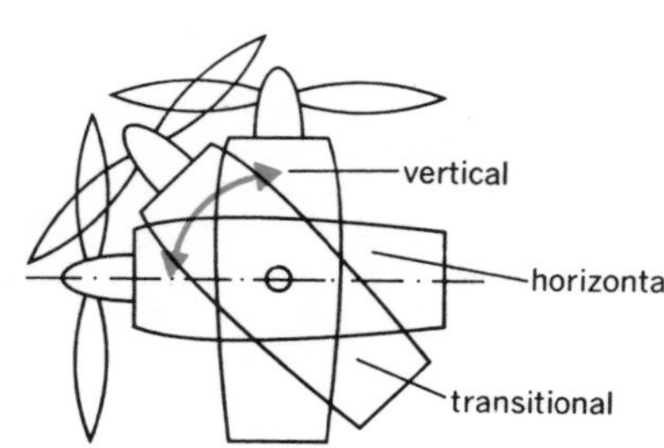

FIG. 2 SWIVELING ENGINE (PRINCIPLE)

FIG. 3

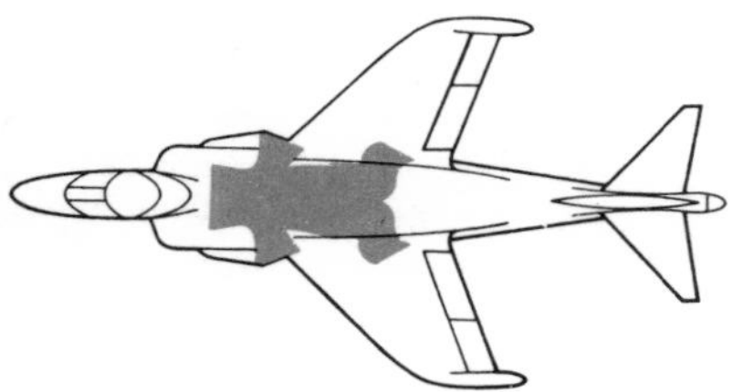

FIG. 4a

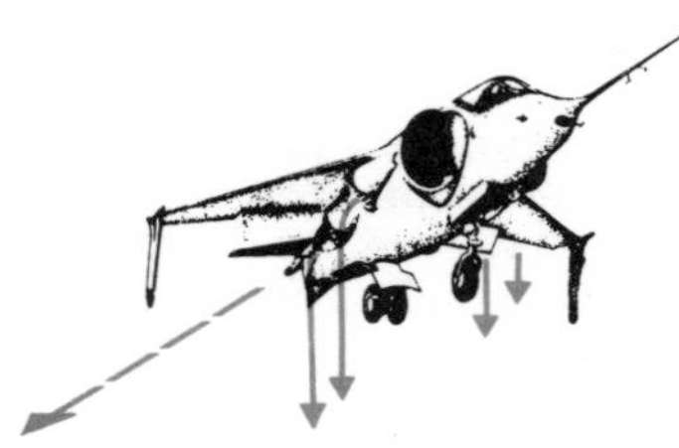

FIG. 4b

FIG. 5

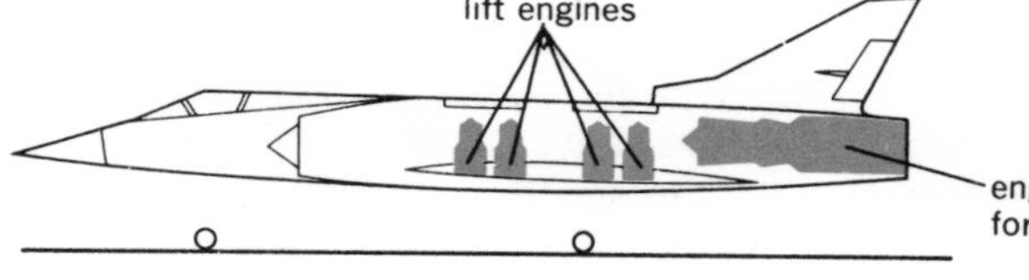

engine for
forward propulsion

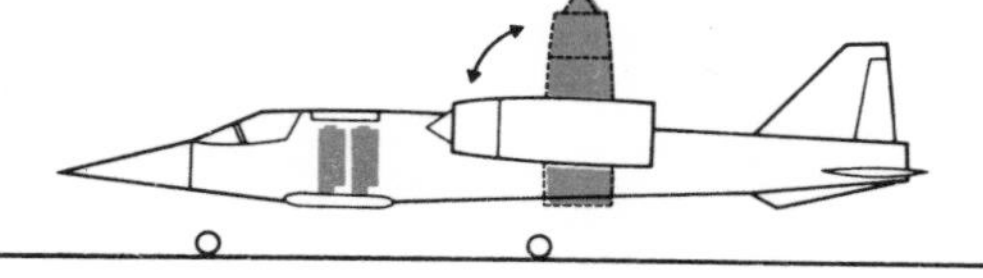

FIG. 6

YACHTS

"Yacht" denotes a comparatively small vessel propelled by sail or power and used for pleasure and for racing purposes. In the present article only sail-driven boats—with or without auxiliary engines—will be considered. Thus "yachting" here refers to the sport of cruising and racing in sailing craft, which may be of many and widely varying types, ranging in size from small boats to large oceangoing yachts.

The term "yacht" is of Dutch origin—"jacht," meaning "hunt" or "chase." From the 14th century onward the seafaring people of Holland had built small, highly maneuverable craft for hunting down pirates and smugglers. At a later period these boats came to be used for pleasure cruising or racing, and it is in this context that the term is now used, to the exclusion of all craft primarily serving commercial or other purposes (fishing boats, cargo ships, etc.). In 1660 the King of England, Charles II, was presented with a Dutch yacht. This marked the beginning of yacht building in England. Tradition has it that the first regatta—a race between small sailing craft—took place in 1662. The year 1720 saw the foundation of the world's first yacht club, the Cork Harbour Water Club, in Ireland. The second yacht club was an English one: the Cumberland Fleet, founded in 1775, of which the Royal Thames Yacht Club is the descendant. Yachting in the modern sense, however, started with the establishment of the Yacht Club (now the Royal Yacht Squadron) at Cowes, Isle of Wight, in 1812. The Yacht Racing Association (Y.R.A.) was founded in 1875 with the object of establishing rules for regatta racing.

American yachting can be said to have started in the early part of the 18th century, but it was not until early in the next century that sailing for pleasure came to be more widely practiced. The New York Yacht Club (N.Y.Y.C.) was founded in 1844. The yachts of that period were usually schooner-rigged, tending to follow the models developed for commercial purposes. The Southern Yacht Club, New Orleans, was founded in 1859, and a number of other American yacht clubs were formed in the next two decades. At present there are close to a thousand yacht clubs in the United States, a high proportion of which are concentrated in the New York area. A very important event in the history of international yachting was the victory of the 100-ft. 170-ton schooner *America* in a 53-mile race around the Isle of Wight against a large number of British yachts in 1851. In that race this yacht won a 100-guinea cup offered by the Royal Yacht Squadron. In 1857 the owners of the *America* presented the cup to the N.Y.Y.C. (henceforth known as the "America's cup") as a perpetual challenge trophy in a race open to competitors from all countries. These contests have had considerable influence on the evolution of modern yacht design.

Figs. 1 and 3 show two basic types of small sailing craft. The small boat illustrated in Fig. 1 has a drop keel which can be raised and lowered. When the boat is sailing before the wind, the keel is raised to reduce resistance and thus increase speed. With side wind, however, the keel is lowered to counteract lateral drift and assist in obtaining a forward-propelling component of the wind force on the sails (Fig. 2; see also Vol. II, p. 274). Most larger yachts have fixed keels, lead-ballasted to reduce the risk of capsizing (Fig. 3). However, the drop keel is not confined entirely to very small craft; it is used in certain boats up to about 30 ft. in length because of the more versatile performance it provides.

(more)

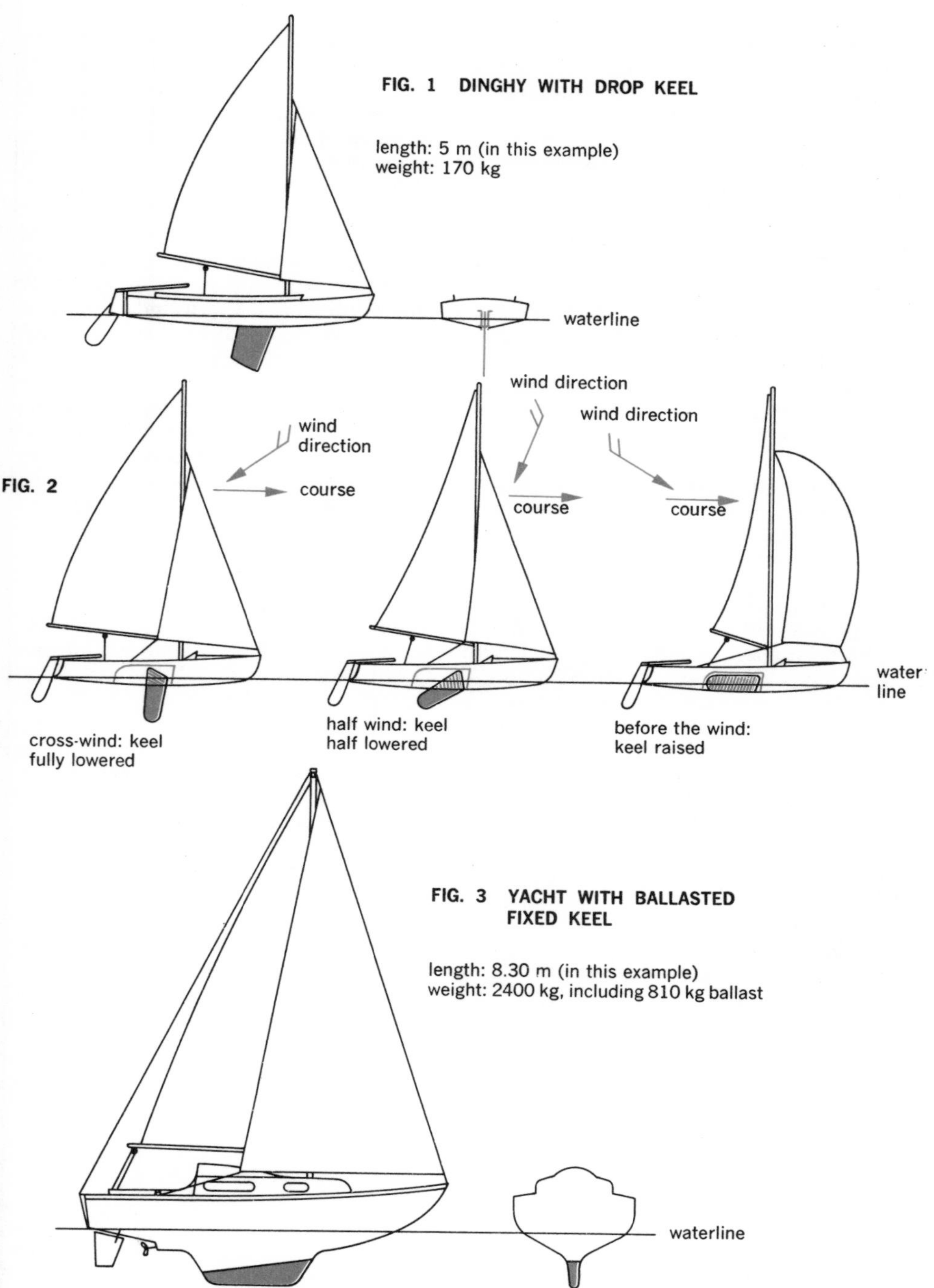
FIG. 1 DINGHY WITH DROP KEEL
length: 5 m (in this example)
weight: 170 kg
waterline
FIG. 2
wind direction
course
wind direction
course
wind direction
course
water line
cross-wind: keel fully lowered
half wind: keel half lowered
before the wind: keel raised
FIG. 3 YACHT WITH BALLASTED FIXED KEEL
length: 8.30 m (in this example)
weight: 2400 kg, including 810 kg ballast
waterline

The early racing yachts differed widely from one another in size and design. In order to obtain something approaching a fair basis of comparison in contests between different types, measurement formulas and rating rules were developed. The competing yachts were measured and appropriate allowances (time allowance, handicap) were made to compensate for the inherent differences in performance between the various types. Essentially the results of races thus came to be judged on the basis of the time taken to complete the course instead of on the basis of "absolute" performance in the sense that the first arrival at the end of the course must necessarily be the winner of the contest. Over the years the formulas employed in various countries and by various yachting organizations have become increasingly complex. For international ocean racing, the British rules and formulas generally employed are those of the Royal Ocean Racing Club (R.O.R.C.), founded in 1925, or those of the Cruising Club of America (C.C.A.), founded in 1922. There is as yet no single internationally adopted set of rules, and it may well occur that a particular type of yacht which receives a favorable rating under one country's rules will not be so favorably rated under another's. However, with the increase in regatta sailing in the present century there has been a trend toward precise specification and classification of yachts, especially in the smaller sizes, so that contests on an "absolute" basis between virtually identical craft can be arranged. In these standard classes even such particulars as the type and thickness of the wood for the hull and other parts are carefully specified, while differences in length and weight between different boats of the same class are not permitted to exceed a few millimeters or a few grams.

Of international interest are more particularly the classes selected by the International Yacht Racing Union (I.Y.R.U.) for Olympic racing:

Finn Dinghy: one-man dinghy, length 4.50 m, beam 1.51 m, weight 105 kg, sail area 10 m^2. The boat is sailed with only a mainsail, no jib (Fig. 4).

Flying Dutchman: two-man dinghy, length 6.05 m, beam 1.80 m, weight 170 kg, sail area 15 m^2. This is the most up-to-date and fastest type of conventional sailing boat (Fig. 5).

Star class: two-man fixed-keel yacht, length 6.92 m, beam 1.73 m, weight 750 kg, sail area 26.13 m^2. The Star is one of the oldest international racing classes (Fig. 6).

Dragon class: three-man fixed-keel yacht with cabin, length 8.90 m, beam 1.90 m, weight approx. 2000 kg, sail area 26.60 m^2. Originally designed (in 1929) as an ordinary cruiser-racer, it has since developed into a pure first-class racing yacht (Fig. 7).

5.5 m class: three-man fixed-keel open yacht (no cabin); dimensions not precisely laid down, but must conform to a specific formula; length a little over 10 m, beam approx. 2 m, weight approx. 2000 kg, sail area approx. 29 m^2. Within the limits permitted by the formula, the designer of this class of boat has a good deal of freedom (Fig. 8).

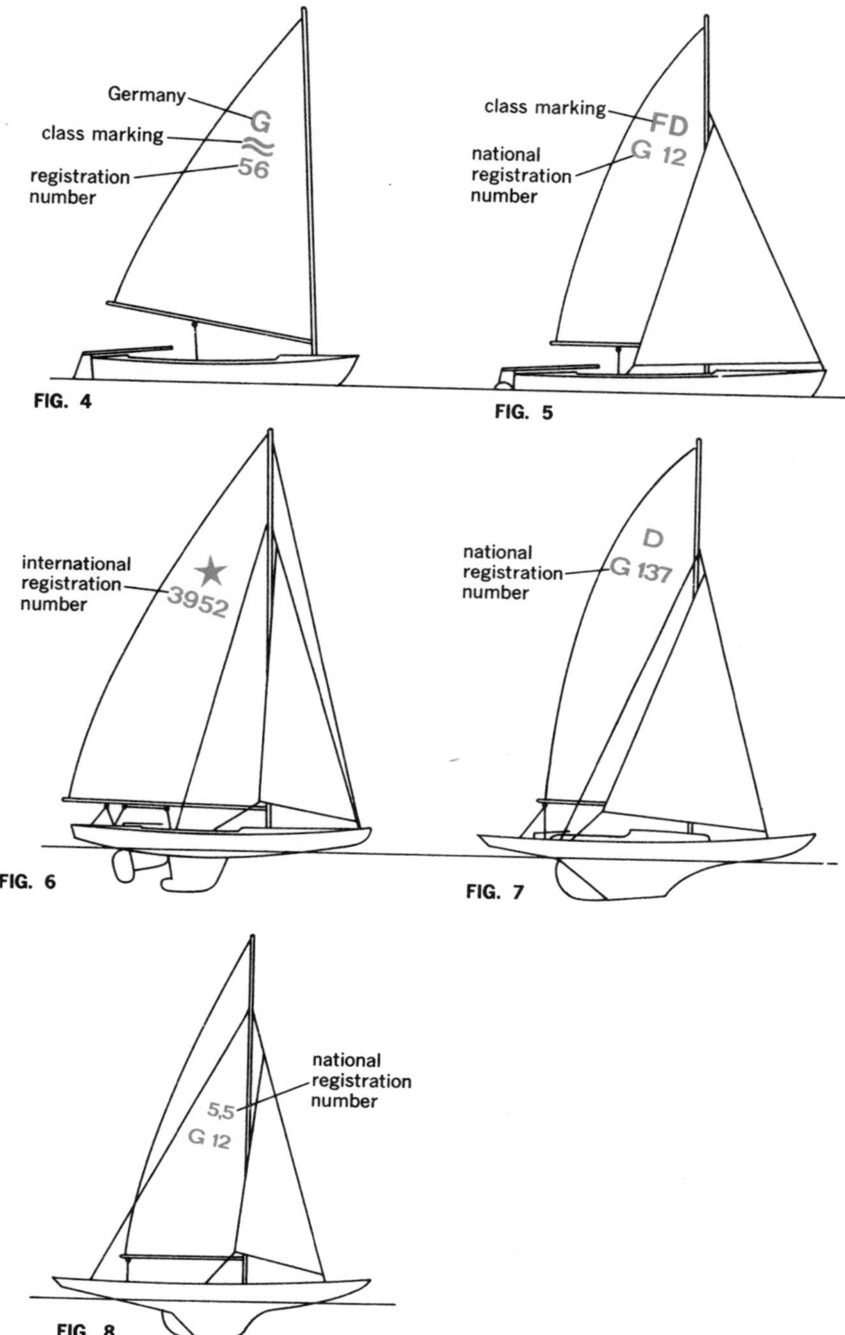
Germany
G
class marking
56
registration
number
FIG. 4
class marking
FD
national
registration
number
G 12
FIG. 5
international
registration
number
3952
FIG. 6
D
national
registration
number
G 137
FIG. 7
5,5
G 12
national
registration
number
FIG. 8

SUBMARINES

A submarine is a naval vessel that can operate on the surface or underwater. A distinction must accordingly be made between the vessel's displacement on the surface and its greater displacement when submerged. For example, these displacements are 1300 tons and 1575 tons, respectively, for the British "T" class submarine, which is a typical conventional submarine developed in World War II. It is 273 ft. in length. Modern submarines range in size from relatively small vessels intended for use in coastal waters (e.g., about 140 ft. long, with 359/430 tons displacement) to large oceangoing long-distance vessels (e.g., about 420 ft. long, with 7900/9000 tons displacement).

When floating on the surface, the submarine displaces a tonnage of water equivalent to the vessel's own weight. In the submerged condition the submarine is in a state of neutral buoyancy, i.e., it can then, with only minor changes in the quantity of water ballast, be made to float at any desired level. Continual adjustment is necessary to maintain this condition, as the submarine uses up fuel when cruising underwater. Consumption of food and water by the crew, and the firing of torpedoes, must also be compensated. Since the center of gravity of the submarine never exactly coincides with the center of buoyancy, motionless "hovering" is hardly possible in actual practice: the submarine must always have a certain amount of forward motion to enable it to maintain its depth with the aid of the hydroplanes, which moreover keep the vessel at the desired angle.

The main part of the submarine is the pressure hull, which usually has a circular shape in cross section (see Figs. 1a to 1e). This cylindrical shape is most suitable for withstanding the water pressure to which it is subjected at great depths. The hulls of modern submarines are always of welded steel construction and are divided into compartments separated by strong bulkheads. Approximately amidships is the superstructure, comprising the conning tower and bridge. The tower is provided with upper and lower hatches giving access to the interior of the submarine.

Under the tower is the control room. Enclosing the pressure hull is a casing; water has free access (through suitable apertures) to the space between this casing

(more)

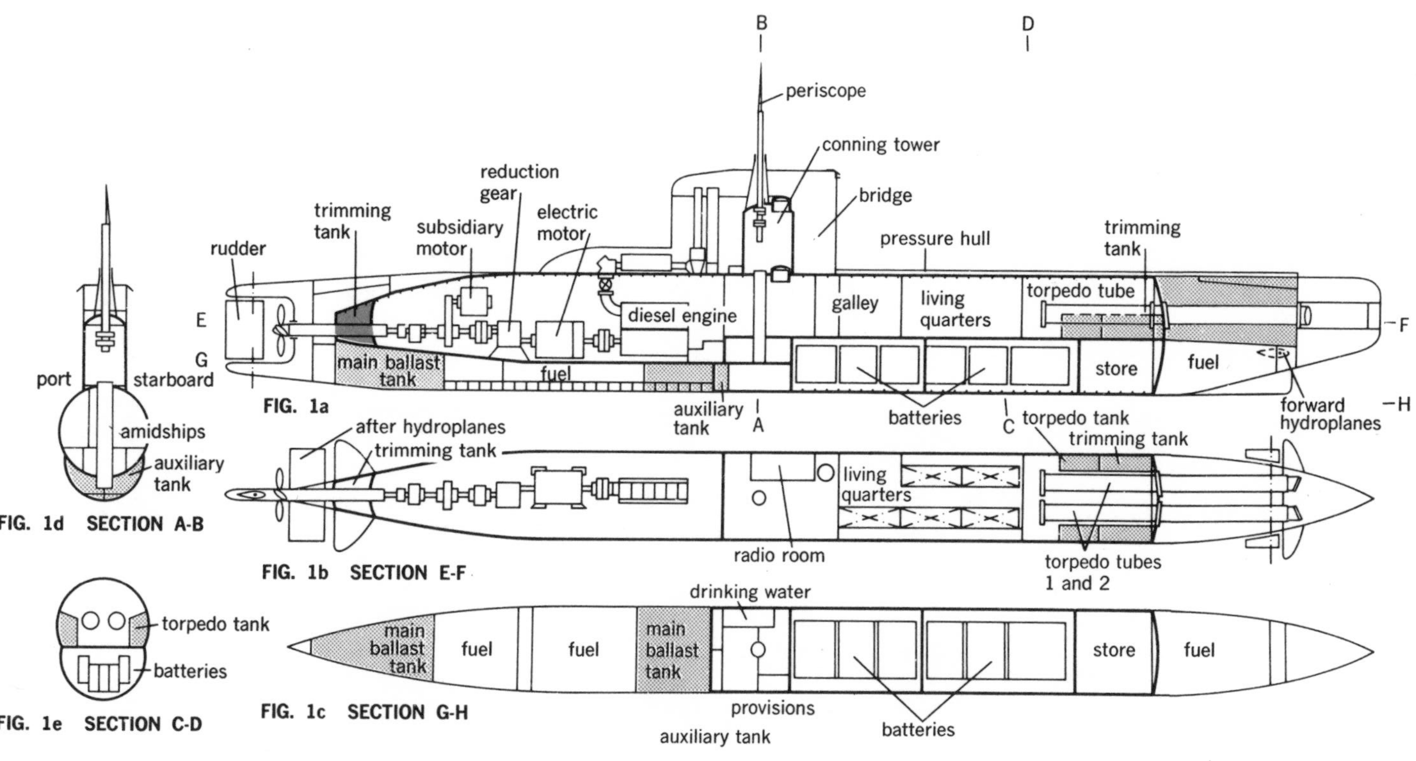

FIG. 1a

FIG. 1b SECTION E-F

FIG. 1c SECTION G-H

FIG. 1d SECTION A-B

FIG. 1e SECTION C-D

Crewmen of the USS Dace in the conning tower during sea trials for this nuclear submarine
Photo USIS

Submarines (continued)

and the hull. Contained within or outside the hull are various tanks, more particularly the fuel tanks and the water-ballast tanks (see Figs. 2a–2e). The latter comprise the main ballast tanks (which are empty when the submarine is on the surface and are completely flooded when it dives), the trimming tanks (forward and after trimming tanks) and the auxiliary tanks (amidships). The two last-mentioned sets of tanks serve to keep the vessel "in trim" by compensating for changes in weight due to fuel consumption, etc. The trimming tanks correct any alteration in the longitudinal distribution weight, while the auxiliary tanks are for control of overall weight. Rapid flooding of the main ballast tanks is essential to enable the submarine to dive quickly; they are provided with large power-operated vents and flood valves.

If the submarine has some forward motion when it dives (as is usually the case), the forward tanks are flooded a few seconds before the after tanks, so that the bow dips and the vessel's motion helps it to glide quickly under the surface, assisted by the hydroplanes. The submerged submarine is controlled by means of the hydroplanes (depth fins) at front and rear. These help to maintain depth and keep the vessel at the desired angle. The control effect of the hydroplanes is greater according as the submarine's forward speed is greater. Surfacing is effected by admitting compressed air to the ballast tanks and thus expelling the water.

The main propulsion of a conventional submarine is provided by diesel engines. As these engines require air, they could formerly be used only for propelling the submarine on the surface. Underwater it was always necessary to use battery-powered electric motors. A large submarine may have four main propulsion diesel engines, each with an output of 1600 hp. In a modern submarine the diesel engines are not, as a rule, directly connected by mechanical means to the propellers. Instead, they drive generators which supply electricity to the motors that drive the propellers. A World War II development is the "schnorkel," a breathing tube which is raised while the submarine is operating at periscope depth. Air for the diesel engines is drawn in through this tube, and the exhaust gases are expelled from a second tube. Diesel-powered propulsion is thus possible even when the submarine is almost totally submerged. For operating at greater depths the diesels and generators are not used, the power for the motors being supplied by storage batteries, which are

(more)

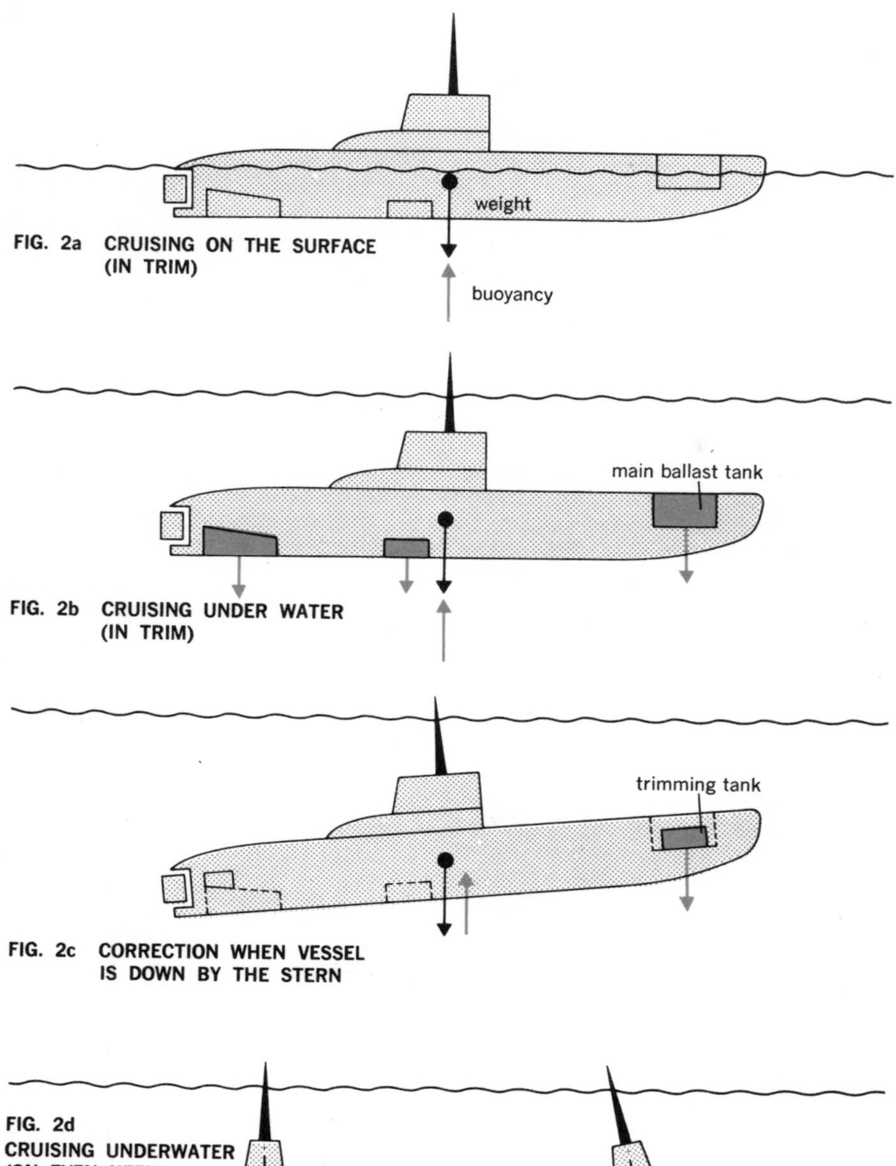

FIG. 2a CRUISING ON THE SURFACE (IN TRIM)

FIG. 2b CRUISING UNDER WATER (IN TRIM)

FIG. 2c CORRECTION WHEN VESSEL IS DOWN BY THE STERN

FIG. 2d CRUISING UNDERWATER (ON EVEN KEEL)

FIG. 2e CORRECTION FOR HEEL

charged when the submarine is cruising on the surface. The top of the inlet tube of the "schnorkel" (also spelled "snorkel" and known as "snort" in Britain) is provided with an automatic quick-closing intake valve which prevents the entry of water (Figs. 3a and 3b).

The first nuclear-powered submarine was the U.S.S. *Nautilus* (1955). The heat produced by a nuclear reactor is used to generate steam which drives the main propulsion turbines and the turbogenerators, both on the surface and submerged. This obviates the need for the submarine to surface for charging the batteries. It can therefore remain submerged for many weeks, if necessary. The heat from the reactor is first transferred to the so-called primary water system, which is superheated under high pressure and is used to generate steam in the secondary water system, in which the water is circulated through a "boiler" in the form of a heat exchanger. The dry saturated steam is passed to the turbines. The spent steam is condensed back into water, which is recirculated through the heat exchanger.

The periscope of a modern submarine is a complicated optical device, comprising prisms and lenses, which gives a view of the surrounding horizon while the vessel remains submerged. A typical periscope is about forty feet in length and can be raised or lowered by telescoping action (Figs. 4a and 4b). It not only provides a view around the horizon, but is equipped with a tilting head prism by means of which the observer can also scan the sky and which permits correction for roll or pitch of the vessel. Navigational sightings on stars can be taken by means of a sextant device. Scales are also provided which enable the observer to gauge distances and estimate the size of objects in the field of view. As a rule, a submarine is equipped with two periscopes, the high-power and the low-power periscope, the latter being used in the final stages of an attack.

On the surface the submarine can avail itself of all modern navigational aids, such as radar. When submerged below periscope depth, sonar apparatus is used ("sonar" is a contraction of "sound navigation and ranging"), which uses sound waves more or less in the manner that radar uses high-frequency radio pulses. The interval between the emission of the pulse and the arrival of its echo enables the distance between the submarine and, for example, an enemy ship to be determined. Large submarines are further equipped with inertial navigation systems, which are independent of outside signals (see page 104).

The torpedo has long been the classic weapon of the submarine (p. 248, Vol. III), for both offensive and defensive purposes. The torpedo tubes can be fired electrically or by hand when surfaced or submerged. Modern developments include various types of rocket-torpedo devices, remote-controlled and/or provided with equipment for automatically homing onto the target. An important development of the past decade has been the missile-launching submarine. In the earlier stages the submarine had to surface before it could fire its missiles, but with the advent of the Polaris ballistic missile, and its successors, launching is now effected from the submerged vessel. Each Polaris submarine carries sixteen of these missiles, which currently have a range of 2500 miles.

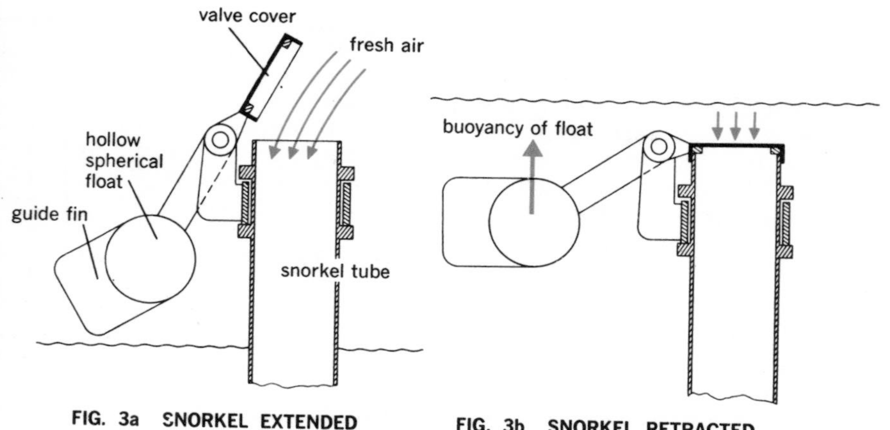

FIG. 3a SNORKEL EXTENDED

FIG. 3b SNORKEL RETRACTED

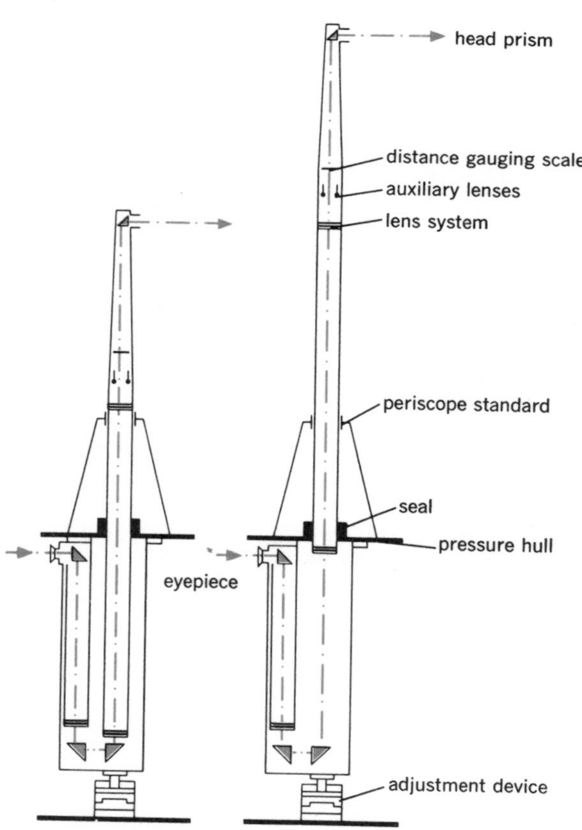

FIG. 4 PERISCOPE: (a) RETRACTED;
(b) EXTENDED (RAISED)

SHIP STABILIZING

A ship at sea performs rolling and pitching movements about its longitudinal and its transverse axis respectively (Fig. 1). Rolling, in particular, is disagreeable to crew and passengers because of its relatively large amplitude, besides presenting problems with regard to the storage of cargo. The rolling motion depends on various factors: the wave movement according to the state of the sea, the vessel's moment of inertia with respect to the rolling axis, the damping moment due to friction between the hull and the water, and the stability moment, determined by the horizontal distance between center of gravity and center of buoyancy (cf. Vol. II, page 272).

Various kinds of devices, known as stabilizers, have been developed for the purpose of reducing the rolling motion of ships. In general these devices are of the "passive" or of the "active" type. The action of a passive stabilizer is initiated by the rolling itself, i.e., such a device *responds* to the motion and takes corrective action. On the other hand, an active stabilizer has preset control whereby the corrective action in the form of a counteracting movement is programed to take place simultaneously with the occurrence of the disturbing movement that causes the rolling of the ship. The wave movements, in particular, are never quite regular, but it is nevertheless possible, by means of appropriately designed active stabilizers, to reduce rolling by at least 75%. The greatest effect is obtained when the stabilizer operates at the natural frequency of the ship, but with a phase difference of 90 degrees in relation to the ship's motion.

The simplest stabilizing device is the bilge keel (Fig. 2), one such keel being fitted on each side and extending about 30–50% of the ship's length. Bilge keels develop considerable resistance to the rolling motion and thus reduce it. The stabilizing effect achieved by these keels depends to a great extent on the speed of the ship. They have the drawback that they present a not inconsiderable resistance and thus slow down the vessel. Instead of being a continuous keel, the stabilizing device may take the form of a series of short fins having a streamlined shape in section so as to reduce the resistance.

Stabilizing (or antiroll) tanks are located on each side of the ship and are interconnected by two pipes (Fig. 3). The tanks are about half filled with water, oil or some other suitable liquid. Water flows through the lower pipe from the upper to the lower side when the ship heels over, while the upper pipe serves to equalize the air pressure in the tanks. This upper pipe contains a throttle which is adjusted to regulate the airflow and thus control the flow of water from one tank to the other in accordance with the rolling conditions. A well-known stabilizing device is the gyrostabilizer (Fig. 4). It consists of a large and heavy steel rotor located on the center line of the ship and mounted in horizontal transverse gudgeon bearings. When the ship is on an even keel, the rotor axis is vertical. A sensitive small control gyroscope responds immediately to any rolling motion of the ship and transmits a counteracting motion to the gyrostabilizer, which thus exerts a righting force against the action of the wave which tends to roll the vessel over.

(more)

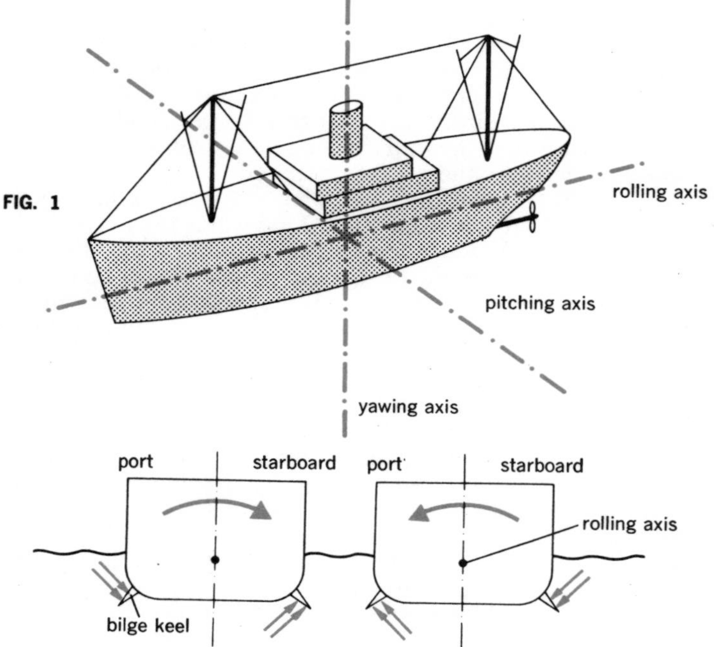

FIG. 1

FIG. 2 BILGE KEEL (PASSIVE)

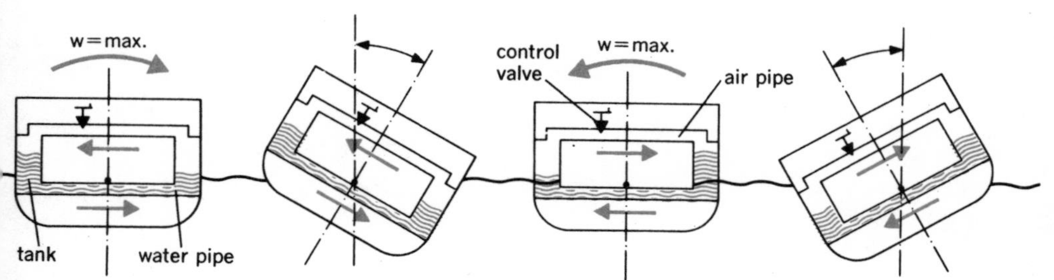

FIG. 3 STABILIZING TANKS (PASSIVE)

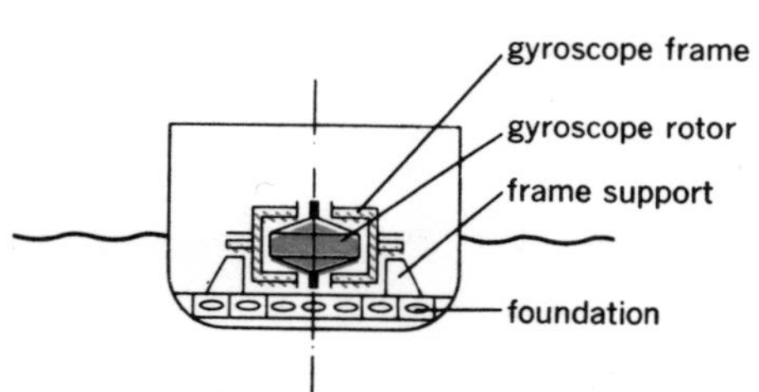

FIG. 4 GYROSTABILIZER (PASSIVE)

The simplest form of active stabilizer is the antiroll device shown schematically in Fig. 5. It comprises a heavily ballasted truck or trolley which travels on a track extending transversely and is so propelled by an electric motor that the moment developed by the trolley's weight counteracts the wave moment that causes rolling. The motor is under the direction of a control gyroscope. This installation can alternatively be used to give the ship a rolling motion in calm water, as is sometimes necessary for experimental and testing purposes.

"Activated" antiroll tanks (Fig. 6) differ from the ordinary "passive" type, already described, in that the movement of the water from one side of the ship to the other is now not made dependent on the action of a throttle valve, but is controlled by a pump installed in the lower pipe or by a blower controlling the airflow and pressure in the upper pipe and air-filled space above the liquid in the tanks. Again the operation of the pump or blower is under the direction of a control gyroscope. This installation can likewise be used to produce rolling motion in calm water.

A fin stabilizing system (Fig. 7) comprises a set of retractable fins mounted approximately amidships on each side of the vessel. These fins can be pivoted in opposite directions about axes extending transversely to the vessel's longitudinal center line. They reduce the rolling motion by developing a counteracting effect which depends on the angle at which the fins are set, the size of the fins, and the speed of the vessel. Control equipment ensures that the fins are at all times swiveled to the appropriate angle for most effectively counteracting the wave action tending to cause rolling. Optimum performance is achieved only within a certain speed range, and careful design of the stabilizing system is necessary to make it as effective as possible. When not in use, the fins can be retracted into the hull or swung back into recesses provided for them.

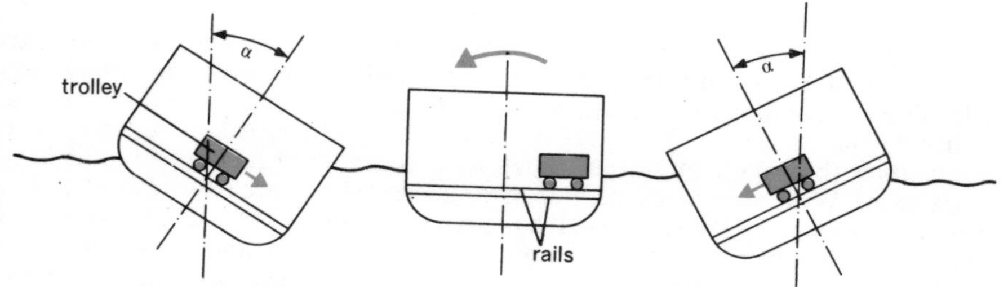

FIG. 5 STABILIZING TROLLEY (ACTIVE)

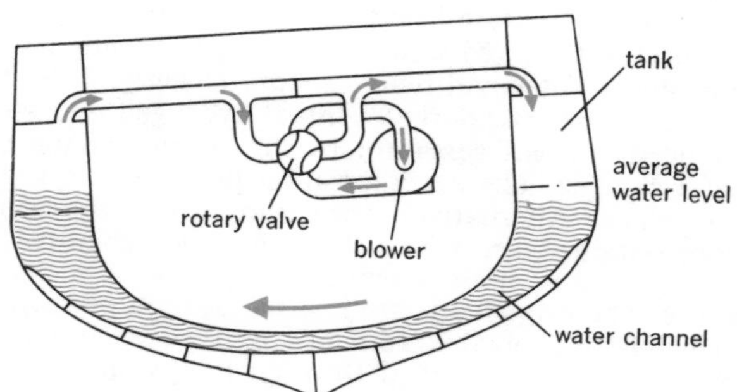

FIG. 6 ACTIVATED ANTIROLL TANKS

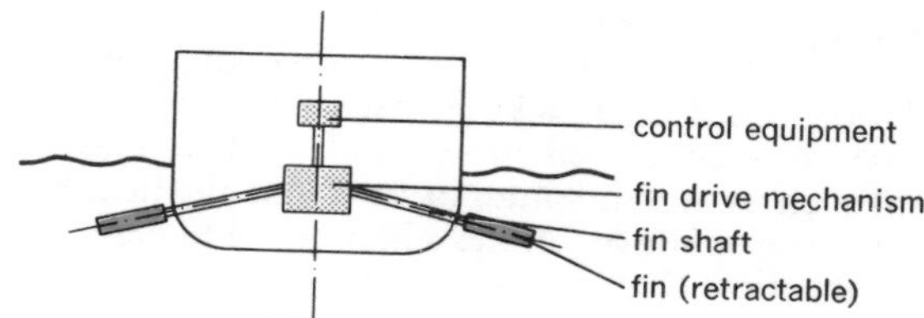

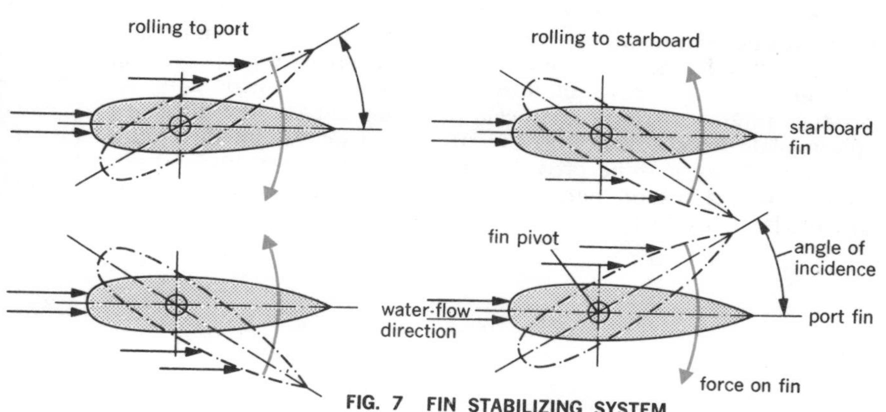

FIG. 7 FIN STABILIZING SYSTEM

A liquid-propellant rocket engine or motor comprises a combustion or thrus chamber, one or more storage tanks for the liquid combustibles, a supply syster for feeding the combustibles to the combustion chamber, and a suitable power uni for driving the propellant pumps (Fig. 1). Most liquid-propellant rockets use tw combustibles (bipropellant system), such as kerosene (the fuel) and liquid oxyge (the oxidant). With modifications, this arrangement, first successfully applied in th German V2 rockets of World War II, has been used in postwar rocket development everywhere. However, efforts to simplify modern rockets and make them mor reliable, particularly for space travel, have led to the utilization of gas pressure a the operating agent for the propellant-supply system, as in Fig. 2. Here the prc pellants (fuel and oxidant) are fed to the combustion chamber by the pressure of a inert gas such as helium and nitrogen. The drawback of gas pressurization is tha the high pressures necessitate heavy tanks. In turbopump supply systems (Fig. 1 the turbine wheel is driven by a high-velocity gas stream and in turn drives singl stage or multistage centrifugal pumps. More recently, axial-flow pumps have als been employed, more particularly for liquid hydrogen. The gas to drive the turbin may be produced in a gas generator by the decomposition of hydrogen peroxid by means of a catalyst. The decomposition products, oxygen and steam, imping on the turbine blades. Alternatively, the gas for driving the turbine for the propellar pumps may be obtained direct from the combustion chamber, or gaseous hydroge from the regenerative cooling system of the combustion chamber may be utilize for the purpose. The propellants are injected at high pressure into the combustio chamber, in which the propellants are atomized, mixed and burned. The hot gaseou combustion products are expelled through the exhaust nozzle. The combustio chamber of a liquid-propellant rocket has to be cooled, for which purpose th regenerative principle is generally applied: one of the propellants flows through jacket around the combustion chamber and cools it before passing to the injecto (The other propellant flows directly to the injector head of the combustion chambe An alternative method is so-called ablation cooling, operating on the same princip as the ablation shield of a rocket capsule on reentry into the atmosphere (see pag 98). The combustion chambers of small rockets may be made of a high-meltin point metal such as molybdenum or tungsten, the heat being dissipated by radiatio from the external surface of the chamber. Efficient injection of the propellan into the combustion chamber is very important, as it must ensure thorough mixir and complete combustion. The injector head atomizes the propellants and contro the feed rate so that they are mixed in the correct ratio. Various types of inject have been developed, such as the impinging spray type in which streams of propella intersect one another at high velocity and are thereby broken up into small drople ("atomized"). In the shower-head type, the propellant is sprayed into the chamb through concentric rows of holes. Sometimes concentric slots are employed produce intersecting conical sheets of propellant; or the injector may embody splash plate which breaks up the streams of propellant directed against it; or swirl-type spray may be provided. Fig. 3 shows a longitudinal section through modern rocket motor, namely, the third-stage motor of a European "Eldo-A satellite launch vehicle.

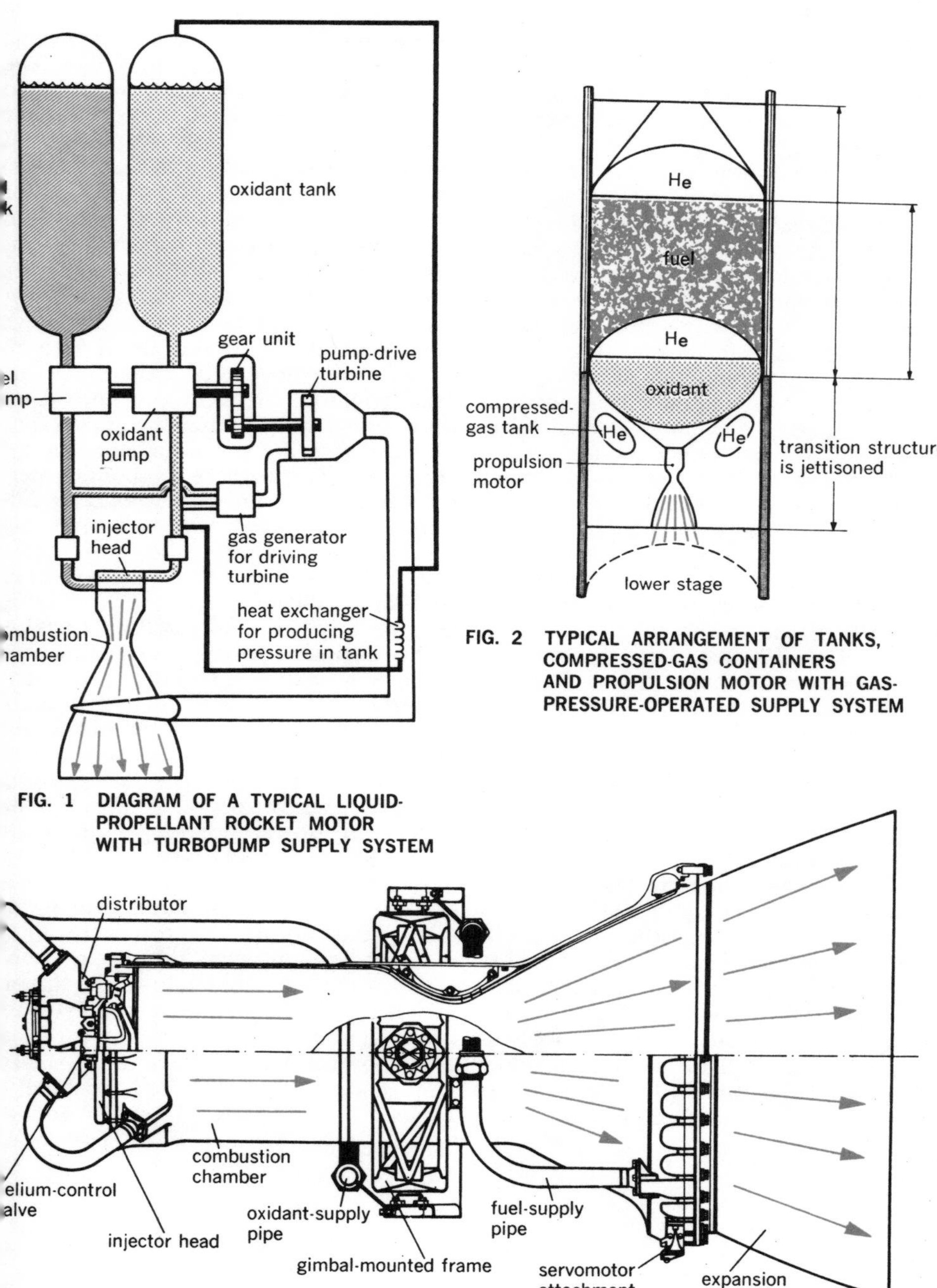

FIG. 1 DIAGRAM OF A TYPICAL LIQUID-PROPELLANT ROCKET MOTOR WITH TURBOPUMP SUPPLY SYSTEM

FIG. 2 TYPICAL ARRANGEMENT OF TANKS, COMPRESSED-GAS CONTAINERS AND PROPULSION MOTOR WITH GAS-PRESSURE-OPERATED SUPPLY SYSTEM

FIG. 3

SOLID-PROPELLANT ROCKET SYSTEMS

The solid-propellant rocket engine or motor embodies the oldest known principle of rocket propulsion. Its major advantage is its relative simplicity in design. The propellant is contained in the combustion (or thrust) chamber, which is provided with an exhaust nozzle for the expulsion of the gases of combustion. For military purposes the solid-propellant rocket has the great advantages of readiness and reliability. Modern solid propellants are usually of the composite (or heterogeneous) type: i.e., they consist of two separate substances, the fuel and the oxidant—for example, the American GALCIT propellants consisting of a mixture of potassium perchlorate (the oxidant) and asphalt oil (the fuel). Other oxidants similarly employed are ammonium perchlorate, ammonium nitrate, etc. Superior results are obtained with certain modern polymer plastics instead of asphalt as fuel. For example, polyurethane fuels were introduced for the Polaris and the second stage of the Minuteman rockets. The liquid polymers are catalyzed and mixed with an oxidant, e.g., ammonium perchlorate, to produce a composite propellant. At first this is of a thickly liquid consistency and is poured into the rocket motor case. After being cured at a slightly elevated temperature, it sets and acquires the appearance of a stiff rubber. Other modern fuels of this category are polybutadienes as, for example, in the first stage of Minuteman, in conjunction with an ammonium perchlorate oxidant. Because of their simplicity, reliability and convenience, solid-propellant rockets are being increasingly used not only for military rockets but also for rockets designed for space flight.

Fig. 1 shows a typical large solid-propellant rocket motor. The motor case—i.e., the combustion chamber—is first provided with a rubber lining; then a molding core is placed in the chamber and the remaining space is filled with a castable propellant. When the latter has set as a result of curing or polymerization, the core is withdrawn, so that a cavity is left in the propellant. As there is no liquid propellant available for regenerative cooling, it may be necessary to employ ablation cooling (see page 98). Various shapes have been devised for the cavity in the propellant charge, all designed to keep the area of the burning surface constant, such as the star-shaped cavity (Fig. 2). Cavities are provided more particularly in fast-burning propellant charges which develop a high thrust over a short period of time. On the other hand, solid-propellant motors which have to operate for longer periods—e.g., for surface-to-air missiles—are usually of the end-burning type, in which the charge burns "cigarette fashion" from one end only. Combinations of internal burning (to give a high initial thrust) and end burning may be employed. The solid-propellant rocket has the drawback that it is relatively difficult to control after ignition; as contrasted with the rocket propelled by liquid combustibles, it is not practicable to swivel the whole motor so as to control the direction of the thrust. Instead, rather complex arrangements to swivel the nozzle are necessary, or thrust control may be effected by the injection of a secondary fluid into the exhaust jet. Most solid propellants contain an admixture of powdered aluminum as an auxiliary fuel, which improves the performance. For example, the propellant of Polaris contains 20% of aluminum powder.

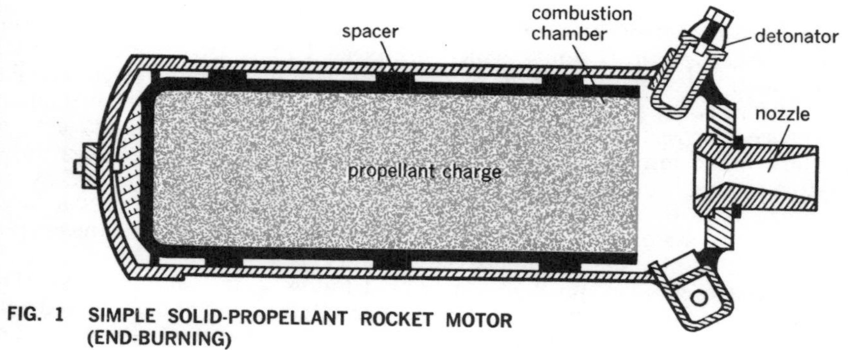

FIG. 1 SIMPLE SOLID-PROPELLANT ROCKET MOTOR (END-BURNING)

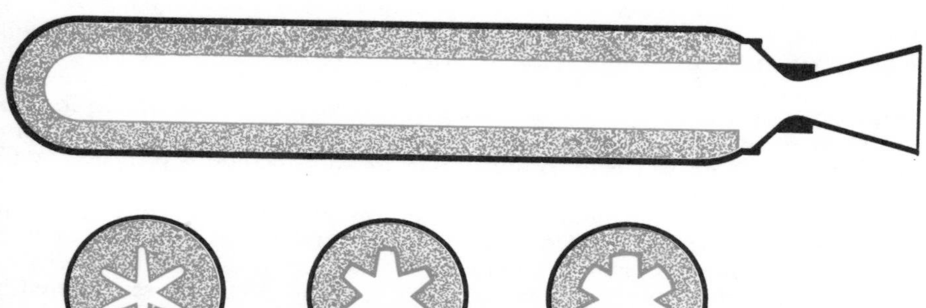

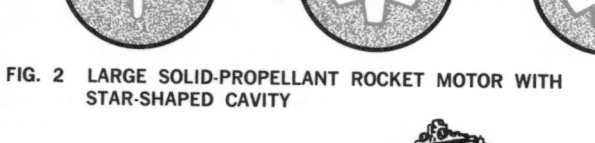

FIG. 2 LARGE SOLID-PROPELLANT ROCKET MOTOR WITH STAR-SHAPED CAVITY

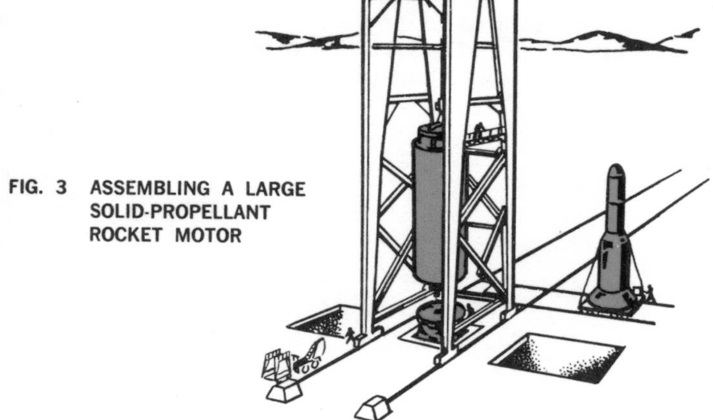

FIG. 3 ASSEMBLING A LARGE SOLID-PROPELLANT ROCKET MOTOR

ION-DRIVE ROCKET PROPULSION SYSTEMS

The ion-drive rocket propulsion system utilizes electrostatic fields to accelerate positively charged particles (ions), which are ejected rearwards. Ions are atoms which have acquired a positive charge by the removal of one or more electrons. The ions may be formed by passing a working fluid, such as cesium vapor, through an ionizing device (electrically heated tungsten grids) whereby the atoms lose electrons and are thus turned into positively charged ions. These ions are first concentrated into a beam by repulsion from positive electrodes and are then accelerated by the attraction exercized by negative electrodes (Fig. 1). To maintain the rocket in an electrically neutral state, it is necessary also to discharge the electrons (negatively charged particles) into space—otherwise the rocket would become negatively charged, so that a cloud of positive ions would follow it and slow it down. The electrons are ejected in the form of a beam from an electron gun and are mixed with the positive ions so that they eventually neutralize the charge of the latter. The velocity attainable by the ions is governed by the difference in voltage along the path they have to traverse in the propulsion motor and by the charge and mass of the ions themselves. Since the acceleration process does not constitute an electric arc or some form of combustion, this is a cold drive system. Very high ejection velocities can be attained without giving rise to the difficulties associated with high temperatures at the exhaust. Typical velocities range from 30 to 300 km/sec.

Various sources of ions can be used. The simplest method of producing ions, as already described, is by direct contact, e.g., between cesium and heated ionizing grids made of tungsten, a metal which can operate at elevated temperatures and has a high affinity for electrons. Another very effective method is provided by the Kaufman system, which embodies a device resembling a magnetron and produces ions by electron bombardment of a metal vapor (Fig. 2). With the aid of a thermionic cathode located at the axis of the ionization chamber and of a magnetic field between the cathode and the chamber wall, the paths of the electrons are so curved by the magnetic field that no anode current will flow until the electrons are scattered by collisions with gas atoms or molecules inside the chamber.

The "ions" employed in an ion drive system may alternatively consist of electrically charged particles other than atomic or molecular ions—namely, dust particles, liquid droplets, or colloidal particles. In the last-mentioned case, half the number of colloidal particles employed are given a positive and the other half a negative charge. These particles are respectively accelerated in two separate chambers and ejected.

Fig. 3 is a schematic representation of an ion-drive system of rocket propulsion. The ion drive is a low-thrust system and can function only in a vacuum. For these reasons it is suitable more particularly for interplanetary space flight.

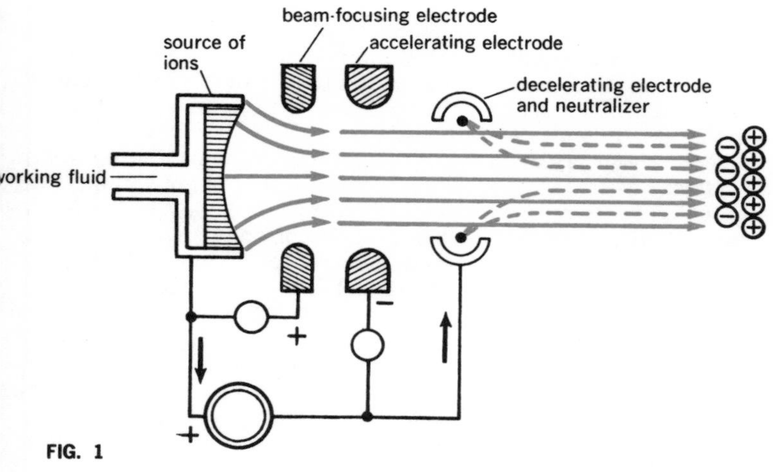

FIG. 1

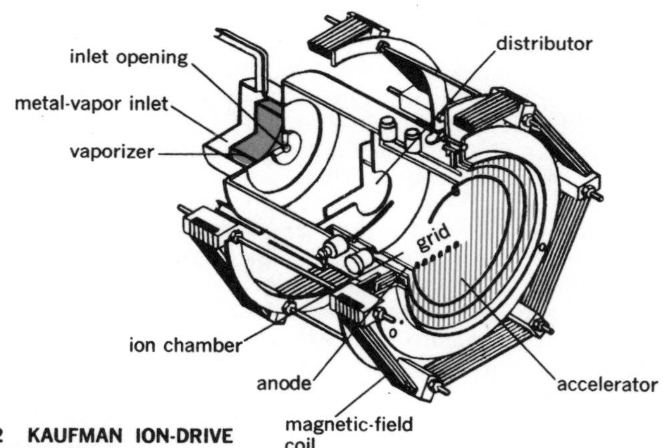

FIG. 2 KAUFMAN ION-DRIVE MOTOR

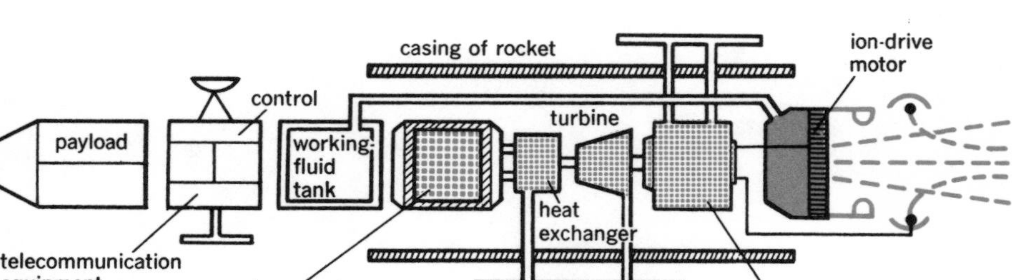

FIG. 3 ION DRIVE SYSTEM FOR ROCKET PROPULSION (SCHEMATIC)

MULTISTAGE ROCKETS

With multistage rockets it is in general possible to attain higher final velocities than with single-stage rockets of equal overall weight. When the propellant in the first stage has been used up, this stage is jettisoned, and the next stage is ignited. The final stage, usually the smallest, carries the payload. Its final velocity is the sum of the final velocities attained by all the rocket stages.

As Fig. 1 shows, there are in principle four different ways of constructing multistage rockets. The system hitherto most widely employed is that of tandem or series staging (Fig. 1a), in which the successive stages are arranged one above the other, the first stage to be ignited and jettisoned being at the bottom. In this way it is possible to combine different types of propulsion and rocket design in the various stages. A typical example of a giant multistage rocket is the Saturn 5, which took America's first astronauts to the moon (Fig. 2e). It stood 263 ft. on the launching pad and weighed about 3000 tons. The first stage was of very heavy and powerful construction, with five F 1 motors powered by kerosene and liquid air, developing a thrust of 7.5 million pounds. The second stage was propelled by five T 2 motors, while the third stage, which contained the Apollo spacecraft, had one T 2 motor. The optimum subdivision of a multistage rocket into its various stages depends to a great extent upon the chosen combination of propellants. A disadvantage of the series-type multistage rocket is that the propulsion systems of the various stages are ignited and operate consecutively, so that they cannot act simultaneously in accelerating the rocket. For this reason the booster-rocket principle has been applied in the Atlas intercontinental ballistic missile (Fig. 1b). The main rocket is essentially a single-stage liquid-propellant vehicle powered by a sustainer motor. In addition there are two booster units, burning the same fuels and developing a very high thrust. The boosters are jettisoned at burnout, and the sustainer accelerates the missile to maximum velocity and is then shut off. In this method only one liquid-propellant supply system is required, whereas separate stages arranged in series each require their own supply system. A third possibility is the parallel-stage rocket (Figs. 1c and 2c), comprising a main rocket and a number of jettisonable solid-propellant booster units for high lift-off thrust and initial acceleration. This arrangement is regarded as most suitable for future space-flight projects. Another possible combination is illustrated in Fig. 1d: a small manned spacecraft is carried into orbit by a launching rocket to which it is attached "piggyback" fashion. Proper separation of the stages at burnout is an important operation, generally carried out in a program-controlled sequence. Actual separation of the stages is effected by means of explosive bolts or similar devices. It is essential that the burned-out stage should become detached simultaneously at all points of connection and that the ignition of the next stage should take place, not immediately upon separation, but with a few seconds' delay. Booster units may be jettisoned by the action of small side-thrust rockets which release the units from the main rocket.

FIG. 1

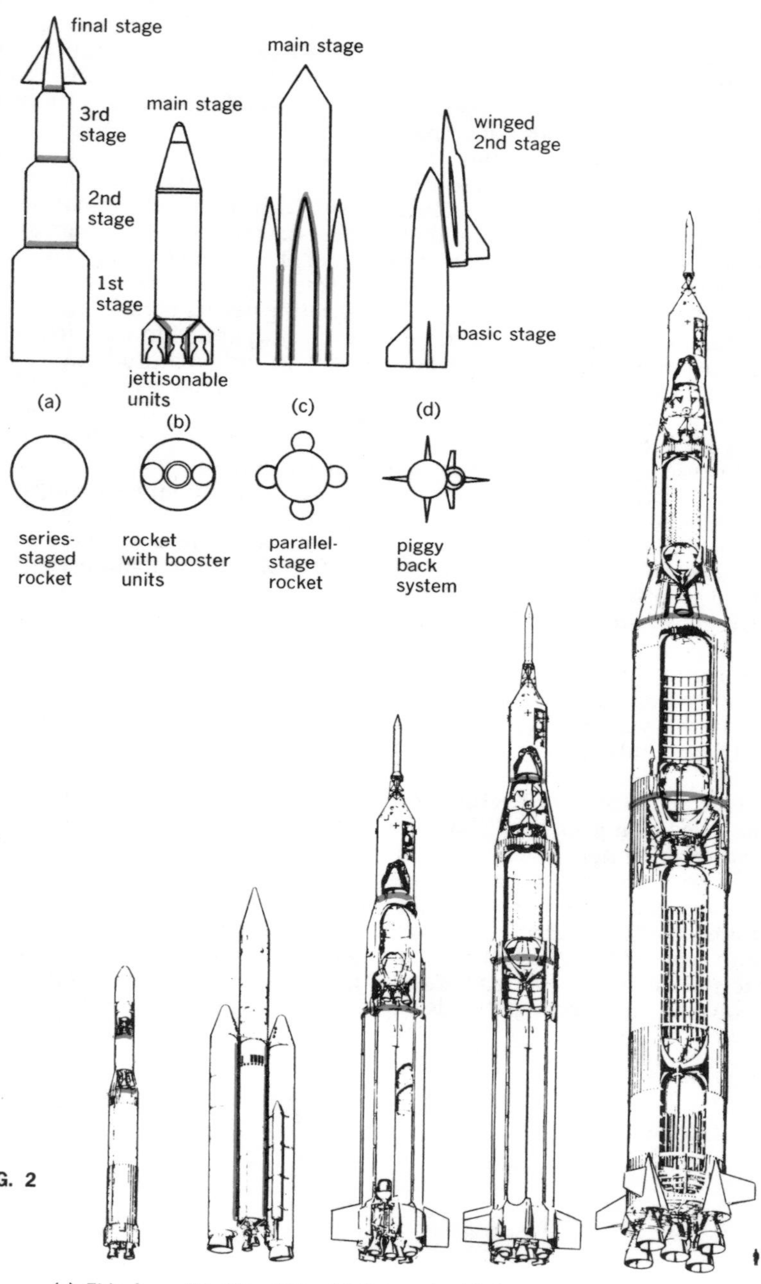

FIG. 2

(a) Eldo-A (b) Titan IIIC (c) Saturn 1 (d) Saturn 1B (e) Saturn 5

REENTRY AND ABLATION

The kinetic energy of a satellite or spacecraft is many times greater than the amount of energy which, in terms of heat, would be needed to bring about complete vaporization of the satellite or spacecraft in question. Retardation and friction with the air on reentry into the earth's atmosphere would release a considerable amount of heat and burn up the reentering body. Indeed, this is the normal fate of meteorites entering the atmosphere from outer space.

After a number of unsuccessful attempts with various protective shields and cooling methods, the problem was solved by the development of the ablating reentry shield. Made of ablative material, the shield dissipates heat by melting and vaporizing. To understand its function more fully, it is necessary to consider in greater detail what happens when a satellite reenters the atmosphere. The first signs of increased air resistance (drag) become noticeable when it enters the thermosphere at an altitude of about 100 km (60 miles), but no significant heating occurs here. When it traverses the mesopause, as yet in a very flat trajectory almost parallel to the earth's surface, some slight heating of the satellite takes place. Then, in an altitude range between about 40 and 25 km (25 and 15 miles), almost the entire kinetic energy is dissipated within a period of approximately one minute. It is in this range that the satellite and its crew are subjected to the severest strains. The front of the satellite is protected by a shield made of synthetic resin or plastic of low combustibility and low thermal conductivity. Friction with the air heats this ablative material to a temperature of several thousand degrees centigrade, so that the resin becomes liquid and "boils off." The layer behind the shock-wave front ahead of the satellite is heated to around 6000° C and is in the gaseous state. About 80% of the thermal energy from the intermediate layer between the liquid and the gaseous layer is dissipated as radiation to the surrounding air (Fig. 1). The low conductivity of the still-solid ablative material prevents any substantial amount of heat from penetrating into the satellite itself during the reentry period (which is of only 50–100 seconds' duration). The resin is reinforced with glass fiber or quartz fiber to maintain the cohesion and strength of the shield. In this way only a few percent of the heat evolved on reentry is absorbed by the satellite; only about ½ to 1 inch thickness of the shield is consumed by ablation.

In the case of a spacecraft returning from the moon or from an interplanetary flight, the speed is higher than that of an earth-orbiting satellite and the reentry problem correspondingly more critical. If the reentry trajectory is too steep, frictional heating will be too severe to be dealt with by ablative cooling. On the other hand, if the trajectory is too flat, the spacecraft traveling at high speed will be in danger of being "bounced off" the earth's atmosphere, thus overshooting it and disappearing forever into space. The optimum reentry angle is between about 5 and 10 degrees in relation to the earth's surface, as indicated in Fig. 2. The Gemini and Apollo space capsules have ablating reentry shields and are steerable within certain limits.

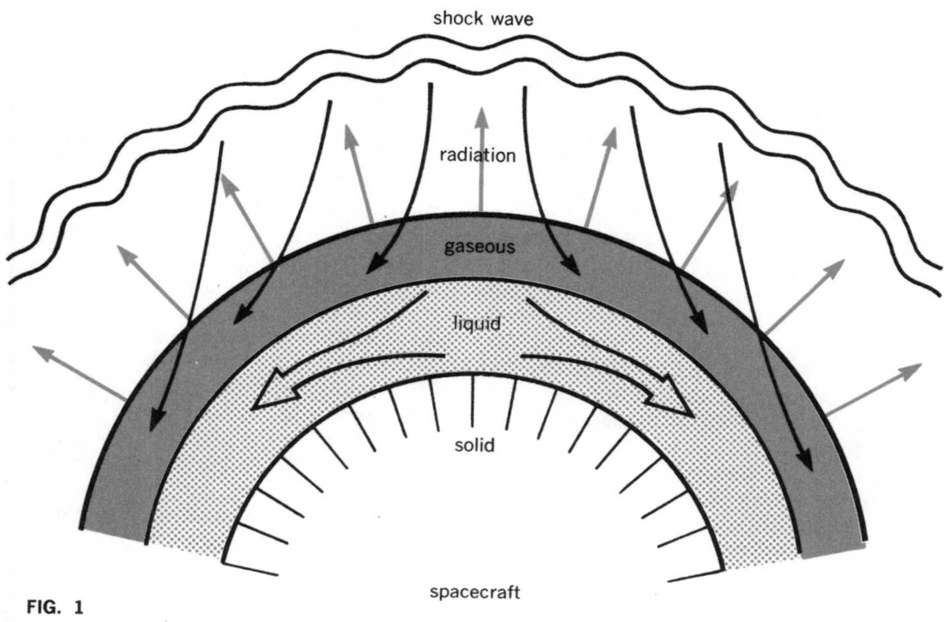

FIG. 1

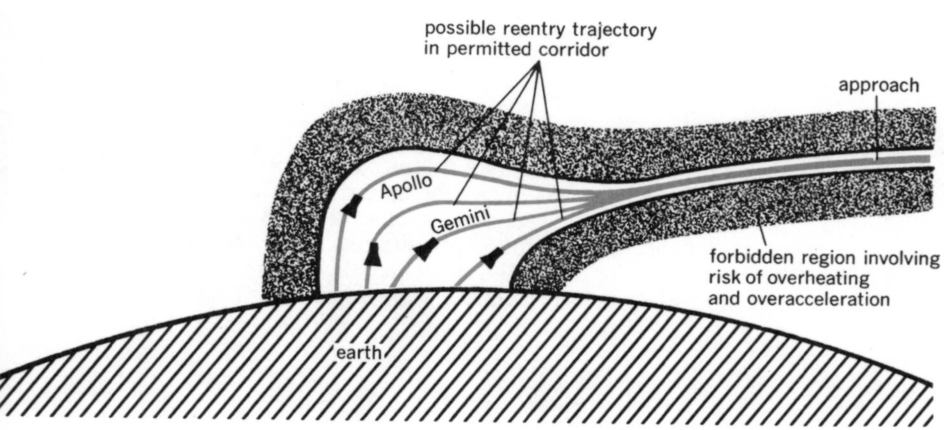

FIG. 2 REENTRY CORRIDOR FOR APOLLO SPACECRAFT (HYPERBOLIC SPEED) AND GEMINI SPACECRAFT (CIRCULAR ORBITAL SPEED)

SPACE SUITS AND SPACE CAPSULES

Man cannot, of course, exist in the near vacuum of interplanetary space, exposed to extreme temperatures, the hazard of meteorites, and bombardment of cosmic rays (very energetic radiation from outer space) and dangerous radiation emitted by the sun. For man to survive in space, he must carry his normal "earthly" environment with him. In the first place, the astronaut wears a space suit and helmet. This equipment keeps him supplied with oxygen for breathing, maintains his body at a controlled temperature, and removes moisture from the air enclosing him. In addition all the important data of his vital functions, such as blood pressure, heart rhythm, body temperature, etc., are continually monitored by sensing devices and automatically transmitted by radio back to earth, where they are supervised and studied by doctors and scientists. Besides wearing this self-contained space suit, the astronaut is additionally enclosed within a fully air-conditioned and temperature-controlled capsule. He can, however, leave the capsule to perform particular tasks outside it ("walk in space"). The capsule is furthermore provided with a complete set of equipment for sustaining human life over a period of days or even weeks, as exemplified by the Apollo spacecraft which performed the first American manned moon flight. With regard to the waste products of the human body this is still an "open" system, on account of the relatively short duration of the space flight—a matter of about eight days. For longer journeys in space—e.g., an interplanetary flight or a sojourn in an orbiting space station—it will be necessary to employ a closed circuit, as represented schematically in Fig. 2. The human waste products are dehydrated, and the water recovered from them is purified and recirculated in the system and can be reused for human consumption over and over again.

The walls of a space suit and of a space capsule are of multilayer construction. An important component of a space suit is a layer of plastic provided with a coat of metal (aluminum or gold) applied to it in vapor form. This metallic coating reflects the intensive solar radiation to which the astronaut is exposed when he ventures outside the capsule. Fig. 1 illustrates the Mercury capsule, which was used in earlier American space flights. A large proportion of the equipment carried in the capsule serves to maintain the controlled conditions in the crew's space suits and in the cabin of the capsule itself. In the Apollo capsule and in future earth-orbiting space stations the crew will live in less cramped conditions and enjoy greater comfort, more particularly because they will be able to remove their cumbersome outer suits inside the cabin. This is possible because these spacecraft are of double-wall construction, with intermediate layers of rubberlike material which are self-sealing in the event of their being punctured by meteorites, so that no sudden loss of pressure within the capsule will occur.

The choice of atmosphere in the cabins of spacecraft is a special problem in itself. The natural air we breathe is essentially a mixture of about 20% oxygen and about 80% nitrogen. Since considerations of weight saving are of paramount importance in all space flights, it has been investigated whether a cabin atmosphere consisting of pure oxygen at appropriately reduced pressure can safely be breathed by astronauts. Another method is to use helium—which is a significantly lighter gas—instead of nitrogen to produce a breathable atmosphere in the spacecraft cabin.

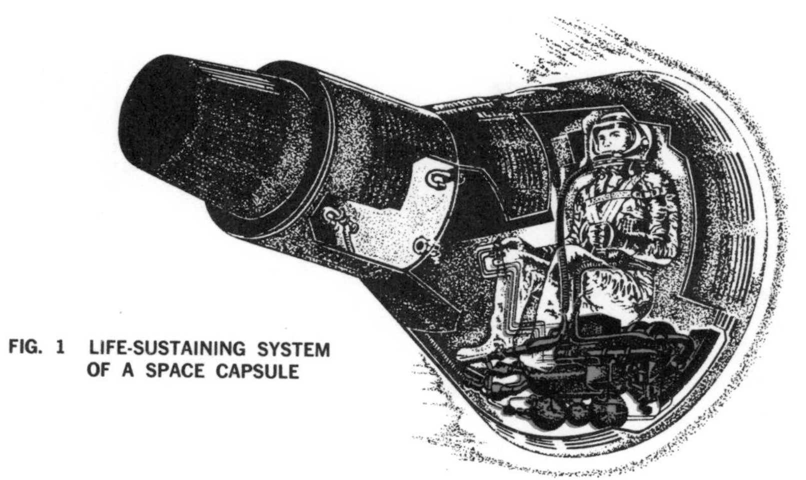

FIG. 1 LIFE-SUSTAINING SYSTEM OF A SPACE CAPSULE

FIG. 2 REGENERATION OF WATER AND AIR IN CLOSED CIRCUIT IN A SPACECRAFT

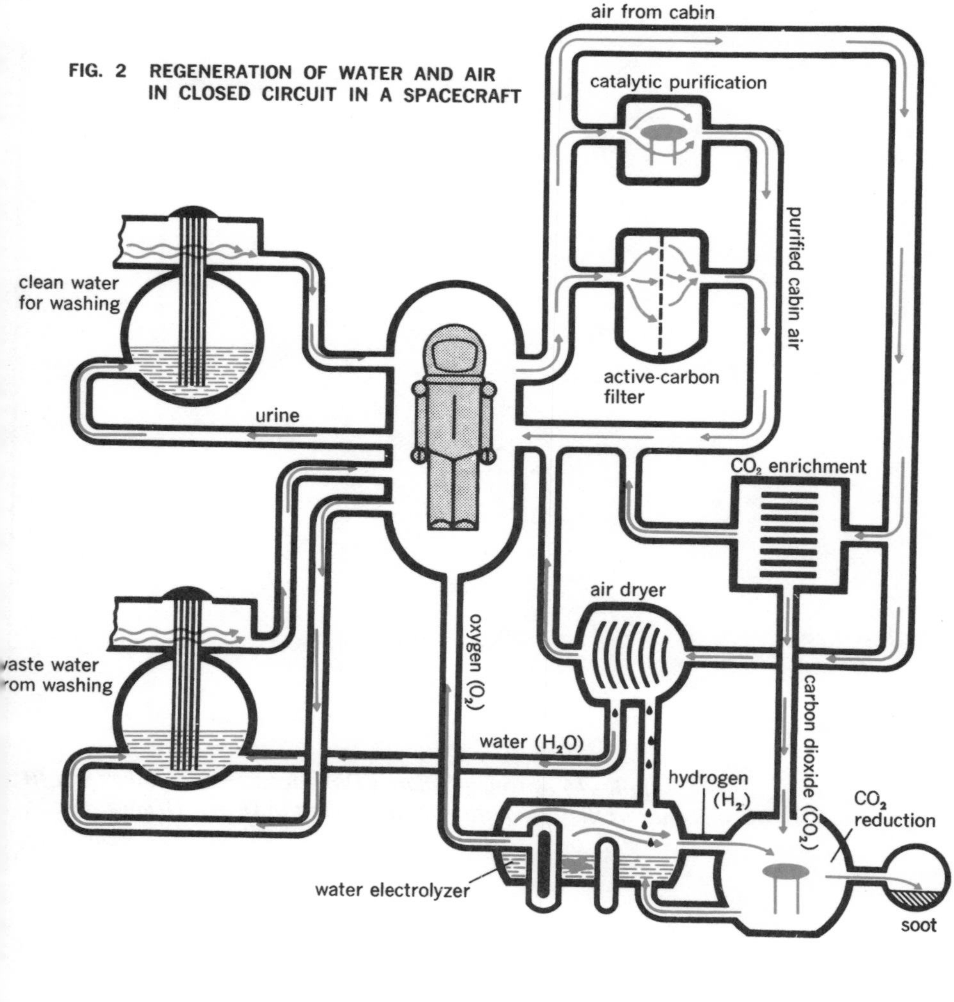

Apollo-16 astronaut Charles Duke tests the flexibility and fit of his spacesuit at the International Latex plant in Dover, Delaware, USA
Photo USIS

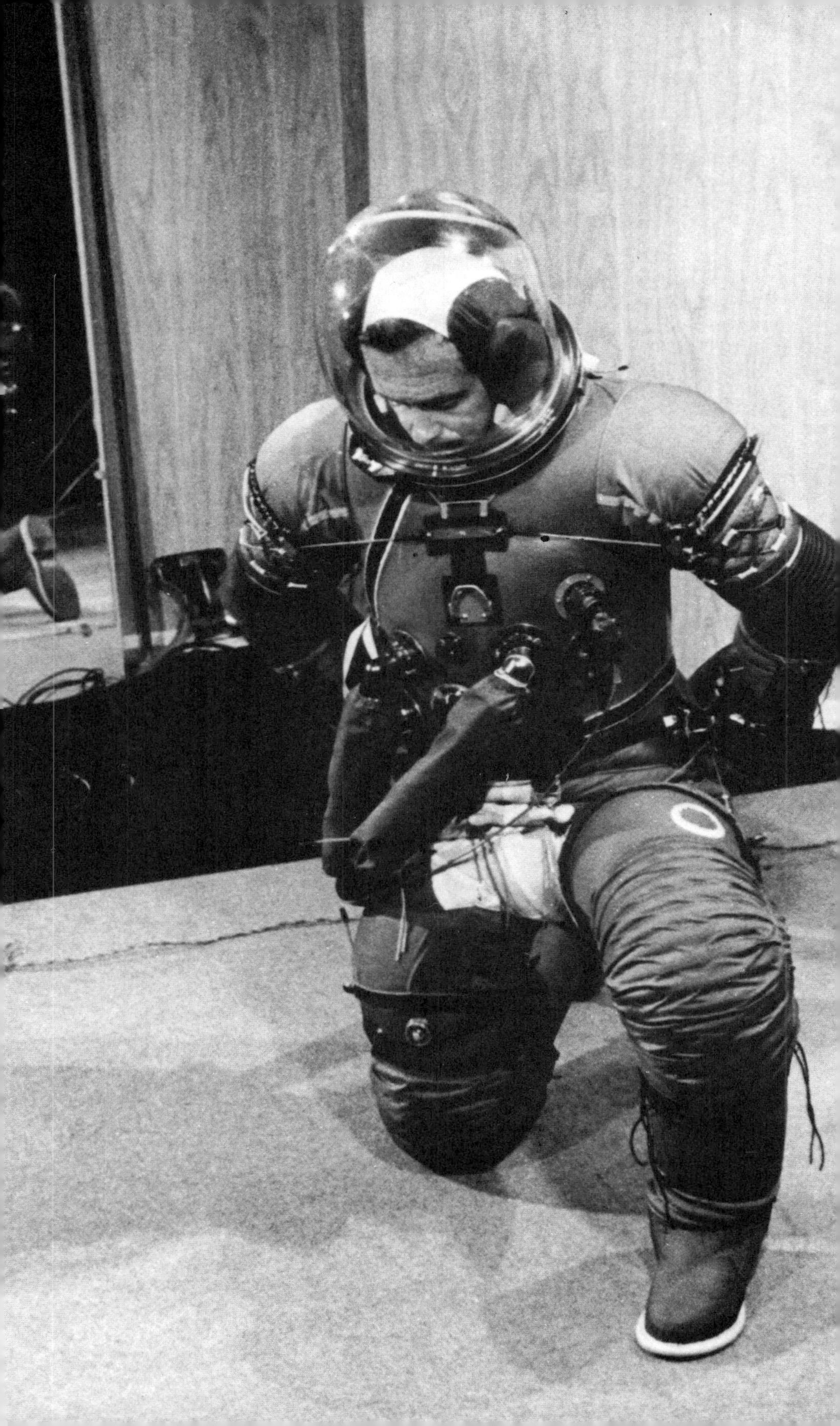

INERTIAL NAVIGATION

Inertial guidance systems are used for controlling the flight of intercontinental missiles. This method of guidance makes use only of the laws of classical mechanics to calculate the flight path of the missile and compel it to follow a programed trajectory from launching site to target. A simple inertial system was incorporated in the German V2 rockets which bombarded London in the final stages of World War II. The basis of a modern inertial guidance system is an arrangement, comprising three mutually perpendicular accelerometers, which can measure forces in any direction in space, coupled with three gyroscopes, also with mutually perpendicular axes, which constitute an independent frame of reference. The inertial system may be supplemented by an independent celestial, or star-tracking, guidance system which maintains the missile in a fixed attitude with reference to the sun or a particular star and thus serves as a check on the inertial system (stellar-monitored inertial guidance). The inertial principle has acquired particular importance for the navigation of spacecraft. Reference axes which take up a fixed position in space are provided by a set of gyroscopes and are independent of any external points of reference such as a lighthouse, beacon, star or the sun, as in conventional navigation. The accelerometers (Fig. 1) measure the acceleration components in three mutually perpendicular directions. By means of successive integration (performed by computer equipment), the speed and the distance traveled can be determined from these acceleration data (Fig. 2). The results of this computation are compared with the precalculated flight path which has been fed into the data-processing computer equipment in advance. The requisite corrections to the course of the spacecraft are then automatically applied. The satellites used in the Lunar Orbiter program relied on astronavigation, based on using the star Canopus (visible in the southern hemisphere) as a fixed point of reference, but in the vicinity of the moon, where Canopus was concealed from view behind the moon, inertial navigation was employed.

An accelerometer measures acceleration or, more particularly, the force that is exerted when a body possessing inertia is accelerated. The inertia tends to resist the acceleration. It is this resistance to a sudden change in speed that is the origin of the force that thrusts a motorist backward into his seat when he suddenly depresses the accelerator pedal. This reaction force is equal to the product of mass (the weight of the motorist's body) and acceleration. In the accelerometer (Fig. 3) a mass is maintained in its neutral position by two springs; it remains in this position so long as the system is at rest or is in motion at constant speed. When the system is accelerated in the arrowed direction, the spring-mounted mass will, on account of its inertia, at first lag behind the movement; the front spring will thus be stretched, and the rear spring compressed. The inertia mass controls a potentiometer contact whose zero position corresponds to the neutral position of the mass. A positive acceleration thus causes the potentiometer to give a positive voltage of corresponding magnitude to the acceleration; a negative acceleration (deceleration) similarly produces a negative voltage of corresponding magnitude. If the voltage is used to drive an electric motor, the total number of revolutions will be proportional to the average speed of the missile or spacecraft over any particular period of time. This combination of the potentiometer and motor thus constitutes an integrating device. A second integrator uses the speed data to compute the total distance traveled (in terms of magnitude and direction). In Fig. 4 this double integration process is illustrated schematically for one coordinate direction (x). Fig. 5 represents an inertial navigation system for a vessel which can move in two dimensions only; in this case only two accelerometers are required. Finally, Fig. 6 shows a three-dimensional inertial guidance system in the nose of a rocket.

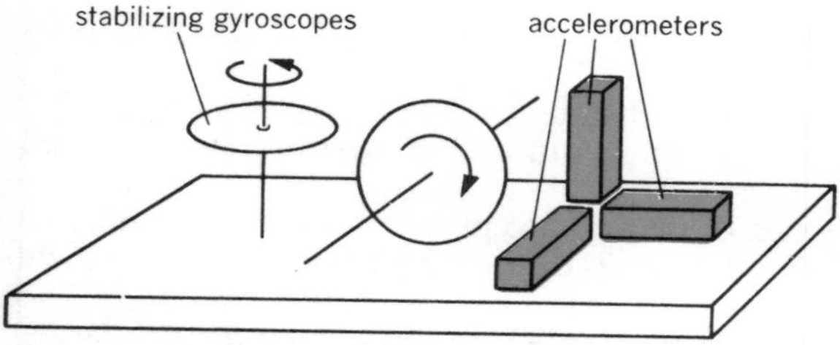

stabilizing gyroscopes
accelerometers

FIG. 1 INERTIAL NAVIGATION SYSTEM (SCHEMATIC)

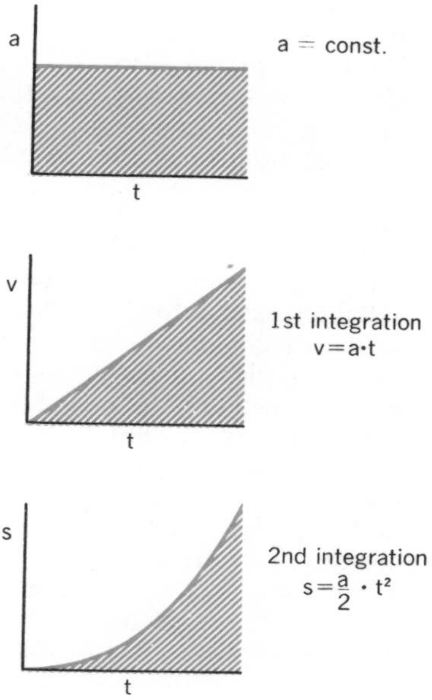

a
t
a = const.
v
t
1st integration
v=a·t
s
t
2nd integration
s=a/2 · t²

FIG. 2 DIAGRAMS FOR ACCELERATION, VELOCITY AND DISTANCE

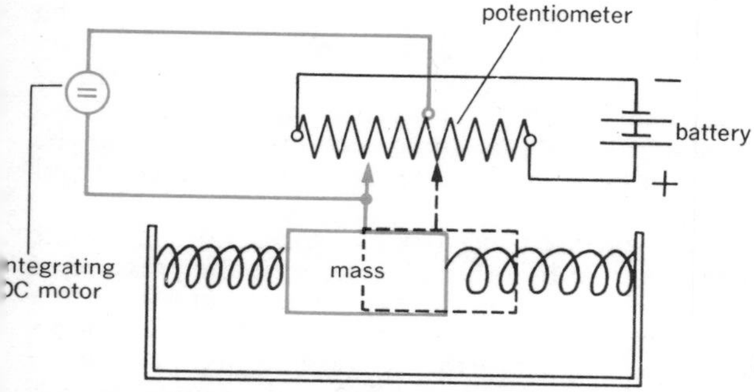

potentiometer
battery
ntegrating
)C motor
mass

FIG. 3 PRINCIPLE OF THE ACCELEROMETER

accelerometer
1st integrator
2nd integrator

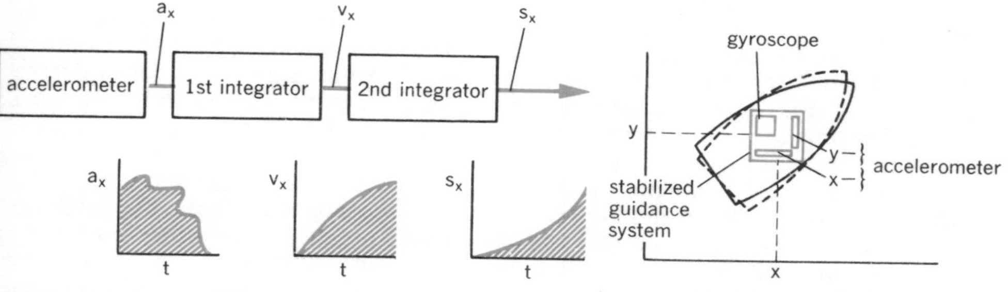

FIG. 4 INERTIAL NAVIGATOR (ONE-DIMENSIONAL, SCHEMATIC)

gyroscope
y
accelerometer
stabilized
guidance
system
x

FIG. 5 TWO-DIMENSIONAL INERTIAL NAVIGATION

accelerometer
guidance system
stabilizing gyroscopes

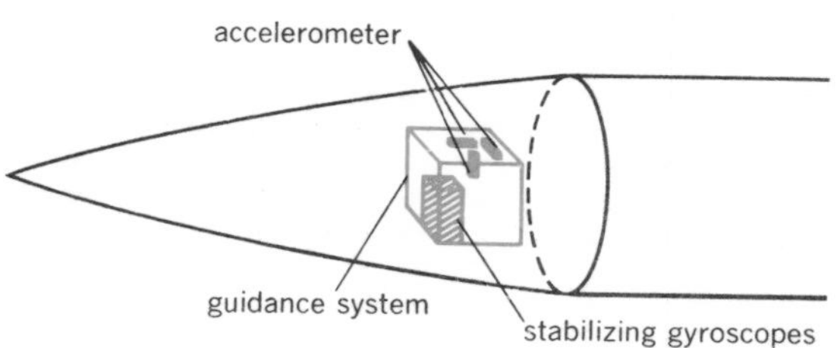

FIG. 6 NOSE OF ROCKET WITH THREE-DIMENSIONAL INERTIAL GUIDANCE SYSTEM

SPACE-FLIGHT ORBITS AND TRAJECTORIES

A spacecraft traveling within the solar system is subject to Kepler's laws of planetary motions (Fig. 1):

(1) Every planet moves in an elliptical orbit having the sun in one of its foci.*

(2) The radius vector (i.e., the line connecting sun and planet) sweeps out equal areas in equal times.

(3) The squares of the periodic times of planets are proportional to the cubes of the mean distances to the sun (the periodic time is the time a planet takes to complete one orbital revolution around the sun).

The same laws apply to any relatively small body orbiting around a much larger one—e.g., a satellite (natural or man-made) orbiting round a planet. Planets and satellites have elliptical orbits, and not all celestial bodies in the solar system necessarily travel in such orbits. The shape of the orbit depends on the speed of the body. For example, comets, which usually move at very high speeds, have very elongated elliptical orbits or, at even higher speeds, parabolic or hyperbolic orbits around the sun. Similarly, depending on the speed and direction of movement imparted to it by its rocket motors, a spacecraft will pursue an elliptical orbit around the earth or travel out into space in a parabolic or hyperbolic trajectory. Ellipses, parabolas and hyperbolas are curves collectively known as conic sections, as they can be conceived as the curves of intersection between the external surface of a cone and a plane set at various angles to the axis of the cone.

Deviations from the mathematically precise trajectory of a spacecraft may occur in consequence of disturbing forces (exerted by other planets or by the pressure of light) or inaccuracies in the quantitative estimation of the intensity of the earth's gravitational field (the theoretical laws of motion are based on the assumption that all the mass of the central body—sun or earth—is concentrated at a single point, whereas in reality the central body is of somewhat flattened spherical shape).

According to Kepler's second law, a planet orbiting around the sun or a satellite orbiting around the earth will attain its highest speed when it passes closest to the sun or earth (Fig. 1). From the third law it follows that satellites moving around the same central body will have equal periodic times if their mean distances to that body and therefore the semimajor axes of their orbits are equal, even if the elliptical orbits have different amounts of eccentricity—i.e., exhibit a greater or lesser degree of flattening (Fig. 2). This applies also to the circular orbit, which can be regarded as the limiting case of an ellipse of zero eccentricity. The periodic times increase with the semimajor axis "a" (proportionally to $a^{3/2}$). Kepler's third law gives rise to a paradoxical phenomenon. If two space vehicles are traveling one behind the other in the same orbit around the earth, and the second vehicle wishes to catch up with the first, it will have to modify its orbital motion not by a forward thrust of its rocket motors, but by means of a retroactive thrust. A thrust to accelerate the spacecraft in its forward motion would cause it to move into a larger orbit, i.e., an ellipse with a larger semimajor axis. Such considerations play a significant part in connection with rendezvous techniques (see page 112).

(more)

* Every ellipse has two points called foci, located on the major axis. The elliptical curve is characterized by the fact that the sum of the distances from any point on the curve to the two foci is constant for that particular ellipse. It is on this principle that the well-known method of drawing an ellipse is based, namely, by means of a pencil and a loop of string around two pins. Each pin corresponds to a focus of the ellipse. A circle may be regarded as the limiting case of an ellipse whose foci coincide at one point, the center of the circle.

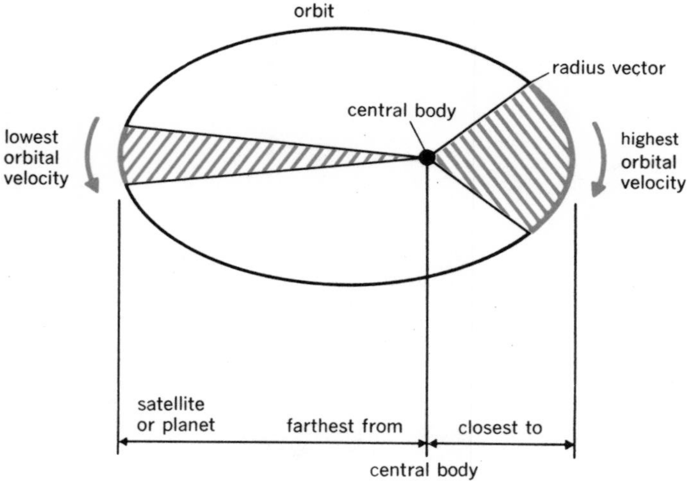

FIG. 1 THE RADIUS VECTOR SWEEPS OUT EQUAL AREAS IN EQUAL TIMES

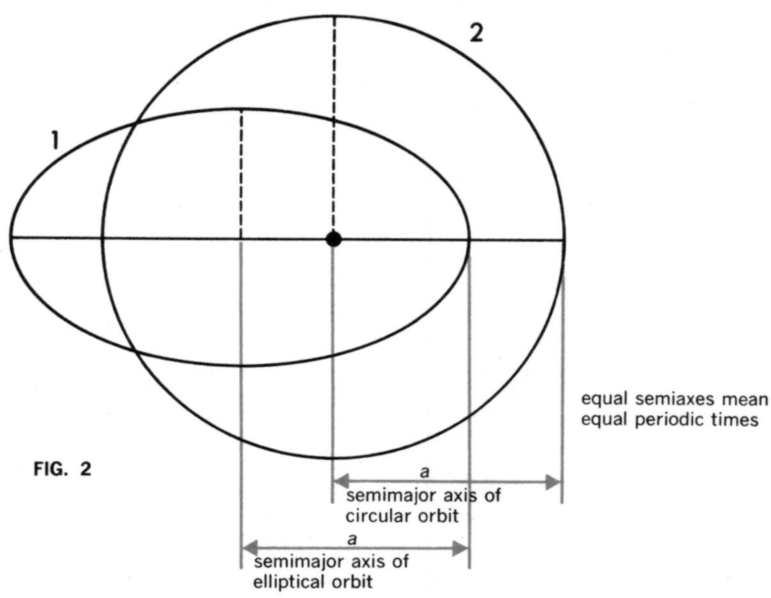

FIG. 2

Ground tracking station for controlling the launch of a space probe and for picking up data transmitted by the probe

Photo Cartier-Bresson, Magnum

I-13

Space-flight Orbits and Trajectories (continued)

As explained in the foregoing, the orbit of a nonpropelled body moving around a central body in space will be a curve belonging to the family of conic sections. Planets and satellites travel in elliptical orbits, i.e., closed curves, whereas bodies moving at high speeds may pursue "open" (parabolic or hyperbolic) orbits. By appropriately firing the rocket motors of a spacecraft it is possible to vary the speed and thus alter the shape of its trajectory in space. Fig. 1 shows some theoretically possible trajectories drawn in red for a spacecraft on a journey from, for example, the earth to Mars. The orbits of these two planets are drawn in black. The part of the trajectory actually traveled by the spacecraft is shown as a full red line. Fig. 1a represents a so-called Hohmann transfer orbit, which is tangential to the inner and outer planetary orbits respectively. The spacecraft, which is first assumed to be moving along with the earth (at A) around the sun, is given an initial thrust which accelerates it in a direction tangential to the earth's orbit. It will then continue to travel, without additional propulsion, along the red trajectory to Mars (at B). In the absence of any further propulsive intervention the spacecraft would then return along the dotted trajectory constituting the other half of the elliptical transfer orbit. If this spacecraft could, on arrival at B, be given a slowing-down thrust in a direction parallel to the surface of Mars, it would go into orbit around that planet. Hohmann orbits are referred to as "minimum-energy" transfer orbits because they have the advantage of requiring relatively low rocket-fuel consumption. A disadvantage, however, is that the spacecraft approaches the destination planet (Mars) at very low speed. Fig. 1c shows an elliptical orbit which permits a more rapid transfer between the two planetary orbits. In addition to these transfer orbits which require two separate propulsive thrusts to put the spacecraft into orbit around the destination planet, there are other possible orbits which would require three or more of such "kick maneuvers" (corrective propulsive thrusts) to achieve that result. Thus, in the case of a bielliptical orbit (Fig. 1d), thrusts would be needed at A, B and C. Figs. 1e and 1f are examples of parabolic and hyperbolic transfer orbits respectively. A special case is represented by the spiral orbits of ion rockets which develop a low-power but continuous thrust during the whole journey (Fig. 1g).

The types of orbit illustrated in Fig. 1 are not confined to the situation where the central body is the sun. In Fig. 1b, for example, the inner circle can be conceived as representing the surface of the earth. Then the curve A–B–C might correspond to the trajectory of an intercontinental ballistic missile. Furthermore, the curves A–B in Figs. 1b and 1c may be conceived as the trajectories of a spacecraft rising to rendezvous with another spacecraft already in orbit around the earth.

Theoretically a great many transfer orbits are conceivable, but in reality their number is limited by various practical considerations. One important requirement is that the launching of the spacecraft must be so timed that the destination planet is in the vicinity of the intersection point of the spacecraft's trajectory and that planet's orbit (Fig. 2). The conditions of illumination of the planet at the time of arrival of the spacecraft is also important with regard to transmission of pictures back to earth. Thus, for a lunar probe (Fig. 3) it is desirable that the observed portion of the moon's surface be situated close to the shadow boundary, where small details show up clearly by the shadows they cast. Because of these and other restricting factors, the actually available time interval ("launch window") for successful launching may be very short (hours, perhaps only minutes).

(more)

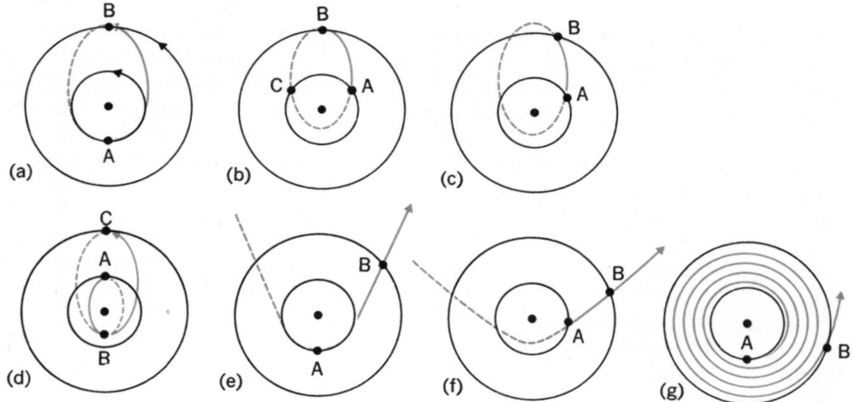

FIG. 1

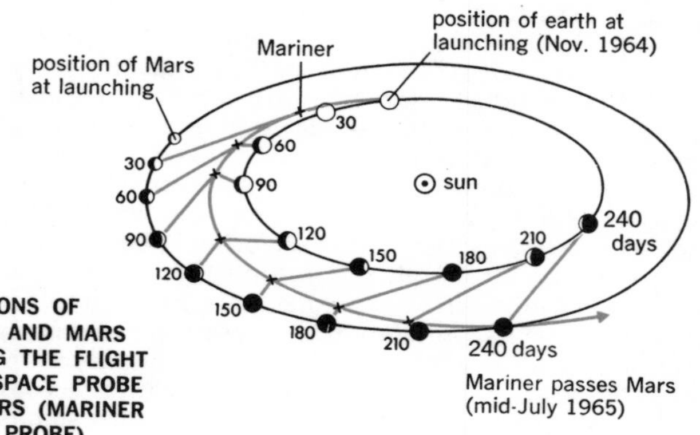

FIG. 2 POSITIONS OF EARTH AND MARS DURING THE FLIGHT OF A SPACE PROBE TO MARS (MARINER SPACE PROBE)

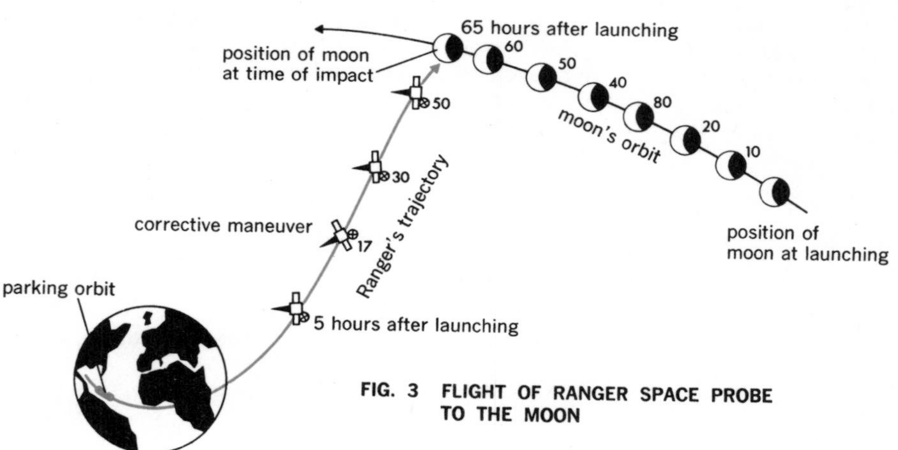

FIG. 3 FLIGHT OF RANGER SPACE PROBE TO THE MOON

Actual space flights are based on the principles described in the foregoing, but often involve complex sequences of the various operations and maneuvers. Thus, for example, the rendezvous procedure for a spacecraft with a satellite already in orbit around the earth comprises four stages. The first stage consists in the flight of the spacecraft and its launching rocket through the atmosphere and the injection of the spacecraft into its elliptical rendezvous trajectory that will carry it into the vicinity of the orbiting satellite. The second stage is the purely "ballistic" flight of the spacecraft along this trajectory. On arrival near the target, the third stage commences, when the crew of the spacecraft take over its control and perform the precision maneuvers to bring it almost into contact with the satellite. Finally, the fourth stage consists in "docking" the spacecraft with the satellite and linking the two space vehicles together.

Fig. 1 shows various possibilities for accomplishing the "ballistic" phase of the flight. In one case (a) the launching is timed to take place exactly when the launching point A is located within the orbital plane of the target satellite. Besides, the satellite itself must, at that instant, be at a particular point of its orbit so that it will arrive at the rendezvous point B simultaneously with the spacecraft. This latter condition, in particular, considerably restricts the interval of time within which the launching must take place. Greater latitude is attainable by first launching the spacecraft into an intermediate orbit (a so-called parking orbit) in which it travels around the earth in a shorter periodic time than that of the satellite. The spacecraft is thus able to "overtake" the satellite and then, by means of a thrust from its rocket motors, be transferred at a suitable moment from the parking orbit to the satellite's orbit (b). Alternatively, it is possible—within certain limits—to waive the condition that the point of launching must be located within the orbital plane of the satellite (c).

The final approach to the target satellite is controlled by the spacecraft's crew themselves, with the aid of radar and optical methods. For example, the spacecraft can be held on a constant course in relation to the satellite as seen against distant stars in the background and the approach speed along this direction be gradually slowed down so that the relative speed of the two space vehicles becomes zero at the instant of contact (Fig. 2a). Alternatively, the spacecraft may, after suitable corrections in its course, approach the target satellite along an elliptical collision trajectory, actual collision being prevented by means of a corrective thrust just before the two vehicles make contact (Fig. 2b). In either case the result is that, on completion of the rendezvous operation, the two space vehicles have the same speed and therefore have no motion in relation to each other. The rendezvous between Gemini 6 (spacecraft) and Gemini 7 (target satellite)—a rather more complex procedure than that just outlined—is illustrated schematically in Fig. 3.

FIG. 1 EXAMPLES OF HOW THE FIRST PHASE OF A RENDEZVOUS OPERATION (BALLISTIC PHASE) CAN BE PERFORMED:
(a) COPLANAR LAUNCHING INTO A BALLISTIC ORBIT
(b) LAUNCHING INTO A PARKING ORBIT
(c) NONCOPLANAR LAUNCHING

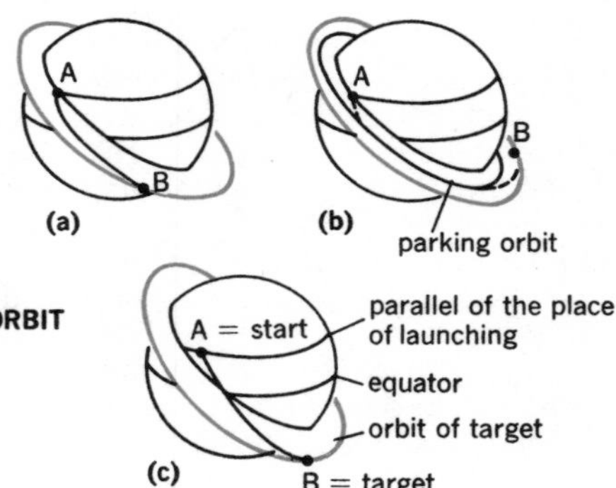

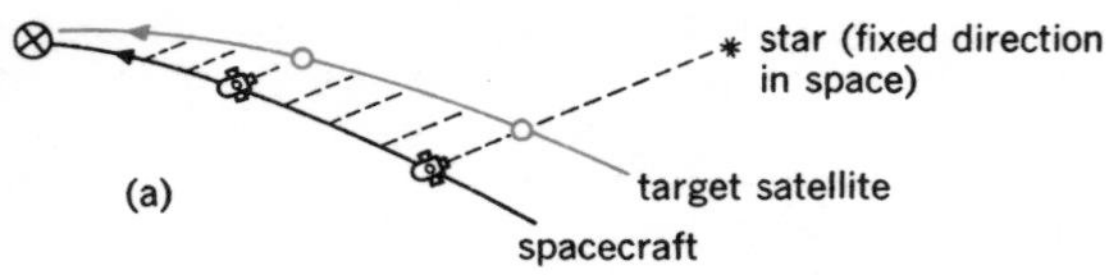

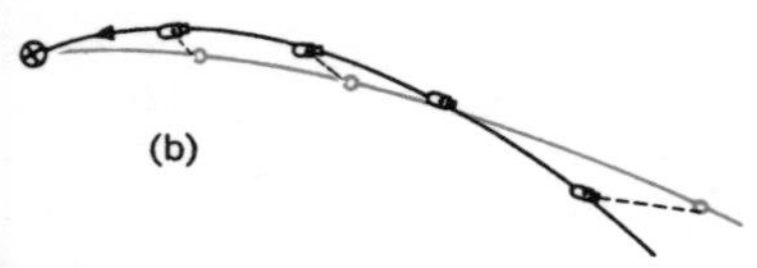

FIG. 2 POSSIBLE METHODS OF ACHIEVING THE FINAL PHASE OF A RENDEZVOUS

FIG. 3 RENDEZVOUS OF GEMINI 6 (BLACK) WITH GEMINI 7 CAPSULE (RED) SERVING AS TARGET

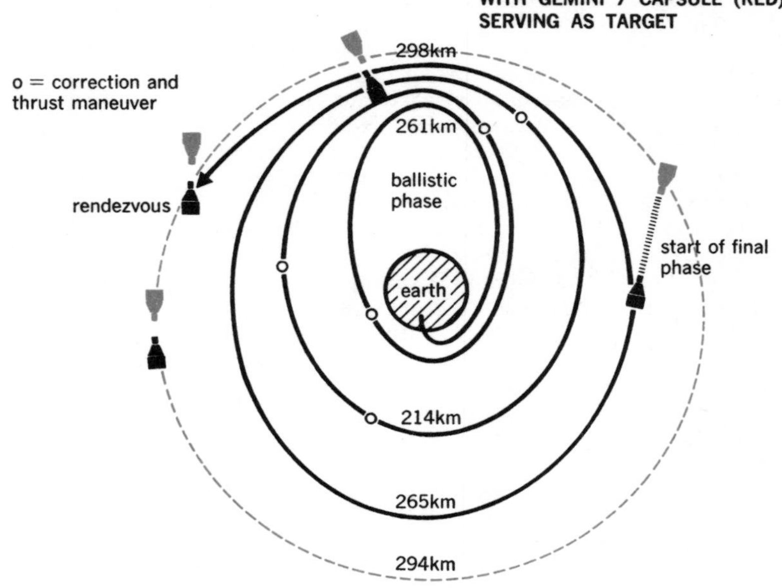

LANDING THE FIRST MEN ON THE MOON

Landing a space vehicle on a celestial body devoid of atmosphere, such as th moon, presents special technical problems of braking the vehicle's descent an accurately controlling the braking action. The conditions of entry are different fro those presented by a major planet enveloped in a relatively dense atmosphere. F a moon landing the entire kinetic energy of the vehicle must be braked by a counte acting thrust developed by rockets.

On arrival in the vicinity of the moon, the spacecraft is first slowed down by firin its retro-rocket motors, so that it goes into a circular parking orbit round the moo This applies more particularly to a manned spacecraft such as the Apollo which th Americans have used for landing men on the moon. In the case of the Apollo X project the actual descent onto the moon's surface was made by two astronauts i a special mooncraft, the "lunar (excursion) module" (abbreviated as "LEM" o "LM"), which was detached from the orbiting spacecraft, in which one astronau remained awaiting the return of the mooncraft.

The entire procedure of releasing the mooncraft, landing it at a predetermine site on the moon and then linking it once again to the spacecraft is one which require precise control of the direction and velocity of both vehicles.When the spacecraft i accurately in orbit and in the correct position on its orbit to ensure a landing in th desired area, the mooncraft briefly fires its rocket motor so that it moves away fro the spacecraft and goes into an elliptical orbit whose point nearest the moon i located some 10 to 20 miles before and six or seven miles above the planned landin area. The periodic time of the mooncraft in this elliptical orbit must be the same a that of the spacecraft in its circular parking orbit. This particular requirement is fo the astronauts' safety; should the landing rockets fail to fire, the mooncraft wi simply continue in orbit and automatically encounter the spacecraft; the latter ca then be maneuvered into a docking position with the mooncraft, so that the tw astronauts in it can return to the spacecraft that will take them back to earth.

When the mooncraft is in the correct position in its orbit, the actual landin maneuver can commence. The landing rocket motor of the mooncraft must be abl to develop a thrust that can be suitably varied, because at the start of the landin operation the craft still carries its full load of rocket fuel, and its speed has to b slowed down from about 5000 mph to zero. In doing this, fuel corresponding t about two-thirds of the mooncraft's initial total weight (with full tanks) is consume The power and direction of the thrust developed by the motor are so controlle that the craft lands at a predetermined point and at a predetermined speed. If th orbit in which the mooncraft is moving around the moon deviates a little from th specified orbit, corrections can be made by means of small steering rocket jets. I this way the horizontal and the vertical speed in relation to the landing area ar reduced. When the horizontal speed has diminished to zero, the mooncraft wi slowly sink towards the surface, the actual speed being kept under control by mean of retroactive rocket motor thrust. By this time the astronauts have taken ove manual control of the mooncraft. Scanning the lunar surface from an altitude o several hundred feet, they select a zone free from boulders, deep cracks or othe hazards and then bring their craft gently down. The final operation calls for ver accurate control of the thrust so that it almost exactly balances the mooncraft' weight. When the feet of the craft touch the surface, the motors are shut off.

On completion of their exploration of the lunar surface, the astronauts return t their mooncraft. The lower half of the craft serves as a launching pad for the uppe half, which is provided with a second, smaller rocket motor just under the cre cabin. This motor propels the ascent stage of the mooncraft back to the spacecraft which will rendezvous and dock with it. The lunar astronauts then transfer to th spacecraft and jettison the mooncraft; the return flight to earth then begins.

The sequence of operations for the Apollo XI moon landing project was as follows (see illustrations on pp. 118–119):

1. Saturn rocket is launched, carrying the Apollo spacecraft with the mooncraft enclosed within it.
2. First stage of the rocket is jettisoned, second stage is fired.
3. Second rocket stage is jettisoned, third stage goes into orbit around the earth ($1\frac{1}{2}$ revolutions).
4. Third stage is fired, thereby increasing the speed from 17,500 mph to the so-called "escape velocity" of almost 25,000 mph.

5a–5d. Third stage burns out. Apollo spacecraft is released. Mooncraft (LEM) and command module are now docked together nose to nose by a complex maneuver. They then reconnect with the third stage and continue the flight. Third stage is then finally jettisoned, and Apollo spacecraft starts up its own rocket motors. Apollo comprises the command module (i.e., the crew capsule), the service module, and the mooncraft.

6. Braking rockets are fired, spacecraft goes into orbit around the moon at an altitude of about 70 miles.
7. Two astronauts enter mooncraft, which is now detached from the spacecraft.
8. Mooncraft goes into its own orbit bringing it over the landing area.
9. Main braking rocket motor of mooncraft is fired. Telescopic legs of mooncraft are extended and it lands on the lunar surface.
10. Ascent stage of mooncraft launched for return flight to orbiting spacecraft.
11. Rendezvous with spacecraft. Lunar astronauts transfer themselves from mooncraft to spacecraft.
12. Mooncraft is jettisoned.
13. Spacecraft starts return flight to earth.
14. Command module is detached from service module.
15. Command module is maneuvered so that the heat shield is facing forward on entering the earth's atmosphere (see page 98).
16. Final parachute descent to earth.

Kennedy Space Centre.
The drawing illustrates how the first laser ever to orbit the moon
is used to map the lunar surface in infinite detail
as it flies aboard the Apollo-15 command module
Photo USIS

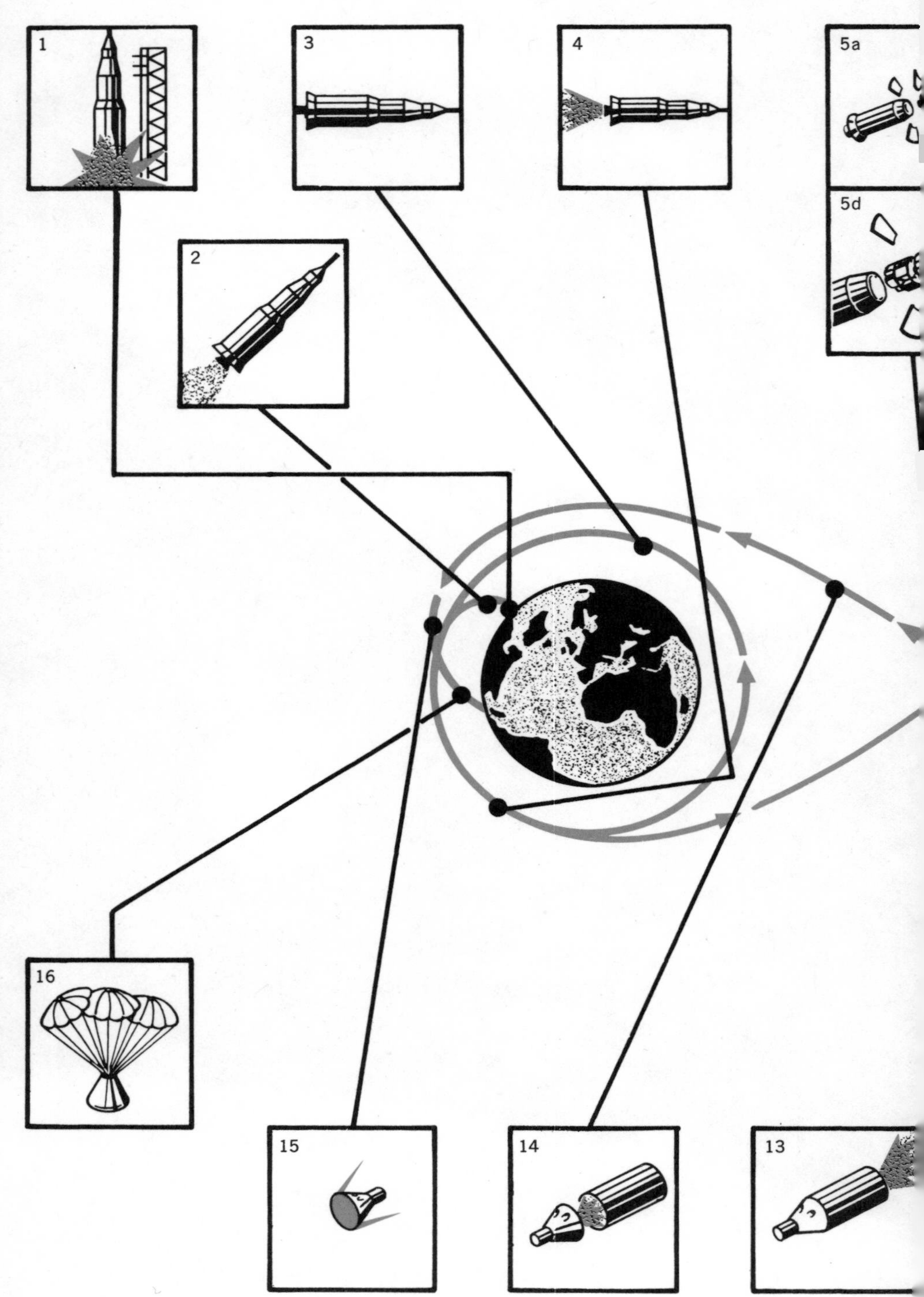

STAGES OF THE MANNED APOLLO SPACECRAFT FLIGHT TO THE MOON

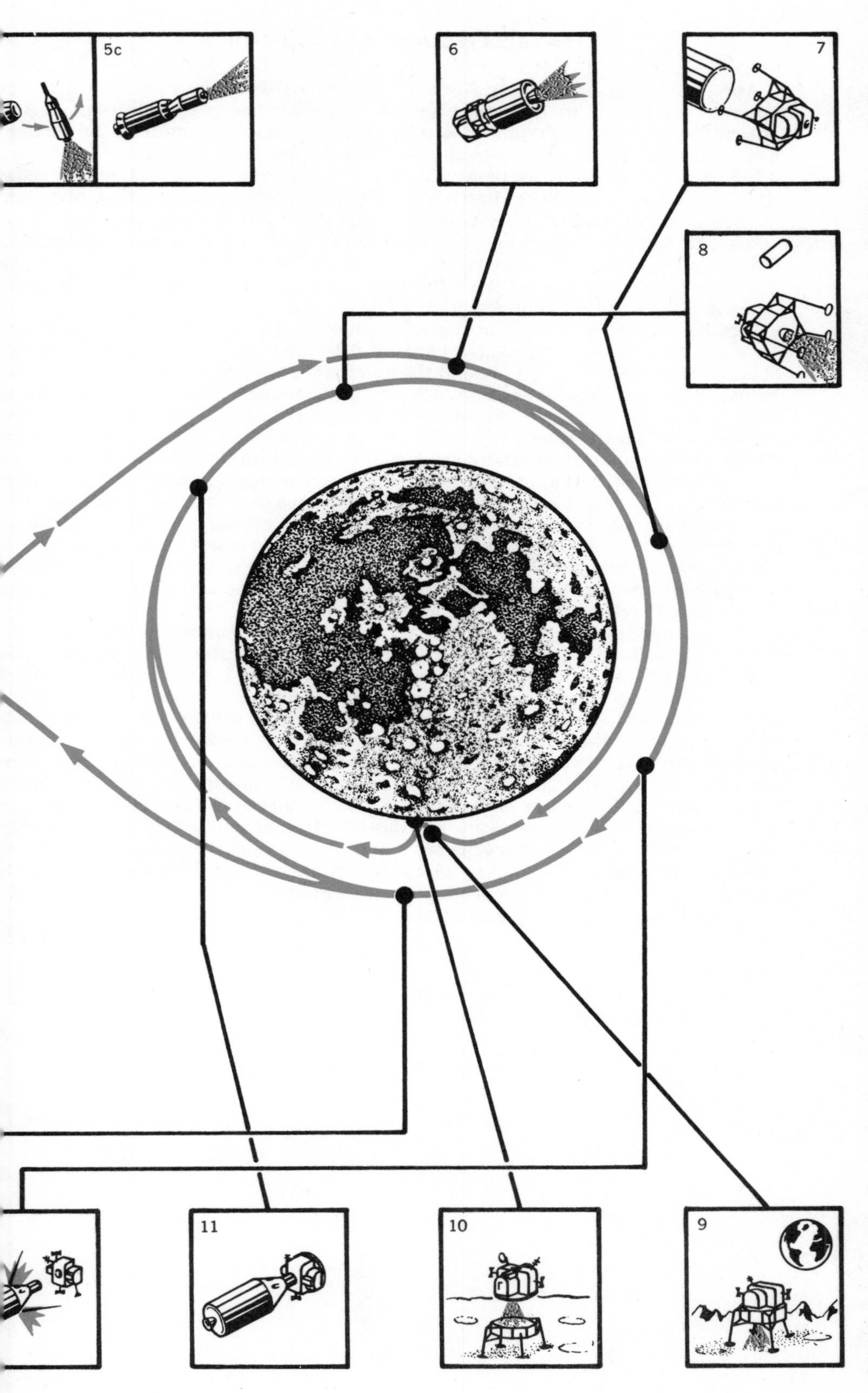

5c
6
7
8
11
10
9

SATELLITES AND SPACE PROBES

About five years after Russia had put the first man-made earth satellite—th Sputnik—into orbit, in 1957, the scientific and economic potentialities of rocket powered space vehicles began to be fully exploited. Scientific study of the weathe made considerable progress with the launching of the Tiros and, later, the Nimbu (1964) weather satellites (both American). The communications satellites Telsta (1962), Relay, Syncom, Echo, Early Bird, and others provided a new and importan transoceanic link, including the possibility of transmitting live television broadcast across the Atlantic. Communications satellites may be either passive reflectors o radio signals, like Echo, or active repeaters, like Telstar. Scientific exploration o interplanetary space started with the space probes of the Ranger and Marine series (U.S.A.) and the Lunik series (Russia).

Weather satellites, communications satellites and probes have one feature i common: they are unmanned. They are put into orbit or space trajectory by mean of launching rockets (see Fig. 1), and their electronic equipment is powered by sola batteries—i.e., storage batteries which are kept charged by current generated i solar cells (Figs. 2a, 5a, 5b; see also Vol. I, page 120). All three types enable dat derived from measurement of conditions in and around the satellite or prob (temperature, radiation, magnetic field, etc.) to be transmitted back to earth, wher they are picked up and monitored. Also, they carry reception equipment for contro signals (Fig. 2a)—e.g., for orbital correction by means of control jets—and are ofte provided with star-tracking systems for automatic orbital control by means o sensing devices for guidance with reference to the sun or a star, such as Canopus i the southern hemisphere. In most cases the space vehicle travels in a predetermine (programed) orbit, so that only the difference between the actual orbital data an the program have to be monitored and corrected.

The ground tracking stations for space probes and communications satellite are of a particular design (Fig. 2b). Their most important feature is a highly sensitiv antenna (Fig. 3) with a gain of 60 db (one million times) in the reception of the wea signals picked up from the probe or satellite. The antenna is continuously swun with a directional accuracy of about one-thousandth of a degree—i.e., 3.6 seconds o arc. Connected to the antenna is a maser amplifier with a low noise factor. "Noise" in the present context denotes unwanted electrical signals generated within th apparatus (more particularly the amplifier) itself and disturbing or distorting th signals received. The maser is an amplifier which converts the energy of atoms int microwave energy (microwaves are very short electromagnetic waves in the frequenc range of 1000–30,000 megacycles/sec.) and uses the electromagnetic waves t stimulate high-energy electrons to release energy, thereby amplifying the stimulatin radiation. The process is independent of the random motion of electrons, so tha maser amplifiers generate less noise than other types of amplifier.

(more

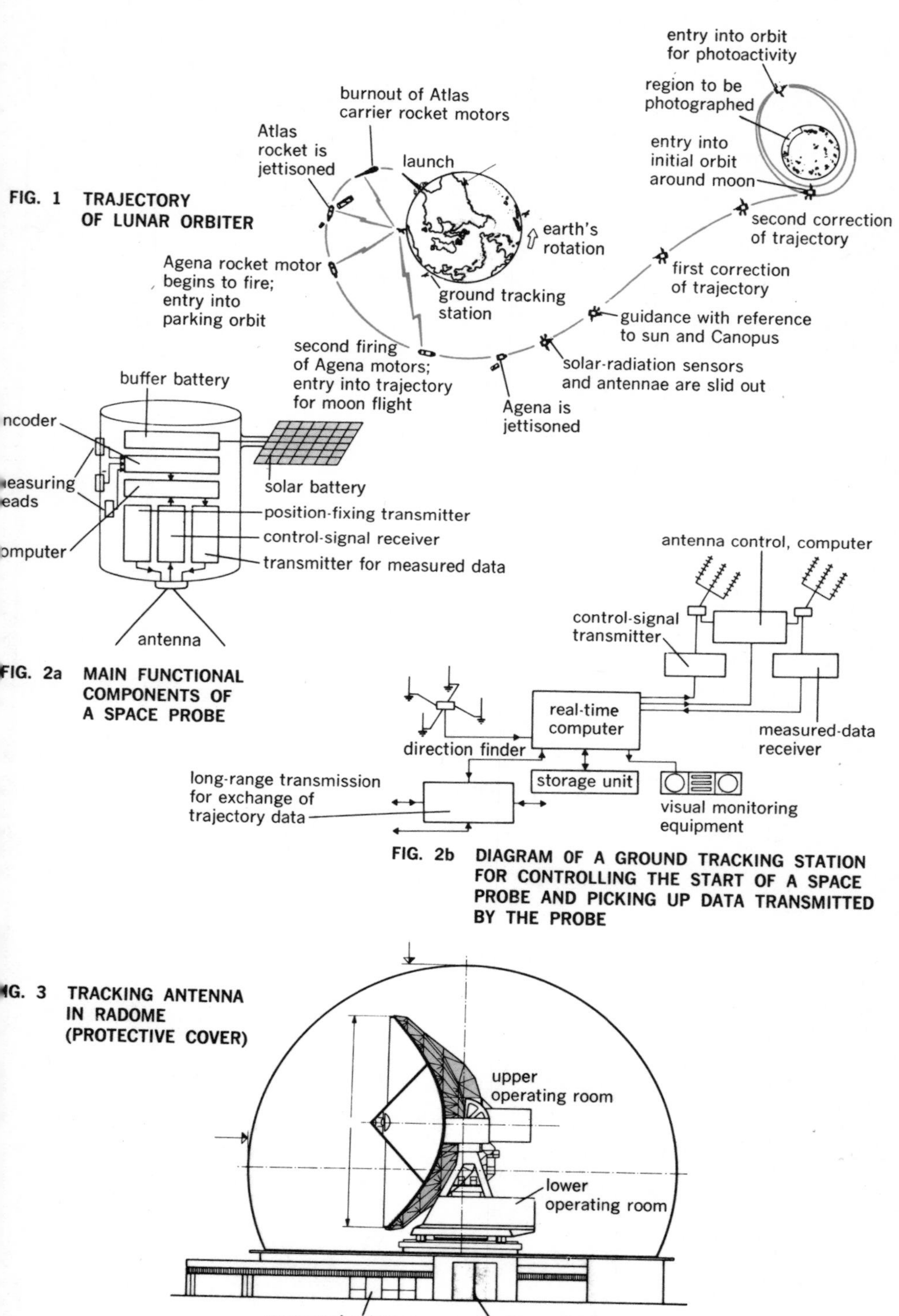

FIG. 1 TRAJECTORY OF LUNAR ORBITER

FIG. 2a MAIN FUNCTIONAL COMPONENTS OF A SPACE PROBE

FIG. 2b DIAGRAM OF A GROUND TRACKING STATION FOR CONTROLLING THE START OF A SPACE PROBE AND PICKING UP DATA TRANSMITTED BY THE PROBE

IG. 3 TRACKING ANTENNA IN RADOME (PROTECTIVE COVER)

In 1973, Mariner, an unmanned U.S. Spacecraft, is scheduled to fly within 625 miles of Mercury and 3,300 miles of Venus to collect information on the physical characteristics of the two planets

Photo USIS

One of the main functions of a *weather satellite* is to report back on cloud formations to the ground tracking stations; in addition, the physical conditions such as temperature are measured and transmitted. The satellite is equipped with a television camera equipped with a vidicon tube (see Vol. I, page 146). In a typical camera of this kind, light is admitted to the single plate in the tube for 1/25 second, and the image is then scanned by an electron beam in 800 lines in a period of 200 seconds. In all, $800 \times 800 = 640{,}000$ picture points are thus scanned; the requisite band width is 1600 cycles/sec.; the transmitter frequency is 136 megacycles/sec.; the output is 5 watts. The antennae for picking up the television pictures from weather satellites need not be so elaborate as those used for communications or for the tracking of space probes far out in the solar system, and ordinary amplifiers instead of masers are generally employed. These satellites orbit at heights varying from about 500 to 1500 miles above the earth. One complete picture is scanned and transmitted every 208 seconds with the type of camera envisaged here; as already stated, the actual scanning time is 200 seconds, which is of course very much longer than in an ordinary television camera.

Space probes: The moon probes of the Ranger series were designed with the object of obtaining high-quality close-up pictures of the lunar surface (from an altitude of about 1000 ft.) and transmitting them back to earth. The three Ranger probes (1964) together sent back 17,000 pictures, some of which provide a thousand times better resolution of detail than could be obtained with moon photographs obtained through telescopes on earth. Ranger was equipped with two television cameras producing 1125-line images with a scanning time of 2.5 seconds. Light was admitted to the signal plate of the special vidicon tube for 1/250 of a second. Each of the two cameras, operating alternatively, took pictures at a rate of one every 5 seconds. They were transmitted at a frequency of 960 megacycles/sec., output 60 watts. The signals were picked up on earth by a parabolic antenna of about 90 ft. diameter and recorded on 35 mm photographic film and on Polaroid film with the aid of a television picture tube. Four other cameras in the probe obtained lower-definition close-up pictures (exposure time 1/500 sec., 282 lines, scanning time 1/5 second). The six cameras operated only during the last 20 minutes before impact.

Although the first pictures of the hidden side of the moon were transmitted back to earth by the Russian moon probe Luna 3 in 1959, serious mapping began with the Lunar Orbiter program. Each of these spacecraft was equipped with two cameras, one for wide-angle, the other for telephoto photography. The spacecraft traveled at a speed of 4500 mph in relation to the surface of the moon, and to prevent blurring, the film was moved slightly between exposures. Lunar Orbiters 1, 2 and 3 photographed the visible face of the moon; Lunar Orbiters 4 and 5 concentrated on the far side.

In 1965 the space probe Mariner IV (Fig. 5) took 21 pictures of the planet Mars from 6000 miles and transmitted them back to earth, a distance of about 140 million miles, using a transmitter with an output of only 10 watts. The spacecraft took 228

(more)

FIG. 4 SPAIN, PORTUGAL AND THE STRAITS OF GIBRALTAR AS PHOTOGRAPHED BY NIMBUS-A WEATHER SATELLITE FROM A HEIGHT OF ABOUT 550 MILES; PICTURE RECEIVED AT A TRACKING STATION AT MUNICH, GERMANY

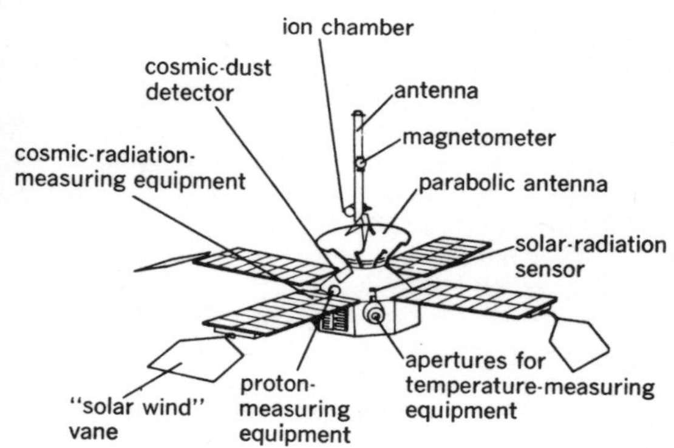

FIG. 5a

solar-radiation sensor
radiation telescope
television camera
Mars sensor
Canopus sensor

FIG. 5b DETAILS OF MARINER IV SPACE PROBE TO MARS

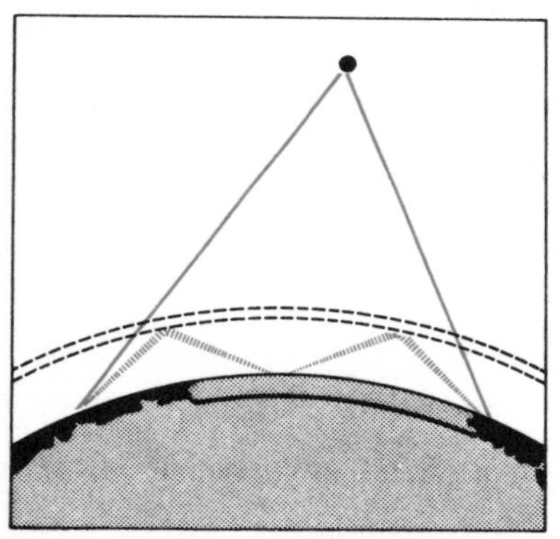

G. 6 UNDERSEA CABLE, SHORT-WAVE RADIO AND COMMUNICATIONS SATELLITE AS MEANS OF INTERCONTINENTAL COMMUNICATION

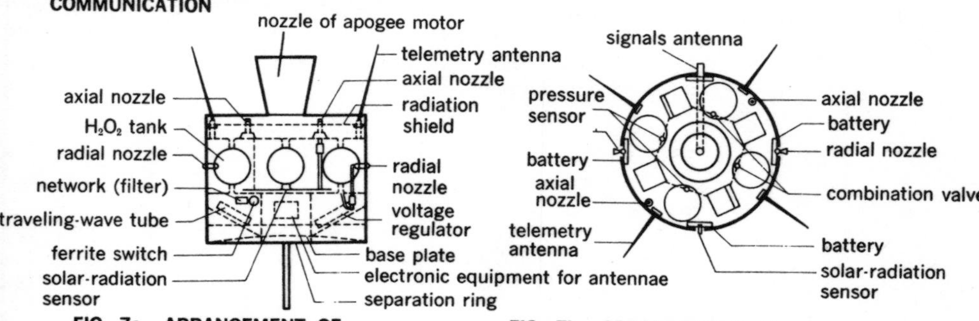

FIG. 7a ARRANGEMENT OF COMPONENT UNITS IN A SATELLITE (SIDE VIEW)

FIG. 7b ARRANGEMENT OF COMPONENT UNITS IN A SATELLITE (REAR VIEW)

days to reach the vicinity of Mars. Its vidicon camera took 200-line pictures, exposure time 1/5 second, scanning time 24 seconds. Each of the $200 \times 200 = 40{,}000$ picture points was assigned a numerical brightness value in a scale of 64 possible values by an analogue-digital converter and these values were stored in binary form on a magnetic tape. For transmission to earth, this tape was subsequently "played back" at a greatly reduced speed (because of the relatively low transmitter power) so that it took 8 hours and 48 minutes to transmit the data of a single picture that had been scanned and taped in 24 seconds (the recording speed of the tape was 13 in./sec., whereas the playback speed was only 0.01 in./sec.). At the tracking station the data were stored on a magnetic tape. When decoded, the numerical values were reproduced in their appropriate brightness intensities in a television picture tube and recorded on 35 mm photographic film.

Communications satellites, more particularly the active repeater type such as Telstar and its successors, are used for long-distance transmission of signals in circumstances that are beyond the performance range of other systems. This applies particularly to band width, which for television transmission is about 5 megacycles/sec. and is thus over a thousand times greater than the band width required for ordinary radiotelephonic communication. ("Band width" denotes the frequency limits of a given wave band; more specifically, it indicates the frequency range occupied by a modulated carrier wave—i.e., a wave generated at a constant frequency whose amplitude, frequency or phase is then varied in accordance with a sound or video signal to be transmitted.) Fig. 7 illustrates an active repeater communications satellite. Externally it carries a communications antenna and several telemetry antennae. Fig. 8 is a block diagram of the electronic system of a satellite of this type, while Fig. 9 represents the electronic system of the ground transmitting and receiving station. The signal beamed to the satellite from the parabolic antenna of the transmitter is equivalent to a power of about 2 million kw. On its journey to the satellite this signal is weakened about 10^{20} times, so that the input at the satellite's receiving antenna is 20×10^{-12} watt. The satellite transmits its signals with a power of 12 watts, which is weakened by a factor of 5×10^{19} on its way to the transatlantic receiving station, so that the input at the receiving antenna is only 2.4×10^{-19} watt. This extremely weak signal is amplified with the aid of maser amplifiers as already described.

Communications satellites of this kind are put into circular orbit around the earth at a distance of about 23,000 miles radius. The periodic time of the satellite in its orbit is 24 hours—i.e., synchronous with the earth's rotation. The advantage of the synchronous satellite is that, because it hovers stationary in relation to the point directly under it on the surface of the earth, it is available for communications work at all times, instead of being only periodically available like the earlier satellites such as Telstar which orbited close to the earth. A synchronous satellite at such an altitude can "see" about 120 degrees of latitude. At least three such synchronous satellites are necessary for complete coverage of the earth's surface.

FIG. 8 REPEATER EQUIPMENT IN SATELLITE

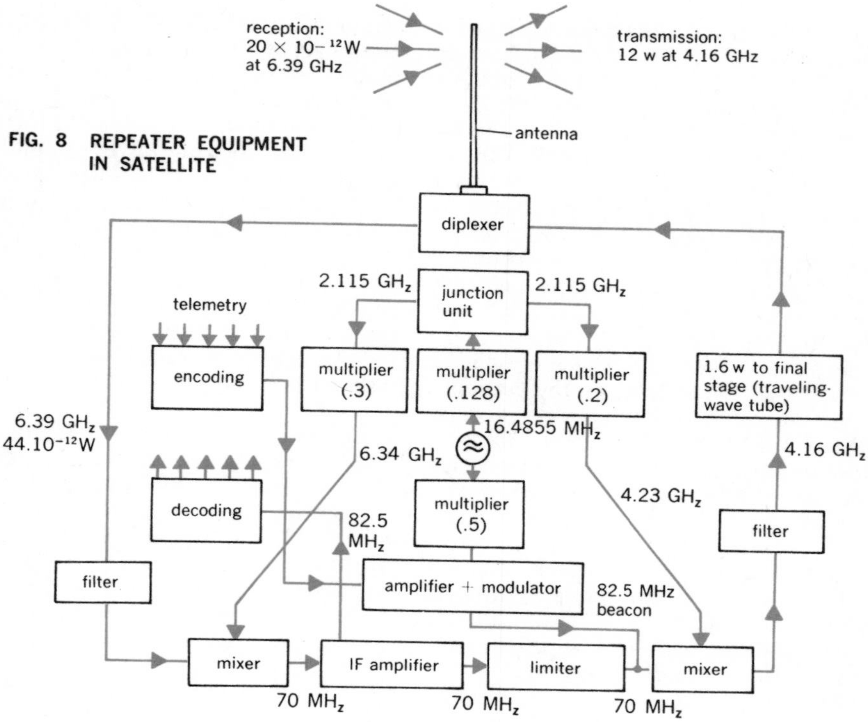

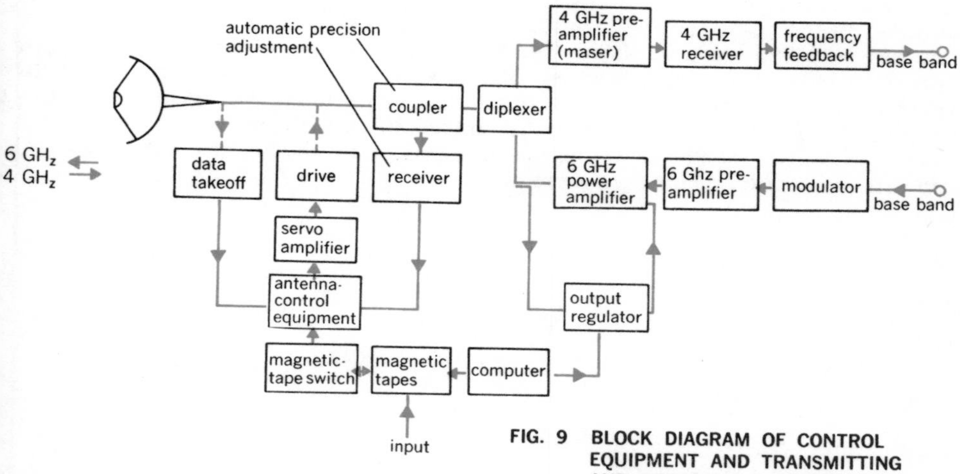

FIG. 9 BLOCK DIAGRAM OF CONTROL EQUIPMENT AND TRANSMITTING AND RECEIVING EQUIPMENT IN GROUND STATION

PLANETARIUM

In modern usage the term "planetarium" denotes an optical system, devised and developed by the German firm of Carl Zeiss in the 1920s, for projecting an artificial night sky on the inside of a hemispherical auditorium and showing the principal motions of planets and other celestial bodies, together with other astronomical phenomena. The forerunner of the modern planetarium was the device known as the orrery, a mechanical model of the solar system in which the planets could be made to move in orbit around the sun in the center by means of handles, spindles and gears. There are three main reasons why the planetary motions as seen by a geocentric observer—i.e., an observer stationed on the earth—are quite complex: first, the orbits of the planets around the sun are elliptical, so that the angular velocity is not constant during one revolution; second, the orbits are located in planes which are inclined at various angles in relation to the ecliptic (or the plane of the earth's orbit); third, the observer is stationed on the earth which is itself in motion around the sun. The ecliptic is the circle of intersection of the earth's orbit with the celestial sphere. To the geocentric observer it is the sun's apparent annual path relative to the stars.

When a dome of at least 50 ft. diameter is used, the effect produced in the planetarium is very realistic. The hemispherical domes of modern planetariums range in diameter from 50 to about 100 ft. At the center of the dome is the projector, a complex piece of equipment (Fig. 1) comprising various individual projectors for the sun, moon, planets and stars. These projectors are moved by motors and precision gear systems to reproduce accurately the motions of the heavenly bodies—speeded up or slowed down, if required. The projector is a "universal instrument" in the sense that it can be made to show the night sky as seen from any place on the earth's surface, and not only as it appears at the present time, but also at any time in the distant past or the distant future.

The modern Zeiss instrument in the London planetarium consists of a 13½ ft. long dumbbell-shaped assembly, weighing over two tons and comprising nearly two hundred optical projectors. It contains about 29,000 individual parts. Besides the sun, moon and planets, the forty-two brightest stars—those of the first and the second magnitude—are produced by individual projectors. In addition, the images of some 8850 other stars, ranging down to the sixth magnitude (the faintest visible to the unaided eye), and including some of lesser magnitude, are projected on to the interior of the dome, as well as a realistic image of the Milky Way. The spectator in the planetarium can be shown in a short time motions which in reality can be observed only by years of watching. The motions can be speeded up, so that the planets can be seen chasing one another, describing loops, advancing and retrograding. Eclipses of the moon and of the sun (complete with corona) can be realistically reproduced, the phases of the moon are correctly shown, and meteorites and comets can be seen racing across the night sky.

(more)

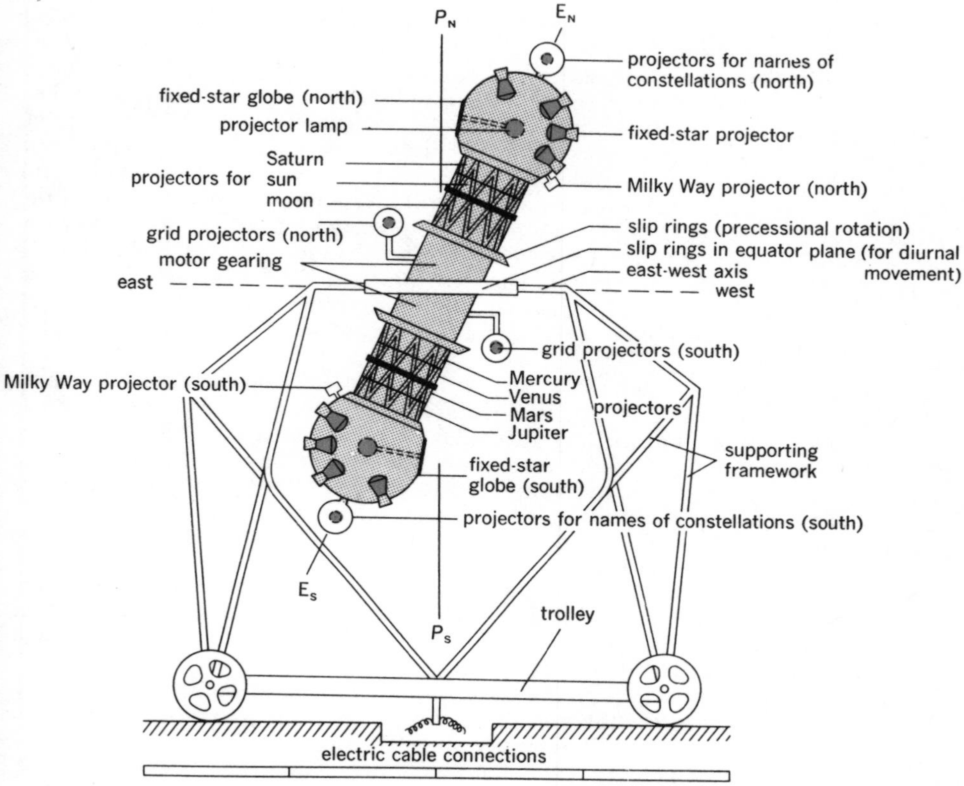

P_N
E_N
projectors for names of constellations (north)
fixed-star globe (north)
projector lamp
fixed-star projector
Saturn
projectors for sun
moon
Milky Way projector (north)
grid projectors (north)
slip rings (precessional rotation)
motor gearing
slip rings in equator plane (for diurnal movement)
east
east-west axis
west
grid projectors (south)
Milky Way projector (south)
Mercury
Venus
Mars
Jupiter
projectors
supporting framework
fixed-star globe (south)
projectors for names of constellations (south)
E_S
P_S
trolley
electric cable connections

FIG. 1 THE ZEISS PLANETARIUM PROJECTOR

east
west
supporting framework
east-west axis
fixed-star globe (south)
grid projector (south)
cover to slip rings for diurnal movement
fixed-star globe (north)
projectors for names of constellations (north)
trolley
supporting framework

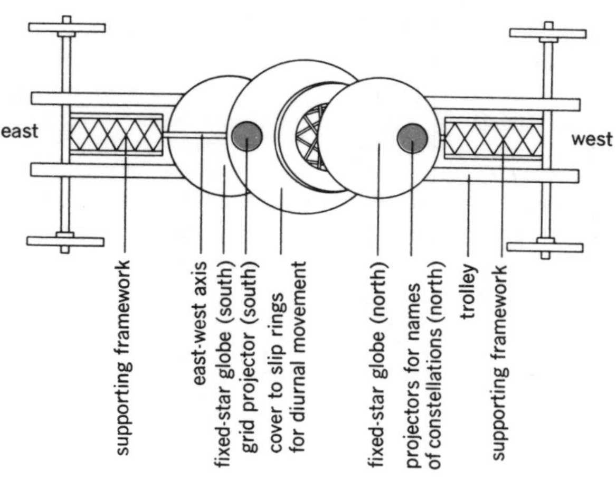

Planetarium (continued)

Fig. 3 shows the earth's annual orbit around the sun. (In reality the orbit is almost circular; its elliptical shape would hardly be apparent on the scale of this diagram; it is here shown in perspective, however.) The earth is represented in four positions in the orbit, corresponding to the four seasons of the northern hemisphere. The earth's axis of rotation (P) is not perpendicular to the orbital plane, but is tilted, forming an angle of 23.5 degrees with the axis of the ecliptic (E). This is also the angle between the polar axis $P_n P_s$ and the ecliptic axis $E_n E_s$ (designated as P-axis and E-axis) of the instrument. Viewed from the earth, the sun moves in the plane of the ecliptic, while the motions of the moon and the planets always occur in the vicinity of that plane. For this reason the projectors for these bodies are located individually along the E-axis of the instrument. The two spherical heads accommodating the projectors for the fixed stars are disposed at the ends of the E-axis. These projectors produce images of some 8900 stars, as well as a number of star clusters, nebulae and the Milky Way.

The simplest motion is due to the earth's diurnal (daily) rotation about its P-axis from west to east, causing an apparent rotation of the heavens from east to west. To reproduce this motion for any particular place on earth, e.g., New York, the instrument must first be set to the geographic latitude of that place. This is done by rotating it about its east-west axis until the P-axis of the instrument makes an angle equal to the angle of latitude with the horizontal line to the north point of the auditorium dome (Fig. 4). The diurnal motion of the heavens is simulated by rotation of the instrument about its P-axis. During this rotation the E-axis traces a double conical surface with its apex at the intersection of the two axes. The earth performs one complete revolution on its axis in the course of a sidereal day which is almost 4 minutes shorter than the (mean) solar day. The instrument performs one complete revolution about its P-axis in a length of time corresponding to the "sidereal day," but speeded up, so that its actual duration is much shorter (it can be varied from 3 to 12 minutes). At the end of this period the instrument returns to its initial position relative to the dome, and the fixed stars occupy the same positions in the sky. Not so the sun, moon and planets. Thus, the projector for the sun has rotated nearly 1 degree to the east, and it is not until 4 "minutes" later (actually a much shorter length of time corresponding to the reduced time scale), when the diurnal rotation motors have rotated the instrument 1 degree farther westward, that the sun regains its initial position in the sky. The "diurnal" motion of the moon, as viewed in the planetarium, is very noticeable, whereas that of the planet Saturn, for example, is almost undetectable. The position of the instrument, in performing the diurnal rotation, must therefore be characterized not by the ordinary time of day, but by sidereal (or stellar) time, as in Fig. 4. This is because of the above-mentioned difference in time between the sidereal day and the solar day. Fig. 3 indicates the positions taken up by the instrument in the course of demonstrating the earth's diurnal rotation in winter (far right) and summer (far left). These diagrams show how the position of the instrument has to be varied with the rotation of the earth in order to keep the E-axis of the instrument parallel to the E-axis of the ecliptic.

(more)

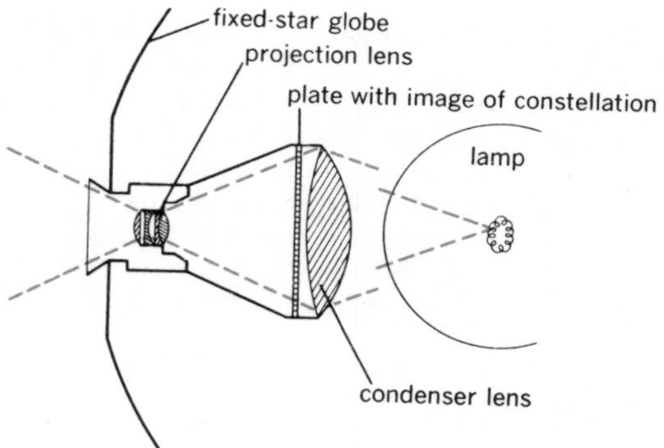

FIG. 2 FIXED-STAR PROJECTOR

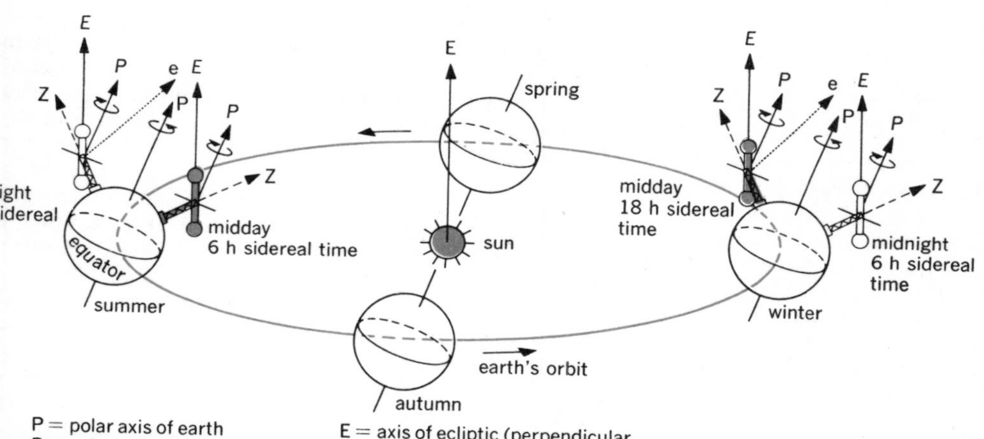

FIG. 3 ANNUAL MOTION OF THE EARTH AROUND THE SUN AND DIURNAL ROTATION OF THE EARTH AROUND ITS POLAR AXIS

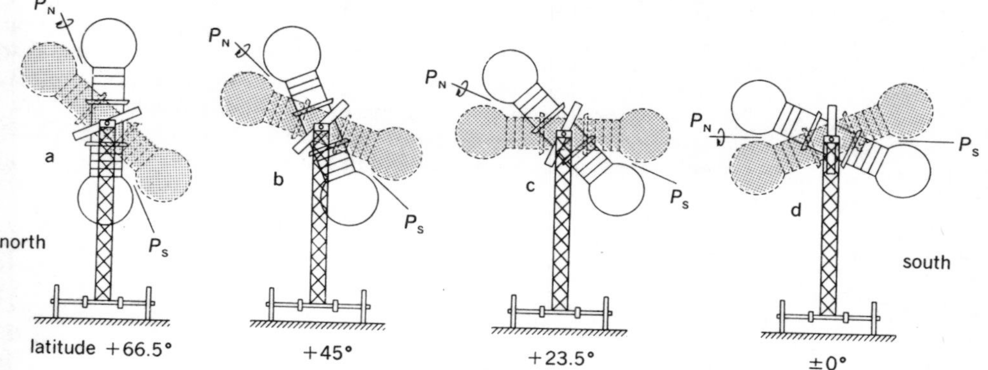

FIG. 4 POSITIONS OF INSTRUMENT AT FOUR DIFFERENT GEOGRAPHIC LATITUDES AND FOR 6 H (RED) AND 18 H (BLACK) SIDEREAL TIME

Planetarium (continued)

The principle of the demonstration of the sun's motion in the planetarium is shown in Fig. 5. Because of the elliptical shape of the earth's orbit, the sun as seen by a geocentric observer moves with varying angular velocity in the course of the year. Since the eccentricity of the orbit is only slight, this variation can adequately be simulated by causing the earth, represented by a pin, to rotate with constant angular velocity on a circular disc whose axis of rotation corresponds to the E-axis, while the sun is given a fixed amount of eccentricity. Earth and sun are interconnected by a guide rod, at one end of which is the sun projector. When the disc is rotated at constant speed, the sun's image projected on to the dome moves at varying speed. The moon's motion is simulated in similar fashion, but the mechanism is more complex because the lunar orbit around the earth is inclined at an angle of 5 degrees to the ecliptic and moreover itself performs a precessional rotation once every $18\frac{1}{2}$ years.

Because of the eccentricity of planetary orbits, the accurate geocentric representation of the motion of a planet is by no means simple, and a full explanation would be outside the present scope. Fig. 6 merely represents the simplified case where the earth's orbit and the planet's orbit are concentric circles situated in the same plane, with the sun at the center. The pins representing the earth and the planet rotate in their respective orbits around the sun. The two pins are interconnected by means of a guide rod, so that the image of the planet (like that of the sun in the mechanism described above) is always projected in the direction away from the earth, and the image is thus always viewed geocentrically. With the planetarium instrument it is also possible to demonstrate the precessional motion of the earth's axis, or "precession of the equinoxes," a phenomenon already known in ancient times and subsequently explained by Newton as being caused by the equatorial bulge (or the flattened shape at the poles) of the earth. It is characterized by the fact that the earth's axis revolves in a small circle about the pole of the ecliptic in a period of 26,000 years. This causes the equinoctial points to move retrograde in the ecliptic by an annual amount of a little over 50 seconds of arc, so that the coordinates of the stars are gradually altered in various ways. The equinox is the instant, occurring twice a year, at which the sun apparently crosses the celestial equator. The two points, diametrically opposite each other, in which the ecliptic cuts the celestial equator are called the equinoctial points. In practical terms the precessional motion means that the earth's axis is not steady in space, but performs a slow "wobble," like the axis of a spinning top. At present the axis points approximately in the direction of the Pole Star (Polaris), in the constellation of Ursa Minor, but in 13,000 years' time the axis will be directed at a point located between the bright star Vega in the Lyre and the star gamma in the Dragon—i.e., at an angular distance of about 47 degrees from Polaris. After another 13,000 years the axis will have returned to its present position, and Polaris will once again be the North Star. In Fig. 7 (upper diagram) the direction P_A is the present position of the earth's axis at midsummer; P_B is the position that the axis will have 13,000 years hence, when the earth is at the same point of its orbit, but—because of the tilt of the axis in the opposite direction as a result of the precessional motion—it will then be midwinter in the northern hemisphere. These variations can be reproduced, greatly speeded up, in the planetarium.

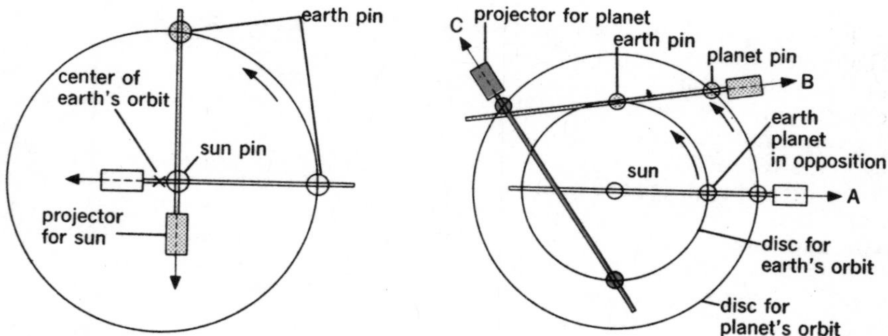

FIG. 5 THE SUN'S ANNUAL ORBIT SEEN BY A GEOCENTRIC OBSERVER

FIG. 6 GEOCENTRIC MOTION OF A PLANET (MARS)

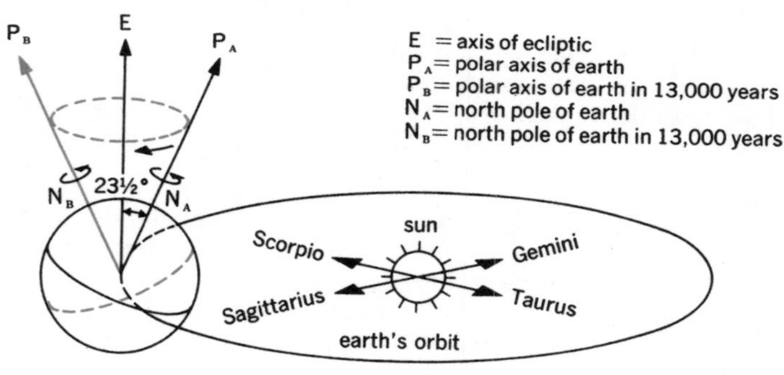

FIG. 7 PRECESSION OF THE EARTH'S AXIS

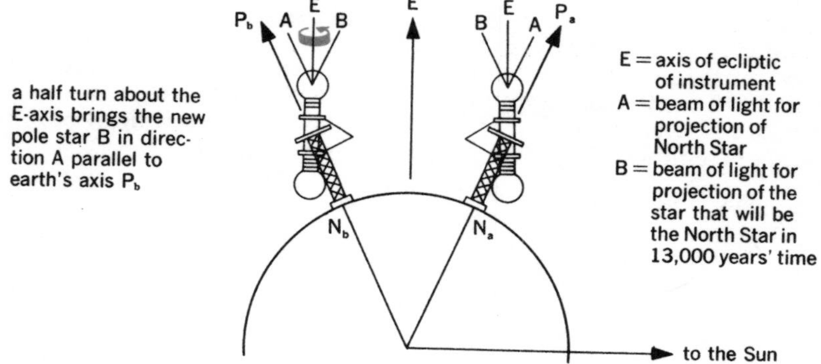

MEDICAL APPLICATIONS OF THE BETATRON

The betatron is an electron accelerator which can produce high-energy electron beams and X-rays of high penetrating power. Acceleration of the electrons traveling in a circular orbit of constant radius is achieved by means of a rapidly changing electric field (see Vol. I, page 126). In medical science the electron beam and X-rays are employed for various therapeutic purposes. For example, the betatron illustrated in Fig. 1 can produce X-rays of an intensity corresponding to that produced in an X-ray tube operating at 42 million volts. Equipment of this kind is large and expensive. Important requirements are that the apparatus be easily movable, simple to operate, safe, and—above all—permitting accurate control of the radiation emitted. Protection against radiation hazard requires special precautions, including concrete walls about five feet thick around the treatment room, in which only the patient remains once the radiation is switched on.

The biological action of electron beams and X-rays is based on the splitting of macromolecules, which is effected through the medium of ionization processes. Cells in pathological growths (tumors, etc.) are more severely affected by the radiation. The actual effect of the radiation on tissues is due to electrons set in motion within them, these electrons being either directly supplied in the radiation (electron beams) or released as a secondary phenomenon from atoms bombarded by electromagnetic radiation of very short wavelength (X-rays). A measure for the radiation dose administered is provided by the ratio of the energy of the electrons to the mass of the irradiated region. The radiation dose produced in the human body by the action of X-rays first increases with the depth of penetration (depending on the energy of the radiation), attains a maximum, and then gradually diminishes according to the attenuation of the rays. Because of this, deep-seated tumors can be subjected to high radiation doses while the intermediate tissues through which the X-rays pass remain relatively unaffected. On the other hand, the radiation administered in the form of an electron beam produces a maximum dose at the surface of the patient's body, and the dose diminishes fairly rapidly with increasing depth. By appropriate choice of the energy it is possible to adjust the radiation to the location of the tumor so that only the latter is attacked and the more deeply situated tissues are spared.

The apparatus as a whole can be swung in various directions. The electrons injected to the annular tube (a) of the betatron (Fig. 2), in which they are accelerated, are either discharged at high velocity direct from the tube or directed on to an anticathode ("target") (b) to produce X-rays (see Vol. I, page 124). The betatron is fed with alternating current which generates a magnetic field (c). The electrons are injected at (d) into the annular tube, which is enclosed in a vacuum jacket (e). An alternating electric field is produced in the tube by the magnetic field and maintains the electrons on a predetermined circular path (f), whereby they are speeded up to extremely high velocities. The magnetic field and the electric field must be accurately interadjusted. The electrons can be emitted from the tube through a thin metal "window" at the periphery, when the magnetic field is weakened (Fig. 3). On the other hand, when the intensity of the magnetic field is increased, the radius of the electron path is reduced, so that the electrons now strike an anticathode (b) at the inner wall of the tube and therefore produce X-rays (Fig. 4).

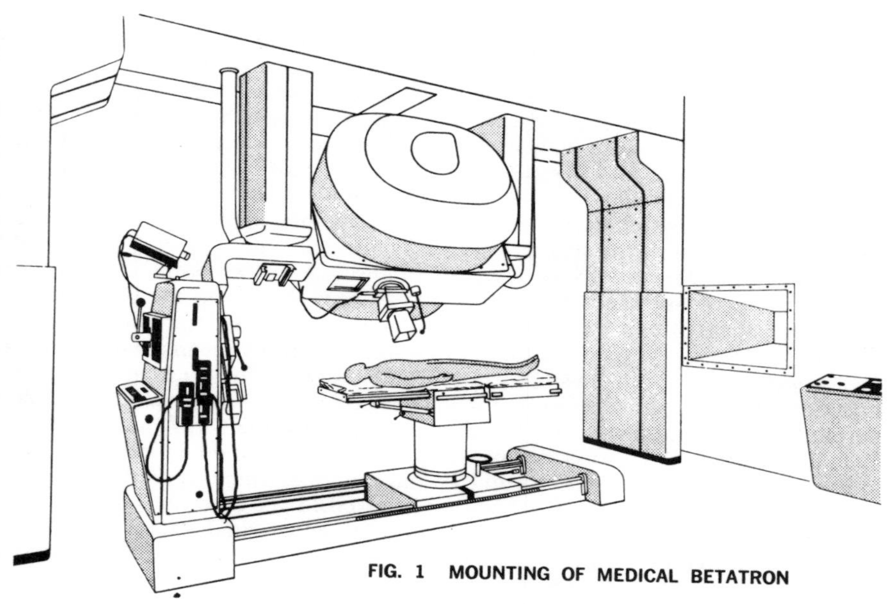

FIG. 1 MOUNTING OF MEDICAL BETATRON

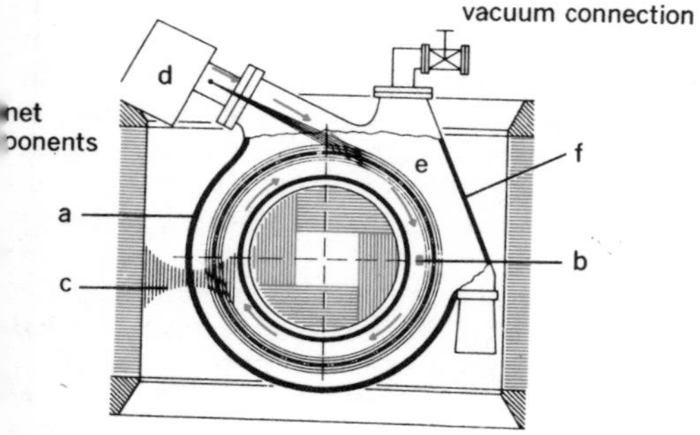

vacuum connection
d
net
ponents
e
f
a
b
c

FIG. 2 BETATRON WITH ANNULAR TUBE

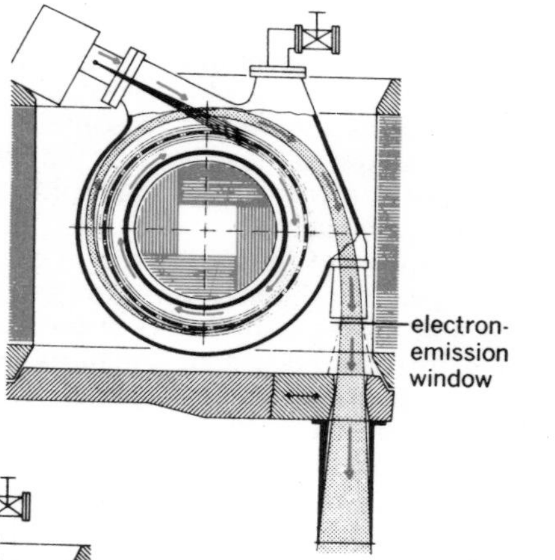

electron-
emission
window

FIG. 3 WEAK MAGNETIC FIELD

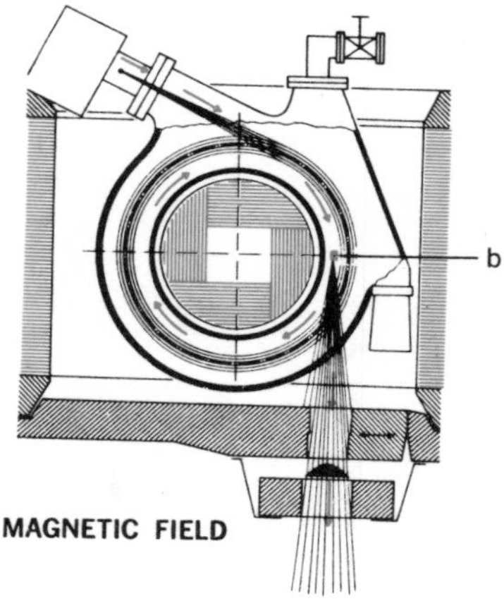

b

FIG. 4 STRONG MAGNETIC FIELD

HEARING AIDS

Fig. 1 shows a section through the human ear, comprising the outer ear, the middle ear, and the inner ear. Beyond the eardrum is the air-filled middle ear cavity bridged by a chain of three small bones (auditory ossicles) forming a mechanical link between the drum and the so-called oval window, which is the entrance to the inner ear. The semicircular canals in the inner ear are concerned with bodily equilibrium, while the fluid-filled spiral, shaped like a snail's shell and divided by a partition, serves for hearing. Located on the partition is the organ of Corti, a complex structure in which the auditory receptor cells are embedded. These cells are connected to the ends of the auditory nerve fibers. Defective hearing may be caused by a functional disorder, due to an accident or disease, at any point in this system including the auditory nerve and indeed the auditory center in the brain. In some cases an impairment can be cured or alleviated by medical treatment or surgery. In other cases it may be possible to obtain improvement by means of a hearing aid.

In general, a hearing aid is a sound amplifier. The earliest form was the ear trumpet which amplifies sound by collecting it with a large mouth and leading it down a tapering tube to a narrow orifice which is inserted into the ear. A modern hearing aid is a transistorized electronic device serving to amplify sound by means of electrical amplification. The sound is picked up by a microphone, which converts it into weak electrical currents. These are amplified and passed to the receiver, which converts them back into sound of greater loudness than the original sound (Fig. 2). The power for the amplifier is supplied by a battery, which may be of the ordinary dry-cell type or a rechargeable storage battery. Present-day hearing aids may comprise several amplification stages combined into a single unit (integrated semiconductor circuit) and are adjustable in various ways to suit them to individual requirements. The user can switch the apparatus on and off, as desired, and he can vary the volume (loudness) to suit the acoustic conditions. Tone control, i.e., a choice of frequency response (the variation of amplification with frequency), may also be provided. The intensity range in which speech is understood may be wide for some deaf people but narrow for others. In some of these latter cases a hearing aid with automatic volume control may help by smoothing out the variations in sound intensity; this kind of control varies the amplification automatically, so that the output intensity is kept constant.

The user of the early type of electrical hearing aid wore earphones held in place by a headband. Later, this external receiver was replaced by the insert receiver clipped to a molded plastic insert in the outer ear. Sometimes a so-called bone-conduction receiver is used, which functions by vibrating the bones of the skull rather than by generating a sound wave. Fig. 3 illustrates a hearing aid which the user carries in a pocket of his clothing, the receiver being connected to the aid by a flexible wire. Other types of hearing aid are small enough to be worn on the head—e.g., behind the ear, or built into an eyeglass frame, or in the ear (Fig. 4). In these small devices all the component parts, including the receiver, are built into one unit.

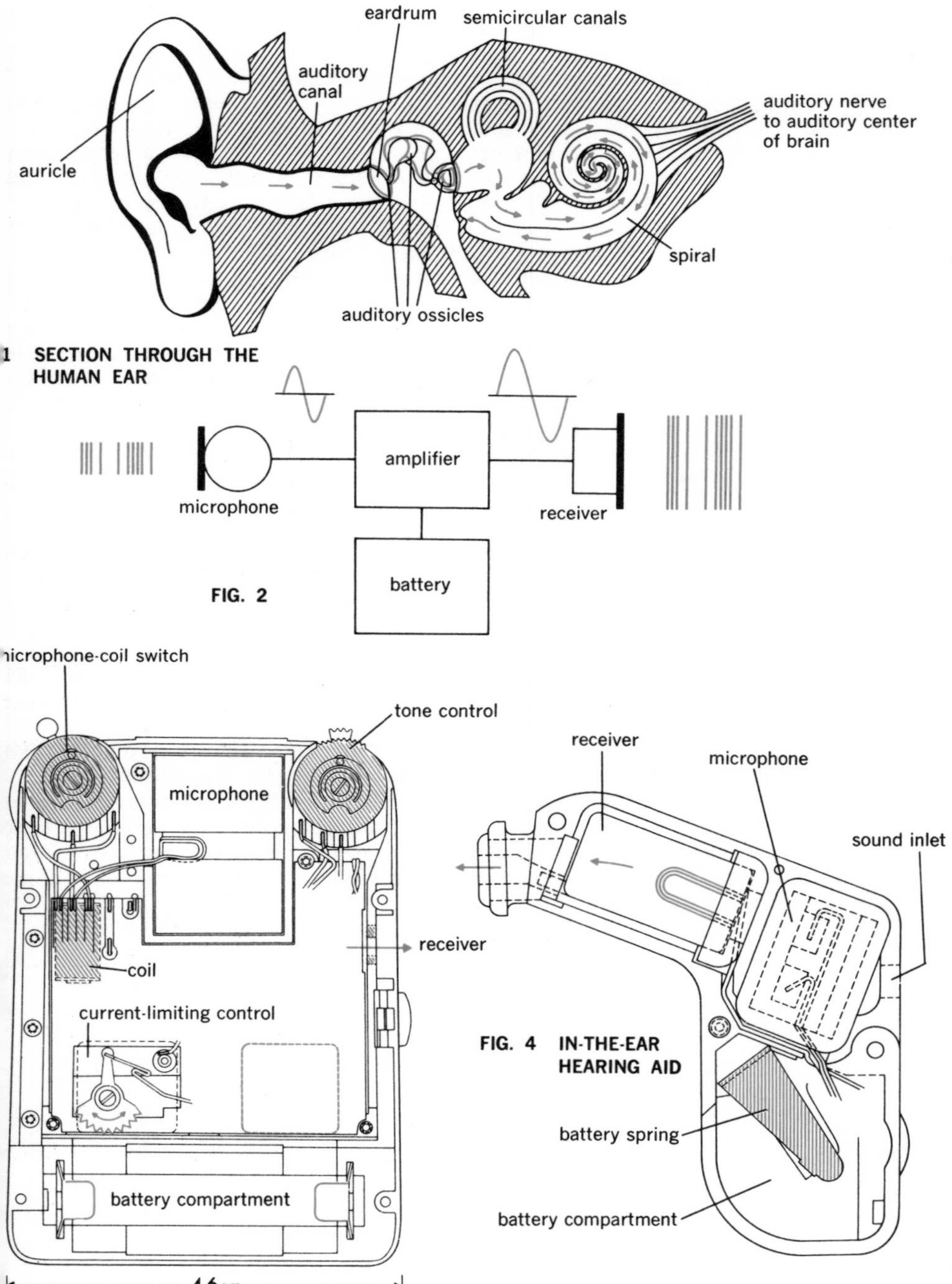

1 SECTION THROUGH THE HUMAN EAR

FIG. 2

FIG. 4 IN-THE-EAR HEARING AID

3 POCKET HEARING AID (REAR COVER OPENED)

HIGH-SPEED TURBINE DRILL

The outer protective layer of a tooth, the enamel (Fig. 1), is difficult to drill an cut because of its great hardness. Considerable progress in dentistry was achieve by the introduction of small drilling tools tipped with hard metal or diamond (Fig. 2 To obtain high cutting efficiency, i.e., faster preparation of cavities for dental treat ment and therefore less pain and discomfort to the patient, it is necessary to emplo high cutting speeds. Diamond and hard-metal-alloy drill bits exert a very effectiv cutting action at speeds of about 60 or 70 ft./sec. To achieve the circumferentia velocities for such cutting speeds with a drill bit which is only about 1/16 in. i diameter it is necessary to rotate it at something like 250,000 revolutions per minut Small turbines driven by compressed air have proved suitable for attaining suc speeds. The operating principle of such a turbine is similar to that of the Pelto wheel (see Vol. I, page 60): a jet of air emerging at high velocity from a nozzl impinging on the blades of a rotor; the spent air is discharged from the rotor chambe through a return duct (Fig. 3). Running under no load, such turbines can reac speeds of about 400,000 rpm; under load the speeds are in the range of 200,000 t 300,000 rpm. Very carefully manufactured high-precision bearings are necessary fo the rotor. As a rule, ball bearings with an external diameter of $\frac{1}{4}$ in. are employe precision-made from stainless steel. For lubrication of the bearings an oil "mist (finely divided oil droplets) is added to the compressed air that drives the turbin The small drill tools (Fig. 2) are inserted directly into a socket in the turbine roto and are secured by means of screw-type or spring-loaded clamping sleeves.

A more recent development has been the introduction of air-cushion, or pneumati bearings (Fig. 4) instead of roller bearings. In this system the rotor "floats" on cushion of air produced by nozzles uniformly distributed around the circumferenc of the rotor chamber (Fig. 5). If the rotor undergoes some displacement and thu moves into an eccentric position within the chamber in consequence of externa loading (lateral pressure developed in drilling), the air-gap between the rotor an the wall of the chamber will become narrower on one side and wider on the opposit side. In the narrow part of the gap the pressure of the cushioning air builds up, whil on the opposite side, where the gap is widest, a decrease in air pressure occurs. Th resulting difference in pressure returns the rotor to its central position.

Very high cutting speeds would, in the absence of cooling, cause excessive heatin of the surfaces being drilled, inasmuch as the tooth material is a poor conductor o heat. To prevent this, the turbine drill is equipped with a cooling system whic directs a number of fine water jets on to the tip of the drill and automatically come into operation as soon as the drill is started (Fig. 1).

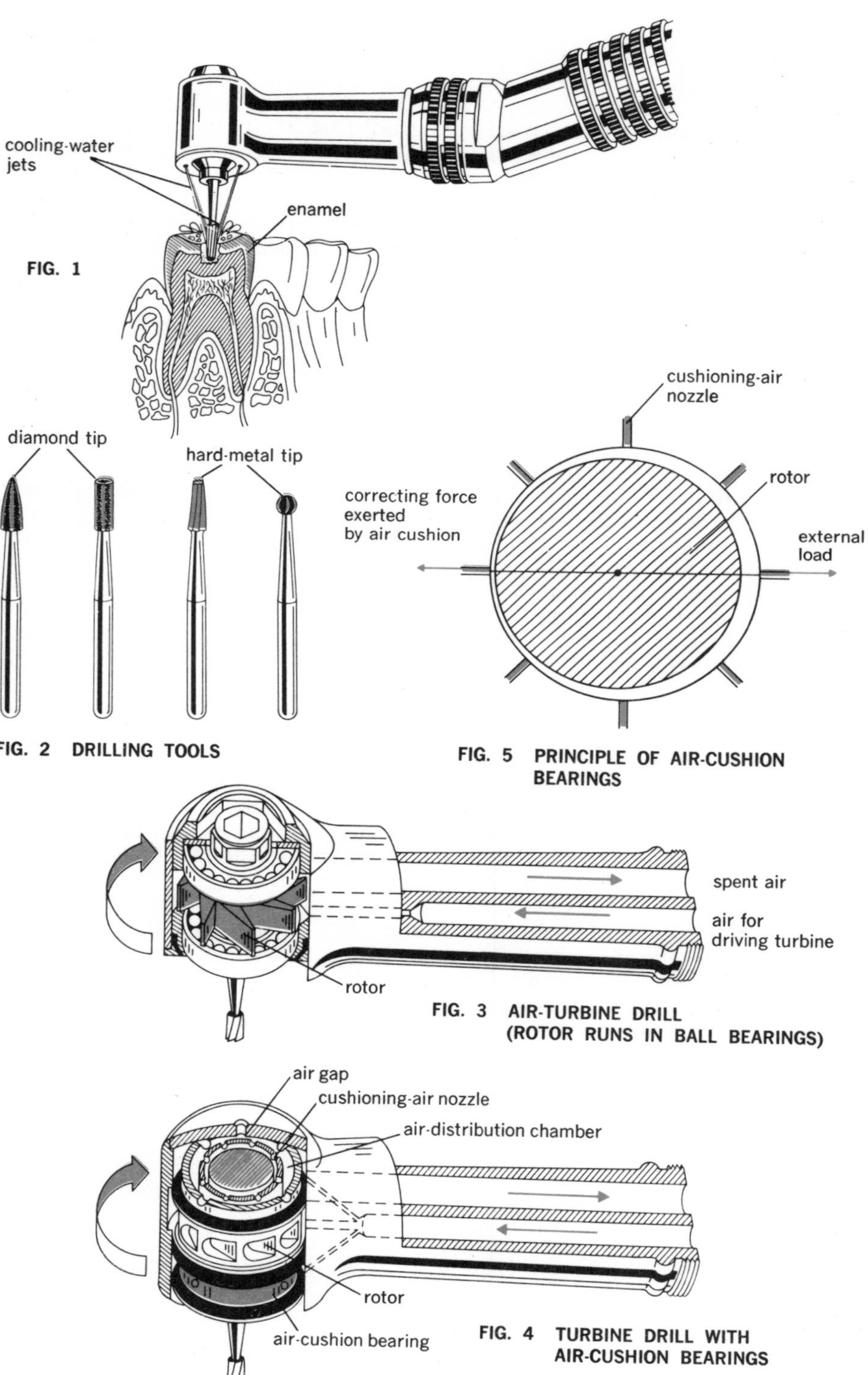

FIG. 2 DRILLING TOOLS

FIG. 5 PRINCIPLE OF AIR-CUSHION BEARINGS

FIG. 3 AIR-TURBINE DRILL (ROTOR RUNS IN BALL BEARINGS)

FIG. 4 TURBINE DRILL WITH AIR-CUSHION BEARINGS

INCUBATOR AND OXYGEN TENT

The function of an incubator (Fig. 1) is to help sustain the life of prematurely born babies who, because of their low weight and weak general constitution, have diminished viability. For such babies, weighing perhaps as little as 2 lb. at birth, the incubator provides an ideal life environment, capable of being varied to suit specific requirements, characterized by: sterility (freedom from germs), temperature (up to 37°C), relative atmospheric humidity (up to 100%), an oxygen concentration (up to 40%—i.e., about twice the normal oxygen content of the atmosphere).

Normally, the prematurely born baby is kept continuously in the incubator for the first few weeks of its life. All nursing manipulations are done by means of special holes through which the nurse inserts her arms and which are provided with sealing devices that fit closely around the arms. The baby is fed, weighed (by means of built-in scales), cleaned and medically treated inside the incubator. Minor operations, transfusions and X-ray photography can likewise be done without having to remove the baby from the incubator.

From the technical point of view the incubator is a special air-conditioned chamber with its own climate-control system. A built-in motor draws in fresh air, which is freed from germs by passing through a bacterial filter and then flows through a thermostatically controlled heating system and a water evaporator (to give it the required humidity). If necessary, oxygen is added. Because of the continuous inflow of air—at a rate of about 6 liters (0.2 cu. ft.) per minute—a slight excess pressure in relation to the surrounding atmosphere is maintained in the incubator. This ensures that the airflow is always directed outwards and the exhaled carbon dioxide is carried away and no external air can penetrate through any small leaks that may be present in the enclosure. The incubator is equipped with various safety devices which sound a warning and/or take preventive action in the event of a failure in the electric power, water or oxygen supply, or if the temperature in the incubator should become too high or too low, or if the oxygen concentration becomes too high.

Comparable in principle to the incubator is the oxygen tent (Fig. 2). It performs two main functions: to supply oxygen-enriched breathing air (30 to 50% oxygen content) to the occupant and to cool the air within the tent by 5 to 8 degrees centigrade. It is used in the treatment of respiratory diseases and heart diseases and in certain cases for the care of persons recovering from serious operations. In cases where the patient's breathing functions are impaired, the oxygen tent can ensure that the normal oxygen content in his blood is maintained, and the body temperature of a patient with very high fever can be kept down.

The oxygen tent consists mainly of a transportable cabinet (accommodating the air-circulating equipment, electric cooling unit, oxygen-dispensing unit, water atomizer, and control apparatus) and the actual tent comprising the supporting frame and the envelope, which is fitted around the patient's bed so as to enclose it completely. A fan draws air out of the tent and passes it through a dust filter to the cooling unit. The moisture in the exhaled air is condensed and thus removed. The air is then recirculated to the tent and is enriched with oxygen. If necessary, the atmospheric humidity can be increased by means of an artificial fog produced by the atomizer. The tent is provided with large openings, closed by zippers (zip fasteners), to give access to the patient.

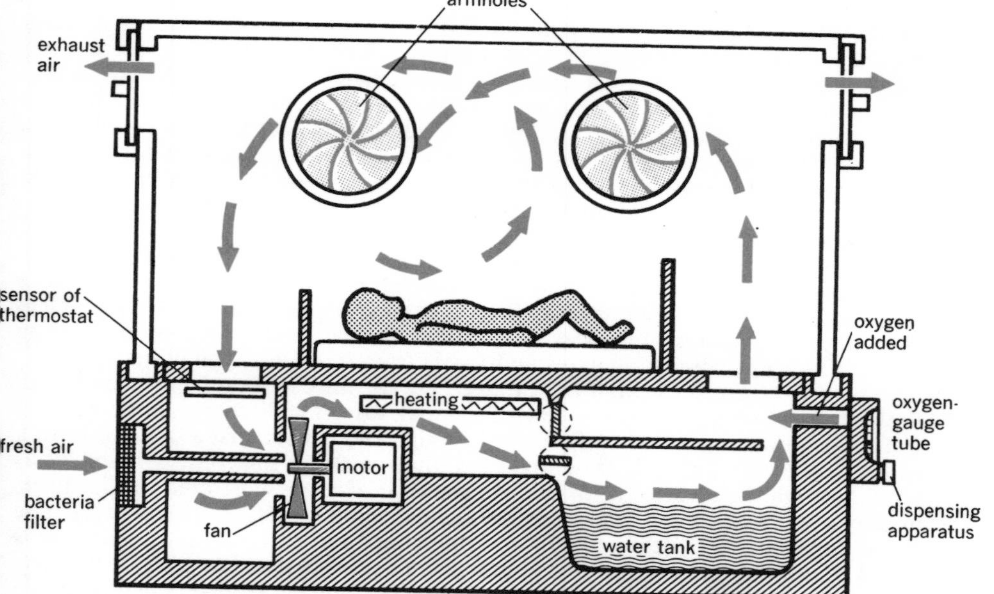

FIG. 1 INCUBATOR

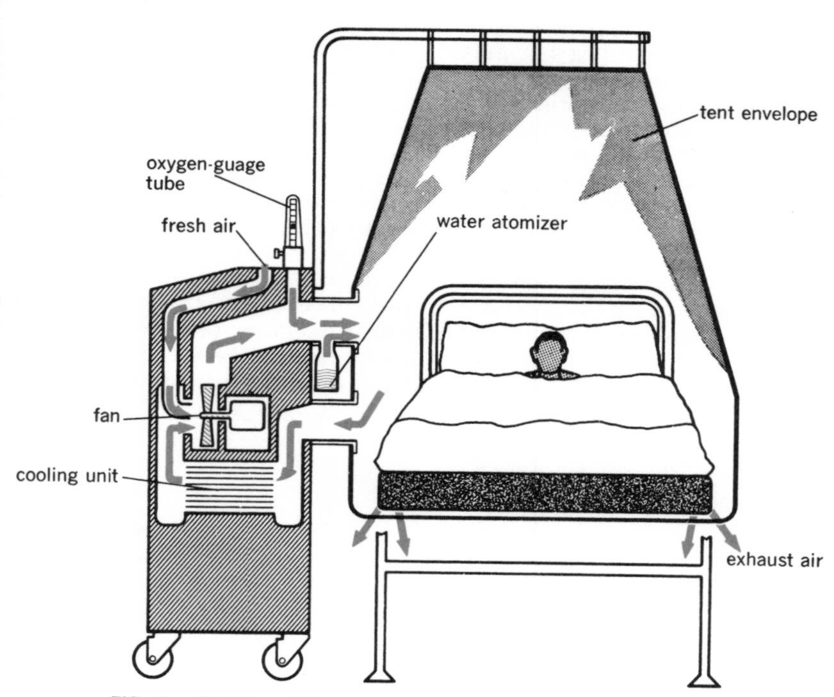

FIG. 2 OXYGEN TENT

GAS MASK

The function of a gas mask is to protect the wearer's respiratory organs and eyes from the effects of poison gases, fumes and dust. Various types of protective mask are used for industrial and for military purposes. For the successful use of a gas mask that filters the air through chemicals in a canister, the basic condition is that the toxic fumes or gas are present in relatively low concentrations (generally not exceeding about 2% by volume) in the air and that the air must also contain a sufficiently high content of oxygen (at least 15% by volume, and at least 17% if carbon monoxide is present). For exposure to atmospheres with a higher content of toxic constituents, a self-contained type of breathing apparatus—i.e., with its own independent oxygen supply—has to be worn.

Gas masks are widely used in industry—e.g., in chemical plants and in certain mining operations where fumes of an injurious character occur. Firemen and rescue squads are also normally equipped with gas masks. A gas mask consists of a facepiece, straps for attaching the mask to the wearer's head, and a canister for filtering the inhaled air and absorbing gases and fumes from it. In one type of mask the exhaled air is discharged through the canister, i.e., air inlet and outlet are combined. Another type is equipped with a separate outlet valve for discharging the exhaled air. The facepiece is molded to fit closely around the wearer's face so as to form a gastight seal around mouth, nose and eyes, thus ensuring that only air which has passed through the canister is inhaled. In the type of mask illustrated in Fig. 1, the canister is screwed to the inlet opening located approximately at chin level. The inhaled air is purified in the canister and thus made safe to breathe. Purification is effected by a combination of physical and chemical processes. Particles or droplets suspended in the air are removed by mechanical filtering performed by a filter made of various fibers (cellulose, glass fibers, asbestos). Sometimes these fibers are of loose texture in the form of a thick felt pad; in other types of mask a folded thin layer of filter paper serves the same purpose (Fig. 2 shows the canister of a dust mask, which protects the wearer from dust but not from gases or vapors). Gas molecules are removed by physical adsorption on surface-active materials (active charcoal with high retention capacity); this principle can be utilized for the removal of all organic vapors (Fig. 3). In addition, the canister may—depending on the nature of the hazard to which the wearer of the mask will be exposed—contain various chemicals for absorbing particular gases or fumes by forming compounds with them—e.g., alkalies for the removal of acid fumes, complex compounds of heavy metals for ammonia, copper salts for hydrocyanic acid. Hopcalite (a mixture of manganese dioxide and cupric oxide) is used for converting carbon monoxide, a highly poisonous gas, into relatively harmless carbon dioxide by oxidation based on catalytic action. After a time, depending on the gas, fume or dust concentration to which the wearer has been exposed and on certain other factors, the canister becomes ineffective—i.e., the neutralizing chemicals have been consumed, or the active charcoal has become saturated, or the filter pad has become clogged with dust, etc. A fresh canister must then be fitted.

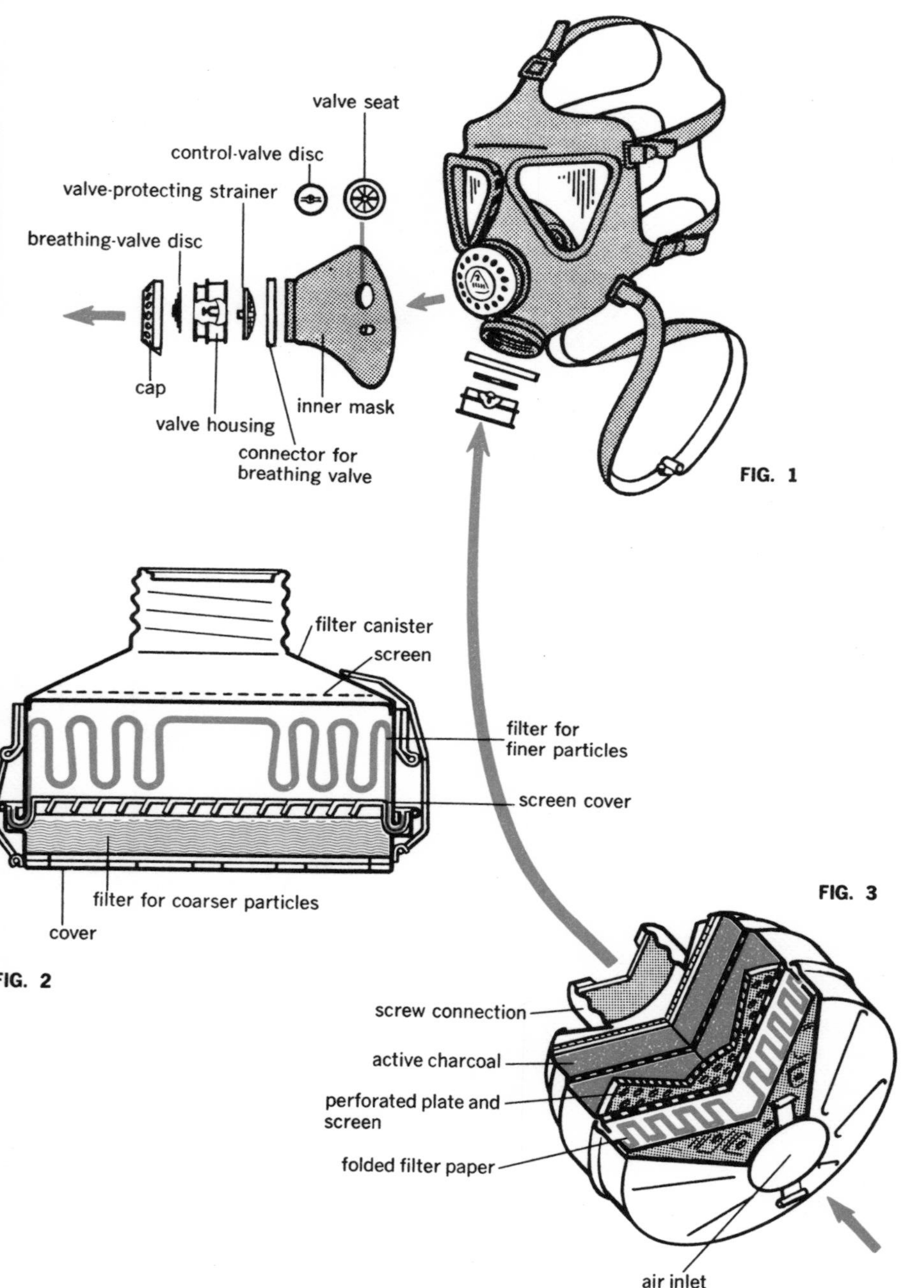
valve seat
control-valve disc
valve-protecting strainer
breathing-valve disc
cap
valve housing
inner mask
connector for
breathing valve
FIG. 1
filter canister
screen
filter for
finer particles
screen cover
filter for coarser particles
cover
FIG. 2
FIG. 3
screw connection
active charcoal
perforated plate and
screen
folded filter paper
air inlet

Gas mask
Photo USIS

ARTIFICIAL HEART

The human heart is a muscular pump comprising four separate cavities and a series of valves allowing blood to pass in one direction only. Man, like other mammals, has a double circulatory system. Blood that has parted with oxygen to the tissues (9 and 13) and absorbed carbon dioxide from them (venous blood) is returned to the heart through the superior and the inferior venae cavae (11 and 10). This blood enters the right auricle (3), whose contractions cause the blood to pass through the tricuspid valve (16) into the right ventricle (1). The contractions of the right ventricle pass the blood through the pulmonary semilunar valves (17) and along the two pulmonary arteries (5) to the lungs (6). In the lungs the blood is oxygenated and returns to the heart through the pulmonary veins (7) and thus enters the left auricle (4). This chamber contracts and passes the blood through the bicuspid, or mitral, valve (15) into the left ventricle (2), whose contractions force the blood through the aortic semilunar valves (18) into the aorta (12 and 13), which is the biggest artery of the body (Fig. 1).

Thus the right side of the heart serves mainly to pump deoxygenated blood through the lungs, while the left side pumps oxygenated blood throughout the rest of the body. This is represented schematically in Fig. 2. The output, or rate of flow, of the blood pumped into the arteries by the ventricles varies to suit the body's requirements. Physical effort—manual labor, running, climbing, etc.—increases the output of blood; when the body is at rest, the output diminishes. The heart varies the output by varying the volume of blood admitted into the ventricles each time the latter are filled and also by varying the rate of contraction (faster or slower heartbeat). The left side of the heart (left auricle and ventricle) has to circulate the blood through all parts of the body, except the lungs, and has thicker and more strongly muscular walls than the right side, which has to perform the pulmonary blood circulation only. For proper functioning, the left side and the right side must be accurately interadjusted, both with regard to the contraction rate of the respective chambers and with regard to the output of blood. In certain diseased conditions there is an imbalance between the two sides of the heart because one side fails to function adequately (e.g., due to valve malfunctioning or other causes) and thus cannot cope properly with the flow of blood pumped by the other (healthy) side. This causes congestion of blood in the blood vessels, especially in the lower part of the body.

What can be done to correct such functional disorders of the heart? For example, consider the relatively simple case where the bicuspid or the tricuspid valve has sustained damage and has ceased to function properly. If it is a case of constriction (stenosis), so that the valve does not open properly, modern surgery can often remedy the defect: dilation of the valve can restore its function and enable the patient to lead a normal life again. In a case where the valve fails to close completely, the valve opening can be reduced in size by stitching. However, if the valves have been destroyed—as a result of disease, for example—the only remedial action consists in the insertion of an artificial valve (Fig. 3, p. 149).

A ball valve is used for the purpose. It comprises a small metal cage in which a plastic ball can move up and down so as to open and close the passage. Such a valve is secured in position in the heart or in a blood vessel (to replace a semilunar valve, for example).

(more)

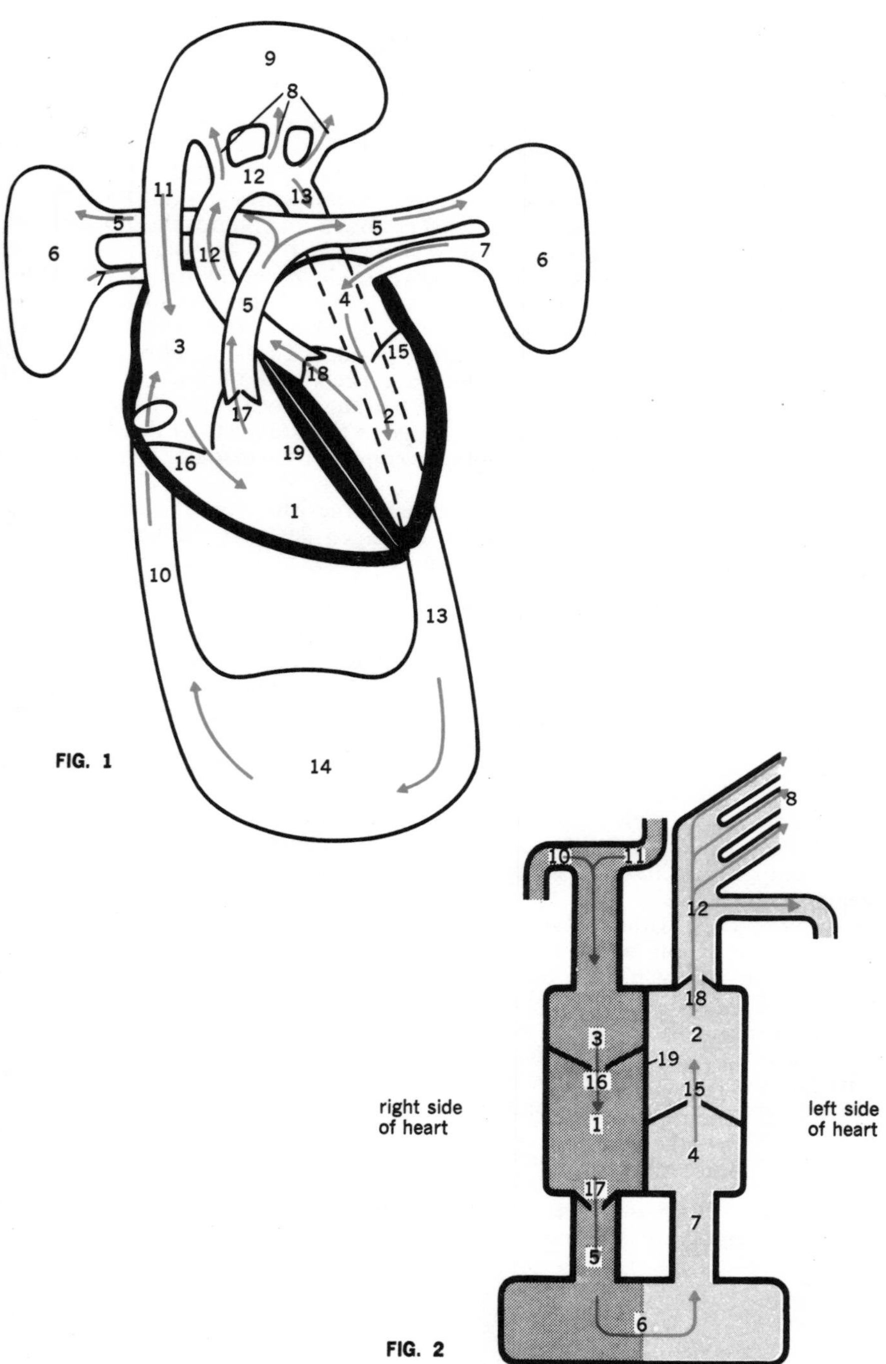

9
8
12
11
13
5
5
6
7
12
7
6
4
5
3
15
18
17
2
19
16
1
10
13
14
FIG. 1
8
10
11
12
18
3
2
19
16
15
right side
of heart
1
left side
of heart
4
17
7
5
6
FIG. 2

Fig. 4 shows the mitral valve of the heart replaced by an artificial valve of this type. In Fig. 4a the left auricle has been filled with oxygenated blood from the lungs. At the instant when the heart muscle slackens and expands, suction is developed in the left ventricle, so that the ball is lifted off its seat and thus opens the valve passage, allowing the ventricle to fill with blood. Simultaneously, the aortic semilunar valves (at the entrance to the aorta, or main artery) close. This rhythmic expansion of the heart whereby blood is drawn into the ventricle is called the diastole. In the next stage, called the systole, the heart contracts and pumps the blood through the arteries, the aortic semilunar valves now being open (Fig. 4b). When this happens, the pressure of the blood in the contracting ventricle forces the ball of the artificial valve back on to its seat, so that no blood can flow back into the auricle.

During operations on the heart it is essential to keep the patient's blood circulating. The best way is to let a machine temporarily perform all the functions of the heart and also of the lungs. The human organism, especially the brain, is very sensitive to oxygen deficiency. If the supply of oxygen (via the blood) to the tissues is stopped for more than ten minutes, permanent damage to the organism or death will ensue. For this reason a device called a heart-lung machine is used in major heart operations (see Vol. II, page 162).

A sensational development in modern cardiac surgery has been the heart transplant —i.e., the replacement of the diseased or damaged heart by the heart of another person, the donor, who usually is the victim of an accident or has died from some cause other than a heart disease. The problems of tissue rejection have not yet been fully overcome, but it is likely that the rejection mechanism, which causes the transplanted heart to be treated as an "intruder" by the body, will be better understood in due course, so that effective measures can be taken to improve the patient's chances of survival and resumption of a more or less normal life.

In a more distant future it may become possible to replace a defective heart by an artificial heart—a wholly man-made pumping machine that can be implanted permanently into the body. An artificial heart of this kind would have to fulfill the following requirements:

1. The "right" and "left" sides must be accurately interadjusted, so that their respective outputs (flow rates) are properly in balance.
2. The pump would have to be double-acting in a case where both sides of the heart are replaced.
3. In order to cope with the body's increased demand for blood under conditions of physical exertion, both the frequency (number of "beats" per minute) and the output (rate of flow in cubic centimeters per minute) must be capable of variation within wide limits.
4. The pressure in the auricles must be kept accurately within specific limits, as it is this pressure that governs the output of the respective ventricles.
5. The output of the right ventricle must not vary too greatly in relation to that of the left ventricle; otherwise congestion of blood in the blood vessels would occur.
6. The artificial heart must not heat up or, alternatively, the heat must be quickly carried away by the bloodstream and dissipated in the lungs and other parts of the body.
7. The artificial heart must be small, and capable of being easily installed in the body, and ensure reliable maintenance-free operation.

(more)

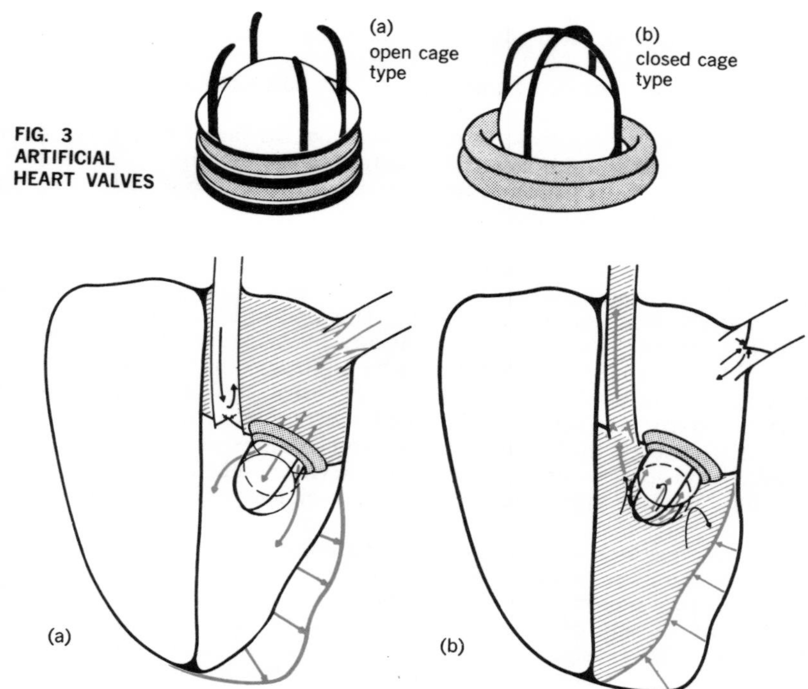

FIG. 3
ARTIFICIAL
HEART VALVES

FIG. 4

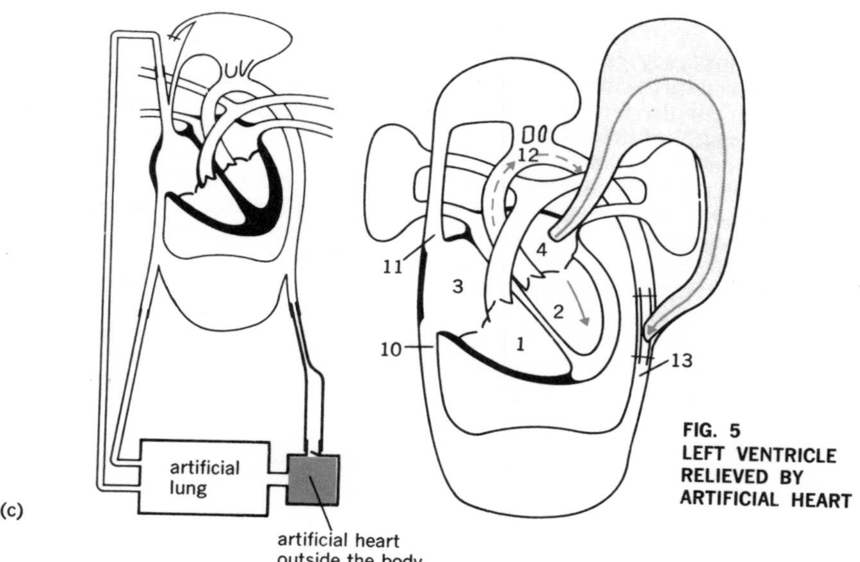

FIG. 5
LEFT VENTRICLE
RELIEVED BY
ARTIFICIAL HEART

Artificial Heart (continued)

Implanting an artificial heart into a living human body presents some major problems:

1. The material of which the heart consists must not call forth a defensive rejection from the body.
2. The material must be smooth so as not to damage the blood corpuscles, as that could have serious effects (thrombosis: clotting of the blood).
3. The artificial heart must not become electrostatically charged inside the body, as this too might cause clotting.

Hence the artificial heart would have to be made of a synthetic material—a plastic—that does not undergo rejection by the body. Such materials already exist. Also, it is possible to cancel changes in the electrical potential by the application of a corrective current from an external source. The artificial heart can moreover be coated with a synthetic substance that can absorb heparin, an anticoagulant which prevents clotting of the blood. And these are by no means all the requirements that the artificial heart must fulfill. Thus, the heart—or rather, the pump—must not suck in too much blood from the veins, as this would cause the latter to collapse and bring the circulation to a standstill. The many factors and variables that must be supervised and controlled require an automatic monitoring device which, for example, regulates the "heartbeats" (i.e., the pulse rate), keeps a check on temperature and output rate, etc.

Because of the functional division of the human heart into two systems—left and right—which operate separate circulations (see Fig. 2), it is, in cases where one side of the heart fails to function properly, possible to bypass that side for a time. This can be done with the aid of relatively simple and inexpensive equipment. Fig. 5 (on p. 149) shows the bypassing of part of the left side of the heart by the interposition of an artificial ventricle between the left auricle and the aorta. This arrangement greatly relieves the strain on the natural ventricle, so that it can rest and get a chance to recover. After a time, the artificial ventricle is removed and the natural ventricle resumes its function. This technique has already been successfully employed in some cases.

Similar temporary replacement of the right ventricle is rather more complex (Fig. 6) because this ventricle receives blood not only from the venae cavae (via the right auricle) but also from the veins coming from the coronary blood vessels, which supply the muscle of the heart wall with blood. The artificial ventricle is implanted in the two venae cavae and the pulmonary artery. Encouraging results have been achieved with this technique, too.

Fig. 7 illustrates the replacement of both ventricles by artificial substitutes. It would appear, however, that more promising results in the future can be expected from artificial parts of compact construction, as illustrated in Fig. 8. The electric motors for driving such hearts present an important problem. Wires for feeding electric current to the motor from an external source might even be dispensed with. There are theoretical possibilities of supplying power to a small electric motor by means of radio waves penetrating through the wall of the chest. Hitherto it has not proved practicable, however, and artificial hearts are usually powered by current from batteries which either are grafted in with the heart or are outside the body.

(more)

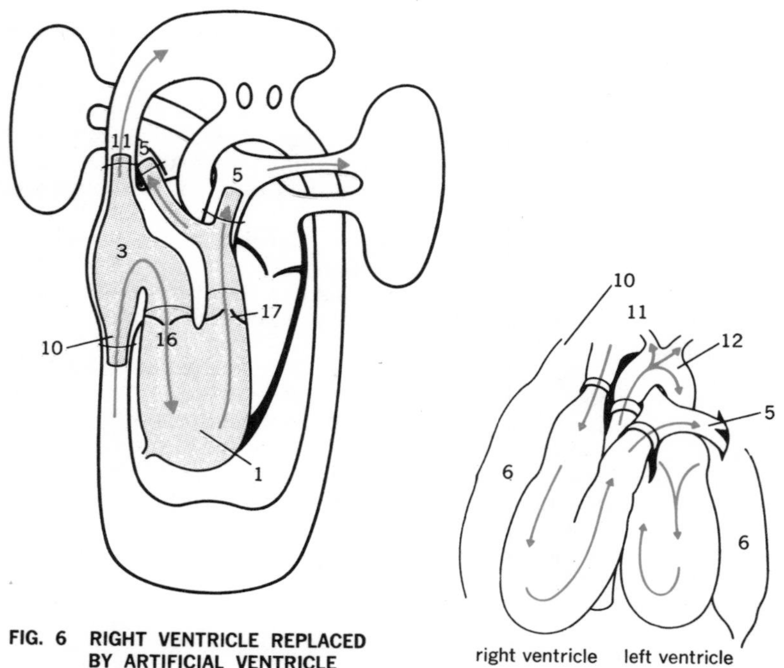

FIG. 6 RIGHT VENTRICLE REPLACED BY ARTIFICIAL VENTRICLE

FIG. 7 BOTH VENTRICLES REPLACED BY TWO SEPARATE ARTIFICIAL VENTRICLES

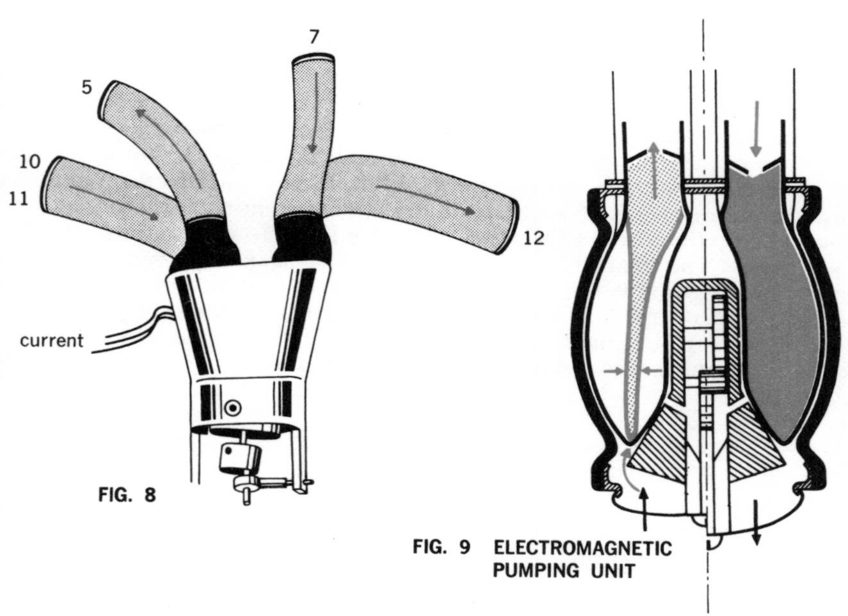

FIG. 8

FIG. 9 ELECTROMAGNETIC PUMPING UNIT

The main problem, however, is presented by the design and construction of the actual pumping unit with its drive system. The following systems have been developed:

1. Devices powered by atomic energy. A device of this kind comprises a capsule containing radioactive isotopes and a miniature steam engine. Such capsules have already been tried experimentally on animals. Weighing about 400 grams, including the radiation-protection shield, they function continuously, and without requiring attention, for about two years.
2. Piezoelectric devices (cf. Vol. I, page 104). A pumping chamber is located between two piezoelectric crystals, which have the property of expansion and contraction when subjected to an alternating electric field and can thus be made to develop a rhythmical pumping action. So far, however, this promising principle has not been put into actual effect.
3. Electromagnetic drive (Fig. 9). The electromagnet consists of a coil and a core which is connected to a diaphragm. The space between the coil and the diaphragm is filled with a liquid. When energized, the coil pulls the core into it, and the diaphragm, actuated by the motion of the core, forces the operating liquid into the spaces around the two flexible "ventricles," thereby compressing them and causing them to pump the blood into the arteries. When the coil is deenergized, the diaphragm springs back to its initial position, so that the liquid returns to the space it originally occupied and blood can flow into the now distended ventricles.
4. Pumping units driven by electric motors. There are several types of artificial heart based on electric motor drive. The first three of these are used mainly for the "extracorporeal hearts" (i.e., outside the body) employed in heart-lung machines:

(a) Screw pump comprising a screw rotating within a flexible-walled chamber (Fig. 10).
(b) Finger pump, in which a series of "fingers" perform a rhythmic wavelike motion, pressing down on to a flexible plastic tube and thus forcing the blood along it (Fig. 11).
(c) Valve-operated pump, in which a ram squeezes the blood alternately out of plastic tubes, while valves synchronized with the ram allow the blood to flow only from right to left (Fig. 12).
(d) Oscillating pump (Figs. 8 and 13). In this type of pumping unit the two ventricles are compressed not simultaneously but alternately. Each time the oscillating "piston" squeezes one "ventricle," it allows the other to expand, and vice versa. This principle of alternate action has certain advantages. Thus, there is better energy utilization in the course of the operating cycle, so that a smaller and lighter motor can be employed. There is also better dissipation of heat from the motor to the bloodstream because the motor in this arrangement is directly adjacent to the ventricles.
(e) Rotary pump (Fig. 14). In this type of pump a lobed rotor forces the blood into the "ventricles." The great advantage of this system is that no inlet valves are needed, such valves with low flow resistance being difficult to construct for artificial hearts. The rotor also performs the function of valves. A cross section through a pump of this kind is shown schematically in Fig. 14a, while Fig. 14b is a diagram which serves to illustrate the pumping principle. Such pumps are of very compact construction, the more so as it is possible to accommodate the motor itself within the rotor.

(more)

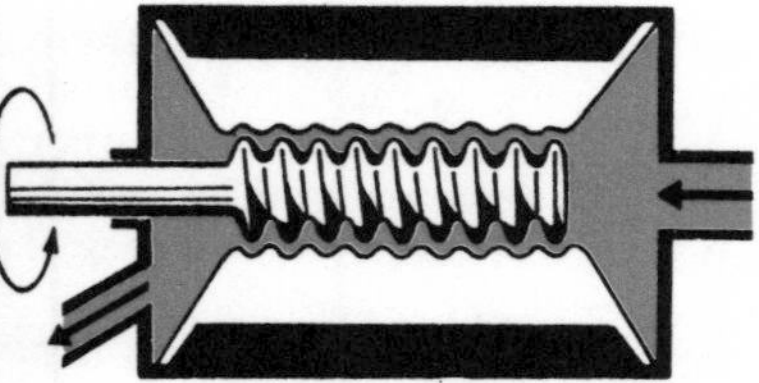
FIG. 10 SCREW PUMP

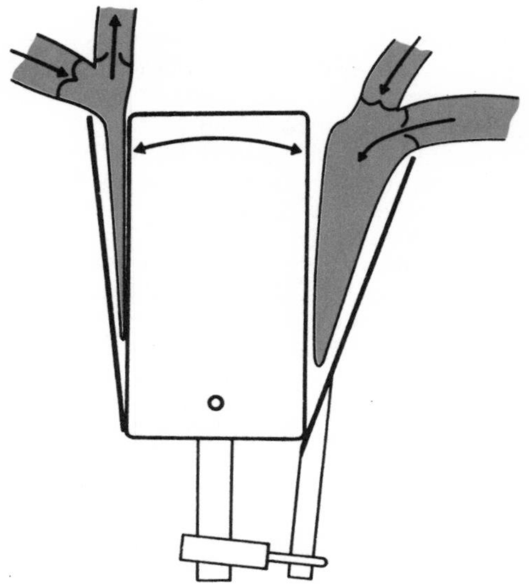
FIG. 13 OSCILLATING PUMP

FIG. 11 FINGER PUMP

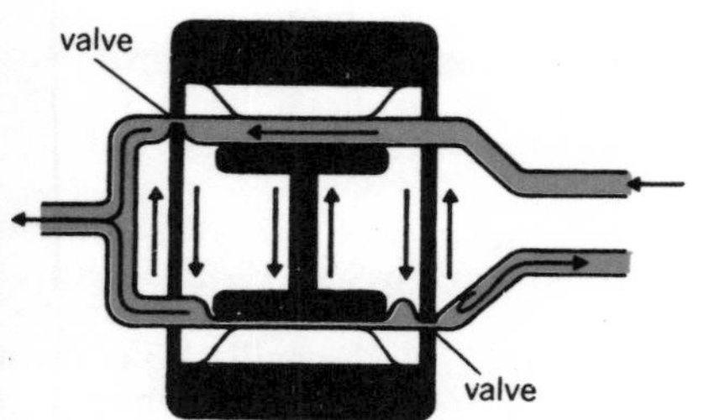

FIG. 12 VALVE PUMP

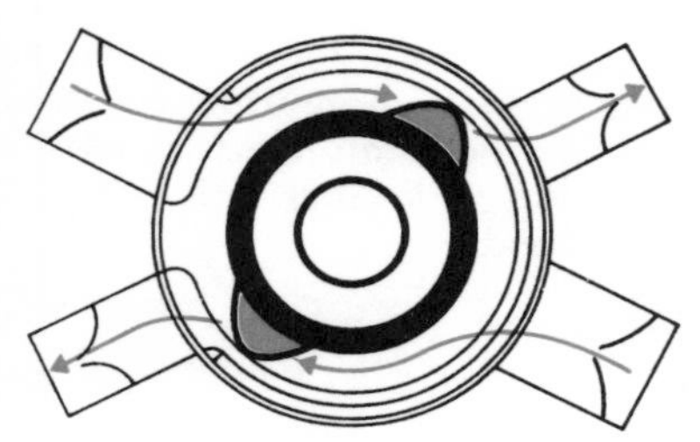
FIG. 14a ROTARY PUMP

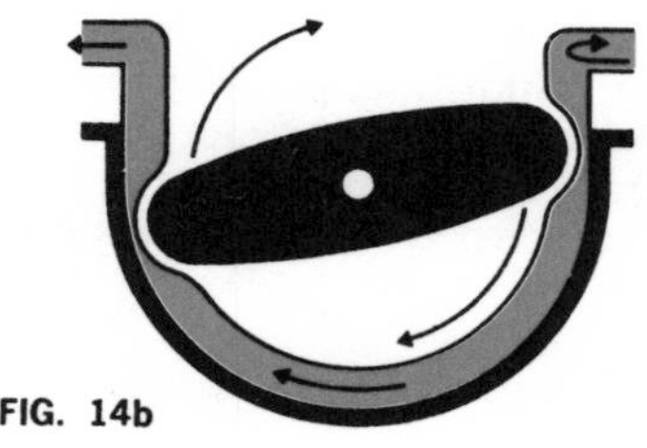
FIG. 14b

5. Pumping units powered by compressed gas or air. The source of power for these artificial hearts is located outside the chest and can be regulated by means of external controls. Such pumps are especially suitable as replacements for one or the other side of the natural heart, as the two sides are fairly easy to separate in this system. This also makes for easier implantation in the patient's chest. There are two types of artificial heart operating on this principle:

(a) Bag-type heart (Fig. 15). A flexible plastic bag is enclosed within a rigid container. Compressed air is admitted into the space between the container and the bag, causing the blood to be squeezed out of the latter. Then, when the air pressure is decreased, the bag expands and automatically fills up with blood again. This type illustrated in Fig. 15a, is intended for use in situ within the human body, whereas Fig. 15b schematically shows the same principle applied to the external "heart" in a heart-lung machine.

(b) An artificial heart may be constructed on the principle represented in Fig. 16 compressed air is admitted, through a pressure regulator and a three-way valve into the space in front of the piston of the artificial heart. With this arrangement the frequency of the heart's rhythm can be regulated at will. The development of a depend-able and efficient pumping unit is an important step in solving the problem o devising a successful and viable artificial heart, but it is by no means the complet solution. The fact that it has hitherto not proved possible to keep an experimenta animal alive for more than a couple of days by means of an artificial heart is i itself sufficient indication of the difficulty of the problem. However, some measur of success has been achieved—even in human subjects—with the temporary replace-ment of one side of the heart by an artificial device. The difficulties and problem associated with the complete surgical substitution of an artificial heart for th diseased or defective natural heart are so complex that success in this field sti appears to be a long way off.

The difficulties can be illustrated with reference to an in itself relatively simpl problem, which could be solved by the arrangement indicated in Fig. 17. The natur heart can vary the power of its beat and the output of blood from its ventricle according to the body's requirements at any particular time. Technically this contr function can be reproduced by installing a piezoelectric transducer (*P*), which is sensing device that measures the blood output rate and controls each stroke of th pump accordingly. The equipment needed for controlling and monitoring th functioning of an artificial heart in an experimental animal in the laboratory very elaborate. Fig. 18 shows—in a schematic and greatly simplified form—a electronic control system for a heart pump powered by compressed air. The diagra shows three interlinked control loops, each of which reports the individual da (pressures, valve position, piston position) back to a higher monitoring center ar causes the latter to adjust and modify the next stroke of the pump. The various stag of the system have to operate as separate computers. (The illustrations for th article were supplied by Professor W. J. Kolff, Cleveland.)

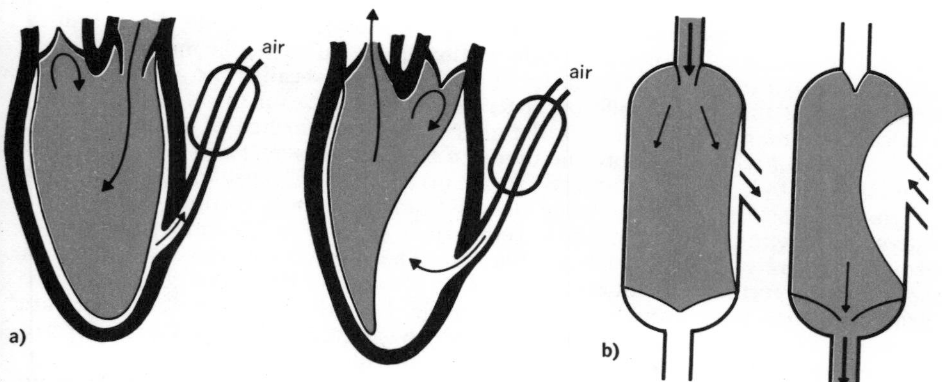

FIG. 15 BAG-TYPE ARTIFICIAL HEART

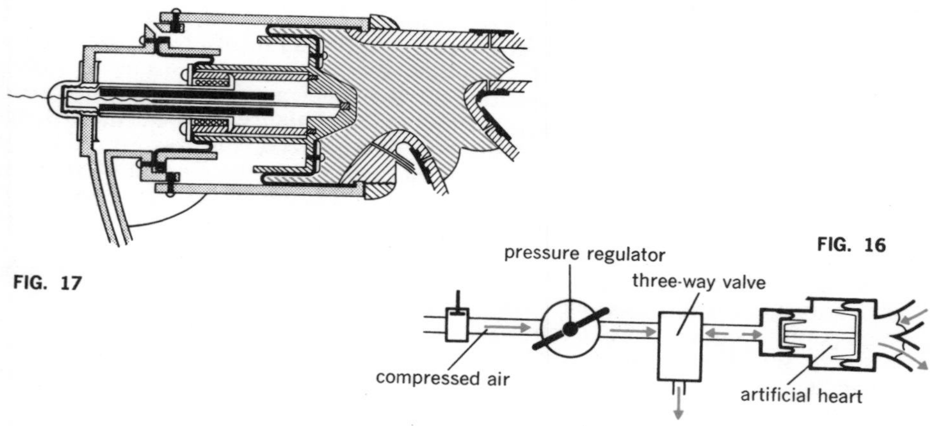

FIG. 17

FIG. 16

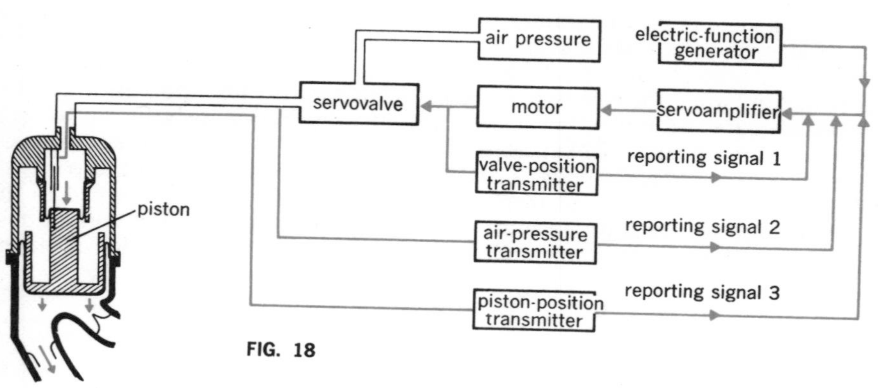

FIG. 18

ARTIFICIAL KIDNEY

The kidneys are two excretory organs which produce the urine. Each kidney (Fig. 1a) is composed of about a million tiny units called nephrons (Fig. 1b). A nephron consists of a tuft of capillaries (fine blood vessels) called the glomerulus (1). Blood enters it through the afferent arteriole (2) and leaves it through the efferent arteriole (3). In its passage through the glomerulus it is purified of waste products, which drain out with fluid from the blood (a filtration process) and are discharged through the tubule leading from the capsule (4) (Bowman's capsule) which encloses the glomerulus (Fig. 1c). The urine drains from the tubule through a branched system of collecting ducts (5, 6, 7, 8) into the pelvic space (9) of the kidney and thence through the ureter into the urinary bladder. The filtration process is a complex one in which certain substances valuable to the body are reabsorbed from the "primary urine" that drains out of the capsule. In addition, other substances are discharged from the blood into the tubule (which is enveloped by capillaries formed by the efferent arteriole). The process in the glomerulus consists of "passive" filtration, whereas the excretion and reabsorption of substances in the tubule is an "active" selective process. An "artificial kidney" can only reproduce the passive filtration process.

The kidneys are important not only as organs of excretion, but also as regulating devices for the body's internal environment—the precise conservation of the salt and water content. Nearly one-fifth of the blood pumped out of the heart (5000–6000 cc per minute) goes to the kidneys; urine is produced at a rate of 1 to 2 cc per minute. If the kidneys fail to function properly, other parts of the body—stomach, bowels, lungs, skin—can, for a time, compensate for the deficiency by taking over part of the excretory function. In the long run, however, the balance will be disturbed, and a diseased condition known as uremia will develop—i.e., the waste products of protein metabolism are retained in the blood. As a result, the content of urea and other waste products in the blood increases. These cause the grave symptoms of toxemia which accompany uremia and are due to the action of poisonous substances in the blood (headache, dizziness, diminished or suppressed urine, rapid pulse; in far advanced cases: nausea, vomiting, coma and death). Remedial treatment may take various forms; the most effective method is by means of the "artificial kidney," which permits more rapid correction of the blood chemistry. In general, the aims of treatment are to give rest to the kidneys, so that they may recover. The artificial kidney can render valuable assistance in this respect. Of course, modern surgery has developed the kidney transplant—replacement of a diseased kidney by a healthy kidney supplied by a suitable donor—as a radical form of treatment. As with heart transplants, the problem of tissue rejection plays a major role in this connection —i.e., the patient's body tends to treat the grafted kidney as an "intruder" which must be got rid of.

Because of the complex character of the kidney's function, it is not possible to construct an artificial kidney that can entirely replace the natural kidneys. However, a considerable amount of success has been achieved with such devices, more particularly in combating the effects of acute kidney disorders. The apparatus required is rather elaborate and bulky, but it need not operate continuously; it can be temporarily switched off, and—what is especially important—no parts of the equipment need be inside the patient's body. The apparatus can be installed in the patient's own home. His blood is passed through the machine and is then returned to the body by intravenous injection. In some cases the treatment need not be continuous; the patient can leave the machine and go normally about his business for considerable lengths of time.

(mor

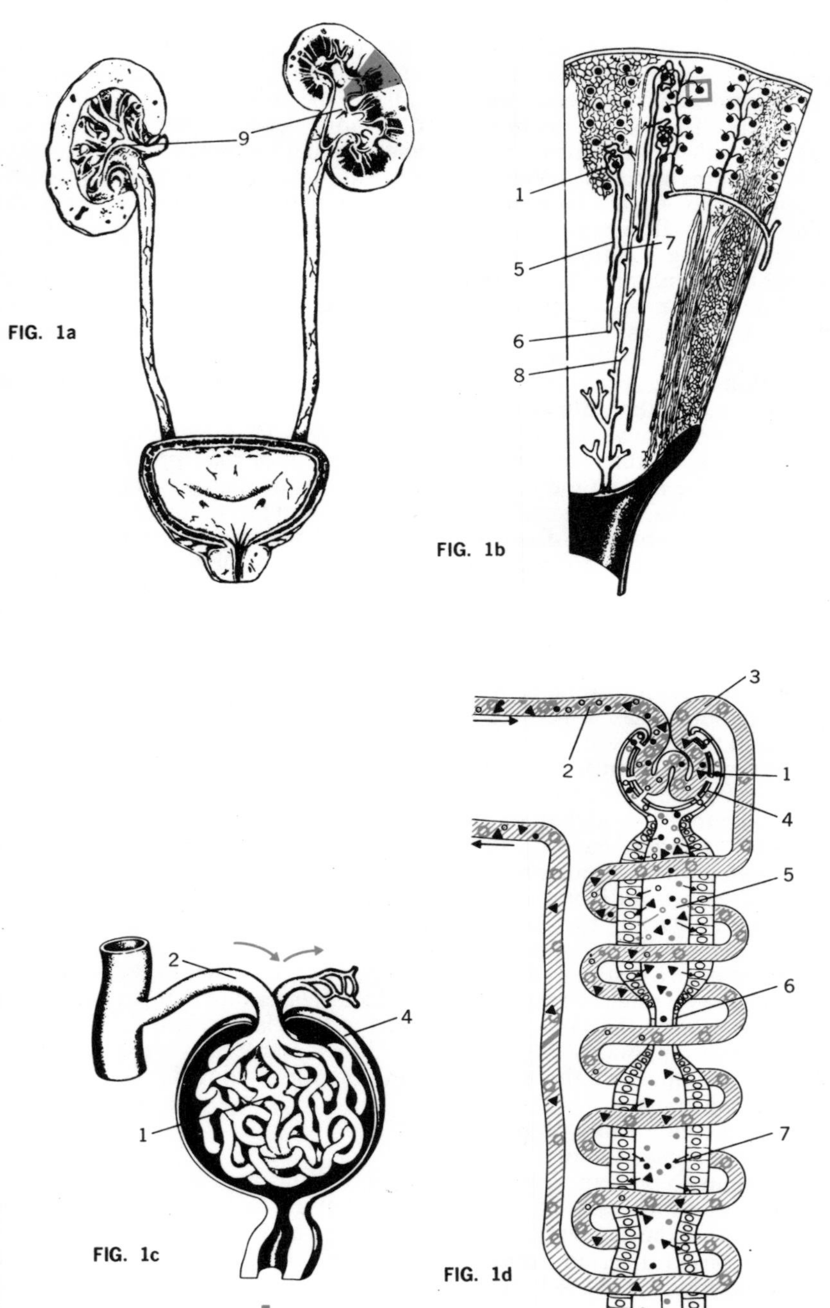

FIG. 1a

FIG. 1b

FIG. 1c

FIG. 1d

Artificial Kidney (continued)

The function of the artificial kidney is based on the physical laws of diffusion and osmosis. The term osmosis denotes the diffusion of a solvent through a semipermeable membrane—a membrane that allows the solvent to pass but is impermeable to the dissolved substances—into a more concentrated solution. In the artificial kidney the semipermeable membrane is similar to the walls of the glomerulus capillaries in some essential respects (pore width, total pore area, filtration effect) and is referred to as the dialyzer. The blood is subjected to a treatment called hemodialysis (Fig. 2): a very thin film of flowing blood (1) is separated from the surrounding rinsing solution (2) by an approximately 0.08 mm (0.003 inch) thick semipermeable membrane (10). Formerly, natural membranes (fishes' air bladders, animals' intestinal membranes) were used for the purpose; at the present time, suitable plastics such as cellophane are employed for the semipermeable membrane. This membrane allows substances in normal molecular solution and the solvent to pass through its pores, but it prevents the passage of very large molecules (proteins, in particular) and of the cellular constituents of the blood (corpuscles, etc., 7, 8, 9). An important advantage is that bacteria and viruses (5, 6) cannot penetrate this membrane either, so that sterilization of those parts of the apparatus which are located outside the membrane is unnecessary. Since the dialyzer obeys the laws of diffusion and osmosis, the rinsing liquid must contain in physiological concentration all those membrane-passing dissolved normal constituents of the blood (electrolytes, in particular) which are required to maintain in the blood and not be lost to the rinsing liquid. On the other hand, this liquid must not contain any of the substances present in above-normal (harmful) concentration in consequence of defective functioning of the natural kidneys—e.g., potassium, urea, harmful acid radicals such as phosphate and sulphate. These substances must be diffused through the membrane into the rinsing liquid. The latter may also contain suitable high concentrations of substances which it is desirable to introduce *into* the blood stream, by diffusion in the opposite direction through the membrane—e.g., drugs, dextrose, etc. The rinsing liquid must furthermore be of the same temperature as the blood it encloses, this being ensured by thermostatic control (4). Also, oxygen (3) must be allowed to bubble through it, so that the stream of blood can absorb this oxygen.

Present-day dialyzers have membranes that function more or less as superfine strainers which allow molecules below a certain size to pass and prevent the passage of larger ones. Efforts are being made to develop membranes that exercize a selective action, not with regard to the size of the molecules, but with regard to the chemical constitution thereof. To be able to pass through the pores in the membrane, the molecule must have a distinctive chemical property that will act like a key to unlock a door. In this way it might be possible to produce membranes that perform selective filtration in somewhat the same manner as the natural kidney does.

The principal components of an artificial kidney are:

1. The dialyzer containing the membrane and the rinsing liquid;
2. The pumping system;
3. The heating equipment with thermostat;
4. The oxygen supply system;
5. Arrangements to prevent clotting of the blood (drugs such as hirudin or heparin; smooth surfaces on all parts of the apparatus that are in contact with the blood).

The prototype of the dialyzer commonly employed at the present time is illustrated in Fig. 3: the blood diverted from an artery (1) has hirudin (2) added to it and is supplied to the apparatus. The latter comprises a number of tubes made of collodion (a cellulose tetranitrate), which constitutes the semipermeable membrane. The rinsing liquid is supplied through a tube (5). After passing through the dialyzer, the blood is introduced into a vein (3) and is thus returned to the patient's body. Constant blood temperature is ensured by a thermostat (6), and oxygen is supplied (7) to the rinsing liquid.

(more)

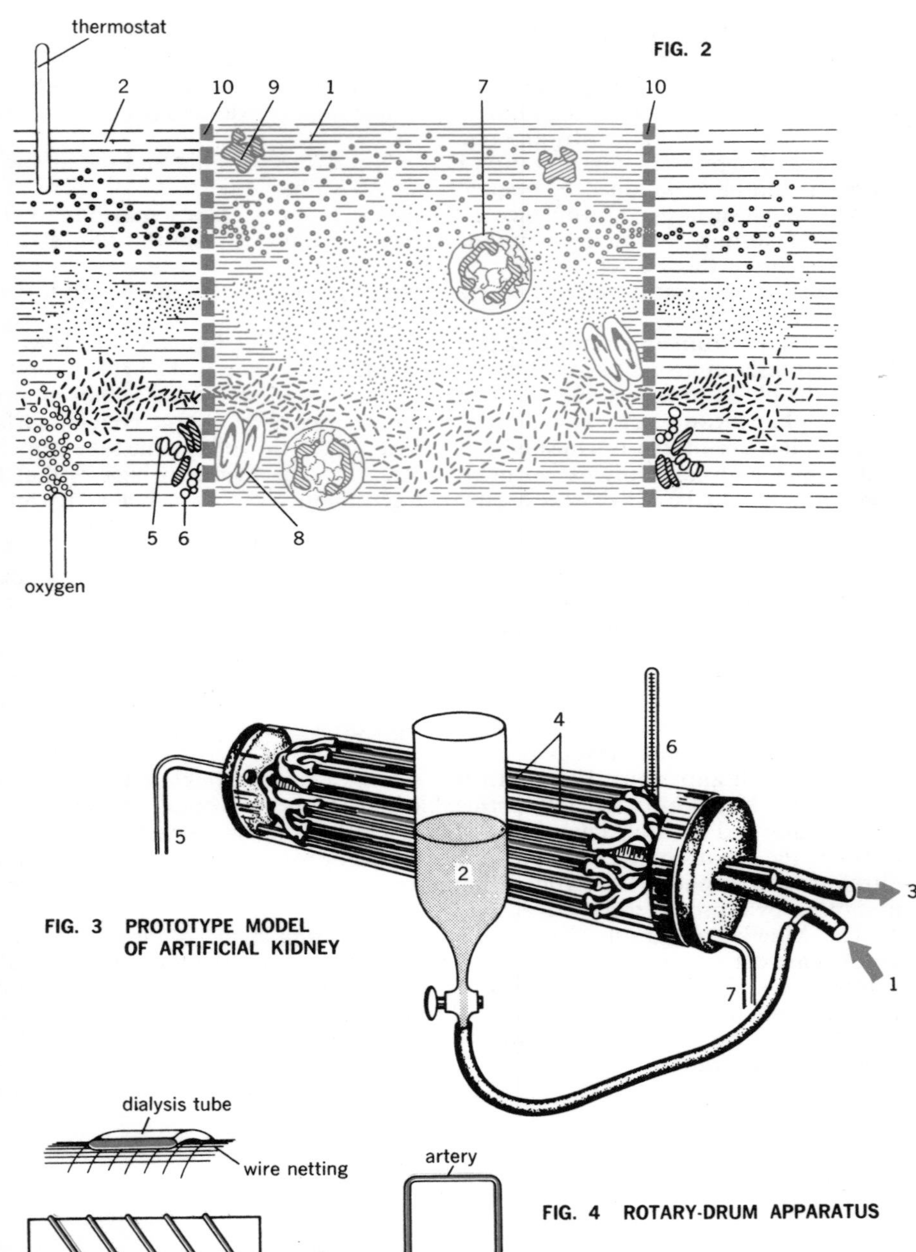

FIG. 3 PROTOTYPE MODEL OF ARTIFICIAL KIDNEY

FIG. 4 ROTARY-DRUM APPARATUS

Artificial Kidney (continued)

The requirements that an artificial kidney has to fulfill are the following:

1. The semipermeable membrane should have a large surface area to ensur adequate osmotic interchange between the blood and the rinsing liquid. This mean that the blood must flow in the thinnest possible film, providing maximum contac with the membrane bathed by the liquid.
2. A large difference in concentration between the rinsing liquid and the inflowin blood should be maintained by frequent renewal of the liquid.
3. Any rough surfaces or turbulence in the flow of blood must be avoided to obviat the risk of clotting. As already mentioned, the use of anticoagulins (hirudin, etc.) ca help to achieve this object.

Medical science has developed several types of blood-dialysis equipment to serv as "artificial kidneys":

1. The rotary-drum apparatus (Fig. 4). A blood-filled flat cellophane tube is woun in helical fashion around a rotating drum made of wire mesh. The rotary motio causes the blood to flow along the tube in the same way that water is moved alon in an Archimedean screw. This device does indeed provide a large contact-surfac area, but it is unsuitable as a means of ultrafiltration, as the cellophane tube stretche and cannot withstand any excess internal pressure. Another drawback is that th apparatus has to be filled with a fairly large quantity of blood before it can b started.
2. The sandwich-type apparatus (Fig. 5). It has a contact-surface area of any desire size and can be used for ultrafiltration under pressure. However, since it has "dea corners," it presents an inherent danger of clotting of the blood. To counterac this, large amounts of anticoagulins have to be used, which is a drawback in th case of recently operated patients and sufferers from gastric disorders, as thes substances are liable to cause serious hemorrhage. In this form of construction flat cellophane bag is sandwiched between grooved plates of plastic. The rinsin liquid flows through the grooves in the opposite direction to the flow of blood in th cellophane bag (countercurrent principle).
3. The Allwall apparatus (Fig. 6). In this system a tube through which the bloo flows and which forms the semipermeable membrane is wound around a wire mesh drum and is itself enclosed within a close-fitting wire-mesh jacket whic restrains the expansion of the tube, so that excess pressure can be used and effectiv ultrafiltration applied. The drum is immersed in the rinsing liquid, which is kep in motion by a propeller device.
4. The Moeller apparatus (Fig. 7) comprises a drum made of plastic in whic grooves are cut and which is enclosed within a plastic outer shell, likewise provide with grooves. The blood-filled dialysis tube is gripped between the inner and oute grooves, and the rinsing liquid flows through the latter in countercurrent to th blood. This arrangement, too, enables the pressure to be made sufficiently high fo effective ultrafiltration.

(more

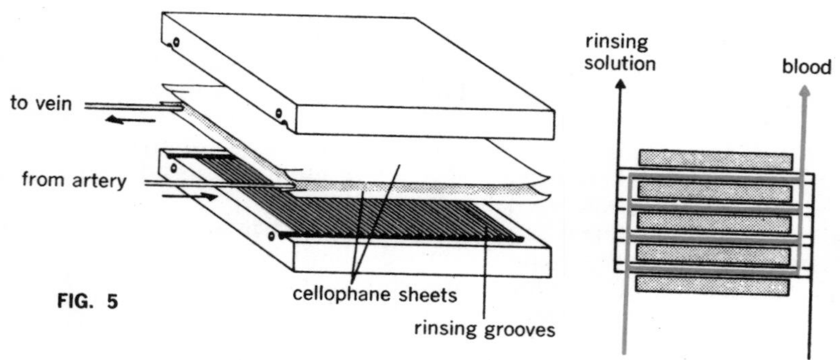
to vein
from artery
cellophane sheets
rinsing grooves
rinsing solution
blood

FIG. 5

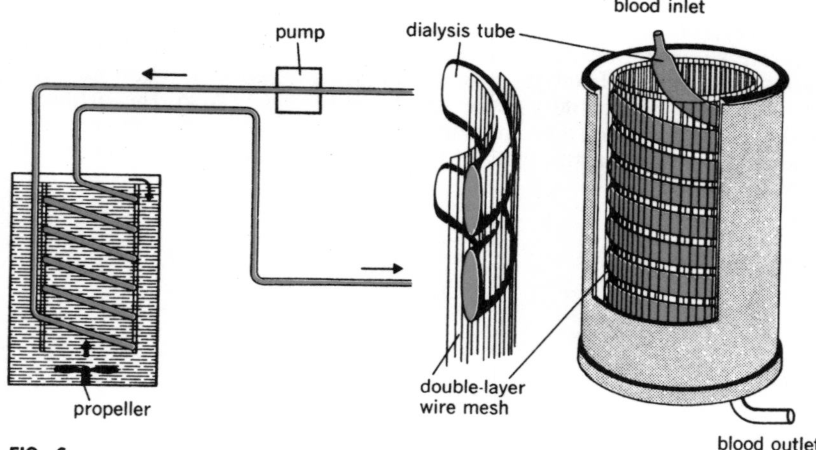
pump
propeller
dialysis tube
blood inlet
double-layer wire mesh
blood outlet

FIG. 6

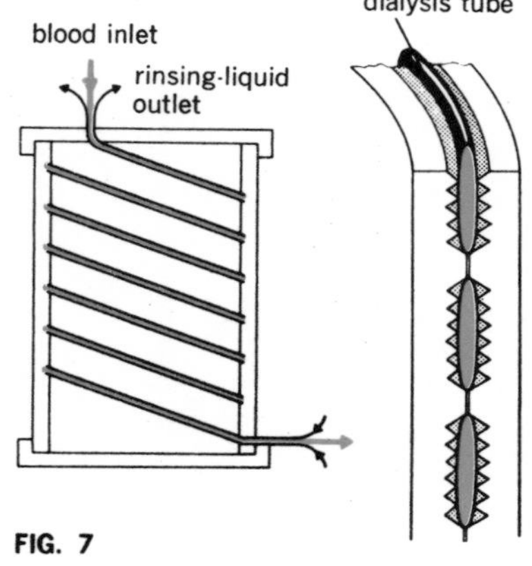
blood inlet
rinsing-liquid outlet
dialysis tube

plastic cylinder

FIG. 7

5. The twin-coil apparatus (Fig. 8a), in which the semipermeable membrane is in the form of a flat, wide cellophane tube which is coiled in two tiers around a hollow core. The coils are mounted inside a container through which the rinsing liquid is passed. A very thin film of blood flows through the coils, which present a large area of contact with the surrounding liquid. Fig. 8b shows the actual dialyzer. It has the advantage that it is supplied sterilized and ready to use inside its container; it can moreover be quickly and easily exchanged.

The artificial-kidney treatment procedure is shown schematically in Fig. 9. The blood is diverted from an artery (1), passes through the dialyzer tubes, and is returned to a vein (2). Circulation of the blood through the apparatus is maintained by a pump. Another pump circulates the rinsing liquid. Before the purified blood enters the vein, it passes through a device in which any air or clots are trapped. The whole procedure takes about six hours and has to be repeated at intervals, depending on the results of blood analyses. In between the successive treatments the patient can lead a more or less normal life. The ideal artificial kidney has not yet been devised. Despite certain shortcomings, however, the results achieved with an artificial kidney are sometimes quite remarkable: as a result of the removal of the noxious metabolic substances from the blood, the patient feels well again and can resume work. Thus his active life can be greatly prolonged. Also, the artificial kidney, though it cannot provide a permanent substitute for nonfunctioning natural kidneys, can be of great value in the relief of reversible kidney damage, giving the kidneys a chance to recover.

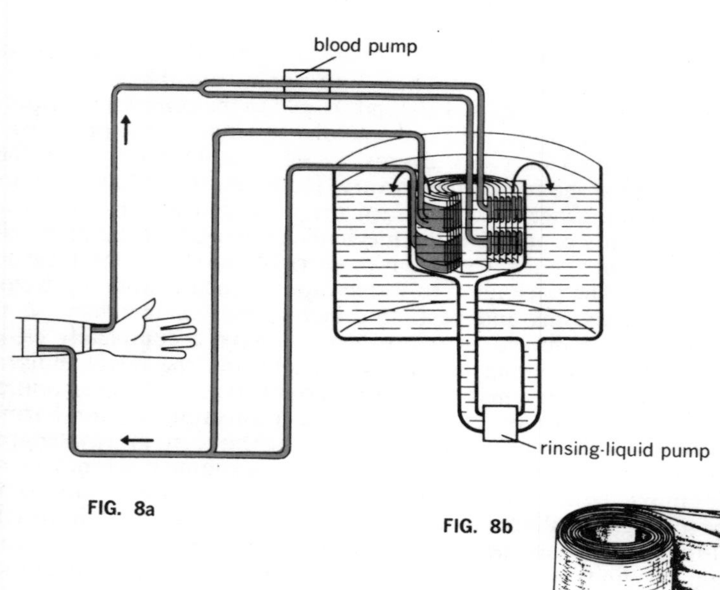

FIG. 8a

FIG. 8b

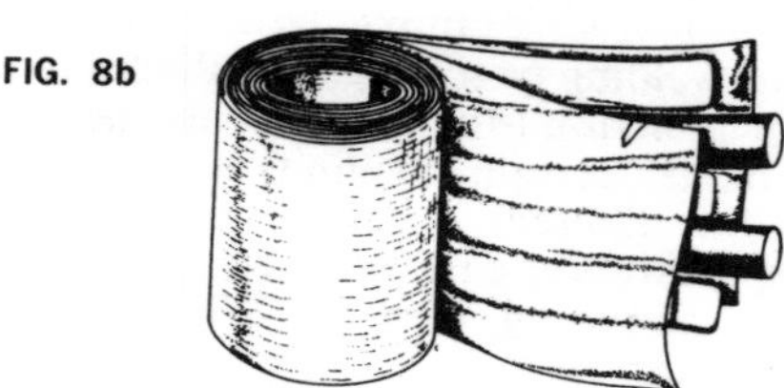

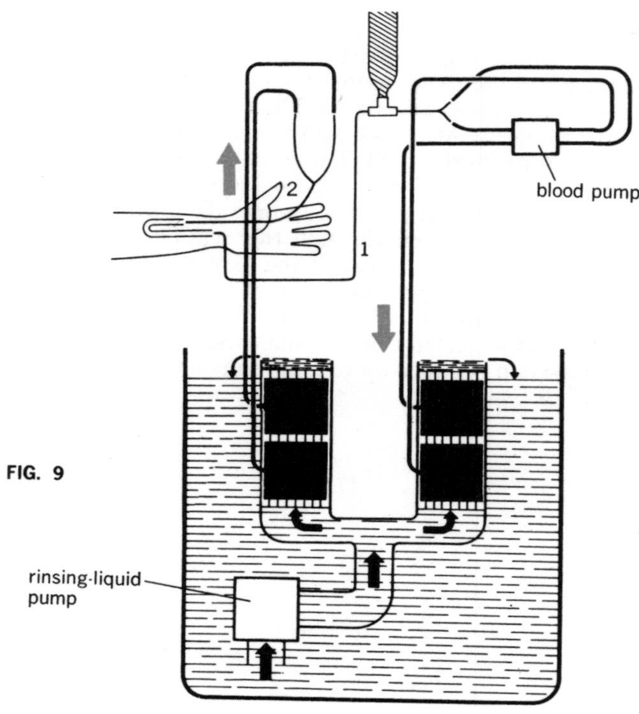

FIG. 9

PACKAGING TECHNOLOGY

A distinction is to be made between consumer packaging and dispatch packaging The former category comprises the wrappers and containers (boxes, tins, jar bottles, bags, etc.) in which merchandise of all kinds is sold to the consumer. Dispatc packaging serves primarily to protect the merchandise in transit from producer t wholesaler or consumer (packing cases, drums, sacks, etc.). Depending on the purpose and their contents, the requirements vary. However, the following factor are usually of major importance: protection of the packaged merchandise fror pressure and knocks (in this connection the mechanical strength of the packagin is all-important), protection against drying out or entry of moisture (with regard t this the impermeability of the packaging to water vapor is the determining factor protection from microorganisms and pests (for many kinds of merchandise th packaging material must be devoid of pores; it must have a completely close surface), protection against fingering and handling, allowing the merchandise t "breathe" (permeability to air—necessary for certain types of commodities preserving the smell and flavor of the merchandise, protection against harmf effects of light (some goods deteriorate on exposure to light of certain wavelengths etc. The packaging materials must be suitable for use in packaging machines. Henc they should, for example, be suitable for printing upon, they should be suitable fc gluing, welding or sealing, and should in many cases moreover withstand destructiv chemical action (due to acids, alkalies, oil, grease, etc.). The customer or consume also makes certain demands as to the quality of the packaging; of course, thes vary for different types of merchandise and may include, for example: goo transportability, ease of opening, easy inspection of the contents (transparency ease of emptying, ease of closing, good stackability (e.g., in a refrigerator), eas disposability, etc.

Modern industry tends to favor the fully automated packaging plant integrate into the production process. For ease and convenience of automatic manufactur filling, closing and printing, various plastics are widely favored as packagin materials. An example is afforded by a machine for producing plastic tubs or cup to serve as containers for foods (Fig. 1). Plastic sheeting (1) is fed intermittently to heating unit (2) and thence to the molding unit (3), in which the cups are formed b pressing and separated by means of a knife (4). The cups are then carried by a be conveyor (5) to the filling unit (6). After passing through a sealing press (7), the cup are provided with printed inscriptions (8). The filled, sealed and printed cups ar ejected at (9) and conveyed to the packing table (10), whence they are dispatched t their destination. Fig. 2 shows another plastic-cup-manufacturing machine based o thermoforming. Plastic sheet is passed through the heating zone and fed to th forming zone. The male mold is pushed forward and carries the plastic sheet into th female mold. To assist the molding operation, air is exhausted from the female mol (vacuum molding) and compressed air is blown into the male mold. The two mold then move apart, and the cup is ejected from the male mold by means of compresse air. A machine of this type can produce up to a million cups a day.

(more

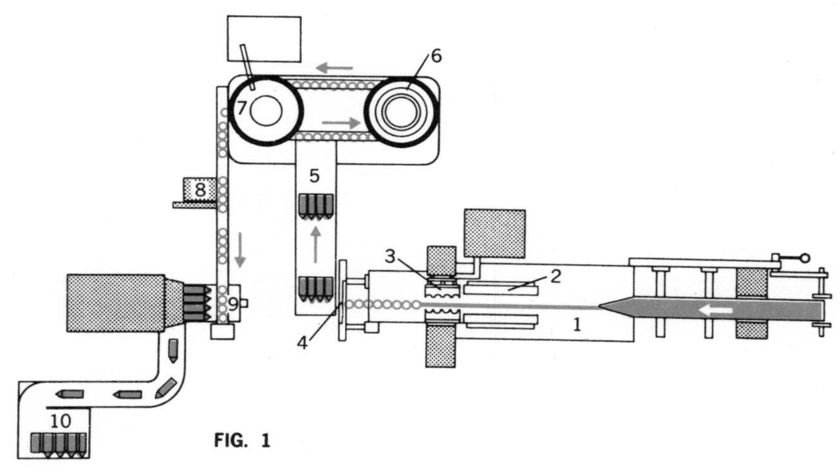

FIG. 1

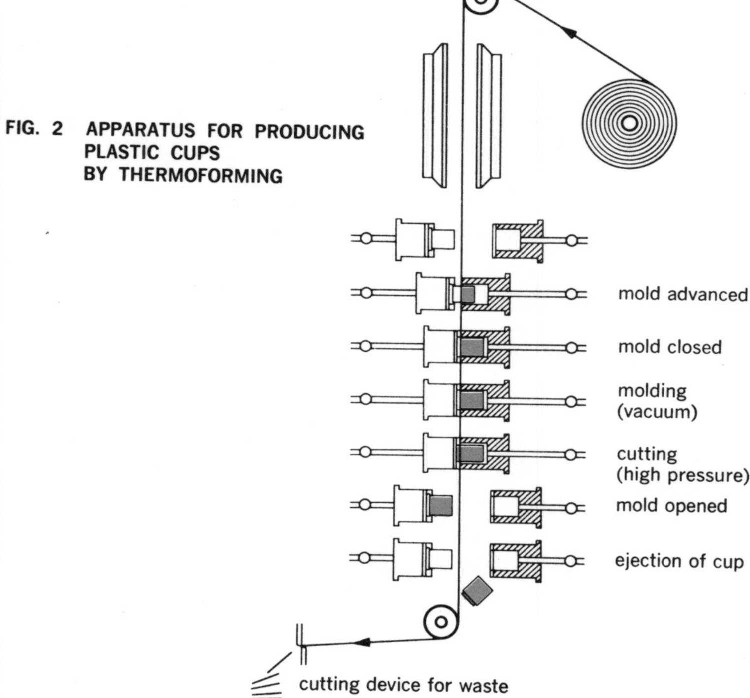

FIG. 2 APPARATUS FOR PRODUCING PLASTIC CUPS BY THERMOFORMING

Packaging machine for bars of chocolate. Sapal, Ecublens, Switzerlan

Photo Sapal, Ecuble

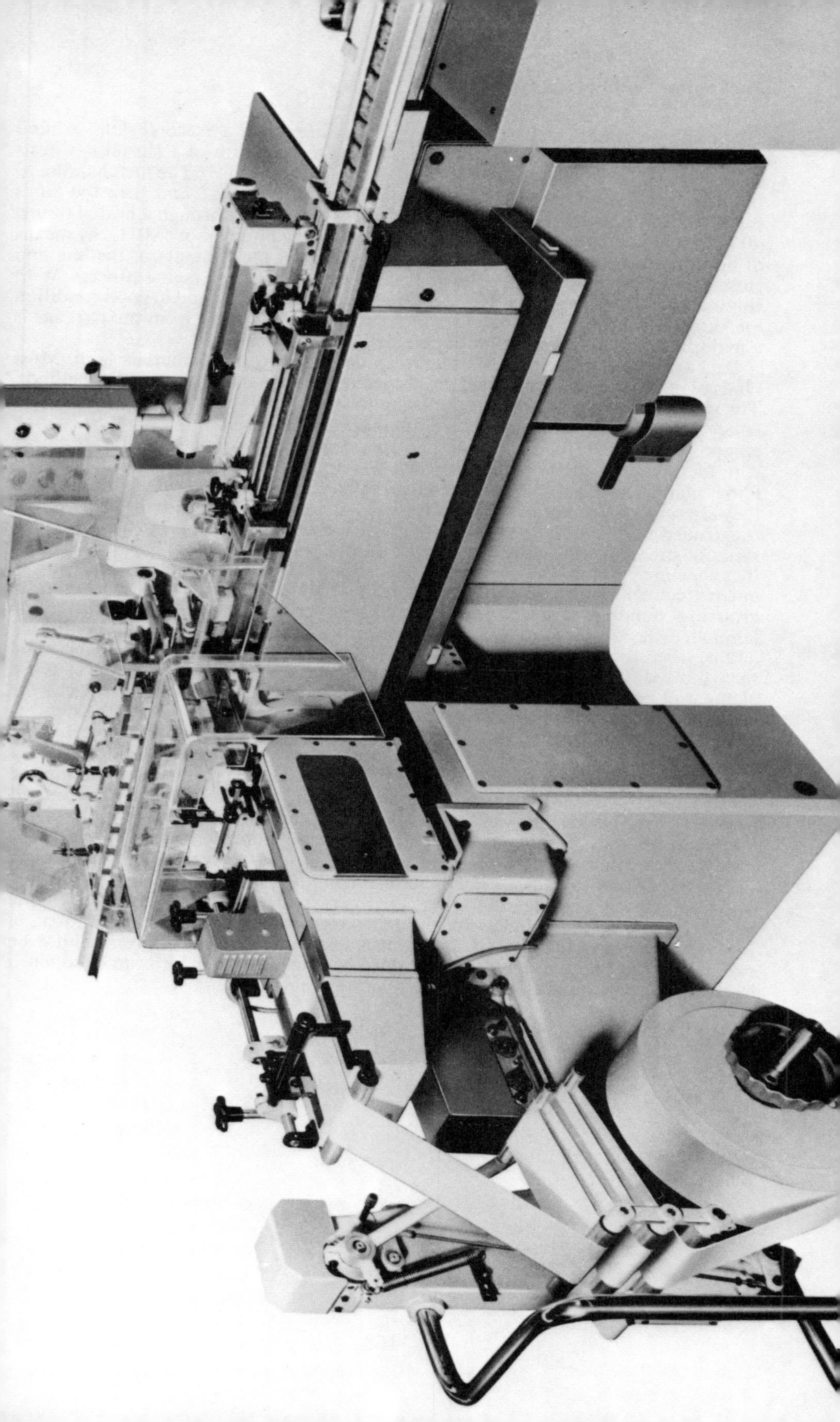

In other processes, packaging consists merely in putting a "second skin" around the goods concerned. More particularly, this takes the form of a shrunk-on heat-sealed wrapping of plastic placed around various foods (Fig. 3). The merchandise to be packaged—i.e., poultry—is first put into a plastic bag (a), and then the air is extracted from the bag (b). The closed bag (c) is then passed through a heated tunnel (d) in which the plastic is heated to above its softening point (above 90° C) by means of hot air. The softened plastic sheet shrinks around the contents of the bag and closely envelops it. A short cooling period completes the packaging process. With this method of preservation it is possible to keep poultry intact and in good condition for human consumption for long periods. Extraction of the air from the package is a major factor in the prevention of putrefaction.

Packaging problems impose basic requirements as to the materials used. Most kinds of merchandise have special properties and call for special packaging methods. The simplest method consists in enclosing the merchandise with a single protective layer of material. However, it is becoming increasingly common practice to employ composite materials (laminates)—e.g., paper combined with plastic sheet, or paper with metal foil, or metal foil sandwiched between sheets of plastic. Plastic sheet or film is manufactured as follows. Granules of plastic are fed into an extruder, in which they are subjected to kneading and mixing, in conjunction with heating. The material is extruded from a slot die in the form of a wide ribbon, which is passed through a series of stretching and calendering rolls. In this way the material is processed into thin sheeting or film. The sheeting produced in this way undergoes various subsequent treatments to improve its mechanical strength: stiffening of the material by grooving, bonding to other plastic sheets (lamination), etc. The manufacture of laminated sheeting is illustrated in Fig. 4. In this process propylene sheet is heated and is, when softened, pressed in contact with a strip of paper or textile fabric and then allowed to cool. In another process—called the "molten bead" process—a hot filament of polyethylene emerging from a small extruder is introduced between the sheets to be bonded together. Fig. 5 shows another process, in which the bond is established by softening of the contact surfaces of two plastic sheets by means of a wedge-shaped heating element, the sheets then being compressed together between rollers so that they remain sticking together. Yet another method of bonding the sheets for forming laminates is by ultrasonic welding: the two sheets are introduced between a "sonotrode" and an "anvil." The sonotrode, which vibrates at ultrasonic frequency, exerts a rhythmically oscillating pressure on the sheets, in which the ultrasonic energy is transformed into heat. The heat softens the plastic and causes the sheet to bond together (Fig. 6). Similar bonding processes are used for sealing (welding) the edges of bags and other containers made of plastic. This may be done by inserting the material between heated jaws which exert a certain amount of pressure and thus effect a seal. If the packaging materials themselves cannot be sealed by direct bonding, a layer of suitable bonding material, which can be softened by the application of heat, is interposed (hot sealing).

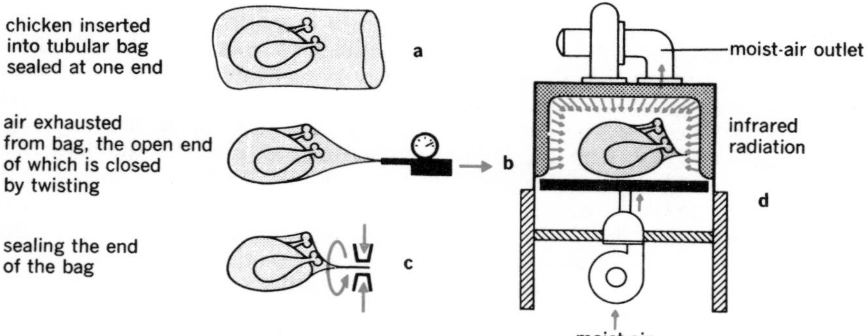

FIG. 3 WRAPPING CHICKENS IN SHRUNK-ON HEAT-SEALED PLASTIC

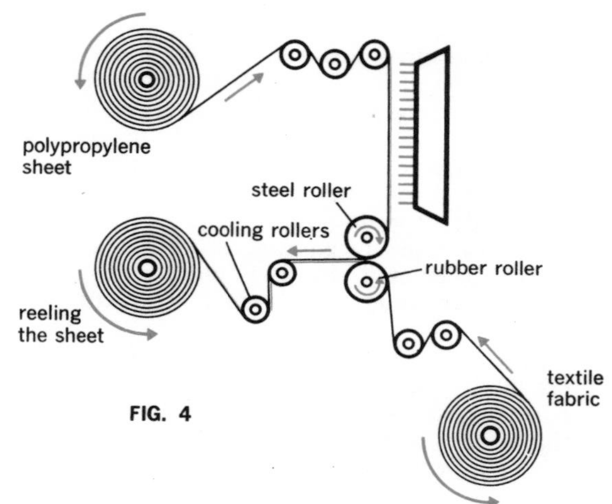

FIG. 4

laminated-sheet manufacture

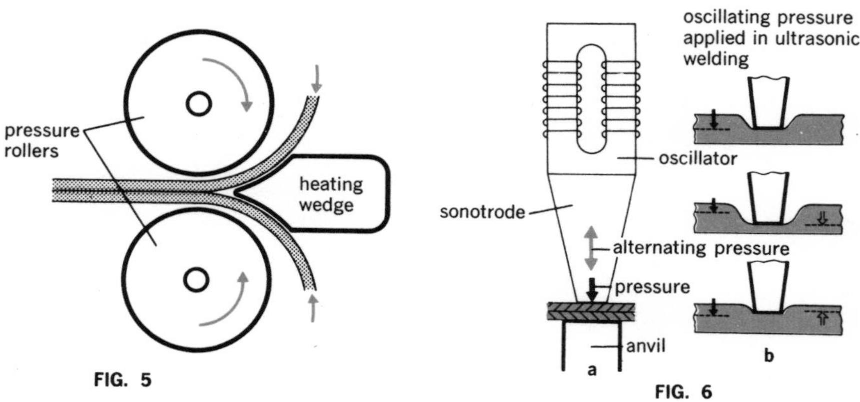

FIG. 5

FIG. 6

SILOS AND SILAGE

The use of silos for the storage and preservation of green fodder (forage) by a process of controlled fermentation is described by the term "ensilage." The fermented foodstuff for farm animals is called "silage." Various crops can be processed in this way: grass crops, leguminous crops (peas, beans), cereals, etc. There are many types of silo. Here only one type, the metal-tower silo, will be dealt with. It is a gastight structure, so designed that fresh forage can be introduced from the top and fermented silage extracted from the bottom at any time, without detriment to the quality of the product. In good silage the composition of the ensiled food crop is largely unchanged, and its feeding value is high if it is made from a protein-rich crop, besides providing a useful source of minerals and vitamins.

The green forage put into the silo has a moisture content of 30–40%. The crop is chopped and elevated to the top of the silo; in modern installations, as shown in the accompanying illustration, this is done pneumatically by means of a blower which provides a stream of air to carry the forage to the top of the silo.

The silage is extracted from the bottom by means of a built-in cutting and conveying device which consists of an endless chain provided with cutter blades. This device removes silage from the bottom of the column and conveys it to the discharge gate at the center. The silage sinks down in the silo under its own weight. As heat is evolved in the fermentation process, there is no risk of the silo contents' freezing and thus remaining blocked in the silo in cold weather. To maintain a fairly constant pressure in the silo despite variations in temperature, the silo is equipped with pressure compensators—baglike flexible containers, communicating with the external air, which take in air at low temperatures and expel it when the temperature rises. The silo wall is made of aluminum alloy or steel plate and is of bolted or welded construction. Advantages of ensilage are that the process is labor-saving because it can be mechanized and that it is independent of weather conditions. Against this, the silo and ancillary equipment involve considerable initial expenditure.

If air is freely admitted to fresh green forage, the biological process of respiration continues for a considerable time. This results in the breakdown of nutritive constituents, so that a loss in feeding value occurs. To prevent this, it is necessary to exclude air from the forage; hence the need for storing it in a closed container. Plant enzymes and bacteria cause fermentation, resulting in the formation of acids, mainly lactic acid.

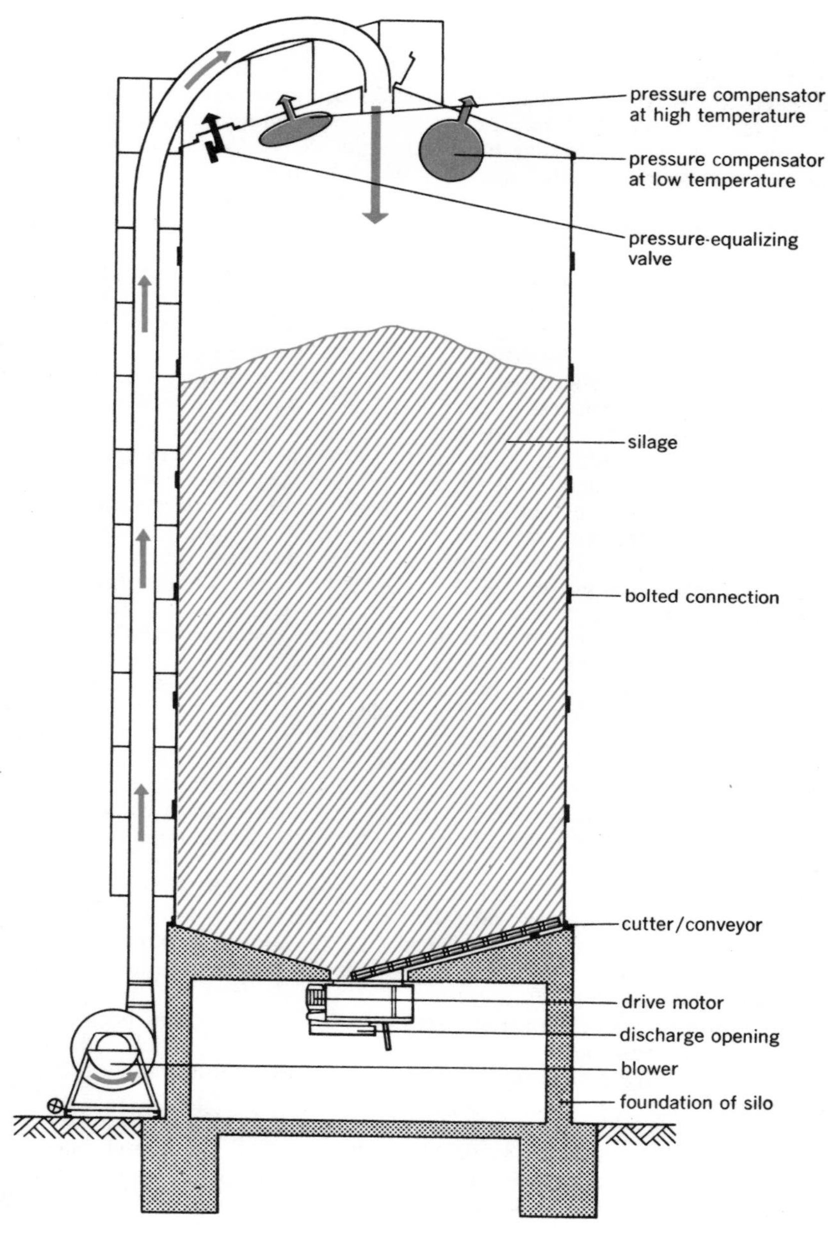
pressure compensator
at high temperature
pressure compensator
at low temperature
pressure-equalizing
valve
silage
bolted connection
cutter/conveyor
drive motor
discharge opening
blower
foundation of silo

THE MODERN CATTLE BARN (COW SHED)

Accommodation for dairy cows is mainly of two types: the stall-barn system and the loose-housing system. In Europe the stall barn is the most extensively used system: each cow is confined in a stall, the stalls being arranged side by side in rows facing on a feedway, which should preferably be wide enough to permit the passage of a wagon for delivering fodder to the troughs. A typical layout comprises two rows of stalls in the longitudinal direction of the barn or shed, with three alleys, or service passages. In cold climates the barns have insulated walls. Ventilation, watering, feed distribution and manure removal may be carried out by power-operated equipment.

The loose-housing system is less costly. The animals can move about freely in one or more large pens inside the shed. Manure is removed only at fairly long intervals by means of power manure loaders. In milder climates the system may take the form of a semiopen shelter adjacent to an outside yard into which the cows may freely move. Hayracks and feed troughs are installed in a feeding area under shelter. Sometimes the cows have access to a self-feeder with an automatic dispensing device which supplies a quantity of hay or grain at predetermined intervals of time. The cows are milked in a milking room adjacent to the shed. They are brought in to be milked and are then returned to the shed or the yard. The loose-housing system with semiopen shelters is for livestock fattening (beef cattle). In modern stall barns with power-operated manure-removal equipment the stalls are usually made 4 to 8 inches shorter than the animals' bodies. Adjacent to the standing area and at a slightly lower level is the manure gutter, which is cleared by means of rope-hauled scrapers or by small two-wheeled power scoops. Alternatively, in some installations the manure mixed with straw is removed by a conveyor system which discharges it on to a manure heap. In recent years, however, manure removal in liquid form has come into increasingly widespread use, because of its convenience and economy. In that case the cows do not lie on straw which is cleared out along with the manure but lie directly on the well-insulated floor of the barn (timber, plastic or ceramic flooring). The liquid mixture of manure and urine produced by the animals flows directly into a gutter which slopes slightly and discharges its contents into a pit outside the building (Fig. 1). With this system it is easier to keep the stalls clean and prevent disease. The cows stand on a clean floor, so that milking is carried out under more hygienic conditions.

Feeding the animals with silage is a simple operation. The silage is brought into the barn either in small wagons on rails or by means of a screw conveyor which brings it straight to the troughs from the silo. Each animal's feed trough is provided with an automatic waterer. When the cow prods the water container with her nose, a valve opens and lets water flow out.

Mechanization of the manure-removal operations is important because they are laborious and disagreeable to do by manual methods. This article will deal more particularly with fully mechanized disposal of cattle manure in liquid form, as already referred to.

The liquid manure that flows into the pit undergoes sedimentation when left to stand. The heavier constituents settle to the bottom and the lighter ones float to the top where they form a surface scum. To prevent this from happening, it is necessary to agitate the manure—i.e., keep it in motion. This can be done in various ways: mechanical (Fig. 2), pneumatic (Fig. 3) or hydraulic agitation (Fig. 4). The manure is spread on the fields. For this purpose it is pumped from the pit into tank wagons by means of centrifugal pumps, plunger pumps, propeller pumps or screw pumps. The pump is driven by an electric motor or from a power-takeoff shaft of the tractor.

(more)

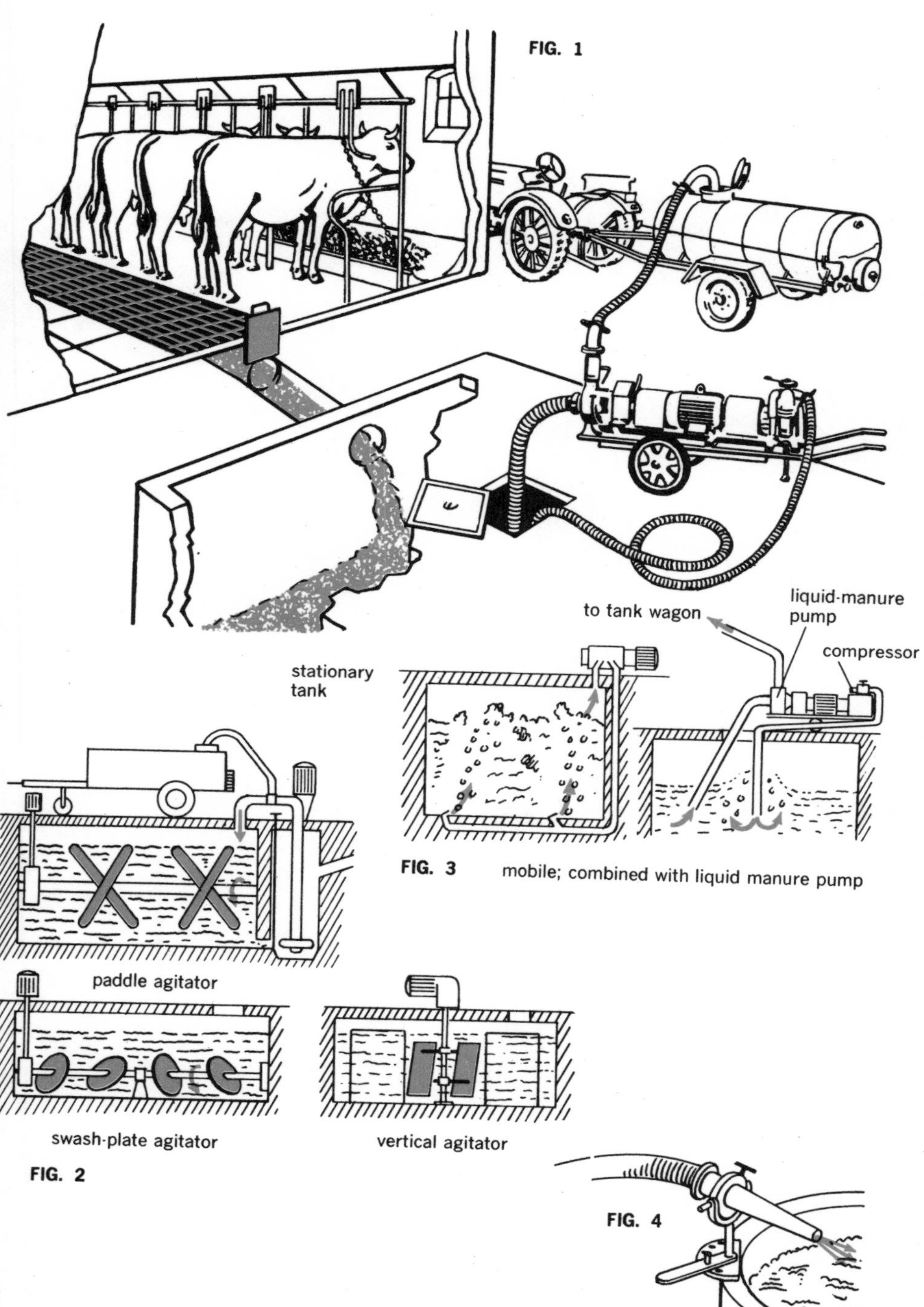
FIG. 1
to tank wagon
liquid-manure pump
compressor
stationary tank
FIG. 3
mobile; combined with liquid manure pump
paddle agitator
swash-plate agitator
vertical agitator
FIG. 2
FIG. 4

Mechanized stalls where cows are washed, dried and milked mechanically during one 12-minute cycle
Photo USIS

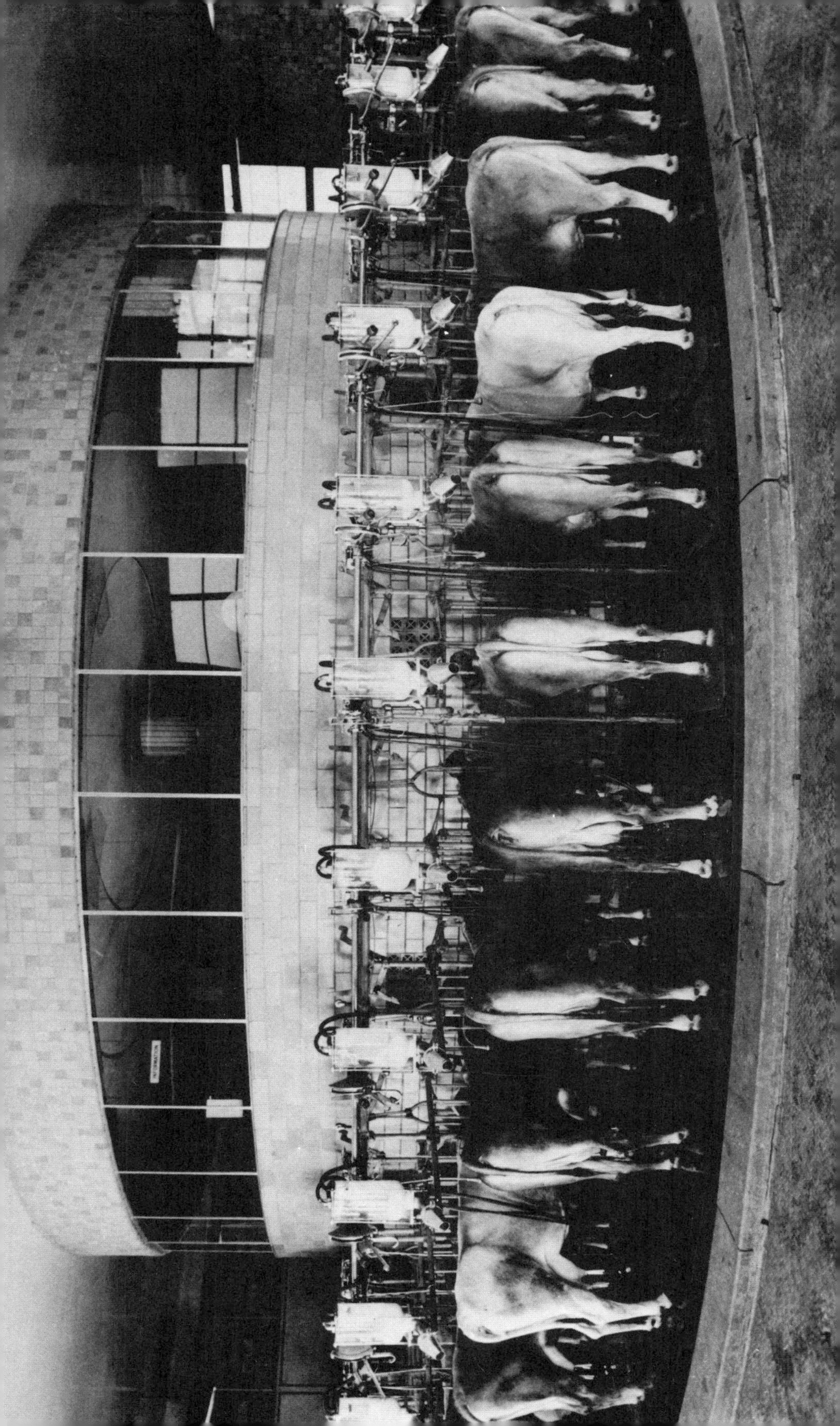

Fig. 5 shows a double-acting (lift-and-force) pump which can be used for agitating the manure and filling the tank wagon. Fig. 6 is an illustration of a propeller pump which can likewise perform both functions. This pump can be so designed that it acts as a comminuter which breaks up the solids (remains of cattle fodder) which might cause blockages in the pump and pipelines. The pump shown in Fig. 7 is merely for the "straight" handling of liquid manure, without having an agitating and/or comminuting action.

Manure may be pumped on to the fields directly through pipelines. For greater distances it is more usual to employ tank wagons for conveying it from the pit to the field. These are usually two-wheeled vehicles with a tank capacity ranging from 1500 to 3500 liters (approx. 330–800 gallons). The actual spreading of the liquid manure on the fields can be done by mechanical (Fig. 10), hydraulic (Fig. 9) or pneumatic (Fig. 8) methods. The quantity dispensed per acre can be appropriately regulated. The power for operating all three types of spreader is supplied by the takeoff shaft of a tractor. The tank wagon may also be equipped with an agitator mechanism for the manure pit and with a pump of its own (Figs. 8 and 9), in which case separate agitating and pumping equipment is not required. On large farms, however, it is more advantageous to use one large separate pump to fill a number of wagons at the pit.

With this liquid-manure-handling procedure it is possible to achieve complete mechanization of the various operations, but it does involve relatively heavy initial capital outlay in providing suitably planned cattle sheds or barns and a manure pit of adequate storage capacity. Each cow produces about 20 m^3 (700 cubic ft.) of liquid manure per year. In addition to general convenience, this method has the advantage that straw-storage facilities can be dispensed with, as no straw is used in the sheds. The straw is chopped up and left on the fields, where it is plowed under.

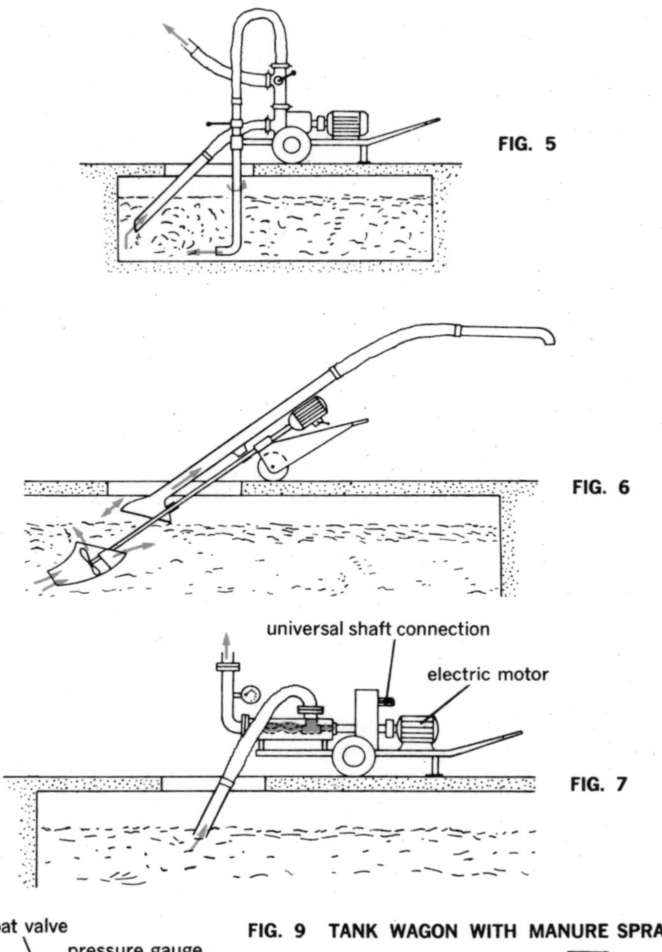

FIG. 5

FIG. 6

FIG. 7

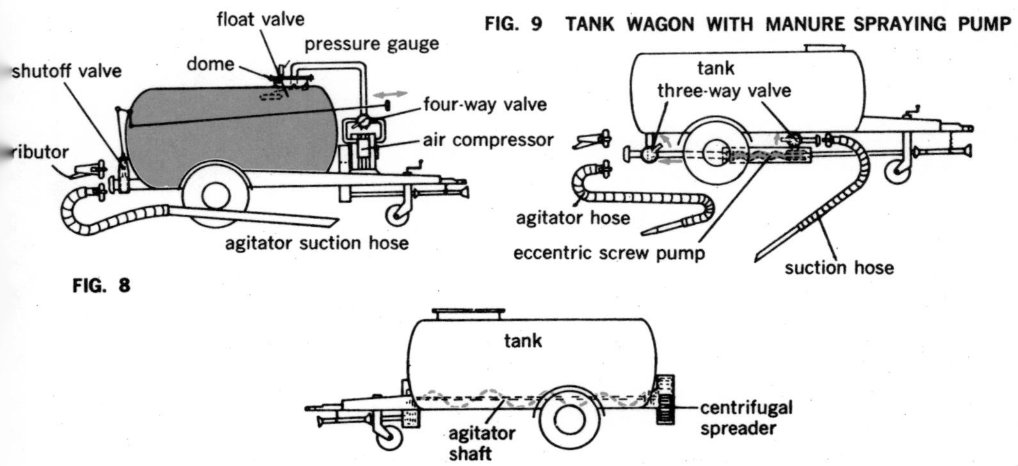

FIG. 8

FIG. 9 TANK WAGON WITH MANURE SPRAYING PUMP

FIG. 10 TANK WAGON WITH CENTRIFUGAL MANURE SPREADER

ROTARY HAYMAKING MACHINE

The rotary haymaking machine is used for scattering and turning the mown hay crop (grass, clover, legumes, etc.). First, the crop is cut off close to the ground by a mower, which is either a tractor-drawn or a self-propelled machine whose cutting mechanism consists of a long flat cutter bar, with forward-pointing slotted fingers, and a reciprocating knife formed by a thin steel strip to which knife blades are attached. As the crop is cut, it falls in a continuous swath on the ground, where it is left to cure until it is sufficiently dry to rake. During or shortly after mowing, the swath is spread out so as to give maximum exposure to sun and wind and thereby promote drying. After a time the spread hay has to be turned. Both these operations are performed by the same machine (Fig. 1). Spreading (scattering) the freshly mown swath is done by double-pronged raking forks mounted at the ends of arms which rotate about a vertical pivot. Each pivot carries four arms in a horizontal cross arrangement; these crosses operate in pairs, rotating in opposite directions (Fig. 2). The whirling prongs rake the mown grass together in front and fling it fanwise behind the machine over a relatively large width. Each rotating cross is supported on a wheel which follows all irregularities of the ground. The machine shown in Fig. 1 has an articulated frame, so that each cross can individually adapt itself to the irregularities. In another system there is a rigid frame, and every alternate wheel has a mounting which can telescope, thus permitting the wheel to move up or down. By means of a screw spindle the rotary crosses can be varied in height in relation to the ground, so that the prongs can be set higher or lower for dealing with different types of crop (e.g., legumes as opposed to grass). The machine is towed behind a tractor or, in some types of machine (with three-point support), the front end is actually supported on the tail of the tractor. Power for rotating the arms carrying the prongs is transmitted through a universal-joint shaft from the tractor. The arms are rotated at speeds of between 10 and 14 rpm. In this type of machine all the motions are rotary; there are no reciprocating parts. This operating principle makes for high efficiency. For instance, a machine with an operating width of 16 ft. (six "crosses"—i.e., sets of rotating arms) and towed at a speed of 9–10 mph can deal with about 18 acres per hour. This high performance rate is important in climates where it is essential to make the most of limited periods of favorable weather.

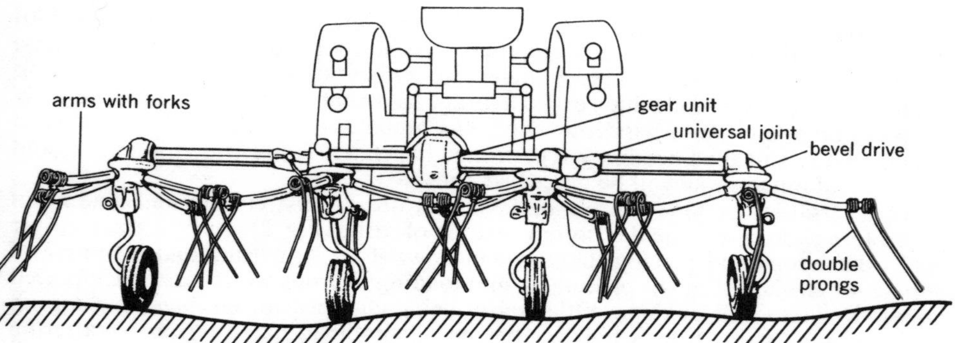

FIG. 1 ROTARY HAYMAKING MACHINE

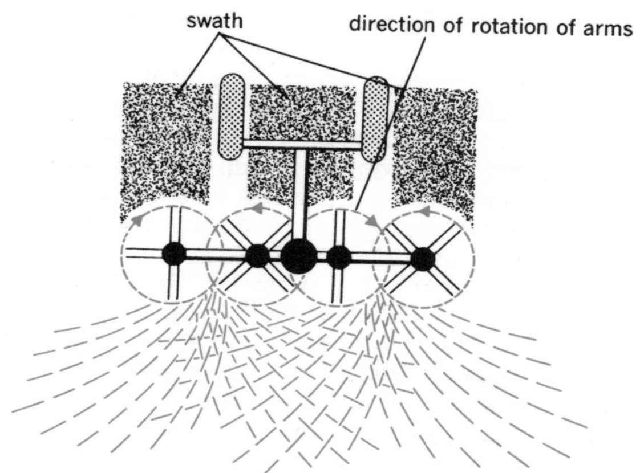

FIG. 2 ROTARY MACHINE SPREADING THE HAY (VIEWED FROM ABOVE)

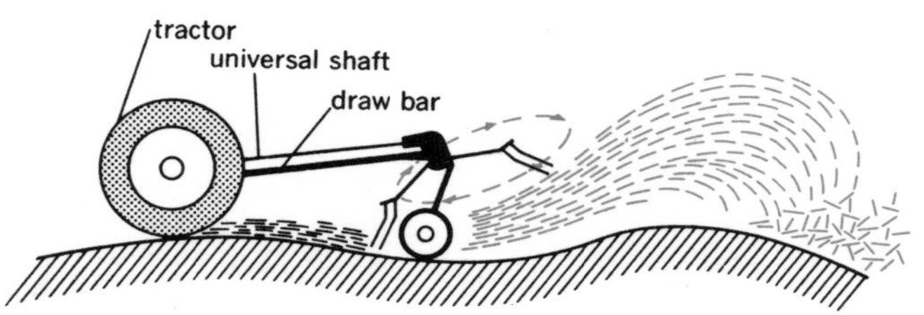

FIG. 3 ROTARY MACHINE TURNING THE HAY (SIDE VIEW)

FORAGE HARVESTERS

Certain crops, such as grass, legumes, and corn, are often ensiled (see page 170) for use as cattle food. To make silage, they must be chopped up so that they can be tightly packed in the silo, whereby anaerobic fermentation is promoted. The crop is cut in the field with a machine called a forage harvester which chops it immediately or picks up and chops a windrow which has been cut and raked earlier. One such machine, the so-called economy-type forage harvester, is illustrated in Fig. 1, and its mode of functioning will be described here.

This versatile machine can perform various operations: cutting and loading of green forage crops for the day-to-day feeding of cattle (Fig. 2); cutting grass, clover and other crops and placing them in windrows (Fig. 3); cutting and chopping of forage for ensilage (Fig. 4); picking up and loading of crops which have been placed in windrows to wilt or dry a little before being chopped for ensilage; picking up and chopping straw from windrows (left by a combined harvester) and scattering the chopped straw on the fields to make it easier to plow it under; cutting and chopping of remains of crops left in the fields, such as potato plants, corn, tobacco or cabbage stalks.

When towed by a tractor, the forage harvester moves along behind, but somewhat to the right of it. Alternatively, the harvester may be fixed to the right-hand side of the tractor. The power for driving the harvester is supplied by the tractor's takeoff shaft connected to a universal-joint shaft provided with a friction clutch. The power is transmitted to the beater shaft through V-belts and pulleys. The belt pulleys are of various sizes and are interchangeable so as to vary the speed of rotation of the beaters (speed range 1000–1700 rpm). The latter are about 2 inches in width and are mounted in a staggered arrangement on the shaft. They cut the growing crop off, or pick up the already cut crop from the windrow, and chop it up by whirling the stalks and leaves past a cutter blade (Fig. 1b) whose distance from the beaters can be adjusted to alter the cutting action. The length of the chopped material depends on the cutter blade setting, the speed of rotation of the beater shaft, and the speed of forward travel of the harvester. When the blade is set close to the beaters and the beaters rotate at high speed, while the machine moves forward at a slow pace, the shortest chopped length is obtained, and vice versa. This length is only an average; actually the chopped material contains a large proportion of oversize pieces—i.e., its chopping action is not accurate, and for this reason the material is not suitable for ensilage in gastight fermentation silos because an excessive proportion of long pieces is liable to interfere with the proper functioning of the discharging mechanism. The chopped material is conveyed up the curved duct by a combination of throwing and blowing. It can thus be discharged into a wagon. Alternatively, it can be deposited in a windrow; in that case the outlet of the duct is fitted with a discharge flap and guide plates which permit varying of the width of the windrow.

(more)

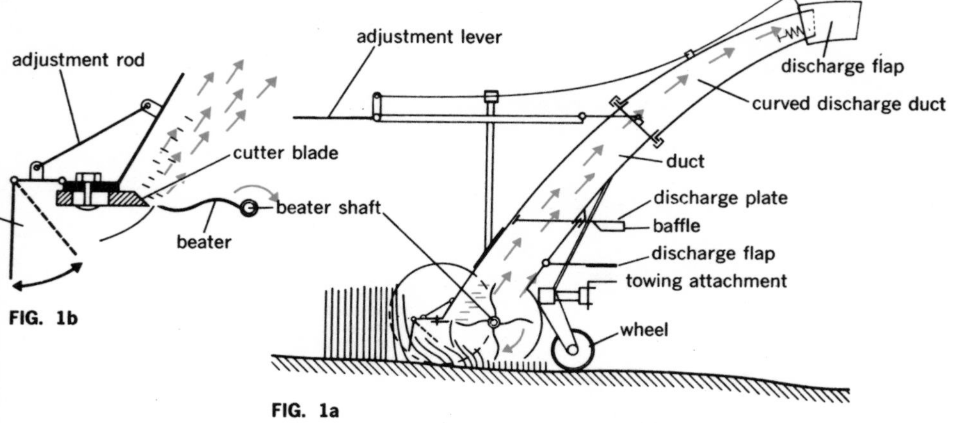

FIG. 1b

FIG. 1a

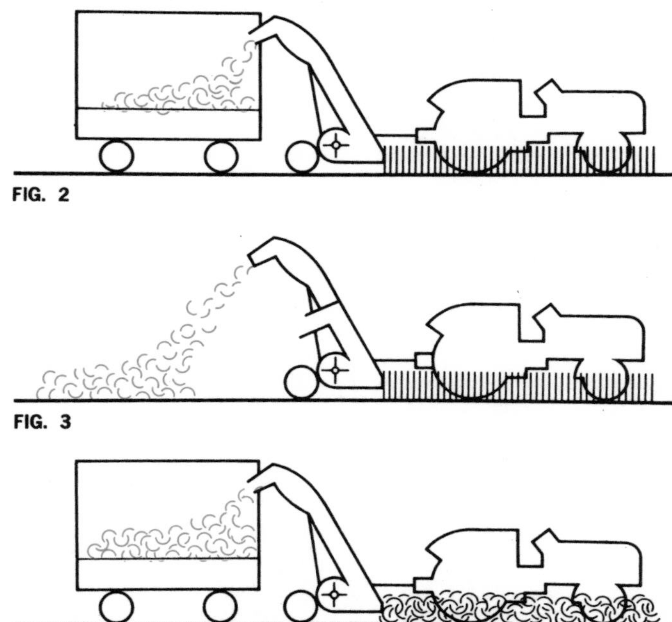

FIG. 2

FIG. 3

FIG. 4

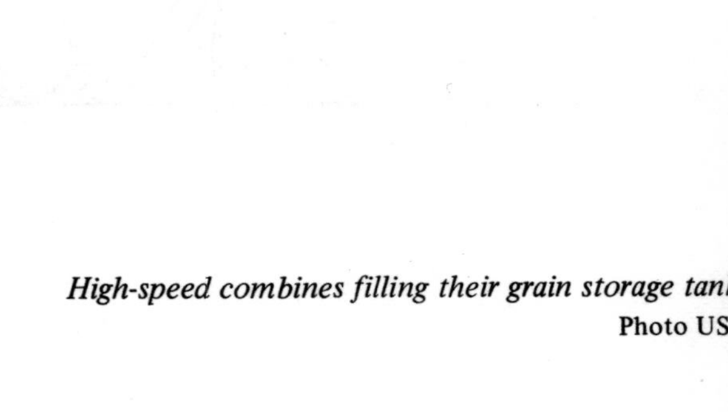

High-speed combines filling their grain storage tank
Photo USI

Forage Harvesters (continued)

Fig. 5 illustrates a forage harvester which enables the length of the chopped material to be controlled with greater precision. According to the arrangement of the cutting knives, these machines are of the flywheel type or the cylinder type. The length of cut can be varied by changing the feed speed or by changing the number of knives. In the cylinder-type machine, which is predominantly used in the U.S., the knives are bolted to a rapidly revolving cylindrical knife holder which chops the material in very short lengths and additionally has an impeller action which flings it upwards through a duct and thus discharges it into a wagon. The knives of the flywheel-type forage harvester are bolted to a rotating flywheel disc which carries up to six knives, each accompanied by an impeller blade. The length of the chopped material can be adjusted between wide limits (about $\frac{5}{16}$ to 12 in.).

These forage harvesters may be tractor-hauled or self-propelled. Cut material deposited in windrows is picked up by means of a cam-controlled pickup mechanism equipped with spring-mounted prongs (a). A cover plate (b) over this mechanism prevents the short material from falling back and subjects it to a certain amount of preliminary pressure. The material compacted in this way is seized by the auger (c) and draw-in chain (d); together they feed it into a duct in which it is compacted by the action of the chain (e) and the roll (f); it is then fed to the cutter bar (g). The cutter wheel (h), revolving at 300–700 rpm, chops off the compressed material, and impeller blades fling it through the curved discharge duct into the wagon. The length of the chopped material can be varied by changing the intake speed, the number of knives (from one to six), and the speed of rotation of the disc carrying the knives. The shortest lengths are employed for material intended for making silage. Instead of the pickup mechanism, the machine can be provided with a row crop attachment for harvesting corn (maize). A knife cuts the stalks close to the ground, while gathering chains carry them to feed rolls which deliver the material to the cutter wheel.

A forage harvester of flywheel or cylinder type, as described on this page, is driven by means of a universal shaft from the power-takeoff shaft of the tractor. A safety clutch protects the machinery against overloading. In the event of blockage of the draw-in and feed devices, a reverse motion can be performed to clear them without the tractor driver's having to leave his seat to attend to the harvester. These harvesters can deal with any kind of forage crop and in any condition—green, wilted or dry.

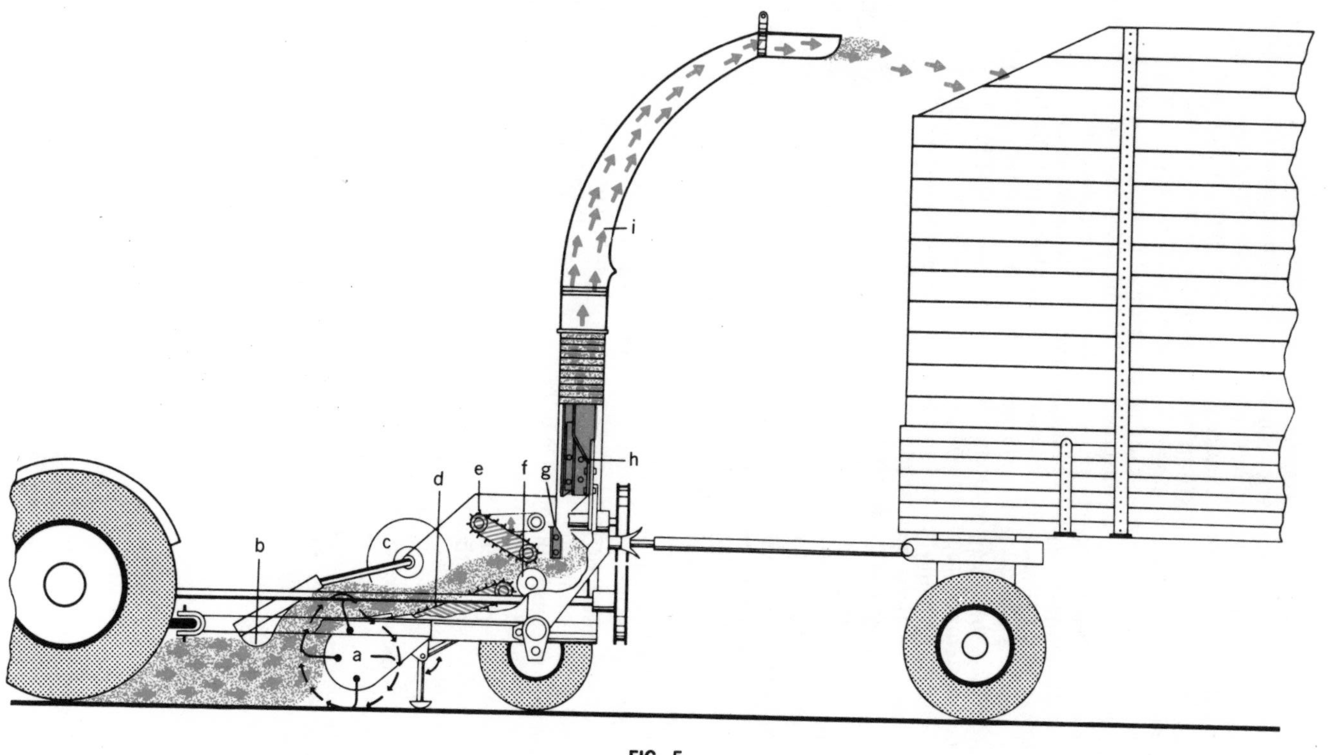

FIG. 5

SELF-CONTAINED UNDERWATER BREATHING APPARATUS (SCUBA)

Apparatus of this general category is used in skin diving, which is practiced as sport as well as for technical, scientific and military purposes. The term "Aqualung is sometimes applied to skin divers' or frogmen's breathing apparatus of any kin but is actually a trade name. A more generally used term is SCUBA. There are tw main types of self-contained equipment: open-circuit and closed-circuit. An oper circuit unit comprises an air supply (one or more cylinders of compressed air) an a mask or mouthpiece to which air is fed through a tube via a demand regulato The exhaled gas is discharged into the water. In the closed-circuit system the breat ing gas is compressed pure oxygen. The exhaled gas is passed into a canister of sod lime or caustic soda which absorbs the carbon dioxide; a flexible respirator (breathin bag) is interposed between the oxygen cylinder and the inhaling tube.

Fig. 1 shows a typical self-contained underwater breathing mouthpiece as use for amateur skin diving. Other items of this open-circuit equipment are compresse air cylinders, demand regulator or pressure-reducing valve, connecting tubes, an pressure gauge. The number and size of the air cylinders carried by the diver depen on the length of time he intends to spend underwater. For dives of maximu duration and depth the diver carries three cylinders, each of 7 liters capacity, co taining air at a pressure of 200 atm. This corresponds to $3 \times 7 \times 200 = 4200$ liters "free" air—i.e., air at ordinary atmospheric pressure. The rate of air consumptio depends on the depth at which the diver is submerged and the amount of physic effort he makes. For example, when swimming at the surface he will need abo 25 liters of air per minute. At a depth of 10 m this will be about 50 liters, and a depth of 20 m it will be about 75 liters per minute.

For greater safety, the underwater breathing apparatus is equipped with a warnin device that alerts the diver when he is nearing the end of his air supply. A reser air supply is then switched on by means of a changeover valve (Fig. 3). So long the air pressure in the air cylinders is above 40 kg/cm^2, the air can flow unhinder to the demand regulator and thence to the mouthpiece. When the pressure fal below that value, the flow to the regulator is gradually throttled down by the pressu of a spring. The resulting increase in breathing resistance serves to warn the dive who now actuates a lever which opens a bypass whereby the rest of the air can flo freely from the cylinders. For example, with three 7-liter cylinders the diver wi then still have $3 \times 7 \times 40 = 840$ liters of air available—sufficient for about 10 minut at a depth of 20 m. This will give him time to return safely to the surface. In Fig. the normal air supply flows through the passage (2) into the chamber (3); the a pressure lifts the valve (4) off its seat, against the force of the spring (5), thus allowin the air to flow through the passage (6) and into the pipe (7) leading to the dema regulator. When the pressure falls below 40 kg/cm^2, the spring (5) gradually clos the valve (4). The diver now actuates the lever (11) whereby the valve (13) is opened, s that the remaining air in the cylinders can flow through the passages (14, 15, 16, and 7) to the regulator.

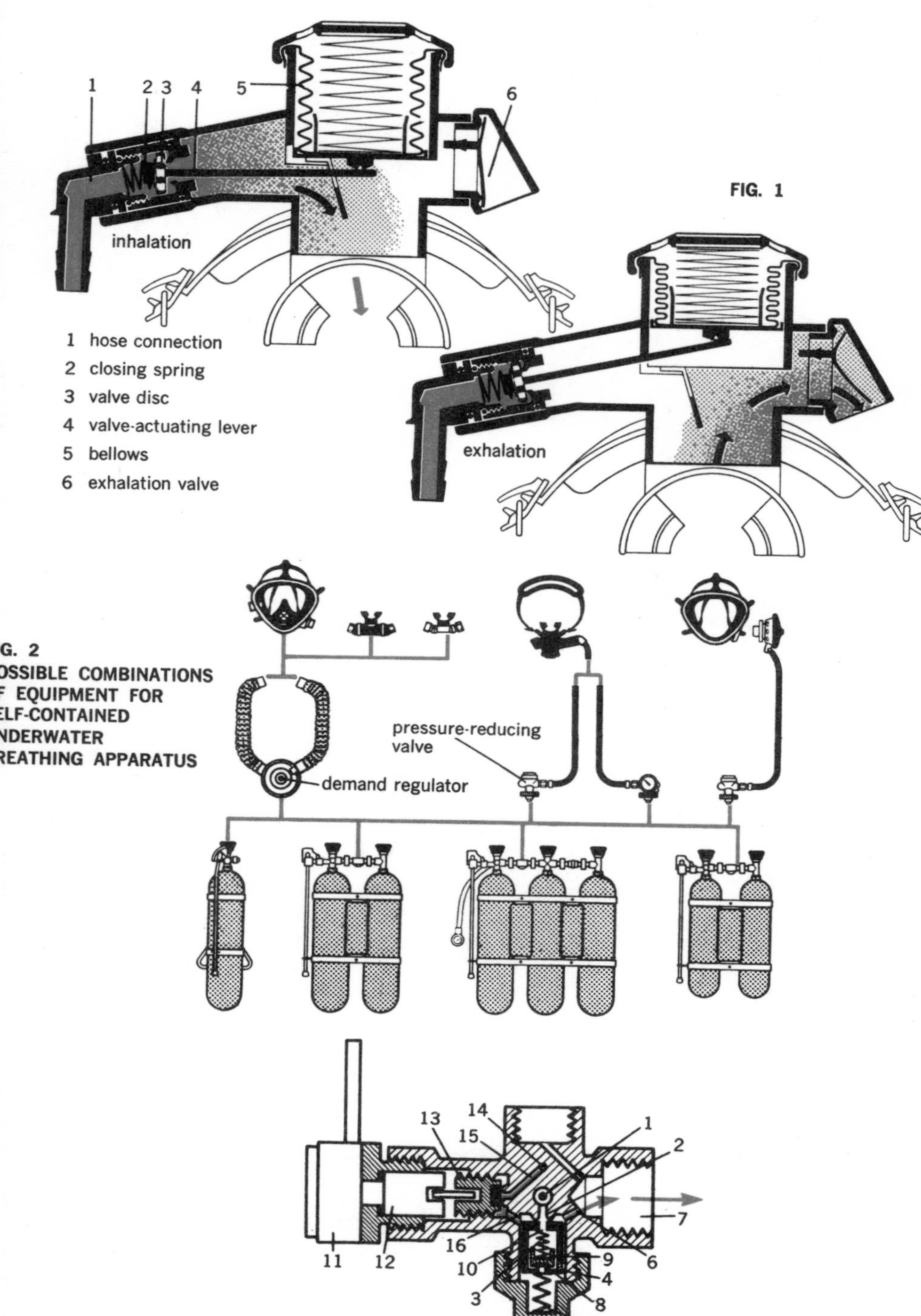

FIG. 1

FIG. 2 POSSIBLE COMBINATIONS OF EQUIPMENT FOR SELF-CONTAINED UNDERWATER BREATHING APPARATUS

FIG. 3 SECTIONAL DRAWING OF CHANGEOVER VALVE

Divers test how fish react, whether they figh[illegible] flee or are curious about their strange shape

Photo USI[illegible]

SAFETY BINDING FOR SKIS

The skier wears heavy boots with stiff soles, which enable him to exercise precise control over the skis. The boots are secured by means of bindings. In the event of a severe fall, the rigid connection between boot and ski is liable to cause injuries. This hazard is reduced by so-called safety bindings (or release bindings), which free the skier's foot when he falls.

The safety binding illustrated in Fig. 1 comprises a swiveling plate (1), which is rotatably secured to the ski with screws (2), and the gripping and release device which is attached to the swiveling plate by means of a cable (3). In a fall, the swiveling plate, which functions in the manner of a "turntable," cooperates by rotating and thus providing an additional degree of freedom. Each end of the cable is provided with a nipple (4 and 5) which bears against a coil spring (6 and 7). The two springs are accommodated in the trapezium-shaped frame (8), to which the middle flap (9) is pivotably connected. A spring catch (14) holds the middle flap (9) in the locked position. The coil spring on the left-hand side is guided by a hole in the nipple and by a pin (10) which is riveted to a rocker (11). The latter is cushioned by a rubber pad (12) and is provided, on the right-hand side, with a hole in which a stud (13), screwed into the nipple (5), can slide longitudinally.

On the right-hand side of the binding is the mechanism which releases it in the event of overloading and thus protects the skier's legs and especially the Achilles tendon. The seating is so designed that the loaded spring tends to swing outwards. However, it is prevented from doing this by the stud (13), which engages with a hole in the rocker. The coil spring can swing outwards only after the stud has been withdrawn downwards out of the hole in the rocker. When this happens, the heel of the boot is automatically released.

Fig. 3 shows the movements that occur in fastening the boot to the binding. If swung about the cable, the binding would move along a curve with radius r_1; but the middle flap bears against a groove at the back of the heel and compels the binding to swing upwards along the curve with radius r_2. As a result, the two coil springs are tensioned and thus keep the boot firmly pressed against the ski. Fig. 2 shows the binding in its "locked" position, gripping the boot. The catch (14) engages with the crosspiece (16), thus preventing accidental release of the binding. Release is effected as a result of a jerk which disengages the catch and dislodges the binding from its "top dead center" position, so that it returns to its bottom position as shown in Fig. 3. To reset the released binding, the stud (13) is reinserted into its hole and the coil spring pressed back into its seating.

(more)

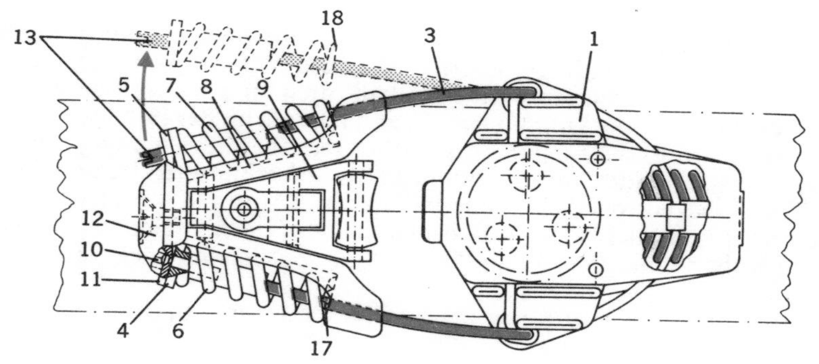

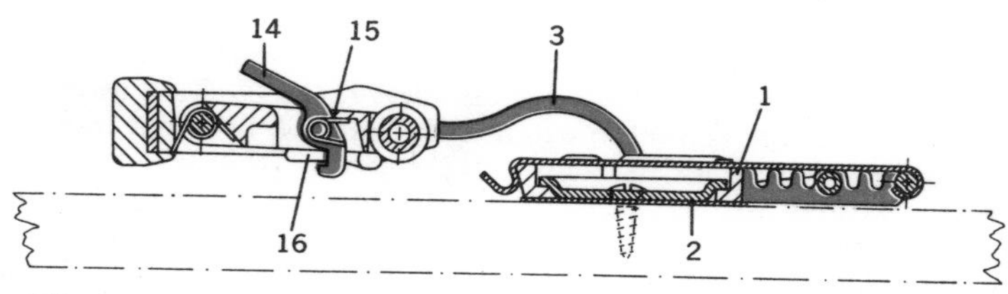

FIG. 1

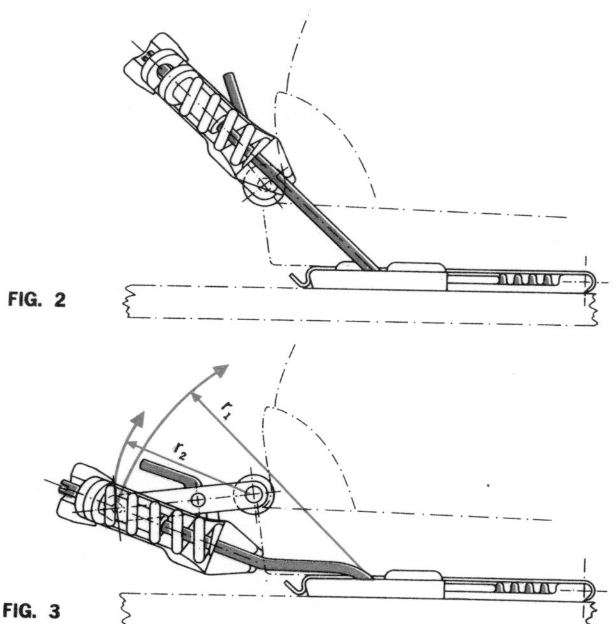

Safety Binding for Skis (continued)

Fig. 5 shows a safety binding whereby the toe of the boot instead of the heel is secured to the ski. This binding comprises the base plate (1) with the supporting pillar (2), the link unit (3) incorporating the ball catch (4) whose gripping force can be adjusted by means of the knurled nut (5), and the sole holder (6). The link unit (3) is loosely screwed on to the supporting pillar, so that the entire binding is vertically adjustable. The sole holder and the link unit are interconnected by another pivot (the stud 7) and locked together by the ball catch. A stop pin (8) screwed into the base plate prevents accidental vertical displacement of the binding. A spring-loaded bush (9) holds the binding in the middle position, but has no effect on the safety-release action.

Fig. 6 shows the binding gripping the boot in the normal position. The two red arrows represent the gripping forces which keep the boot secured by the binding. The sole holder balances on the two teeth; the stud (7) is the fulcrum. In Fig. 7 the binding is shown in the "release" position. The device functions as follows: when the skier falls and the toe of the boot is jerked sideways, the movement dislodges the binding from its normal position.

It first swivels about its main pivot (the supporting pillar), while as yet the ball catch keeps the link unit locked to the sole holder. If the twisting force is relatively small and of short duration, the catch will merely "give" a little but remain engaged. The binding will then swing back to its normal position, so that the stable equilibrium of the system is restored. On the other hand, if the force is of longer duration and attains the maximum value that the ball catch can resist (this value can be varied by adjusting the gripping force by means of the nut 5), the catch will disengage and release the sole holder, so that now the link unit and the sole holder can also swivel in relation to each other. From Fig. 7 it is apparent that the binding swivels farther about the main pivot and that release is longer deferred according as the ball catch engages more firmly (this being adjusted by means of the nut). Between the main pivot, the loaded tooth, and the ankle a toggle action is developed, which ensures that release will always occur, no matter how firmly the catch engages. Hence there is no risk that the binding will fail to perform its releasing action even if the skier sets the gripping force of the catch to a high value. Once the ball catch disengages the binding completely and instantly releases the toe of the boot (Fig. 8).

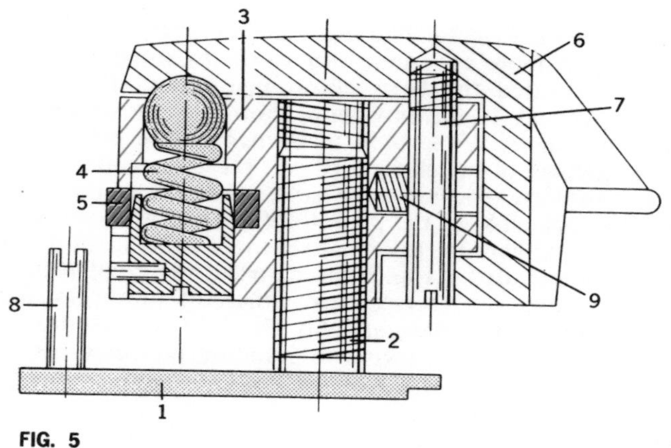

FIG. 5

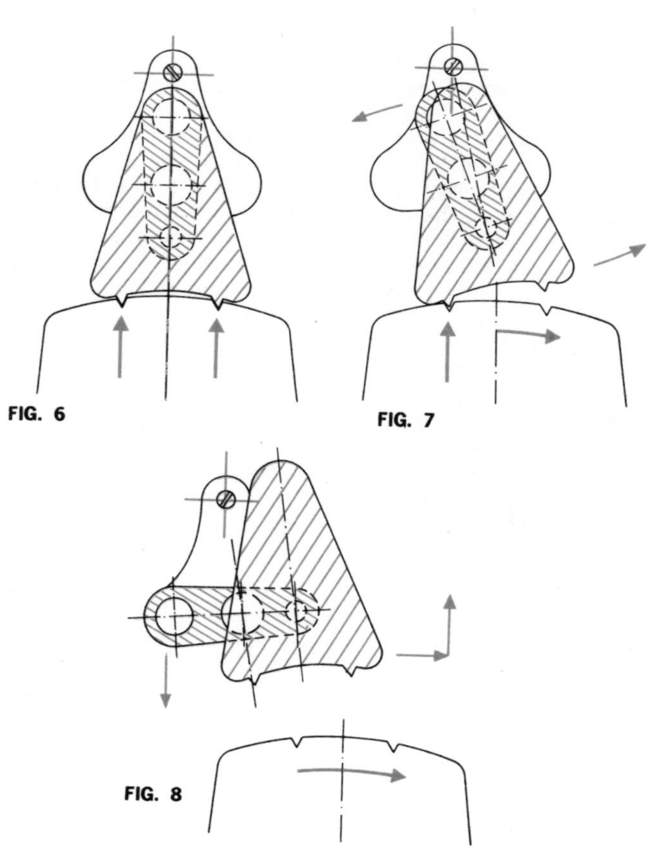
FIG. 6

FIG. 7

FIG. 8

PIANOFORTE

Forerunners of the piano include such instruments as the virginals, the harpsichord and the clavichord. A more advanced form of the harpsichord was the spinet. The mechanism that operated the harpsichord involved quills that "twanged" the strings of the instrument. In the clavichord, however, the strings were struck from below by brass hammers. While both instruments were played through the 18th century, the mechanism of the clavichord was the immediate ancestor in principle of the modern pianoforte (the full name for the instrument now commonly known as the piano). The principle of the pianoforte appears to have originated with an Italian harpsichord maker, Bartolommeo Cristofori, who in 1720 produced the escapement action illustrated in Fig. 2, based on less advanced forms of a mechanism introduced by him some ten years earlier. Cristofori's invention was perfected by Gottfried Silbermann, a German, and his pupil Johann Andreas Stein. In 1821 Sebastian Erard, an Alsatian working in London, perfected his invention of the repetition, or double-escapement, action, which is now, in modified forms, employed in most pianos.

The modern grand piano comprises the following main parts:

1. The cast-iron frame, which has to resist the pull of about 18 tons exerted by the more than 220 strings.
2. The soundboard, consisting of a carefully prepared wooden panel 9 to 11 mm (about $\frac{3}{8}$ inch) thick. The vibrations of the strings are transmitted through a bridge to the soundboard, which intensifies the sound.
3. The casing and wrest plank (fixed to the iron frame) provided with holes into which the tuning pins are inserted.
4. The action, i.e., the system of levers whereby the hammers are actuated, and the keyboard.
5. The strings: in present-day grand pianos the over- or cross stringing introduced by Steinway in the 19th century is employed. In this arrangement the bass strings are made to cross over the tenor strings, so that longer bass strings can be used and the area of bridge pressure on the soundboard can be increased (Fig. 1).

The action of a grand piano is illustrated in Fig. 3. This is essentially the Steinway action introduced in 1884. When the key t1 is depressed, its other end t2 is raised. The damper is lifted off the string, and the lever system abc pivots about the point p until the bell-crank lever (the lower arm of the hopper c) comes into contact with the setoff button s1. The hammer h has now moved much closer to the string. With further depression of the key, the hopper must (since c1 is against the button) rotate to the right. The hammer is thus further raised and strikes the string. Continued pressure on the key causes the hopper to escape from under the roller. The hammer automatically falls back, allowing the string to vibrate freely. If the pressure on the key is now reduced a little, the spring f causes the hopper c to come back under the roller, so that the hammer can again be struck without first having to let the key return to the initial position (repetition action).

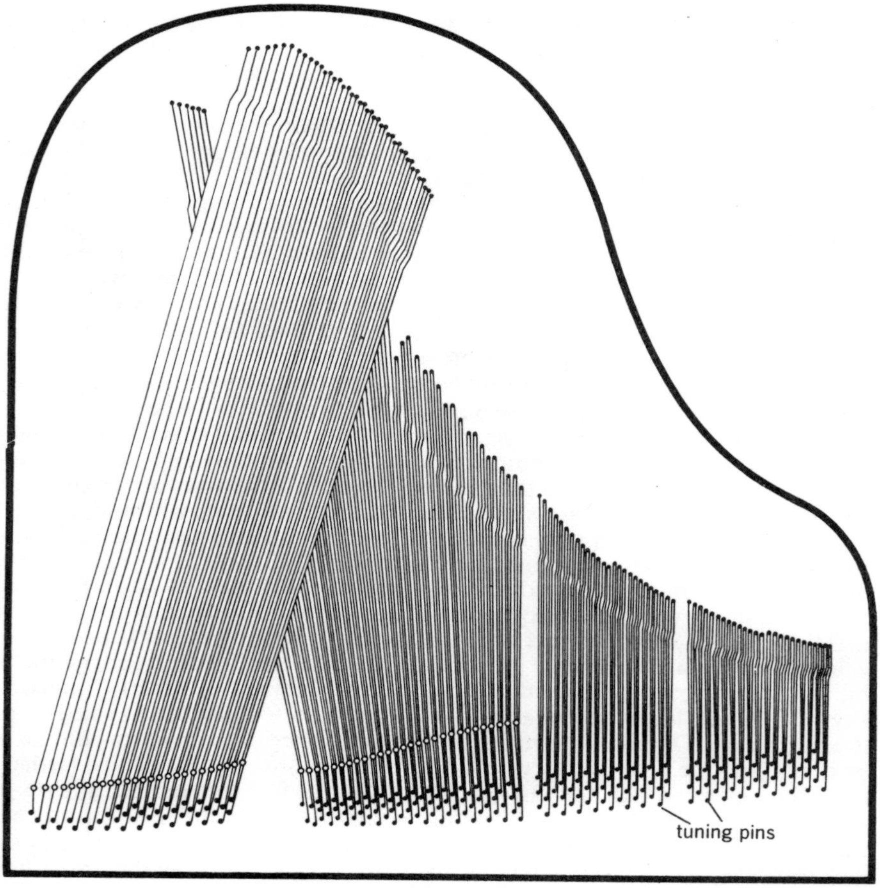

tuning pins

FIG. 1

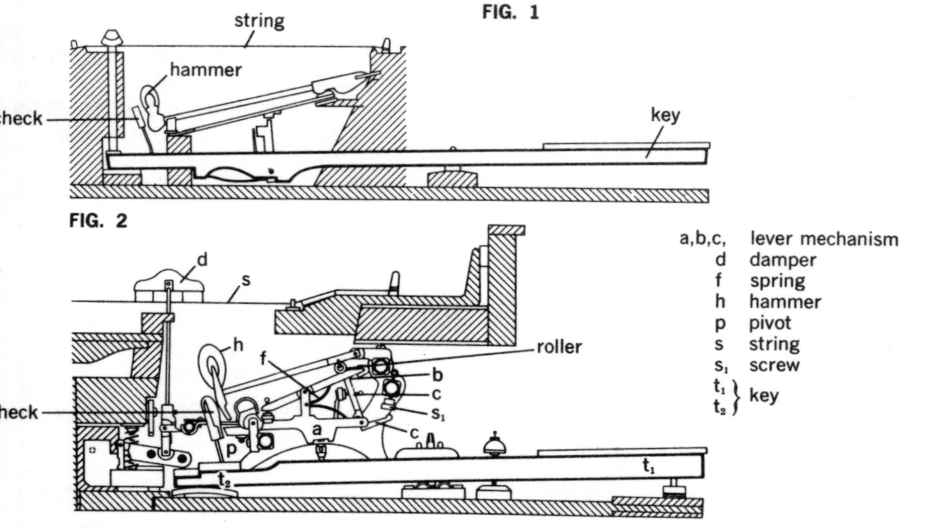

FIG. 2

FIG. 3

PIANO TONE AND TUNING

The sounds produced by a piano are caused by the vibration of strings (Fig. 1) which are struck by hammers. The loudness (intensity) of the tone depends on the amplitude of the vibration—i.e., the maximum distance to which the string is deflected from its stationary position.

On the other hand, the pitch of the tone depends on the frequency of the vibration—i.e., the number of oscillations that the string performs per second. The string in Fig. 1 is performing what is known as its fundamental vibration. Under certain conditions a string can be made to vibrate in two or more "waves" (Fig. 2); the points of maximum amplitude are called nodes. In this way so-called harmonic vibrations, producing overtones, are formed. In reality the fundamental vibration as well as several harmonic vibrations (and therefore several overtones) occur simultaneously. For example, in Fig. 2 the string vibrates not only over the lengths AB, BC, CD and DE, but also over the length AC and EC and the length AD and BE, as well as performing its fundamental vibration. Thus, each tone produced by a stringed instrument such as the piano is a compound, consisting of a fundamental tone and its overtones. The frequencies of the overtone are whole multiples of the frequency of the fundamental tone. Thus, the overtone frequencies are in the ratios of 1:2:3:4:5 etc. (Fig. 3: the notes marked correspond only approximately to these overtones), which is known as the "harmonic series." The notes of various frequency which constitutes the harmonics of, for example, the tone of "middle C" blend together pleasingly, with the exception of the seventh and ninth harmonics, which are dissonant. The best tone quality is produced by striking the strings at one-eighth of their length; this is believed to discourage the seventh and ninth harmonics.

With "exact" tuning, the frequencies of the note within an octave are proportional to 24, 27, 30, 32, 36, 40, 45 and 48. This is known as the "natural scale" and can be achieved only in instruments of continuously variable pitch, such as the violin, but not in keyboard instruments. A piano could indeed be "exactly" tuned for the key of C major, for example, as in Fig. 4; but if the pianist then wished to play in the key of, say, D major, the ratios of the frequencies of the notes would no longer be exact. And the discrepancy would be greater according as he moved farther away from the key for which the instrument was tuned. For this reason, among others, so-called "equal temperament" tuning is used for keyboard instruments such as the piano. This is based on the "tempered scale," in which each octave is divided into twelve equal semitone intervals, so that any two successive semitones have the same frequency ratio. Since each note has to vibrate at twice the frequency of the same note an octave below, the semitone ratio from note to note is taken as the twelfth root of 2, namely, 1.05946. This gives a continuous geometrical progression throughout the keyboard. This progression is not in precise agreement with the natural scale, but does provide a sufficiently close approximation, as appears from the "tempered" ratios in the octave compared with the corresponding "natural" ratios:

Tempered ratios:	1.00000	1.05946	1.12246	1.18921	1.25992	1.33484
Natural ratios:	1.00000		1.12500		1.25000	1.33333

Tempered ratios:	1.41421	1.49831	1.58740	1.68179	1.78180	1.88775	2.00000
Natural ratios:		1.50000		1.66667		1.87500	2.00000

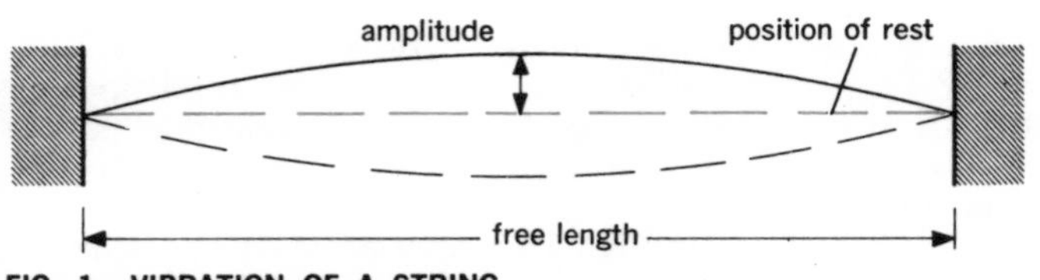

FIG. 1 VIBRATION OF A STRING

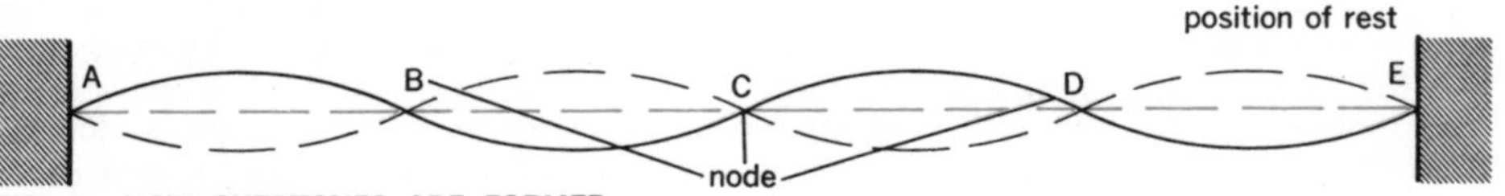

FIG. 2 HOW OVERTONES ARE FORMED

FIG. 3 OVERTONES ASSOCIATED WITH THE FUNDAMENTAL TONE C

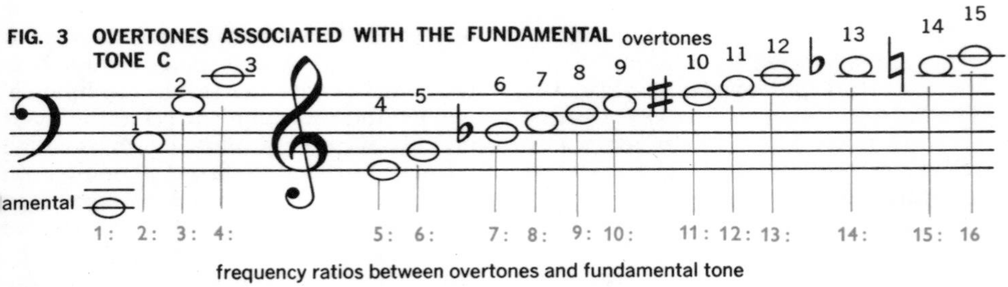

overtones

1 2 3 4 5 6 7 8 9 10 11 12 13 14 15

amental

1: 2: 3: 4: 5: 6: 7: 8: 9: 10: 11: 12: 13: 14: 15: 16

frequency ratios between overtones and fundamental tone

FIG. 4 "EXACT" TUNING IN C MAJOR

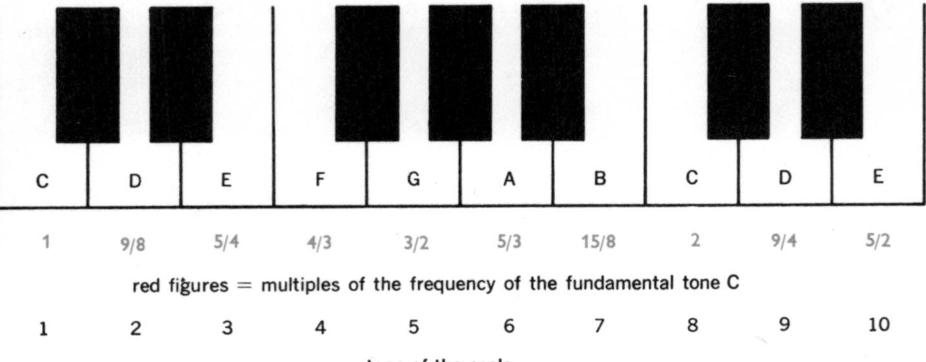

ACCORDION

The accordion is a free-reed instrument which was developed in the first half of the 19th century. Each reed consists of a metal tongue over a slot in a metal plate, the pitch of the reed being determined by the length and thickness of the tongue. The tongue is "sprung up" above its frame and vibrates when air flows around the reed from its upper side.

Fig. 1 represents a section through a modern accordion. It comprises a bellows secured between two wooden end units in which the reeds are accommodated. The wind is admitted selectively to the reeds through valves controlled by finger buttons or by keys on a keyboard. In the double-action or "piano" accordion each button or key operates a pair of reeds both sounding the same note, one of which sounds on the "press," and the other on the "draw," of the bellows. Thus every note is available from one key with both directions of movement of the bellows. On the other hand, with the single-action accordion the two reeds of a pair produce two adjacent notes of the scale, each note being available with a bellows movement in one direction only. For the left hand there are usually two keys or buttons to produce bass notes and major or minor, etc., chords respectively.

On the treble side of the accordion, the fingerboard and the frame of the instrument are separated by a soundboard of wood or metal, which serves to intensify the tone and improve its quality. The soundboard covers the treble mechanism. The "action" whereby the keys operate the valves and thus admit wind to the reeds is illustrated in Fig. 2. The modern accordion is furthermore provided with so-called registers, whereby slides are operated which can cut out or bring in individual tonalities or whereby, in some instruments, extra sets of reeds are brought into action, one set pitched an octave below the main set and the other off-tuned to give a tremulant, so that the sound emitted has a pulsating or tremolo effect. The reeds are screwed or riveted over slots in metal plates. These rectangular plates each have two slots and cover the air ducts through which the wind for blowing the reeds is admitted. The reeds themselves are made of watch-spring steel (brass was used in earlier accordions) and can vibrate freely in their slot ("free reeds"). To minimize the air consumption, the slots are closed by flexible flaps of leather.

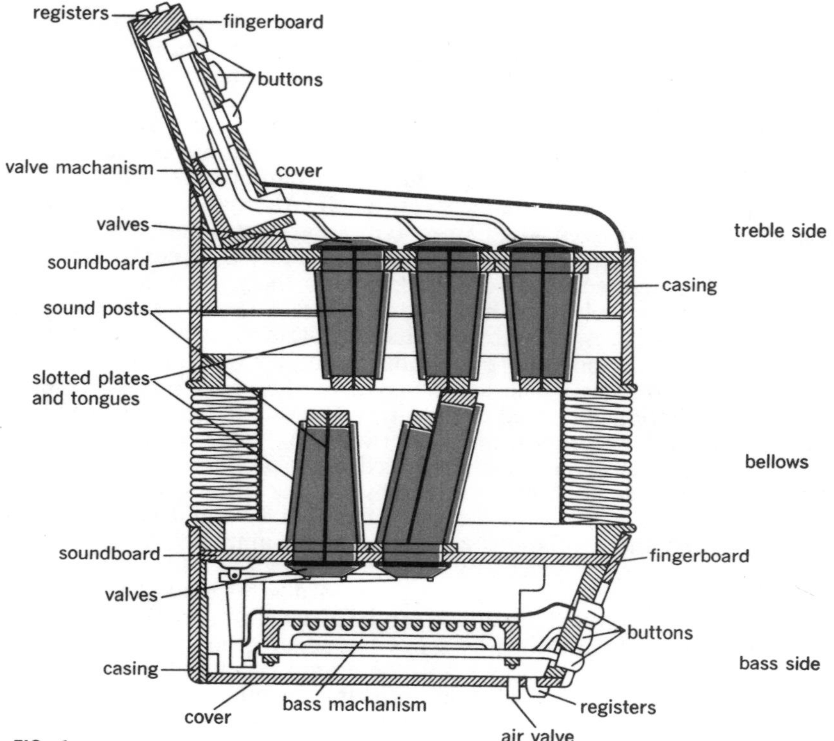
registers
fingerboard
buttons
valve machanism
cover
valves
treble side
soundboard
casing
sound posts
slotted plates
and tongues
bellows
soundboard
fingerboard
valves
buttons
bass side
casing
bass machanism
registers
cover
air valve

FIG. 1

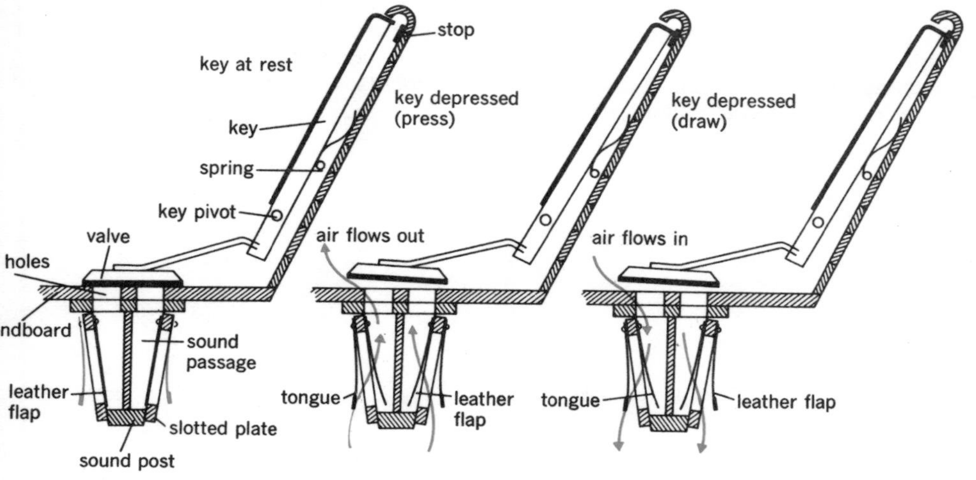
stop
key at rest
key depressed
(press)
key depressed
(draw)
key
spring
key pivot
valve
air flows out
air flows in
holes
ndboard
sound
passage
leather
flap
tongue
leather
flap
tongue
leather flap
slotted plate
sound post

FIG. 2

ELECTRONIC ORGAN

The main components of an electronic organ are a set of generators for producing electrical oscillations, one or more keyboards whereby the oscillations are passed to filters, whence they are fed to an amplifier, and finally to a loudspeaker which converts them into audible sound waves (Fig. 1). The generators for producing the electrical oscillations in the audio-frequency range consist of feedback oscillators employing electronic tubes (valves) or transistors, and are connected to frequency dividers, which are devices for producing an output wave whose frequency is a submultiple of the input frequency (Fig. 2). Alternatively, the generators may comprise so-called reed oscillators (vibrating metal reeds acting as variable capacitors) or toothed iron discs which rotate in front of electromagnets in which voltages are generated which are used to form the pitch note for each key; there are a number of such discs rotating at different speeds, each corresponding to one semitone of the equally tempered scale; other discs provide harmonics which can be added to the pitch note to produce complex tone colors.

The switch contacts which are actuated by the key of the keyboard cause the electrical oscillations to be fed to the filters. The oscillations produced by the generators contain a high proportion of overtones. By means of electronic filters those overtones are filtered out which are needed for producing certain typical sounds resembling those emitted, for example, by various string instruments and wood or metal wind instruments (Figs. 3 and 4). Through a volume-control device, usually pedal-operated, the oscillations are passed to the amplifier. In some instruments a reverberation signal, produced by a special unit, can be added to the amplifier. The amplified electrical oscillations are finally passed to the loudspeaker, which converts them into sound waves. The sounds can be given a more realistic quality by means of a vibrato device controlled by a low-frequency generator (Fig. 5). Also, devices for controlling the rate of attack and the rate of decay of the musical sounds may be provided (Fig. 6). The multiplex principle is applicable in that the individual oscillations of the generators can be utilized in multiple fashion by suitably combining and adding together the tones.

In the electronic organ provided with frequency dividers, as envisaged here, there are twelve oscillators for the top octave (twelve semitones). All the lower octaves are obtained from these oscillators by circuits which divide the frequency by two in each successive octave. In the so-called free phase system, however, one oscillator is provided for each note. The earlier electronic organs were comparatively large and bulky. With the advent of semiconductor components (transistors) it has become possible to build very compact instruments, some of which are reduced to suitcase size for convenient portability.

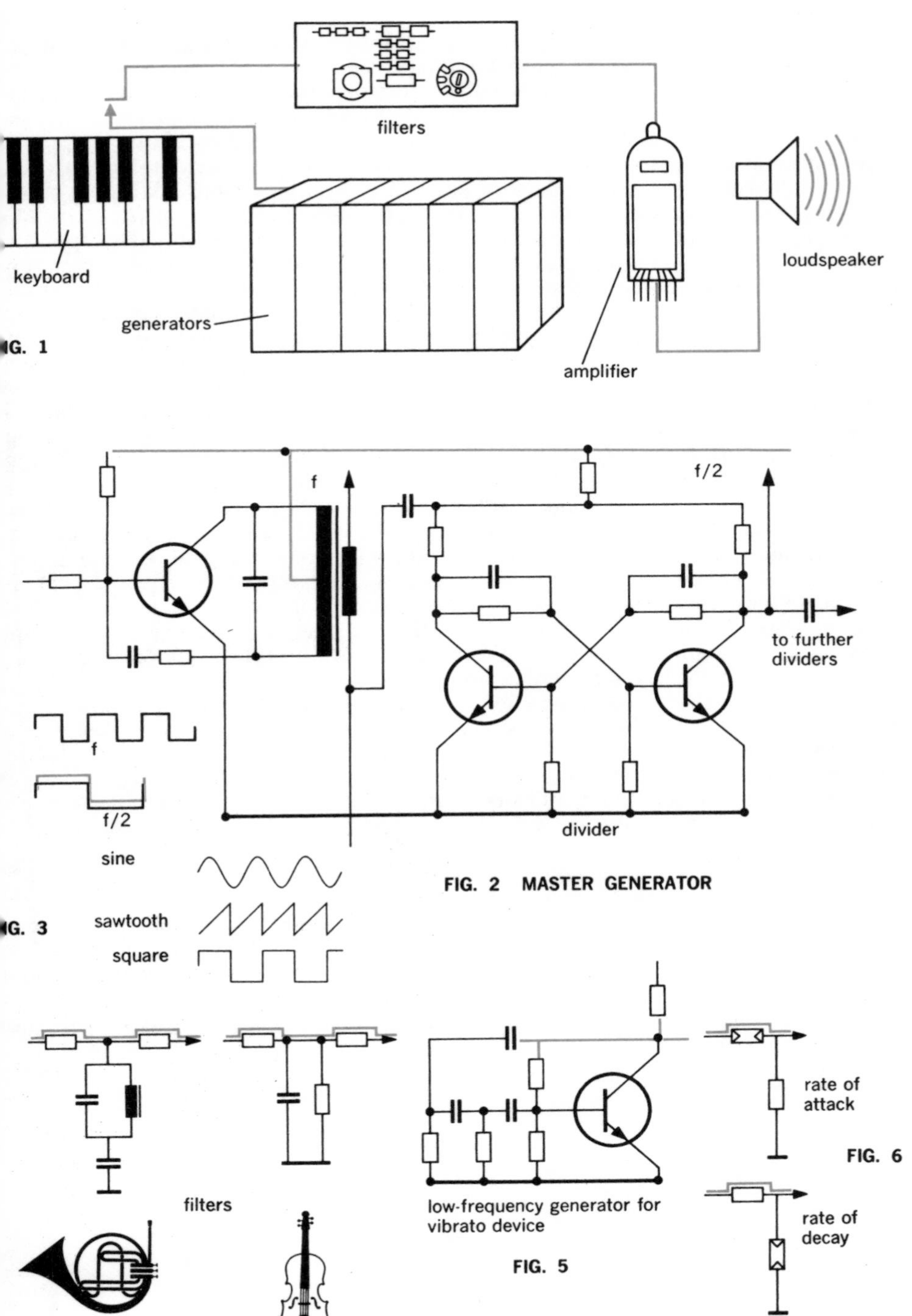
filters
keyboard
generators
loudspeaker
amplifier
FIG. 1
f
f/2
to further dividers
f
f/2
divider
FIG. 2 MASTER GENERATOR
sine
sawtooth
square
FIG. 3
filters
FIG. 4
low-frequency generator for vibrato device
FIG. 5
rate of attack
rate of decay
FIG. 6

Oscillations in the audio-frequency range are produced and processed with t aid of electronic equipment, stored on tape, and converted into audible sou waves by loudspeakers. The "material" of electronic music can, in acoustical terr be subdivided into tones, sounds, tone mixtures, sound mixtures, and noises. *To* are the simplest acoustic effect and are based on sinusoidal oscillations. They not occur in conventional music. *Sounds*, which in musical terminology are co ventionally called "tones," consist of harmonic overtones (sinusoidal tones wh frequencies bear whole-numbered ratios to one another). *Tone mixtures* conta sinusoidal tones of different, arbitrary frequencies. *Sound mixtures* correspond the chords of conventional music and consist of sounds. *Noises* are either to mixtures of very high density or have a continuous acoustic spectrum (sounds a tone mixtures have line spectra). An acoustic effect is essentially defined by fo parameters: frequency (pitch), amplitude (loudness), time (duration), and qual (timbre). Frequency is measured in cycles/second (Hertz, Hz), amplitudes in decib (db), duration in seconds or in a sound track in centimeters (cm). Timbre (to quality) is the result of the overtone composition of a sound. In a sound studio it possible to produce any frequency in the range from 1 to 20,000 cycles/second (ra of audibility: 16 to 20,000 cycles/sec.), any loudness (sound intensity) in the ra from the threshold of audibility (0 phon) to the threshold of pain (130 phons), a any sound duration from about 1/500 second upwards. Suitable measuring inst ments are available for measuring these quantities (frequency, sound, level, et The various types of apparatus for producing (generators), processing (filte modulators, etc.), storage (magnetic recorders), and reproduction (loudspeake of the sounds, as well as the measuring instruments, have for the most part be adopted and adapted from communication engineering, electroacoustics, a electrical measurement technology. Electromechanical and electronic (electrophon musical instruments serve merely to supplement the apparatus. Fig. 1 schematica shows the layout of the equipment for an electronic music studio. The precise natu and the number of the units can be varied. Each unit is manually operated, but some studios semiautomatic or fully automatic control equipment is additionally e ployed. An electronic composition generally consists of a number of "layers," wh are first produced separately and stored and are then mixed. Composing electro music comprises numerous individual operations and is quite time-consuming. T composer monitors and controls each step directly by means of loudspeakers; can immediately intervene and make such corrections as he considers necessa When the composer has completed the composition, it is ready for playing electronic reproduction equipment—no human interpreter of the music is need

Production of tone, sound and noise: The composer of electronic music alwa begins by producing the "audio" raw material. This consists essentially of sinusoid square-wave (rectangular) and sawtooth tones of various frequencies and intensiti as well as "white" (all-frequency) noise. The material either is immediately used is first stored on tape.

(mor

FIG. 1 BLOCK DIAGRAM OF AN ELECTRONIC MUSIC STUDIO (ACCORDING TO K. DIENERT)

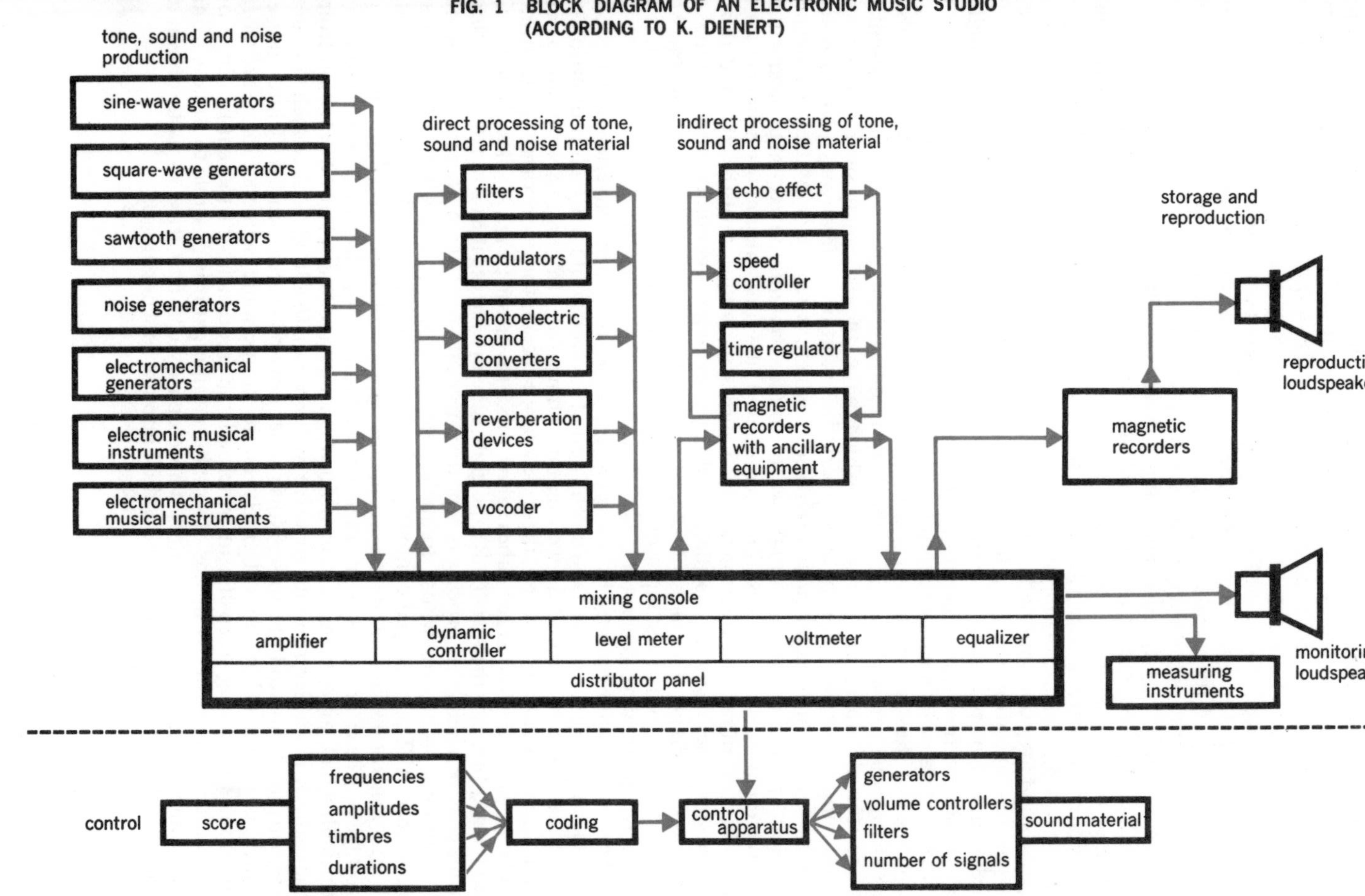

Sine-wave generators produce sinusoidal electrical oscillations in the audio-frequency range. These oscillations are reproduced as tones which have only one frequency and one amplitude per oscillation period and constitute the elementary "building blocks" of all acoustic processes (Fig. 2). A sine-wave generator consists in principle of an electron tube (valve) and an oscillatory circuit. Feedback circuits are often employed. So-called RC (resistance-capacitance) generators (or oscillators) do not use coils, their function being based solely on resistors and capacitors (Fig. 3). The frequency of the oscillations depends on the design of the oscillatory circuit and the properties of the electron tubes. Each oscillator can cover only one particular frequency range, the frequencies being capable of either continuous or stepwise variation. All frequencies in the audible range can be produced by means of an arrangement called a *beat-frequency oscillator* (Fig. 4) and comprising two high-frequency generators, a rectifier (or modulator) and a low-pass filter. Two high-frequency sinusoidal oscillations with a frequency difference of only a few cycles per second are superimposed to form what is known in acoustics as a "beat"—i.e., a periodic pulsation resulting from the interference of two wave trains of different frequency. This pulsation is then rectified; the low-pass filter suppresses the high-frequency portions. In all generators not only the frequency but also the amplitude can be regulated by means of continuously variable controls. Sometimes the building-up time and the decay time can also be adjusted. With some generators it is possible to change the sinusoidal oscillations directly into rectangular square-wave oscillations. Finally, there are generators which have an additional sweep device for producing a so-called vibrato effect (periodic variation of frequency). *Square-wave generators* produce rectangular oscillations which, when made audible by means of a loudspeaker, emerge as "square-wave" sounds containing a very high proportion of overtones. A sound of this kind is composed of a fundamental (or primary) tone and the odd-numbered overtones. Fig. 5 shows the addition of the first and third overtones; the resultant oscillation already exhibits something approaching a rectangular shape. The *multivibrator* (Fig. 6), an oscillator which comprises two stages coupled so that the input of each is derived from the output of the other, is a suitable square-wave generator.

The oscillations produced by *sawtooth generators* are, when converted into audible sound waves, perceived as "sawtooth" sounds, which contain a high proportion of overtones (even-numbered as well as odd-numbered). In contrast with sine-wave and square-wave generators, these sawtooth generators (or ramp generators) operate with gas-discharged tubes (glow tube, thyratron; Fig. 7). The capacitor C is charged through the resistor R; the glow tube discharges it as soon as its ignition voltage is reached; this process is repeated over and over again, thereby producing a sawtooth oscillation whose frequency depends on the capacitance C and the resistance R. The overtone content (timbre) of the sound produced can be varied. *Noise generators* are used for producing noise voltages (irregular alternating voltages). These are caused by random fluctuations of electrons in a conductor through which an electric current is flowing (resistance noise) or on emission from the cathode in an electron tube or valve (valve noise). In a loudspeaker such voltages are converted into audible noise. Noise generators produce so-called "white" noise, which is composed of an extremely dense nonperiodic sequence of very short impulses, of varying intensity, in which all the frequencies of the entire range of audibility are present. By means of suitable equipment it is possible to isolate, from this white noise, impulse sequences whose density can be varied so as to obtain a continuous transition from the individual impulse to white noise.

(more)

2 cycles per second (2 Hz);
duration 1.5 sec.

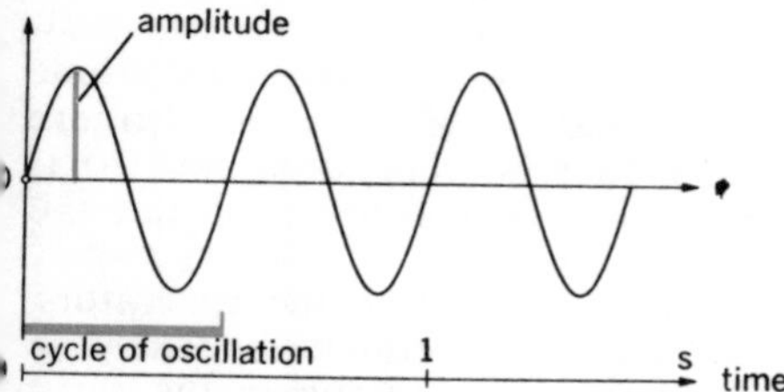

FIG. 2 SINE-WAVE OSCILLATION

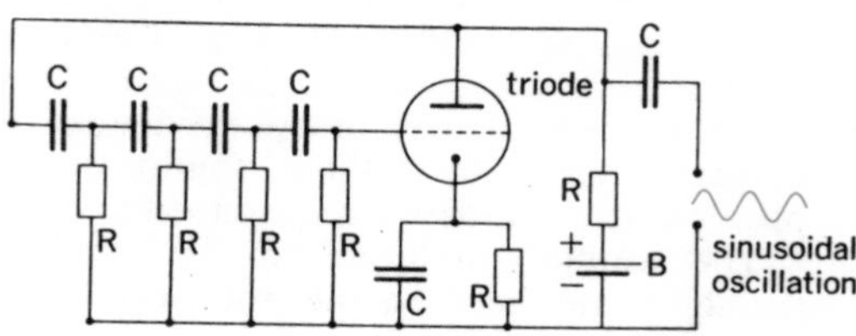

FIG. 3 SINE-WAVE GENERATOR

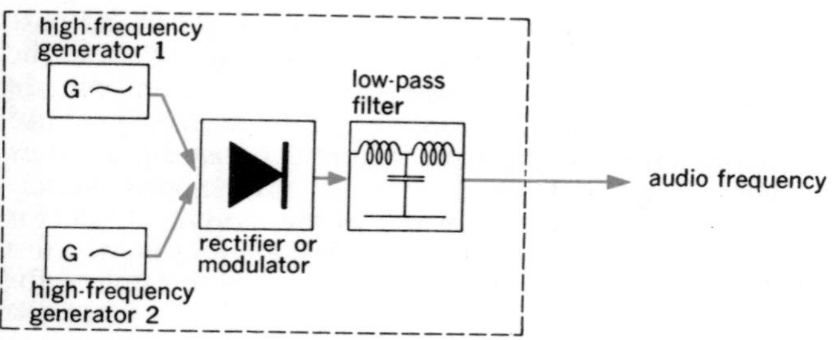

FIG. 4 BEAT-FREQUENCY OSCILLATOR

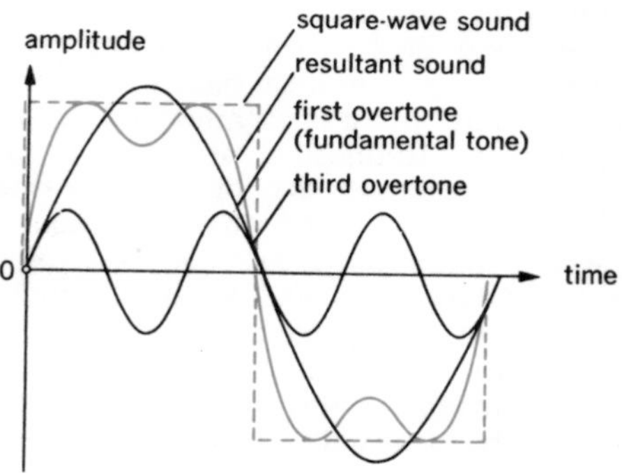

FIG. 5 ADDITION OF FIRST AND THIRD OVERTONES

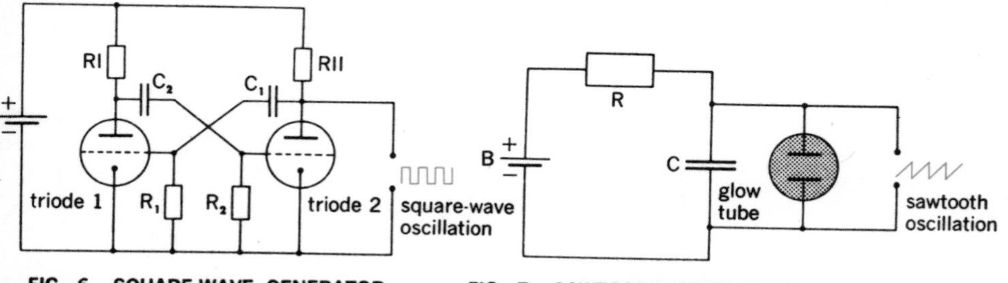

FIG. 6 SQUARE-WAVE GENERATOR (MULTIVIBRATOR)

FIG. 7 SAWTOOTH GENERATOR (DIAGRAM ILLUSTRATING PRINCIPLE)

The audio-frequency oscillations from *electromechanical generators* are produced by mechanical systems (e.g., oscillating diaphragms, rotating discs). Electromagnetic, electrostatic or photoelectric sound-pickup devices convert the mechanical oscillations into electrical oscillations. The oscillator systems are employed in electronic organs and other *electronic musical instruments* (see page 200), as also are electronic-tube generators in feedback circuits, glow-tube generators, and beat-frequency generators. Pitch, loudness and timbre can be controlled to suit the player's or composer's requirements.

The "audio" material can be directly utilized by connecting the generators, through amplifiers, to the appropriate equipment (filters, modulators, etc.). The "processing" of the material is concerned primarily with producing the tonal qualities (timbres) to give the desired musical effects. It is then stored on tape.

Electric *filters* are composed of capacitors and choke coils and are used for intensifying or suppressing certain frequency ranges (frequency bands). A low-pass filter (Fig. 8) allows only frequencies below a certain predetermined value to pass, whereas a high-pass filter (Fig. 9) allows only high frequencies to pass. The band-pass filter (Fig. 10) allows a certain frequency band—bounded on both the high- and the low-frequency side—to pass and suppresses all other frequencies. Tone-control (actually timbre-control) devices and equalizers (antidistortion devices) are also forms of filter. In the studio, combinations comprising a number of band-pass filters connected in parallel are mainly employed, which together cover approximately the whole range of audible frequencies. The band width of the individual filters is usually equivalent to a third or an octave—hence the designations "one-third octave filter" and "octave filter." It is advantageous to be able to control the amplitude of each individual filter, e.g., the Albis variable filter (Fig. 11). With the aid of filters it is possible to obtain sounds having a particular overtone structure—i.e., a particular desired timbre—from "audio" material with a high content of overtones. Certain frequency bands can be filtered out of "white" (colorless) noise so that "colored" noise is obtained, which possesses timbre ("sound color").

Modulators: Modulation produces a major change in the given frequency spectrum—more particularly by the process termed multiplicative mixing, as distinct from additive mixing in which the frequencies are merely superimposed upon one another. If a sound (frequencies 50, 100, 150 cycles/sec.) is modulated with a carrier frequency of 160 cycles/sec., a sound combination with the frequencies 210, 260, 310 and 110, 60, 10 cycles/sec. is obtained. All the frequencies are displaced to a different range (upwards and downwards); intervals between the several frequencies remain unchanged, but the ratios of the frequencies are altered. Multiplicative mixing is often done by means of a so-called ring modulator (or double-balanced modulator). The *frequency converter* (Fig. 12) functions on the same principle, except that it suppresses one of the two newly formed frequency bands (side bands), so that either the sum or the difference (in absolute value) can be obtained separately.

(more)

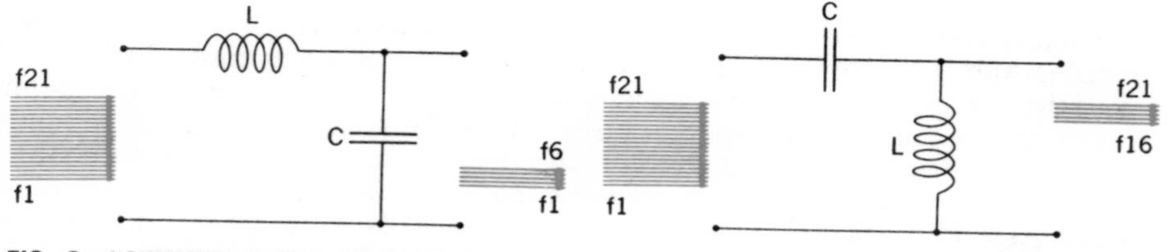

FIG. 8 LOW-PASS FILTER (PRINCIPLE)

FIG. 9 HIGH-PASS FILTER (PRINCIPLE)

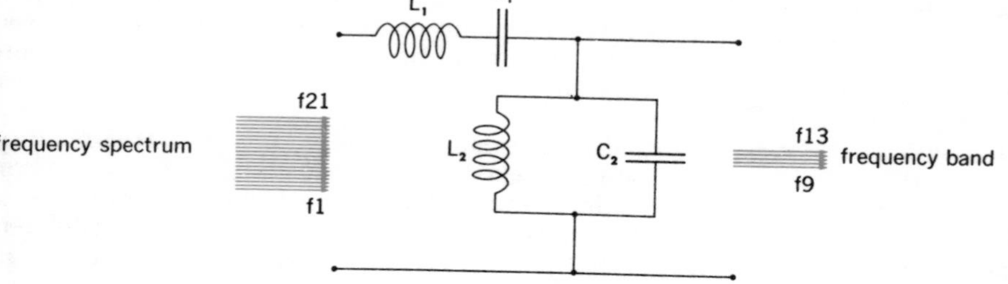

FIG. 10 BAND-PASS FILTER (PRINCIPLE)

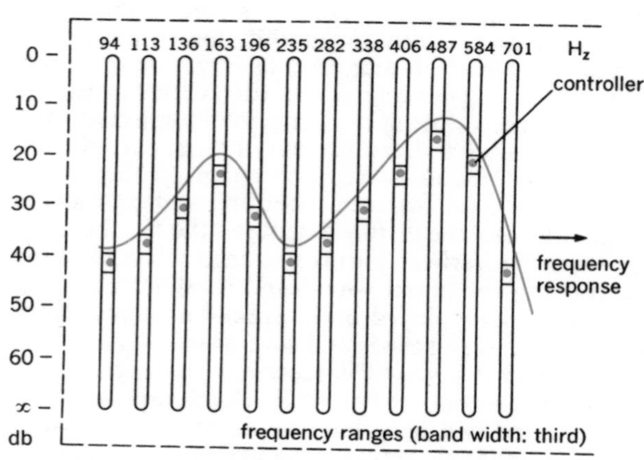

FIG. 11 ALBIS VARIABLE FILTER (PORTION OF SCALE)

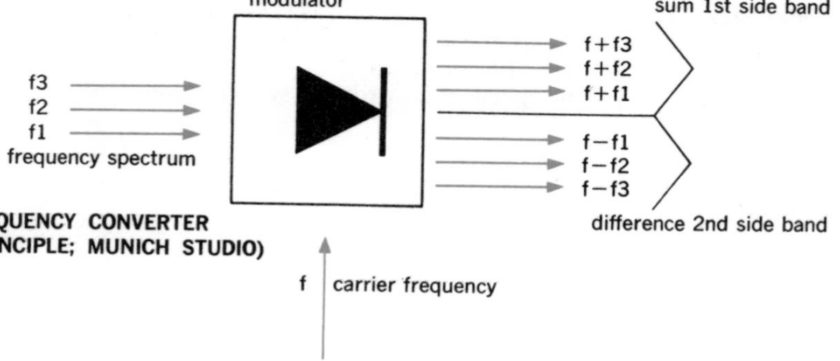

FIG. 12 FREQUENCY CONVERTER (PRINCIPLE; MUNICH STUDIO)

Photoelectric sound converters: In the *photomodulator* (Fig. 13) the cathode-ray oscillograph is controlled by audio-frequency electrical oscillations which, together with the sawtooth oscillation generated in the apparatus, produces a corresponding oscillogram on the screen of the cathode-ray tube. This oscillogram (i.e., the luminous pattern produced on the screen) is focused by lenses on the photocathode of a photomultiplier, a device which converts the image into electrical oscillations (see Vol. I, page 140). The image can be varied by means of control devices on the oscillograph; in this way the timbre of a given sound can be continuously varied. In a *picture scanner* a diapositive (transparency) is scanned point by point by means of an electron beam which can be controlled either by electrical oscillations or by hand. The light-transmitting capacity of each individual point of the diapositive image is different from that of other points, depending on the composition of the image. A photoelectric cell records the fluctuations of brightness and converts them into electrical oscillations. The picture composition determines the contents of overtones (timbre) of the sound produced.

Reverberation devices: A loudspeaker emits the sound into a reverberation chamber (Fig. 14). Part of the sound is picked up directly by a microphone and part of it is reflected from the walls of the chamber. The reflected sound waves reach the microphone slightly later, thus producing an echo effect (reverberation). In a different type of reverberation device a metal plate (*reverberation plate*) is made to vibrate by electrical means. An acoustic pickup converts the mechanical vibrations into electrical oscillations. The echo effect is produced by the dying away of the vibrations of the plate. A *vocoder* is a device comprising filters, modulators and two generators (impulse generator, noise generator) which is used in the studio for special modulation processes, more particularly for modulation of speech with sound and noises.

"Audio" material stored on magnetic tape can be modified to produce an *echo effect* by means of a magnetic tape recorder with feedback circuit (Fig. 15); the recording head and reproducing head are interconnected. A sound is recorded on the tape and is then, after a short interval of time, played back by the reproducing head. The reproduced sound is recorded again on the same tape; this process is repeated. The time interval between recording and reproduction is determined by the speed of the tape and the distance between the two heads. If this interval is very short, an echo effect (reverberation) is obtained when the tape with the composite recording comprising the initial sound and its slightly delayed second and subsequent recordings is finally played back. Special machines embodying this principle operate with very high tape speeds and several sets of heads.

Tape-speed control: If a sound is recorded on magnetic tape at a speed of, for example, $7\frac{1}{2}$ inches per second and played back at a tape speed of 15 inches per second, the played-back sound will have half the duration and twice the frequency of the original sound. The intervals between the various frequencies composing the sound are likewise doubled, the frequency band is widened, and the buildup and dying-out effects are altered. On the other hand, the frequency ratios remain unchanged. Playback of the tape at reduced speed has the opposite result. Special tape-recording and playback equipment embodies continuous ("infinitely variable") speed control from 0 to 60 inches per second by means of a suitable amplifier with a sine-wave generator (frequency range approx. 15 to 100 cycles/sec.). The synchronous motors driving the tape vary their speed in accordance with the frequency.

(more)

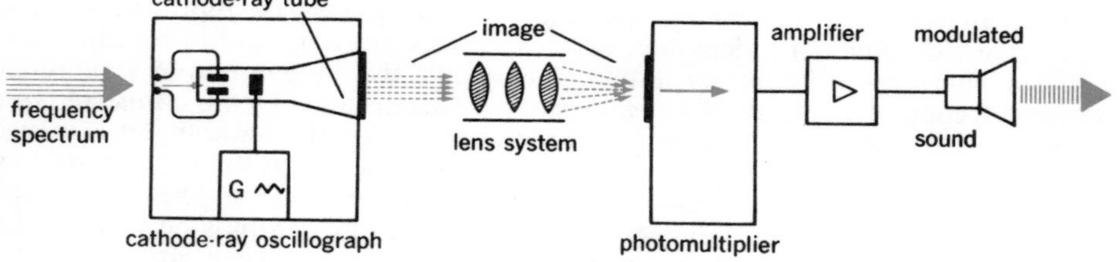

FIG. 13 PHOTOMODULATOR (DARMSTADT STUDIO)

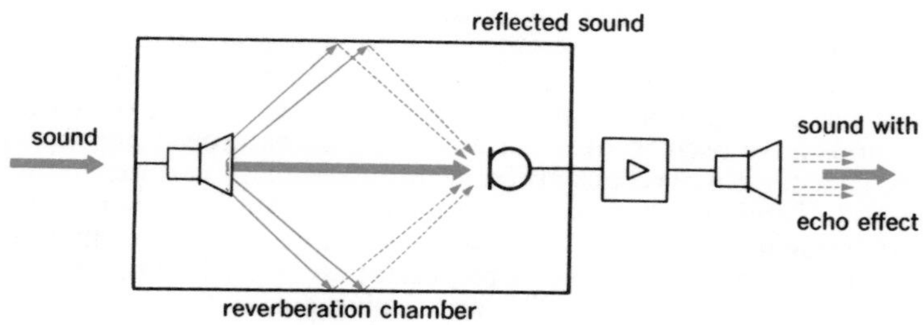

FIG. 14 REVERBERATION CHAMBER

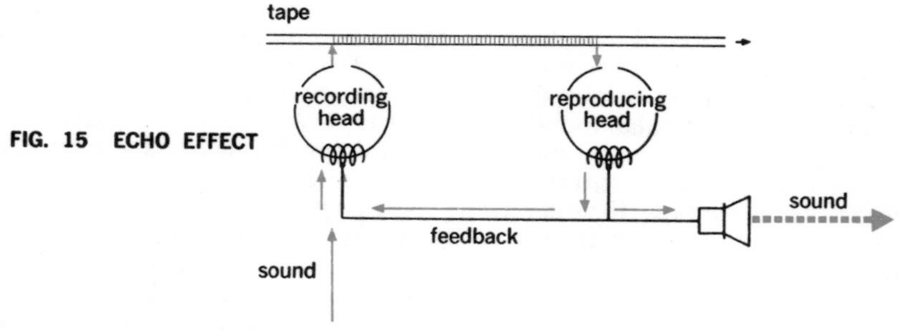

FIG. 15 ECHO EFFECT

FIG. 16 REPRODUCING HEAD WITH FOUR SCANNERS FOR TIME REGULATOR (ACCORDING TO SPRINGER)

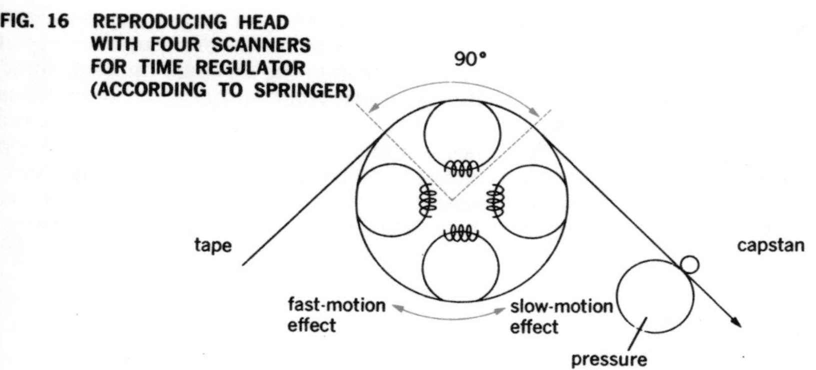

As an alternative to varying the speed, it is possible to vary the reproduction time of a recorded sound—i.e., lengthen or shorten its duration—within certain limits without altering the frequency (pitch). This is effected by continuous ("infinitely variable") control by means of a *time regulator*. This device, which is connected to a tape recorder, comprises a cylindrical reproducing head with four scanners disposed around its circumference (Fig. 16, p. 209). The tape is passed around the head at an angle of 90 degrees and is in contact with only one scanner at a time. The reproducing head can be rotated in both directions; the scanning rate can thus be varied independently of the tape speed. To increase the reproduction time, any particular section of the tape is scanned a number of times; conversely, to shorten the reproduction time, certain sections are skipped. A variant of the time regulator is the tone-pitch regulator, a device whereby the frequencies of a sound can be transposed without changing the reproduction time.

A wide range of effects can be obtained by the suitable cutting and editing of magnetic tape recordings. In this way it is possible to control the rhythm, the buildup and dying-out effects, and the enveloping curves of the recorded sound. Fig. 17a illustrates the editing of an impulse sequence: strips of tape of selected length, on which sounds have been recorded, are stuck to blank tape at appropriately selected intervals. At a certain playback speed of this assembly, a certain rhythm is obtained. The method of splicing the tape also has an effect: straight splices produce abrupt, or "hard," transitions (Fig. 17b), whereas oblique splices produce more gradual, or "soft," transitions (Fig. 17c), in respect of both the buildup and the dying out of particular sound sequences. The enveloping curves (or envelopes) can likewise be modified to some extent by cutting the tape to vary its width (Fig. 17d). (The envelope is the curve enclosing the peak values of a high-frequency oscillation.) Looped tapes can be used to give any desired number of repetitions of recorded sound sequences.

Using "audio" material stored on tape, the composer of electronic music determines the timing and overall dynamic structure of his composition and applies such corrections as may be necessary (blending in of sounds, adjusting the volume, intensifying or attenuating certain frequency ranges by means of equalizers, fading in and fading out of particular sounds). *Mixing* the various "layers" of an electronic musical composition is done by means of several synchronized tape recorders or by means of a four-track instrument whereby the recordings on three tapes are recorded on the fourth tape, the operations being controlled from a mixing console. Fig. 18 schematically shows that re-recording procedure. First, the sound sequence is recorded, through the stereo reproducing head, on to the bottom track of the tape. The tape is then rewound and again run through the recorder; this time the recording is transferred through the full-track recording head, amplifier and stereo reproducing head to the top track. At the same time another sound sequence can be recorded on the bottom track, as the full-track erasing head has meanwhile wiped the tape clean. During the third run of the tape through the machine the two sound recordings are mixed and transferred to the top track, while another sound sequence can again be recorded on the bottom track. Each time the tape is run through the machine, the last recorded sound sequence is added to the previous one on the top track (additive mixing), while a fresh sequence can be recorded on the bottom track. During the recording operations the composer can monitor the sounds both before and after final recording and apply such corrections as he considers necessary.

(more)

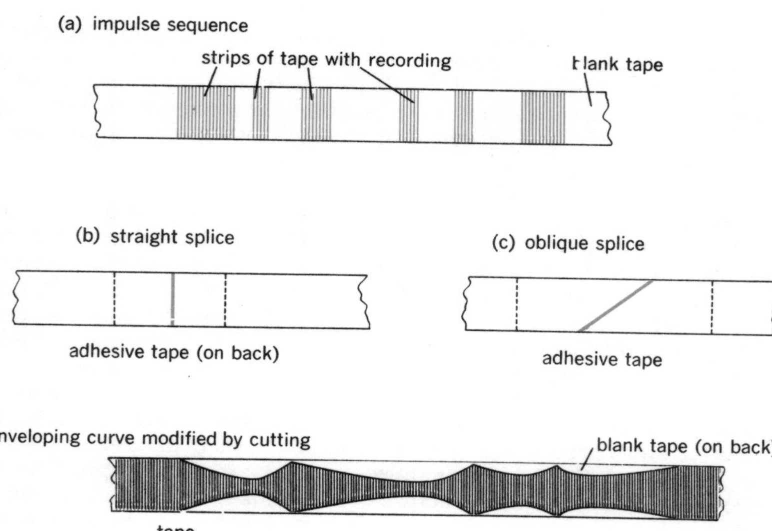

FIG. 17 TAPE CUTTING AND EDITING

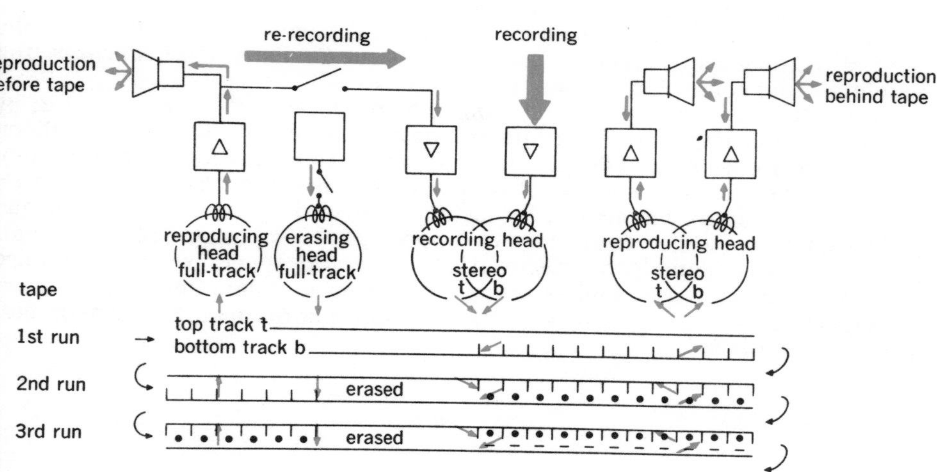

FIG. 18 SPECIAL TAPE-RECORDING APPARATUS (PRINCIPLE) (ACCORDING TO HEISS/VOLLMER)

Storage and reproduction: Recording the electronic composition on magnetic or perforated magnetic film is the final stage of the process. Reproduction of the composition may be monaural (single-channel), in which only one loudspeaker (or set of speakers) is used; with stereophonic (or binaural) reproduction two channels are used; some systems use four reproduction channels. With these multichannel systems two or more loudspeakers are suitably positioned in the room or hall, whereby a "three-dimensional" effect can be obtained.

Control: In recent years, electronic data-processing equipment has been utilized for automatically controlling the production process. Computers and punched-tape equipment are used for the purpose. Such apparatus comprises generators, volume regulators and filters which are controlled by punched tape; for this it is necessary first to convert the frequencies, amplitudes, timbres and durations into a suitable code system. By means of automatic control systems it is possible to produce highly differentiated musical compositions; for instance, four hundred variations in pitch, volume and timbre per second can be achieved by means of punched-tape control.

Notation: The score of an electronic musical composition contains precise instructions for the technical production, represented in the form of diagrams provided with numerical data, symbols and explanatory notes. The method of presentation varies and depends primarily on the structure of the composition. The example of a score presented in Fig. 19 is read from top to bottom (time values in centimeters, referred to a tape speed of 19 cm or 7½ inches per second) and from right to left (loudness in decibels; 0 db = minimum damping, i.e., maximum loudness). The frequencies are indicated at the beginning of the respective sounds. The line diagram indicates the loudness as a function of time.

In the score illustrated in Fig. 20, only the enveloping curves (volume-time curves) of the sound sequence are indicated, distributed over four channels (tracks). Each of the four channels is played back over a separate loudspeaker. The figures relate to the "audio" material for which the frequencies, timbres, amplitudes and time values are separately recorded in another score.

Fig. 21 indicates data for preparing a punched tape which will automatically control the frequency ranges of the filters (timbre). Similarly, the frequencies and amplitudes are controlled by other punched tapes.

Electronic music may also, within limits, be produced without a score—i.e., by a process of free improvisation by the composer, who records his work directly on tape. There are no hard-and-fast rules or clear-cut standards for the composition of electronic music. The character of an electronic composition depends not only on the composer's ideas, but also on the facilities provided by the studio; artistic and technical factors have an equal share in the process of composing. True "electronic music" is based entirely on electronically produced sound, whereas so-called "musique concrète" uses sounds actually occurring in nature and in human environment (train whistles, factory sirens, automobile horns, industrial sounds, etc.) as its "raw material."

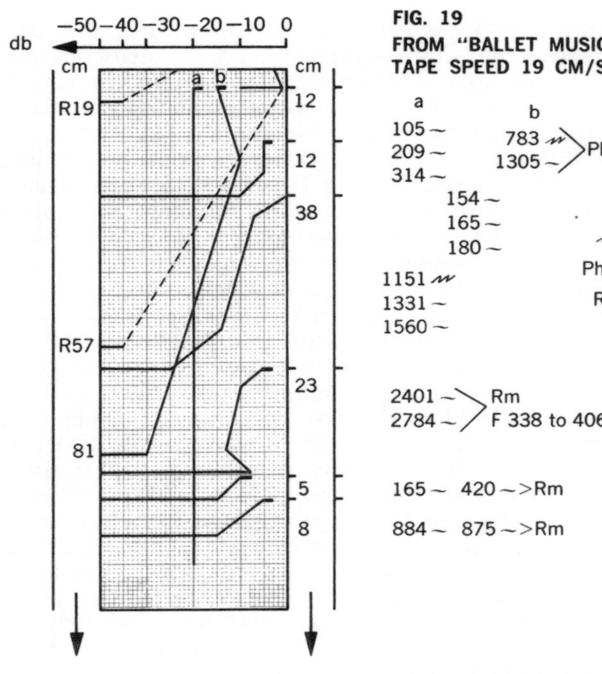

FIG. 19
FROM "BALLET MUSIC" BY H. HEISS, DARMSTADT, TAPE SPEED 19 CM/SEC.

a
b
105 ~
209 ~
314 ~
783 ≁ > Phm
1305 ~
154 ~
165 ~
180 ~
1151 ≁
1331 ~
1560 ~
2401 ~ > Rm
2784 ~ F 338 to 406 Hz
165 ~ 420 ~ >Rm
884 ~ 875 ~ >Rm

~ = sinusoidal frequency
≁ = sawtooth frequency
Phm = photomodulator
Rm = ring modulator
R = reverberation
F = filter

FIG. 20 FROM "ZUORDNUNG VIER" BY H. HEISS, DARMSTADT

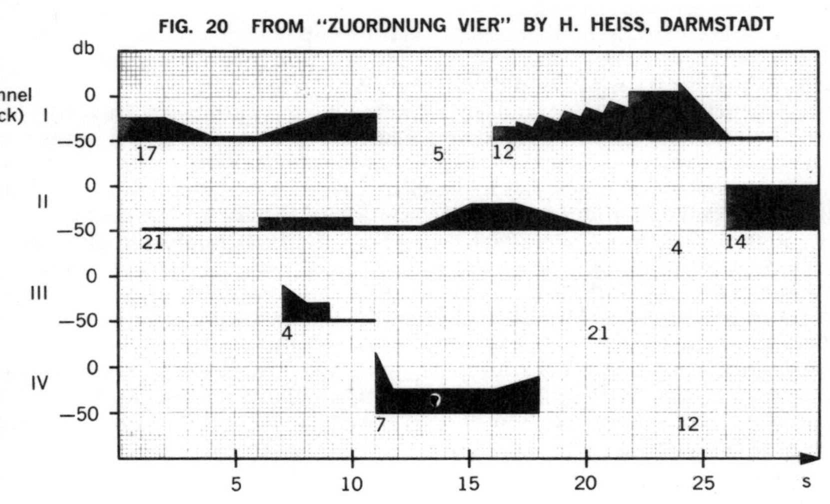

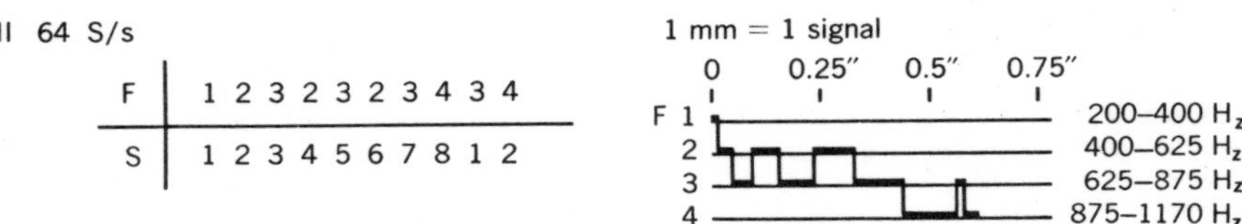

F	1	2	3	2	3	2	3	4	3	4
S	1	2	3	4	5	6	7	8	1	2

FIG. 21 FROM "COMPOSITION NO. 2" BY J. A. RIEDL, MUNICH

III = punched-tape loop III
F = filter
F1 = filter 1
64 S/s = 64 signals per second
S = signal
S2 = 2 signals

HIGH FIDELITY

The term "high fidelity" ("hi-fi") is applied to sound recording and reproducing equipment whereby a reasonably faithful reproduction of the quality of the original sound can be obtained. Oscillations, however complex they may be, can always be conceived as the sum of various pure sine and cosine oscillations (the latter are of precisely the same shape as sine oscillations, but are displaced one-quarter of a wavelength in relation to them). This possibility of splitting up any oscillation into an assembly of sine (and cosine) oscillations (Fig. 1) is important because the electronic components which are used for the transfer of oscillations can retransmit pure sine oscillations as oscillations which are again at least approximately sinusoidal in form, but amplified by a factor depending on the frequency and delayed by a length of time likewise depending on the frequency (Fig. 2). Such components are referred to as "linear" transfer elements; their performance is fully characterized by the amplification and the delay (phase displacement) as a function of the frequency. Together these two data determine the frequency response of the equipment (in Fig. 2 only the amplification response, not the phase response, is indicated). The "overall frequency response" of a high-fidelity system is determined by the product of the amplification responses and by the sum of the phase responses of all the transfer elements. The system should provide constant amplification and phase displacement (delay) over the entire range of audibility (approx. 16 to 20,000 cycles/sec.). Since the frequency dependence of the amplification is generally linked to the frequency dependence of the phase displacement, the amplification must not suddenly decrease at the limits of the audibility range, for otherwise phase displacements will occur within that range. This is especially important for stereophonic reproduction, inasmuch as the "three-dimensional" effect is produced partly by particular phase relations between the two channels corresponding to the hearer's left and right ears respectively. Between the amplification response and the phase response of the system there must exist a mathematical relationship which ensures that in the "overall frequency response" a constant amplification over a certain range is associated with a constant phase displacement within that range.

Rigorously linear behavior of transfer elements is an idealization. In reality the pure sine oscillations will always undergo some distortion. Thus, if a sinusoidal voltage is applied to a loudspeaker, the diaphragm responds accurately to the voltage only at low amplitudes. With increasing amplitudes the deflection of the diaphragm reaches a maximum value; the variation of the acoustic pressure is then no longer sinusoidal, but has flattened peaks (Fig. 3). Such nonlinear distortions, once they have developed, can—in contrast to linear distortions—be corrected only in exceptional cases. This is done, for example, in certain disc-recording procedures: the oscillations to be recorded are so distorted prior to recording that the nonlinear distortions which subsequently occur are largely compensated. The oscillation which results from nonlinear distortion of a sinusoidal oscillation can be resolved into a number of purely sinusoidal oscillations in the manner shown in Fig. 1. For each transfer element, the proportion of higher frequencies produced by nonlinear distortion can be stated as a percentage.

(more)

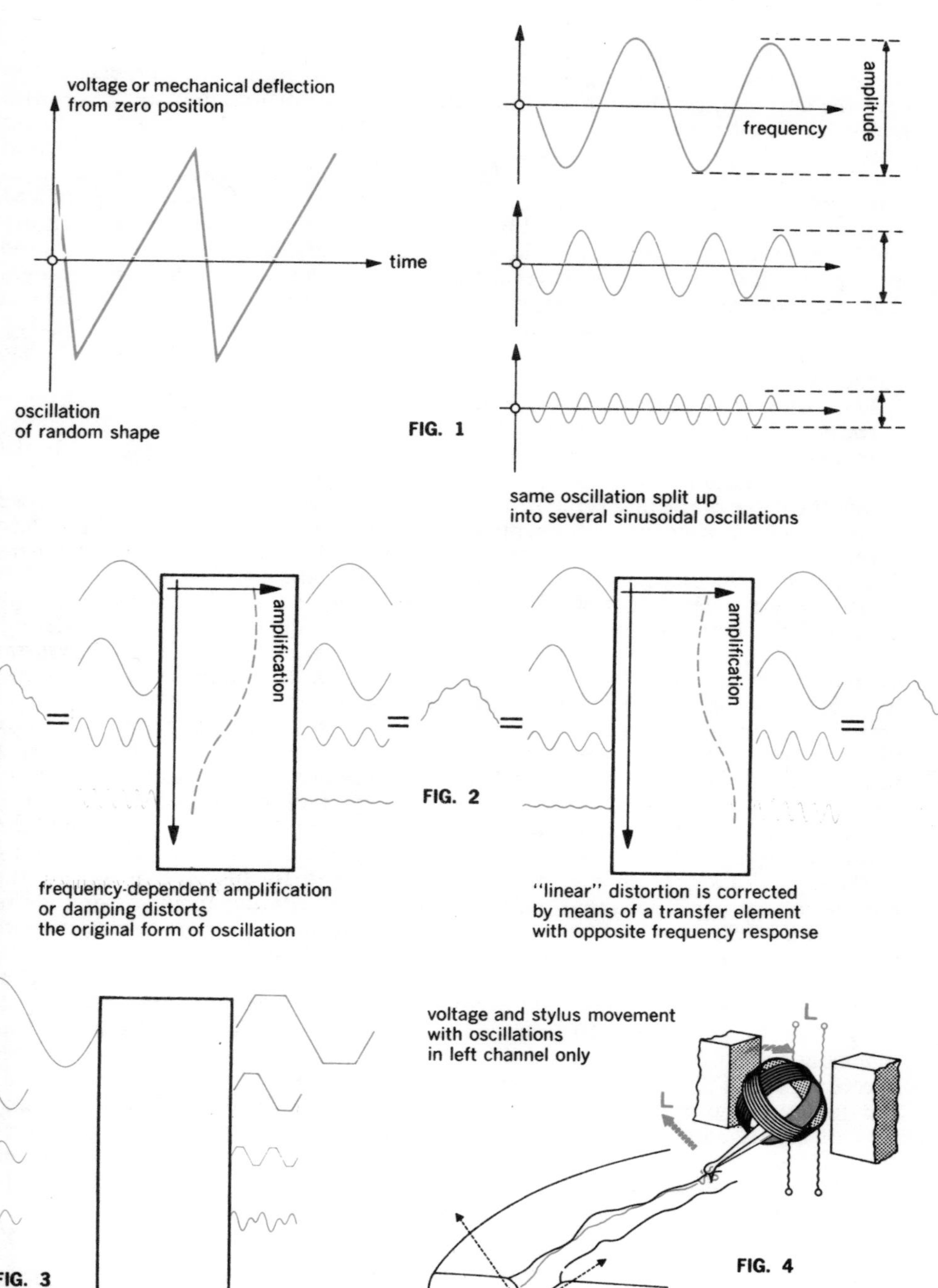
voltage or mechanical deflection
from zero position
time
oscillation
of random shape
FIG. 1
amplitude
frequency
same oscillation split up
into several sinusoidal oscillations
amplification
amplification
FIG. 2
frequency-dependent amplification
or damping distorts
the original form of oscillation
"linear" distortion is corrected
by means of a transfer element
with opposite frequency response
FIG. 3
nonlinear transfer elements
cause distortion even of
purely sinusoidal oscillations
voltage and stylus movement
with oscillations
in left channel only
L
L
FIG. 4
magnetic pickup and movement
of stylus in a stereo groove

This is called the distortion factor and should not exceed 1% in the case of high-fidelity systems. The whole object of hi-fi technique is to attain faithful reproduction over the entire range of audibility (minimum linear distortion) in conjunction with minimum distortion of the individual frequency components (minimum nonlinear distortion). Simpler amateur equipment will generally give faithful reproduction only of a narrower range of audio frequencies (standard broadcast radio up to 9000 cycles/sec.; record players approx. 50 to 5000 cycles/sec.). The sound reproduced by such equipment is "darker" and lacking in clarity, but the nonlinear distortions, which are much more objectionable, are reduced in advance, since they are caused more particularly at low frequencies and high frequencies—i.e., the frequency ranges that such equipment does not reproduce at all. Ultrashort-wave radio (VHS) can transmit audio frequencies ranging from approx. 30 to 15,000 cycles/sec., but few amateur receivers are actually able to reproduce the whole of this range of frequencies.

The reduction of distortion by technical measures will be explained with reference to the example of a record player (see also Vol. II, page 14). Fig. 4 (page 215) shows a stereo groove and the needle movement it produces in a magnetic pickup. In the case of a monaural phonograph record (or disc), only a radial movement component within the plane of the disc is recorded, whereas the groove of a stereophonic record comprises two movement components which are inclined at 45 degrees to the surface of the disc, each component corresponding to one of the two reproduction channels. The magnetic or electromagnetic pickup separates the two components: i.e., it transmits two independent signals, which are amplified and fed to two separate loudspeakers. This separation is achieved as follows: if the left channel is oscillating, whereas the right channel is receiving no signals, the needle (or stylus) will perform the movement indicated by the thick red arrow in Fig. 4. This causes the black coil to rotate in its plane; in doing this it intersects no magnetic lines of force and so no voltage is induced in this coil. The red coil L is so rotated that the magnetic flux (the number of magnetic lines of force) passing through the coil changes. As a result of this change a voltage is induced which is proportional to the velocity of the needle. The crystal pickup (Fig. 5) utilizes the piezoelectric effect (see Vol. I, p. 104 and II, 16). The resilient W-shaped coupling element ensures that each of the two mutually perpendicular movement components causes flexing movement only of the crystal assigned to that particular component. In this type of pickup, the output voltage is proportional not to the needle velocity but to the magnitude of the needle's deflection from its neutral position. Accurate proportionality is more difficult to achieve than with the magnetic pickup. Besides, with the crystal the counteracting force to the deflection of the needle is greater, so that much higher contact pressure between disc and needle is needed to guide the latter properly in the groove: between 5 and 10 grams, as compared with as little as 0.5 gram for the magnetic pickup. Stereo records should not be subjected to needle-contact pressures exceeding about 5 grams, as these are liable to damage the groove and thus impair the quality of the record. This deterioration first affects the higher frequencies and may at first remain undetected in amateur equipment which does not reproduce these frequencies. More recently, ceramic pickups have been developed which operate with contact pressures of about 3 grams and are not much inferior to magnetic pickup systems as regards freedom from distortion.

(more)

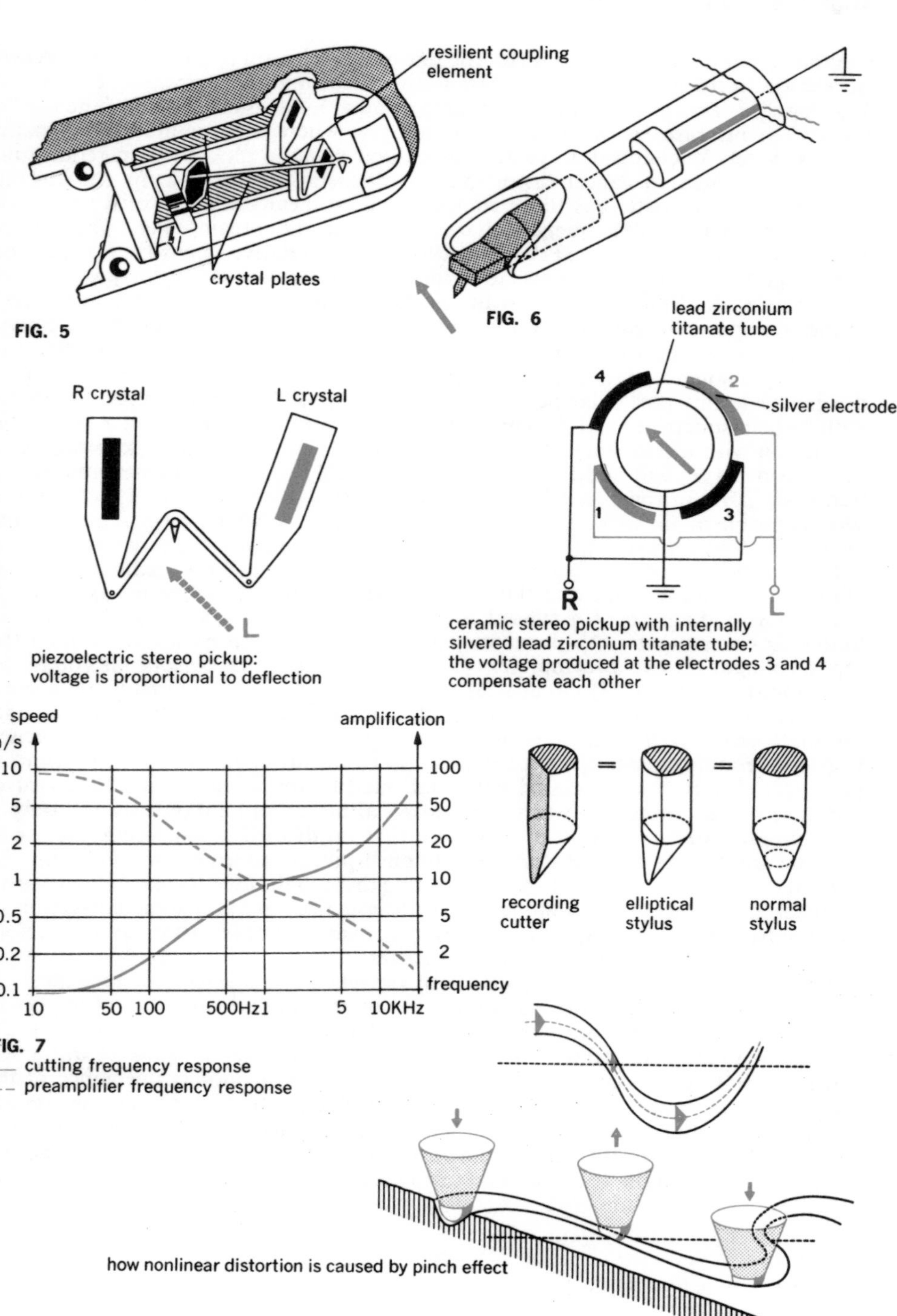
resilient coupling element
crystal plates
FIG. 5
FIG. 6
lead zirconium titanate tube
4
2
silver electrode
1
3
R
L
R crystal
L crystal
L
piezoelectric stereo pickup:
voltage is proportional to deflection
ceramic stereo pickup with internally
silvered lead zirconium titanate tube;
the voltage produced at the electrodes 3 and 4
compensate each other
speed
cm/s
amplification
10
5
2
1
0.5
0.2
0.1
100
50
20
10
5
2
frequency
10
50 100
500Hz1
5 10KHz
FIG. 7
cutting frequency response
preamplifier frequency response
recording cutter
elliptical stylus
normal stylus
how nonlinear distortion is caused by pinch effect

FIG. 8

When a phonograph record is cut, the low frequencies are intentionally weakened in relation to the high ones, as appears from the cutting frequency characteristic in Fig. 7, p. 217. This means that for the same original loudness the speed of the needle (or stylus) increases with increasing frequency, whereas the amplitudes remain approximately unchanged. Crystal pickups and ceramic pickups then require no corrective devices to cancel distortion. In magnetic pickup systems the cutting frequency characteristic has to be compensated by means of a corrective network with a counteracting frequency characteristic in the preamplifier. The higher frequencies are thereby toned down to their correct relative intensity; this has the advantage that background noise (due to surface irregularities or dust) is reduced.

Nonlinear distortions occur already in the process of transfer of the movement to the pickup needle (sapphire or diamond): the shape of the recording cutter causes the width of the groove to remain constant in the radial direction, but there is nevertheless some variation in width measured perpendicularly to the direction of the groove at any particular point thereof (Fig. 8, p. 217). Hence the pickup needle with its hemispherical head dips more or less deeply into the groove. If a sinusoidal oscillation with a frequency W is recorded and played back, the pickup needle of the record player will additionally perform vertical oscillatory movements with a frequency 2 W. In the case of "mono" pickups this so-called pinch effect is not a serious problem, but with "stereo" pickup equipment, in which vertical movements also have to be resolved into "right" and "left" components, the pinch effect must —for high-fidelity reproduction—be reduced by use of a pickup needle that has an elliptically rounded shape and thus more closely resembles the recording cutter.

Fig. 9 is a diagram of a typical high-fidelity amplifier system comprising the following components: (1) filter sections with large capacitors for smoothing the input voltage; (2) two preamplifiers (a magnetic pickup has an output voltage of only about 0.01 volt); (3) circuits for obtaining a frequency characteristic corresponding to the dotted curve in Fig. 7; (4) separately adjustable transfer elements for high and low frequency range, for compensation of loudspeaker frequency response, room acoustics, etc.; (5) push-pull output stage for compensation of nonlinear distortions associated with high modulation of individual tube (valve) outputs; power output 15 watts and more—although only about 3 watts output is required in ordinary rooms—to ensure that no distortion will occur even with extreme amplitudes of short duration; (6) push-pull transformer for combining the currents from the two output tubes and suiting them to the loudspeakers; (7) negative feedback for reducing the nonlinear distortions: also provides some correction of the loudspeaker's defects, but reduces the overall amplification and therefore necessitates a large number of amplifier stages.

The reproduction of low frequencies by detached loudspeakers or loudspeakers mounted in small open cabinets is impaired by the mutual canceling of the direct and the indirect compression wave (Fig. 10). This can be avoided by installing the speaker in an enclosed cabinet or an acoustic baffle. A large loudspeaker with good low-frequency reproduction, on the other hand, gives a poor performance in the high-frequency range; if its diaphragm is very flexible, at high frequencies only a limited zone around the moving coil is effectively actuated. On the other hand, a rigid diaphragm does indeed move as a single unit even at high frequencies, but the amplitudes remain small because of the greater inertia to be overcome.

(more)

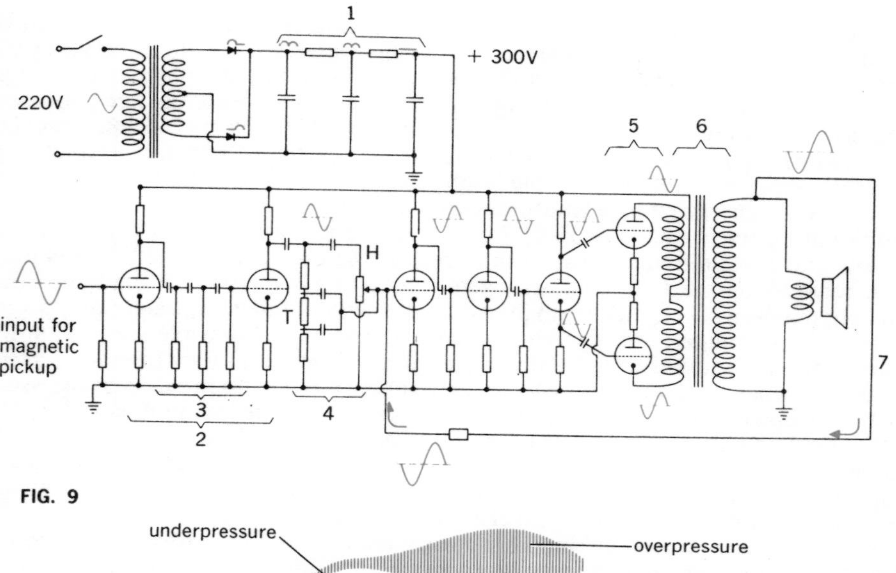

FIG. 9

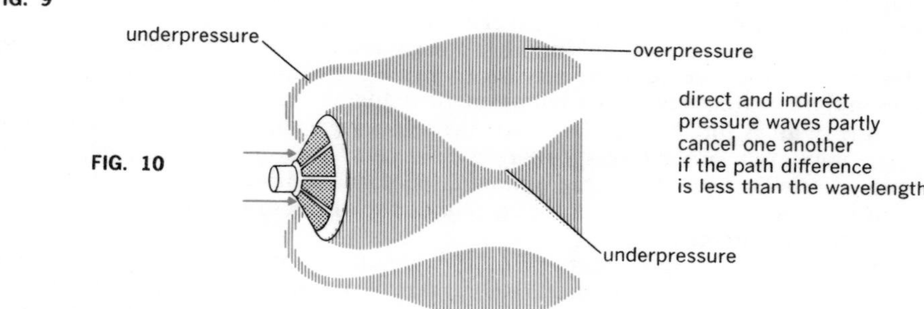

FIG. 10

FIG. 12

3
2
1

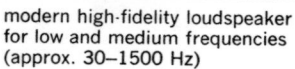

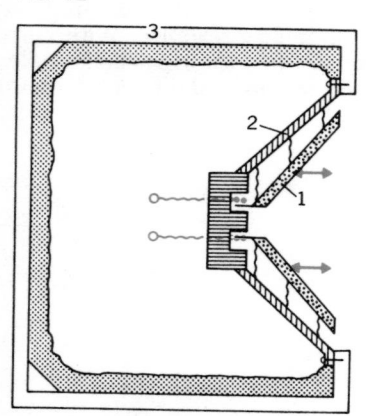

modern high-fidelity loudspeaker
for low and medium frequencies
(approx. 30–1500 Hz)

FIG. 11

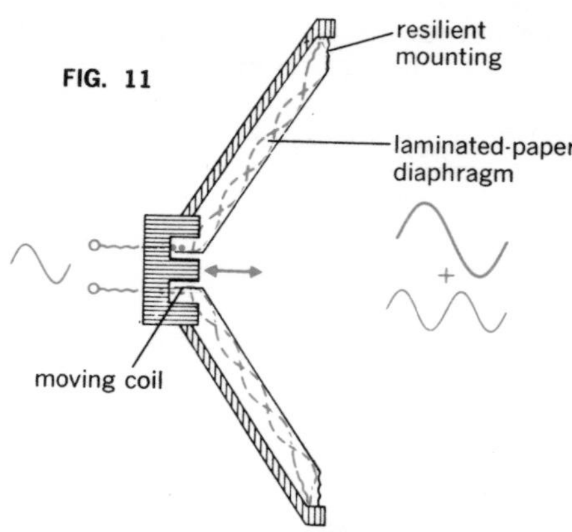

formation of harmonic oscillations
due to nodes in the diaphragm
of an ordinary loudspeaker

In a wide-range loudspeaker the frequency range is increased by subdivision of the diaphragm into a rigid inner and a flexible outer zone, with a very flexible transition region in between. At high frequencies only the inner part vibrates; at low frequencies the whole diaphragm is actuated. A more consistent solution consists in dividing the incoming frequency mixture between special loudspeakers for low and for high frequencies with the aid of electrical filter circuits. The laminated paper diaphragm (cone) of a simple loudspeaker tends to develop harmonic components when energized by a sinusoidal oscillation (Fig. 11, p. 219) and thus to emit additional higher frequencies. Fig. 12 (p. 219) illustrates a high-fidelity loudspeaker for low and middle frequencies; in this speaker the above-mentioned defects have been reduced by the following arrangements: (1) rigid diaphragm made of thick but light material (1 cm thick foam plastic coated with tinfoil, total weight only about 10 grams) to obviate harmonic components; (2) very flexible triple suspension for exact centering and ensuring accurately axial movement and for obtaining a resonance frequency at the bottom end of the frequency range (approx. 25 cycles/sec.); (3) thick cabinet stiffened by ribs and corner blocks, to obviate harmonic components, with sound-absorbing lining to absorb the sound emitted into the interior of the cabinet and to prevent stationary waves from forming; the cabinet is moreover amply dimensioned, because the stiffness of the air cushion in a small cabinet would shift the resonance of the loudspeaker to higher frequencies.

In a completely closed cabinet the energy emitted in the rearward direction is absorbed. In the bass-reflex speaker cabinet (Fig. 13), however, the energy is utilized also in the low frequencies. By enlarging or reducing the reflex opening, the enclosed volume of air is tuned to such a resonance frequency that, instead of the steep resonance maximum of the loudspeaker, two flat resonance curves, characteristic of two coupled oscillating systems, are obtained. Also, the indirect pressure wave emerging from the reflex opening undergoes a phase displacement of such magnitude that it intensifies the direct wave.

Like any oscillating system, a loudspeaker does not exactly respond to a force that suddenly commences and then remains constant. It oscillates about a new middle position (Fig. 14b, black curve). In the schematic model (Fig. 14a) such an oscillation induces a current in the damping coil. At low damping resistance this current becomes very strong, and its magnetic field damps the oscillation. In a loudspeaker the moving coil functions both as driving coil and as damping coil. The output circuit of the amplifier serves as a damping resistance. With correct design of the equipment this damping resistance is of just the right magnitude to provide optimum damping (continuous red curve in Fig. 14b) and thus ensure faithful reproduction of steplike modes of oscillation.

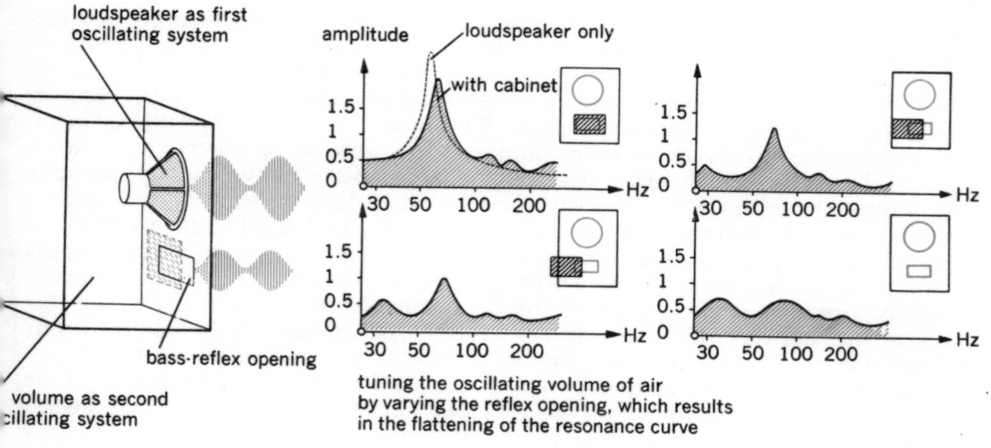

. 13 BASS-REFLEX SPEAKER

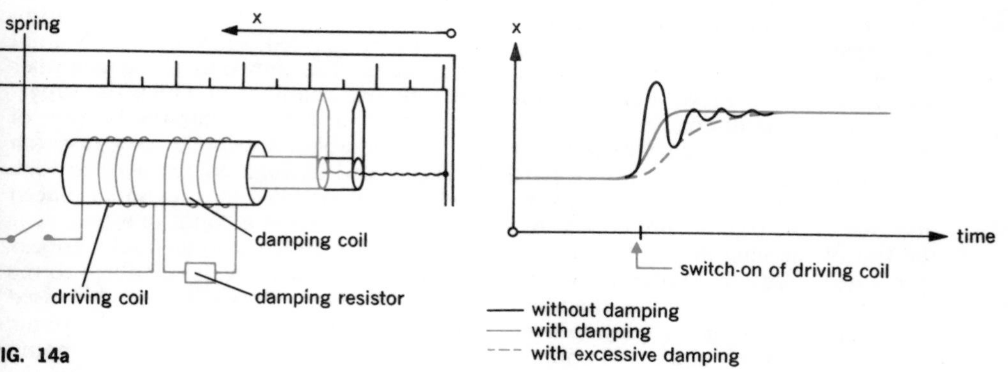

'IG. 14a

FIG. 14b MOVEMENT OF AN OSCILLATING SYSTEM WITH AND WITHOUT DAMPING

CLOUD CHAMBER AND BUBBLE CHAMBER

Important contributions to the discovery and investigation of elementary particles such as electrons and positrons and of the particles such as protons and neutrons which are the components of atomic nuclei have been made by experimental methods of detection. An important apparatus for this kind of research is the cloud chamber, of which there are two main types: the Wilson cloud chamber and the diffusion cloud chamber. By means of such equipment it is possible to observe and photograph the paths of high-speed electrically charged particles. When such particles pass through a gas, they collide with, and dislodge electrons from, the gas atoms, so that the latter become positively charged ions. The dislodged electrons (negative particles) and the gas ions function as centers of condensation upon which droplets form if the gas is supersaturated with a vapor. The succession of droplets along the path of a particle is visually observable as a so-called cloud track. It was this discovery that led C. T. R. Wilson to develop the first cloud chamber in 1912. In its original form, the Wilson cloud chamber consists of a circular glass cylinder closed at the top by a glass observation window (Fig. 1). The bottom and side wall of the chamber are of a black color to reveal the cloud tracks. The bottom, which is formed by a plunger, is covered with wet absorbent paper to keep the air in the chamber saturated with water vapor. An electric field is applied between the top and bottom of the chamber in order to remove any ions that may already be present. When the plunger is suddenly withdrawn (lowered) a certain distance, the expansion causes the gas and vapor in the chamber to cool, whereby the gas becomes supersaturated with vapor. When this happens, the electrically charged particles introduced into the chamber leave characteristic cloud tracks formed by tiny droplets of condensed vapor, as exemplified in Fig. 2, where the longer and finer track is due to the smashing of an atom, causing a proton to be liberated. A limitation of the Wilson cloud chamber is that it allows only instantaneous observations, since the supersaturated conditions suitable for the formation of cloud tracks exist only very briefly during the expansion. Various modifications have been applied to Wilson's original chamber, but the principle is essentially the same. The diffusion cloud chamber was developed in 1950. It is a continuously sensitive chamber in which the supersaturation is maintained more or less permanently in a layer near the bottom of the chamber. This apparatus has acquired considerable importance as a research tool, particularly in the study of particles discharged by high-energy accelerators. The prototype of this cloud chamber consisted of an air-filled glass cylinder placed in a pan of methyl alcohol cooled by dry ice. Warm methyl alcohol in a tray near the top of the chamber evaporated and diffused downward. Cloud tracks appear in a zone where a state of diffusion equilibrium is established. A device allied to the cloud chamber is the bubble chamber, developed by D. A. Glaser in 1952. It is used more particularly for studying collision of high-speed charged particles with atomic nuclei. A pressure-tight vessel contains a liquid heated far above its boiling point, but maintained at high pressure so that boiling is prevented (Fig. 3). When the pressure is suddenly reduced, the liquid becomes superheated. Charged particles passing through the liquid in this condition produce strings of tiny bubbles along their paths (Fig. 4). These bubble tracks are recorded by high-speed photography; precision measurements on the photographs provide information on the nuclear processes concerned. One important advantage over the cloud chamber is that in the bubble chamber rare nuclear events are of relatively frequent occurrence because of the high density in the liquid.

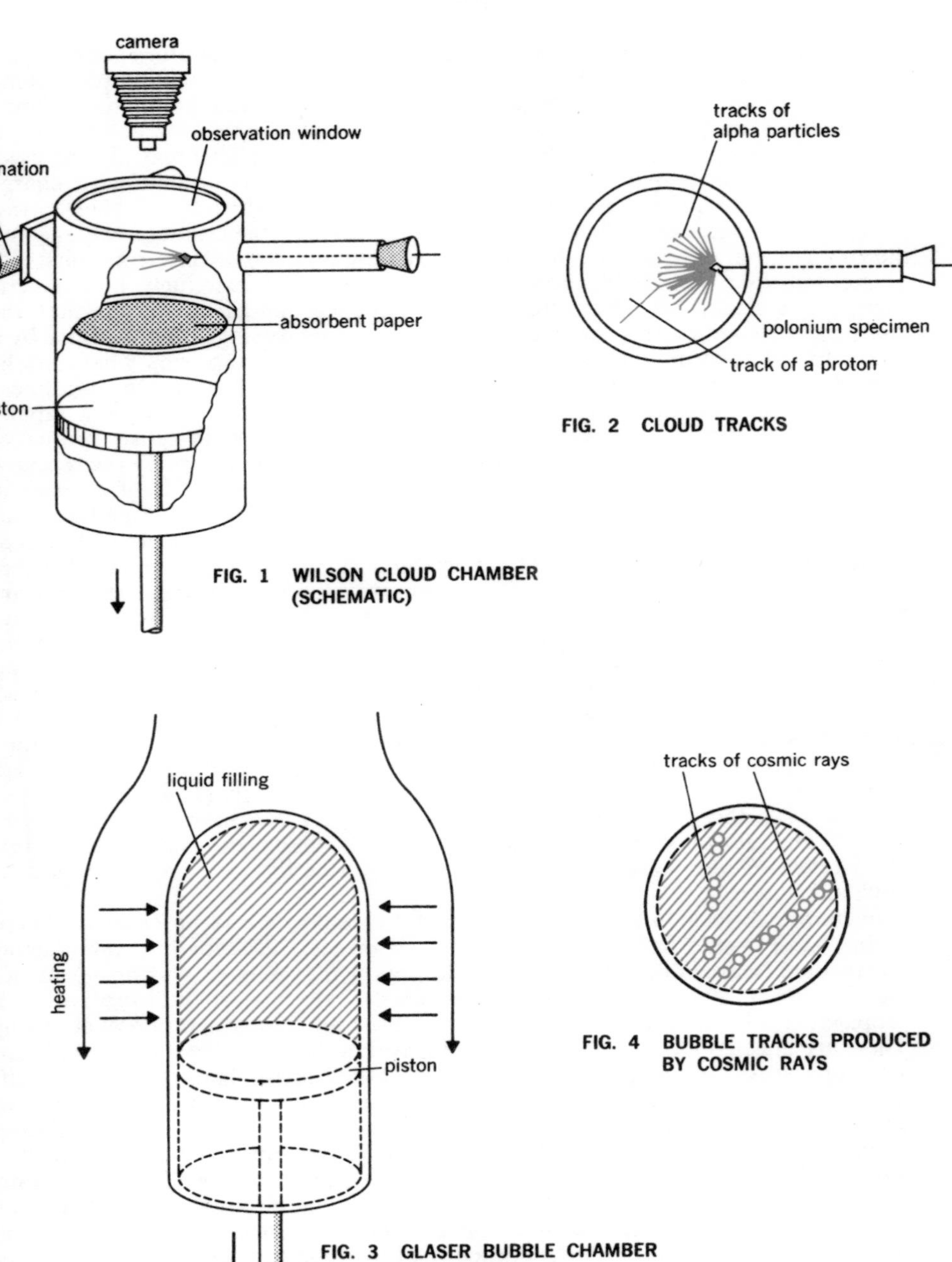

FIG. 1 WILSON CLOUD CHAMBER (SCHEMATIC)

FIG. 2 CLOUD TRACKS

FIG. 3 GLASER BUBBLE CHAMBER (SCHEMATIC)

FIG. 4 BUBBLE TRACKS PRODUCED BY COSMIC RAYS

LINEAR ACCELERATOR

Devices of various types collectively known as particle accelerators are of major importance in nuclear research. The particles accelerated to velocities corresponding to many millions of volts, and used as high-energy projectiles for bombarding atoms and for other purposes, are usually the nuclei of light atoms such as the proton from hydrogen or the alpha particle from helium; heavier nuclei may also be used. In the accelerator the particle acquires a kinetic energy equal to its electric charge multiplied by the difference in electric potential through which it falls. The corresponding unit of energy is the electron-volt (ev), based on the electronic charge and the volt as a unit of potential; the unit Mev represents 1,000,000 electron-volts.

The principle of multiple acceleration whereby these extremely high kinetic energies are attained is illustrated by the mechanical model in Fig. 1, where the "particle" (the red ball) is speeded on its way at an increasingly high velocity by a succession of rotating hammers. The class of apparatus comprising what may be termed "circular accelerators" has been dealt with in Vol. I, page 126. In a linear accelerator the particles travel in a straight line and are accelerated by a rapidly alternating potential. The earlier linear accelerators were so-called resonance accelerators (Fig. 2a), in which the particles are accelerated in steps by the repeated application of a relatively small voltage. The accelerator consists of a series of tubular units which are alternately connected to the poles of a high-frequency generator. Acceleration of the particles (e.g., low-energy ions) occurs at the gaps between the units, the frequency of the accelerating voltage being so adjusted that the correct polarity to speed the particle on its way is applied at the correct instant when the particle arrives at the gap (Figs. 2b and 2c). In simple terms: when a positive particle enters a gap just when the next tubular unit is negative and the preceding unit is positive, it will be attracted by the former and repelled by the latter and thus accelerated; by the time the particle reaches the next gap, the polarity has reversed, and it is again similarly attracted and repelled. To satisfy this condition there must be the following relation between the frequency f, the length l of a tubular unit, and the velocity v of the particle: $fl = v$. Since v increases as the particle proceeds along the accelerator, while f remains unchanged, this means that l must progressively increase—i.e., the gaps must be spaced farther apart (the tubular units must be longer). The ions to be accelerated are produced by an ion source and injected into the accelerator at a suitable high initial velocity with the aid of an appropriately applied voltage.

In its present-day form the linear accelerator makes use of an electromagnetic (radio) wave, with a frequency of around 3000 megacycles/second, traveling along an evacuated waveguide: i.e., a hollow metal conductor (see page 276) through which high-frequency microwaves—more particularly, very short radio waves—are propagated (Fig. 4). This type of apparatus is used for the acceleration of electrons. These are injected into the waveguide and travel in the same direction as the wave. The apparatus is so designed that the wave and the electron have the same velocity at all points along the guide; the electron thus travels synchronously with the wave. The latter has an electric field component which is directed along the axis of the waveguide. An electron which enters the guide at the correct time (or phase) is propelled along by a force arising from the interaction of its charge and the electric field. Since the wave and the electron travel at the same velocity, the electron is subjected to this force all along the waveguide and thus travels faster and faster. To achieve the desired synchronization, the phase velocity of the high-frequency wave is adjusted to the electron velocity by means of suitably dimensioned diaphragms (with circular openings in them) spaced at intervals equal to one-quarter of the wavelength (Fig. 3).

The world's largest linear accelerator is at Stanford University, in Palo Alto, California. It is nearly 2 miles long and can, in its present stage of development, accelerate electrons to energies of 20 million electron-volts (20,000 Mev). The electron beam can easily be brought out from the accelerator, so that certain precision experiments can be performed which are not possible with circular accelerators.

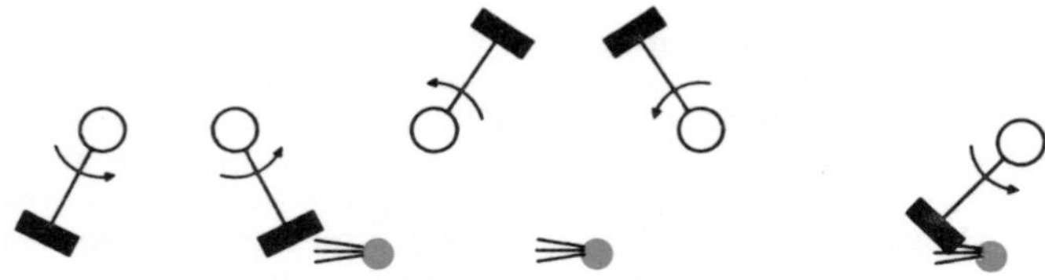

FIG. 1 MECHANICAL ANALOGY OF ACCELERATION PRINCIPLE

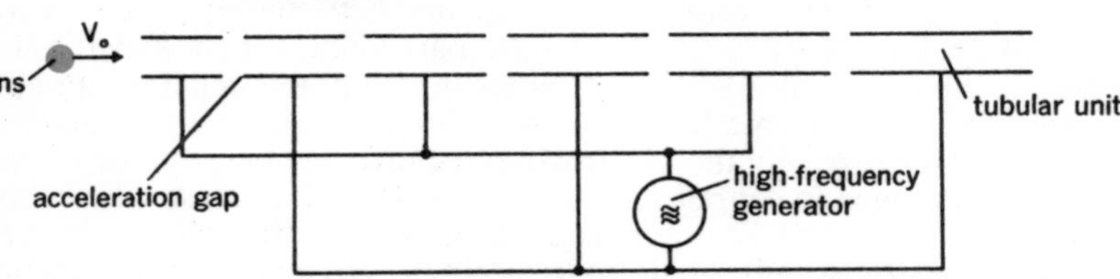

FIG. 2a SCHEMATIC DIAGRAM OF LINEAR ACCELERATOR

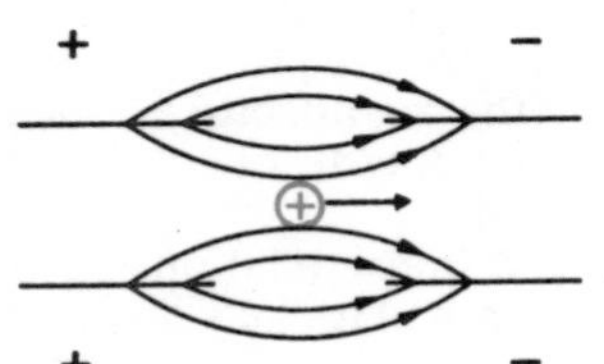

FIG. 2b IONS IN THE ACCELERATION GAP

FIG. 2c IONS IN THE FIELD-FREE INTERIOR OF THE TUBE

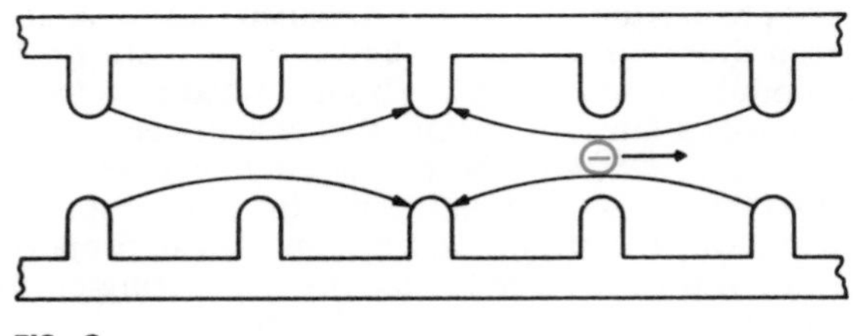

FIG. 3

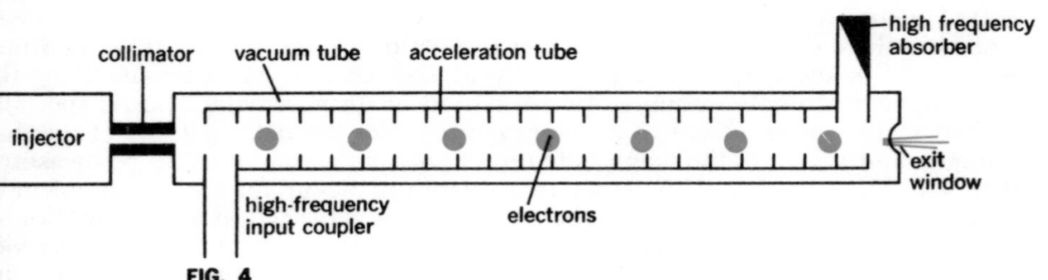

FIG. 4

ELECTRIC-RESISTANCE STRAIN GAUGE

Strain denotes the specific deformation, often expressed as a percentage, caus in a material by the action of a stress—i.e., a force per unit area (e.g., lb./in.^{2}, kg/cn kg/mm^2, etc.). In an elastic material such as steel there is direct proportionali between stress and strain. Because of this definite relationship it is possible determine the magnitude of the stresses in a structure if the strains are known. T latter can be measured by devices termed strain gauges, which are extensively used science and engineering for purposes of research and testing. There are vario types of strain gauge. One very widely applied type is the bonded electric-resistan strain gauge, first developed some thirty years ago. In its simplest form it consists a length of fine wire in a zigzag or grid pattern cemented between two thin sheets paper (Figs. 1 and 2). The gauge is bonded to the part being tested, and the w grid participates in the deformations thereof, either in compression (shortening) tension (elongation) so that the length and cross-sectional area of the wire under changes, which cause changes in the electrical resistance of the wire which a proportional to the changes in length (elongation causes an increase, shorteni causes a decrease in resistance). These changes in resistance, though usually ve small, can be measured by means of suitable electrical circuits and instrumen The relationship between the unit change in resistance and strain is expressed by t formula: $\Delta R/R = k.\Delta l/l$, where k is the so-called gauge factor, ΔR is the change resistance caused by the strain, R is the original resistance of the gauge, and Δ is the strain under the gauge (l is the original gauge length and Δl is the change length). The gauge factor (k) and the original resistance (R) are predetermined valu for any particular strain gauge and are supplied by the manufacturer. Such gaug are very sensitive; strains as low as 0.001% (corresponding to one millionth of inch over a gauge length of one inch) can be detected.

As already stated, for an elastic material there is a linear relationship (i.e., pr portionality) between stress and strain. This is known as Hooke's law and can expressed by the following formula: $\sigma = \varepsilon.\ E$, where σ is the stress, ε is the stra and E is a coefficient termed the modulus of elasticity (or Young's modulus). Eve elastic material has its own modulus of elasticity, which—for that material— constant within certain limits. (In reality, no material is completely elastic; ev steel has a limit of stress above which the stress is no longer proportional to t strain; below this limit of proportionality, in the so-called elastic range of behavi Hooke's law is fairly accurately conformed to, however.) For steel below the lin of proportionality the modulus of elasticity is about 2,100,000 kg/cm^2 (30,000,0 lb./in.^{2}). According to Hooke's law this means that when steel is subjected to strain of, for example, 0.1% ($\varepsilon = 0.001$) the corresponding stress in the steel $\sigma = \varepsilon \cdot E = 0.001 \times 30{,}000{,}000 = 30{,}000$ lb./in.^{2}. Since the electrical resistance of t strain gauge is proportional to the strain, and this in turn is proportional to t stress, the strain gauge can also be regarded as a stress-measuring device and it c be calibrated to give stress readings for any particular material.

A single strain gauge measures strains in one direction only. To measure strai in more than one direction at any particular point, two or more gauges can affixed there—for example, three gauges in a rosette arrangement which meas strains in three directions at 120 degrees in relation to one another (Fig. 3). Str gauges can be used for a variety of technical and scientific purposes involving t measurement of small amounts of deformation or displacement. Thus, a specia shaped strain gauge affixed to a diaphragm enables the deformations of the d phragm, and therefore the magnitude of the pressure acting on it, to be measur (Fig. 4, p. 227). Fig. 5 (p. 227) shows an acceleration pickup for the measurement accelerations varying with time. When the device is subjected to an acceleration the direction of the arrow, the part A with the bonded-on strain gauge underg a deflection (in the opposite direction) which is directly proportional to t acceleration.

(mor

FIG. 1 ELECTRIC-RESISTANCE STRAIN GAUGE WITH ZIGZAG WIRE

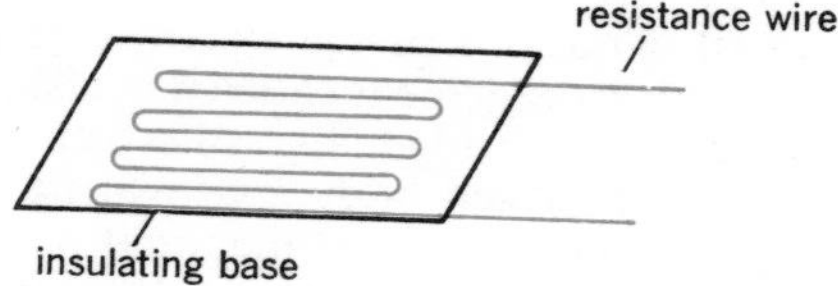

FIG. 2 ELECTRIC-RESISTANCE STRAIN GAUGE WITH WIRE GRID

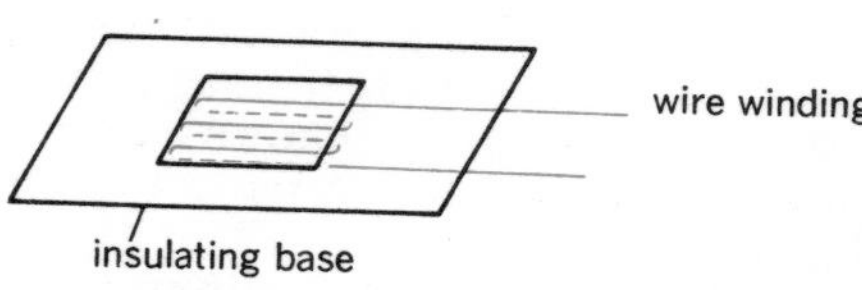

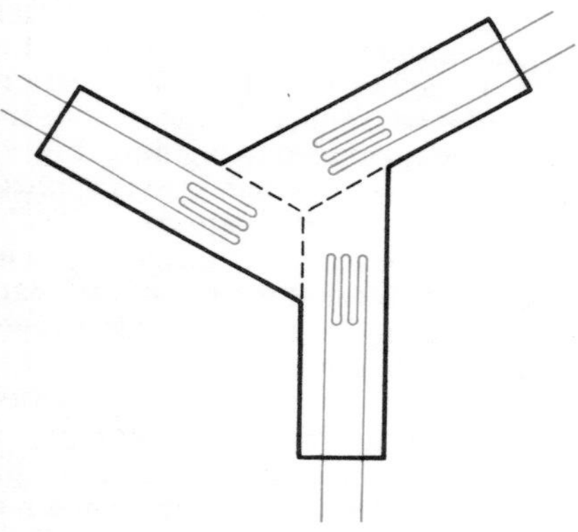

FIG. 3 THREE STRAIN GAUGES IN ROSETTE ARRANGEMENT

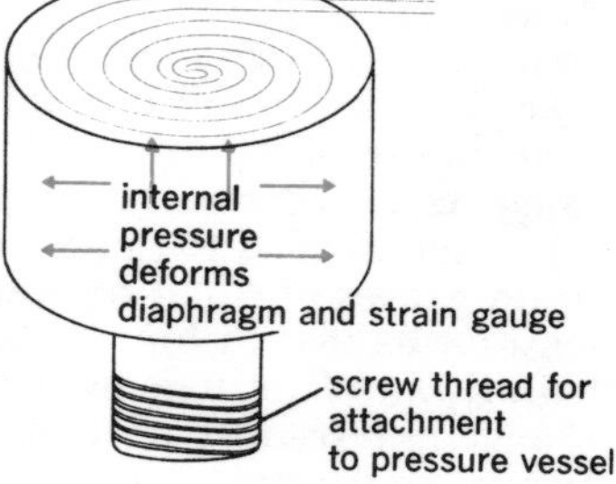

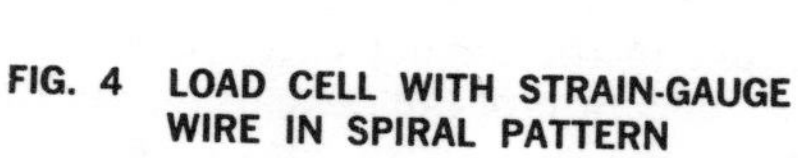

FIG. 4 LOAD CELL WITH STRAIN-GAUGE WIRE IN SPIRAL PATTERN

FIG. 5 ACCELERATION PICKUP WITH ELECTRIC-RESISTANCE STRAIN GAUGE

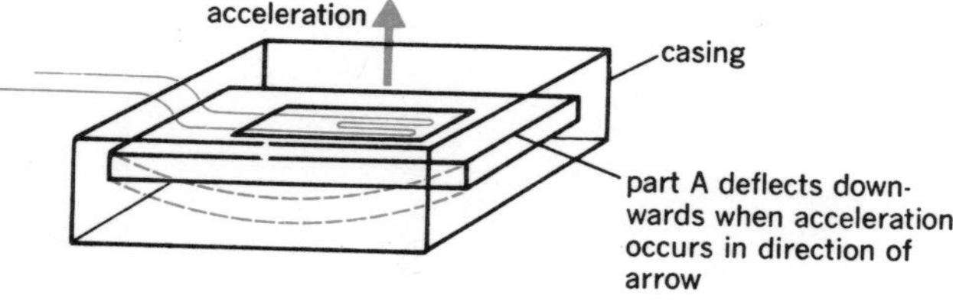

Electric-resistance Strain Gauge (continued)

The small variations in the electrical resistance of a strain gauge are measured by means of an arrangement called a measuring bridge which embodies the principle of the Wheatstone bridge (Fig. 6) which comprises two resistance branches connected in parallel, each branch consisting of two resistances in series. The supply voltage is applied at the two diagonal points I and II. The measuring instrument (galvanometer) connected between the other two diagonal points III and IV will give a zero voltage reading only when the same voltage drop occurs between I and III as between I and IV—for example, when $R_1 = R_4$ and $R_2 = R_3$, and also when $R_1 = R_2$ and $R_3 = R_4$. In general, the bridge will be "in equilibrium"—i.e., the measuring instrument will give a zero reading, when the mathematical relationship $R_1 : R_2 = R_4 : R_3$ is satisfied. If three of the resistances are of known value, e.g., R_2, R_3 and R_4, then the (unknown) fourth resistance R_1 can be determined by "balancing" the bridge (by varying the resistance R_2) and calculating it from $R_1 = R_2 R_4/R_3$.

For measurements performed with strain gauges, all four resistances of the bridge may be replaced by strain gauges, all of equal resistance (Fig. 7); alternatively, only two equal strain gauges may be connected into the bridge circuit, while the other two resistances are incorporated in the measuring-bridge apparatus itself (Fig. 8). When the bridge has been "balanced," i.e., the measuring instrument has been brought to a zero reading, a variation in the magnitude of one or more of the resistances will cause the needle of the instrument to deflect from the zero position. The arrangement shown in Fig. 7 may, for example, be applied in measuring the strains occurring at the top and at the underside of a beam loaded in bending (Fig. 9). When there is no load on the beam, the bridge is in equilibrium; when load is applied, the two gauges R_1 and R_3 undergo an equal tensile strain (elongation), while the two gauges R_2 and R_4 undergo an equal compressive strain (shortening). The purpose of the arrangement in Fig. 10 is to measure the strain at the top of the beam subjected to a combination of flexural and tensile loading. Only the strain gauges R_1 and R_3 are affixed to the beam; the gauges R_3 and R_4 are dummies in that they do not participate in the strain of the beam, but provide temperature compensation —i.e., they are installed in the vicinity of the other two, so that any changes in the temperature of the surroundings (whereby the resistances are altered) affect all the gauges equally. Similar compensation can be provided in the arrangement shown in Fig. 8 and applied to the strain measurement on a beam as shown in Fig. 11. With strain gauges of equal resistance the measuring arrangement in Fig. 10 is twice as sensitive as that in Fig. 11, because in the former case the change in resistance of both R_1 and R_3 causes twice the deflection of the measuring instrument as does the change in resistance of R_1 alone in the latter case. Fig. 12 shows strain gauges for measuring the strains in a shaft subjected to a torque (twisting moment). The largest strains occur in directions at 45 degrees to the center line of the shaft.

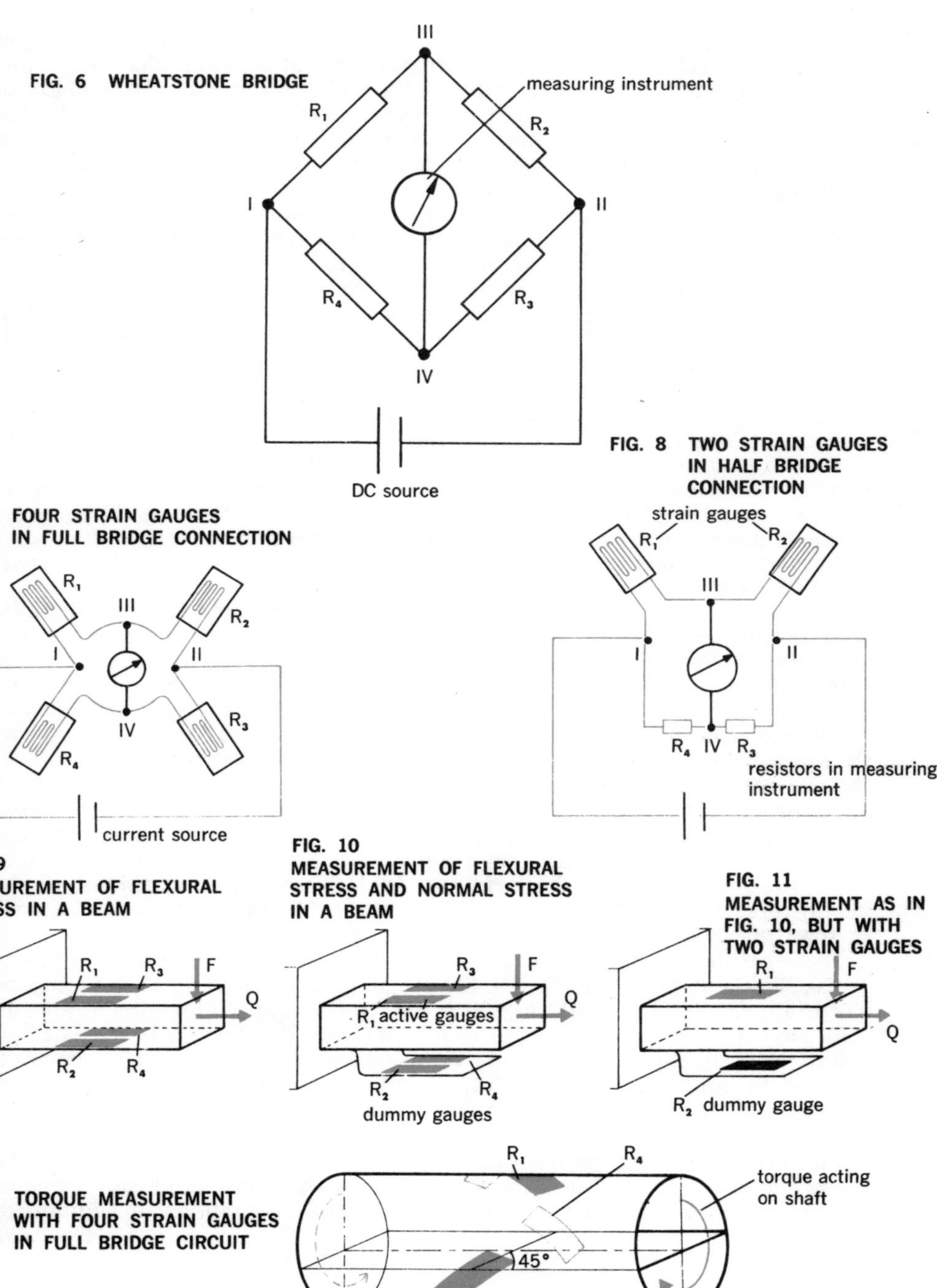

FIG. 6 WHEATSTONE BRIDGE
III
measuring instrument
R1
R2
I
II
R4
R3
IV
DC source
FIG. 8 TWO STRAIN GAUGES IN HALF BRIDGE CONNECTION
7 FOUR STRAIN GAUGES IN FULL BRIDGE CONNECTION
strain gauges
current source
resistors in measuring instrument
FIG. 10 MEASUREMENT OF FLEXURAL STRESS AND NORMAL STRESS IN A BEAM
.9 ASUREMENT OF FLEXURAL RESS IN A BEAM
FIG. 11 MEASUREMENT AS IN FIG. 10, BUT WITH TWO STRAIN GAUGES
F
Q
active gauges
dummy gauges
dummy gauge
2 TORQUE MEASUREMENT WITH FOUR STRAIN GAUGES IN FULL BRIDGE CIRCUIT
torque acting on shaft
45°

SLIDE RULE

The slide rule is widely used in engineering, science and commerce for rapidly performing calculations involving multiplication and division which have to be accurate to not more than three or four decimal places. It can also be used for such operations as involution (raising to a power) and evolution (extraction of a root) and for calculations with trigonometric functions (sine, cosine, tangent, cotangent). In addition to those for general use there are many different types of special-purpose slide rules. What they all have in common is logarithmic scales.

To understand how a slide rule works it is essential to know about logarithms. In general, the logarithm of a value a to base b is the exponent n denoting the power to which b must be raised in order to obtain a; i.e., if $a = b^n$, then $\log_b a = n$, where a itself is called the antilogarithm. Hence logarithms are exponents. In particular, so-called common, or Briggsian, logarithms are exponents of the base 10, this being the most convenient base for purposes of general computation. (In theory, any other base could be adopted for a system of logarithms. Of special importance, besides common logarithms, are the natural, or Naperian, logarithms, which have the value $e = 2.718\ldots$ for their base and are important in higher mathematical analysis.)

Since $1 = 10^0$, $10 = 10^1$, $100 = 10^2$, $1000 = 10^3$, etc., the common logarithms of 1, 10, 100, 1000, etc., are equal to 0, 1, 2, 3, etc. This is set forth in Table 1. Any number between 1 and 10 has a logarithm which lies between 0 and 1; numbers between 10 and 100 have logarithms between 1 and 2; etc. Whereas the logarithms of whole powers of 10 are whole numbers, the logarithms of intermediate values are decimal fractions, as exemplified by the logarithms of the numbers between 0 and 10 listed in Table 2.

When two (or more) values which are powers of the same base are multiplied, their product is obtained by adding the exponents. For example: $10^2 \times 10^3 = 100 \times 1000 = 100{,}000 = 10^5$. Similarly, division is done by subtraction of exponents. For example: $10^5 \div 10^3 = 100{,}000 \div 1000 = 100 = 10^2$. In general: $10^m \times 10^n = 10^{m+n}$ and $10^m \div 10^n = 10^{m-n}$. Thus multiplication and division can be reduced to the simpler operations of addition and subtraction if, instead of the actual numbers, the logarithms of those numbers are employed. For this purpose the logarithms of the numbers to be multiplied or divided are looked up in suitable tables and are added or subtracted. The result thus obtained is the logarithm of the required answer, which can be looked up (as the antilogarithm) in the same logarithm tables. Example: to calculate 2×3 using logarithms: $\log 2 \times 3 = \log 2 + \log 3 = 0.301 + 0.477 = 0.778$; the antilogarithm of 0.778 is 6 (see Table 2, where the logarithms are given in only three decimal places; in actual logarithm tables they are given in five, seven or sometimes even more places, thus providing greater accuracy).

The logarithms of the numbers 1, 2, 3, 4, etc., have the same values as those of 10, 20, 30, 40, etc., and 100, 200, 300, 400, etc., in so far as the decimals are concerned. For example: $\log 2 = 0.301$; $\log 20 = \log 2 \times 10 = \log 2 + \log 10 = 0.301 + 1 = 1.301$; $\log 200 = \log 2 \times 100 = \log 2 + \log 100 = 0.301 + 2 = 2.301$; etc. The figure before the decimal point is called the characteristic of the logarithm; it denotes the range of the antilogarithm—e.g., 0 to 10, 10 to 100, 100 to 1000, etc. The figures after the decimal point constitute the mantissa.

The above principles are utilized in the slide rule. The scale divisions represent not the actual numbers, but the logarithms (or, to be more precise, the mantissas) of those numbers. Fig. 1 shows the logarithmic scale. Thus, as already explained, multiplication and division are reduced to simple operations of addition and

(more)

Table 1

power	exponent	value of the power
10^0	0	1
10^1	1	10
10^2	2	100
10^3	3	1000
10^4	4	10,000
10^5	5	100,000
10^6	6	1,000,000
...	...	......

Table 2

number antilogarithm	power	exponent (logarithm)
1	10^0	0
2	$10^{0.301...}$	0.301...
3	$10^{0.477...}$	0.477...
4	$10^{0.602...}$	0.602...
5	$10^{0.699...}$	0.699...
6	$10^{0.778...}$	0.778...
7	$10^{0.845...}$	0.845...
...	...	......

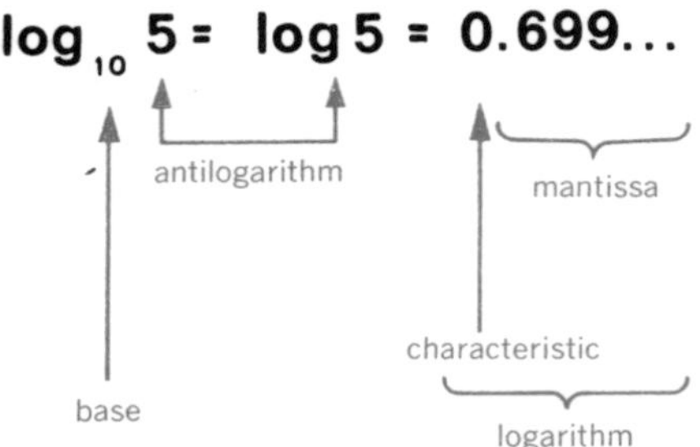

$$\log_{10} 50 = \log 50 = 1.699...$$

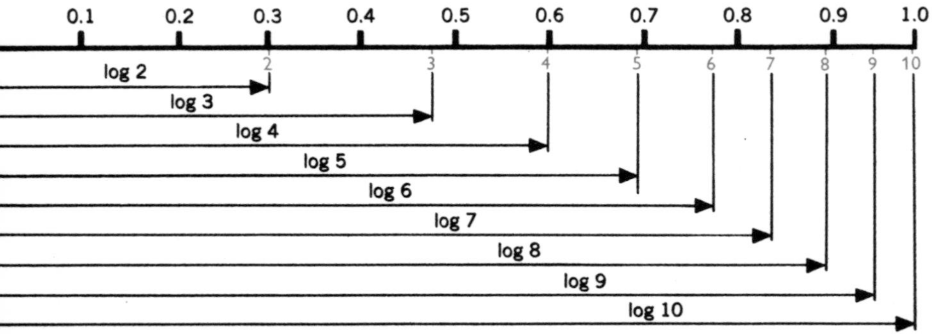

FIG. 1 THE LOGARITHMIC SCALE

subtraction, performed by sliding one part of the rule in relation to the other. It should be noted that in logarithmic calculations the position of the decimal point is determined by the characteristic of the logarithm. The slide rule, however, gives only the mantissa. It is up to the user to determine the position of the decimal point independently. In actual practice this is not a serious difficulty, as it is usually a simple matter to estimate the approximate magnitude of the answer and thus know where to place the decimal point.

An ordinary slide rule consists of the actual rule, the slide, and the transparent cursor with a hairline. Various logarithmic scales are engraved on the rule and the slide (Fig. 2). When the rule is "closed," the pairs of scales A and B, and C and D, respectively, coincide. The divisions on A and B extend from 1 to 100; those on C and D extend from 1 to 10. To determine the square of a value, the hairline is moved to that value on scale C or D, and the square is indicated by the hairline on scale B or A (Fig. 3). Square roots are obtained by the reverse procedure (Fig. 4). The scale K (above A in Fig. 2) gives the cubes of the values on scale D (Fig. 3). Conversely, scale D gives the cube roots of the values on K (Fig. 4).

For multiplication, the scales C and D are preferably employed (Fig. 5). It may occur that the slide has to be moved too far to the right to give a reading of the answer. In that case the slide should be moved back to the left until the figure 10 instead of the figure 1 on scale C is opposite the first factor of the multiplication. The result is then obtained in the usual way on scale D, opposite the second factor on scale C. Alternatively, the scales A and B may be used, though with reduced accuracy of the readings.

Division is performed as indicated in Figs. 7 and 8. Operations involving both multiplication and division may be carried out in accordance with Fig. 9. On a standard slide rule there is, between the scales C and D, another scale, usually marked CI. It gives the reciprocals of the values on scale C (Fig. 10). For the values on scale B the scale CI gives the reciprocals of the square roots; for example, a value a on scale B corresponds to $1/\sqrt{a}$ on scale CI. Reciprocals can be used advantageously for multiplying (dividing by the reciprocal value) and also for complex multiplications and divisions involving several factors (Fig. 11).

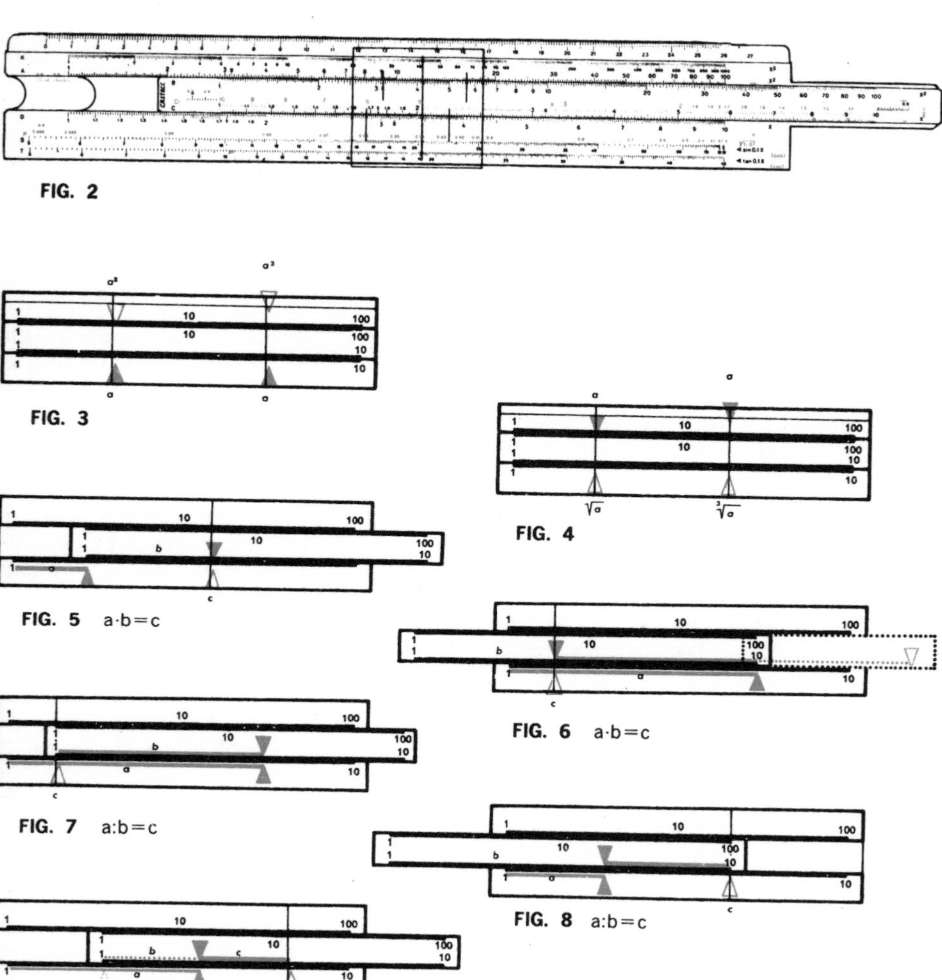

FIG. 2

FIG. 3

FIG. 4

FIG. 5 $a \cdot b = c$

FIG. 6 $a \cdot b = c$

FIG. 7 $a : b = c$

FIG. 8 $a : b = c$

FIG. 9 $(a : b) \cdot c = d$

FIG. 10

FIG. 11 $a \cdot b \cdot c = d$

STRAIGHT-LINE LINK MECHANISMS

A variety of link mechanisms, or linkages, enable movements to be produced which are exactly or at least approximately rectilinear—i.e., directed along a straight line. The applied motion may be circular or rectilinear. A four-bar linkage (see pp. 212, 214, Vol. III) can be so contrived that certain points of the mechanism describe substantially straight paths. One such contrivance, proposed by Hoecken, is shown in Fig. 1. Particularly favorable dimensions are obtained when the stationary link *d* is made twice as long as the crank *a* and all the other dimensions (*b*, *c*, *e*) are made 2.5 times as long as *a*. In the case of the oscillating crank (Fig. 2), the point C travels in an approximately straight path. A mechanism whereby the circular motion of the point A is converted into the accurately rectilinear motion of the point B is illustrated in Fig. 3.

In the straight-line link mechanism devised by Watt (Fig. 4a), the point S travels along a so-called lemniscoidal curve, two parts of which are close approximations of straight lines. Fig. 4b shows the mechanism for a particular type of gas-pressure indicator used with a piston-operated machine; the pressure is exerted upon a spring-loaded measuring piston K in a measuring cylinder, so that the piston is raised a greater or lesser amount, depending on the magnitude of the gas pressure. This motion is so transmitted to the recording stylus S that the latter performs a rectilinear vertical motion and records the pressure as a function of the position of the machine's working piston, the rotation of the recording drum being synchronized with the movement of this last-mentioned piston. Accurately rectilinear motion can also be obtained by a pantograph-type mechanism (Fig. 5; cf. Vol. III, page 214) whereby the length of travel of a motion can be enlarged or reduced as required. In the cardan gears (invented by Cardano) shown in Fig. 6 the inner wheel has half the radius of the outer. Any particular point on the circumference of the inner wheel, as the latter rotates within the outer wheel, moves on a straight line which passes through the center of the outer wheel and through the two points where that circumferential point on the inner wheel comes into contact with the outer wheel in the course of each revolution. Instead of completely circular wheels it is possible to use parts of circles—i.e., circular arcs, as in Fig. 7, where this principle is utilized in the cam lever (or rolling contact lever).

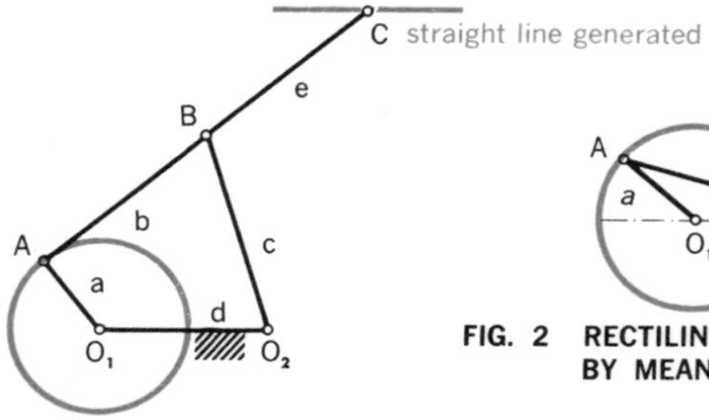

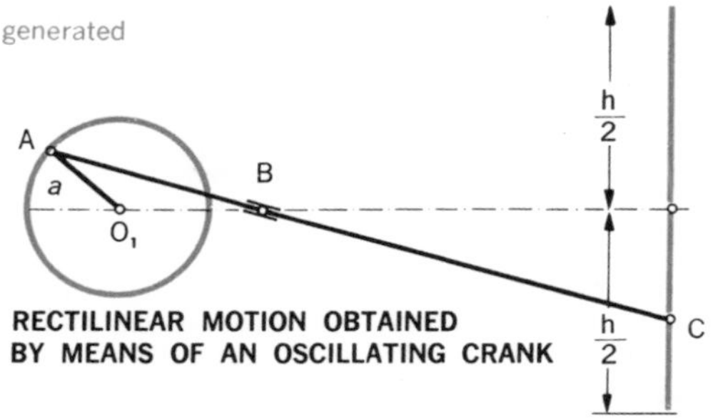

C straight line generated

FIG. 1 APPROXIMATELY RECTILINEAR MOTION OBTAINED WITH A FOUR-BAR LINKAGE (ACCORDING TO HOECKEN)
$b = c = e = 2.5\ a$;
$d = 2a$

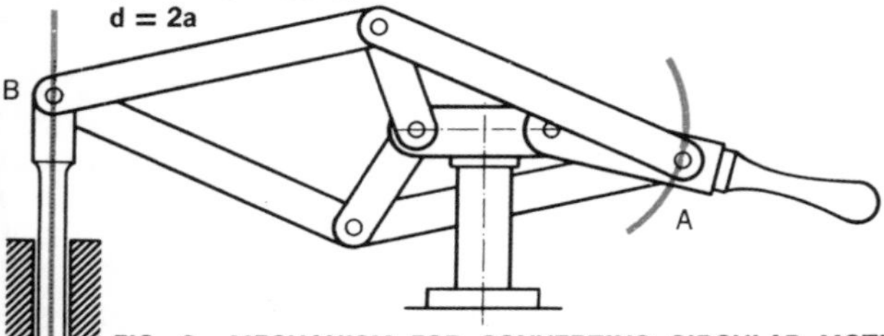

FIG. 2 RECTILINEAR MOTION OBTAINED BY MEANS OF AN OSCILLATING CRANK

FIG. 3 MECHANISM FOR CONVERTING CIRCULAR MOTION OF POINT A INTO RECTILINEAR MOTION OF POINT B (FOUR SHORT AND FOUR LONG LINKS, THE LATTER HAVING 2½ TIMES THE LENGTH OF THE FORMER)

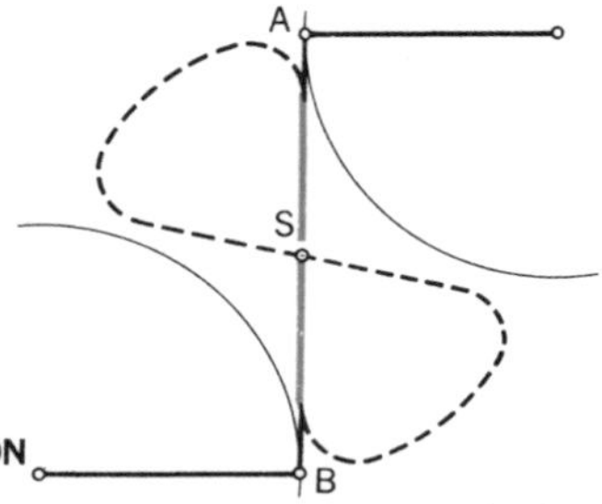

FIG. 4a

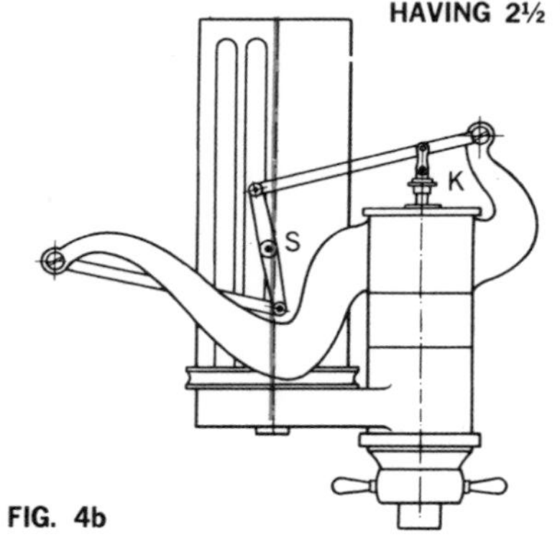

FIG. 4b

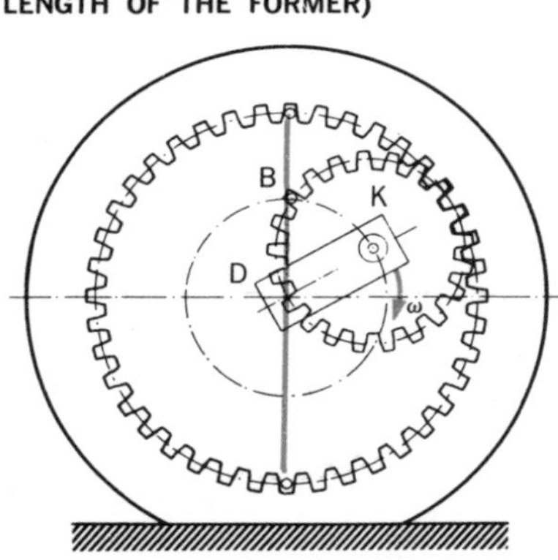

FIG. 6 CARDAN GEARS

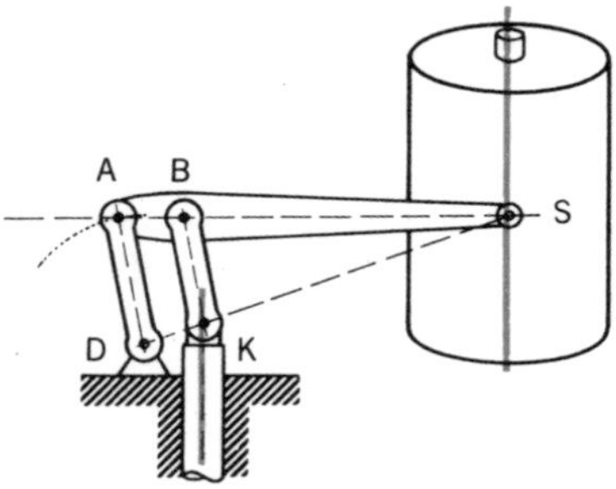

FIG. 5 INCREASING THE LENGTH OF TRAVEL OF A RECTILINEAR MOTION

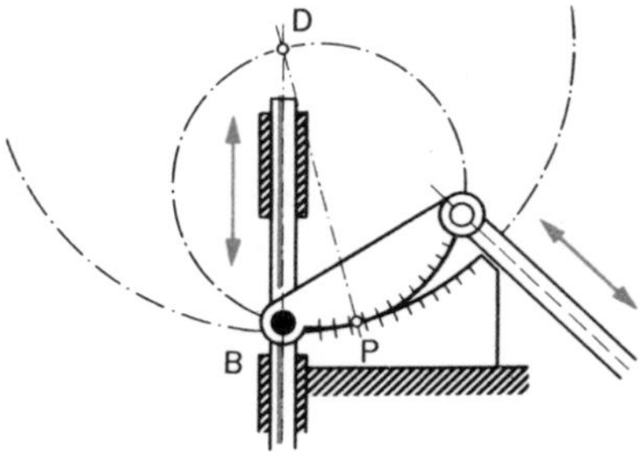

FIG. 7 CAM LEVER BASED ON CARDAN GEAR PRINCIPLE

MEASUREMENT OF PRESSURE

The pressure of a fluid (gas or liquid) is defined as the force it exerts in a direction perpendicular to a surface of unit area. A distinction is to be made between "absolute pressure," which is measured with respect to zero (absolute vacuum), and "gauge pressure," which is the amount by which the pressure exceeds the atmospheric pressure. Hence: gauge pressure + atmospheric pressure = absolute pressure. This relationship is further clarified in Fig. 1 for the case where the pressure to be measured is higher and lower than the atmospheric pressure respectively.

The simplest form of pressure gauge is the U-tube manometer (Fig. 2). It may either have both arms open to the atmosphere (a) or one sealed arm (b) in which there exists a vacuum (Torricellian vacuum) over the sealing liquid. With type (a) one arm is connected to the pressure p_1 to be measured and the other arm is in communication with the pressure of the atmosphere (the reference pressure p_b). The difference in level H is a measure of the difference in pressure $p_1 - p_b$; i.e., H represents the gauge pressure (as defined above) measured, for example, in millimeters or inches of sealing-liquid column. If the sealing liquid is water, then H will represent the pressure in units (mm or inches) of water column (or "water gauge"). If the sealing liquid has a specific gravity γ, then H can be converted to "water gauge" by multiplying it by γ; hence: $p_1 - p_6 = \mathrm{H}\,\gamma$ (w.g.). The U-tube manometer open at both ends can be employed as a differential gauge for measuring difference between two pressures p_1 and p_2—as, for example, in Fig. 2c, where an inverted U tube is used to measure the pressure difference $p_1 - p_2$ in millimeters or inches of the liquid to which the two arms of the gauge are connected, the sealing medium being a gas in this case.

The ring-balance pressure gauge (Fig. 3), comprising a pivotably mounted annular tube containing a partition and a sealing liquid, may be regarded as a combination of a U-tube gauge and a balance. It is particularly used for measuring small differential pressures. Thus the pressure difference $p_1 - p_2$ acting on the partition produces a rotating movement which causes the partition to swing through an angle α in relation to the vertical, so that a state of equilibrium is established, when the turning moment $M_p = (p_1 - p_2)$ AR is equal to the counteracting moment $M_G = G \sin\alpha.\ a$, where A is the cross-sectional area and R is the mean radius of the annular tube, while G is a known weight and a is its distance to the center. The differential pressure $p_1 - p_2$ can be calculated from the condition $M_p = M_G$.

An important and widely used instrument is the Bourdon-tube pressure gauge (or spring-tube pressure gauge, Fig. 4) in which pressure measurement is based on the deformation of an elastic measuring element (in this case a curved tube) by the pressure to be measured. The deformation is indicated by a pointer on a dial calibrated to give pressure readings. The tube, which is of circular or oval cross-sectional shape, is closed at one end, and the pressure to be measured is applied to the other end, causing the radius of curvature of the tube to increase (i.e., the tube tends to straighten itself out, as shown dotted in the right-hand diagram of Fig. 4). In the diaphragm-pressure gauge (Fig. 5) the elastic element is a stiff metallic diaphragm held between two flanges; pressure is applied to the underside of the diaphragm, and the movement of the latter is transmitted to a pointer. In the capsule-type pressure gauge (Fig. 6) the elastic element is a capsule to the interior of which the pressure is admitted. The piston-type pressure gauge (Fig. 7) is a so-called dead-weight apparatus in which the pressure to be measured is balanced by adjustment of the weight G placed on the piston. This is a very accurate type of gauge, usually employed for the calibration and testing of other gauges.

(more)

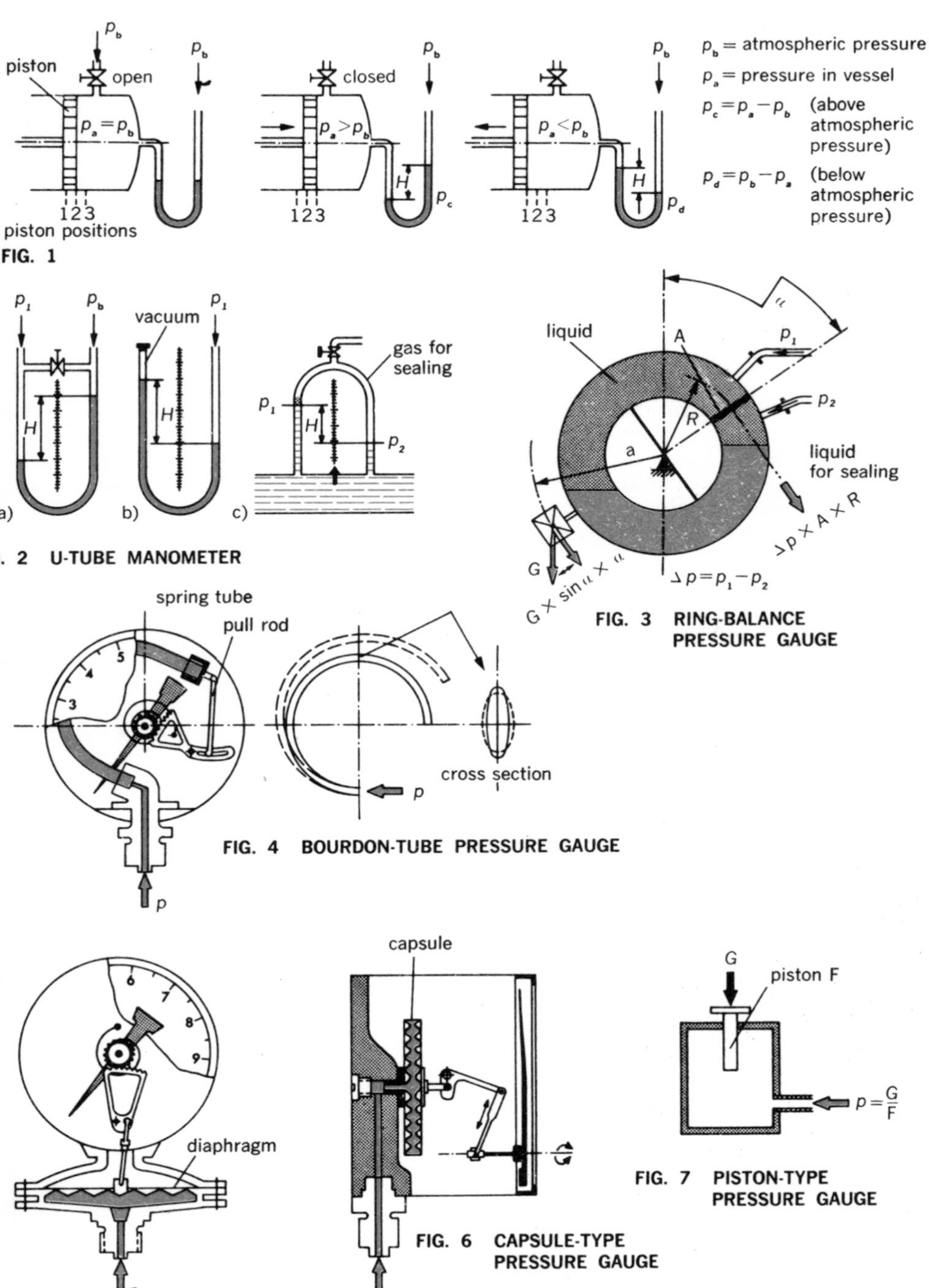

FIG. 1

FIG. 2 U-TUBE MANOMETER

FIG. 3 RING-BALANCE PRESSURE GAUGE

FIG. 4 BOURDON-TUBE PRESSURE GAUGE

FIG. 5 DIAPHRAGM PRESSURE GAUGE

FIG. 6 CAPSULE-TYPE PRESSURE GAUGE

FIG. 7 PISTON-TYPE PRESSURE GAUGE

Measurement of Pressure (continued)

The operation of electric pressure gauges is based on quite a different principle: namely, that pressure causes changes in the electrical properties of various substances such as manganin (a copper-base alloy containing manganese and nickel), carbon, etc. These devices are called resistance pressure gauges. Other substances, e.g., quartz, acquire an electric charge when subjected to pressure (piezoelectric effect). This principle is utilized in pressure-measuring instruments (piezoelectric gauges), as is also the phenomenon that the capacity of a condenser (or capacitor) varies under the action of pressure (capacitive gauges).

Figs. 1, 2 and 3 show examples of pressure gauges employed in level measuring and indicating devices. In the arrangement illustrated in Fig. 1 the hydrostatic pressure of the liquid, or its level, is indicated by the gauge—a mercury-float pressure gauge—illustrated in Fig. 4. This device is essentially a U-tube gauge with mercury as the sealing liquid. The variable pressure of the liquid in the tank (in which the level is to be measured) is applied to the "positive" pressure-measuring chamber, and the "negative" chamber is connected to the atmospheric pressure. The movements of the float on the mercury are proportional to the variations in the level of the liquid in the tank and are transmitted through a rack-and-pinion mechanism to a pointer. Another system is shown in Fig. 2: gas (air, nitrogen, carbon dioxide) under pressure is introduced into the pipes so that bubbles constantly emerge from the mouth of the pipe immersed in the liquid. The gas is kept flowing at a constant rate by means of a metering device and acquires a pressure corresponding to the liquid level in the tank at any particular moment. This pressure is transmitted to the float pressure gauge. If the liquid in the tank is under more than atmospheric pressure, as in Fig. 3, the pressure acquired by the gas in the pipes corresponds to the liquid level plus the pressure of the saturated vapor over the liquid. The vapor pressure must be compensated; it is applied to the "negative" chamber of the float pressure gauge, so that the latter indicates only the liquid pressure or the depth of the liquid in the tank.

When a fluid flows through a constriction (orifice, diaphragm, nozzle) in a pipeline, the difference in pressure between two points which are respectively located immediately before and after the constriction provides a measure of the rate of flow. More particularly, the flow rate is proportional to the square root of this pressure difference. The flow rate can thus be measured by means of a pressure gauge—of the type shown in Fig. 4, for example—whose scale is appropriately divided to give direct flow-rate readings (in ft.^{3}/sec., m^3/min., etc.). By appropriate design of the parts containing the sealing liquid, it is possible to ensure that the float movement is proportional to the square root of the pressure difference, so that the scale can be provided with a linear division (Fig. 5). Fig. 6 shows a rate-of-flow measuring system comprising a float pressure gauge of this type and a U-tube gauge for checking the float pressure gauge.

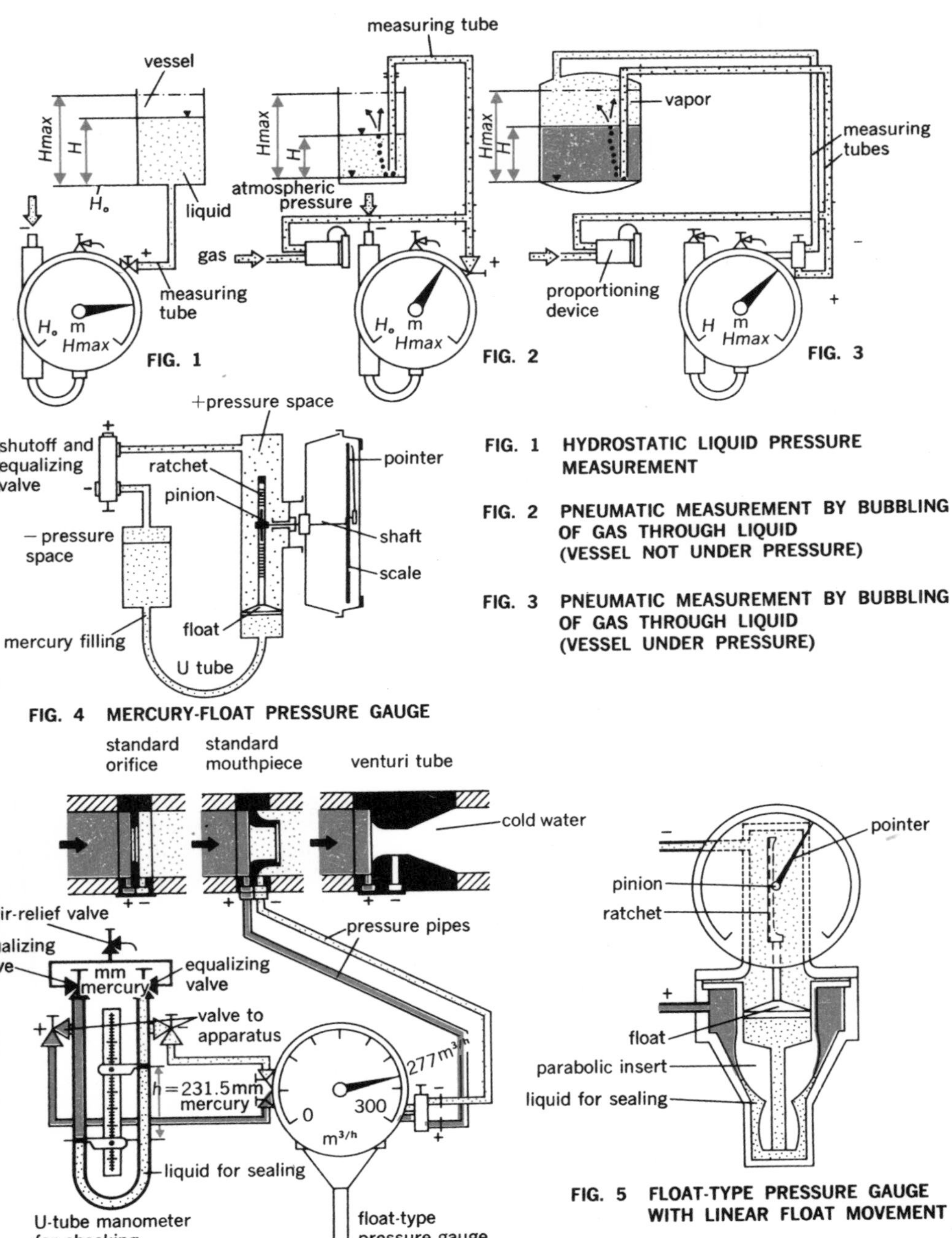

FIG. 1 HYDROSTATIC LIQUID PRESSURE MEASUREMENT

FIG. 2 PNEUMATIC MEASUREMENT BY BUBBLING OF GAS THROUGH LIQUID (VESSEL NOT UNDER PRESSURE)

FIG. 3 PNEUMATIC MEASUREMENT BY BUBBLING OF GAS THROUGH LIQUID (VESSEL UNDER PRESSURE)

FIG. 4 MERCURY-FLOAT PRESSURE GAUGE

FIG. 5 FLOAT-TYPE PRESSURE GAUGE WITH LINEAR FLOAT MOVEMENT

FIG. 6 RATE-OF-FLOW-MEASURING EQUIPMENT

In modern industrial technology, pipelines are extensively used for conveying a wide variety of gases, liquids and even solids. Obviously it is important to be able to measure the rate of flow of materials conveyed through pipelines—i.e., the quantity that passes in the unit of time (ft.^{3}/sec., m^3/min., etc.). Flow-measuring devices are of various kinds. The present article is concerned only with so-called volumetric meters. Such meters—used more particularly for the measurement of gas and water, respectively—have been dealt with in Vol. I, pp. 258–261.

Flow-measuring devices of the "direct" type for liquids function on either of two principles: (1) a measuring chamber of known capacity is repeatedly filled and emptied (Fig. 1; see also Vol. I, page 260); (2) the rotating measuring element displaces a known quantity of liquid in performing each revolution (Figs. 2 to 5). These displacement-type meters, though differing in design and technical features, all operate on the same principle, which will here be described more particularly with reference to the oval-runner meter (Fig. 5). It comprises two rotating elements of oval cross-sectional shape which mesh with each other. They are enclosed within a cylindrical casing which forms the measuring chamber and is provided with an inlet and an outlet. Fig. 6 shows the oval rotating elements in four successive positions in the course of one revolution, during which each crescent-shaped space at the top and bottom of the measuring chamber is twice filled. The total volume of liquid that is passed through the measuring chamber from inlet to outlet during each revolution of the oval elements is equal to 4 $F_s h$, where F_s is the cross-sectional area of each crescent-shaped space and h is the transverse dimension of the measuring chamber (perpendicularly to the plane of the drawing in Fig. 6). The power for driving the oval elements is supplied by the liquid flow itself (Fig. 7a). The pressure difference Δp across the meter acts upon the major and minor projected areas f and F of the lower oval element in Fig. 7a, which areas are thus subjected to the resultant forces P_F and P_f respectively (Fig. 7b). Since P_F is larger than P_f and moreover has a larger lever arm with respect to the center of rotation of the oval element, the latter is thus subjected to a torque (turning moment) which causes it to rotate. The upper oval element, when in the position shown in Fig. 7b, is subjected to a torque of zero magnitude, since the resultant forces acting on each side of the center balance each other. When the two elements have each rotated through 90 degrees, the situation is reversed, in that now the upper element is subjected to its maximum torque and on the lower element there is momentarily no torque acting at all. In intermediate positions, the two elements are subjected to torques of varying magnitude: the torque on the lower element (as shown in Fig. 7a) diminishes to zero, while that on the upper element increases to its maximum value. The meter is self-starting in the sense that the oval elements will begin to rotate from any position as soon as the liquid flow commences, provided that the liquid to be measured has a pressure

(more)

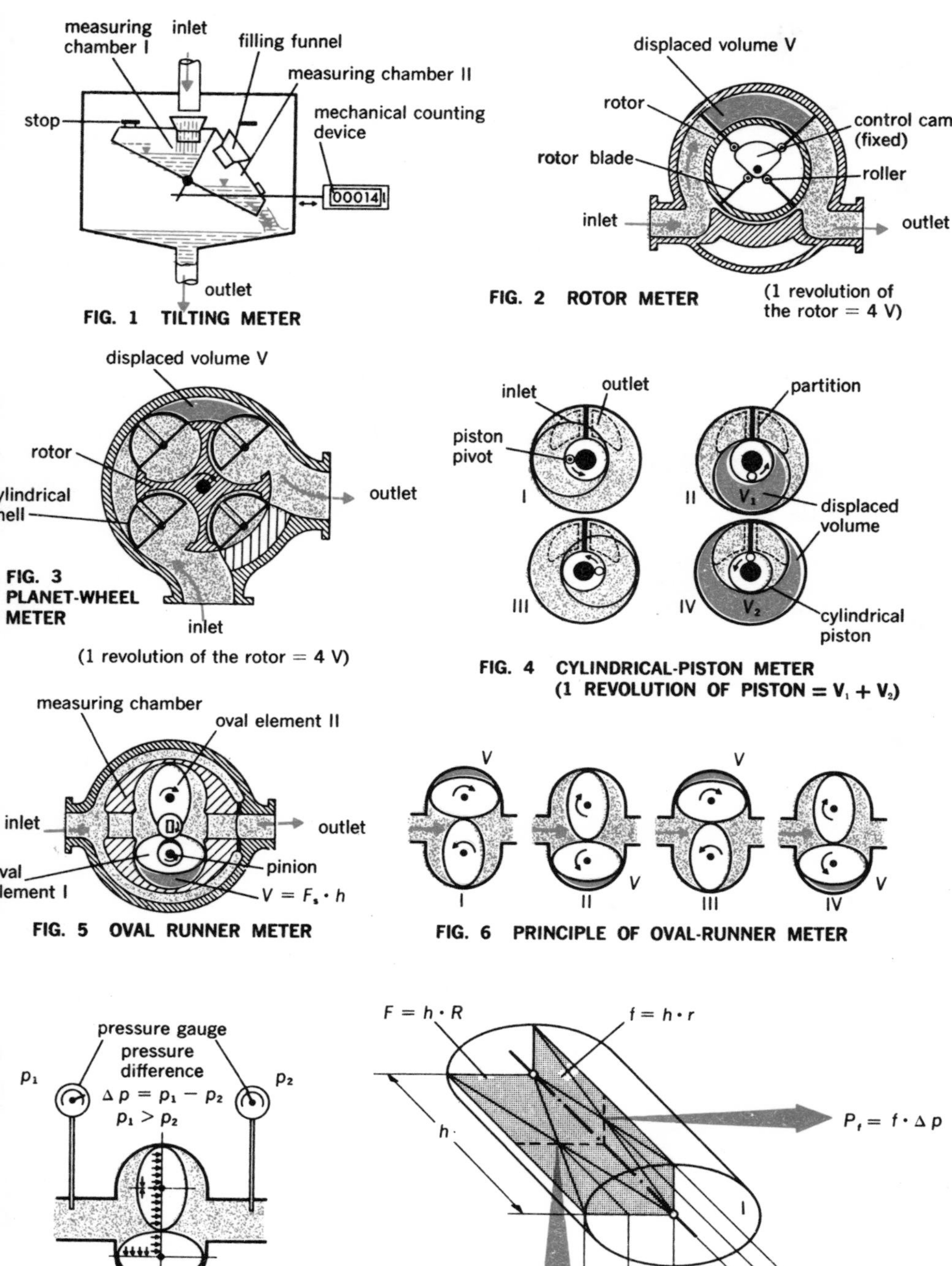

FIG. 1 TILTING METER

FIG. 2 ROTOR METER (1 revolution of the rotor = 4 V)

FIG. 3 PLANET-WHEEL METER (1 revolution of the rotor = 4 V)

FIG. 4 CYLINDRICAL-PISTON METER (1 REVOLUTION OF PISTON = $V_1 + V_2$)

FIG. 5 OVAL RUNNER METER

FIG. 6 PRINCIPLE OF OVAL-RUNNER METER

FIG. 7a

FIG. 7b

sufficient to overcome the inertia and friction of the elements. To minimize friction, the latter are not in contact with the wall of the measuring chamber. There is thus a slight gap between each element and the wall, so that a certain small amount of leakage occurs. If this leakage is neglected, the speed of rotation is proportional to the rate of flow of the liquid, since the quantity that passes through the measuring chamber in each revolution of the oval elements is constant (and equal to Fig. 4 $F_s h$).

Fig. 1 shows the construction of an oval-runner meter. The two oval elements can rotate freely on their spindles. The upper element is connected to a gear wheel which drives another gear wheel, mounted at the center of the casing, and this in turn drives a magnetic coupling. The latter transmits the rotation of the oval elements and prevents the penetration of liquid into the indicating mechanism. Fig. 2 shows a single-pointer dial mechanism with a pointer which rotates continuously while measuring is in progress. The pointers of the two-pointer dial mechanism illustrated in Fig. 3 can be reset to zero on completion of the measuring operation.

As already stated, a certain amount of leakage occurs in consequence of the clearances between the rotating elements and the wall of the chamber. The amount of leakage, besides obviously being dependent on the precision of manufacture of the meter and the rate of flow, is dependent on the viscosity of the fluid passing through the meter. Fig. 4 shows an installation for testing the performance of an oval-runner meter, more particularly with liquids of different viscosity. The object of the gas separator is to remove any gas dissolved in the liquid, as its presence produces errors in the measurements. With this equipment the accuracy of the meter can be checked for different flow rates and different liquids.

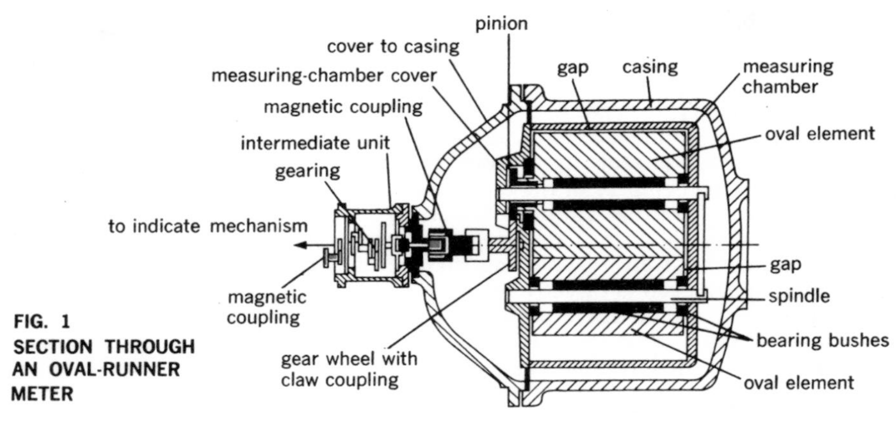

FIG. 1 SECTION THROUGH AN OVAL-RUNNER METER

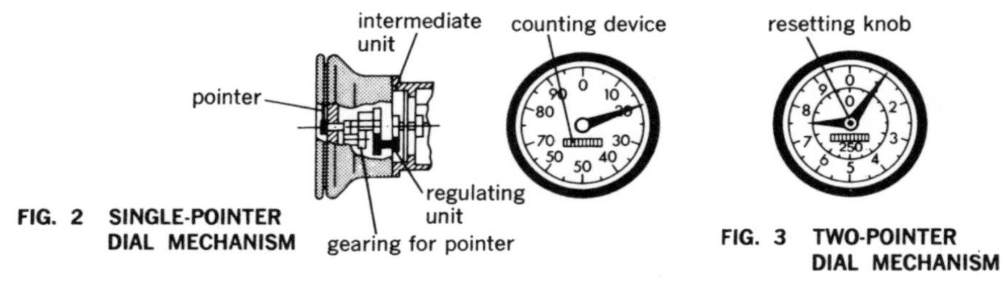

FIG. 2 SINGLE-POINTER DIAL MECHANISM

FIG. 3 TWO-POINTER DIAL MECHANISM

FIG. 4 TESTING INSTALLATION

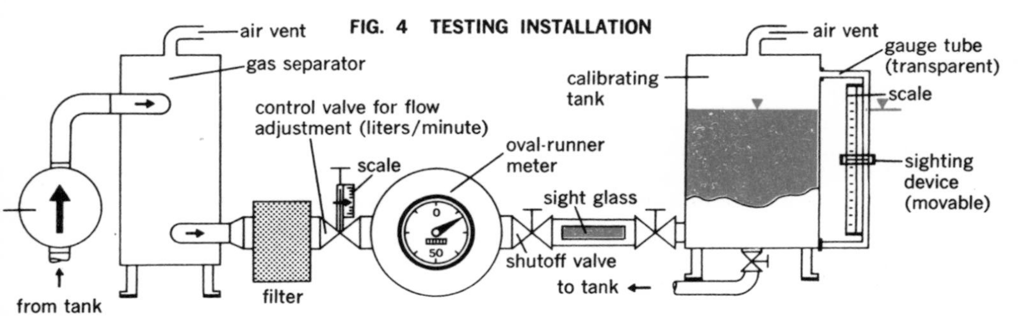

MIXING OF MATERIALS

Operations involving the mixing of solid, liquid and gaseous substances occur in innumerable industrial manufacturing processes. Each industry has developed mixers unique to its own use and has in most cases done this chiefly on an empirical basis, which has given rise to considerable diversification of the equipment employed. The main requirement applicable to any mixing operation, however, is to achieve as homogeneous a mixture as possible. In many cases some kind of chemical reaction and/or physical change of the materials concerned is required to take place during mixing—e.g., heating, cooling, dissolving, aeration, de-aeration, change of state (e.g., liquid to solid or vice versa), agglomeration, granulation, dispersion (suspension, emulsion), wetting, coloring, change of viscosity, etc. The intimacy or degree of mixing achieved is directly related to the homogeneity of the mixture. Absolute homogeneity would correspond to theoretically perfect mixing; in actual practice only a certain degree of homogeneity, sufficient to fulfill the requirements of the process concerned, is aimed at. The individual components of a mixture sometimes offer considerable resistance to the attainment of uniform distribution and dispersion in the specified proportions (by weight or by volume). This may be due to difference in specific gravity or bulk density of the component materials, the action of adhesive or cohesive forces, surface features of the particles, etc. In particular, when solids are mixed with liquids, undesirable agglomerations are liable to occur which prevent uniform wetting of the solid particles unless such agglomerations are broken up in the course of the mixing operation. This can be achieved by appropriate design of the mixing elements and the mixing container, appropriate speed of rotation of the mixing elements, and adequate driving-power input. In difficult cases it may be necessary to perform the mixing operation in two or more stages—e.g., a coarse preliminary mixing operation (macromixing) followed by a homogenizing process (micromixing) in which a high power input is applied to the premixed material so that large shearing forces are produced whereby the agglomerations are broken up.

Friction is an attendant phenomenon of every mixing operation. Intensification of the frictional effect in conjunction with an increase in power input causes the actual mixing effect to diminish in importance as compared with the comminuting (or disintegrating) effect associated with friction. Machines which thus develop a comminuting action are called mixing mills. An essential requirement applying to every mixing operation is that both horizontal and vertical flow of sufficient intensity occur and that all the material is moved frequently into the zone of intense mixing action in the vicinity of the mixing element (i.e., the mixing paddle, impeller, etc.). Stratification, settling and segregation of the material in the container must on no account take place. These phenomena are liable to occur as the result of gravity or centrifugal force and must be prevented by suitable mixing action.

(more)

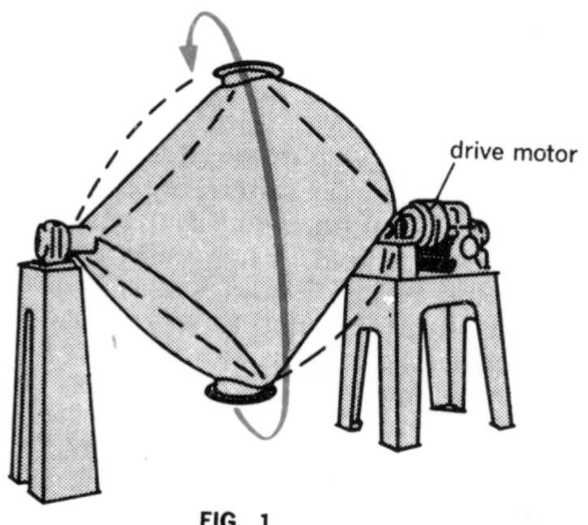

FIG. 1

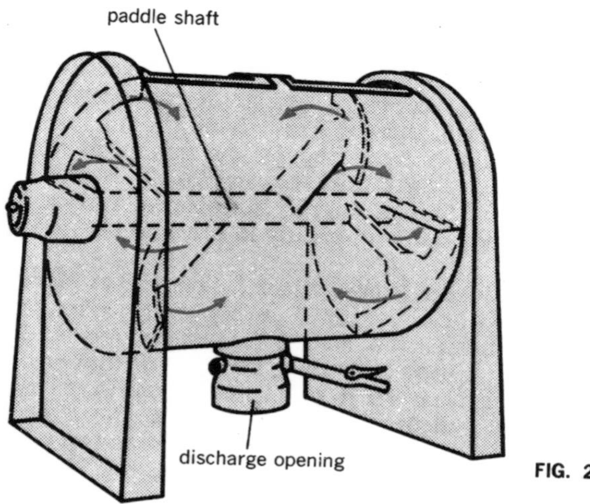

FIG. 2

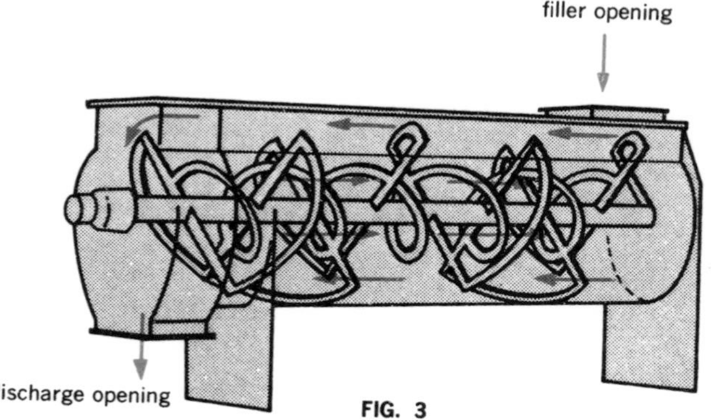

FIG. 3

Mixing of Materials (continued)

As already mentioned, mixers for various purposes present a wide diversity of types, only a few of which can be dealt with here. Four main classes of mixing appliances can be distinguished, however: (1) flow mixers: these are used in circulating systems for the mixing of miscible fluids, the mixing effect being produced by interference with the flow (jet mixers, injectors, turbulence mixers, etc.); (2) paddle mixers: one or more blades rotate on a shaft within the container so that the material to be mixed is moved around in a circular path; (3) propeller mixers: mixing is effected by revolving helical blades which constantly push the material along; (4) turbine (or centrifugal impeller) mixers: broadly speaking, these operate on the principle of the centrifugal pump, the material being accelerated by the impeller vanes and discharged tangentially. The mixers of classes (2), (3) and (4) are positive-action mixers, characterized in that a power-driven mixing element moves (rotates) within a stationary container, as exemplified by the paddle mixer in Fig. 2 (p. 245), in which the rotating paddle blades move the material toward the center of the container, while the arms on which the blades are mounted move it back toward the periphery (counterflow principle). A different class of mixing equipment, not included in the above classification, is formed by the so-called gravity mixers, of which there are various types, one of which is illustrated in Fig. 1 (p. 245). The container is constantly rotated, so that the material inside it is tumbled about. The interior of the container may be fitted with lifting scoops or similar devices which lift the material a certain distance and let it fall, thereby intensifying the mixing action. Gravity mixers can sometimes be suitably employed for the mixing of materials which must not be subjected to the severer mechanical stresses exerted by the mixing elements of positive-action mixers, but they are hardly suitable for mixing sticky or highly viscous materials or for solids differing greatly in physical character and therefore difficult to mix.

Fig. 3 (p. 245) shows a so-called double-helical mixer (belonging to class 3) in which mixing is performed by two helical "ribbons" in concentric arrangement one a right-hand and the other a left-hand screw, so that the material is moved back and forth in the container. This type is used for mixing powders or thin pastes. In Fig. 4 a turbodisperser is illustrated (class 4); it comprises a centrifugal turbine impeller which rotates at high speed and produces flow patterns whose direction and intensity depend on the shape of the container and on the shape and speed of the impeller. A kneader (class 2) has two sets of paddle blades rotating in opposite directions; in the machine shown in Fig. 5 the two bladed shafts not only rotate at high speed on their own axes but also perform a combined rotary motion about their common center (planetary kneader). The blades are disposed in a helical pattern around the shafts and are staggered in relation to one another, thus producing intensive radial and axial counterflow in the material. Such mixers are more particularly suitable for mixing materials of a viscous, sticky or plastic consistency. Another type of kneader is illustrated in Fig. 6; it has two Z-shaped kneading blades rotating in opposite directions on horizontal shafts at different speeds. The bottom of the container is shaped like a divided trough, with a raised ridge along the center line. These kneaders are especially suitable for highly viscous materials.

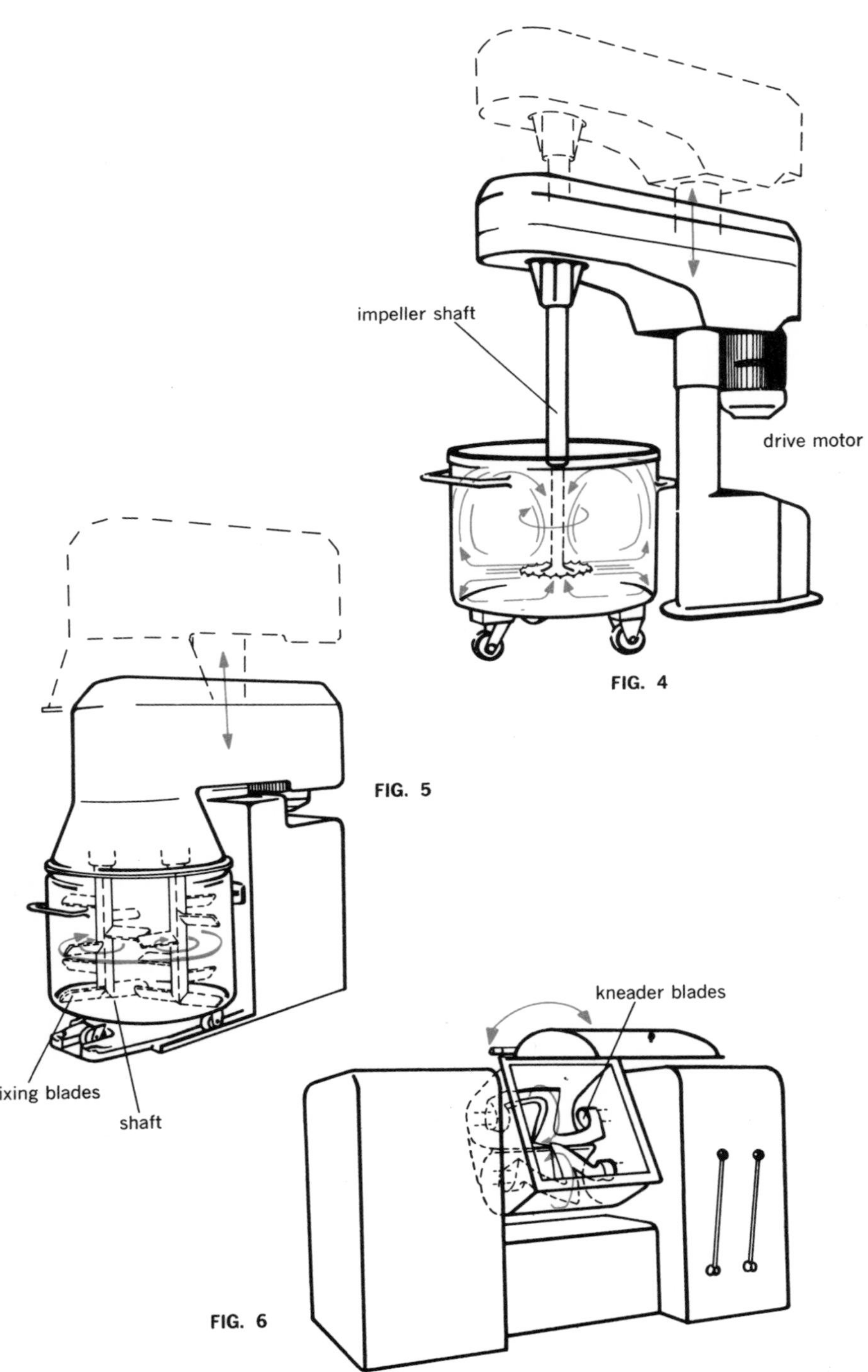
impeller shaft
drive motor
FIG. 4
FIG. 5
mixing blades
shaft
kneader blades
FIG. 6

ELECTROMAGNETS

Iron (or steel) can be conceived as consisting of numerous randomly disposed magnetic units, or domains, which cancel one another so that the piece of metal as a whole exhibits no magnetic polarity (Fig. 1). When the iron is magnetized, these domains become aligned in the same direction and thus act in combination to produce overall magnetic properties: the iron has thus become a magnet (Fig. 2). This can be done by placing the iron in the field of force of an existing magnet or by placing it within a coil of insulated wire (Fig. 3) through which an electric current is passed; in the latter case the coil with its iron core forms an electromagnet. If the core is of soft iron, it loses its magnetism almost immediately after the current in the coil is switched off—i.e., when the electromagnet is de-energized. On the other hand, steel will retain a substantial proportion of the magnetism it acquires and thus form a permanent magnet, in which the magnetic domains persist in retaining their aligned orientation after the external magnetic field which produced this orientation has been removed. The orientation can be disrupted by heating the steel, whereby the magnetic domains revert to their random condition and the steel becomes partly or wholly demagnetized. The electromagnet is based on the fact that an electric current passing through a circular conductor (Fig. 4) produces a magnetic field—i.e., is surrounded by magnetic lines of force which together form the so-called magnetic flux. A coil consisting of many turns of wire (Fig. 5) can be conceived as the superposition of a corresponding number of circular conductors. If the coil is provided with an iron core (Fig. 6), the flux density (or magnetic induction) is greatly increased. This is due to the property of ferromagnetism possessed by iron and certain other metals. A ferromagnetic material has a high magnetic permeability (μ), this being the ratio of the magnetic induction (B) in a piece of magnetic material to the external magnetic field strength (H) producing the induction. The permeability of air and nonmagnetic materials is unity.

Fig. 5 shows the magnetic field set up by a coil in which a current is flowing. Externally its properties are generally similar to those of a bar magnet, with south and north pole respectively. The highest field strength occurs at the center (Fig. 7). As already stated, the presence of a ferromagnetic material (in particular, iron) in the magnetic field gives rise to magnetic induction in that material, which is linked to the field strength of the coil itself by the relation $B = \mu H$, where μ denotes the permeability (which has the order of magnitude of 10^3 to 10^4 for ferromagnetic materials). The permeability may be conceived as the criterion for the increase in the number of magnetic lines of force brought about by the orientation of the magnetic domains in the iron. In practical terms, the presence of an iron core within the coil makes the magnetic field very much stronger. The permeability varies for different values of the magnetic induction, even for the same material (Fig. 8, p. 251). The magnetic-field strength of the coil increases in proportion to the strength of the current flowing through it; as a result, more and more of the domains in the iron core become aligned until finally they are all oriented in the same direction (Fig. 2). The iron is then said to have become magnetically saturated. Any further increase in the magnetic-field strength (H) will produce little or no change in the magnetic induction (B).

(more)

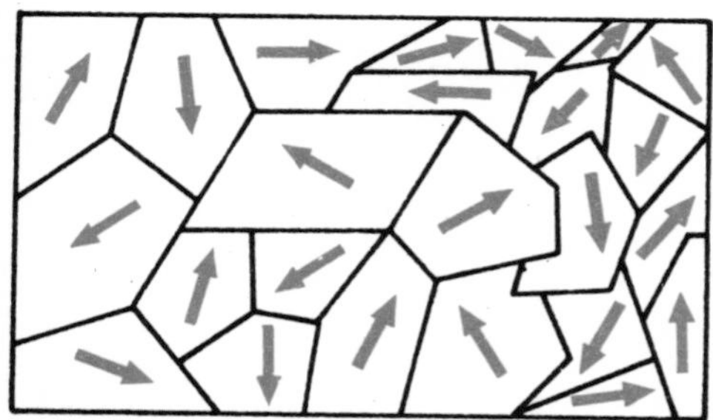

FIG. 1 ELEMENTARY MAGNETIC DOMAINS IN A POLYCRYSTALLINE MATERIAL WHICH BEHAVE LIKE TINY MAGNETS WITH RANDOMLY ORIENTED FIELD DIRECTIONS (ARROWED)

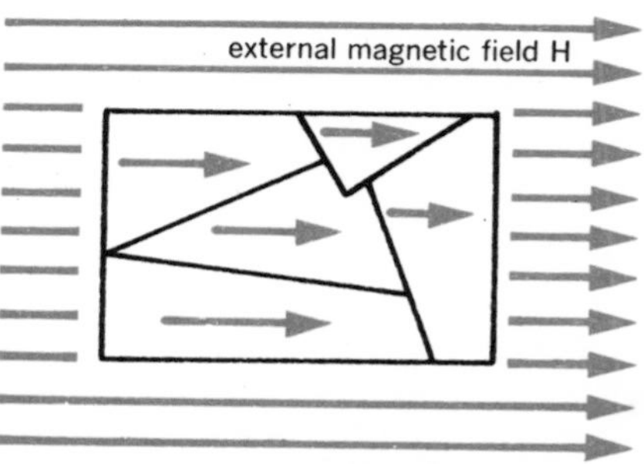

FIG. 2 FERROMAGNETIC SATURATION: ALL THE ELEMENTARY DOMAINS ARE NOW ORIENTED PARALLEL TO THE EXTERNAL MAGNETIC FIELD

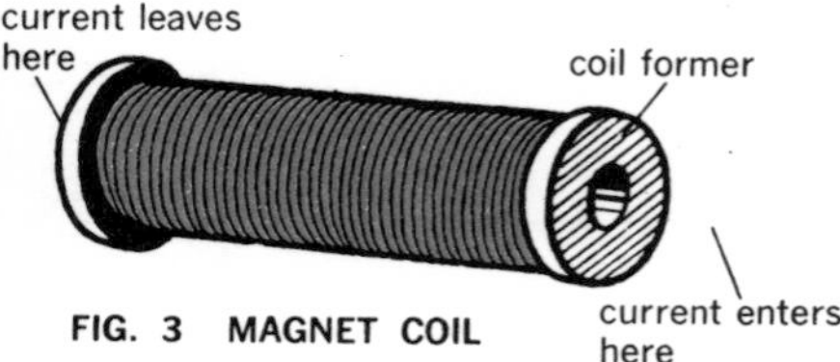

FIG. 3 MAGNET COIL

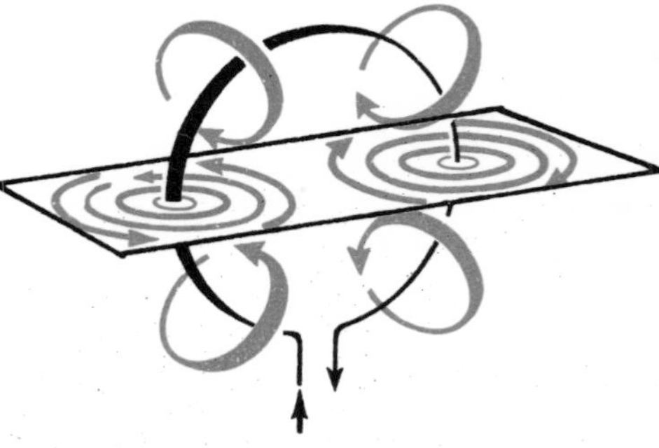

FIG. 4 MAGNETIC FIELD OF A CIRCULAR CONDUCTOR

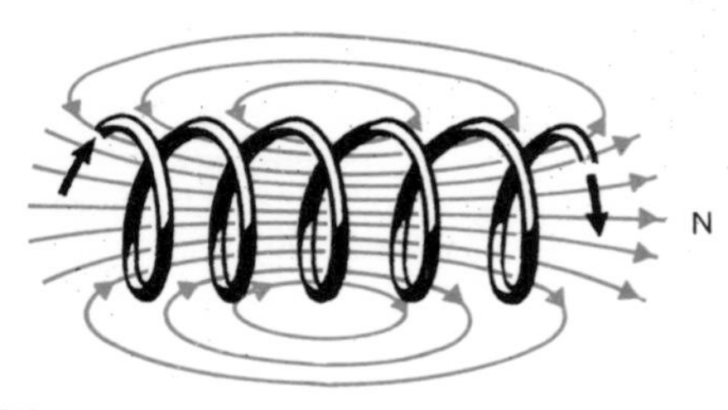

FIG. 5 MAGNETIC FLUX (LINES OF FORCE) IN A COIL THROUGH WHICH A CURRENT IS FLOWING

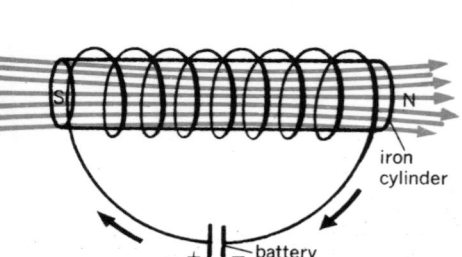

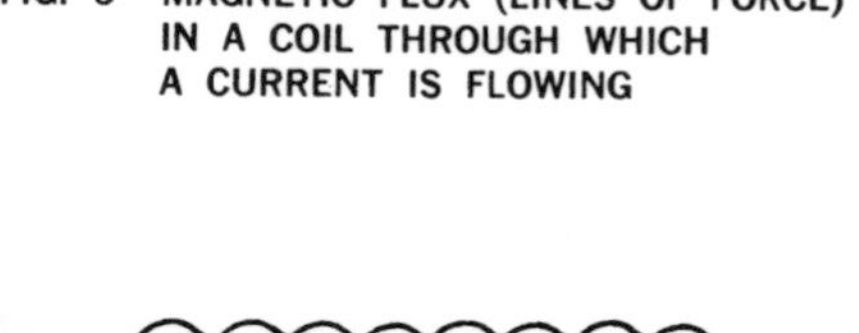

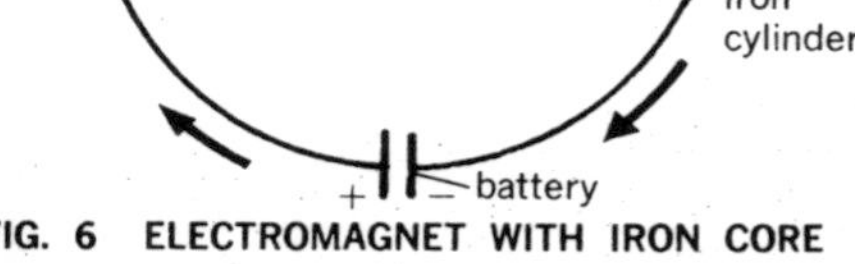

FIG. 6 ELECTROMAGNET WITH IRON CORE

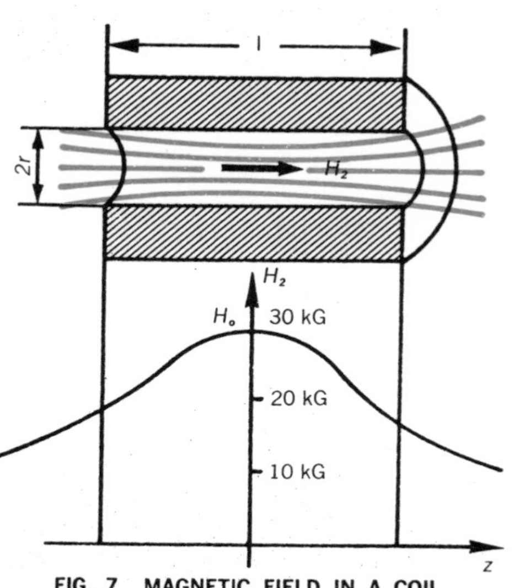

FIG. 7 MAGNETIC FIELD IN A COIL

Electromagnets (continued)

Small electromagnets are used in a wide variety of electrical equipment. Familiar examples presented in Vol. I include the electric bell, the relay, the loudspeaker the telephone, etc. There are innumerable other types of apparatus and electrical machinery in which electromagnets play an essential role: measuring equipment television tubes, switch gear, remote-control equipment, tape recorders, signaling devices, telecommunication equipment, etc. The magnetic lenses in electron microscopes are basically electromagnets. Electric motors and generators are, of course very important applications of electromagnets. Lifting magnets are used for handling scrap iron, steel plates, etc.; such magnets may have lifting capacities of several tons Powerful electromagnets play an important part in various branches of research—e.g., in cyclotrons and similar equipment.

To produce a powerful magnetic field, the electromagnet should have a core which resembles as closely as possible a ring interrupted only by a narrow gap (Fig. 10); it is within this gap that the powerful field is developed, especially if the two poles are so shaped as to produce a concentration of the lines of force (Fig. 11). Examples of electromagnets embodying this principle and designed to produce high field strengths are illustrated in Figs. 12 and 13. The unit of magnetic-field strength is the oersted, this being the force in dynes which acts on a unit magnetic pole at any point in a magnetic field; the unit of magnetic flux is the weber; the gauss is the unit of magnetic induction. To obtain high field strengths in large volumes of space, it is necessary to dispense with the iron core: a large and long coil with a large number of windings and a powerful electric current will produce a strong and fairly homogeneous magnetic field in its interior. Theoretically it would be possible to increase the field strength to any desired value, but in actual practice the heat evolved in the windings causes major difficulties. Water cooling is usually employed for large magnets: the water circulates through pipes embedded in the windings, or the wires themselves are hollow and conduct both electricity and water.

An interesting application of the electromagnet in research is in the production of extremely low temperatures close to absolute zero ($-273°$ C) by the adiabatic demagnetization of a paramagnetic salt. The specimen to be cooled is embedded in such a salt, and the latter is cooled in liquid helium (about $-269°$ C). A strong magnetic field is then applied, which serves to orient all the magnetic dipoles (elementary "atomic magnets" formed by the orbiting electrons) in the salt, releasing heat from this into the helium, so that the temperature of the salt drops and comes very close to absolute zero.

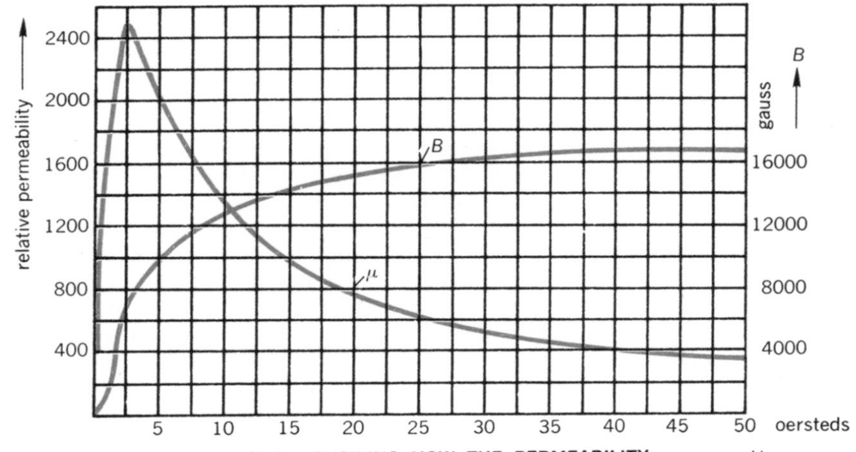

FIG. 8 DIAGRAM SHOWING HOW THE PERMEABILITY AND THE MAGNETIC INDUCTION B ARE RELATED TO THE FIELD STRENGTH H

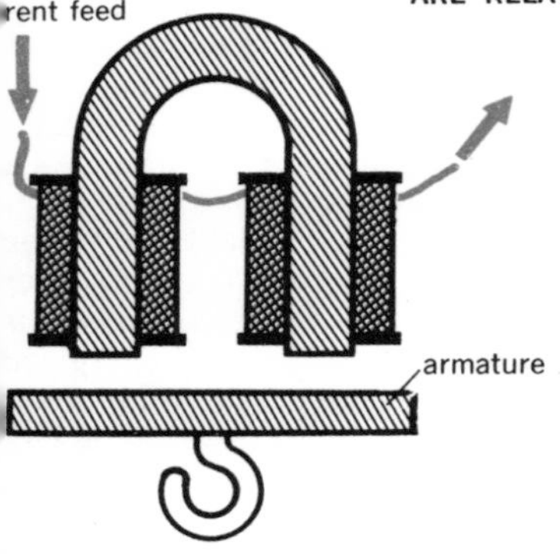

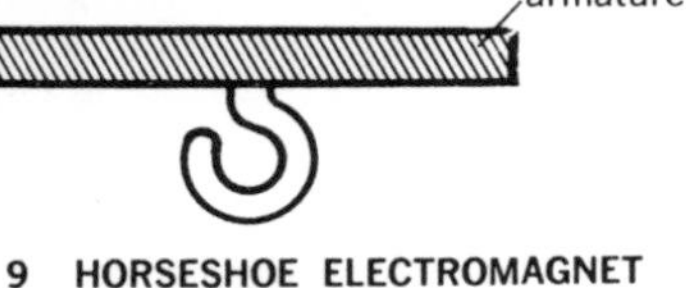

9 HORSESHOE ELECTROMAGNET WITH ARMATURE

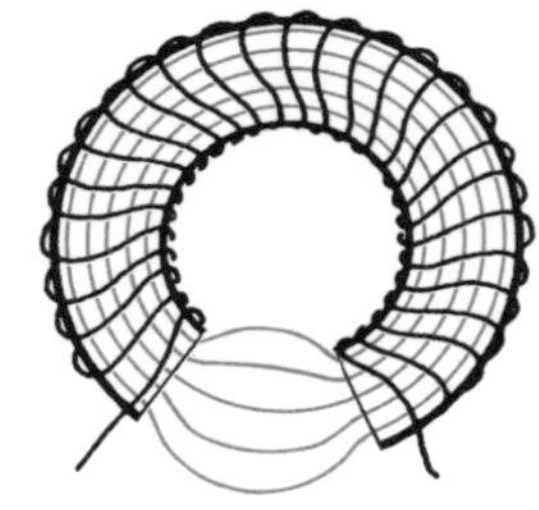

FIG. 10 MAGNETIC LINES OF FORCE IN AN INTERRUPTED MAGNETIC CIRCUIT

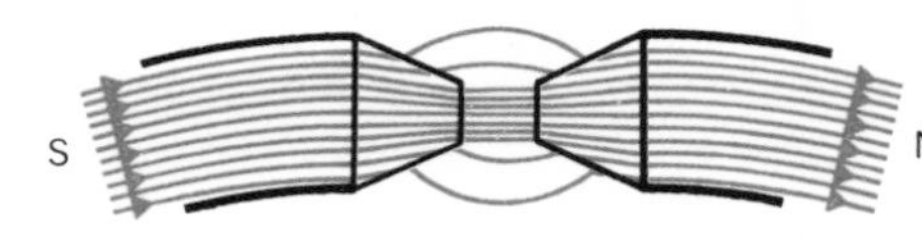

FIG. 11 TAPERED POLE SHOES

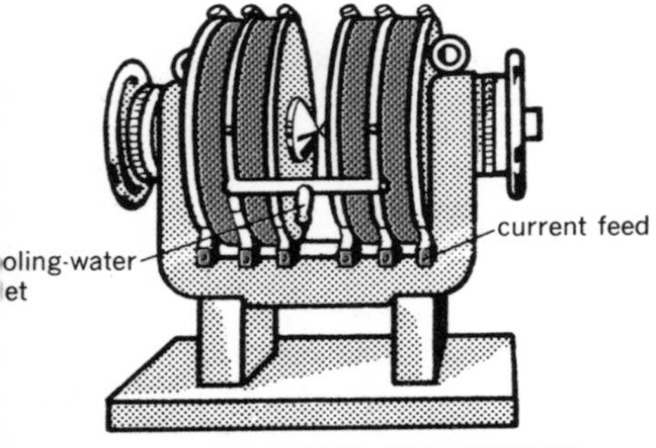

FIG. 12 WATER-COOLED FARADAY-TYPE ELECTROMAGNET

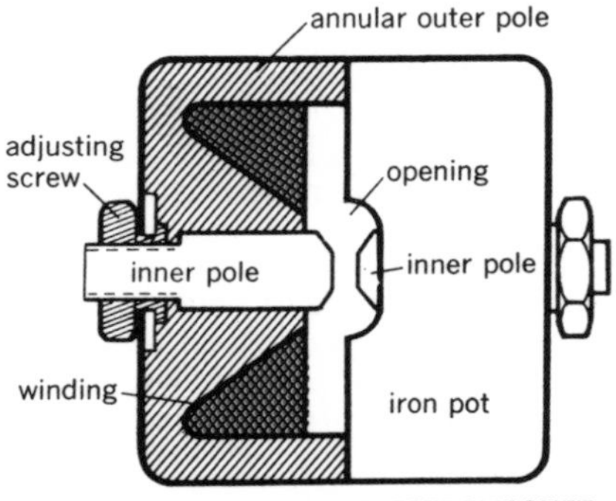

FIG. 13 A MODERN ELECTROMAGNET (DOUBLE-POT TYPE)

DIRECT-CURRENT MACHINES

A direct-current (or DC) machine is either an electric motor fed by a DC power supply or a generator (dynamo) which produces direct current. The motor and the generator are essentially identical in construction: in general, a DC machine can be used for either purpose. Fig. 1 schematically illustrates such a machine. It comprises the stator, which (in this example) has two magnetic poles for producing the magnetic field, and the rotor (usually called the armature in a DC machine) which rotates between the poles. In very small motors the field may be produced by a permanent magnet; otherwise electromagnets are used, the stator poles being provided with windings (known as field windings or exciting windings) through which current flows. The armature also has a winding consisting of conductors (coils of wire) disposed in grooves formed in the armature core, the latter being composed of sheet-steel laminations. The ends of the armature coils are each connected to one of the insulated copper segments of the commutator. In a generator the current for the external circuit is collected from the commutator by brushes (spring-loaded contact pieces, usually of carbon). Conversely, the current for driving a motor is applied to the armature through the brushes and commutator; at the same time part of the current is used to energize the field windings. The commutator is mounted on the armature shaft and rotates with it. Fig. 2 schematically shows the "developed" armature winding and the commutator segments, which in reality are of course arranged in a cylindrical shape. In this example the armature has a so-called lap winding. Motors usually have a wave winding, however, in which the winding does not overlap its previous course in loops, but follows a wavelike course.

When current is passed through the armature winding of a motor, the magnetic fields of armature and stator strive to place themselves parallel to each other. As a result, the armature develops a torque (turning moment) about its shaft. The magnitude of the torque is proportional to the strength of the magnetic field and of the current. Several types of DC motor can be distinguished according to the manner of connection of the armature and field windings respectively. In the *shunt motor* the field winding is connected in parallel with the armature and is thus energized by a current of constant voltage, so that the magnetic field is constant. When load is applied to the motor, the speed decreases, but not considerably. Thus this type of motor has a fairly constant speed at all loads and is especially suitable for driving machine tools, lifts, etc. In the *series motor* the field and armature windings are connected in series, so that the strength of field is dependent on the motor load and varies with the armature current. Such motors develop a high torque at starting and run at a speed depending on the load; they are suitable for cranes, traction, etc. because of the high starting torque and their flexibility of operation. Under no-load conditions the speed may become dangerously high, however. The third form of DC motor is the *compound motor*, which has, in addition to the shunt field winding (in parallel with the armature), a series winding which reinforces the field and gives a fairly high starting torque while retaining the speed-limiting properties of the shunt winding. It is used for driving machine tools, presses, shearing machines, etc. Its characteristic properties are a compromise between those of the two foregoing types of motor.

The DC generator is the reverse of the motor in that the armature is rotated by an external source of power, so that the armature conductors intersect the lines of force of the magnetic field of the stator. The principle of the generator has already been dealt with on page 44. In the *separately excited generator* (Fig. 3) the field winding (or exciting winding) is supplied with current from an independent source

(more)

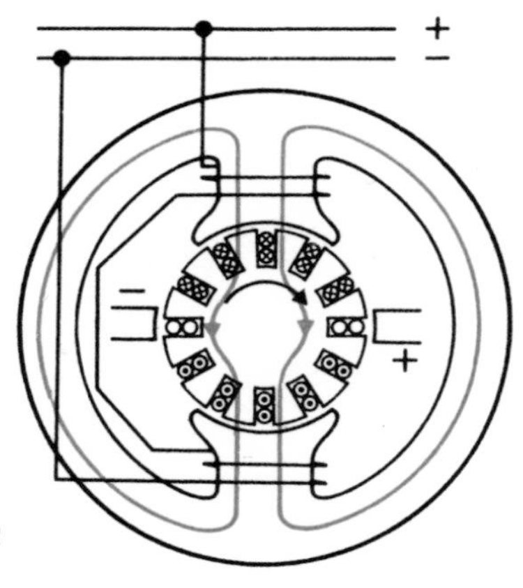

FIG. 1 DC GENERATOR

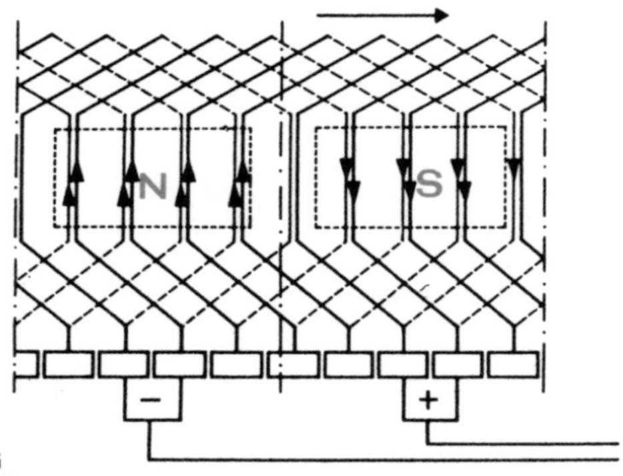

FIG. 2 LAP WINDING ON ARMATURE

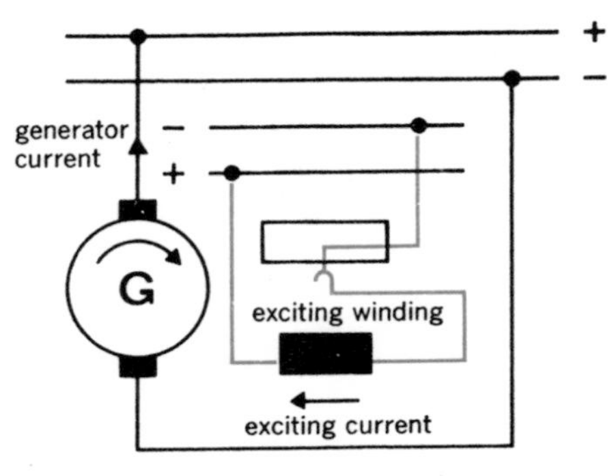

FIG. 3

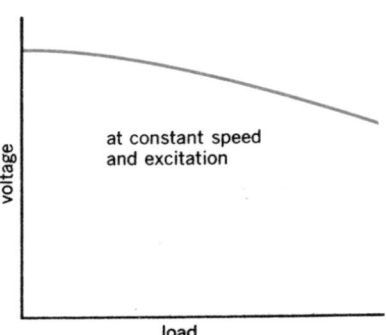

Wiring of an electric motor. Brown Boveri, Baden, Switzerland
Photo Roland Schneider, Len Sirman Press

at constant voltage. With increasing (electrical) load, the voltage at the output terminals of the generator undergoes some decrease. If necessary, this decrease can be compensated, and the voltage thus kept constant, by appropriately increasing the excitation voltage applied to the field winding. This type of generator is suitable for supplying current to an electrical system of constant voltage—e.g., for the charging of storage batteries.

In analogy with those DC motors already discussed, there are three main types of *self-excited generator*: shunt, series and compound. In all these machines a portion of the current produced by the generator itself is used for energizing the field windings. In the *shunt generator* the field winding is in parallel with the armature winding (Fig. 4). With increasing load there is a greater decrease in voltage than in the case of the separately excited generator; nevertheless, at not too high loads the decrease is only gradual, so that this type of generator is also suitable—in conjunction with a shunt rheostat—for constant-voltage systems. However, with increasing load the voltage falls off more rapidly, and above a certain maximum load the characteristic curve even becomes retrograde, with the voltage decreasing to zero at short-circuit. The shunt generator is the commonest type; it is used in power stations, electrochemical works, etc.—i.e., in situations where no frequent and no excessively large load variations occur; it can also be used for the charging of storage batteries. The *series generator* has the field winding connected in series with the armature winding (Fig. 5). The voltage becomes higher as the load increases. This type of generator is seldom used: only as an auxiliary device for loss compensation in long-distance power transmission systems or in constant-current distribution systems in which the current, not the voltage, is kept constant. (Normally, a constant-voltage system is used, in which the voltage remains constant at all currents and all consuming appliances—lamps, motors, etc.—are connected in parallel across the mains.) The *compound generator* has a shunt winding (in parallel with the armature) and, in addition, a series field winding to compensate for the drop in voltage with increasing load. With appropriate design of the respective windings it is possible to obtain a voltage which remains virtually constant at all loads (Fig. 6). The compound generator is used for systems in which the voltage remains constant without need for adjustment to compensate for frequent and large variations of load, e.g., in rolling mills.

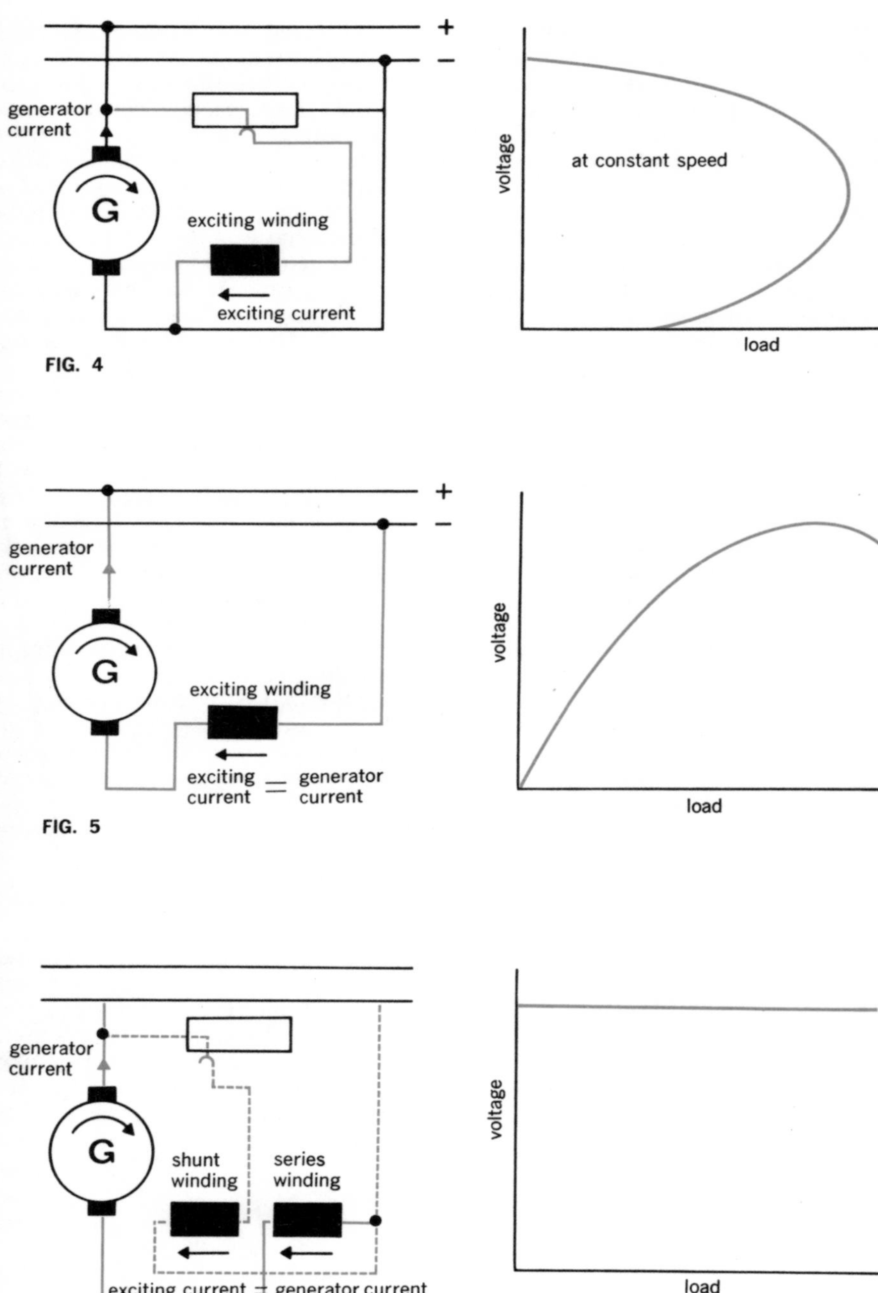
+
–
generator current
G
exciting winding
exciting current
voltage
at constant speed
load
FIG. 4
+
–
generator current
G
exciting winding
exciting current = generator current
voltage
load
FIG. 5
generator current
G
shunt winding
series winding
exciting current = generator current
voltage
load
FIG. 6

If the armature winding of a DC generator is connected to continuous slip rings instead of to a segmented commutator, an alternating current (AC) is collected from these rings by the brushes (see page 44). There may be two slip rings, connected to two opposite points of the rotor winding, or three slip rings, connected to three equidistant points; in the latter case a three-phase alternating current is obtained. To avoid the technical difficulty of collecting a high-intensity current from slip rings, the form of design now usually adopted for an alternator (AC generator) is that of the "revolving field alternator." In this machine the armature winding, in which the output current is generated, is on the stator (the stationary frame of the machine), while the field system revolves on the rotor, the latter being called the magnet wheel in this type of machine. The direct current for excitation—i.e., for energizing the winding of the magnet wheel—is supplied through brushes and slip rings; as it is a current of much lower strength than the output current of the generator, the technical problem is greatly reduced.

The voltage produced by the AC generator depends on the strength of the excitation current, the speed of rotation, and the number of pairs of poles on the magnet wheel. The frequency of the voltage is also directly dependent on the speed and the number of pole pairs. Figs. 1 and 2 show a two-pole and a four-pole rotor (i.e., with one and two pole pairs respectively). The number of tappings (connections) of the stator winding increases in proportion to the number of pole pairs. Since it is desired to maintain a certain frequency (usually 50 or 60 cycles/sec.), it is not possible to vary the speed of rotation to adjust the voltage to the required value. This can be done only by varying the excitation current, i.e., varying the intensity of the magnetic field.

Fig. 4 is a sectional drawing of a two-pole three-phase *synchronous alternator*, with DC excitation and a fixed frequency, as envisaged in the preceding paragraph. Fig. 3 is a diagram of the voltage generated by a three-phase alternator with star-connected stator winding. It is this type of machine that is most widely used for generation of electricity. The driving power is provided by steam, water or gas turbines or by internal-combustion engines. Depending on the speed of these prime movers, two-pole or four-pole generators are used to obtain the required frequency of 50 or 60 cycles/sec.

If a synchronous alternator is run up to its normal speed (synchronous speed)—i.e., the speed corresponding to the frequency of the circuit—and connected to an existing power-distribution system, it will continue to run as a *synchronous motor* on removal of the external driving power. Such an AC motor, which is similar in construction to a synchronous alternator, always needs an external agency—e.g., a small auxiliary motor—to run it up to speed before being put on to load. It will then continue running at constant speed, "in step" with the frequency, at any load up to a certain overload; if this is exceeded, the motor will fall "out of step" and stop. This ability to run at constant speed, irrespective of the load, makes it very useful for certain applications. Small synchronous motors are used to drive electric clocks timing mechanisms, etc. The drawback of the synchronous AC motor is that it is not self-starting; it needs an auxiliary starting motor or the rotor must be provided with an auxiliary starting winding; in either case the starting torque is poor.

(more)

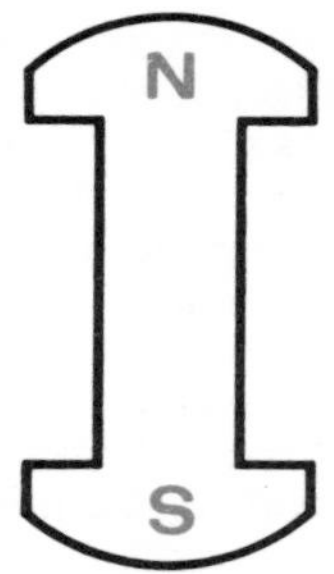

FIG. 1

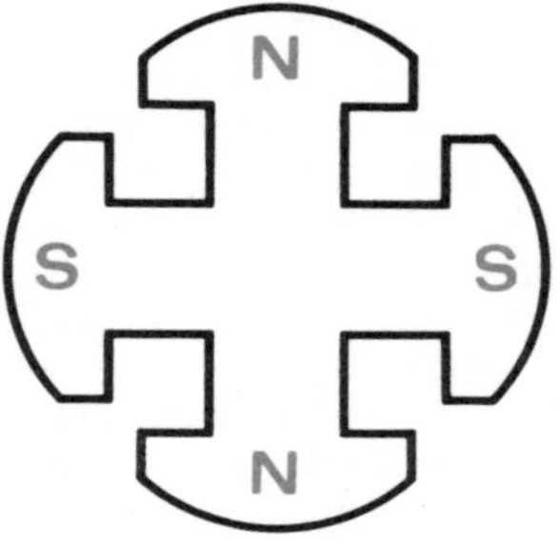

FIG. 2

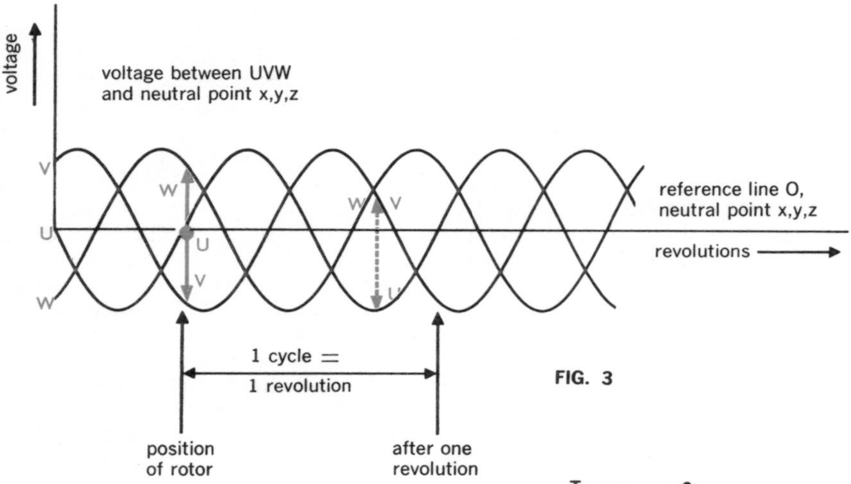

voltage

voltage between UVW
and neutral point x,y,z

reference line O,
neutral point x,y,z

revolutions

1 cycle =
1 revolution

position
of rotor

after one
revolution

FIG. 3

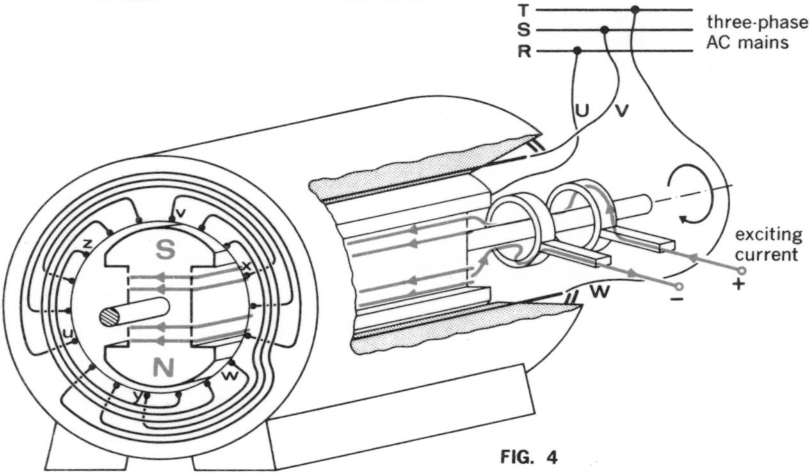

T
S
R

three-phase
AC mains

U V W

exciting
current

– +

FIG. 4

A three-phase winding such as the stator of a three-phase synchronous motor produces a so-called rotating magnetic field which has an effect similar to that of a mechanically rotated magnet system. In the machine shown in Fig. 4 (p. 259), conceived as a motor, the rotor consists of an iron core provided with peripheral slots in which the "winding" is disposed in the form of longitudinal copper or aluminum bars connected to rings at each end forming a short-circuited winding without any external connection through slip rings. This is known as a squirrel-cage rotor (Fig. 1). The motion of the rotating field in relation to the rotor bars causes a voltage to be induced in them. This voltage, and the current associated with it, depends on the strength of the magnetic field and on the speed of the field relative to the bars. The squirrel-cage motor is a particular type of *induction motor*. Such motors are in general characterized by having only the stator connected to the external circuit. The stator produces a rotating field. The current induced in the rotor causes it to follow the rotating field and run at a speed slightly lower than that of the field. Because of this slight difference in speed, these motors are called *asynchronous motors*: i.e., the rotor speed is asynchronous, not an exact multiple of the frequency (as in the case of synchronous motors). The difference between the actual speed of an induction motor and the speed of the rotating field is called the "slip" and is expressed as a percentage of the synchronous speed. The stator of an induction motor is usually fed with three-phase current, but it is also possible to build single-phase induction motors with special arrangements to produce a rotating field. When the *squirrel-cage induction motor* is switched on, a large initial rush of current occurs. The current induced in the rotor when the latter is still at rest is very large; then, as the rotor gains speed, so that the difference between its speed and that of the rotating field decreases, the current induced in the rotor correspondingly decreases in strength. It might thus be supposed that the torque developed by the rotor is highest on starting and decreases to a minimum at full speed, when the slip has dropped to a small value. However, because of the phase displacement of the rotor current in relation to the rotor voltage, the maximum torque does not occur at starting. With increasing rotor speed the said phase displacement decreases, and the resulting torque is dependent on the speed of rotation. The maximum torque that the motor can develop is called the breakdown torque; if the load exceeds this, the motor stops. The rotor of an induction motor always adjusts its speed to a certain value corresponding to the load, so that the motor torque is equal to the load torque. Even under "no-load" conditions there is always a certain amount of load due to friction; the rotor therefore never quite reaches synchronous speed; there is always some slip.

(more)

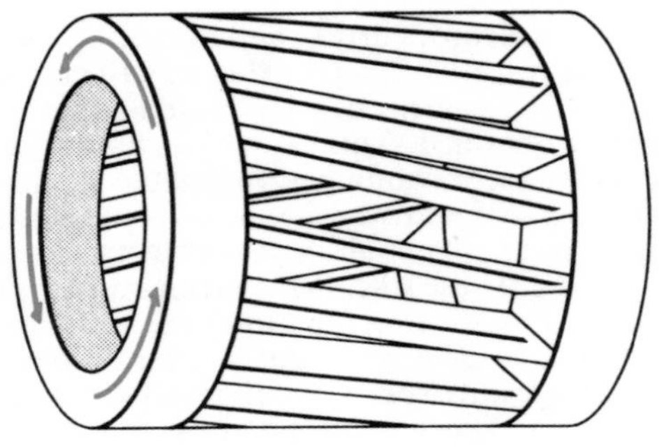

FIG. 1 SQUIRREL-CAGE ROTOR

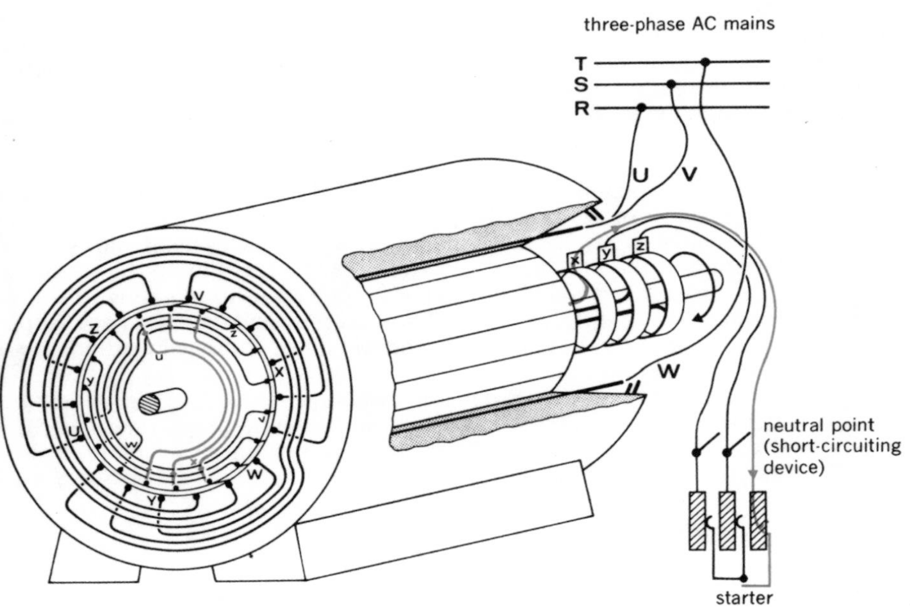

FIG. 2 SLIP-RING ROTOR

The phase displacement between rotor current and magnetic field can be modified by varying the resistance of the rotor winding. In this way the torque characteristic can be altered, so that the starting current can be limited while a reasonably high starting torque is nevertheless obtained. This is not possible with a squirrel-cage induction motor, however, as the rotor winding is unsuitable for this kind of control. Instead, it is necessary to have a wound rotor, i.e., a rotor provided with a winding connected to slip rings (Fig. 2, page 261), enabling variable resistors (rheostats) to be connected in series to the winding. These so-called starting resistors may be regarded as an extension of the winding. For starting the motor the resistors are temporarily connected into the rotor circuit, to give good starting conditions. Then, when the motor has attained its normal working speed, the resistors are disconnected and no longer perform any function; the brushes are lifted off the slip rings in order to reduce wear. The slip rings are short-circuited and the rotor then functions essentially in the manner of a squirrel-cage rotor. This type of motor is called a *slip-ring induction motor*. To reduce the starting current, any motor may initially be connected to a voltage which is lower than the nominal voltage. This can be done by means of a variable resistor connected in series with the stator winding; the resistance is reduced as the motor gains speed; when working speed is reached, the resistor is bypassed and performs no further function. Another method of reducing the voltage at starting is by using an autotransformer starter whereby a reduced voltage from a transformer is applied, in one or more steps, to the stator. A third method, applicable to three-phase induction motors, is provided by star-delta control, whereby the stator winding is temporarily connected in star instead of in delta. The voltage is thereby reduced in the ratio of $1/\sqrt{3}$, and the starting current is reduced to one-third of that drawn at full voltage. The changeover is effected by means of a star-delta switch.

Speed control of induction motors can be obtained by various methods: frequency control (the frequency of the power supply is varied by means of a special device; this alters the synchronous speed of the revolving magnetic field); pole-changing control (alteration of the number of effective poles by regrouping the stator coils; this method enables the speed to be changed stepwise in fixed ratios; it does not allow continuous variation); addition of rotor or secondary resistance (slip-ring induction motor); stator voltage control. The two first-mentioned methods are also applicable to synchronous motors.

A third type of AC motor (besides the induction motor and the synchronous motor) is the *commutator motor*, constructed on the same general lines as the DC motor and used in household appliances such as vacuum cleaners, food mixers etc. They are sometimes called universal motors because they can be used on DC or AC.

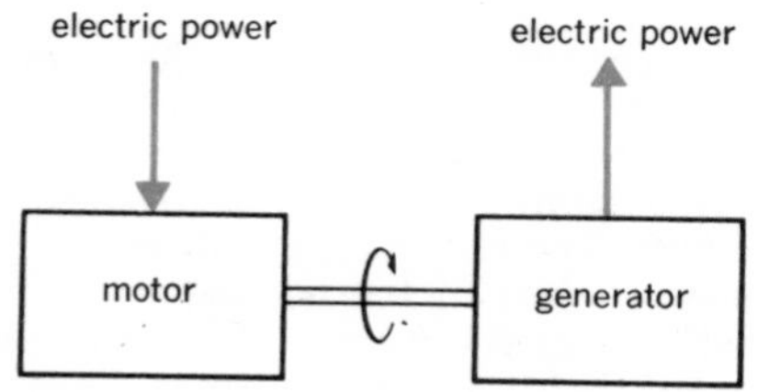

FIG. 1

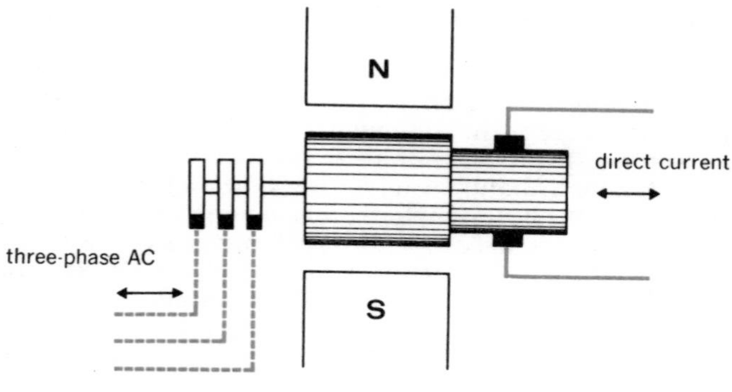

FIG. 2

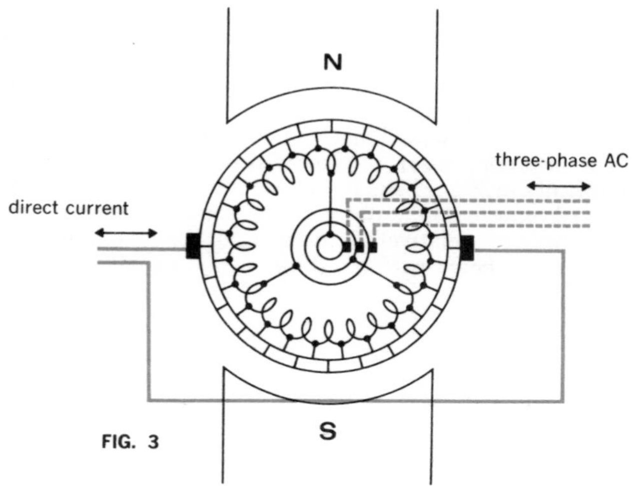

FIG. 3

Converter is a general term applicable to a rotary machine or combination of machines whose function is to convert AC to DC or vice versa, or which is used for AC phase conversion or frequency conversion.

The *motor-generator* is a combination of an electric motor and a generator connected to the same shaft. The motor, fed with one type of current, drives the generator, which produces current of the desired type. For instance, alternating current can be converted into direct current. The principle is indicated in Fig. 1 (page 263). An advantage of the motor-generator is that the input and the output current can be independently controlled. Against this, however, the overall efficiency is relatively low, being the product of the efficiencies of the two machines individually and therefore lower than either of them.

The *rotary converter* (or synchronous converter) is a rotating machine, resembling a multipolar DC generator in construction, with the addition of slip rings. It has a stationary field-magnet system and a rotating armature whose winding is connected to a commutator upon which are brushes connected to the DC terminals. At the opposite end of the armature to the commutator are slip rings connected to tappings in the armature winding; the brushes on these rings are connected to the AC terminals. The machine and the armature winding are shown schematically in Figs. 2 and 3 (page 263); in this particular example the machine has been designed for three-phase AC. If AC is supplied to the converter, it will run as a synchronous motor, and DC can be taken from the commutator. Alternatively, if DC is supplied to the machine, AC can be taken from the slip rings. The efficiency of the rotary converter is higher than that of the motor-generator and the cost is lower, but it is not possible —unless special methods are employed—to vary the DC voltage independently of the AC voltage.

The *cascade converter* (or motor-converter) comprises a wound-rotor induction motor mounted on the same shaft as a rotary converter. Suitable points of their windings are interconnected. The set runs at half the synchronous speed of the induction motor, and the slip energy from the rotor of the motor is fed to the armature of the converter and converted to DC. The other part of the energy input to the motor is transmitted mechanically by the shaft to the converter, which converts it to DC output (in doing this the converter acts as a DC generator). The combination of electrical and mechanical power transmission is symbolized in Fig. 1. This machine is intermediate between a motor-generator and a rotary converter, combining some of the advantages of both. It is more expensive than a rotary converter, but has the advantage that it can be supplied at higher voltages, and the commutating difficulties are less severe. The interconnection of motor rotor and the converter armature is illustrated schematically in Fig. 2. The induction motor is fed with three-phase AC, and DC is collected from the commutator of the rotary converter.

Converters are nowadays relatively seldom used, their function—conversion of AC to DC in most cases—being performed more economically by silicon rectifiers.

three-phase AC
N
stator
direct
current
starter
S
rotary converter
asynchronous
motor

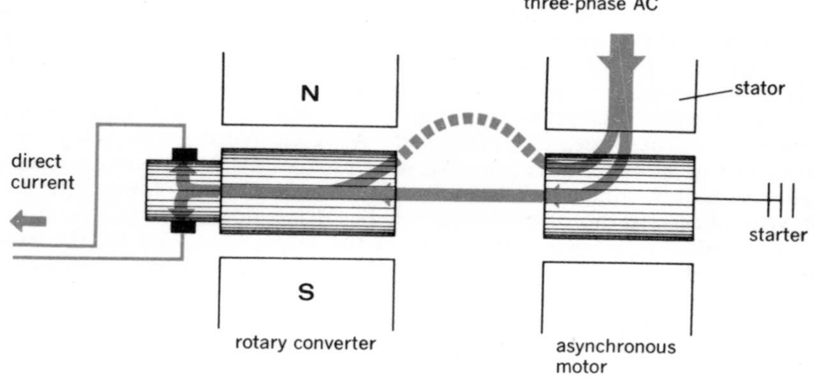

FIG. 4

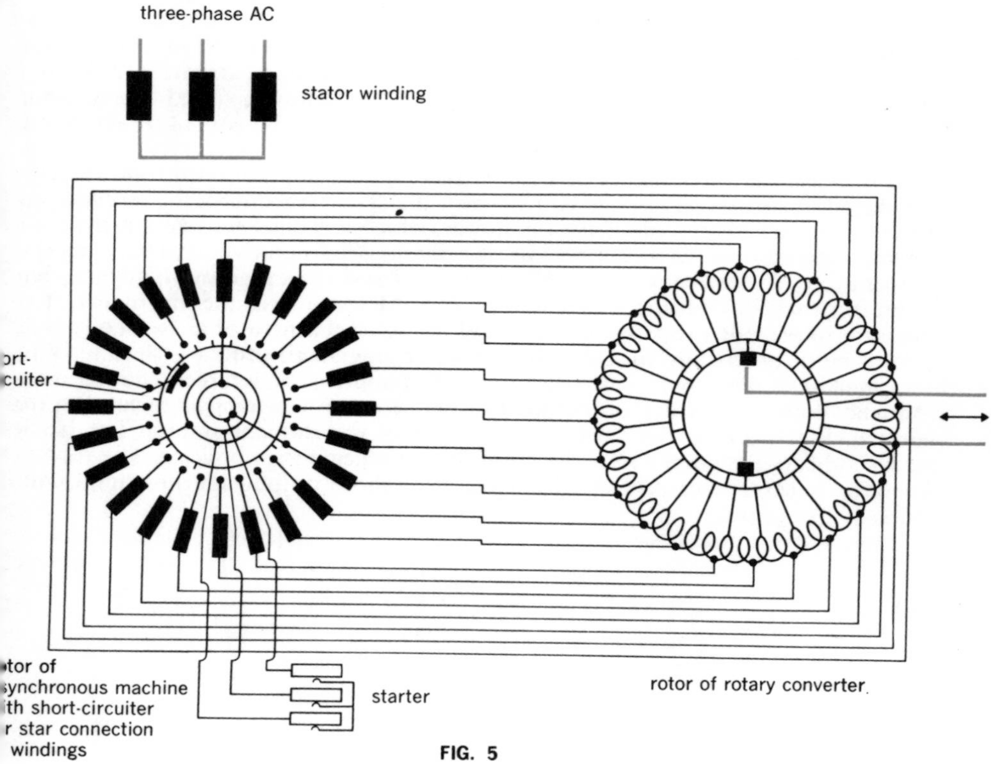

three-phase AC
stator winding
ort-
cuiter
tor of
synchronous machine
ith short-circuiter
r star connection
windings
starter
rotor of rotary converter

FIG. 5

WARD-LEONARD CONTROL

This is a control system whereby the speed of a DC motor (see page 252) can be very accurately varied by the application of a variable voltage obtained from a motor-generator by shunt regulation. This system provides a wide range of speed control in both directions of rotation of the motor and low power losses. It is expensive and used only for large motors driving such machinery as rolling mills, cranes, winding engines, rotary printing presses, etc. A typical Ward-Leonard control circuit is shown in Fig. 1. The main motor M, which drives the machinery, is a separately excited DC motor which is fed by the continually running control generator G of the Ward-Leonard motor-generator set. The drive motor A of this set (usually an induction motor) is fed with current from the mains. The DC for the excitation (energizing the field windings) of the motor M and the generator G may be supplied by an external source or, if this is not available, by a small self-exciting DC generator E mounted on the shaft of the drive motor A.

With constant excitation, the speed of a shunt motor is very largely dependent on the voltage of the current supplied to it and is only slightly affected by the magnitude of the load. The voltage applied to the terminals of the main motor M (which in general has constant excitation) is supplied by the control generator G. By means of the field rheostat F, the excitation of the control generator can be so adjusted that the generator produces a voltage that can cause the main motor to run at the desired speed. With this rheostat it is thus possible to obtain "infinitely variable" speed control and also to reverse the direction of rotation of the main motors, this being done by reversing the direction of the field current. With Ward-Leonard control the speed of the main motor can be accurately varied to any value from zero to nominal speed, without involving any appreciable loss of power. Since the motor speed is moreover inversely proportional to the field current, a further speed increase can be obtained by field weakening, though the torque will thereby be reduced. A further advantage is that when the speed is reduced, the momentum of the driven machinery will drive the motor, which will thus act temporarily as a dynamo and supply energy back to the mains (regenerative braking: energy recuperation). A drawback of the Ward-Leonard system is its cost, this being due to the fact that, in addition to the main motor M that drives the machinery, it is necessary to provide the drive motor A and the control generator G, both of which have to be of practically the same power as M; the small generator E is also an extra item. The main motor M can be installed some considerable distance away from the Ward-Leonard motor-generator set, as only electrical connections are required. Fig. 2 shows the various main units of this control system. The black arrows indicate the energy-flow direction during regenerative braking. The motor-generator is sometimes replaced by a rectifier whose output can be varied continuously from zero.

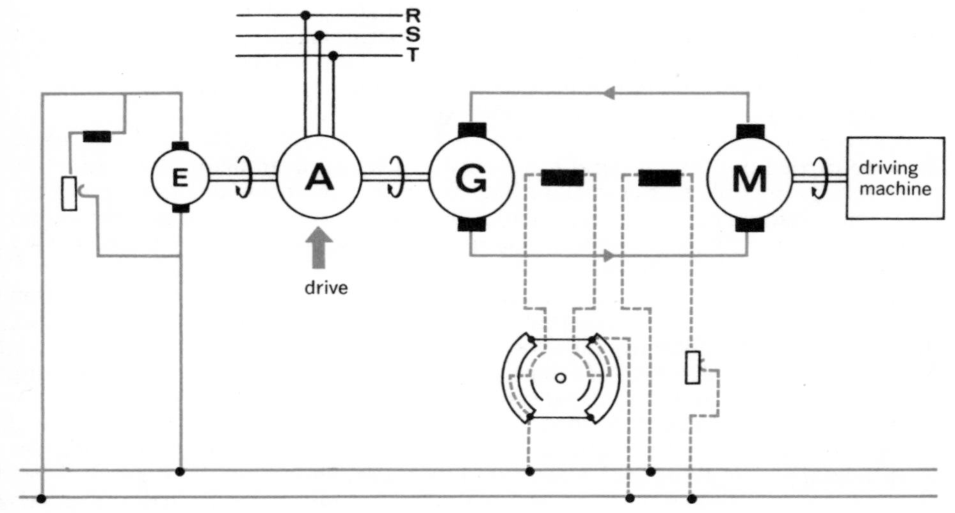
R
S
T
E
A
G
M
driving machine
drive
+
–

FIG. 1

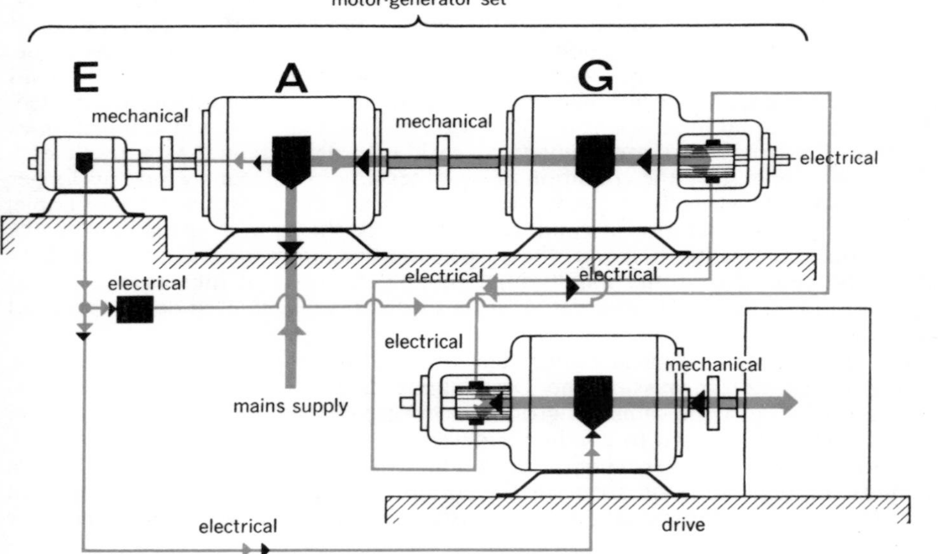
motor-generator set
E
A
G
mechanical
mechanical
electrical
electrical
electrical
electrical
electrical
mechanical
mains supply
electrical
drive

FIG. 2

The two methods available for the transmission and distribution of electric power are: underground insulated cables; bare conductors suspended at a safe height aboveground. The latter method—i.e., overhead lines—is generally adopted for high-voltage long-distance transmission, because the cost is lower than for corresponding buried cables, especially at higher voltages.

Before an overhead transmission line is built, a survey of the proposed route must be carried out. The general route may be selected from maps, approximating as closely as possible to the straight line connecting the beginning and end of the route, but avoiding natural or man-made obstacles. If possible, the alignment should avoid woods and forests; it should also not pass close to towns or villages, having regard to their probable future expansion.

The overhead line must not be located too close to railway overhead electrification lines, or to telephone and telegraph lines, because of the danger of induction. Also, it must be routed sufficiently far away from airfields, artillery training ranges, etc. Major terrain obstacles, such as extensive marshy areas, unstable hillsides presenting a landslide hazard, and mining subsidence areas, must likewise be avoided.

Once the route has been decided, a final detailed survey must be made. Ground levels are determined at frequent intervals for the purpose of establishing the longitudinal profile along the route. Part of such a profile is shown in Fig. 1. It shows all the significant topographical features along the route and is plotted to a greatly exaggerated vertical scale in relation to the horizontal scale—e.g., 1:250 vertically and 1:1250 horizontally. The purpose of the profile is to enable the positions and heights of the supports to be determined, so as to conform to requirements of minimum ground clearance and special arrangements at crossings of railways, roads, etc. The positions of the supports and the curve representing the maximum sag of the bottom conductor (corresponding to highest temperature) are plotted. As a rule, in order to avoid unfavorable conditions of vibration of the conductors due to wind load, successive spans are not made exactly equal. When the conductors are erected, the tension is equal in all spans of the section of line concerned. On completion of erection, the conductors are clamped at each suspension point. As a result of a change in temperature the condition of equal tension in all spans would no longer be satisfied if the suspension points were rigid. A fall in temperature, for example, would cause a greater rise in conductor tension in the shorter spans than in the longer ones. In reality, however, the suspension insulators are flexible enough to allow the conductor some longitudinal (in-line) freedom of movement, so that equalization of tension in adjacent spans is automatically achieved despite rise and fall of temperature.

Fig. 2 illustrates a typical lattice steel tower ("pylon") for supporting a high-voltage overhead transmission line. Determining the requisite tower height is based on the need to provide sufficient ground clearance of the conductors at maximum sag and with due regard to conductor deviation caused by swinging in the wind. Horizontal and vertical spacing of the conductors must ensure adequate clearance at midspan, depending on span length, sag and voltage. Fig. 2 shows a so-called wire-clearance diagram based on these considerations. The sag curve of a conductor

(more)

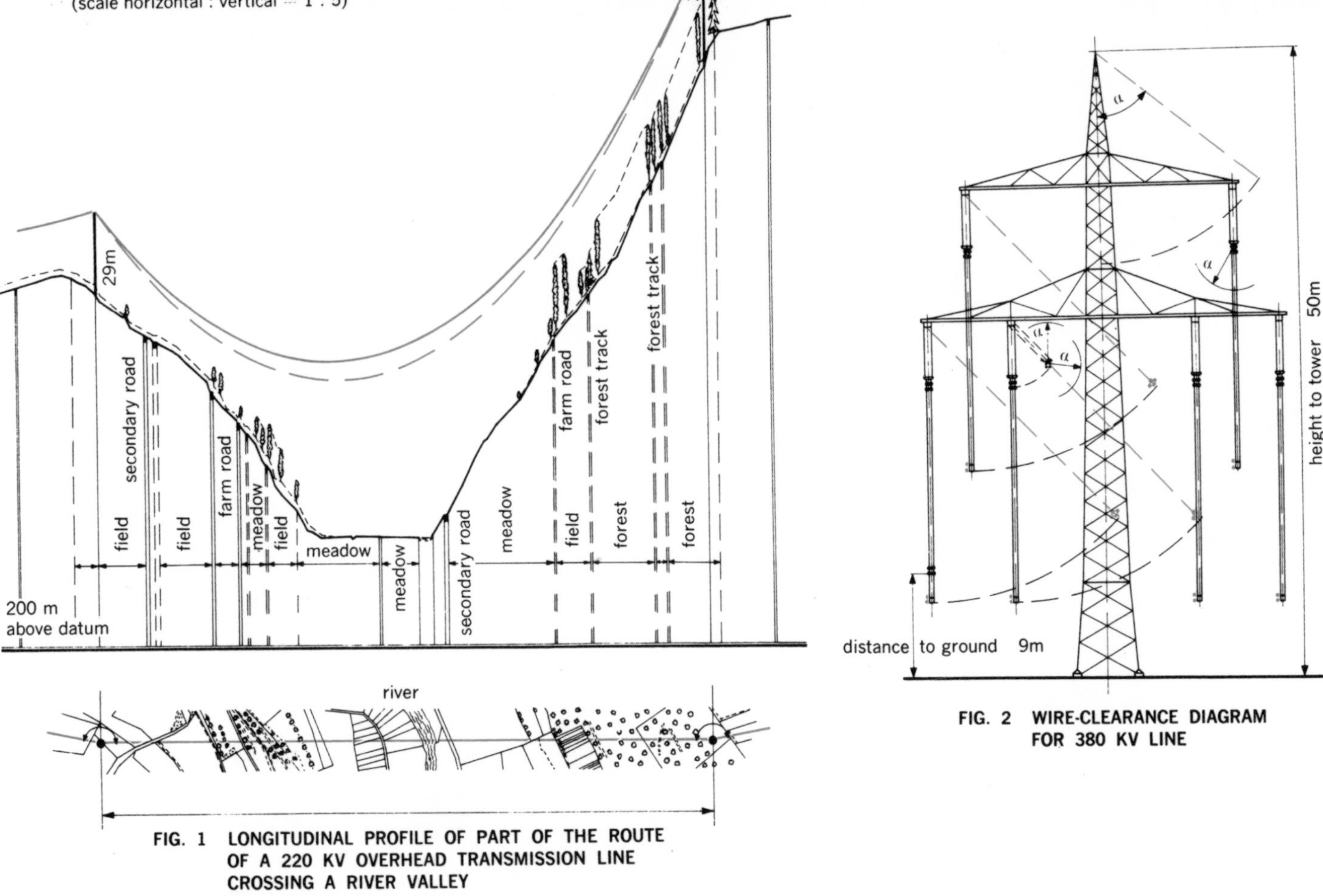

FIG. 1 LONGITUDINAL PROFILE OF PART OF THE ROUTE OF A 220 KV OVERHEAD TRANSMISSION LINE CROSSING A RIVER VALLEY

FIG. 2 WIRE-CLEARANCE DIAGRAM FOR 380 KV LINE

Insulators on an overhead transmission line
Photo Pierre Berger, Len Sirman Press

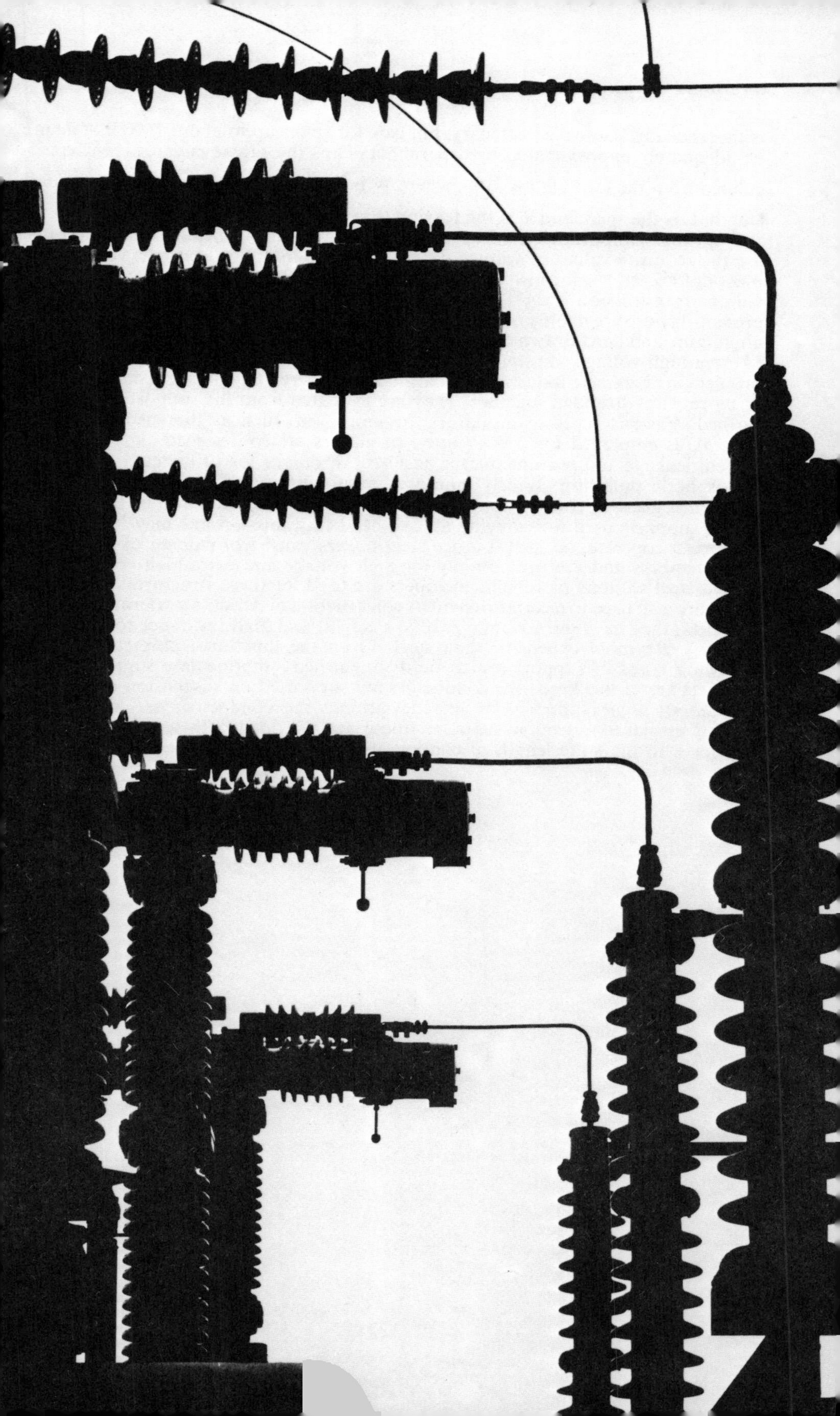

is theoretically a so-called catenary, but can, for spans up to about 1600 ft. (500 m), be adequately approximated by a parabola. Thus the sag at midspan can be calculated from the formula $f = \frac{WL^2}{8T}$, where W is the weight of the conductor per unit length, L is the span, and T is the tension (Fig. 3).

Of primary importance to the electrical design of an overhead transmission line are the requisite values of voltage drop and power loss. For example, voltage loss must not exceed 6% for low voltage, 10% for high voltage, and 15% for extra-high-voltage transmission lines. Power loss should not exceed 7%. The conductors in present-day use are mainly of three types: steel-cored aluminum (Fig. 4), hard-drawn aluminum, and hard-drawn copper; the first-mentioned type is used for the majority of extra-high-voltage transmission lines. Corrosion of conductors may be a serious problem in aggressive industrial or marine atmospheres. Conductors consist of three or more wires stranded together. They are insulated from the supports, which are earthed. Various types of insulators are employed, such as the suspension type (Fig. 5), as employed for 220 kv lines. Insulators are so designed as to minimize current leakage and prevent surface flashover in rain or fog or under conditions of atmospheric pollution. Widely employed insulating materials are porcelain and toughened glass, in conjunction with fittings of galvanized cast iron or steel.

The supports used for carrying an overhead transmission line may be of wood, reinforced concrete, or steel. Lattice steel towers consist of painted or galvanized steel members and are used mainly for high-voltage and extra-high-voltage lines. Rolled-steel sections or tubular members are used for these structures. Aluminum alloys are also used to a certain extent as construction materials for transmission-line supports; they have the advantages of low weight and high resistance to corrosion, but they are more expensive than steel. From the functional point of view the following types of support are to be distinguished: intermediate supports (most supports are of this kind; the conductors are supported on suspension or pin type insulators); angle supports (at line deviations; the conductors are attached to tension insulators); section supports (these are provided with tension insulators and serve to limit the length of continuous line); terminal supports (at each end of the line).

(more)

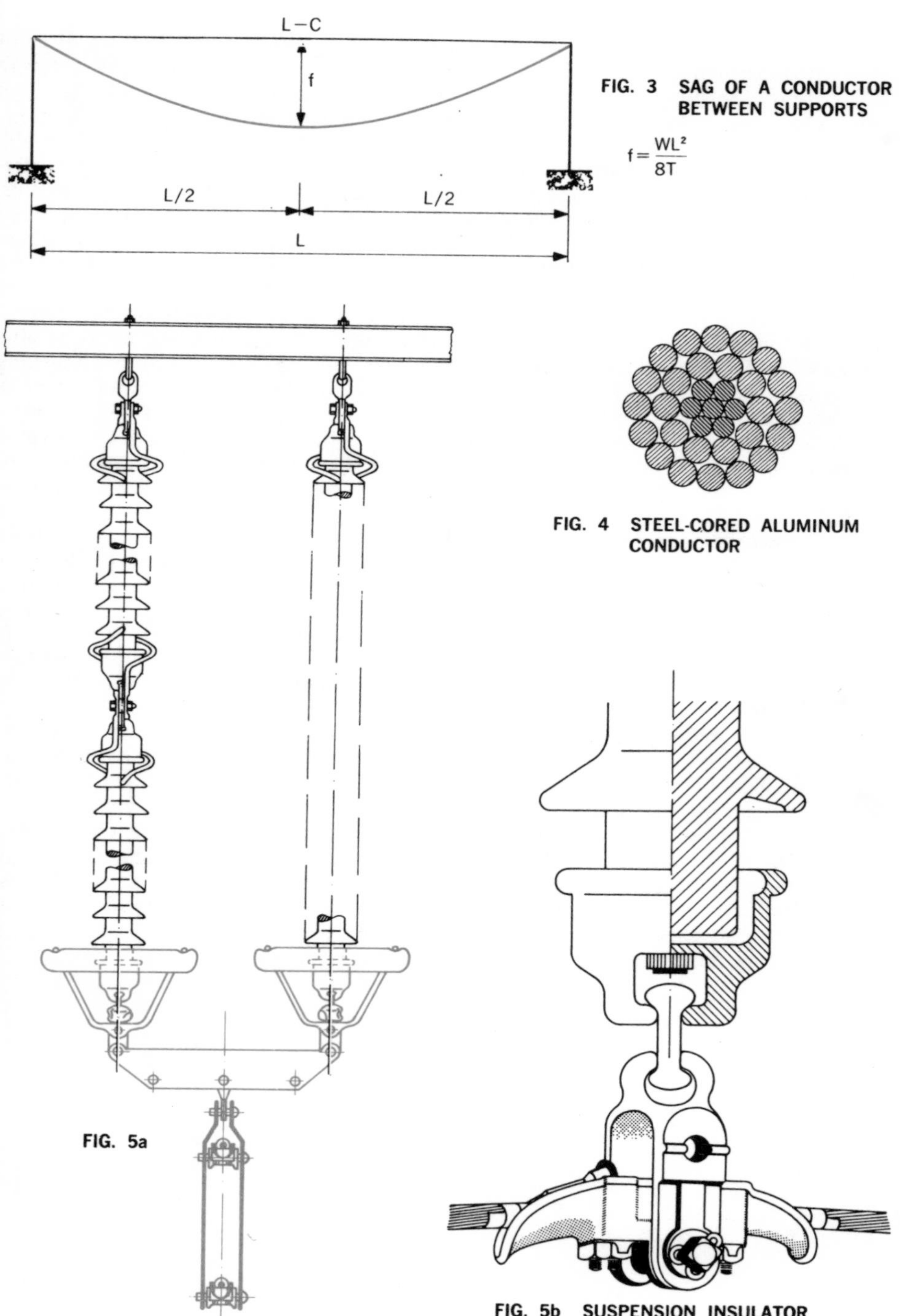

FIG. 3 SAG OF A CONDUCTOR BETWEEN SUPPORTS

$$f = \frac{WL^2}{8T}$$

FIG. 4 STEEL-CORED ALUMINUM CONDUCTOR

FIG. 5b SUSPENSION INSULATOR

Overhead Transmission Lines (continued)

The foundations for overhead transmission line supports depend on the type of support and on the nature of the soil. Wooden-pole supports and light concrete poles are often simply installed in excavated or bored holes. Broad-base lattice steel towers for high-voltage and extra-high-voltage lines generally have concrete foundations (Fig. 6). These may be so-called uplift and compression foundations (Fig. 6b), which have to resist upward and downward forces, produced by wind pressure, conductor tension, dead weight, etc. If the soil has very poor structural properties, it may be necessary to use pile foundations. Steel or concrete piles may be employed for the purpose. In firm soil, the foundations can be formed by placing concrete and reinforcement in bored holes, which may be widened at the bottom to form enlarged footings. The corner members of the towers are embedded in the concrete. Overvoltages in transmission lines may be due to internal causes (switching operations and faults); the line insulation and clearances are so contrived as to be able to withstand these overvoltages. External overvoltages are caused by lightning strokes on the line. The line conductors are shielded against lightning by means of overhead earth wires suitably earthed at the supports. There is usually a single earth wire running centrally, above the power conductors; sometimes two earth wires are installed. The supports themselves are also earthed. Fig. 7 shows how the potential due to a fault current is dissipated in the earth at the base of a broad-base tower.

In British practice, high-voltage transmission lines carry voltages ranging from 66 kv to 132 kv; extra-high-voltage lines carry voltages from 220 kv to 380 kv; in all cases the power is transmitted in the form of three-phase alternating current at 50 cycles/sec. The cost of an overhead line depends largely on conductor size and voltage. It is necessary to select the most economical combination of the two. In various countries the trend is toward the construction of much-higher-voltage transmission lines, e.g., 750 kv. These voltages result in greater economy in the transmission of electric power over long distances.

Conductor erection: The conductors are supplied wound on drums, which are installed in position at the end of a section. They are mounted to revolve freely and are controlled by a braking device. The conductors are usually hauled along the ground by a winch or sometimes a tractor. As the conductors pass each support, hauling is stopped, and they are fitted through running blocks, which are then hoisted up to the crossarms of the supports. Alternatively, the conductor may be run out clear of the ground, i.e., pulled through pulleys suspended overhead (Fig. 8). This is done mainly to avoid causing damage to the conductors. Finally, after suitable adjustment and check of the amounts of sag, the conductors are clamped at each suspension point (a conductor suspension clamp is shown in Fig. 5b).

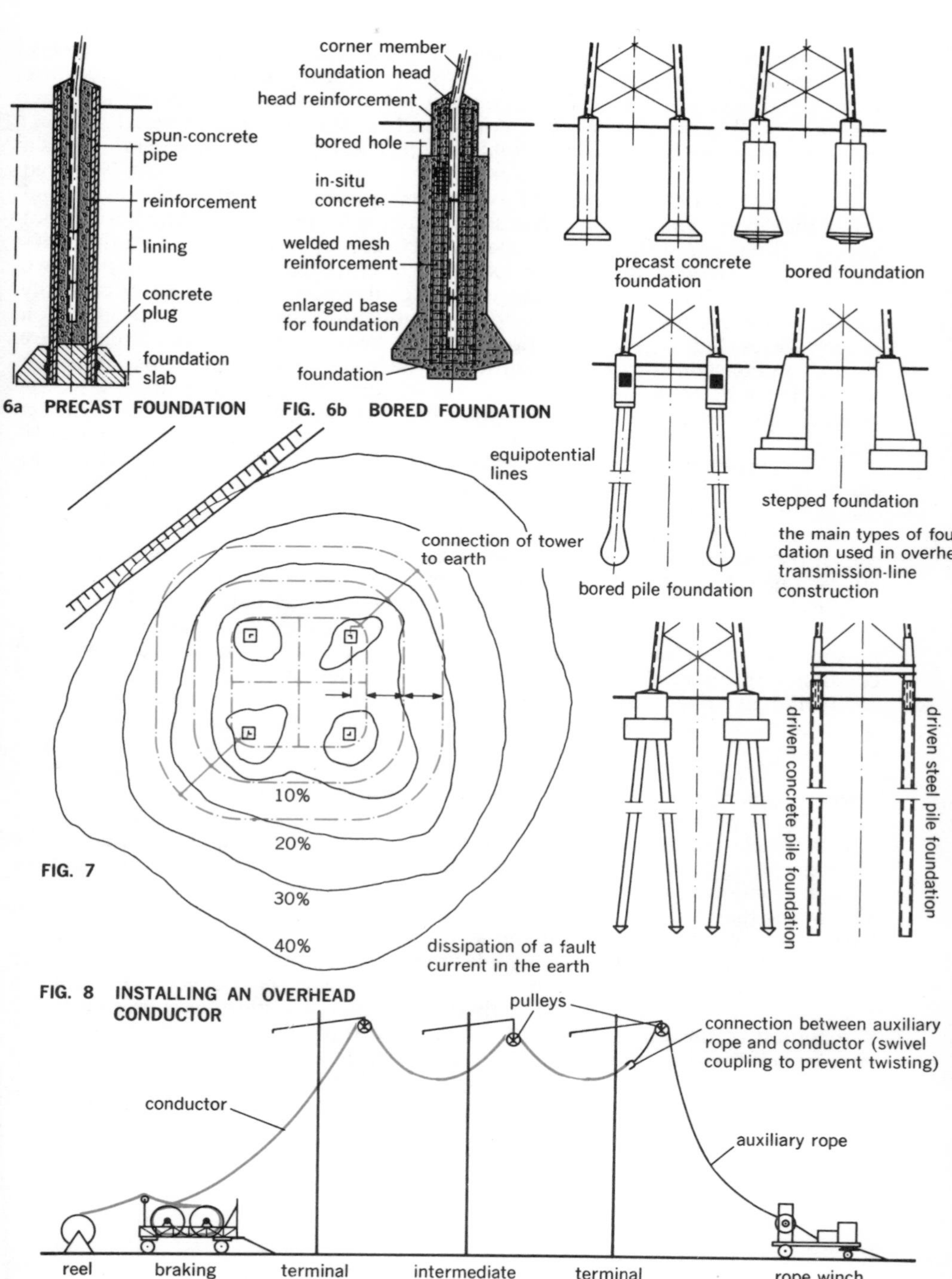
spun-concrete pipe
reinforcement
lining
concrete plug
foundation slab
6a PRECAST FOUNDATION
corner member
foundation head
head reinforcement
bored hole
in-situ concrete
welded mesh reinforcement
enlarged base for foundation
foundation
FIG. 6b BORED FOUNDATION
precast concrete foundation
bored foundation
equipotential lines
stepped foundation
connection of tower to earth
the main types of foun
dation used in overhea
transmission-line
construction
bored pile foundation
driven concrete pile foundation
driven steel pile foundation
FIG. 7
10%
20%
30%
40%
dissipation of a fault current in the earth
FIG. 8 INSTALLING AN OVERHEAD CONDUCTOR
pulleys
connection between auxiliary rope and conductor (swivel coupling to prevent twisting)
conductor
auxiliary rope
reel
braking device
terminal tower
intermediate tower
terminal tower
rope winch

WAVE GUIDES

High-frequency electromagnetic energy, i.e., high-frequency alternating currents, in the form of electromagnetic waves or displacement currents (see page 278) require no material medium for their propagation. Because of this property, standing electrical oscillations of very high frequencies can be established in metal cavities; this is the principle of the cavity resonator (see Vol. I, page 86). In general, this is a space bounded by conducting walls in which electromagnetic energy can be stored as oscillations (standing waves) whose frequency is determined by the shape and size of the cavity. The resonator has a lower frequency limit below which it will not respond. If one end wall of a cylindrical cavity resonator is removed and the cylindrical wall is extended, the tubular hollow conductor obtained in this way is known as a wave guide. It is so named because it can guide electromagnetic waves coaxially with its axis. More specifically it is a hollow conducting tube used for the propagation of such waves (Fig. 1). The oscillation nodes of the waves in the radial direction are located on concentric cylindrical surfaces which are concentrated closer together toward the wall of the wave guide; in the circular direction they are located on planes which are spaced at equal angular distances and pass through the cylinder axis (Fig. 2). At very high frequencies (from about 100 megacycles/sec. onwards) the electromagnetic fields in the wave guide do not break down, because they alternate so rapidly that no charge exchange at all can take place in the wall, as the conducting electrons travel too slowly for this. Hence considerable instantaneous current may flow between two points of the wall. Slots in the wall present no obstacle; they are bridged by displacement currents. The longitudinal edges of a slot function like the plates of a condenser, whereas the transverse edges (which extend axially, i.e., in the direction of the currents in the wall) act inductively (Fig. 3). The displacement currents between the longitudinal edges are surrounded by circular magnetic flux lines (or lines of force) similar to those around a straight conventional conductor through which a current is passing. These flux lines emerge from the cavity and give rise to circular electric flux lines, which in turn produce a magnetic flux, and so on. In this way an electromagnetic radiation is generated which withdraws energy from the wave guide. A slot in a wave guide (Fig. 3) thus functions similarly to an electric dipole (see Vol. I, page 86), except that in this case a magnetic field is primarily created. For this reason it is called a magnetic dipole. Both in respect of its geometric form and its mode of functioning it constitutes the counterpart of the electric dipole (rather in the manner of the positive and the negative of a photograph). The radiation properties described here are put to practical use for the construction of antennae (or aerials), such devices being known as slot radiators. The waves that occur in wave guides are classified into two groups: waves which have only an electric component and waves which have only a magnetic component in the axial direction of the wave guide; these are known as TM waves (transverse magnetic waves) and TE waves (transverse electric waves) respectively. The numbers of circular and radial nodal surfaces (in this sequence) are added as subscripts to the designation of the wave; thus TM_{12} denotes a transverse magnetic wave with 1 circular nodal surface and 2 radial nodal cylinders (Fig. 4). Wave guides are employed more particularly in radio engineering, where they are used for the transmission of electrical energy from transmitter to antenna and from antenna to receiver.

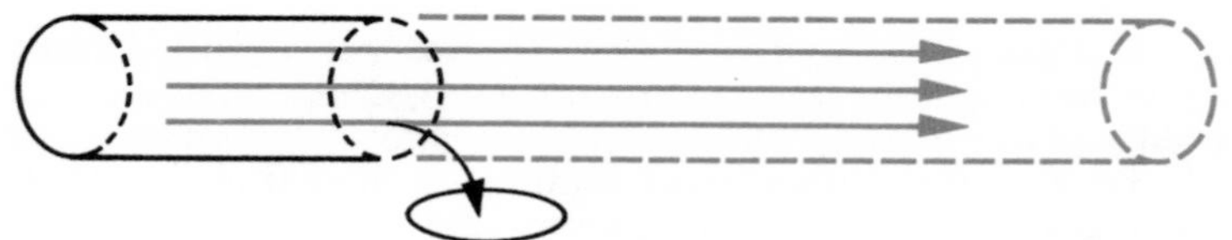

FIG. 1 TRANSFORMATION OF CAVITY RESONATOR INTO WAVEGUIDE

FIG. 2 NODAL PLANES (TWO CYLINDRICAL, ONE PLANE)

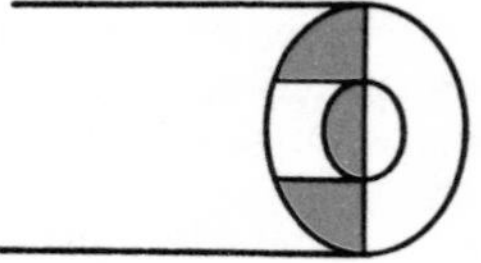

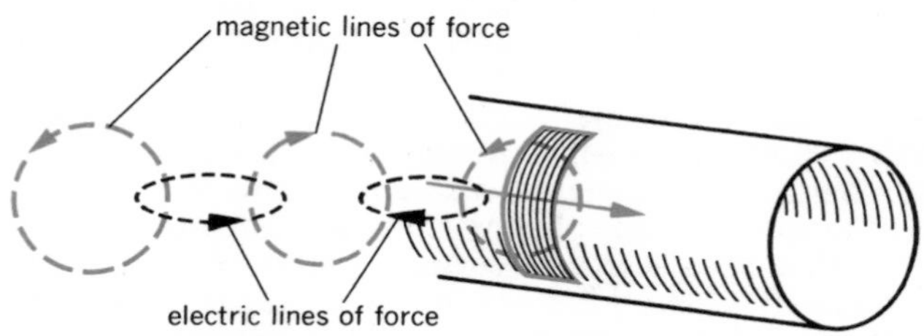

FIG. 3 RADIATION OF ELECTROMAGNETIC ENERGY THROUGH A SLOT IN A WAVEGUIDE

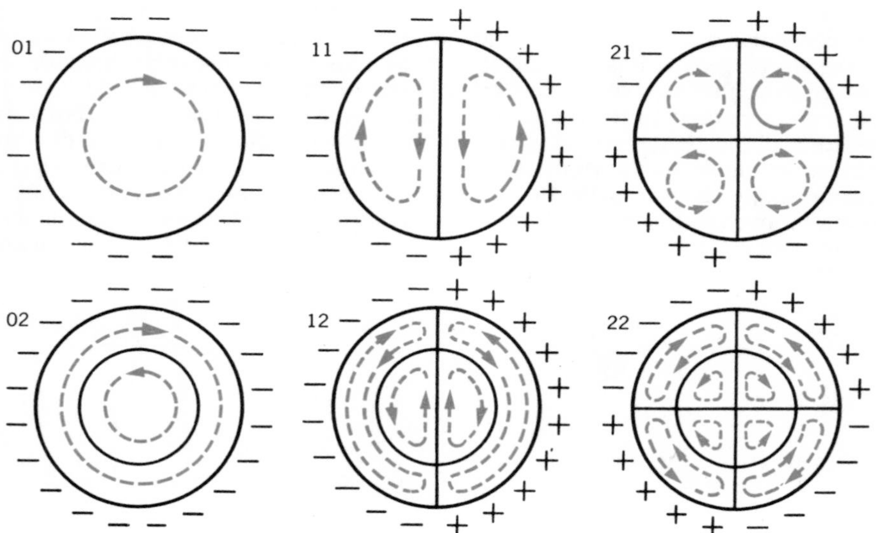

FIG. 4 NODAL PLANES AND MAGNETIC LINES OF FORCE OF VARIOUS WAVE TYPES IN CYLINDRICAL WAVEGUIDES

DISPLACEMENT CURRENT

If a charged capacitor (or condenser) is connected into a direct current circuit, i causes an interruption of the flow of current (Fig. 1). On the other hand, if the sam circuit is fed with alternating current, the capacitor is alternately charged an discharged—i.e., the alternating current continues to flow (Fig. 2); the electric fiel between the capacitor plates, whose intensity and direction vary with time, thu constitutes an immaterial link in the transmission of electric energy through th circuit. This energy flow of alternating direction between the plates behaves like a electric current; it is associated with circular magnetic flux lines (or lines of force whose direction of rotation varies synchronously with the electric field (Fig. 3). Thi transmission of electric energy by the action of an "immaterial" electromagneti field instead of by the action of charge carriers such as electrons or ions is calle displacement current. In actual practice, the plates of a capacitor are separate not by an air gap but by a dielectric (an insulating material) through which inductio can take place, i.e., allowing magnetic or electric lines of force to pass, for example mica, glass, plastics, etc. (Fig. 4). The alternating electromagnetic field causes displacement of the positive in relation to the negative charges in the atoms or of th dielectric (Fig. 5b); normally these charges (positive atomic nuclei surrounded b electrons) are so disposed that the atoms are outwardly neutral (Fig. 5a).

Under the influence of an alternating field the charges oscillate about their center of neutrality. Moving charges produce an electric current; with periodically oscilla-ting charges an alternating current is formed, and since this is due to displacemen of electric charges, the term "displacement current" was applied to it. However although this conception of the current as being associated with the displacemen of electric charges in a material medium (the dielectric) is a convenient aid t visualizing the nature of this phenomenon, it is not an accurate one. This is eviden from the fact that a displacement current is produced even when there is a vacuum —i.e., no material of any kind—between the capacitor plates. The presence of a suitable dielectric does, however, play a part in that it intensifies the transfer o electromagnetic energy in the alternating field. This intensification is expressed by the dielectric constant (or permittivity), which is the ratio of the electric displacemen produced in a particular medium to the electric force producing it as a compare with the ratio for a vacuum; it indicates how many times higher a capacitor with that particular dielectric can be charged than a similar capacitor with a vacuum between its plates; i.e., it is the ratio of the capacitances for those two respective cases The oscillating motion of charges extracts energy from the electric field, however this is more evident as the frequency of the alternating field increases. The inertia resistance of the charge carriers (which transfer the electric charge to the dielectric opposes the high accelerations and decelerations associated with very high fre-quencies of the alternating field. Consequently, increased damping of the oscillations occurs, more particularly with substances having a high dielectric constant, in which case the displacement current becomes very small. If the dielectric is removed and a vacuum substituted for it, the current increases in intensity.

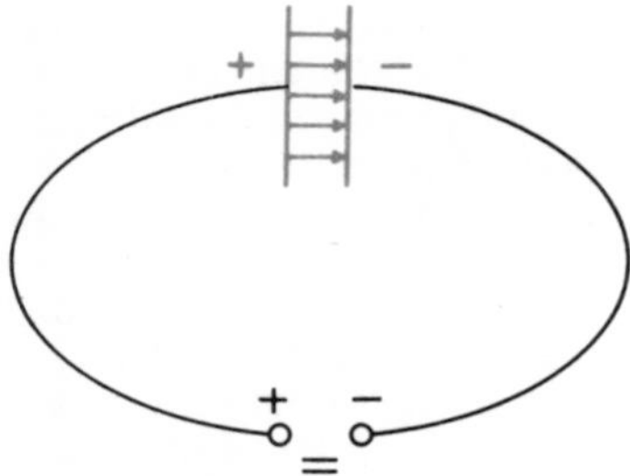

FIG. 1 CAPACITOR IN DC CIRCUIT

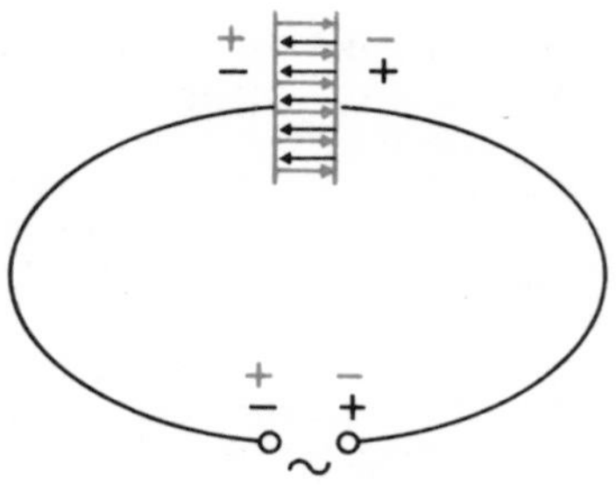

FIG. 2 CAPACITOR IN AC CIRCUIT

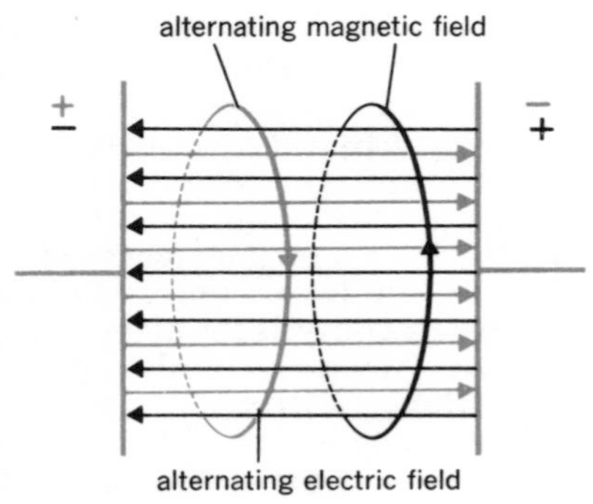

FIG. 3 LINES OF FORCE IN ALTERNATING ELECTROMAGNETIC FIELD

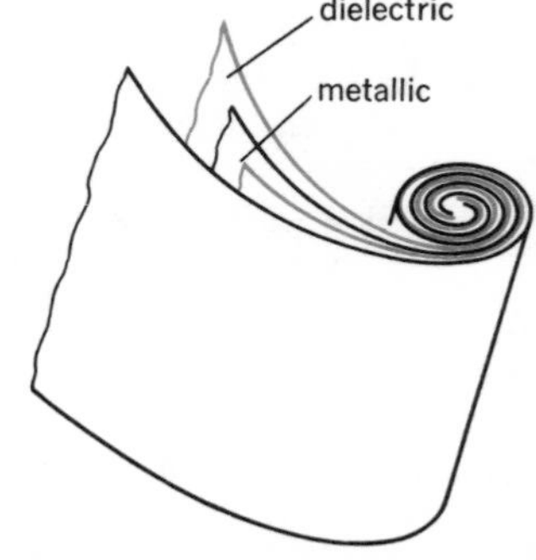

FIG. 4 CYLINDRICAL CAPACITOR COMPOSED OF SHEETS OF METAL AND INSULATING MATERIAL

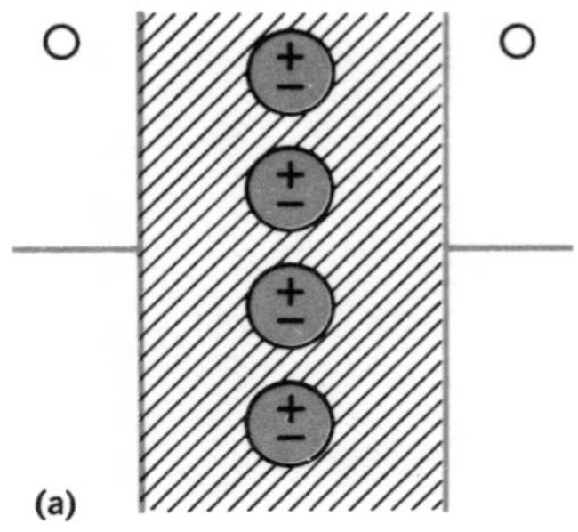

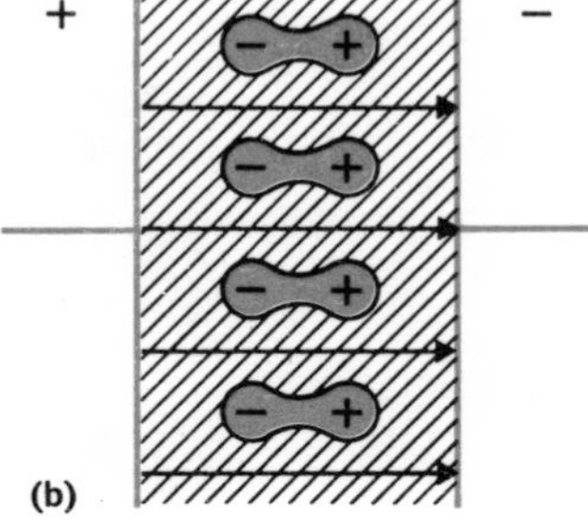

FIG. 5 ATOMS OF THE DIELECTRIC IN THE NEUTRAL CONDITION (a) AND IN AN ELECTRIC FIELD (b)

BASIC ELECTRONIC CIRCUITS

When a current I flows through a series of resistors (Fig. 1), the voltage E between two points is proportional to I and the resistance R that the current encounters; this is expressed by the formula: $E = I \cdot R$ (Ohm's law). In this way a voltage can be divided into two or more lower voltages in any desired ratio. If I is an alternating current of frequency ω, an ordinary (ohmic) resistor has no effect on the frequency; but if the circuit includes a capacitor with a capacitance C, the capacitive reactance thereof is $R = \omega/C$, and if the circuit comprises an inductor (a coil) with inductance L, the inductive reactance due to this is $R = \omega L$. Because of these effects, voltage dividers with inductors and capacitors will divide a high-frequency alternating current in a different ratio from a low-frequency one. Examples of the application of this principle are afforded by the high-pass and the low-pass filter (Fig. 2). To calculate the impedance, or total apparent resistance, of an AC circuit with ohmic resistors, inductors and capacitors, the principle indicated in Fig. 3 is applied. Impedance is a complex property comprising the ohmic resistance of the circuit, the inductive reactance (due to the inductance of the circuit), and the capacitive reactance (due to the capacitance), the last two being frequency-dependent as indicated above. To explain the underlying theory would be outside the scope of this article. At a certain frequency the inductor and the resistor have resistances which are exactly equal but of opposite effect. As a result, the impedance of a series oscillating circuit (Fig. 4a) attains a minimum at this frequency, whereas that of a parallel oscillating circuit (Fig. 4b) attains a maximum. This is known as the resonance frequency ($\omega = \sqrt{LC}$). In high-frequency electronic engineering such oscillating circuits are utilized for filtering out a particular frequency from a frequency mixture.

Electronic equipment requires a certain DC voltage for its operation; this is supplied by a so-called power unit which appropriately converts the main voltage—for example, 240 volts AC. Fig. 5 shows how the AC voltage supplied by the transformer is converted into a pulsating DC voltage whose "alternating" components are suppressed by low-pass filter stages. The smoothing action of the capacitors presents an analogy with that of elastic containers (balloons) in a compressed-air pipeline, whereby the initially existing pulsations in air pressure are smoothed away as a result of the equalizing action of the balloons.

(more)

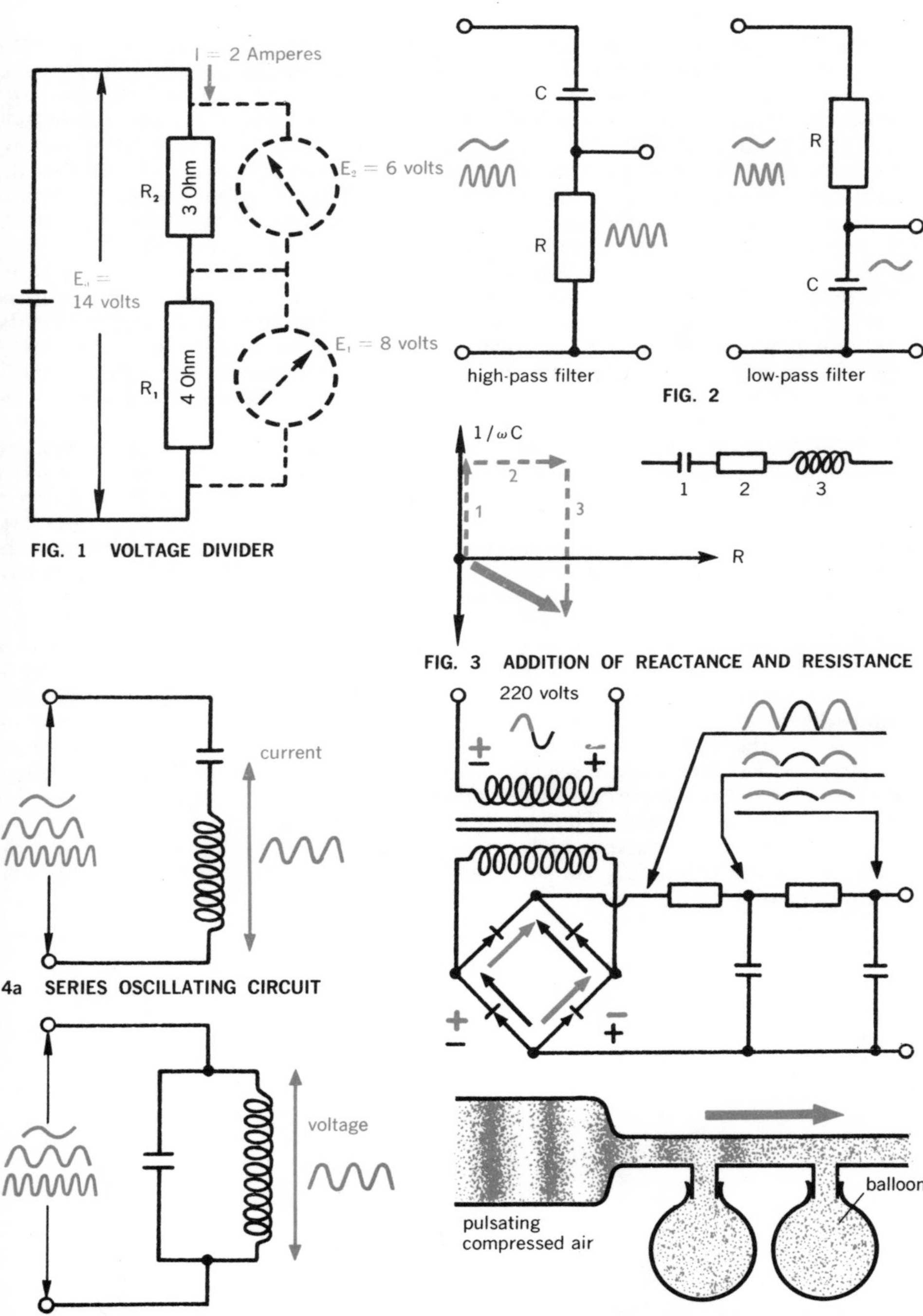

FIG. 1 VOLTAGE DIVIDER

FIG. 2

FIG. 3 ADDITION OF REACTANCE AND RESISTANCE

4a SERIES OSCILLATING CIRCUIT

FIG. 4b PARALLEL OSCILLATING CIRCUIT

FIG. 5 RECTIFICATION AND SMOOTHING OF AN AC VOLTAGE

Fig. 6 shows a commonly adopted circuit for an amplifier tube (or valve). The input AC voltage applied to the grid of the tube causes the anode current I to be increased and decreased in the same rhythm (see also Vol. I, page 90). The current I flows through the anode resistor R_a and the cathode resistor R_k and produces a voltage drop in both. The higher the value of R_a, the higher becomes the output AC voltage. The value of R_k (and therefore the voltage drop in R_k) is so chosen that the grid remains negative in relation to the cathode. The AC voltage produced by the variations of I in R_k is often undesirable. (It should be borne in mind that the current I is controlled by the difference between grid voltage and cathode voltage.)

In the circuit known as a cathode follower (Fig. 7) there is no anode resistor; the output voltage is taken across the cathode resistor R_k. Voltage variations at the grid produce anode (and therefore cathode) current variations in phase, so that the cathode potential rises and falls in sympathy with the grid voltage. This arrangement provides a high input impedance and low output impedance. The voltage amplification of the cathode follower is equal to unity (or less). There is no phase inversion between input and output with a resistive load.

A certain proportion of the output voltage of an amplifier can be so fed back to the input that the input voltage is in part compensated. This so-called negative feedback at first merely causes some reduction of the amplification. Now, in every amplifier there occur deviations from exact proportionality between input and output voltage (linearity). The actual voltage of an amplifier may be conceived as the sum of a truly linear output voltage and an error voltage. The feedback adds part of the error voltage to the input voltage, so that a correcting voltage is produced at the output of the amplifier. The residual error in the output voltage is reduced to such an extent that it just suffices to produce the correcting voltage. In a case where a very constant DC voltage is required, the arrangement known as a stabilizing circuit is employed (Fig. 9). The voltage is regulated, for example, by reference to a glow-discharge lamp (such as a neon lamp) in which there is practically no voltage drop—i.e., the voltage across the electrodes remains constant irrespective of the strength of the current discharged through the lamp. A fixed proportion of the voltage to be stabilized is compared with the glow-lamp voltage, and the difference is fed to the input of the amplifier. The output voltage of the differential amplifier controls the grid of a tube (or valve) which determines the current in the voltage divider and thus keeps the voltage E_2 constant (apart from a residual error) even when load variations occur.

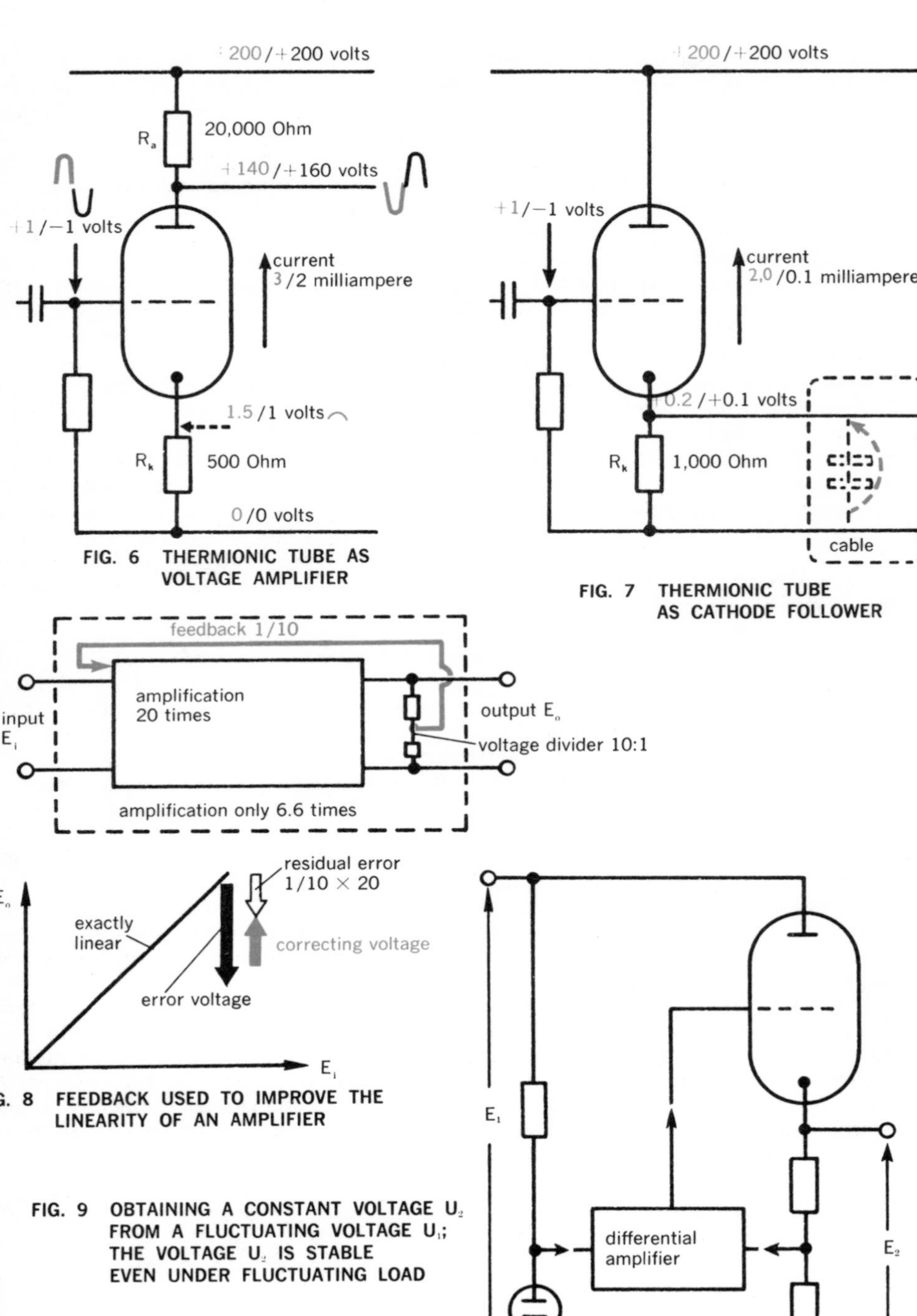

FIG. 6 THERMIONIC TUBE AS VOLTAGE AMPLIFIER

FIG. 7 THERMIONIC TUBE AS CATHODE FOLLOWER

IG. 8 FEEDBACK USED TO IMPROVE THE LINEARITY OF AN AMPLIFIER

FIG. 9 OBTAINING A CONSTANT VOLTAGE U_2 FROM A FLUCTUATING VOLTAGE U_1; THE VOLTAGE U_2 IS STABLE EVEN UNDER FLUCTUATING LOAD

CARRIER TRANSMISSION

The high cost of telecommunication systems—whether on the "wire" or the "wireless" principle—soon led to the development of methods for the multiple utilization of the circuits. This is known as channeling and denotes the technique of using one telecommunication path for simultaneously carrying a number of channels for the transmission of messages. To do this successfully, it is obviously necessary to possess the technical means of suitably combining and separating the channels at the start and at the end of the telecommunication path respectively. The means employed for effecting the separation is the so-called *carrier frequency*. Each channel corresponds to a different carrier frequency or, to be more precise, a different frequency range or band of frequencies. For example, the transmission of speech requires a band width of 3400 Hz ("Hz" is the abbreviation of "hertz," the unit of frequency equal to one cycle per second). Accordingly, the frequencies of the carrier waves are spaced at intervals of 4 kHz (= 4000 Hz)—e.g., 4 kHz, 8 kHz, 12 kHz, 16 kHz, 20 kHz for a six-channel system. With this frequency spacing the intermediate range of 600 Hz between each pair of neighboring channels ensures effective separation of the transmissions and suppresses the disturbance known as cross talk, due to spillover of sound from other channels. The terms "carrier wave" and "carrier frequency" indicate that the wave can be modulated to carry the lower speech frequency—i.e., the amplitude of the wave is varied in sympathy with the frequency of the sounds to be transmitted (Fig. 1). A simple system comprising only two channels will be considered in order to illustrate the principle (Fig. 2). The speech frequency band in channel 1 is produced by a microphone and is modulated upon the carrier by means of a modulator, whence it is passed to the transmission path (drawn in black in Fig. 2). The same procedure is applied in the case of channel 2 with its carrier 2, whose frequency, however, is higher than that of the carrier 1 (red in Fig. 2). By way of the transmission path the modulated frequency mixture of the two channels travels to the receiving end, where suitable filters respectively permit the frequencies of channel 1 and channel 2 to pass. After this frequency separation has been effected, the modulated carrier waves are demodulated—i.e., the original information is separated from the carrier waves in a device called a demodulator—and the speech frequencies are turned into audible speech in a telephone or loudspeaker.

From the foregoing discussion of the principle it is apparent that, if f_{max} denotes the maximum carrier frequency range and Δf denotes the frequency band width required for each individual channel, then it will theoretically be possible to accommodate $f_{max}/\Delta f$ channels within that range. In reality the number of channels must be smaller, because of the need to have adequately wide frequency margins between neighboring channels.

Fig. 3 is a diagram of a so-called ring modulator, comprising two transformers (U1 and U2) and four rectifiers (tracks 1–4). To the center of the inner winding of each transformer is connected the carrier frequency CF, whose high frequency causes very rapid reversal of polarity of the rectifiers. As a result, the rectifiers 1 and 2 allow current to pass during one half-wave of the carrier frequency, while 3 and 4 block the flow of current; during the next half-wave the situation is

(more)

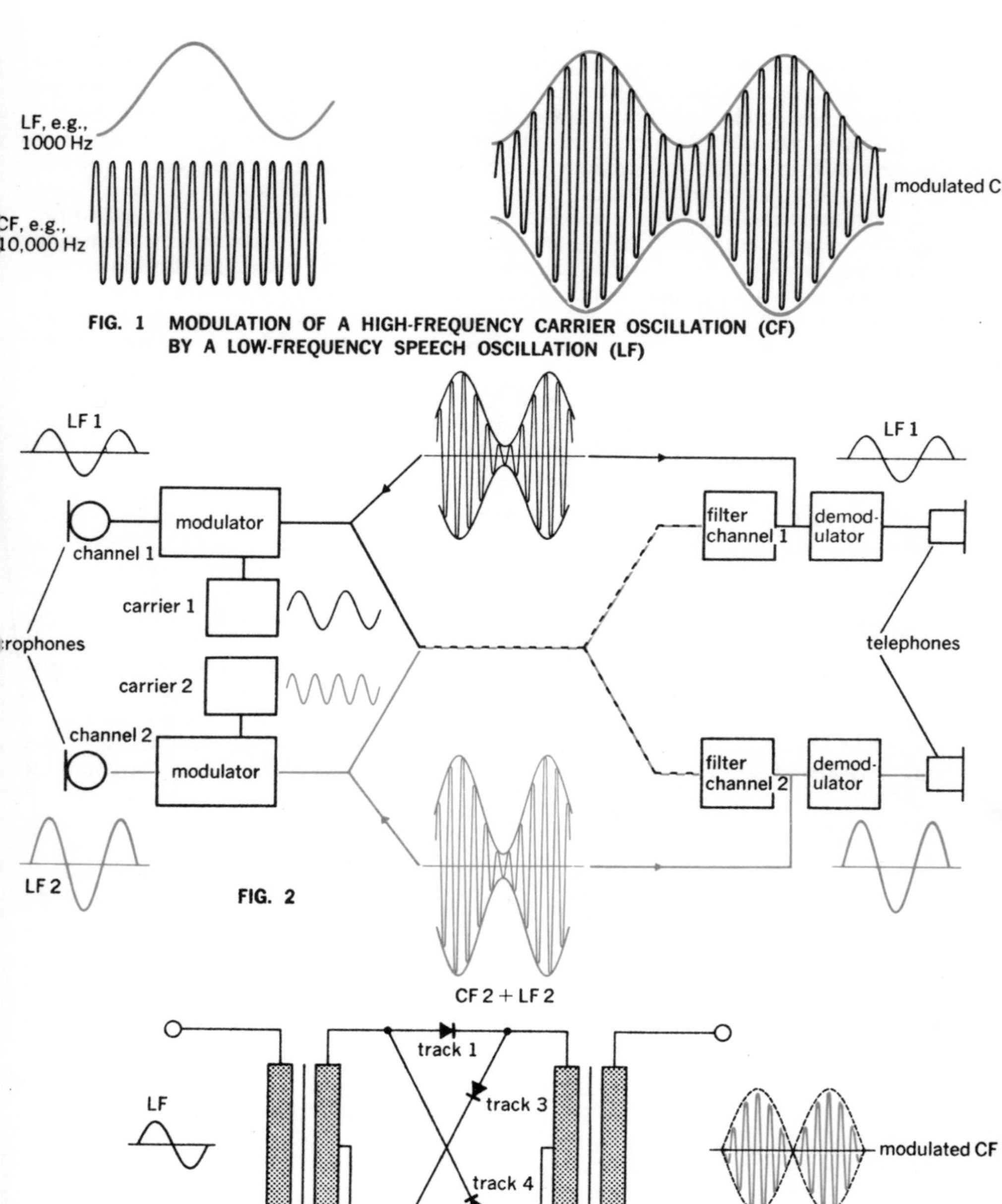

FIG. 1 MODULATION OF A HIGH-FREQUENCY CARRIER OSCILLATION (CF) BY A LOW-FREQUENCY SPEECH OSCILLATION (LF)

FIG. 2

FIG. 3 RING MODULATOR

reversed. The low-frequency current LF is applied to the input winding of the first transformer and, in consequence of the cross connections in the circuit, undergoes a phase displacement of 180 degrees. On the output side, a carrier frequency whose amplitude is modulated to the low frequency emerges from the ring modulator. On the right in Fig. 3 the low frequency is represented by the enveloping curve (dotted) of the high-frequency amplitudes.

A mathematical analysis shows that the two frequencies (LF and CF) fed to the modulator are present in it as a sum and a difference of the frequencies. The sum is referred to as the upper side frequency f_s, and the difference as the lower side frequency f_d. Speech transmission requires not just a single frequency, but a frequency range from 0.3 kHz to 3.4 kHz, and an upper and a lower side band are formed. Let f_c denote the carrier wave frequency and let Δf_s and Δf_d denote the respective side bands; then

$$\Delta f_s = f_c + (0.3 \rightarrow 3.4\ \text{kHz})$$
$$\Delta f_d = f_c - (0.3 \rightarrow 3.4\ \text{kHz})$$

With a carrier frequency of 16 kHz, the side bands are:

$$\Delta f_s = 16.3 \rightarrow 19.4\ \text{kHz}$$
$$\Delta f_d = 12.6 \rightarrow 15.7\ \text{kHz}$$

These data are indicated in Fig. 4. The apexes of the triangles each correspond to the position of the lowest speech frequency (0.3 kHz). The triangle in the LF band occupies the standard position. The upper side band is similarly positioned, whereas the lower side band is symmetrically reversed. Each side band contains the same amount of information as the other. For this reason only one side band is used for the transmission of the message; the other side band is suppressed by suitable filters before it enters the transmission path. A filter which allows only a particular frequency range to pass is known as a band-pass filter. Fig. 5 shows the circuit arrangement and the damping curve of a band-pass filter for the upper side band in the transmission of speech with a carrier frequency of 16 kHz. The filter consists of a high-pass and a low-pass filter. The high-pass filter (H P) is so designed that it allows frequencies above 16.3 kHz to pass almost without damping; the low-pass filter (L P) is so designed that it strongly damps all frequencies above 19.4 kHz. From the shape of the damping curve it is evident that only the upper side band is let through by the band-pass filter: at the highest frequency of the lower side band (in this example 15.7 kHz) the band-pass filter already has a high degree of damping.

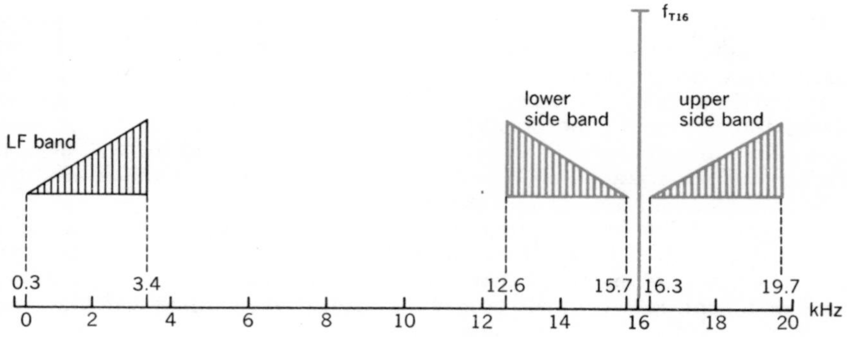

FIG. 4 MODULATION OF A SPEECH BAND WITH CARRIER FREQUENCY $f_{T16} = 16$ kHz (LF AND UPPER SIDE BAND IN STANDARD POSITION LOWER SIDE BAND IN REVERSED POSITION)

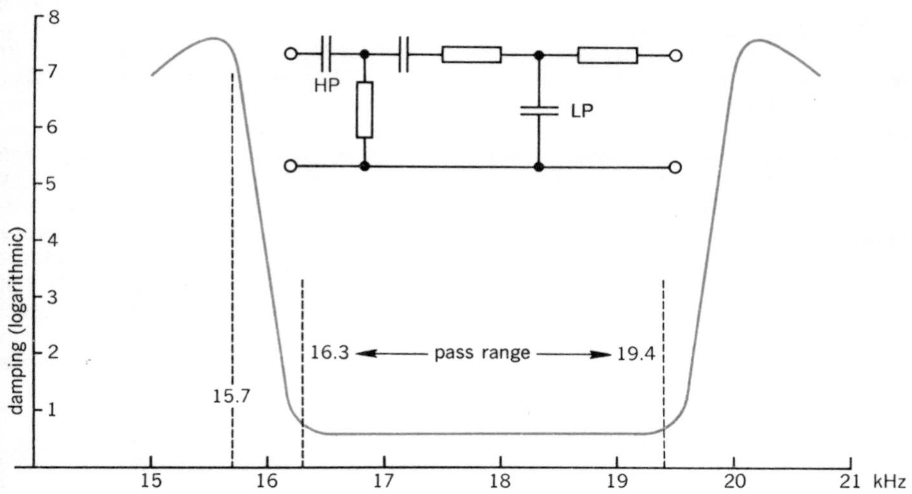

FIG. 5 BAND-PASS FILTER FOR UPPER SIDE BAND OF CARRIER FREQUENCY $f_{T16} = 16$ kHz (CIRCUIT DIAGRAM AND DAMPING CURVE)

In VHF (very high frequency) broadcasting with ultrashort waves, the frequency of the waves radiated from the transmitter is increased and decreased in sympathy with the acoustic vibration that must be transmitted. Fig. 1 shows a simple acoustic vibration and the associated voltage-variation pattern at the antenna of a frequency-modulated transmitter. In the demodulator of the VHF receiver, the frequency variations are converted back into variations of voltage; i.e., at the output of the demodulator an AC voltage is obtained which is a copy of the acoustic vibration. It can be amplified and used to energize a loudspeaker.

In VHF stereophonic broadcasting, the two acoustic vibrations intended for the hearer's right and left ear respectively must be separately transmitted and reproduced. Transmission by means of two transmitters and two receivers would be an expensive and technically complex procedure. Instead, the method which will now be described is employed (pilot frequency method).

The two microphones in Fig. 2 (p. 291) produce two AC voltages R and L, from which first the sum signal $(R+L)$ and the difference signal $(R-L)$ are formed. In the arrangement in Fig. 2 this is achieved by means of transformers; other circuits may be used in practice.

Instead of using the AC voltage direct from the microphone, a so-called multiplex signal is transmitted. This signal is composed as follows (Fig. 3):

The amplitude of a 38 kHz oscillation (for example) is varied proportionally to the signal $(R-L)$ just as in medium-frequency broadcasting (amplitude modulation). As a result, an AC voltage (C) is produced, which varies the 38 kHz frequency between the values $(+1)\cdot(R-L)+T$ and $(-1)\cdot(R-L)-T$, where T denotes a constant 38 kHz frequency (the carrier). The AC voltage (C) is added to the signal $(R+L)$. The signal (D) thus obtained oscillates 38,000 times per second between the values $(R+L)+(R-L)+T = 2R+T$ and $(R+L)-(R-L)-T = 2L-T$. It is used to modulate the frequency of the transmitter just as in ordinary VHF radio, and at the receiver it emerges again as the output from the demodulator. In an ordinary VHF receiver the signal is merely amplified and fed to a loudspeaker. However, no human ear can hear a 38 kHz oscillation, nor indeed can a loudspeaker reproduce such a high-frequency oscillation anyway. Hence only the mean value, corresponding to the sum signal $(R+L)$, becomes acoustically audible. The signals R and L can, however, be separated in a stereo decoder. Thus if the multiplex signal (D) is fed to the input of the circuit shown in Fig. 4, only the branch R carries current during the positive half-wave, and only the branch Lduring the negative half-wave. As a result, voltages corresponding to the signals R and L respectively are produced in the resistors of these branches. Superimposed on both these signals is still a 38 kHz oscillation, but this is suppressed in the following resistance-capacitance sections.

(more)

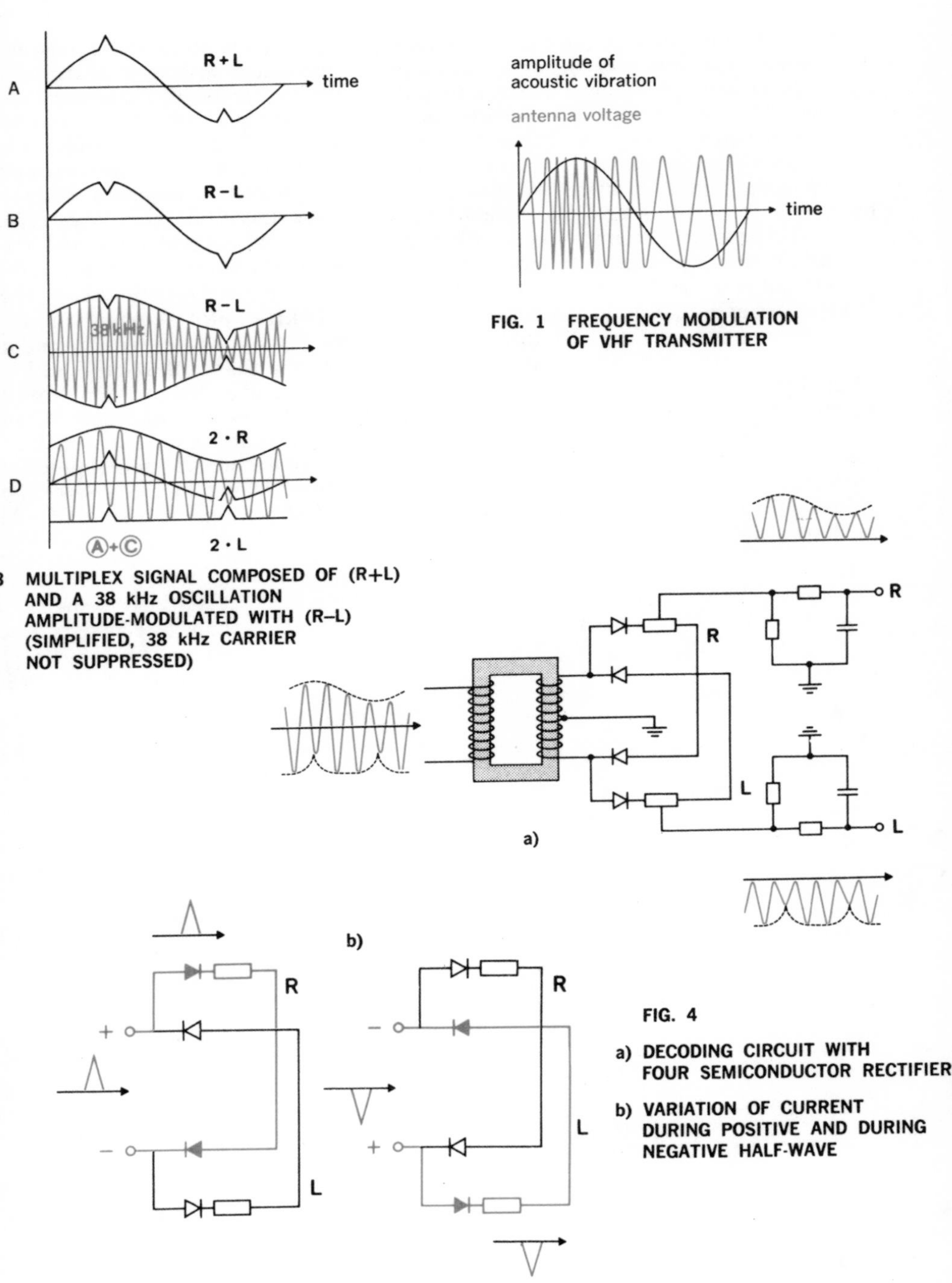

FIG. 1 FREQUENCY MODULATION OF VHF TRANSMITTER

3 MULTIPLEX SIGNAL COMPOSED OF (R+L) AND A 38 kHz OSCILLATION AMPLITUDE-MODULATED WITH (R–L) (SIMPLIFIED, 38 kHz CARRIER NOT SUPPRESSED)

FIG. 4

a) DECODING CIRCUIT WITH FOUR SEMICONDUCTOR RECTIFIERS

b) VARIATION OF CURRENT DURING POSITIVE AND DURING NEGATIVE HALF-WAVE

The procedure that is adopted in actual practice differs from the foregoing description: The multiplex signal (D) contains the frequencies arising from the sum signal, up to approximately 15 kHz, and additionally the frequency range between $38-15 = 23$ kHz and $38+15 = 53$ kHz arising from the signal $(R-L)$(Fig. 5a). In the upper frequency range the frequency of 38 kHz is especially prominent, inasmuch as it occurs also when the difference signal $(R-L)$ temporarily vanishes (sound source in the middle position). Accurate transmission of such a frequency mixture by a VHF transmitter would require a large frequency deviation, i.e., a large peak difference between the instantaneous frequency of the modulated wave and the carrier frequency. It is possible to manage with a smaller frequency deviation and yet obtain the same quality of transmission by completely suppressing the 38 kHz carrier and, instead, transmitting a constant 19 kHz "pilot frequency" along with the signal. In the decoder this 19 kHz frequency is filtered out by a resonant circuit and nonlinearly amplified. The 38 kHz harmonic that is thus produced is again filtered out in a 38 kHz resonant circuit, amplified, and added to the multiplex signal as a substitute for the suppressed carrier. The further process of decoding can then again be performed in the same manner as described above for the simplified multiplex signal (D). Fig. 6 is a block diagram of a stereo decoder. In actual practice the signal $(R+L)$ is added only after the decoding circuit shown in Fig. 4, since the splitting up into a positive and a negative half-wave concerns only the signal $(R-L)$ oscillating at 38 kHz.

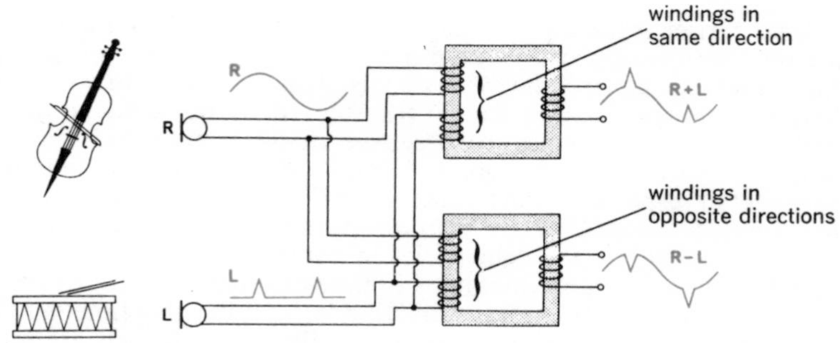

FIG. 2 OBTAINING THE SIGNALS (R+L) AND (R–L) FROM THE OUTPUT VOLTAGES OF TWO MICROPHONES R AND L WITH THE AID OF TWO TRANSFORMERS

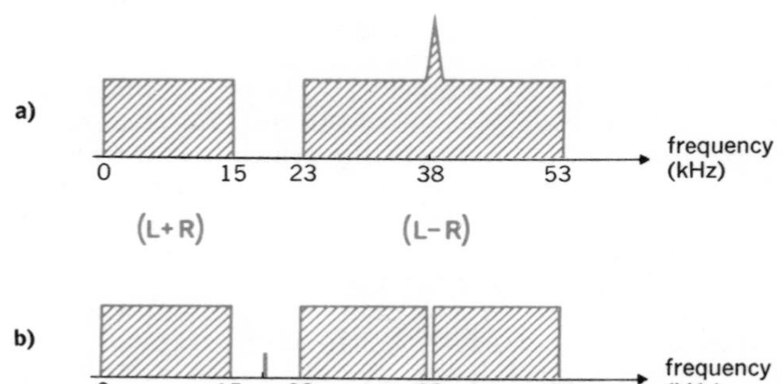

FIG. 5 FREQUENCY DISTRIBUTION IN THE MULTIPLEX SIGNAL
a) 38 kHz CARRIER IS PRESENT
b) 38 kHz CARRIER SUPPRESSED AND REPLACED BY kHz PILOT FREQUENCY

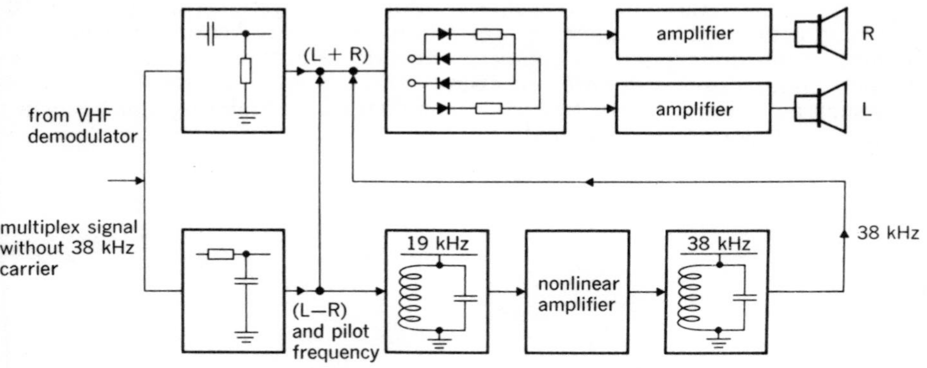

FIG. 6 BLOCK DIAGRAM OF A STEREO DECODER WITH LOW-FREQUENCY AMPLIFIERS CONNECTED IN SERIES BEHIND IT

TIME DIVISION MULTIPLEXING

Like carrier signaling (see page 284), time-division multiplexing is a technique for the transmission of two or more signals over a common path, using different time intervals for the different signals. However, instead of employing different frequency ranges (speech bands) transmitted by the modulation of progressively higher carrier frequencies in successive channels, time-division multiplexing telescopes the various speech signals together, as it were, by availing itself of the relative slowness of response of the human sense of hearing, which fails to detect gaps of up to 25 milliseconds' (25/1000 sec.) duration in the transmission and which is even able to compensate for deficiencies in continuity or clarity. Because of this, it is possible to pack a large number of "time channels," each carrying a message (i.e., a separate conversation), into this time lag. Within this time lag the two speakers conducting a conversation along one of the time channels are interconnected for brief periods of 0.5 microseconds (1/2,000,000 sec.) by means of electronic gate circuits operating at a repetition frequency of 10 kHz (10,000 cycles/sec.). Thus 250 connections are established within the duration of the time lag, each connection lasting only for 0.125 millisecond. Thus about 2000 time channels can be packed into the time lag. Multiple use of the transmission path is thus achieved by telescoping together a number of impulse sequences, each associated with a particular speech connection (Fig. 1). The speed of the impulse sequence is measured in bits/sec. or kbits/sec., a "bit" being a unit of information content (see Vol. I, page 334). Based on the time-division multiplexing principle is the TASI system (an abbreviation of "time assignment speech interpolation"), developed more particularly for use with undersea telephone cables, as it enables more channels to be transmitted than is economically feasible with carrier-signaling techniques. Fig. 2 schematically shows this system applied to a cable which carries 36 channels and through which 72 lines can be connected. Speech detectors ascertain whether a particular channel is engaged or free. As soon as more than 36 speech connections are simultaneously required, a central control device, operating with electronic gate circuits, initiates multiple utilization of the transmission path by time-division multiplexing. The control operations, for which a separate channel is reserved (channel 37 in Fig. 2), must likewise take place within the time lag. Faulty transmission is liable to occur only if it takes the speech detectors more than 100 milliseconds to find a free channel; in that case a syllable of speech (average duration 120 milliseconds) will be lost.

Time-division multiplexing is also coming into use in general telephone engineering, as it cuts down the amount of technical equipment by getting rid of the elaborate switching network and in improved operational reliability because it reduces the number of junctions (points of contact). The most important application of time-division multiplexing is in data processing, however, in which impulse sequences play such an important role. In Fig. 3, time-division multiplexing and frequency-division multiplexing are compared.

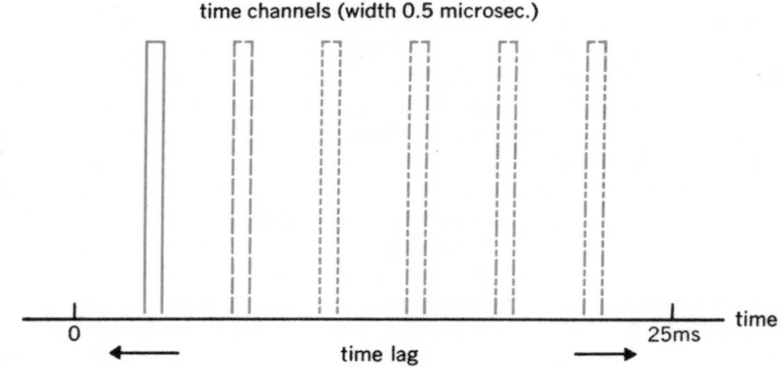

FIG. 1 MULTIPLE UTILIZATION OF A TRANSMISSION PATH BY SIX TIME CHANNELS (WIDTH NOT TO SCALE)

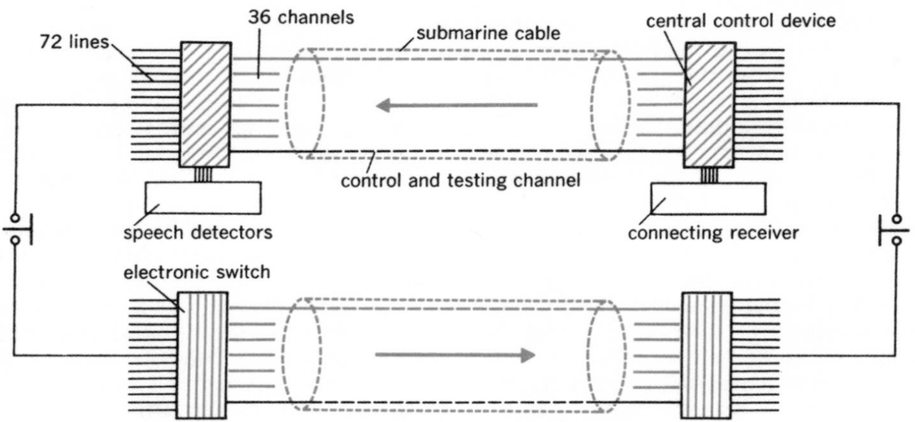

FIG. 2 SCHEMATIC DIAGRAM TO SHOW HOW THE TASI SYSTEM FUNCTIONS

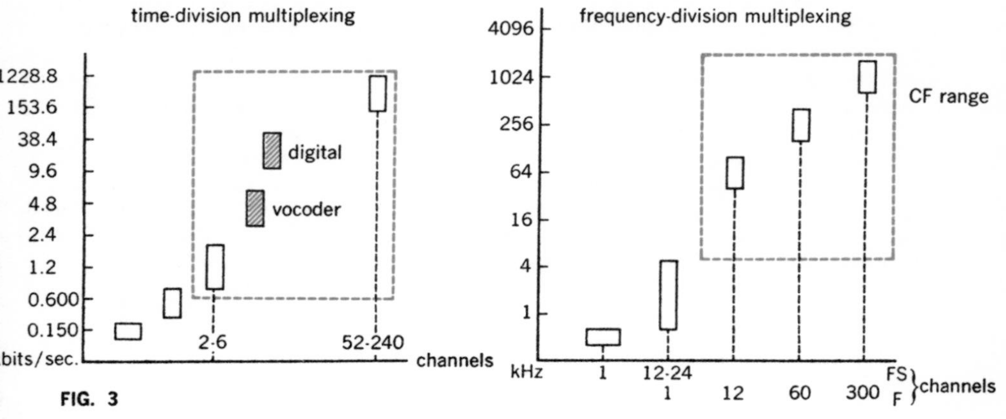

FIG. 3

The procedure in making a telephone call is as follows. The caller picks up the receiver; the contact U1 (Fig. 1) closes and bypasses the capacitor C. Now a direct current flows through the line and serves to prepare the equipment at the telephone exchange for dealing with the call. When the dial tone is heard, the caller can dial the desired number. When he does this, the contact nsa short-circuits the microphone and telephone circuit until the dial has returned to its original position. During the return motion the contact nsi is opened and closed as many times as corresponds to the digit that has been dialed. When the receiver is resting in its cradle, the contact nsr bridges the contact nsi. When the caller speaks into the microphone M, the latter modulates the above-mentioned current or—in the case of an electrodynamic microphone—produces an alternating speech current which oscillates in sympathy with the acoustic vibrations. The greater part of this current travels along the line to the other person's instrument. A small proportion flows through the short circuit consisting of the winding 1 of the telephone transformer and the resistor 4. Most of the speech current also flows through a winding 2 of the transformer before reaching the line. The windings 1 and 2 are so connected that their effects almost entirely cancel each other out. Hence only a small proportion of the speech current is transmitted to the winding 3, so that the caller's own voice is only faintly heard in his own receiver. This arrangement suppresses the disturbing influence of background noises in the room from where the caller is speaking. The speech current coming in from the distant instrument flows through the two windings 1 and 2 of the transformer in the same direction and is therefore passed without loss of strength to the third winding. The telephone connected to this winding reproduces the speech of the distant speaker. The two rectifiers (GL) connected in parallel to the telephone serve to eliminate crackling and contact noises arising in the line. W denotes the alternating-current bell.

Behind the dial (Fig. 2) of the telephone instrument is a small gear mechanism with a contactor. When a number is dialed, the spiral spring is tensioned. When the dial is released, the spring force returns it to its initial position. This return motion has to be performed at a controlled constant speed, which is ensured by means of a centrifugal governor. During the return motion the interrupter arms open the contact nsi as many times as corresponds to the digit dialed. The cam on the shaft of the dial actuates the contact nsa/nsr only when the dial is in its initial position (position of rest) and for two-thirds of the distance between the initial position and the finger hole "1."

Some telephone systems have push-button dialing by means of 10 or 12 buttons. When a button is depressed, a transistor generator sends two audio frequencies—out of a possible eight such frequencies—through the line to the telephone exchange (Fig. 3). The circuit (Fig. 4) functions as follows: When the caller picks up the receiver, the contact GU is closed, but the transistor is short-circuited by the contact *r*. When one of the push buttons is depressed, this contact *r* opens and activates the transistor. The contact *a* short-circuits the microphone-telephone circuit, so that no interfering tones can be transmitted by the microphone during the transmission of the signals. At the same time, the resonant circuit capacitors C3 and C4 are each connected, by respective contacts, to a tapping of the transformers U2 and U3 respectively. While the contacts *u* and *r* are actuated by every button, each button closes a different combination of two resonant circuit contacts. The bell and speech circuit arrangements are similar to those in the rotating dial system already described.

(more)

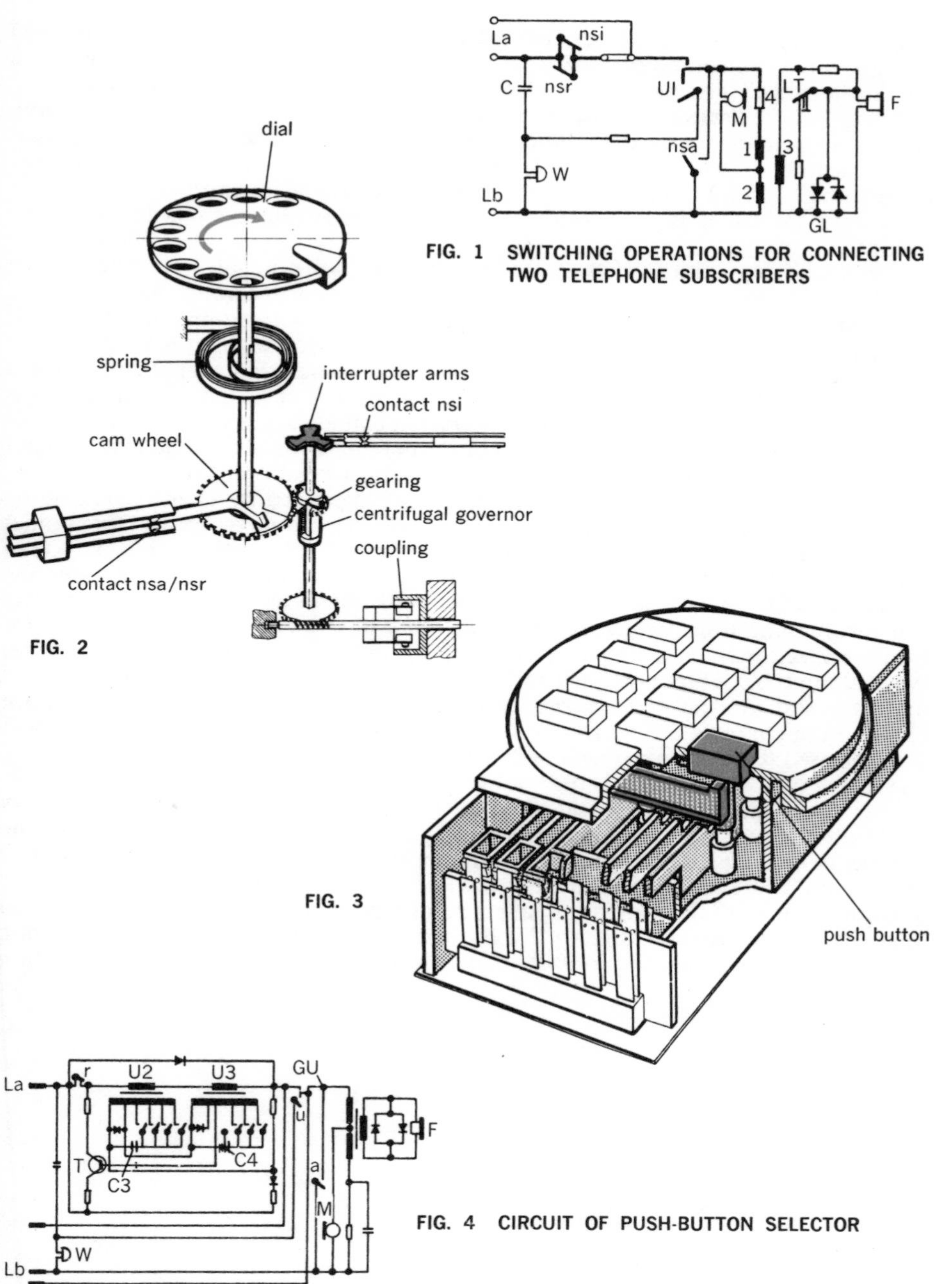

FIG. 1 SWITCHING OPERATIONS FOR CONNECTING TWO TELEPHONE SUBSCRIBERS

FIG. 2

FIG. 3

FIG. 4 CIRCUIT OF PUSH-BUTTON SELECTOR

When the caller dials a number, the circuit to the telephone exchange is interrupted as many times as corresponds to that number. Each digit on the dial controls a "selection stage" comprising an electromagnetic multiple-contact (or stepping) switch called the "selector." The latter has one input and can connect this to many outputs. Depending on the digit dialed, the first selector connects the caller to a local line or a long-distance (trunk) line, and further selectors—at distant exchanges, when trunk calls are made—connect one section of line after another in successive steps until the caller is connected to the telephone of the persons he wishes to speak to.

The selector equipment of the type known as a "noble metal uniselector motor switch" comprises a motor, an adjusting element, and a contact bank (Fig. 1). The motor is of a somewhat unusual type: it has two electromagnets placed at right angles to each other and a Z-shaped soft-iron rotor without a winding. The rotor shaft actuates two contacts which alternately switch the magnet coils on and off; each time, the coil which has attracted the rotor is switched off. The Z shape ensures that the attracting force of the energized coil always acts in the same direction. With each half revolution of the rotor the contact arms of the adjusting element are rotated a distance corresponding to one contact position of the contact bank. To stop the motor, both coils are simultaneously energized by a relay, causing the rotor to be arrested in an intermediate position between the magnet poles; the contact arms are then located accurately at the center of a contact position. This method of stopping the rotation is a distinctive feature of this selector, as it eliminates the vibrations and the wear and tear associated with the older forms of construction. For local connections, selectors with four pairs of arms are used; those used for trunk connections have eight pairs. Two of the arms (or four in the eight-arm selector) move along the contact positions and serve to control the running and stopping of the rotor and transfer certain control currents. The other two (or four) arms are lifted off the contacts during rotation. Only when the motor has stopped are these arms pressed (by electromagnetic action) against the contact positions.

Another important device is the "noble metal rapid-contact relay" (Figs. 2 and 3), used in the construction of so-called couplers, which can take the place of selectors in telephony and are becoming increasingly important. In this type of relay the number of moving parts is reduced to a minimum. Five of these relays are combined into a unit. There are no separate mechanical parts for actuating the contacts. The movable springs of the four or six contacts of a relay are pressed against the fixed opposite contact springs directly by the magnetic field of the coil. The moving masses are so small that the contacts close within 2/1000 second after the operating coil is energized.

(more)

contact bank
contact
assembly
adjusting
element
contacts
electromagnets
rotor

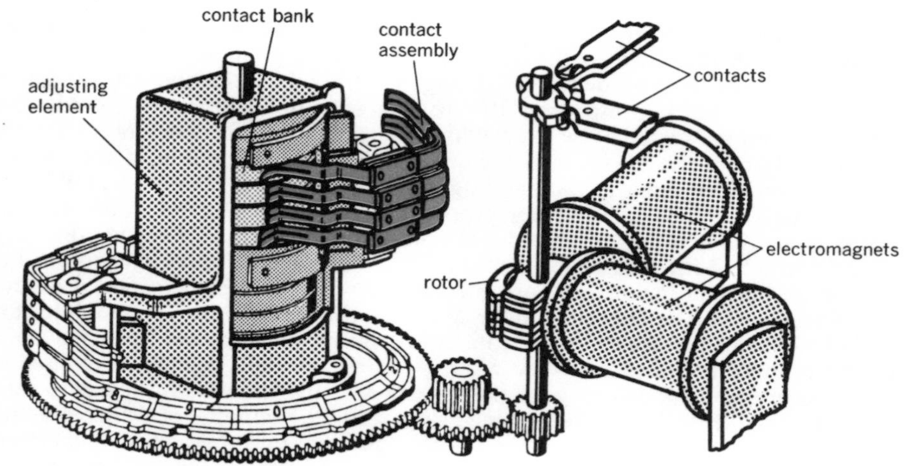

FIG. 1 UNISELECTOR MOTOR SWITCH

FIG. 2 RAPID-CONTACT RELAY

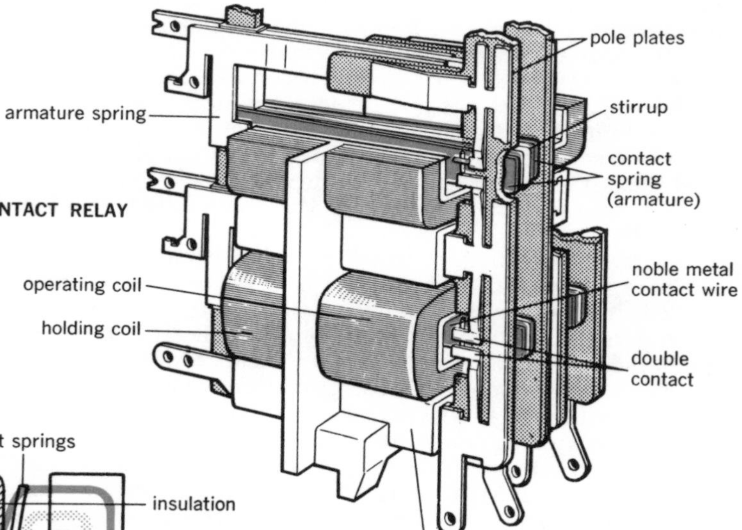

pole plates
armature spring
stirrup
contact
spring
(armature)
noble metal
contact wire
operating coil
holding coil
double
contact
guide chamber

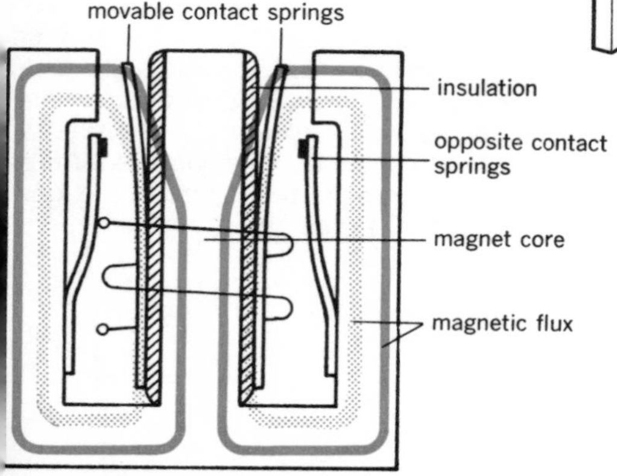

movable contact springs
insulation
opposite contact
springs
magnet core
magnetic flux

FIG. 3 DIAGRAM SHOWING MODE OF FUNCTIONING OF RAPID-CONTACT RELAY WITH SUPERIMPOSED MAGNETIC FLUXES

The number-selection procedure in a telephone exchange can most suitably be explained with reference to the selection of a two-digit number. Formerly two-motion selectors were used (see Vol. I, page 130), in which the number was selected from a square bank comprising 10 × 10 contacts. In the modern "noble metal uniselector motor switch" (see page 296), however, all the 100 contacts are arranged side by side in a semicircle. Hence when the digit corresponding to the "tens" is dialed, the selector must, at each dialing impulse, jump over ten contacts. When the "ones" digit is dialed, the selector proceeds step by step, i.e., from one contact to the next. At the first current impulse the relay A energizes the delay-action relay V (Fig. 1), which in turn closes the motor circuit. The selector cannot yet rotate, however, since both motor magnets are energized through the zero position contact nr. When the relay A is de-energized at the end of the current impulse, the rotor is released, and the selector rotates to the first main rest position, where the first "ten" of the dialed number commences. Now when a second current impulse is emitted, the changeover contact *a* de-energizes the magnet M_2, and the selector begins to rotate. It completes its first "tens" step, which brings it to the beginning of the second "ten." The cam contacts nr and zr on the selector play an important part in controlling the selector movements. The main rest contact hr marks the end and also the beginning of a "ten." The intermediate rest contact zr serves to stop the motion of the selector if the number-dialing impulses are emitted too slowly. As appears from the—greatly simplified— circuit diagram in Fig. 1, the selector is stopped at the intermediate rest position ZR (always the sixth step within each "ten") if the contact *a* is still reversed when the selector reaches this intermediate rest position. On the other hand, if the relay A has already become de-energized when the selector reaches the intermediate rest position, it does not stop there, but continues to the main rest position. Here it is held by the action of the reset contact *a* and the main rest contact. When the next current impulse is emitted, the same procedure is repeated. After the last impulse of a series of current impulses has brought the selector to the relevant main rest, the control relay V is de-energized; selection of the "ones" then commences.

This latter operation, in which the selector moves along one "step" at a time, can be explained with reference to Fig. 2. When the first dialing current impulse is emitted, the relay A causes the delay-action control relay V to be energized. A contact *v* energizes the motor circuit. Through the contact *a* (in series with the low-ohmic relay winding D) both magnets are now energized, so that the motor remains stationary. The second winding D is energized through another contact *v* and a contact *a*. In that case the relay D does not respond, as the current flows in the opposite direction through the winding connected in the motor circuit. At the end of the first current impulse, with release of the relay A, the motor holding current circuit is broken. The motor magnet M_1 is energized. The selection performs only one step, since the magnet M_1 remains energized through the rest contact *a* and the contact *d*, notwithstanding that the contact m_1 is open. At the next current impulse the relay D responds because the current flows in the same direction through both windings. When this impulse has ended, the selector can perform its next step, but is once again stopped by the relay D because now the magnet M_2 remains energized.

(more)

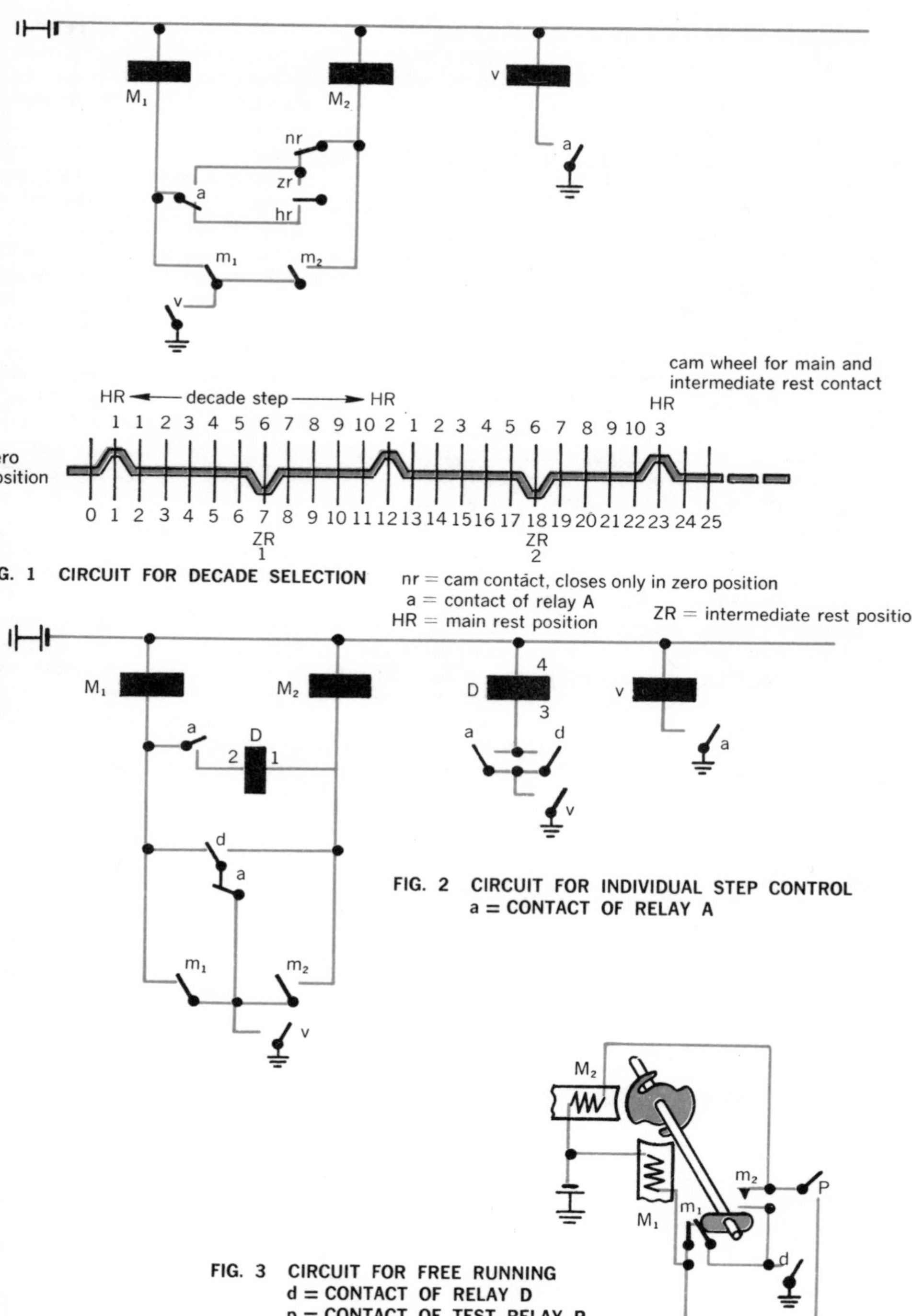

FIG. 1 CIRCUIT FOR DECADE SELECTION

nr = cam contact, closes only in zero position
a = contact of relay A
HR = main rest position
ZR = intermediate rest position

FIG. 2 CIRCUIT FOR INDIVIDUAL STEP CONTROL
a = CONTACT OF RELAY A

FIG. 3 CIRCUIT FOR FREE RUNNING
d = CONTACT OF RELAY D
p = CONTACT OF TEST RELAY P

Telephony and Telephone-exchange Techniques (continued)

As a result of the advances in switching techniques described in the foregoing, there are already a number of experimental telephone exchanges operating with electronic switch gear. In principle, any relay having two functional positions ("on" and "off") can be replaced by a system of electronic components (e.g., diodes, transistors) in which a flow of electrons is permitted to pass or is blocked. These technical advances have, broadly speaking, been reflected in developments in the telephone system itself, including the direct dialing of numbers in foreign countries by any subscriber. A feature which has not changed, however, is the "star-shaped" pattern, as exemplified by the accompanying map showing central and main telephone exchanges in the Federal Republic of Germany (West Germany). There are eight central exchanges, to each of which are connected eight main exchanges. These in turn are each connected to eight junction exchanges, and each of these has up to eight end exchanges connected to it. In cases where the number of junction exchanges or end exchanges is larger than the maximum that can be connected to the main exchange or the junction exchange concerned, these last-mentioned exchanges have to be doubled. This may be the case in the vicinity of major cities, where large numbers of telephone subscribers are concentrated in a relatively limited area. The "star" arrangement has advantages and disadvantages. An advantage is that the expensive long-distance selection equipment need be installed only at the center of the star. The disadvantage associated with it is that, in the event of a breakdown or technical trouble of any kind in these important exchanges, large sections of the telephone system are immediately put out of action. For gradual enlargement and extension of a telephone system the "star" arrangement provides the least expensive solution.

However, really economical operation can be achieved only by sufficient intermeshing of the telephone system so as to fulfill the requirements of telephone operation and reliability. Instead of having to pass all calls through the central exchanges it might well be possible in certain cases to bypass these and, for example, employ a more economical cross connection between two main exchanges. Now that the "star" system has been completed in Germany, further development for the moment consists in the addition of such connections as and when the need arises.

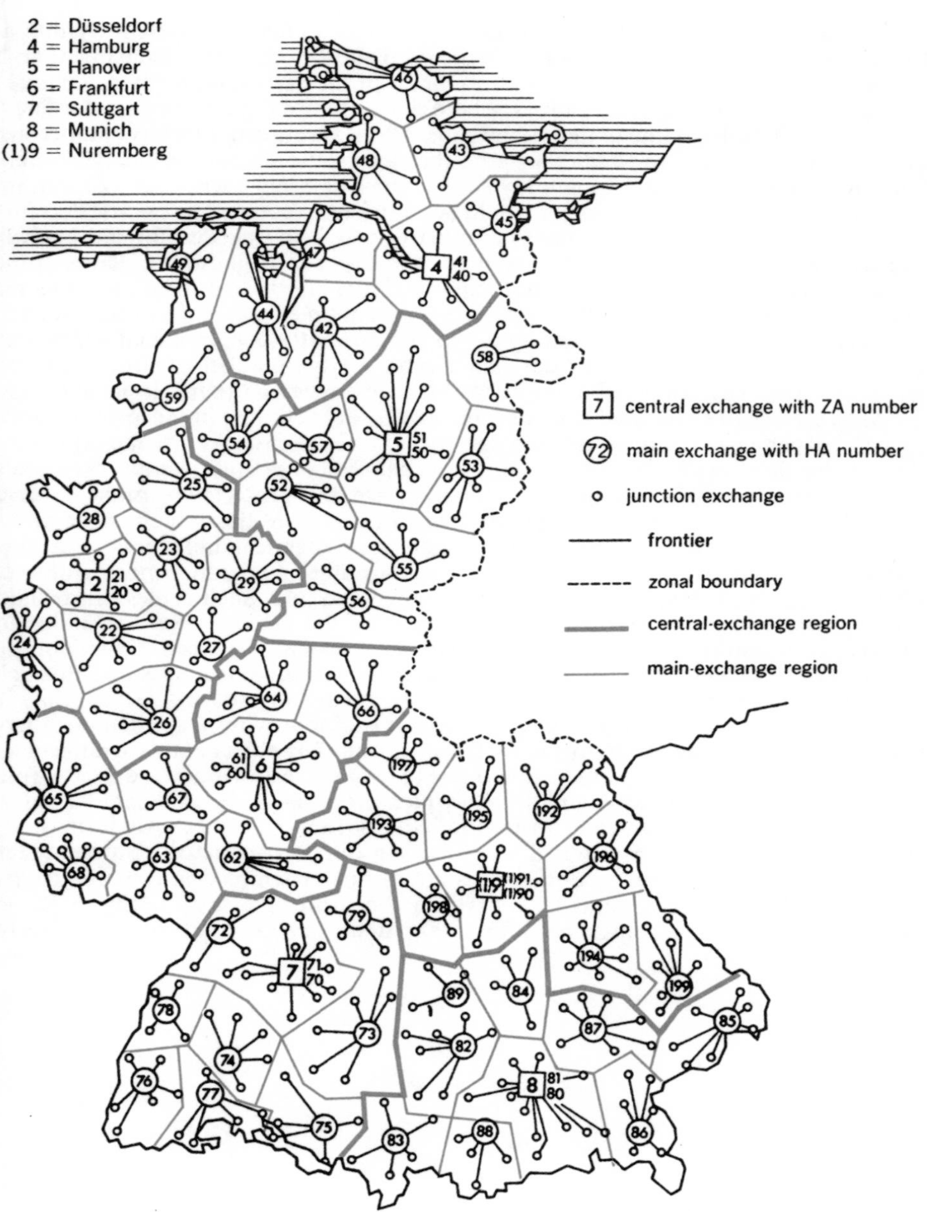

Central and main-exchange telephone regions for the Federal Republic of Germany, not including Berlin

TELEPHONE CABLES

The telephone lines are the most expensive part of a telephone system. Within a particular locality they connect all the individual subscribers to the exchanges, and the exchanges are interconnected by trunk lines. In the early days of the telephone overhead lines were usual; nowadays, where these are used at all, they are confined to short final lengths of line to individual subscribers. Overhead lines have numerous disadvantages: stresses to which they are subjected by the action of wind, ice formation, etc., make it necessary to employ hard copper or bronze wires up to 3 mm in diameter, whereas 0.6 mm diameter would be sufficient to convey the electric current i.e., such lines are wasteful in material, most of this being needed for mechanical strength. Besides, overhead telephone wires are exposed to inductive action from adjacent high-voltage equipment (particularly if it is faulty) and from atmospheric electricity (especially thunderstorms). In the course of time most of the overhead lines were replaced by cables, thus getting rid of the unsightly congestion of wires that disfigured some cities in prewar days. In a cable a large number of circuits can be accommodated, each of which comprises two wires, called a "pair." In local cables the pairs are usually insulated from one another by dry cellulose in the form of paper pulp or paper tape wrapped around the wires; in long-distance (or trunk) cables they are insulated with plastics, e.g., polyvinyl chloride or polyethylene. Since cables are, with few exceptions, laid underground, they are thus protected from the adverse influences affecting overhead telephone lines. In addition, the cable can be given appropriate strength and resistance to aggressive chemical influences. For this purpose it is provided with a metal sheath (lead or aluminum), an armoring of steel tape, and an outer wrapping of bitumen-impregnated jute. Such cables can be laid directly in the ground. In local telephone systems the cables may be installed in underground multiple-way ducts (Fig. 1) which extend between cable-jointing chambers (manholes). These cables, which are not armored, are threaded through the ducts and are connected to one another by means of jointing sleeves (Fig. 3). The cable is composed of eight quads, i.e., groups of four wires (conductors); there are two pairs forming two circuits in each such group. The object of this arrangement is to prevent cross talk (unwanted sound due to capacitive and inductive action from adjacent circuits). There are two forms in which the wires in the cable are stranded, i.e., twisted together: "star-quad formation" (Fig. 4a) and "multiple-twin formation" (Fig. 4b). Five quads are assembled into a basic group of conductors containing ten pairs of wires (Fig. 5). Such basic groups are in turn assembled into main groups which are disposed in several layers within the protective sheath. Fig. 6 shows typical cross-sectional arrangements for a 300-pair and a 1500-pair cable respectively.

(more)

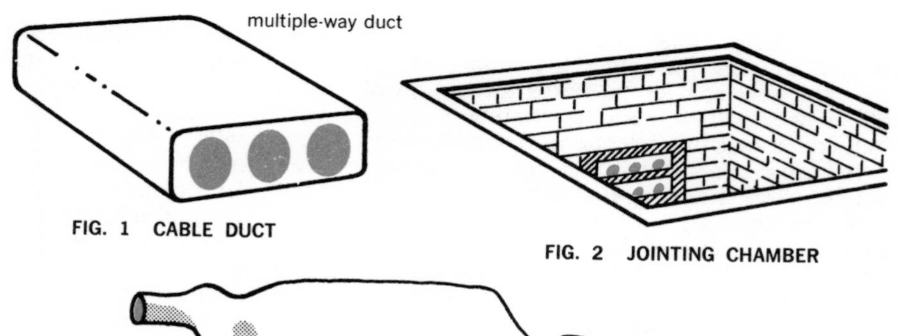

FIG. 1 CABLE DUCT

FIG. 2 JOINTING CHAMBER

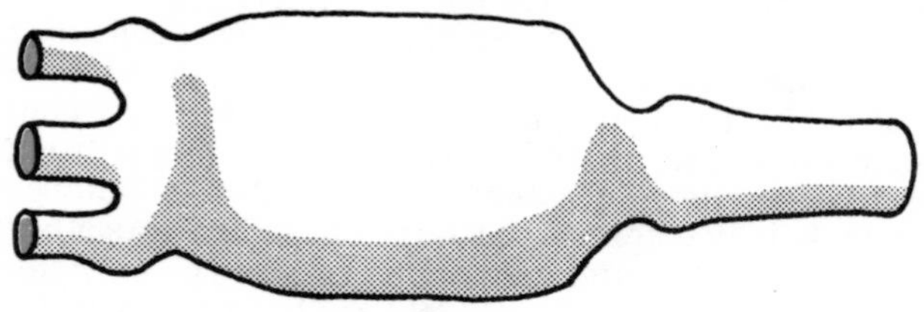

FIG. 3 LEAD JOINTING SLEEVE AT BRANCHING OF ONE MULTIPAIRED CABLE INTO THREE SMALLER CABLES

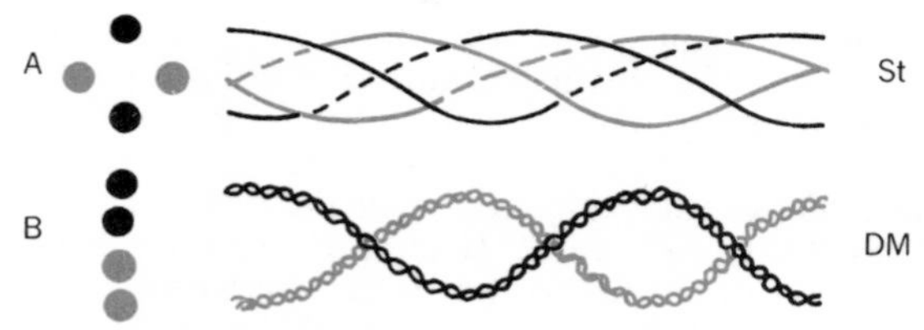

FIG. 4 STAR-QUAD FORMATION (St) AND MULTIPLE-TWIN FORMATION (DM)

FIG. 5 BASIC GROUP CONTAINING PAIRS OF CONDUCTORS

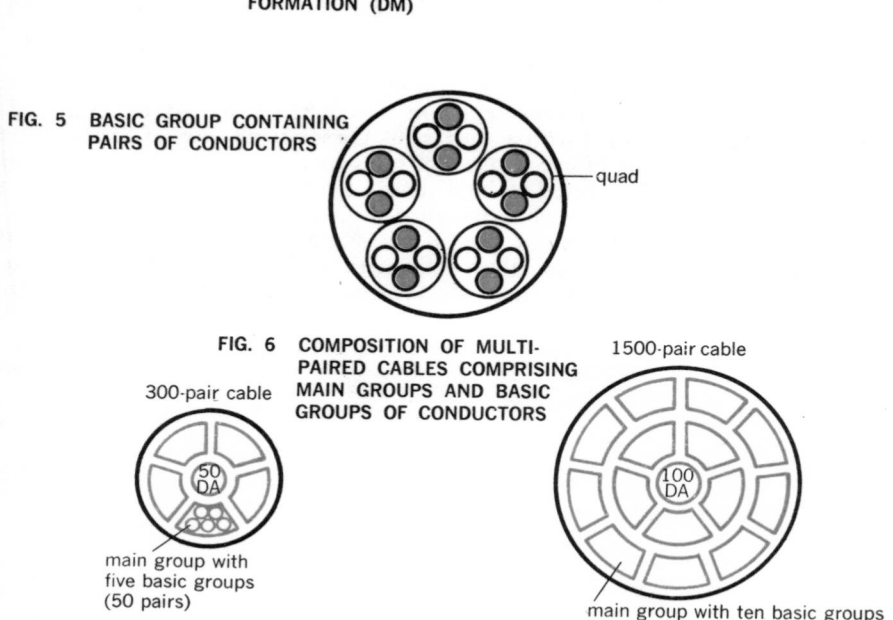

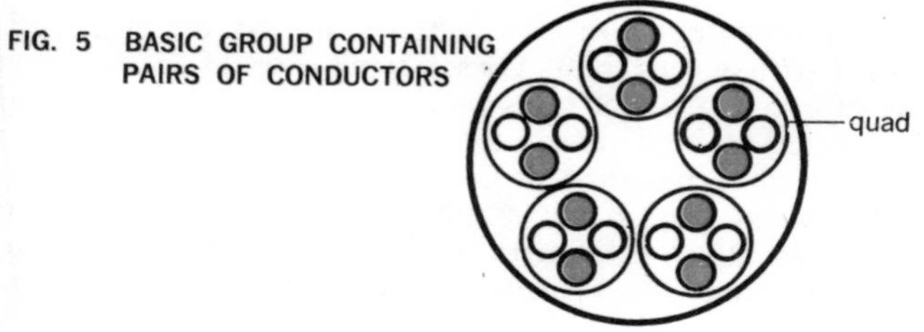

FIG. 6 COMPOSITION OF MULTI-PAIRED CABLES COMPRISING MAIN GROUPS AND BASIC GROUPS OF CONDUCTORS

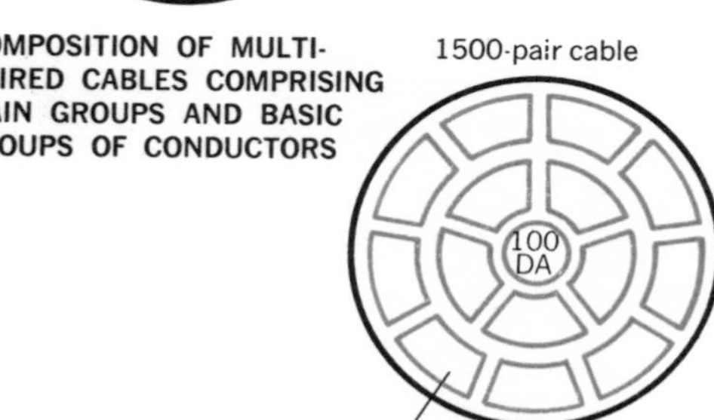

The telephone cables extend between distribution boxes and dividing boxes; the individual subscribers' lines are connected to the latter. In the telephone exchange the cables are split up into separate groups of conductors in multiple cable joints and connected to a main distributing frame (Fig. 7). The branching of a cable into individual lines in a telephone system is shown schematically in Fig. 8.

In local systems each subscriber is connected to the exchange by a pair of individual copper wires. For long-distance cables, however, multiplex carrier techniques are being increasingly adopted (see page 284); time-division multiplexing is more particularly preferred for submarine cables. These methods make new demands upon the cables; the use of high-frequency carrier waves (e.g., 240 kHz for 300 speech channels) increases the likelihood of cross talk between adjacent conductors. Attempts to overcome these and other difficulties led to the development of the so-called coaxial cable. The two conductors of a coaxial unit consist of a hollow cylinder and a central wire respectively (Fig. 9), separated by a distance of 2 to 5 mm (0.08 to 0.4 inch). Sometimes a cable is composed of a number of such units. Alternatively, a cable may comprise one large coaxial unit together with a number of ordinary quads grouped around it (Fig. 10). A coaxial cable of this kind can carry as many as 960 speech channels or it can be used to carry the wide frequency band of a television transmission. At higher carrier frequencies the electromagnetic energy tends to "become detached" from the metal conductor and to be propagated into space as waves (a property which, at still higher frequencies, is utilized in the wave guide: see page 276). For this reason it is essential to ensure that the coaxial unit is geometrically accurate, i.e., the axial wire must be precisely central within the cylindrical tube surrounding it. If this condition is not satisfied, the carrier waves will be reflected back from the cylinder wall, causing "ghost" images in the case of a television transmission. This requirement of geometric precision, which is essential to ensure good electromagnetic performance of the line, must be fulfilled without undue sacrifice of flexibility of the cable. It should, for example, be possible to bend it to a radius of about 4 ft. ($1\frac{1}{4}$ m) so that it can be wound on a reel. To obtain this flexibility, the cylindrical tube of the coaxial cable is made of coiled copper tape, the central wire being maintained in position by means of spacer discs made of trolitul (an insulating material) or by means of a helix made of styroflex (Fig. 9). Despite progress in cable-manufacturing technology, higher carrier frequencies undergo considerable damping. Thus, about 99.9% of the input energy is lost over a distance of five or six miles, so that amplification becomes necessary. These intermediate amplifiers, called repeaters, are now often installed underground, completely buried, or provided with access shafts for servicing (Fig. 11). Submarine telephone cables have to be of much stronger construction than cables for normal use on land, as they are subjected to high tensile forces (especially at the time of laying) and very high pressures when installed in great depths of water. For this reason, coaxial cables for submarine use do not contain a cavity between central wire and cylindrical tube, but are filled solid with a suitable insulating material (gutta-percha, plastic), besides containing steel "armor" wires for additional strength.

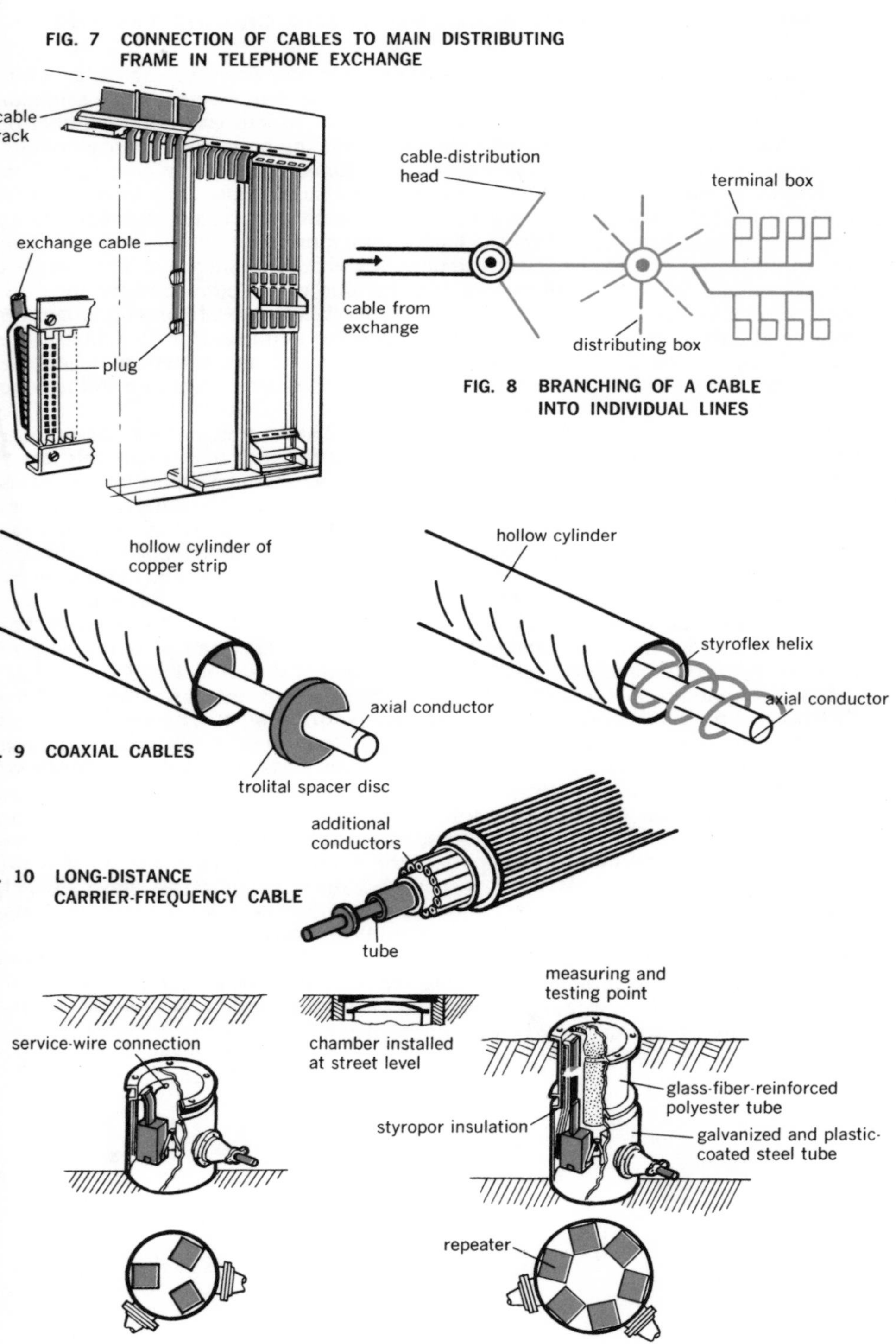

FIG. 7 CONNECTION OF CABLES TO MAIN DISTRIBUTING FRAME IN TELEPHONE EXCHANGE

FIG. 8 BRANCHING OF A CABLE INTO INDIVIDUAL LINES

FIG. 9 COAXIAL CABLES

FIG. 10 LONG-DISTANCE CARRIER-FREQUENCY CABLE

FIG. 11 REPEATERS FOR MULTIPLE-TUBE COAXIAL CABLES IN UNDERGROUND CHAMBERS (UP TO SIX REPEATERS PER CHAMBER)

AUTOMATIC MESSAGE ACCOUNTING AND CIRCUIT TESTING

In telephony, the automatic recording of data for preparing the subscriber's bill is closely related to automatic switching. The simplest method consists in using an electromechanical counter, called a message register, which records the number of calls made by a subscriber. In modern telephone systems, however, a more elaborate procedure, known as multiunit registration, according to the distance and duration of the call, is usually employed. In some systems this procedure is applied only to long-distance calls, while local calls are charged at a flat rate, irrespective of duration; in others, all calls are charged on the basis of the number of "message units." The registration of calls is based on electrical impulses which actuate relays. The impulses are continually fed to the call-metering device during the conversation; they are fed in quicker succession according as the call distance is longer. In practice, a certain number of "distance zones" is introduced—nine, for example. For each zone there is a different standard impulse rate, the time interval between two impulses (the zone time) being the length of time corresponding to one message unit in the zone concerned.

The impulses are emitted by a call timer (Fig. 1). This comprises an electric motor which drives a shaft at constant speed. Mounted on the shaft are cam wheels which actuate contacts and thus produce the impulse sequences. The spacing of the cams is different on the wheels corresponding to the different zones. The difference between normal tariff and the cheaper evening and night tariff is obtained by changing the speed of the motor. The metering devices are installed in the telephone exchange, where they are read at regular intervals; the number of message units indicated by each meter provides the basis for billing each subscriber. Each metering device comprises several drums on which the numerals for "units," "tens," "hundreds," etc., are marked and which are rotated by means of a ratchet-and-pawl mechanism actuated by electromagnets (Fig. 2). The meter dial is shown in Fig. 3.

Every telephone selector has, in addition to the wipers (contact arms) for switching the speech circuit, other wipers for testing and control (Fig. 4). The wiper C is used for "engaged" testing (or testing for free circuit). Connected to this wiper is the test relay P; the speech circuit is connected through only when this relay is energized; for this there must be a sufficiently high voltage at the contact that the wiper reaches on completion of the dialing operation. If this voltage is sufficient, the energizing current can flow through the relay P. As soon as the armature of this relay has been attracted, its contacts short-circuit part of the winding, so that the voltage at the selector contact decreases. While P is energized, the winding of the relay C (which is connected to the selector contact and belongs to the next selection stage) and the reduced winding of P form a "voltage divider." When the wiper C of another selector reaches a contact which is connected to the same relay C, its relay P receives too low a voltage and cannot become energized. The control circuit of this second selector tests whether the relay P has responded within a certain time; if not, the "engaged" signal is transmitted to the subscriber.

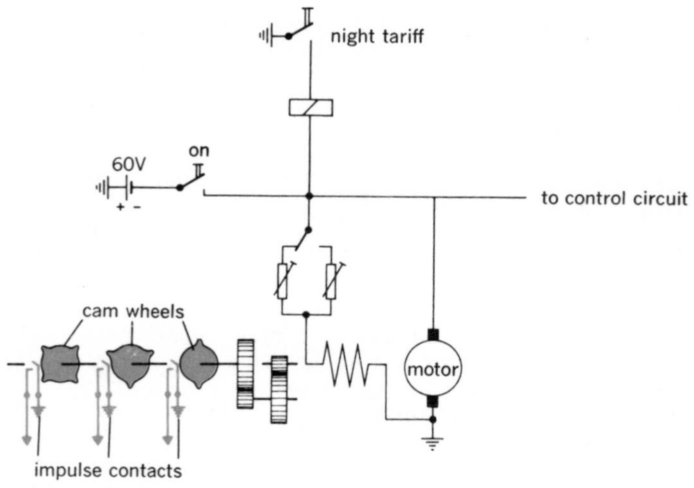

FIG. 1 DIAGRAM OF A CALL TIMER

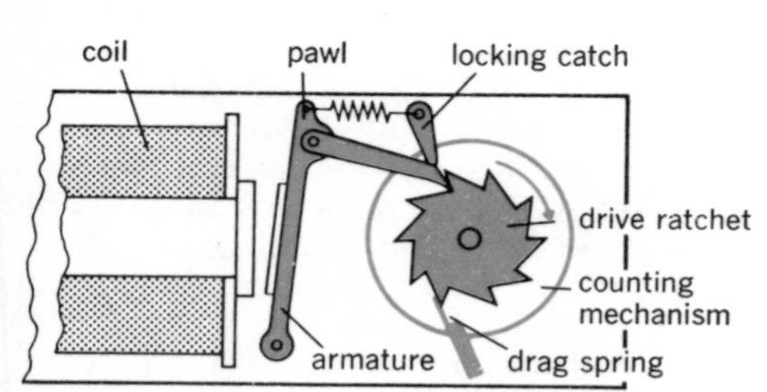

FIG. 2 RATCHET-AND-PAWL COUNTING DEVICE

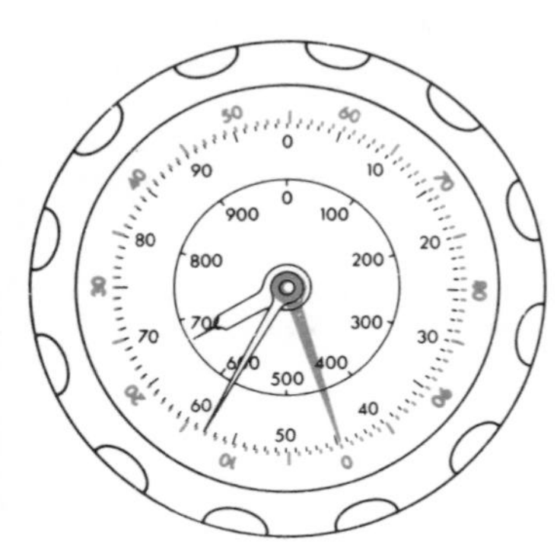

FIG. 3

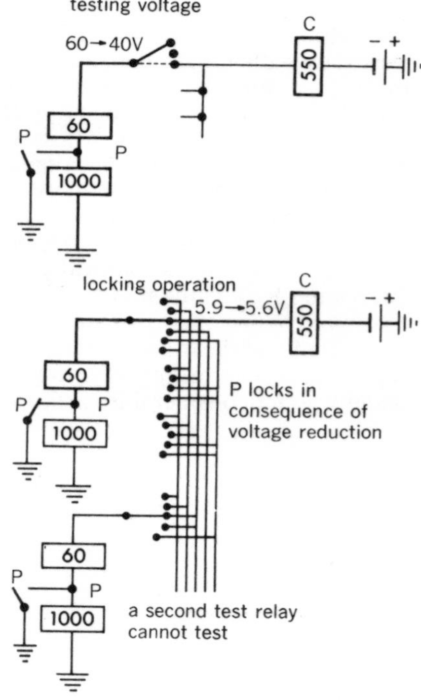

FIG. 4 TESTING AND LOCKING PROCEDURE FOR SELECTORS

CURRENT SUPPLY FOR TELECOMMUNICATION SYSTEMS

The suitable supply of current is an essential factor for the proper functioning of a telephone system. The public electricity supply mains as such are not a suitable source of current, as the permissible tolerances with regard to voltage and the occasional power failures would seriously interfere with proper telephonic communication. Besides, the requirements as to the type of current, voltage, current strength, and frequency vary greatly. What is primarily essential in telephony is a completely undisturbed supply of direct current; the lines and equipment are designed for 60 volts, whereas the public mains generally supply alternating current at a substantially higher voltage. The alternating main current is transformed down, rectified, and used to charge a storage battery of sufficient capacity to supply the telephone system with current for at least six hours in the event of a supply failure of the main (Fig. 1). In about 97% of the cases this is a sufficient length of time to put right the fault in the main and thus resume the recharging of the battery. Otherwise a standby generating set, consisting of a diesel engine coupled to a generator, must temporarily supply charging current.

Certain types of telecommunication equipment require an alternating-current supply. Even in such cases the main's alternating current is first converted into direct current—because this can be stored in a storage battery which gives a constant supply of current independent of the mains and possible troubles affecting them—and then converted back into alternating current. This last-mentioned conversion can be done by means of a motor-generator, i.e., a DC motor driving an AC generator, or by means of an inverter (also known as an inverted rectifier) (Figs. 2 and 3). Two motor-generators or two inverters are connected in parallel, in order to improve operational reliability. For telecommunication installations which are in remote locations with no on-the-spot attendant personnel—e.g., directional radio transmitters—it may be advantageous to connect the power supply directly with a standby supply system. The requisite electric power for operating the equipment is obtained from a generator whose shaft is coupled to that of an electric motor (with a flywheel) which in turn is connected, through an induction coupling, to a diesel engine (Fig. 4). Under normal operating conditions the motor, supplied with current from the main, drives the generator and the flywheel. In the event of a power failure in the main, the induction coupling engages, and the momentum of the flywheel provides sufficient mechanical power to start the diesel engine. The latter runs at the same speed as the motor, which has now been automatically disconnected from the main. When the main supply is restored, the diesel engine is mechanically disconnected and the motor is electrically reconnected to the main. An automatic fault-reporting system brings these events to the attention of a central monitoring station, usually some considerable distance away.

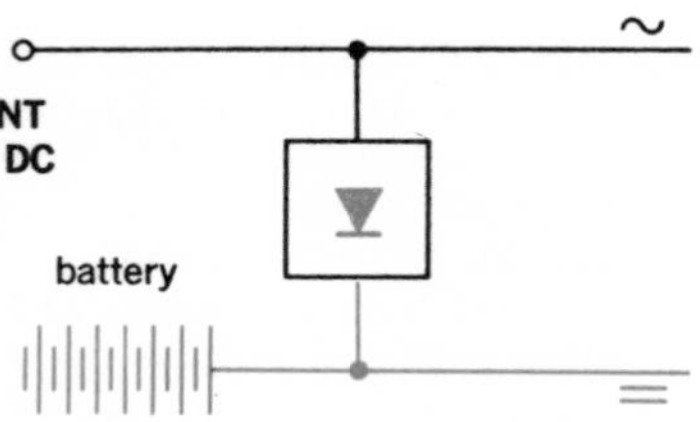

FIG. 1 CONTINUOUS CURRENT SUPPLY FOR SMALL DC REQUIREMENTS

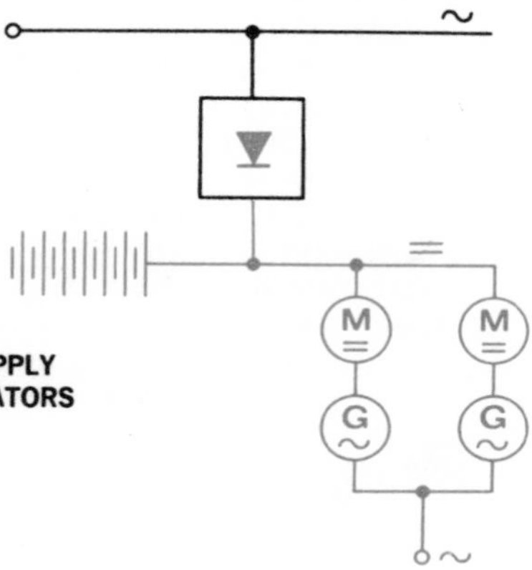

battery

FIG. 2 CONTINUOUS AC SUPPLY WITH MOTOR-GENERATORS

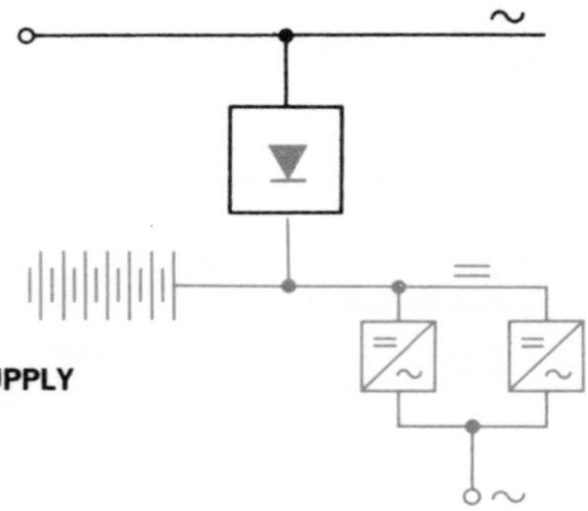

FIG. 3 CONTINUOUS AC SUPPLY WITH INVERTERS

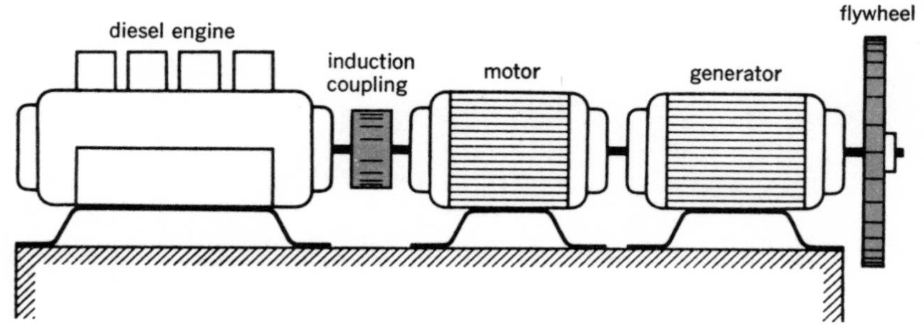

FIG. 4 MOTOR-GENERATOR WITH STANDBY DIESEL ENGINE

VIDEO TAPE RECORDING

Video tape recording (magnetic picture recording) is the "visual" counterpart of audio tape recording. It is the technique of storing video signals by means of a tape magnetized along its length in accordance with the signals impressed upon it. The tape, consisting of a plastic material coated with magnetic oxide, is fed past a recording head, and the signals are stored in the magnetized oxide particles. This type of recording has the important advantage of being ready for immediate playback without development or other processing. For this reason it is now extensively used for the recording of both monochrome and color television programs.

An early forerunner of tape-recording technique was Poulsen's "telegraphone" (1898) for the recording of telegraphic messages and, later on, of speech on thin steel wire as the magnetic storage medium. A subsequent development was the "magnetophone," a device developed by the German electrical-engineering firm of AEG in 1930 and based on an invention by Pleumer. It used iron oxide powder as the storage material applied to a base consisting of a paper or plastic tape. In 1953 the Radio Corporation of America (RCA) developed Olson's video tape recorder, operating with a tape speed of 6 m/sec., longitudinal recording (Fig. 1a). with a fixed recording or reproducing head. Because of the very high tape speed, this apparatus was not very suitable for practical purposes. In the Ampex machine developed by Ginsburg in 1956 the signals are recorded transversely (Fig. 1b), the tape speed being 38 cm/sec. This apparatus had four recording heads (and four reproducing heads) positioned at intervals of 90 degrees around a rotating disc. It was the first really serviceable video tape recorder for commercial use, giving a picture of such good quality that a prerecorded television transmission was no longer distinguishable from a "live" one. Besides, the tape speed was similar to that of the audio tape recorders used in broadcasting. With appropriate ancillary equipment this video recorder was also suitable for color-picture recording for television (NTSC system used in America). In 1959 the Japanese firm of Toshiba introduced a recorder with a tape speed of 19 cm/sec. and oblique recording (Fig. 1c) on a helically guided tape by means of a single rotating head. This machine has about half the resolving power of the Ampex and is suitable for industrial and educational purposes and private use.

Fig. 2 schematically shows the Ampex video tape-recording system. The video signal frequency-modulates a carrier-frequency oscillation of approximately 50 MHz with a deviation from −0.9 to +2.1 MHz—i.e., giving a frequency band of 49.1 to 52.1 MHz. For the purpose of recording, the band of 49.1–50–52.1 MHz is converted

(more)

FIG. 1

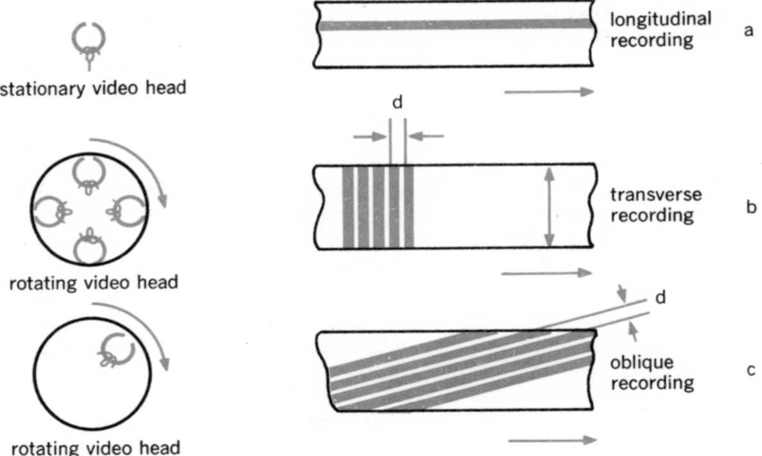

FIG. 2 SIMPLIFIED BLOCK DIAGRAM OF A VIDEO TAPE-RECORDING SYSTEM OPERATED ON THE FOUR-HEAD AMPEX PRINCIPLE

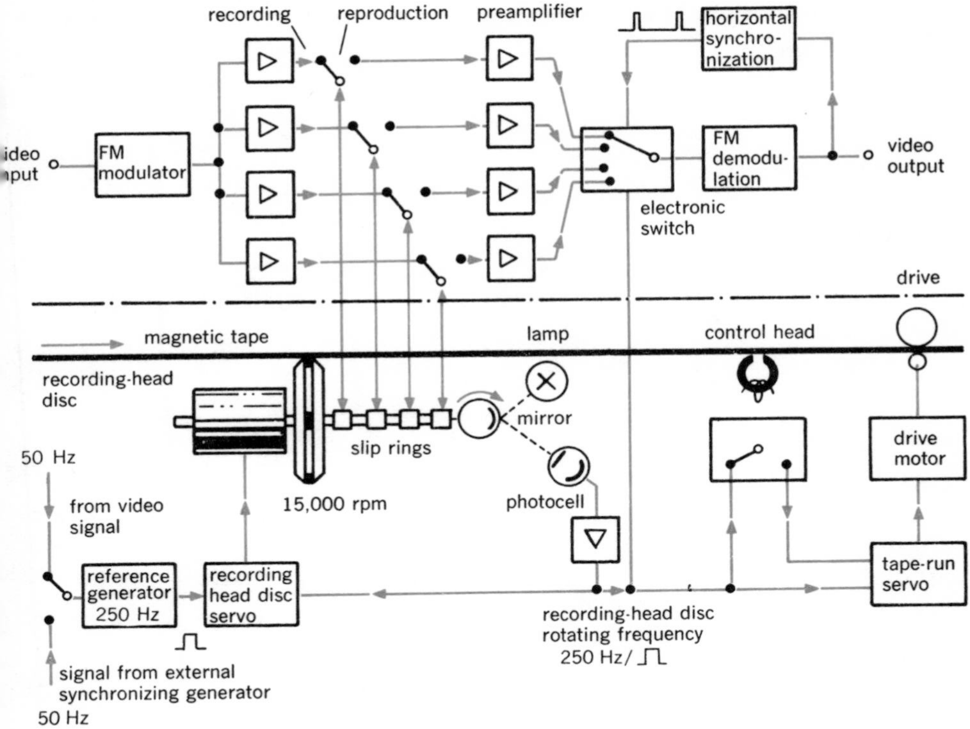

recording
reproduction
preamplifier
horizontal synchro-nization
video input
FM modulator
electronic switch
FM demodu-lation
video output
drive
magnetic tape
lamp
control head
recording-head disc
mirror
slip rings
drive motor
50 Hz
from video signal
15,000 rpm
photocell
reference generator 250 Hz
recording head disc servo
tape-run servo
recording-head disc rotating frequency 250 Hz/
signal from external synchronizing generator
50 Hz

to 6.3–7.2–9.3 MHz and is fed simultaneously to the four rotating recording heads (Fig. 3). A picture line of 64 microseconds' duration is recorded on a track length of 2.4 mm—i.e., at a speed of 38.1 m/sec. The tracks are 0.25 mm wide and are 0.131 mm apart; a complete 625-line picture is recorded on a 15.2 mm length of the 50.8 mm wide tape. One revolution of the recording-head assembly corresponds to a tape length of 4 × 0.381 = approx. 1.6 mm; for a speed of 250 revolutions per second the tape travels at a speed of 38.1 cm/sec. Reproduction of the recording is done by means of the same head assembly. It converts the magnetic recording into frequency-modulated signal voltages. These are converted to 49–52 MHz and demodulated to produce a video signal. In contrast with the recording process, the four reproducing heads are *consecutively* connected to the demodulator in order to obviate the overlaps between the individual heads during recording. For recording, the tape speed and the rotational speed of the heads need not fulfill very exacting requirements of uniformity. On the other hand, for reproduction the head and the tape must be synchronized with an accuracy of 0.1 microsecond (or 0.15 micron). For this purpose the tape speed is controlled by means of a control frequency corresponding to the actual recording-head speed and recorded on the tape along with the picture, and the speed of rotation of the heads is controlled by the frame-synchronizing impulse of the video signal. Additional electronic control devices compensate for inaccuracies in the positioning of the four heads in relation to one another. The reproduction of color video signals calls for something like 100 times greater accuracy even than for monochrome. The audio signal, i.e., the sound accompanying the picture, is recorded on a 1 mm wide track at the edge of the tape. The video and audio signals are exactly synchronized. The control frequency for the tape speed is likewise recorded on a 1 mm wide edge track. The complete Ampex video-tape recording machine is shown in Fig. 4.

(more)

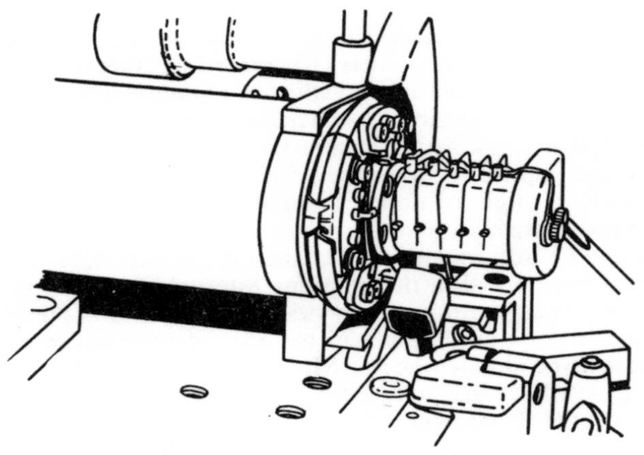

FIG. 3 AMPEX MACHINE (RECORDING-HEAD DISC WITH MAGNETIC RECORDING HEADS AT 90-DEGREE SPACING AND COLLECTOR SPRINGS FOR HEAD CONTACTS ON THE ROTATING SHAFT)

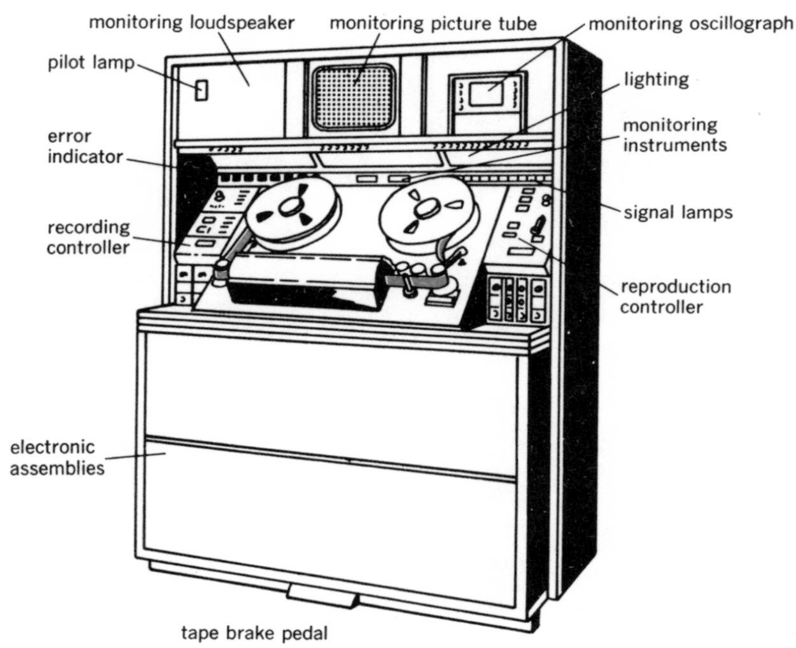

FIG. 4 FOUR-HEAD VIDEO TAPE-RECORDING MACHINE

Because of the convenience associated with the immediate readiness for reproduction of the recorded pictures, video tape recording is used not only in television broadcasting but also for industrial and educational purposes, as well as for amateur use in the home. Somewhat simpler machines operating with a single recording head are employed in these cases, where rather less exacting requirements as to picture quality are applied. A machine of this type which records the signals in tracks inclined at an angle of about 4 degrees is shown schematically in Fig. 5. The tape is wrapped around a tilted tape-guide cylinder containing one rotating head. One inclined track records half a picture ($\frac{1}{50}$ second); the jump from one track to the next occurs within the blanking interval—i.e., during the fraction of a second when there is no picture on the video screen—and is therefore not seen. As the speed of the head is only about 20 m/sec., the resolving power is only about half that of the four-head machine (2.5 MHz as against 5 MHz). The tape speed has been reduced to 19.05 cm/sec. without adversely affecting the signal-to-noise ratio to a significant degree. The audio track and control track are likewise located at the edge of the tape. The video tape recorder (Fig. 6) can be connected to a television set.

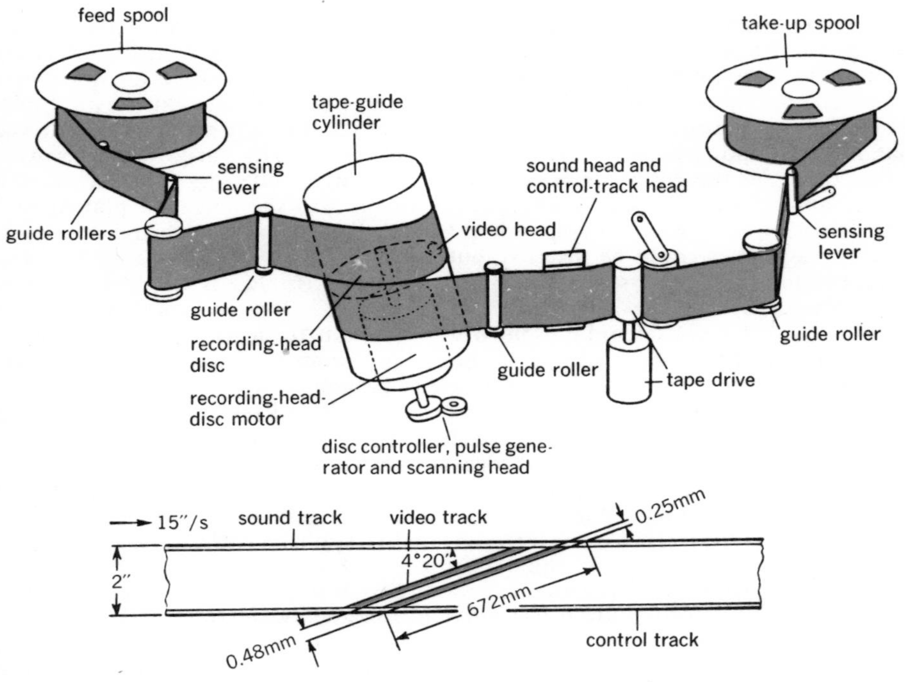

FIG. 5 DIAGRAM OF VIDEO RECORDING IN OBLIQUE TRACKS ON MAGNETIC TAPE; THE TRACKS ARE FORMED BY GUIDING THE TAPE ON A RECORDING-HEAD DISC WITH INCLINED AXIS

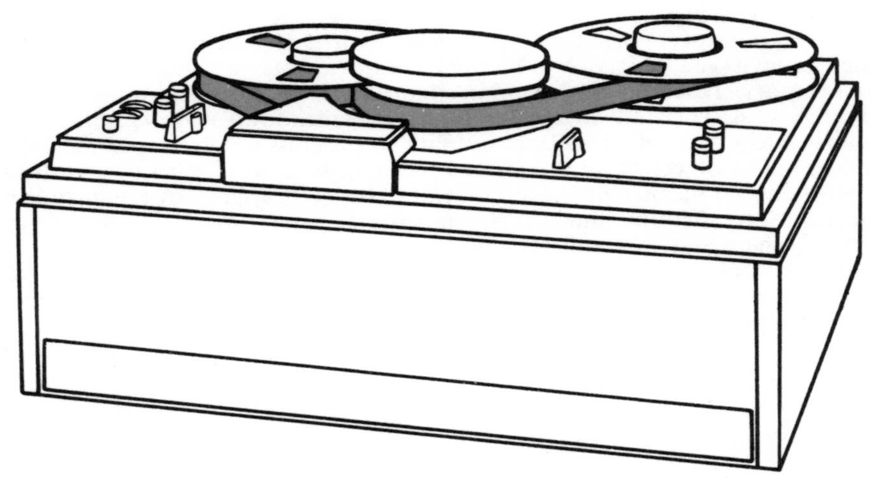

FIG. 6 VIDEO TAPE RECORDER FOR INDUSTRIAL USE

TEACHING MACHINES

Teaching machines are of various types, some of which are shown in the accompanying illustrations. Fig. 1 represents Pressey's machine dating from 1927. Its only function was to pose questions. To each question four possible answers were presented; the learner had to choose the correct one by pressing a button (multiple-choice method). Pressey was aiming to rationalize the teaching process. He believed that material inducements and rewards were helpful. His early machines were designed to give the deserving pupil a piece of candy or chewing gum each time a correct answer was chosen. A later device of his was the so-called punchboard (Fig. 2) with holes—each corresponding to an answer—into which the point of a pencil or a pricker could be inserted, but only if the answer was the correct one. Other machines were devised in which the choice of possible answers was increased to twenty—e.g., in Briggs's "subject matter trainer" (Fig. 3). Another inventor, Norman Crowder, considered it useful also to evaluate the learner's wrong answers. In his machine (Fig. 4) he tried to lead the erring learner back to the correct answer by roundabout paths (on the principle called "branching").

Skinner, who was more successful than his predecessor Pressey in publicizing and gaining acceptance of teaching by machine (1954), considered that the correct answer must always be brought to the learner's attention: the machine must present the correct answer for comparison after the learner has made his choice. Fig. 5 shows one of Skinner's machines, with the answers recorded on a disc. In Porter's machine (Fig. 6) the learner's answer was fed into a slot; the correct answer was then revealed to the learner. The machine illustrated in Fig. 7 is similar in principle, but is worked by a knob which the learner rotates. For dealing with programs consisting entirely of text matter the knob has proved to be the means of manipulation best suited to human sensomotoric requirements. On the other hand, push buttons are preferable for audiovisual machines. Fig. 8 illustrates a special teaching machine which instructs the learner in the operation of a piece of apparatus and shows the correct manipulations on a television screen. In some machines the correct answer is not directly given; instead, the progress of the program is made dependent on the learner's giving the correct answer. Some machines of this type are shown in Figs. 9–12, including a digital computer (Fig. 11).

From the viewpoint of educational psychology, the use of teaching machines is based on concepts of behavioristic learning theories and the principle of "conditioning" as envisaged by Pavlov in his famous experiments on animals at the end of the last century. Teaching machines have indeed proved successful in many branches of education. Their advantage lies in skillful breakdown and organization of the course into a series of steps. Responsibility for progress devolves upon the individual student. The object of all programed teaching is to let the learner teach himself "privately," at his own pace, without fear of being "trapped" by a human teacher's questions. At the same time, he is compelled to master every step in the program actively; he is at all times directly involved, whereas in an ordinary school class the pupil gets only a limited amount of opportunity to demonstrate his knowledge or grasp of the subject matter actively; for most of the time he has to be content with a passive listening role.

(more)

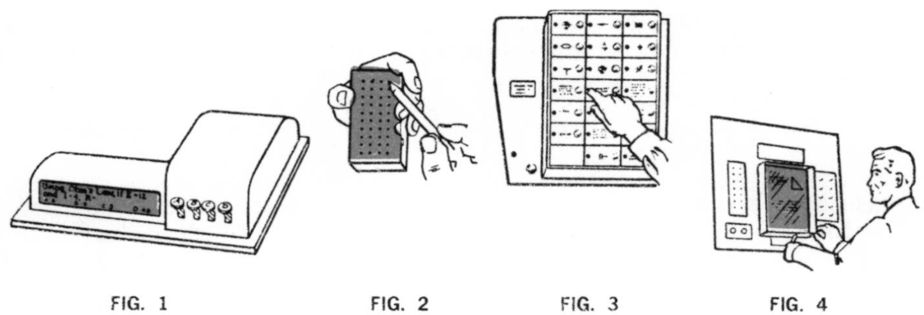

FIG. 1 FIG. 2 FIG. 3 FIG. 4

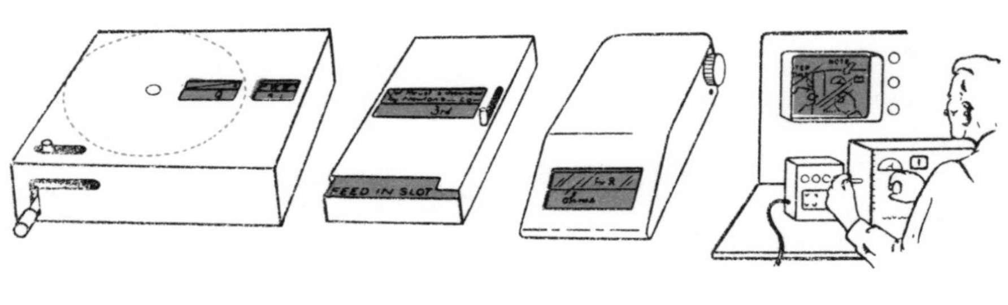

FIG. 5 FIG. 6 FIG. 7 FIG. 8

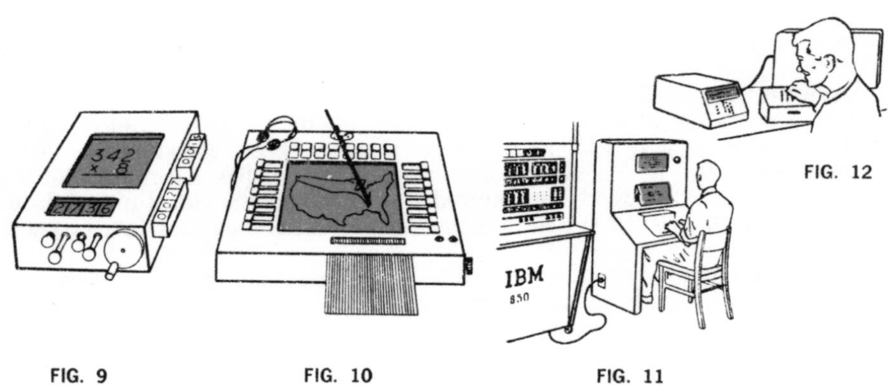

FIG. 9 FIG. 10 FIG. 11 FIG. 12

In the teaching program, the subject matter must be so organized that the learner can easily follow the flow of instruction, as represented by a flow diagram or an algorithm:

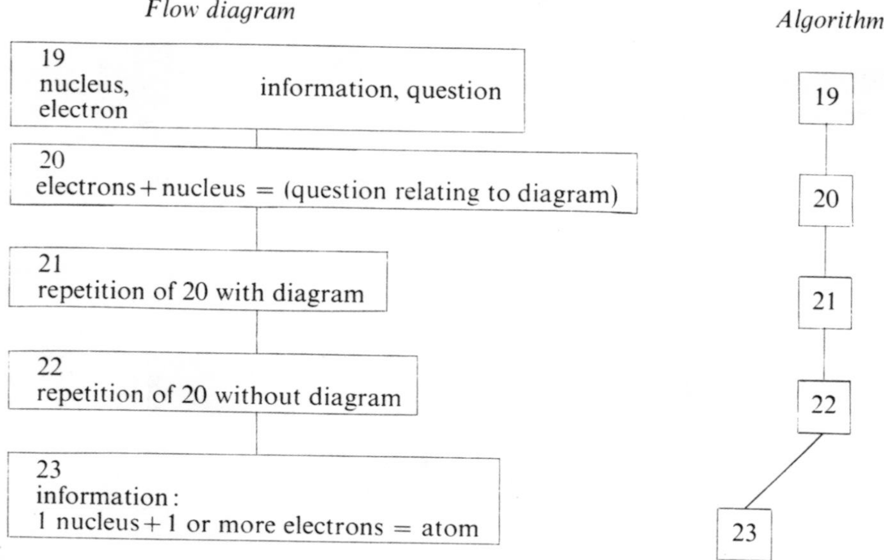

(The above example is part of a program on electronics.)

The meaning of the symbolic representation embodied in the algorithm (this term simply means a systematic process or method of solving any particular problem in a number of steps conforming to well-defined rules) is that the machine presents the learner with a series of "learning elements" (LE): LE 19 to 21 give and repeat information, but in LE 22 it is of decisive importance that the learner indeed give the answer; if so, he proceeds to LE 23; if not, then he must again go through the routine from LE 19 to 22.

The incorporation of additional LE to allow for individual differences between learners is exemplified by LE 119, 94 and 95 in Fig. 1. These are known as "simple program steps." In Fig. 2 a "simple subsequence" to LE 101 is included. If simple program steps are frequently introduced, the procedure is called a "wash-back program" (Fig. 3), and if a system of subsequences is adopted, it is called a "wash-ahead program" (Fig. 4).

Fig. 5 is part of an algorithm that makes use of explanatory steps, subsequences and repetitions ("complex wash-back program"). Repetitions, jumps, detours may be presented to the learner. In general, the teaching machine performs the functions of teaching (imparting the information) and of controlling the learning process. It can perform these functions separately or in any desired combination. When programed teaching is introduced, it is not a good thing to let the machine at once take charge of all the functions involved. Depending on the extent to which the machine undertakes various functions, the following types of equipment may be distinguished:

(more)

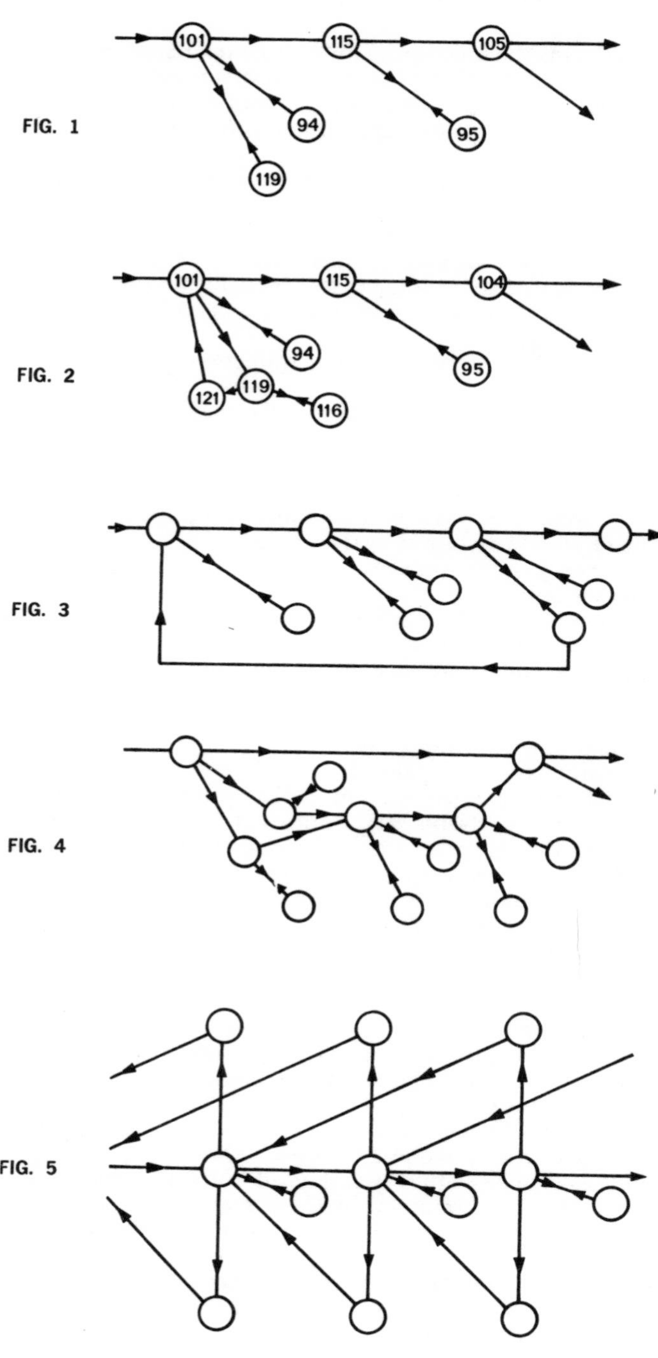

FIG. 1

FIG. 2

FIG. 3

FIG. 4

FIG. 5

Teaching Machines (continued)

1. The machine performs the function of instructing (giving information). The other functions (repetition, confirmation of correctness of answers, etc.) are embodied in the program and are under the learner's free control. He can set his own pace.
2. The machine performs the function of instructing and reduces physiological strain in various ways:
(a) elimination of the need to turn pages, reduction or optimization of the number of eye movements, etc.;
(b) sensomotoric function (the learner turns knobs); sometimes several sensory paths are utilized: acoustic plus visual presentation (push-button control); instruction given by the machine may in some cases be augmented by experiments.
3. The machine performs the function of instructing and of giving a visual presentation of the subject:
(a) a tape recorder supplies information, in conjunction with visual presentation of tables, diagrams, pictures, etc.;
(b) visual presentation of text (i.e., information obtained by reading) alternates with pictures, diagrams, etc.;
(c) taped sound track linked to a slide projector.
4. The machine presents information and calls for reactions from the learner in the form of a reply or some other active participation; the running of the program is stopped until the required reaction is forthcoming:
(a) the program continues after every reaction (writing or speaking into the machine, or pressing a selector button);
(b) the program continues only when the correct reaction is given (the machine checks the correctness of the reaction).
5. The machine presents information, calls for reactions and confirms their correctness (or otherwise) in any of the following ways:
(a) the program continues, without feedback;
(b) the program continues, with feedback;
(c) a signal is presented (visual, audio, etc.).
5(a) controls the learning process without explicit confirmation of the correctness of replies. In the case of 5(b) and 5(c) the learner is told whether or not he has answered correctly; this is regarded as advantageous in giving him positive encouragement. Encouragement is also provided when the learner himself is made to compare the answer that he has formulated with the correct answer. The program may achieve this by direct or indirect means.
6. The machine presents information, calls for reactions and confirms their correctness; it also prepares the subject matter systematically and presents it in accordance with the rules of educational psychology; such machines are more elaborate and are to be classed as computers:
(a) a computer-type teaching machine can be programed to present variant problems of the same type; it can set arithmetical problems to a whole classroom of pupils and speedily check the answers;
(b) electronic equipment is being increasingly used in organizing the subject matter itself and presenting it in a systematic form; the correct sequence of instruction is mapped out in accordance with psychological rules to which the computer is adjusted; in some cases the optimum learning sequence may be deduced by the computer itself from the "experience" it gains in the performance of teaching programs.
7. Language laboratories may be regarded as a special type of teaching machines whose main object is to train students in the oral use of foreign languages. There are, broadly speaking, three types:
(a) the listening laboratory (the student plays only a passive role);
(b) the listening and speech laboratory (active participation);
(c) the listening, speech and recording laboratory.

(more)

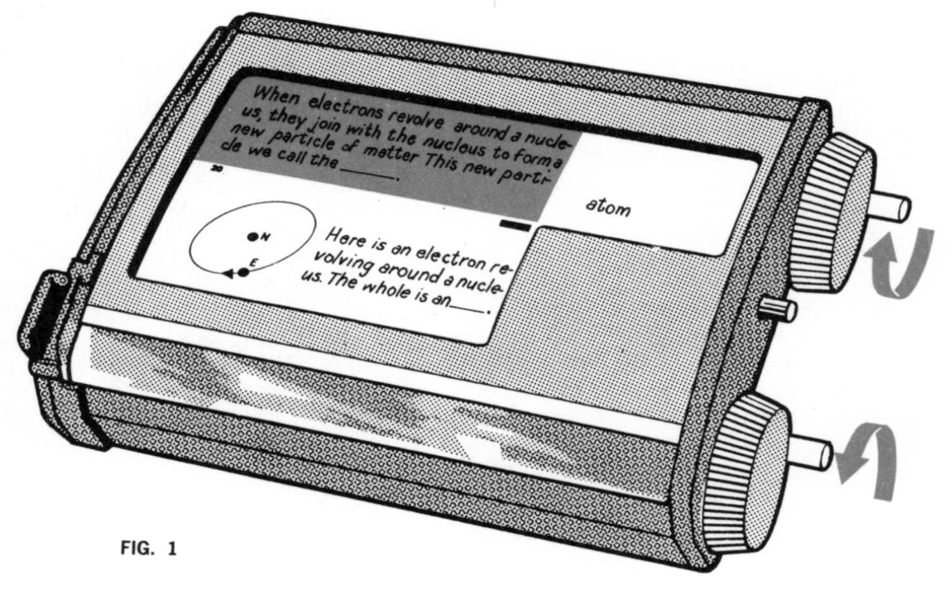
When electrons revolve around a nucle-
us, they join with the nucleus to form a
new particle of matter This new partr
cle we call the_____.
20
atom
N
E
Here is an electron re-
volving around a nucle-
us. The whole is an____.

FIG. 1

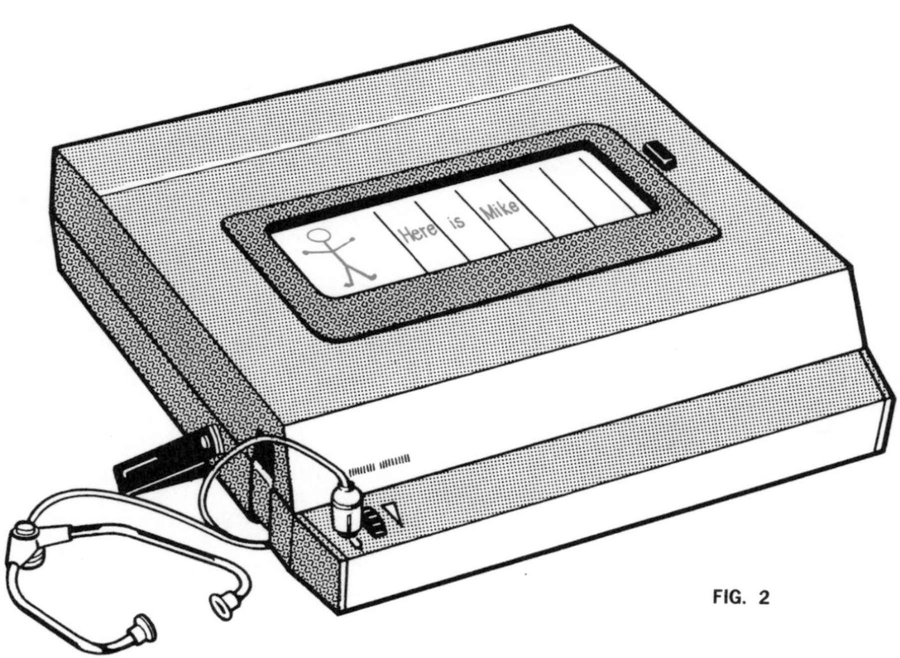
Here
is
Mike

FIG. 2

Teaching Machines (continued)

Programed instruction by machines aims to give the student immediate confirmation of the correctness of his answers to the questions and problems presented to him and thus to reinforce the acquisition of each step by knowledge of progress. However, the machine should not take complete control of the teaching process to the exclusion of all initiative on the learner's part. He should always be allowed a certain amount of independence of decision or choice—i.e., a controlled degree of freedom. The teaching machine has a psychological effect in stimulating the learner's interest: he feels a desire to manipulate it and is thus stimulated to learn.

The illustrations on pp. 321 and 323 show some teaching machines which have been developed in Germany. Fig. 1 (p. 321) shows the "Promentaboy," a machine which presents written information in simple easy-to-understand form, whereby much of the physiological strain is taken out of the reading-and-learning process. The second machine is the "Probiton," developed by Zielinski and Schöler, which gives audiovisual instruction (Figs. 1–3, p. 323): spoken and read text, pictures and sound illustrations together provide the optimum learning conditions. Finally, Correll's teaching machine (Fig. 2, p. 321) is an example of an audiovisual device for teaching very young children to read.

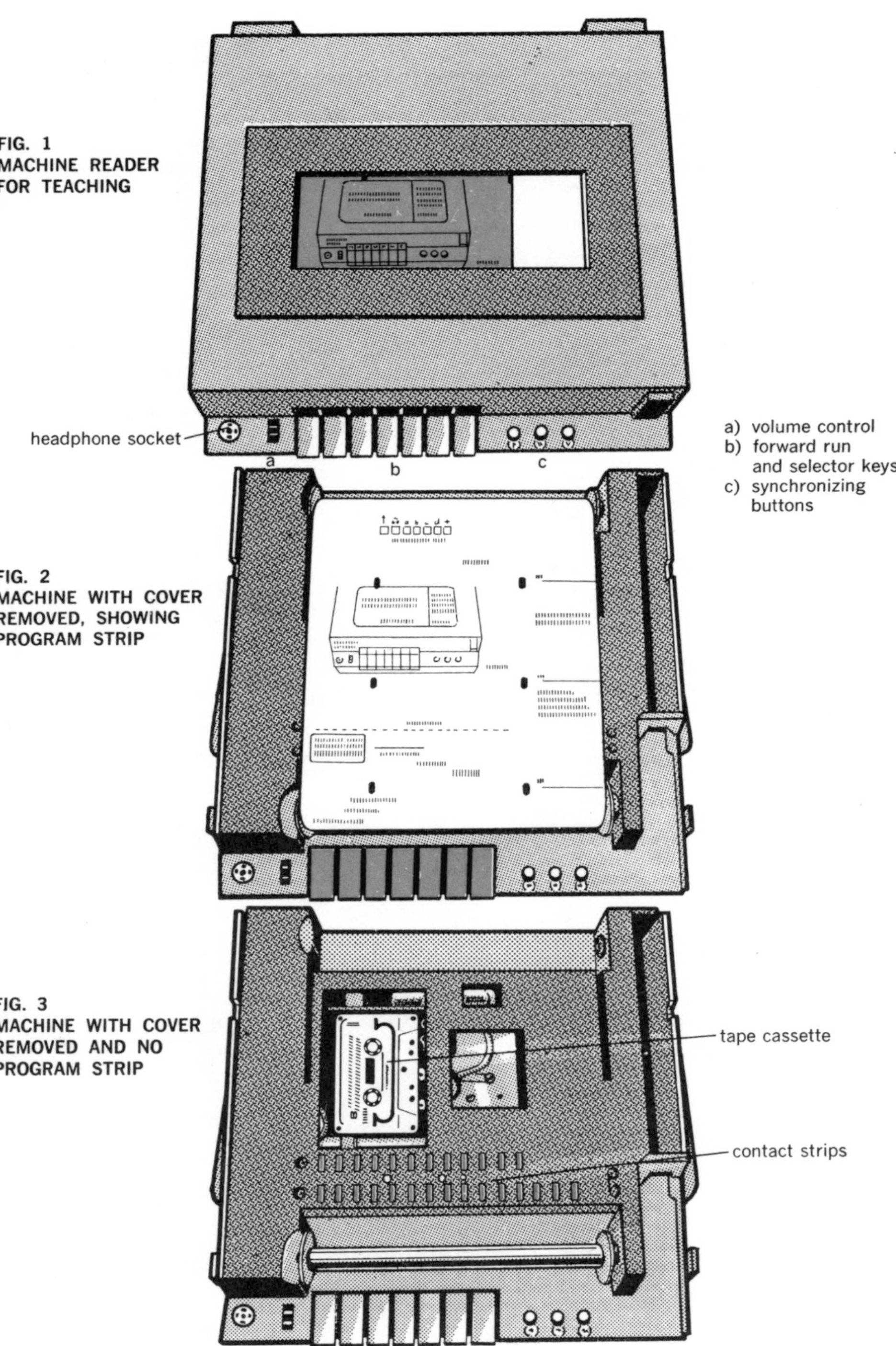
FIG. 1
MACHINE READER
FOR TEACHING
headphone socket
a
b
c
a) volume control
b) forward run
and selector keys
c) synchronizing
buttons
FIG. 2
MACHINE WITH COVER
REMOVED, SHOWING
PROGRAM STRIP
FIG. 3
MACHINE WITH COVER
REMOVED AND NO
PROGRAM STRIP
tape cassette
contact strips

INDEX

Biostatistical Design and Analysis Using R

Companion website

A companion website for this book is available at:

www.wiley.com/go/logan/r

The website includes figures from the book for downloading.

Biostatistical Design and Analysis Using R

A Practical Guide

Murray Logan

WILEY-BLACKWELL

A John Wiley & Sons, Inc., Publication

Blackwell Publishing was acquired by John Wiley & Sons in February 2007. Blackwell's publishing program has been merged with Wiley's global Scientific, Technical and Medical business to form Wiley-Blackwell.

Registered office: John Wiley & Sons Ltd, The Atrium, Southern Gate, Chichester, West Sussex, PO19 8SQ, UK

Editorial offices: 9600 Garsington Road, Oxford, OX4 2DQ, UK
The Atrium, Southern Gate, Chichester, West Sussex, PO19 8SQ, UK
111 River Street, Hoboken, NJ 07030-5774, USA

For details of our global editorial offices, for customer services and for information about how to apply for permission to reuse the copyright material in this book please see our website at www.wiley.com/wiley-blackwell

Library of Congress Cataloguing-in-Publication Data

Logan, Murray.
Biostatistical design and analysis using R : a practical guide / Murray Logan.
p. cm.
Includes bibliographical references and index.
ISBN 978-1-4443-3524-8 (hardcover : alk. paper) – ISBN 978-1-4051-9008-4 (pbk. : alk. paper)
1. Biometry. 2. R (Computer program language) I. Title.
QH323.5.L645 2010
570.1′5195 – dc22

2009053162

A catalogue record for this book is available from the British Library.

Typeset in 10.5/13pt Minion by Laserwords Private Limited, Chennai, India
Printed and bound in Singapore by Markono Print Media Pte Ltd

4 2013

Contents

Companion website for this book: wiley.com/go/logan/r

Preface

R is a powerful and flexible statistical and graphical environment that is freely distributed under the GNU Public Licence[a] for all major computing platforms (Windows, MacOSX and Linux). This open source licence along with a relatively simple scripting syntax has promoted diverse and rapid evolution and contribution. As the broader scientific community continues to gain greater instruction and exposure to the overall project, the popularity of R as a teaching and research tool continues to accelerate.

It is now widely acknowledged that R proficiency as a scientific skill set is becoming increasingly more desirable and useful throughout the scientific community. However, as with most open source developments, the emphasis of the R project remains on the expansive development of tools and features. Applied documentation still remains somewhat sparse and somewhat incomprehensible to the average biologist. Whilst there are a number of excellent texts on R emerging, the bulk of these texts are devoted to the R language itself. Any featured examples therein are used primarily for the purpose of illustrating the suite of commonly used R features and procedures, rather than to illustrate how R can be used to perform common biostatistical analyses.

Coinciding with the increasing interest in R as both a learning and research tool for biostatistics, has been the success of a relatively new major biostatistics textbook (Quinn and Keough, 2002). This text provides detailed coverage of most of the major statistical concepts and tests that biologists are likely to encounter with an emphasis on the practical implementation of these concepts with real biological data. Undoubtedly, a large part of the appeal of this book is attributable to the extensive use of real biological examples to augment and reinforce the text. Furthermore, by concentrating on the information biologists need to implement their research, and avoiding the overuse of complex mathematical descriptions, the authors have appealed to those biologists who don't require (or desire) a knowledge of performing or programming entire analyses from scratch. Such biologists tend to use statistical software that is already available and specifically desire information that will help them achieve reliable statistical and biological outcomes. Quinn and Keough (2002) also advocate a number of alternative

[a] This is an open source licence that ensured that the application as well as its source code is freely available to use, modify and redistribute.

texts that provide more detailed coverage of specific topics and that also adopt this real example approach.

Typically, most biostatistical texts focus on the principles of design and analysis without extending into the practical use of software to implement these principles. Similarly, R/S-plus texts tend to concentrate on documenting and showcasing the features of R without providing much of a biostatistical account of the principles behind the features or illustrating how these tools can be extended to achieve comprehensive real world analyses. Consequently, many biological students and professionals struggle to translate the theoretical advice into computational outcomes. Although some of these difficulties can be addressed after extensively reading through a number of software references, many of the difficulties remain. The inconsistency and incompatibility between theory texts and software reference texts is mainly the result of differing intentions of the two genres and is a source of great frustration.

The reluctance of biostatistical texts to promote or instruct on any particular statistical software (except for extremely specialized cases where historically only a single dedicated program was available) is in part an acknowledgment of the diversity of software packages available (each of which differs substantially in the range of features offered as well as the user interface and output provided). Furthermore, software upgrades generally involve major alternations to the way in which preexisting tasks are performed and thus being associated with a single software package tends to restrict the longevity and audience of the text. In contrast, although contributers are constantly extending the feature set of R environments, overall the project maintains a consistent user interface. Consequently, there is currently both a need and opportunity for a text that fills the gap between biostatistics texts and software texts, so as to assist biologists with the practical side of performing statistical analysis.

Many biological researchers and students have at one stage or another used one or other of the major biostatistics texts and gained a good understanding of the principles. However, from time to time (and particularly when preparing to generate a new design or analyse a new data set), they require a quick refresher to help remind them of the issues and principles relevant to their current design and/or analysis scenarios. In most cases, they do not need to re-read the more discursive texts and in many cases express a reluctance to invest large amounts of valuable research time doing so. Therefore, there is also a need for a quick reference that summarizes the key concepts of contemporary biostatistics and leads users step-wise through each of the analysis procedures and options. Such a guide would also help users to identify their areas of statistical naivete and enable them to return to a more comprehensive text with a more focused and efficient objective.

Therefore, the intended focus of this book will be to highlight the major concepts, principles and issues in contemporary biostatistics as well as demonstrate how to use R (as a research design, analysis and presentation tool) to complete examples from major biostatistics textbooks. In so doing, this proposed text acknowledges the important role that statistical software and real examples play in reinforcing statistical principles and practices.

Hence in summary, the intentions of the book are three-fold

(i) To provide very brief refresher summaries of the main concepts, issues and options involved in a range of contemporary biostatistical analyses
(ii) To provide key guides that steps users through the procedures and options of a range of contemporary biostatistical analyses
(iii) To provide detailed R scripts and documentation that enable users to perform a range of real worked examples from statistics texts that are popular among biological and environmental scientists

Worked examples

Where possible and appropriate, this book will make use the same examples that appear in the popular biostatistical texts so as to take advantage of the history and information surrounding those examples as well as any familiarity that users may have with those examples. Having said this however, access to these other texts will not be necessary to get good value out of the materials.

Website

This book is augmented by a website (http://www.wiley.com/go/logan/r) which includes:

- raw data sets and R analysis scripts associated with all worked examples
- the `biology` *package* that contains many functions utilized in this book
- an R reference card containing links to pages within the book

Typographical convensions

Throughout this book, all R language objects and functions will be printed in courier (`monospaced`) typeface. Commands will begin with the standard R command prompt (>) and lines continuing on from a previous line will begin with the continuation prompt (+). In syntax used within the chapter keys, `dataset` is used as an example and should be replaced by the name of the actual data frame when used. Similarly, all vector names should be replaced by the names used to denote the various variables in your data set.

Acknowledgements

The inspiration for this book came primarily from Gerry Quinn and Mick Keough towards whom I am both indebted and infuriated (in equal quantities). As authors of a statistical piece themselves, they should known better than to encourage others to attempt such an undertaking! I also wish to acknowledge the intellectualizing and suggestions of Patrick Baker and Andrew Robinson, the former of whom's regular supply of ideas remains a constant source of material and torment. Countless numbers of students and colleagues have also helped refine the materials and format of this book. As almost all of the worked examples in this book are adapted from the major biostatistical texts, the contributions of these other authors cannot be overstated. Finally, I would like to thank Nat, Kara, Saskia and Anika for your support and tolerance while I wrote this "extremely quite boring book with rid-ic-li-us pictures" (S. Logan, age 7).

R quick reference card

Session management

`> q()` Quitting R (see page 8)

`> ls()` List the objects in the current environment (see page 7)

`> rm(...)` Remove objects from the current environment (see page 7)

`> setwd(dir)` Set the current working directory (see page 7)

`> getwd()` Get the current working directory (see page 7)

Getting help

`> ?function` Getting help on a function (see page 8)

`> help(function)` Getting help on a function (see page 8)

`> example(function)` Run the examples associated with the manual page for the function (see page 8)

`> demo(topic)` Run an installed demonstration script (see page 8)

`> apropos("topic")` Return names of all objects in search list that match "topic" (see page 9)

`> help.search("topic")` Getting help about a concept (see page 9)

`> help.start()` Launch R HTML documentation (see page 9)

Built in constants

`> LETTERS` the 26 upper-case letters of the English alphabet (see page 17)

`> letters` the 26 lower-case letters of the English alphabet (see page 17)

`> month.name` English names of the 12 months of the year

`> month.abb` Abbreviated English names of the 12 months of the year

`> pi` π – the ratio of a circles circumference to diameter (see page 105)

Packages

`> installed.packages()` List of all currently installed packages (see page 44)

`> update.packages()` Update installed packages (see page 44)

`> install.packages(pkgs)` Install package(s) (pkgs) from CRAN mirror (see page 45)

`R CMD INSTALL package` Install an add-on package (see page 43)

`> library(package)` Loading an add-on package (see page 45)

`> data(name)` Load a data set or structure inbuilt into R or a loaded package.

Importing/Exporting

`> source("file")` Input, parse and sequentially evaluate the file (see page 45)

`> sink("file")` Redirect non-graphical output to file

`> read.table("file", header=T, sep=)` Read data in table format and create a data frame, with variables in columns (see page 51)

`> read.table("clipboard", header=T, sep=)` Read data left on the clipboard in table format and create a data frame, with variables in columns (see page 51)

`> read.systat("file.syd", to.data.frame=T)` Read SYSTAT data file and create a data frame (see page 52)

`> read.spss("file.sav", to.data.frame=T)` Read SPSS data file and create a data frame (see page 52)

`> as.data.frame(read.mtp("file.mtp"))` Read Minitab Portable Worksheet data file and create a data frame (see page 52)

`> read.xport("file")` Read SAS XPORT data file and create a data frame (see page 52)

`> write.table(dataframe, "file", row.names=F, quote=F, sep=)` Write the contents of a dataframe to file in table format (see page 53)

`> save(object, file="file.RData")` Write the contents of the object to file (see page 53)

`> load(file="file.RData")` Load the contents of a file (see page 53)

`> dump(object, file="file")` Save the contents of an object to a file (see page 53)

Generating Vectors

`> c(...)` Concatenate objects (see page 6)

`> seq(from, to, by=, length=)` Generate a sequence (see page 12)

`> rep(x, times, each)` Replicate each of the values of x (see page 13)

Character vectors

`> paste(..., sep=)` Combine multiple vectors together after converting them into character vectors (see page 13)

`> substr(x, start, stop)` Extract substrings from a character vector (see page 14)

Factors

`> factor(x)` Convert the vector (x) into a factor (see page 15)

> **`factor(x, levels=c())`** Convert the vector (x) into a factor and define the order of levels (see page 15)
> **`gl(levels, reps, length, labels=)`** Generate a factor vector by specifying the pattern of levels (see page 15)
> **`levels(factor)`** Lists the levels (in order) of a factor (see page 54)
> **`levels(factor)`** **`<-`** Sets the names of the levels of a factor (see page 54)

Matrices

> **`matrix(x,nrow, ncol, byrow=F)`** Create a matrix with `nrow` and/or `ncol` dimensions out of a vector (x) (see page 16)
> **`cbind(...)`** Create a matrix (or data frame) by combining the sequence of vectors, matrices or data frames by columns (see page 16)
> **`rbind(...)`** Create a matrix (or data frame) by combining the sequence of vectors, matrices or data frames by rows (see page 16)
> **`rownames(x)`** Read (or set with **`<-`**) the row names of the matrix (x) (see page 17)
> **`colnames(x)`** Read (or set with **`<-`**) the column names of the matrix (x) (see page 17)

Lists

> **`list(...)`** Generate a list of named (for arguments in the form `name=x`) and/or unnamed (for arguments in the form (x) components from the sequence of objects (see page 17)

Data frames

> **`data.frame(...)`** Convert a set of vectors into a data frame (see page 49)
> **`row.names(dataframe)`** Read (or set with **`<-`**) the row names of the data frame (see page 49)
> **`fix(dataframe)`** View and edit a dataframe in a spreadsheet (see page 49)

Indexing

Vectors
> **`x[i]`** Select the ith element (see page 21)
> **`x[i:j]`** Select the ith through j^{th} elements inclusive (see page 21)
> **`x[c(1,5,6,9)]`** Select specific elements (see page 21)
> **`x[-i]`** Select all except the ith element (see page 21)
> **`x["name"]`** Select the element called `"name"` (see page 21)
> **`x[x > 10]`** Select all elements greater than 10 (see page 22)
> **`x[x > 10 & x < 20]`** Select all elements between 10 and 20 (both conditions must be satisfied) (see page 22)
> **`x[y == "value"]`** Select all elements of x according to which y elements are equal to "value" (see page 22)
> **`x[x > 10 | y == "value"]`** Select all elements which satisfy either condition (see page 22)

Matricies
> **`x[i,j]`** Select element in row i, column j (see page 23)
> **`x[i,]`** Select all elements in row i (see page 23)
> **`x[,j]`** Select all elements in column j (see page 23)
> **`x[-i,]`** Select all elements in each row other than the ith row (see page 23)
> **`x["name",1:2]`** Select columns 1 through to 2 for the row named `"name"` (see page 23)
> **`x[x[,"Var1"]>4,]`** Select all rows for which the value of the column named `"Var1"` is greater than 4 (see page 23)
> **`x[,x[,"Var1"]=="value"]`** Select all columns for which the value of the column named `"Var1"` is equal to "value"

Lists
> **`x[[i]]`** Select the ith object of the list (see page 24)
> **`x[["value"]]`** Select the object named `"value"` from the list (see page 24)
> **`x[["value"]][1:3]`** Select the first three elements of the object named `"value"` from the list (see page 24)

Data frames
> **`x[c(i,j),]`** Select rows i and j for each column of the data frame (see page 56)
> **`x[,"name"]`** Select each row of the column named `"name"` (see page 56)
> **`x[["name"]]`** Select the column named `"name"`
> **`x$name`** Refer to a vector named `"name"` within the data frame (x) (see page 53)

Object information

> **`length(x)`** number of elements in x (see page 34)
> **`class(x)`** get the class of object x (see page 18)
> **`class(x)<-`** set the class of object x (see page 18)
> **`attributes(x)`** get (or set) the attributes of object x (see page 19)
> **`attr(x, which)`** get (or set) the *which* attribute of object x (see page 19)
> **`is.na(x), is.numeric(x), is.character(x), is.factor(x), ...`** methods used to assess the type of object x (`methods(is)` provides full list) (see page 18)

Object conversion

> **`as.null(x), as.numeric(x), as.character(x), as.factor(x), ...`** methods used to covert x to the

specified type (`methods(is)` provides full list) (see page 20)

Data manipulations

> **`subset(x, subset=, select=)`** Subset a vector or data frame according to a set of conditions (see page 56)

> **`sample(x, size)`** Randomly resample `size` number of elements from the x vector without replacement. Use the option `replace=TRUE` to sample with replacement. (see page 76)

> **`apply(x, INDEX, FUN)`** Apply the function (*FUN*) to the margins (`INDEX=1` is rows,`INDEX=2` is columns, `INDEX=c(1,2)` is both) of a vector, array or list (*x*) (see page 29)

> **`tapply(x, factorlist, FUN)`** Apply the function (*FUN*) to the vector (*x*) separately for each combination of the list of factors (see page 30)

> **`lapply(x, FUN)`** Apply the function (*FUN*) to each element of the list x (see page 30)

> **`replicate(n, EXP)`** Re-evaluate the expression (EXP) *n* times. Differs from `rep` function which repeats the result of a single evaluation (see page 28)

> **`aggregate(x, by, FUN)`** Splits data according to a combination of factors and calculates summary statistics on each set (see page 58)

> **`sort(x, decreasing=)`** Sorts a vector in increasing or decreasing (default) order (see page 26)

> **`order(x, decreasing=)`** Returns a list of indices reflecting the vector sorted in ascending or descending order (see page 26)

> **`rank(x, ties.method=)`** Returns the ranks of the values in the vector, tied values averaged by default (see page 27)

> **`which.min(x)`** Index of minimum element in x

> **`which.max(x)`** Index of maximum element in x

> **`rev(x)`** Reverse the order of entries in the vector (x) (see page 27)

> **`unique(x)`** Removes duplicate values (see page 337)

> **`t(x)`** Transpose the matrix or data frame (x) (see page 387)

> **`cut(x, breaks)`** Creates a factor out of a vector by slicing the vector x up into chunks. The option `breaks` is either a number indicating the number of cuts or else a vector of cut values (see page 111)

> **`which(x == a)`** Each of the elements of x is compared to the value of a and a vector of indices for which the logical comparison is true is returned

> **`match(x,y)`** A vector of the same length as x with the indices of the first occurance of each element of x within y

> **`choose(n,k)`** Computes the number of unique combinations in which k events can be arranged in a sequence of n

> **`combn(x,k)`** List all the unique combinations in which the elements of x can be arranged when taken k elements at a time

> **`with(x,EXP)`** Evaluate an expression (EXP) (typically a function) in an environment defined by x (see page 59)

Search and replace

> **`grep(pattern, x, ...)`** Searches a character vector (x) for entries that match the pattern (pattern) (see page 24)

> **`regexpr(pattern, x, ...)`** Returns the position and length of identified pattern (`pattern`) within the character vector (x) (see page 25)

> **`gsub(pattern, replacement, x, ...)`** Replaces ALL occurrences of the pattern (`pattern`) within the character vector (x) with replacement (`replacement` (see page 26)

> **`sub(pattern, replacement, x, ...)`** Replaces THE FIRST occurrence of the pattern (`pattern`) within the character vector (x) with replacement (`replacement` (see page 26)

Formating data

> **`ceiling(x)`** Rounds vector entries up to the nearest integer that is no smaller than the original vector entry (see page 27)

> **`floor(x)`** Rounds vector entries up to the nearest integer that is no smaller than the original vector entry (see page 27)

> **`trunc(x)`** Rounds vector entries to the nearest integer towards '0' (zero) (see page 27)

> **`round(x, digits=)`** rounds vector entries to the nearest numeric with the specified number of decimal places (`digit=`). Digits of 5 are rounded off to the nearest even digit (see page 27)

> **`formatC(x, format=, digits=, ...)`** Format vector entries according to a set of specifications (see page 28)

Math functions

Summary statistics

> **`mean(x)`** Mean of elements of x (see page 70)

> **`var(x)`** Variance of elements of x (see page 70)

> **`sd(x)`** Standard deviation of elements of x (see page 70)

> **`length(x)`** Number of elements of x (see page 34)

> **`sd(x)/sqrt(length(x))`** Standard error of elements of x (see page 70)

> **`quantile(x, probs=)`** Quantiles of x corresponding to probabilities (default: `0,0.25,0.5,0.75,1`)

> **`median(x)`** Median of elements of x (see page 70)

> **`min(x)`** Minimum of elements of x (see page 70)

> **max(*x*)** Maximum of elements of x (see page 70)
> **range(*x*)** Same as c(min(x), max(x)) (see page 111)
> **sum(*x*)** Sum of elements of x (see page 106)
> **cumsum(*x*)** A vector the same length as *x* and whose i^{th} element is the sum of all elements up to and including *i*
> **prod(*x*)** Product of elements of x
> **cumprod(*x*)** A vector the same length as *x* and whose i^{th} element is the product of all elements up to and including *i*
> **cummin(*x*)** A vector the same length as *x* and whose i^{th} element is the minimum value of all elements up to and including *i*
> **cummax(*x*)** A vector the same length as *x* and whose i^{th} element is the maximum value of all elements up to and including *i*
> **var(*x,y*)** variance between *x* and y (matrix if x and y are matrices of data frames)
> **cov(*x,y*)** covariance between *x* and y (matrix if x and y are matrices of data frames)
> **cor(*x,y*)** linear correlation between *x* and y (matrix if x and y are matrices of data frames) (see page 226)

Scale trasformations

> **exp(*x*)** Transform values to exponentials (see page 212)
> **log(*x*)** Transform values to log_e (see page 69)
> **log(*x*, 10)** Transform values to $log_1 0$ (see page 69)
> **log10(*x*)** Transform values to $log_1 0$ (see page 69)
> **sqrt(*x*)** Square root transform values of x (see page 69)
> **asin(sqrt(*x*))** Arcsin transform values of x (which must be proportions) (see page 69)
> **rank(*x*)** Transform values of x to ranks (see page 27)
> **scale(*x*, center=, scale=)** Scales (mean of 0 and sd of 1) values of x to ranks. To only center data, use scale='FALSE', to only reduce data use center='FALSE' (see page 220)

Distributions

The following are used for the following list of distribution functions

x= a vector of quantiles
q= a vector of quantiles
p= a vector of probabilities
n= the number of observations

> **dnorm(x, mean, sd), pnorm(q, mean, sd), qnorm(p, mean, sd), rnorm(n, mean, sd)** Density, distribution function, quantile function and random generation for the normal distribution with mean equal to mean and standard deviation equal to sd (see page 63)
> **dlnorm(x, meanlog, sdlog), pnorm(q, meanlog, sdlog), qnorm(p, meanlog, sdlog), rnorm(n, meanlog, sdlog)** Density, distribution function, quantile function and random generation for the log normal distribution whose logarithm has a mean equal to meanlog and standard deviation equal to sdlog (see page 63)
> **dunif(x, min, max), punif(q, min, max), qunif(p, min, max), runif(n, min, max)** Density, distribution function, quantile function and random generation for the uniform distribution with a minimum equal to min and maximum equal to max (see page 63)
> **dt(x, df), pt(q, df), qt(p, df), rt(n, df)** Density, distribution function, quantile function and random generation for the t distribution with df degrees of freedom
> **df(x, df1, df2), pf(q, df1, df2), qf(p, df1, df2), rf(n, df1, df2)** Density, distribution function, quantile function and random generation for the F distribution with df1 and df2 degrees of freedom
> **dchisq(x, df), pchisq(q, df), qchisq(p, df), rchisq(n, df)** Density, distribution function, quantile function and random generation for the chi-squared distribution with df degrees of freedom (see page 499)
> **dbinom(x, size, prob), pbinom(q, size, prob), qbinom(p, size, prob), rbinom(n, size, prob)** Density, distribution function, quantile function and random generation for the binomial distribution with parameters size and prob (see page 63)
> **dnbinom(x, size, mu), pnbinom(q, size, mu), qnbinom(p, size, mu), rnbinom(n, size, mu)** Density, distribution function, quantile function and random generation for the negative binomial distribution with parameters size and mu (see page 63)
> **dpois(x, lambda), ppois(q, lambda), qpois(p, lambda), rpois(n, lambda)** Density, distribution function, quantile function and random generation for the Poisson distribution with parameter lambda (see page 63)

Spatial procedures

sp package

> **Polygon(*xy*)** Convert a 2-column numeric matrix (xy) with coordinates into a object of class Polygon. Note the first point (row) must be equal to the last coordinates (row) (see page 79)
> **Polygons(*Plygn*, *ID*)** Combine one or more Polygon objects (*Plygn*) together into an object of class Polygons. (see page 80)
> **SpatialPolygons(*xy*)** A list of one or more Polygons . (see page 80)
> **spsample(*x*, *n*, *type=*)** Generate approximately n points on or within a SpatialPolygons object (x). The

option type= indicates the type of sampling ("random", "regular", "stratisfied" or "non-aligned") (see page 80)

Plotting

> **hist(x, *breaks*)** Histogram of the frequencies of vector x. The option breaks specifies how the bins are constructed and is typically either a number (number of bins), a vector of breakpoints (see page 116)

> **plot(x)** Plot the values of x (on *y*-axis) ordered on *x*-axis (see page 85)

> **plot(x, y)** Scatterplot of y (on *y*-axis) against x (*x*-axis) (see page 37)

> **plot(*formula*)** If all vectors numeric - Scatterplot of lhs (on *y*-axis) against rhs (*x*-axis), otherwise a "box-and-whisker" plot with a separate box for each combination of rhs categories (see page 37)

> **boxplot(x)** "Box-and-whiskers" plot for vector or formula x (see page 119)

> **pairs(x)** Scatterplot matrices for multiple numeric vectors or formula x (see page 122)

> **Mbargraph(dv, iv)** Bargraph (*biology package*) of mean dv against categorical iv with error bars (see page 268)

> **interaction.plot(x.fact, trace.fact, response)** Plots the mean (or other summary) of the response (response) for two-way combinations of factors (*x*-axis factor: x.fact and trace factor: trace.fact), thereby illustrating possible interactions (see page 126)

> **scatterplot(x)** (car package) Fancy scatterplot for a pair of numeric vectors or formula x. Includes boxplots on margins and regression line (see page 121)

> **scatterplot.matrix(x)** (car package) Fancy scatterplot matrices for multiple numeric vectors or formula x. Includes univariate displays in diagonals (see page 122)

Low-level plotting commands

> **points(x, y)** Adds points with coordinates x, y. Option type= can be used (see page 99)

> **lines(x, y)** Adds lines with coordinates x, y. Option type= can be used (see page 109)

> **abline(*fit*)** Adds a regression line from the linear model fit (see page 109)

> **abline(a, b)** Adds a regression line with a *y*-intercept of a and a slope of b

> **axis(*text, at, labels, ...*)** Adds an axis to the bottom (side=1), left (side=2), top (side=3) or right (side=4) plot margin. Options at and labels can be used to specify where to draw tick marks and what labels to put at each tick mark (see page 107)

> **box(*which=, bty=, ...*)** Draws a box around the plot (which="plot"), figure (which="figure"), inner (which="inner") or outer (which="outer") region of the current plot. Option bty specifies the type of box to draw ("o", "l", "7", "c", "u" or "]" result in boxes that resembles the corresponding upper case letter) (see page 127)

> **mtext(*text, side, line=0, ...*)** Adds text (text) to the plot margin specified by side (see axis() above). Option line specifies the distance (in lines) away from the axis to put the text (see page 101)

> **matlines(x, y, ...)** Adds confidence or prediction (y) limits along a sequence (x) to the plot (see page 113)

> **data.ellipse(x, y, *levels*, ...)** Adds data ellipses from vectors (x, y) to the plot (see page 184)

> **confidence.ellipse(x, y, *levels*, ...), confidence.ellipse(*model*, ...)** Adds confidence ellipses to the plot for linear models from vectors (x, y) or fitted model

Model fitting

> **contrasts(x)** View the contrasts associated with the factor x (see section 7.3.1)

> **contrasts(x) <- value** Set the contrasts associated with the factor x. The value parameter can either be a numeric matrix of coefficients or else a quoted name of a function that computes the matrix.(see section 7.3.1)

> **lm(formula)** Fit linear model from formula of format response ~ predictor1 + predictor2 + ... use I($x*y$) + I(x^2) to include nonlinear terms (see chapters 8&10)

> **lm.II(formula)** (biology package) Fit linear model II regression from formula of format response~predictor. (see chapter 8)

> **rlm(formula)** (MASS package) Fit M-estimator linear model from formula of format response~predictor. (see chapter 8)

> **mblm(formula)** (mblm package) Fit nonparametric regression model from formula of format response~predictor. (see chapter 8)

> **glm(formula, family)** Fit generalized linear model from formula. Error distribution and link function are specified by family - see family() (see chapter 17)

> **aov(formula)** Fit an anova model by making a call to lm for each stratum within formula (see chapters 10-15)

> **nls(formula, start)** Determine the nonlinear least-squares estimates of the parameters of a nonlinear model formula. Starting estimates are provided as a named list or numeric vector (start) (see chapter 9)

> **lme(fixed, random, correlation, ...)** (*nlme package*) Fit linear mixed effects models from

a specification of the fixed-effects formula (`fixed`) and random-effects formula (`random`) and correlation structure (`correlation`) (see chapters 11-14)

> **`lmer(formula, ...)`** (*lme4 package*) Fit (generalized) linear mixed effects models from a specification of a formula (`formula`) (see chapters 11-14)

> **`gam(formula, family=, ...)`** (*gam package*) Fit generalized additive models from the formula (`formula`). Error distribution and link function are specified by `family` - see `family()` (see chapter 17)

> **`pvals.fnc(.lmer, nsim, withMCMC, ...)`** (*languageR package*) Calculate p-values from lmer models (`.lmer`) via Markov Chain Monte Carlo sampling. (see chapters 11-14)

> **`VarCorr(fit)`** (*nlme package*) Calculate variance components from a linear mixed effects model (`fit`). (see chapters 11-14)

Fit diagnostics *The following generic functions can be applied to some of the above fitted model objects*

> **`plot(fit)`** Diagnostic plots for a fitted model `fit` (see chapters 8-15)

> **`av.plots(fit)`** Added-variable (partial-regression) plots for a fitted model `fit` (see chapter 9)

> **`residuals(fit)`** Residuals from a fitted model `fit` (see chapters 8-15)

> **`deviance(fit)`** Deviance of a fitted model `fit` (see chapter 17)

> **`influence.measures(fit)`** Regression diagnostics for a fitted model `fit` (see chapters 8-15, 17)

> **`vif(fit)`** Calculate variance-inflation factor for a fitted model `fit` (see chapters 9, 17)

> **`1/vif(fit)`** Calculate tolerance for each term in a fitted model `fit` (see chapters 9, 17)

> **`predict(fit, data.frame)`** Predicted responses from a fitted model `fit` given a set of predictor values `data.frame` (see chapters 8-15, 17)

> **`confint(fit)`** Parameter confidence intervals from a fitted model `fit` (see chapters 8-15, 17)

> **`replications(formula)`** Determine the number of replicates of each term in `formula` (see chapters 11-15)

> **`is.balanced(formula)`** (*biology package*) Determine whether the design specified by the `formula` is balanced (see chapters 11-15)

> **`tukey.nonadd.test(fit)`** (*alr3 package*) Perform Tukey's test for nonadditivity from a model (`fit`) fitted via `lm()` (see chapters 13-15)

Measures of model fit

> **`extractAIC(fit, ...)`** Compute AIC for parametric model (fit). Equivalent BIC using `k=log(rnow(dataset))` argument. (see chapters 9 & 17)

> **`AIC(fit, ...)`** Compute AIC for any model (fit). Equivalent BIC using `k=log(rnow(dataset))` argument. (see chapters 9 & 17)

> **`AICc(fit)`** (*MuMIn package*) Compute AIC corrected for small sample sizes for a fitted model (*fit*). (see chapters 9 & 17)

> **`QAIC(fit)`** (*MuMIn package*) Compute quasi-AIC corrected for overdispersion for a fitted model (*fit*). (see chapters 9 & 17)

> **`QAICc(fit)`** (*biology package*) Compute quasi-AIC corrected for overdispersion and small sample sizes for a fitted model (*fit*). (see chapters 9 & 17)

> **`deviance(fit)`** Compute deviance for a fitted model (*fit*). (see chapters 9 & 17)

> **`Model.selection(fit)`** (*biology package*) Generate various model fit estimates and perform model averaging for all possible combinations of predictor variables in a supplied model `fit`. (see chapters 9 & 17)

> **`dredge(fit)`** (*MuMIn package*) Select most parsimonious model from all possible combinations of predictor variables in a supplied model `fit` based on information criteria (`rank=` either `"AICc"`, `"QAIC"` or `"BIC"`). (see chapters 9 & 17)

> **`model.avg(ml)`** (*MuMIn package*) Perform model averaging from a supplied fitted model object `ml` returned from model dredging. (see chapters 9 & 17)

Post-hoc analyses

> **`mainEffects(fit, at)`** (*biology package*) Perform main effects tests from the fitted model (`fit`) (see chapters 12-15, 17)

> **`glht(fit, linfct=mcp(FACTOR=type))`** (*multcomp package*) Post-hoc, pairwise comparisons of factor (`FACTOR`). Option `type` specifies what type of post-hoc test to perform (`"Dunnett"`, `"Tukey"`, `"Sequen"`, `"AVE"`, `"Changepoint"`, `"Williams"`, `"Marcus"`, `"McDermott"`) (see chapter 10)

> **`npmc(dataset, ...)`** (*npmc package*) Non-parametric post-hoc, pairwise comparisons on a specifically constructed dataset (`dataset`). (see chapter 10)

> **`mt.rawp2adjp(pvalues, proc)`** (*multtest package*) Multiple pairwise comparison p-value (`pvalues`) adjustments . (see chapter 10)

> **`p.adjust(pvalues, method)`** Multiple pairwise comparison p-value (`pvalues`) adjustments . (see chapter 10)

Statistics and summaries

> **`t.test(x, y), t.test(formula)`** One and two sample t-tests on vectors (`x, y`) or formula `formula`. Option `var.equal` indicates whether pooled or separate variance t-test and option `paired` indicates whether independent or paired t-test (see chapter 6)

> **cor.test(*x, y*), cor.test(*formula*)** Correlation between sample pairs from separate vectors (x, y, ...) or formula formula, ... Option method indicates the form of correlation ('pearson', kendall or spearman') (see chapter 8)

> **hier.part(y, data, gof)** (*hier.part package*) Hierarchical partitioning given a vector of dependent variables y and a data frame data. Option gof= used to specify assessment of fit (root mean square prediction error: "RMSPE", Log-Likelihood: "logLik" or R-squared: "Rsqu") (see chapter 9)

> **anova(fit, ...)** Compute analysis of variance table for a fitted model fit or models (see chapters 8-15, 17)

> **summary(fit)** Summarize parameter estimates for a fitted model fit (see chapters 8-15, 17)

> **AnovaM(fit, ...)** (*biology package*) Compute analysis of variance table for a fitted model fit accommodating unbalanced hierarchical designs (see chapters 11-15)

> **wilcox.JN(*fit*)** (*biology package*) Perform Wilcoxon modified Johnson-Neyman procedure on fitted ANCOVA model (fit) (see chapter 15)

> **tree(formula, ...)** (*tree package*) Perform binary recursive partitioning (regression tree) from response and predictors specified in formula. (see chapter 9)

Robust statistics

> **wilcox.test(*x, y*), t.test(*formula*)** One and two sample ("Mann-Whitney") Wilcoxon testson vectors (x, y) or formula formula. Option indicates whether independent or paired Wilcoxon-test (see chapter 6)

> **oneway.test(*formula,...*)** Perform Welch's test comparing the means of two or more groups specified by formula formula, ... (see chapter 10)

> **kruskal.test(*formula,...*)** Perform Kruskal-Wallis rank sum test, specified by formula formula, ... (see chapter 10)

> **friedman.test(*formula,...*)** Perform Friedman rank sum test with unreplicated blocked data, specified by formula formula, ... (see chapter 13)

> **friedmanmc(*DV, FACTOR, BLOCK*)** (*pgirmess package*) Multiple pairwise comparison test following Friedman's test. (see chapter 13)

Frequency analysis

> **chisq.test(*x*)** Performs chi-squared goodness-of-fit tests and contingency table tests. (see chapter 16)

> **fisher.test(*x*)** Performs fishers exact test goodness-of-fit tests and contingency table tests. (see chapter 16)

> **ks.test(*x*)** Performs Kolmogorov-Smirnov tests. (see chapter 16)

> **g.test(*x*)** (*biology package*) Performs G-test for goodness-of-fit tests and contingency table tests. (see chapter 16)

> **oddsratios(*xtab*)** (*biology package*) Calculate pairwise odds ratios from a contingency table (xtab). (see chapter 16-17)

Bootstrapping

> **boot(*data, stat, R, sim, rand.gen*)** (*boot package*) Generates R bootstrap replicates from a statistical function (stat) incorporating a particular simulation (sim= one of "parametric", "balanced", "permutation" or "arithetic"). Function rand.gen defines how randomization occurs (see page 149)

Power analysis

> **power.t.test(*n, delta, sd, power*)** Calculate one of; sample size (n), true difference in means (delta), standard deviation (sd) or power (power) of t-test. The option type indicates the type of t-test ("two.sample", "one.sample", "paired")

> **pwr.r.test(*n, r, power*)** (*pwr package*) Calculate one of; sample size (n), correlation coefficient (r) or power (power) of t-test. > **power.anova.test(*groups, n, between.var, within.var, power*)** Calculate one of; number of groups (groups), sample size (n), between group variance (between.var), within group variation (within.var) or power (power) of ANOVA.

> **pwr.chisq.test(*w, N, df, power*)** (*pwr package*) Calculate one of; effect size (w), total number of observations (N), degrees of freedom (df) or power (power) of chi-square test.

General key to statistical methods

1 a. Testing a specific null hypothesis or effects .... Go to 3
b. Not testing a specific null hypothesis .... Go to 2

2 a. Statistical or numerical summaries .... Chapter 3
b. Graphical summaries .... Chapter 5

3 a. Response variable continuous .... Go to 4
b. Response variable categorical or frequencies .... Go to 10

4 a. One or more categorical predictor (independent) variables .... Go to 6
Testing a null hypotheses about group differences
b. One or more continuous predictor (independent) variables .... Go to 5
Investigating relationships

5 a. Single predictor variable and linear relationship .... Chapter 8
Correlation and simple linear regression
b. Multiple predictor variables or curvilinear/complex relationship ...... Chapter 9
Complex regression analysis

6 a. A single predictor variable .... Go to 7
b. Multiple predictor variables .... Go to 8

7 a. Predictor variable with two levels (two groups) .... Chapter 6
Simple hypothesis testing, *t*-tests
b. Predictor variable with multiple levels (more than two groups) ...... Chapter 10
Single factor Analysis of Variance (ANOVA)

8 a. All predictor variables categorical .... Go to 9
Multifactor and complex Analysis of Variance ANOVA
b. Continuous and categorical predictor variables .... Chapter 15
Analysis of Covariance

9 a. All levels within each predictor variable fully replicated .... Chapter 12
Multifactor Analysis of Variance ANOVA

b. All predictor variables blocked within a random factor .... Chapter 13
Unreplicated factorial designs – randomized block and simple repeated measures

c. Within and between blocking factors .... Chapter 14
Partly nested designs – split-plot and complex repeated measures

10 a. Binary response variable (presence/absence, alive/dead, yes/no etc) .. Chapter 17
Logistic regression

b. Response variable frequencies .... Chapters 16&17
Counts from classifying units according to one or more categories
Chi-squared test, contingency tables, log-linear modeling.

1

Introduction to R

1.1 Why R?

R is a language and programming environment for statistical analysis and graphics that is distributed under the GNU General Public License[a] and is largely modeled on the powerful proprietary S/Splus (from ATT Bell Laboratories). R provides a flexible and powerful environment consisting of a core set of integrated tools for classical data manipulation, analysis and display. An ever expanding library of additional modules (packages) provide extended functionality for more specialized procedures. Initially written by Ross Ihaka and Robert Gentleman of the Department of Statistics at the University of Auckland (NZ), the R project is currently maintained by an international cooperative (the 'R Core Team') who oversee and adjudicate on the continual development of the project.

The GNU General Public License and flexible language ensure that the R project has the potential to rapidly support any newly conceived procedures. Consequently, R has (and will continue to), evolved rapidly as statisticians from a wide range of scientific backgrounds recognize the power of universally adopted tools and offer their contributions. Moreover, the universality, freedom and extensibility of R has resulted in its rapid expansion in popularity among biological teaching and research professionals and students alike. Source code and binaries (executable files) are also freely available for the Windows, Mac[b] and Unix/Linux families of operating systems from the Comprehensive R Archive Network (CRAN) site at 'http://cran.r-project.org/'. Not surprisingly then, R is quickly becoming the universal statistical language of the international scientific community, and correspondingly, R proficiency skills are becoming increasingly more valuable.

As R is a copy of S, documentation on either are generally relevant (however, it should be noted that there are a number of differences between the two dialects). In particular, Everitt (1994), Pinheiro and Bates (2000) and Venables and Ripley (2002) are excellent S/S-PLUS references whilst Dalgaard (2002), Fox (2002), Maindonald and Braun (2003), Crawley (2002, 2007), Murrell (2005) and Zuur et al. (2009) are excellent R reference texts for biologists. In addition, there is an extensive amount of

[a] Under the GNU General Public License, anyone is free to use, modify and (re)distribute the software.
[b] Support for the Mac OS Classic ended with R 1.7.1.

Biostatistical Design and Analysis Using R: a Practical Guide, 1st edition. By M. Logan.
Published 2010 by Blackwell Publishing.

information available on-line at the CRAN site ('http://r-project.org') and in the help files packaged with the distributions and extension packages.

1.2 Installing R

At the time of writing the current version of R is R.2.9.1. Since Windows, Unix/Linux and Mac OS systems differ extensively in areas of user privileges and software management, different installation files and procedures are required for each of the systems. Irrespective of the system, the latest version of an installation binary or the source code can be downloaded from the CRAN. Binary installation files or compressed source code for version R.2.9.1 can also be found on the accompanying website www.wiley.com/go/logan/r.

1.2.1 Windows

Obtain a copy of the R installation binary file (e.g. R-2.9.1-win32.exe). Run this self-extracting and self-installation file as Administrator (right click on the executable and select Run as Administrator) if you know the appropriate password. This will install R in the default (and best) location. If you do not know the Administrator password for the computer (or do not have adequate privileges), R will be installed within your user account. The installer will guide you through the installation, but for most purposes the default options are adequate. During the installation process, startup menu and desktop icon links to *RGui.exe* (the main R interface) will be automatically created.

1.2.2 Unix/Linux

Obtain a copy of the compressed R source code (e.g. R.2.9.1.tgz) and unpack it to an appropriate location (typically `/usr/local`) with:

```
tar xvfz R.2.9.1.tgz
```

Note: if you do not have root status, or you wish to have R installed in an alternative location for some reason, you are referred to the R-admin.html help file included in the packed source. From the top directory of the unpacked source, issue the following commands to configure, build and check the system:

```
./configure
make
make check
```

If there are no failures, the manuals can be built in dvi, pdf and/or info formats using the following commands:

```
make dvi
make pdf
make info
```

Install the R tree (and manuals) on your system using the following commands:

```
make install
make install-dvi
make install-pdf
make install-info
```

A symbolic link (`R`) will be added to `/usr/local/bin` and thus R can be run by entering `R` at a terminal command prompt.

1.2.3 MacOSX

Obtain a copy of the R disk image file (e.g. R.2.9.1.tgz). Start the installation by running (double-clicking on) the disk image file. This will bring up a new Finder window containing the installation package. Run the installation package (double-click) and if you are not already logged in as Administrator, you will be prompted for the administrator password. The installer will then guide you through the installation, but for most purposes the default options are adequate.

1.3 The R environment

Let's begin with a few important definitions:

Object R is an object oriented language and everything in R is an object. For example, a single number is an object, a variable is an object, output is an object, a data set is an object that is itself a collection of objects, etc.

Vector A collection of one or more *objects* of the same type (e.g. all numbers or all characters etc).

Function A set of instructions carried out on one or more objects. Functions are typically used to perform specific and common tasks that would otherwise require many instructions. For example, the *function* `mean()` is used to calculate the arithmetic mean of the values in a given *numeric vector*. Functions consist of a name followed by parentheses containing either a set of *parameters* (expressed as *arguments*) or left empty.

Parameter The kind of information that can be passed to a function. For example, the `mean()` *function* declairs a single required parameter (a valid object for which the mean is to be calculated is a compulsary) as well as a number of optional parameters that facilitate finer control over the function.

Argument The specific information passed to a function to determine how the function should perform its task. Arguments are expressions (in the form of `name=value`) given between the parentheses that follow the name of the function. For example, the `mean()` function requires at least one argument - either the name of an object that contains the values from which the mean is to be generated or a vector of values.

Operator Is a symbol that has a pre-defined meaning. Familiar operators include `+` `-` `*` and `/`, which respectively perform addition, subtraction, multiplication and division. The `=` operator is used within functions to assign values to arguments. Logical operators are queries returning either a TRUE or FALSE response. Familiar logical operators include < ('is the left hand side less than the right?'), > ('greater than?'), <= ('less than or equal?') and >= ('greater than or equal?'), while less familiar logical operators include == (which translates to 'does the entry on the left hand side of the == operator equal the entry on the right hand side?'), != (logical NOT – 'is the left hand side not equal to the right?'), && (logical AND – 'are both left hand and right hand conditions TRUE?') and || (logical OR – 'is either condition TRUE?').

1.3.1 The console (command line)

The R command prompt (>) is where you interact with R by entering commands (expressions). Commands are evaluated once the **Enter** key has been pressed, however, they can also be separated from one another on a single line by a semicolon character (;). A continuation prompt (+) is used by R to indicate that the command on the preceding line was syntactically incomplete. R ignores all characters on a line that are followed by a hash character (#). These statements or *comments* are commonly used in R literature and scripts for explaining or detailing the surrounding commands.
Enter the following command at the R command prompt (>):

```
> 5 + 1
[1] 6
```

R evaluates the command `5+1` (5 plus 1) and returns the value of an object whose first (and only) element is 6. The `[1]` indicates that this is the first (and in this case only) element in the object returned.

Command history

Each time a command is entered at the R command prompt, the command is also added to a list known as the command history. The up and down arrow keys scroll backward and forward respectively through the session's command history list and place the top most command at the current R command prompt. Scrolling through the command history enables previous commands to be rapidly re-executed, reviewed or modified and executed.

1.4 Object names

All objects have unique names to which they are refered. Names given to any object in R can comprise virtually any sequence of letters and numbers providing that the following rules are adhered to:

- Names must begin with a letter (names beginning with numbers or operators are not permitted)
- Names cannot contain the following characters; `space , - + * / # % & [ ] { } ( ) ~`

Whilst the above rules are necessary, the following naming conventions are also recommended:

- Avoid names that are the names of common predefined functions as this can provide a source of confusion for both you and R. For example, to represent the mean of a head length variable, use something like `MEAN.HEAD.LENGTH` or `MeanHeadLength` rather than `mean`.
- In R, **all commands are case sensitive** and thus `A` and `a` are different and refer to different objects. Almost all inbuilt names in R are lowercase. Therefore, one way to reduce the likelihood of assigning a name that is already in use by an inbuilt object is to only use uppercase names for any objects that you create. This is a convention practiced in this book.
- Names should reflect the content of the object. One of the powerful features of R is that there is virtually no limit to the number of objects (variables, datasets, results, models, etc) that can be in use at a time. However, without careful name management, objects can rapidly become misplaced or ambiguous. Therefore, the name of an object should reflect what it is, and what has happened to it. For example, the name `Log.FISH.WTS` might be given to an object that contains log transformed fish weights.
- Although there are no restrictions on the length of names, shorter names are quicker to type and provide less scope for typographical errors and are therefore recommended (of course within the restrictions of the point above).
- Separate any words in names by a decimal point. For example, the name `HEAD.LENGTH` might be used to represent a numeric vector of head lengths.

Attempts have been made to always adhere to the above naming conventions throughout the rest of the worked examples in this book, so as to provide a more extensive guide to good naming practices.

1.5 Expressions, Assignment and Arithmetic

An **expression** is a command that is entered at the R command prompt, evaluated by R, printed to the current output device (usually the screen), and then discarded. For example:

```
> 2 + 3                          ← an expression
[1] 5                            ← the evaluated output
```

Assignment assigns a name to a new object that may be the result of an evaluated expression or any other object. The assignment operator `<-` is interpreted by R as 'evaluate the expression on the right hand side and assign it the name supplied on the left hand side'[c]. If the object on the left hand side does not already exist, then it is created, otherwise the object's contents are replaced. The contents of the object can be viewed (printed) by entering the name of the object at the command prompt.

```
> VAR1 <- 2 + 3                  ← assign expression to the object VAR1
> VAR1                           ← print the contents of the object VAR1
[1] 5                            ← evaluated output
```

[c] Assignment can also be made left to right using the `->` assignment operator.

A single command may be spread over multiple lines. If either a command is not complete by the end of a line, or a carriage return is entered before R considers that the command syntax is complete, the following line will begin with the prompt + to indicate that the command is incomplete.

```
> VAR2 <-          ← an incomplete assignment/expression
+ 2 + 3            ← assignment/expression completed
> VAR2             ← print the contents of VAR2, the evaluated output
[1] 5
```

When the contents of a vector are numeric (see section 1.10 below), standard arithmetic procedures can be applied.

```
> VAR2 - 1               ← print the contents of VAR2 minus 1
[1] 4
> ANS1 <- VAR1 * VAR2    ← evaluated expression assigned to ANS1
> ANS1                   ← print the contents of ANS1 the evaluated output
[1] 25
```

Objects can be concatenated (joined together) to create objects with multiple entries using the `c()` (concatenation) *function*.

```
> c(1, 2, 6)         ← concatenate 1, 2 and 6
[1] 1 2 6            ← printed output
> c(VAR1, ANS1)      ← concatenate VAR1 and ANS1 contents
[1] 5 25             ← printed output
```

In addition to the typical addition, subtraction, multiplication and division operators, there are a number of special operators, the simplest of which are the quotient or integer divide operator (`%/%`) and the remainder or modulus operator (`%%`).

```
> 7/3
[1] 2.333333
> 7%/%3
[1] 2
> 7%%3
[1] 1
```

1.6 R Sessions and workspaces

1.6.1 Cleaning up

So far we have created a number of objects. To view a list of all current objects that have been created:

```
> ls()               ← list current objects in R environment
[1] "ANS1" "VAR1" "VAR2"
```

The `ls()` *function* is also useful for searching for the name of objects that you created and can't remember:

```
> ls(pat = "VAR")                    ← list objects that begin with VAR
[1] "VAR1" "VAR2"
> ls(pat = "A*1")                    ← list objects that contain an A and a 1 with
[1] "ANS1" "VAR1"                      any number of characters in between.
```

Since objects are easily created (and forgotten about) in R, an R session's workspace can rapidly become cluttered with extraneous and no longer required objects. To avoid this, it is good practice to remove objects as they become obsolete. This is done with the `rm()` *function*.

```
> rm(VAR1, VAR2)                     ← remove the VAR1 and VAR2 objects
> rm(list = ls())                    ← remove all user defined objects
```

1.6.2 Workspaces

Throughout an R session, all objects (including loaded packages, see section 1.19) that have been added are stored within the R global environment, called the workspace. Occasionally, it is desirable to save the workspace and thus all those objects (vectors, functions, etc) that were in use during a session so that they are automatically available during subsequent sessions. This can be done using the `save.image()` *function*. Note, this will save the workspace to a file called `.RData` in the current working directory (usually the R startup directory, see section 1.6.3), unless a filename (and path) is supplied as an argument to the `save.image()` *function*. A previously saved workspace can be loaded by providing a full path and filename as an argument to the `load()` *function*. Whilst saving a workspace image can sometimes be convenient, it can also contribute greatly to organizational problems associated with large numbers of obsolete or undocumented objects.

1.6.3 Current working directory

By default, files are read and written to the current working directory-the R startup directory (location of the R executable file) unless otherwise specified. To enable read and write operations to take place in other locations, the current working directory can be changed with the `setwd()` *function* which requires a single argument (the full path of the directory[d]). The current working directory can be reviewed using the `getwd()` *function*

```
> setwd("~/Documents/")              ← set the current working directory
> getwd()                            ← review the current working directory
[1] "/home/murray/Documents"
```

[d] Note that R using the Unix/Linux style directory subdivision markers. That is, R uses the forward slash / in path names rather than the regular \ of Windows.

```
> list.files(getwd())
[1] "addressbook.vcf"
[2] "Introduction.rnw"          ← list all in the current working directory
[3] "Introduction.rnw.map"
[4] "Rplots.ps"
[5] "Rscripts.R"
```

1.6.4 Quitting R

To quit R elegantly, use the `q()` *function*. You will be asked whether or not you wish to save the workspace image. If you answer yes (`y`), the current state of your environment or workspace (including all the objects and packages[e] that were added during the session) will be stored within the current working directory.

1.7 Getting help

There are a variety of ways to obtain help on either specific functions or more general procedures within the R environment. Specific information on any inbuilt and add-in objects (such as functions) as well as the R language can be obtained by either providing the name of the object as a character string argument for the `help()` *function* or by using the name of the object as a suffix to a `?` character[f]. As an example, the following two statements both display the R manual page on the `mean()` *function*:

```
> help(mean)
> ?mean
```

Help files are in a standard format such that they all include a description of the object(s), a template of how the object(s) are used, a description of all the arguments and options, more information on any important specific details of the use of the object(s), a list of authors, a list of similar objects and finally a set of examples that illustrate the use of the object(s).

The examples within a manual page can also be run on the R command line using the `example()` *function*. To see an example use of the `mean` *function*:

```
> example(mean)
```

R includes some inbuilt demonstration scripts that showcase the general use of functions on certain topics. The `demo()` *function* provides a user-friendly interface for running these demonstrations. For example, to get an overview of the use of some of the basic graphical procedures in R, run the `graphics demo`:

```
> demo(graphics)
```

[e] Packages provide a flexible means of extending the functionality of R, see section 1.19.

[f] Help on objects within a package is only available when the package is loaded.

Calling the `demo()` *function* without any arguments returns a list of demonstration topics available on your system:

```
> demo()
```

The `apropos()` *function* returns a set of object names from the current search list that match a specific pattern, and is therefore useful for recalling the name of functions. For example, the following expression returns the name of all currently available objects that contain the characters `"mea"` in their names.

```
> apropos("mea")
 [1] "colMeans"              "influence.measures"
 [3] "kmeans"                "mean"
 [5] "mean.data.frame"       "mean.Date"
 [7] "mean.default"          "mean.difftime"
 [9] "mean.POSIXct"          "mean.POSIXlt"
[11] "rowMeans"              "weighted.mean"
```

The `help.search()` and `help.start()` *functions* both provide ways of searching through all the installed R manuals on your system for specific terms. The name of the term or 'keyword' is provided as a character string argument (supports regular expression matching) to the `help.search()` *function* which returns a list of relevant manual pages and their brief descriptions. Using the character string as suffix to `??` command provides similar functionality. For example,

```
> help.search("mean")
> ??mean
```

The `help.start()`*function* is a more comprehensive and general help system that launches a web browser that displays various local HTML documents containing specific R documentation, a search engine and links to other resources.

In addition to the official help files and manual pages, there are numerous R mailing lists accessible via the R Project's website. The `RSiteSearch()` *function* sends a key word or phrase search query to the R Project search engine and displays the result in a web browser.

```
> RSiteSearch("mean")
```

There are also numerous books written on the use of R (and/or S/PLUS), see section 1.22 for a list of recent publications.

1.8 Functions

Functions are sets of commands that are conveniently wrapped together such that they can be initiated via a single command that encapsulates all the user inputs to any of the internal commands. Hence, functions provide a friendly way to interact with a set of commands. Most functions require one or more inputs (called *arguments*), and, while a particular function may have a number of arguments, not all need to be specified each time the function is *called*. Consider the `seq()` *function*, which generates a sequence of values (a *vector*) according to the values of the arguments. This function has the following common usage structures:

```
> seq(from, to)                     ← a sequence of numbers from 'from' to
                                      'to' incrementing by 1
> seq(from, to, by = )              ← a sequence of numbers from 'from' to
                                      'to' incrementing by 'by='
> seq(from, to, length.out = )      ← a sequence of 'length.out' numbers
                                      from 'from' to 'to'
```

If only the first two arguments are provided (as in the first form above), the result is a sequence of integers from `'from'` to `'to'`. Note that this is equivalent to the sequence generator of the form `'from:to'`. When the arguments are provided unnamed (such as `seq(5,9)`), the order of arguments is assumed to be as provided in the usage structure. Therefore, the following two expressions do **not** yield the same sequences:

```
> seq(5, 9)
> seq(9, 5)
```

Named arguments are used to distinguish between alternative uses of a function. For example, in the expression `seq(2,10,4)`, the `4` could mean either that the sequence should increment by 4 (`by=4`) or that the sequence should consist of 4 numbers (`length.out=4`). Furthermore, when named arguments are provided, the order in which the arguments are included is no longer important. Thus, the following are equivalent:

```
> seq(from = 5, to = 9, by = 2)
> seq(to = 9, by = 2, from = 5)
```

Argument names can also be truncated provided the names are not ambiguous. Therefore, the above examples could be shortened to `seq(f=5, t=9, b=2)`. If a function had the arguments `length` and `letter`, for that particular function, the arguments could be truncated to `len` and `let` respectively.

Many functions also provide default values for some compulsory arguments. The default values represent the 'typical' conditions under which the function is used, and these arguments are only required if they are to be different from the default. For example, the `mean` *function* calculates the arithmetic mean of one or more numbers. In addition to an argument that specifies an object containing numbers (to be averaged), the function has the arguments `trim=0` and `na.rm=FALSE` which respectively indicate what fraction of the data to trim to calculate the trimmed mean and whether or not to remove missing entries before calculation. The expression `mean(X)` is therefore equivalent to `mean(X, trim=0, na.rm=FALSE)`.

1.9 Precedence

The rules of operator precedence are listed (highest to lowest) in Table 1.1. Additionally, expressions within parentheses '`()`' always have precedence. Arguments and

Table 1.1 Precedence and description of operators within R listed from highest to lowest.

<table>
<tr><th>Operator</th><th>Description</th></tr>
<tr><td>[[[</td><td>indexing</td></tr>
<tr><td>::</td><td>name space</td></tr>
<tr><td>$</td><td>component</td></tr>
<tr><td>^</td><td>exponentiation (evaluated right to left)</td></tr>
<tr><td>- +</td><td>sign (unary)</td></tr>
<tr><td>:</td><td>sequence</td></tr>
<tr><td>%special%</td><td>special operators (e.g. %/%, %%)</td></tr>
<tr><td>* \</td><td>multiplication, division</td></tr>
<tr><td>+ -</td><td>addition and subtraction</td></tr>
<tr><td>< > <= >= == !=</td><td>ordering and comparison</td></tr>
<tr><td>!</td><td>logical negation (not)</td></tr>
<tr><td>& &&</td><td>logical AND</td></tr>
<tr><td>| ||</td><td>logical OR</td></tr>
<tr><td>~</td><td>formula</td></tr>
<tr><td>-> ->></td><td>assignment (left to right)</td></tr>
<tr><td>=</td><td>argument assignment (right to left)</td></tr>
<tr><td><- <<-</td><td>assignment (right to left)</td></tr>
<tr><td>?</td><td>help</td></tr>
</table>

expressions within a function are always evaluated before the function. Consider the following set of commands that use the `c()` (concatenation) *function* to generate a vector of two numbers (2 and 4) and then use the `rep()` (repeat) *function* to repeat the vector thrice.

```
> X <- c(2, 4)
> rep(X, 3)
[1] 2 4 2 4 2 4
```

Alternatively, by nesting the `c()` *function* within the `rep()` *function*, the same result can be achieved with a single command:

```
> rep(c(2, 4), 3)
[1] 2 4 2 4 2 4
```

1.10 Vectors - variables

The basic data storage unit in R is called a *vector*. A vector is a collection of one or more entries of the same *class* (type). Table 1.2 below defines the four major vector classes and provides simple examples of their use. Vectors are one-dimensional arrays of entries. That is, a vector is a single column (or row) of entries whose length is the number of rows in the column or vice versa. Each entry has a unique index number that is equivalent to a row number that can be used to refer to that particular entry within the vector.

Table 1.2 Object vector classes in R. The *operator* : is used to generate a sequence of integers. The *function* called `c()` is short (very short) for concatenate and can be used to generate a vectors. The *operator* == evaluates whether the left hand side is equal to the right hand side.

Vector class	Example	

integer
(Whole numbers)
	`> 2:4`
	`[1] 2 3 4`
	`> c(1,3,9)`
	`[1] 1 3 9`
		`#vector of integers from 2 to 4`
		
		`#vector of integers`

numeric (Real numbers)	`> c(8.4, 2.1)` `[1] 8.4 2.1`	`#vector of real numbers`
character (Letters)	`> c('A', 'ABC')` `[1] "A" "ABC"`	`#vector of letters`
logical (TRUE or FALSE)	`> c(2:4)==3` `[1] FALSE TRUE FALSE`	`#evaluate the expression` `#the printed logical vector`

Biological variables are collections of observations of the same kind (e.g. a temperature variable contains a collection of temperature measurements) and are therefore, appropriately represented by vectors. Continuous biological variables are represented by *numeric vectors*, whereas, categorical variables are best represented by *character vectors*. For example, a *numeric vector* (variable) might represent the air temperature within ten (10) quadrats.

```
> TEMPERATURE <- c(36.1, 30.6, 31, 36.3, 39.9, 6.5,
+      11.2, 12.8, 9.7, 15.9)
> TEMPERATURE
 [1] 36.1 30.6 31.0 36.3 39.9  6.5 11.2 12.8  9.7 15.9
```

1.10.1 Regular or patterned sequences

Inclusive sequences of integers can be generated using the : operator

```
> #a sequence from 10 to 18 inclusive
> 10:18
[1] 10 11 12 13 14 15 16 17 18
> #a sequence from 18 to 10 inclusive
> 18:10
[1] 18 17 16 15 14 13 12 11 10
```

The `seq()` *function* is used to generate numeric sequences

```
> #every 4th number from 2 to <= 20
> seq(from=2, to=20, by=4)
[1]  2  6 10 14 18
```

```
> seq(from = 2, to = 20, length = 5)
[1]  2.0  6.5 11.0 15.5 20.0
```

Sequences of repeated entries are supported with the `rep()` *function.*

```
> rep(4, 5)                     #repeat the number 4 five times
[1] 4 4 4 4 4
> rep("no", 4)                  #repeat the word 'no' four times
[1] "no" "no" "no" "no"
> rep(c(2, 5), 3)               #repeat the series 2 & 5 three times
[1] 2 5 2 5 2 5
> rep(c(2, 5), c(3, 2))         #repeat the number 2 three times
[1] 2 2 2 5 5                   # and then the number 5 twice
```

Note that in the two examples immediately above, there are functions within functions. That is the `c()` *function* is used within the `rep()` *function.* When there are functions within functions, the inner most function is evaluated first. Hence in the above examples, the `c()` *function* is evaluated and expanded first and then the `rep()` function uses the resulting object(s) as an argument.

1.10.2 Character vectors

Names of experimental or sampling units (such as sites, quadrats, individuals...) can be stored into character vectors.

```
> QUADRATS <- c("Q1", "Q2", "Q3", "Q4", "Q5", "Q6",
+      "Q7", "Q8", "Q9", "Q10")
> QUADRATS
 [1] "Q1"  "Q2"  "Q3"  "Q4"  "Q5"  "Q6"  "Q7"  "Q8"  "Q9"
[10] "Q10"
```

A more elegant way to generate the above character vector is to use the `paste()` *function.* This function converts multiple vectors into character vectors before combining the elements of each vector together into a single character vector. A `sep=` argument is used to indicate a separation character (or set of characters) to appear between combined vector elements:

```
> QUADRATS <- paste("Q", 1:10, sep = "")
> QUADRATS
 [1] "Q1"  "Q2"  "Q3"  "Q4"  "Q5"  "Q6"  "Q7"  "Q8"  "Q9"
[10] "Q10"

> paste("Quad", 1:10, sep = ".")
 [1] "Quad.1"  "Quad.2"  "Quad.3"  "Quad.4"  "Quad.5"
 [6] "Quad.6"  "Quad.7"  "Quad.8"  "Quad.9"  "Quad.10"
```

Such a character vector can then be used to name the elements of a vector. For example, we could use the `names()` *function* to name the elements of the `TEMPERATURE` vector according to their quadrat labels:

```
> names(TEMPERATURE) <- QUADRATS
> TEMPERATURE
  Q1   Q2   Q3   Q4   Q5   Q6   Q7   Q8   Q9  Q10
36.1 30.6 31.0 36.3 39.9  6.5 11.2 12.8  9.7 15.9
```

The `paste()` *function* can also be used in conjunction with other functions to generate lists of labels. For example, we could combine a vector in which the letters A, B, C, D and E (generated with the `LETTERS` *constant*[g]) are each repeated twice consecutively (using the `rep()` *function*) with a vector that contains a 1 and a 2 to produce a character vector that labels sites in which the quadrats may have occurred.

```
> SITE <- paste(rep(LETTERS[1:5], each = 2), 1:2,
+     sep = "")
> SITE
 [1] "A1" "A2" "B1" "B2" "C1" "C2" "D1" "D2" "E1" "E2"
```

The `substr()` *function* is used to extract parts of string (set of characters) entries within character vectors and thus is useful for making truncated labels (particularly for graphical summaries). For example, if we had a character vector containing the names of the Australian capital cities and required abbreviations (first 3 characters) for graph labels:

```
> AUST <- c("Adelaide", "Brisbane", "Canberra",
+     "Darwin", "Hobart", "Melbourne", "Perth",
+     "Sydney")

> substr(AUST, 1, 3)
[1] "Ade" "Bri" "Can" "Dar" "Hob" "Mel" "Per" "Syd"
```

Alternatively, we could use the `abbreviate()` *function.*

```
> abbreviate(AUST, minlength = 3)
 Adelaide  Brisbane  Canberra    Darwin    Hobart Melbourne
    "Adl"     "Brs"     "Cnb"     "Drw"     "Hbr"     "Mlb"
    Perth    Sydney
    "Prt"     "Syd"
```

Categorical variables with discrete levels can be represented by *character vectors*. For example, a *character vector* might represent whether or not each of the quadrats (from which the above temperatures were measured) were shaded. The first entry in each vector (the numerical temperature vector and the categorical shade vector), corresponds to the first quadrat measured, and so on such that both vectors (variables) are of the same length.

[g] The object, `LETTERS`, is a 26 character vector inbuilt into R that contains the uppercase letters of the English alphabet. Similarly, `letters`, contains the equivalent lowercase letters.

```
> SHADE <- c("no", "no", "no", "no", "no", "full",
+     "full", "full", "full", "full")
> SHADE
 [1] "no"   "no"   "no"   "no"   "no"   "full" "full" "full"
 [9] "full" "full"
```

1.10.3 Factors

To properly accommodate factorial (categorical) variables, R has an additional class of vector called a *factor* which stores the vector along with a list of the levels of the factorial variable. The `factor()` *function* converts a vector into a factor vector.

```
> SHADE <- factor(SHADE)
> SHADE
 [1] no   no   no   no   no   full full full full full
Levels: full no
```

Note the differences between the output of the factor vector and the previous character vector. Firstly, the absence of quotation marks indicate that the vector is no longer a character vector. Internally, the factor vector (`SHADE`) is actually a numeric variable containing only 1's and 2's and in which 1 is defined as the level 'full' and 2 is defined as the level 'no' (levels of a factor are defined alphabetically by default). Hence, when printed, each entry is represented by a label and the levels contained in the factor are listed below.

There are a number of more convenient ways to generate factors in R. Combinations of the `rep()` *function* and concatenation (`c()`) *function* can be used in a variety of ways to produce identical results:

```
> SHADE <- factor(c(rep("no", 5), rep("full", 5)))
> SHADE <- factor(rep(c("no", "full"), c(5, 5)))
> SHADE <- factor(rep(c("no", "full"), each = 5))
> SHADE
 [1] no   no   no   no   no   full full full full full
Levels: full no
```

Another convenient method of generating a factor when each level of the factor has an equal number of entries (replicates) is to use the `gl()` *function*. The `gl()` *function* requires the number of factor levels, the number of consecutive replicates per factor level, the total length of the factor, and a list of factor level labels, as arguments.

```
#generate a factor with the levels 'no' and 'full', each repeated
five times in a row

> SHADE <- gl(2, 5, 10, c("no", "full"))
> SHADE
 [1] no   no   no   no   no   full full full full full
Levels: no full
```

```
> SHADE <- gl(2, 1, 10, c("no", "full"))
> SHADE
 [1] no   full no   full no   full no   full no   full
Levels: no full
```

Notice that by default, the `factor()` *function* arranges the factor levels in alphabetical order, whereas the `gl()` *function* orders the factor levels in the order in which they are included in the expression. Issues relating to the ordering of factor levels will be covered in section 2.6.1.

1.11 Matrices, lists and data frames

1.11.1 Matrices

A vector has only a single dimension – it has length. However, a vector can be converted into a matrix (2 dimensional array), whereupon it will display height and width. For example, we could convert the `TEMPERATURE` vector into a matrix by specifying the number of rows (or columns) within the `matrix()` *function*:

```
> matrix(TEMPERATURE, nrow = 5)
     [,1] [,2]
[1,] 36.1  6.5
[2,] 30.6 11.2
[3,] 31.0 12.8
[4,] 36.3  9.7
[5,] 39.9 15.9
```

By default, the matrix is filled by columns. The optional argument `byrow=T`, causes filling by rows instead.

Matrices can also be used to represent the binding of two or more vectors of equal length (and class[h]). For example, we may have the X and Y coordinates for five quadrats within a grid. Vectors are combined into a single matrix using the `cbind()` (combine by columns) or `rbind()` (combine by rows) *functions*:

```
> X <- c(16.92, 24.03, 7.61, 15.49, 11.77)
> Y <- c(8.37, 12.93, 16.65, 12.2, 13.12)
> XY <- cbind(X, Y)
> XY
         X     Y
[1,] 16.92  8.37
[2,] 24.03 12.93
[3,]  7.61 16.65
[4,] 15.49 12.20
[5,] 11.77 13.12
```

[h] when vectors of different types are combined, they are all be converted into a suitable common type.

```
> rbind(X, Y)
   [,1]  [,2]  [,3]  [,4]  [,5]
X 16.92 24.03  7.61 15.49 11.77
Y  8.37 12.93 16.65 12.20 13.12
```

Row and column names can be set (and viewed) using the `rownames()` and `colnames()` *functions*:

```
> colnames(XY)
[1] "X" "Y"
> rownames(XY) <- LETTERS[1:5]
> XY
      X     Y
A 16.92  8.37
B 24.03 12.93
C  7.61 16.65
D 15.49 12.20
E 11.77 13.12
```

1.11.2 Lists

Whilst matrices store vectors of the same type (class) and length, *lists* are used to store collections of objects that can be of differing lengths and types. Lists are constructed using the `list()` *function*. For example, we have previously created a number of isolated vectors (temperature, shade and names and coordinates of sites) that may actually represent data or information from a single experiment. These objects can be grouped together such that they all become *components* of a *list* object:

```
> EXPERIMENT <- list(SITE = SITE, COORDINATES = paste(X,
+     Y, sep = ","), TEMPERATURE = TEMPERATURE,
+     SHADE = SHADE)
> EXPERIMENT
$SITE
 [1] "A1" "A2" "B1" "B2" "C1" "C2" "D1" "D2" "E1" "E2"

$COORDINATES
[1] "16.92,8.37"  "24.03,12.93" "7.61,16.65"  "15.49,12.2"
[5] "11.77,13.12"

$TEMPERATURE
  Q1   Q2   Q3   Q4   Q5  Q6   Q7   Q8  Q9  Q10
36.1 30.6 31.0 36.3 39.9 6.5 11.2 12.8 9.7 15.9
```

```
$SHADE
 [1] no   full no   full no   full no   full no   full
Levels: no full
```

Note that this list consists of four components made up of two character vectors (SITE and COORDINATES: a vector of XY coordinates for sites A, B, C, D and E), a numeric vector (TEMPERATURE) and a factor (SHADE). Note also that while three of the components have a length of 10, the COORDINATES component has only five.

1.11.3 Data frames - data sets

Rarely are single biological variables collected in isolation. Rather, data are usually collected in sets of variables reflecting investigations of patterns between and/or among the different variables. Consequently, data sets are best organized into matricies of variables (*vectors*) all of the same lengths yet not necessarily of the same type. Hence, neither lists nor matrices represent natural storages for data sets. This is the role of *data frames* which are used to store a list of vectors of the same length (yet potentially different types) in a rectangular matrix.

Data frames are generated by combining multiple vectors together such that each vector becomes a separate column in the data frame. In this way, a data frame is similar to a matrix in which each column can represent a different vector type. For a data frame to faithfully represent a data set, the sequence in which observations appear in the vectors must be the same for each vector, and each vector should have the same number of observations. For example, the first, second, third...etc entries in each vector must represent respectively, the observations collected from the first, second, third...etc sampling units.

Since the focus of this book is in the exploration, analysis and summary of data sets, and data sets are accommodated in R by data frames, the generation, importation/ exportation, manipulation and management of data frames receives extensive coverage in chapter 2.

1.12 Object information and conversion

1.12.1 Object information

Everything in R is an object and all objects are of a certain type or *class*. The class of an object can be examined using the class() *function*. For example:

```
> class(TEMPERATURE)
[1] "numeric"
```

There is also a family of *functions* prefixed with is. that evaluate whether or not an object is of a particular class (or type) or not. Table 1.3 lists the common object query functions. All object query functions return a *logical vector*. Enter methods(is) for a more comprehensive list.

Table 1.3 Common object query functions and their corresponding return values.

Function	Returns TRUE:
`is.numeric(x)`	if **all** elements of x are numeric or integer (`x <-c(1,-3.5)`)
`is.null(x)`	if x is NULL (the object has no length) (`x <-NULL`)
`is.logical(x)`	if **all** elements of x are logical (`x <- c(TRUE,FALSE)`)
`is.character(x)`	if **all** elements of x are character strings (`x <- c(,A,,,Quad,)`)
`is.vector(x)`	if the object x is a vector (a single dimension). Returns `FALSE` if object has any attributes other than `names`
`is.factor(x)`	if the object x is a factor
`is.matrix(x)`	if the object x is a matrix (2 dimensions but not a data frame)
`is.list(x)`	if the object x is a list
`is.data.frame(x)`	if the object x is a data frame
`is.na(x)`	for **each** missing (`NA`) element in x (`x <- c(NA,2)`)
`!`	('not') character as a prefix converts the above functions into '`is.not.`'

Many R objects also have a set of *attributes*, the number and type of which are specific to each class of object. For example, a matrix object has a specific number of dimensions as well as row and column names. The attributes of an object can be viewed using the `attributes()` *function*:

```
> attributes(XY)
$dim
[1] 5 2

$dimnames
$dimnames[[1]]
[1] "A" "B" "C" "D" "E"

$dimnames[[2]]
[1] "X" "Y"
```

Similarly, the `attr()` *function* can be used to view and set individual attributes of an object, by specifying the name of the object and the name of the attribute (as a character string) as arguments. For example:

```
> attr(XY, "dim")
[1] 5 2
> attr(XY, "description") <- "coordinates of quadrats"
> XY
      X     Y
A 16.92  8.37
B 24.03 12.93
```

```
C  7.61 16.65
D 15.49 12.20
E 11.77 13.12
attr(,"description")
[1] "coordinates of quadrats"
```

Note that in the above example, the attribute `"description"` is not a regular attribute of a matrix. When a new attribute is set, this attribute is displayed along with the object. This provides a useful way of attaching a description to an object, thereby reducing the risks of the object becoming unfamiliar.

1.12.2 Object conversion

Objects can be converted or coerced into other objects using a family of *functions* with a `as.` prefix. Note that there are some obvious restrictions on these conversions as most objects cannot be completely accommodated by all other object types, and therefore some information (such as certain attributes) may be lost or modified during the conversion. Objects and elements that cannot be successfully coerced are returned as `NA`. Table 1.4 lists the common object coercion functions. Use `methods(as)` for a more comprehensive list.

Table 1.4 Common object coercion functions and their corresponding return values.

Function	Converts object to
`as.numeric(x)`	a numeric vector ('integer' or 'real'). Factors converted to integers.
`as.null(x)`	a `NULL`
`as.logical(x)`	a logical vector. Values of `>1` converted to `TRUE`, otherwise `FALSE`
`as.character(x)`	a character vector
`as.vector(x)`	a vector. All attributes (including `names`) are removed.
`as.factor(x)`	a factor. This is an abbreviated version of `factor`
`as.matrix(x)`	a matrix. Any non-numeric elements result in all matrix elements being converted to character strings
`as.list(x)`	a list
`as.data.frame(x)`	a data frame. Matrix columns and list columns are converted into a separate vectors of the data frame, and character vectors are converted into factors. All previous attributes are removed

1.13 Indexing vectors, matrices and lists

This section makes use of a number of objects created in earlier sections. Importantly, the `TEMPERATURE` object is a named vector and thus output will differ slightly from unnamed vectors in that returned elements are headed by their row names.

1.13.1 Vector indexing

It is possible to print or refer to a subset of a vector by appending an *index vector* (enclosed in square brackets, `[]`), to the vector name. There are four common forms of vector indexing used to extract a sub-set of vectors:

(i) **Vector of positive integers**. A set of integers that indicate which elements of the vector are to be selected. Selected elements are concatenated in the specified order.

- Select the nth element

```
> TEMPERATURE[2]
  Q2
30.6
```

- Select elements n through m

```
> TEMPERATURE[2:5]
  Q2   Q3   Q4   Q5
30.6 31.0 36.3 39.9
```

- Select a specific set of elements

```
> TEMPERATURE[c(1, 5, 6, 9)]
  Q1   Q5   Q6   Q9
36.1 39.9  6.5  9.7
```

(ii) **Vector of negative integers**. A set of integers that indicate which elements of the vector are to be excluded from concatenation.

- Select all but the nth element

```
> TEMPERATURE[-2]
  Q1   Q3   Q4   Q5   Q6   Q7   Q8   Q9  Q10
36.1 31.0 36.3 39.9  6.5 11.2 12.8  9.7 15.9
```

(iii) **Vector of character strings**. This form of vector indexing is only possible for vectors whose elements have been named. A vector of element names can be used to select elements for concatenation.

- Select the named element

```
> TEMPERATURE["Q1"]
  Q1
36.1
```

- Select the names elements

```
> TEMPERATURE[c("Q1", "Q4")]
  Q1   Q4
36.1 36.3
```

(iv) **Vector of logical values**. The vector of logical values must be the same length as the vector being sub-setted and usually are the result of an evaluated condition. Logical values of `T` (`TRUE`) and `F` indicate respectively to include and exclude corresponding elements of the main vector from concatenation.

- Select elements for which the logical condition is true

```
> TEMPERATURE[TEMPERATURE < 15]
  Q6   Q7   Q8   Q9
 6.5 11.2 12.8  9.7
> TEMPERATURE[SHADE == "no"]
  Q1   Q3   Q5   Q7   Q9
36.1 31.0 39.9 11.2  9.7
```

- Select elements for which multiple logical conditions are true

```
> TEMPERATURE[TEMPERATURE < 34 & SHADE == "no"]
  Q3   Q7   Q9
31.0 11.2  9.7
```

- Select elements for which one or other logical conditions are true

```
> TEMPERATURE[TEMPERATURE < 10 | SHADE == "no"]
  Q1   Q3   Q5   Q6   Q7   Q9
36.1 31.0 39.9  6.5 11.2  9.7
```

1.13.2 Matrix indexing

Like vectors, matrices can be indexed from vectors of positive integers, negative integers, character strings and logical values. However, whereas vectors have only a single dimension (length) (thus enabling each element to be indexed by a single number), matrices have two dimensions (height and width) and, therefore, require a set of two numbers for indexing. Consequently, matrix indexing takes on the form of `[row.indices, col.indices]`, where `row.indices` and `col.indices` respectively represent sequences of row and column indices of the form described for vectors in section 1.13.1.

Before proceeding, re-examine the `XY` matrix generated in section 1.11.1:

```
> XY
      X     Y
A 16.92  8.37
B 24.03 12.93
C  7.61 16.65
D 15.49 12.20
E 11.77 13.12
attr(,"description")
[1] "coordinates of quadrats"
```

The following examples will illustrate the variety of matrix indexing possibilities:

```
> XY[3, 2]                     # select the element at row 3,
[1] 16.65                        column 2

> XY[3, ]                      # select the entire 3rd row
    X     Y
 7.61 16.65

> XY[, 2]                      # select the entire 2nd column
    A     B     C     D     E
 8.37 12.93 16.65 12.20 13.12

> XY[, -2]                     # select all columns except the
    A     B     C     D     E    2nd
16.92 24.03  7.61 15.49 11.77

> XY["A", 1:2]                 #select columns 1 through 2 for
    X     Y                      row A
16.92  8.37

> XY[, "X"]                    #select the column named 'X'
    A     B     C     D     E
16.92 24.03  7.61 15.49 11.77

> XY[XY[, "X"] > 12, ]         #select all rows for which the
      X     Y                    value of the column X is
A 16.92  8.37                    greater than 12
B 24.03 12.93
D 15.49 12.20
```

1.13.3 List indexing

Lists consist of collections of objects that need not be of the same size or type. The objects within a list are indexed by appending an *index vector* (enclosed in double square brackets, `[[]]`), to the list name. A single object within a list can also be referred to by appending a string character (`$`) followed by the name of the object to the list names (e.g. `list$object`). The elements of objects within a list are indexed according to the object type. *Vector indices* to objects within other objects (lists) are placed within their own square brackets outside the list square brackets:

Recall the `EXPERIMENT` list generated in section 1.11.2

```
> EXPERIMENT
$SITE
 [1] "A1" "A2" "B1" "B2" "C1" "C2" "D1" "D2" "E1" "E2"
```

```
$COORDINATES
[1] "16.92,8.37"  "24.03,12.93" "7.61,16.65"  "15.49,12.2"
[5] "11.77,13.12"

$TEMPERATURE
  Q1   Q2   Q3   Q4   Q5   Q6   Q7   Q8   Q9  Q10
36.1 30.6 31.0 36.3 39.9  6.5 11.2 12.8  9.7 15.9

$SHADE
 [1] no   full no   full no   full no   full no   full
Levels: no full
```

The following examples illustrate a variety of list indexing possibilities:

```
> #select the first object in the list
> EXPERIMENT[[1]]
 [1] "A1" "A2" "B1" "B2" "C1" "C2" "D1" "D2" "E1" "E2"

> #select the object named 'TEMPERATURE' within the list
> EXPERIMENT[['TEMPERATURE']]
  Q1   Q2   Q3   Q4   Q5   Q6   Q7   Q8   Q9  Q10
36.1 30.6 31.0 36.3 39.9  6.5 11.2 12.8  9.7 15.9

> #select the first 3 elements of 'TEMPERATURE' within
> #'EXPERIMENT'
> EXPERIMENT[['TEMPERATURE']][1:3]
  Q1   Q2   Q3
36.1 30.6 31.0

> #select only those 'TEMPERATURE' values which correspond
> #to SITE's with a '1' as the second character in their name
> EXPERIMENT$TEMPERATURE[substr(EXPERIMENT$SITE,2,2) == '1']
  Q1   Q3   Q5   Q7   Q9
36.1 31.0 39.9 11.2  9.7
```

1.14 Pattern matching and replacement (character search and replace)

It is often desirable to select a subset of data on the basis of character entries that match more general patterns. Furthermore, the ability to search and replace character strings within a character vector can be very useful.

1.14.1 grep - pattern searching

The `grep()` *function* searches within a vector for matches to a pattern and returns the index of all matching entries.

```
# select only those 'SITE' values that contain an 'A'
> grep("A", EXPERIMENT$SITE)
[1] 1 2
> EXPERIMENT$SITE[grep("A", EXPERIMENT$SITE)]
[1] "A1" "A2"
```

By default, the pattern comprises any valid *regular expression*[i] which provides great pattern searching flexibility.

```
# convert the EXPERIMENT list into a data frame
> EXP <- as.data.frame(EXPERIMENT)
# select only those rows that contain correspond to a 'SITE'
  value of either an A, B or C followed by a '1'
> grep("[A-C]1", EXP$SITE)
[1] 1 3 5
> EXP[grep("[A-C]1", EXP$SITE), ]
   SITE COORDINATES TEMPERATURE SHADE
Q1   A1  16.92,8.37        36.1    no
Q3   B1  7.61,16.65        31.0    no
Q5   C1 11.77,13.12        39.9    no
```

1.14.2 regexpr - position and length of match

Rather than return the indexes of matching entries, the `regexpr()` *function* returns the position of the match within each string as well as the length of the pattern within each string (`-1` values correspond to entries in which the pattern is not found).

```
#recall the AUST character vector that lists the Australian
  capital cities
> AUST
[1] "Adelaide"  "Brisbane"  "Canberra"  "Darwin"
[5] "Hobart"    "Melbourne" "Perth"     "Sydney"
#get the position and length of string of characters containing
  an 'a' and an 'e' separated by any number of characters
> regexpr("a.*e", AUST)
[1]  5  6  2 -1 -1 -1 -1 -1
attr(,"match.length")
[1]  4  3  4 -1 -1 -1 -1 -1
```

[i] A regular expression is a formal computer language consisting of normal printing characters and special *metacharacters* (which represent wildcards and other features) that together provide a concise yet flexible way of matching strings.

1.14.3 gsub - pattern replacement

The `gsub()` *function* replaces all instances[j] of an identified pattern within a character vector with an alternative set of characters.

```
> gsub("no", "Not shaded", EXP$SHADE)
 [1] "Not shaded" "full"       "Not shaded" "full"
 [5] "Not shaded" "full"       "Not shaded" "full"
 [9] "Not shaded" "full"
```

It is also possible to extend the functionality to accomodate perl-compatible regular expressions.

```
#convert all the capital values entries into uppercase identify
  (and store) all words (\\w) convert stored pattern (\\1) to
  uppercase (\\U)
> gsub("(\\w)", "\\U\\1", AUST, perl = TRUE)
[1] "ADELAIDE"  "BRISBANE"  "CANBERRA"  "DARWIN"
[5] "HOBART"    "MELBOURNE" "PERTH"     "SYDNEY"
```

1.15 Data manipulation

1.15.1 Sorting

The `sort()` *function* is used to sort vector entries in increasing (or decreasing) order. Note that the elements of the `TEMPERATURE` vector were earlier named (see section 1.10.2). This assists in the distinction of the following functions, however it does result in slightly different format (each element has a name above it, and the braced index is absent).

```
> sort(TEMPERATURE)
  Q6   Q9   Q7   Q8  Q10   Q2   Q3   Q1   Q4   Q5
 6.5  9.7 11.2 12.8 15.9 30.6 31.0 36.1 36.3 39.9

> sort(TEMPERATURE, decreasing = T)
  Q5   Q4   Q1   Q3   Q2  Q10   Q8   Q7   Q9   Q6
39.9 36.3 36.1 31.0 30.6 15.9 12.8 11.2  9.7  6.5
```

The `order()` *function* is also used to sort vector entries in increasing (or decreasing) order, but rather than return a sorted vector, it returns the position (order) or the sorted entries in the original vector. For example:

```
> order(TEMPERATURE)
 [1]  6  9  7  8 10  2  3  1  4  5
```

---

[j] The similar `sub()` *function* replaces only the first match of a pattern within a vector.

Indicating that the smallest entry in the TEMPERATURE vector was at position (index) 6 and so on.

The rank() *function* is used to indicate the ranking of each entry in a vector:

```
> rank(TEMPERATURE)
 Q1  Q2  Q3  Q4  Q5  Q6  Q7  Q8  Q9 Q10
  8   6   7   9  10   1   3   4   2   5
```

Indicating that the first entry in the TEMPERATURE vector was ranked eighth in increasing order. Ranks from decreasing order can be produced by then reversing the returned vector using the rev() *function*.

```
> rev(rank(TEMPERATURE))
Q10  Q9  Q8  Q7  Q6  Q5  Q4  Q3  Q2  Q1
  5   2   4   3   1  10   9   7   6   8
```

1.15.2 Formatting data

Rounding

The ceiling() *function* rounds vector entries up to the nearest integer

```
> ceiling(TEMPERATURE)
 Q1  Q2  Q3  Q4  Q5  Q6  Q7  Q8  Q9 Q10
 37  31  31  37  40   7  12  13  10  16
```

The floor() *function* rounds vector entries down to the nearest integer

```
> floor(TEMPERATURE)
 Q1  Q2  Q3  Q4  Q5  Q6  Q7  Q8  Q9 Q10
 36  30  31  36  39   6  11  12   9  15
```

The trunc() *function* rounds vector entries to the nearest integer towards '0' (zero)

```
> trunc(seq(-2, 2, by = 0.5))
[1] -2 -1 -1  0  0  0  1  1  2
```

The round() *function* rounds vector entries to the nearest numeric with the specified number of decimal places. Digits of 5 are rounded off to the nearest even digit.

```
> round(TEMPERATURE)
 Q1  Q2  Q3  Q4  Q5  Q6  Q7  Q8  Q9 Q10
 36  31  31  36  40   6  11  13  10  16
```

```
> round(seq(-2, 2, by = 0.5))
[1] -2 -2 -1  0  0  0  1  2  2
```

```
> round(TEMPERATURE/2.2, 2)
   Q1    Q2    Q3    Q4    Q5    Q6    Q7    Q8    Q9   Q10
16.41 13.91 14.09 16.50 18.14  2.95  5.09  5.82  4.41  7.23

> round(TEMPERATURE, -1)
 Q1  Q2  Q3  Q4  Q5  Q6  Q7  Q8  Q9 Q10
 40  30  30  40  40  10  10  10  10  20
```

Other formating

Occasionally (mainly for graphical displays), it is necessary to be able to adjust the other aspects of the formatting of vector entries. For example, you may wish to have numbers expressed in scientific notation (2.93e-04 rather than 0.000293) or insert commas every 3 digits left of the decimal point. These procedures are supported via the `formatC()` *function.*

```
> seq(pi, pi * 10000, length = 5)
[1]     3.141593  7856.337828 15709.534064 23562.730300
[5] 31415.926536

# scientific notation
> formatC(seq(pi, pi * 10000, length = 5), format = "e",
+     digits = 2)
[1] "3.14e+00" "7.86e+03" "1.57e+04" "2.36e+04" "3.14e+04"

# scientific notation only if it saves space
> formatC(seq(pi, pi * 10000, length = 5), format = "g",
+     digits = 2)
[1] "3.1"     "7.9e+03" "1.6e+04" "2.4e+04" "3.1e+04"

# floating point format with 1000's indicators
> formatC(seq(pi, pi * 10000, length = 5), format = "f",
+     big.mark = ",", digits = 2)
[1] "3.14"      "7,856.34"  "15,709.53" "23,562.73"
[5] "31,415.93"
```

1.16 Functions that perform other functions repeatedly

The `replicate()` *function* repeatedly performs the function specified in the second argument the number of times indicated by the first argument. The important distinction between the `replicate()` *function* and the `rep()` *functions* described in section 1.10.1, is that the former repeatedly performs the function whereas the later performs the function only once and then duplicates the result multiple times. Since most functions produce the same result each time they are performed, for many uses, both functions produce identical results. The one group of functions that do not produce identical results each time, are those involved in random number generation. Hence, the `replicate()` *function* is usually used in conjunction with random number generators (such as `runif()`, which will be described in greater detail in chapter 4) to produce sets of random numbers. Consider first the difference between `rep()` and `replicate()`:

```
> rep(runif(1), 5)
[1] 0.4194366 0.4194366 0.4194366 0.4194366 0.4194366

> replicate(5, runif(1))
[1] 0.467324683 0.727337794 0.797764456 0.007025032
[5] 0.155971928
```

When the function being run within `runif()` itself produces a vector of length > 1, the `runif()` *function* combines each of the vectors together as separate columns in a matrix:

```
> replicate(5, runif(5))
          [,1]      [,2]      [,3]      [,4]        [,5]
[1,] 0.3266058 0.3313832 0.2113326 0.4744742 0.257732622
[2,] 0.5241960 0.9801652 0.6642341 0.5292882 0.799982207
[3,] 0.1894848 0.8300792 0.7178351 0.7262750 0.698298026
[4,] 0.1464055 0.6758495 0.9940731 0.3015559 0.288537242
[5,] 0.5491748 0.4052211 0.9923927 0.4074775 0.002170782
```

1.16.1 Along matrix margins

The `apply()` *function* applies a function to the margins (1=row margins and 2=column margins) of a matrix. For example, we might have a matrix that represents the abundance of three species of moth from three habitat types:

```
> MOTH <- cbind(SpA = c(25, 6, 3), SpB = c(12, 12,
+     3), SpC = c(7, 2, 19))
> rownames(MOTH) <- paste("Habitat", 1:3, sep = "")
> MOTH
         SpA SpB SpC
Habitat1  25  12   7
Habitat2   6  12   2
Habitat3   3   3  19
```

The `apply()` *function* could be used to calculate the column means (mean abundance of each species across habitat types):

```
> apply(MOTH, 2, mean)
      SpA       SpB       SpC
11.333333  9.000000  9.333333
```

1.16.2 By factorial groups

The `tapply()` *function* applies a function to the vector separately for each level of a factor combination. This provides a convenient way to calculate group statistics (pivot tables). For example, if we wanted to calculate the mean `TEMPERATURE` for each level of the `SHADE` factor:

```
> tapply(TEMPERATURE, SHADE, mean)
   no  full
25.58 20.42
```

1.16.3 By objects

The `lapply()` and `sapply()` *functions* apply a function separately to each of the objects in a list and return a list and vector/matrix respectively. For example, to find out the length of each of the objects within the `EXPERIMENT` list:

```
> lapply(EXPERIMENT, length)
$SITE
[1] 10

$COORDINATES
[1] 5

$TEMPERATURE
[1] 10

$SHADE
[1] 10

> sapply(EXPERIMENT, length)
       SITE COORDINATES TEMPERATURE       SHADE
         10           5          10          10
```

1.17 Programming in R

Although the library of built-in and add-on tools available for the R environment is extensive (and continues to grow at an incredible rate), occasionally there is the need to perform a task for which there are no existing functions. Since R is itself a programming language (in fact most of the available functions are written in R), extending its functionality to accommodate additional procedures can be a relatively simple exercise (depending of course, on the complexity of the procedure and your level of R proficiency).

1.17.1 Grouped expressions

Multiple commands can be issued on a single line by separating each command by a semicolon (`;`). When doing so, commands are evaluated in order from left to right:

```
> A <- 1;  B <- 2;  C <- A + B
> C
[1] 3
```

When a series of commands are grouped together between braces (such as `{command1; command2;...}`), the whole group of commands are evaluated as a single expression and the value of the last evaluated command within the group is returned:

```
> D <- {A <- 1; 2 -> B; C <- A + B}
> D
[1] 3
```

Grouped expressions are useful for wrapping up sets of commands that work together to produce a single result and since they are treated as a single expression, they too can be further nested within braces as part of a larger grouped expression.

1.17.2 Conditional execution – `if` and `ifelse`

Conditional execution is when a sequence of tasks is determined by whether a condition is met (`TRUE`) or not (`FALSE`), and is useful when writing code that needs to be able to accommodate more than one set of circumstances. In R, conditional execution has the forms:

```
if(condition) true.task
if(condition) true.task else false.task
ifelse(condition) true.task false.task
```

If `condition` returns a `TRUE`, the statement `true.task` is evaluated, otherwise the `false.task` is evaluated (if provided). If `condition` cannot be coerced into a logical (a yes/no answer), an error will be reported.

To illustrate the use of the `if` conditional execution, imagine that you were writing code to calculate means and you anticipated that you may have to accommodate two different classes of objects (vectors and matrices). I will use the vector `TEMPERATURE` and the matrix `MOTH`:

```
> NEW.OBJECT <- TEMPERATURE
> if (is.vector(NEW.OBJECT)) mean(NEW.OBJECT)
+     else apply(NEW.OBJECT, 2, mean)
[1] 23
```

```
> NEW.OBJECT <- MOTH
> ifelse(is.vector(NEW.OBJECT), mean(NEW.OBJECT),
+     apply(NEW.OBJECT, 2, mean))
[1] 11.33333
```

1.17.3 Repeated execution – looping

Looping enables sets of commands to be performed (executed) repeatedly.

for

A `for` loop iteratively loops through a vector of integers (a counter), each time executing the set of commands, and takes on the general form of:

```
for (counter in sequence) task
```

where `counter` is a loop variable, whose value is incremented according to the integer vector defined by `sequence`. The `task` is a single expression or *grouped expression* (see section 1.17.1) that utilizes the incrementing variable to perform a specific operation on a sequence of objects. For a simple example of a for loop, consider the following snippet that counts to six:

```
> for (i in 1:6) print(i)
[1] 1
[1] 2
[1] 3
[1] 4
[1] 5
[1] 6
```

As a more applied example, let's say we wanted to calculate the distances between each pair of sites in the XY matrix generated in section 1.11.1. The distance between any two sites (e.g. `'A'` and `'B'`) could be determined using Pythagoras' theorem ($a^2 + b^2 = c^2$).

```
> sqrt((XY["A", "X"] - XY["B", "X"])^2 + (XY["A",
+     "Y"] - XY["B", "Y"])^2)
# OR equivalently
> sqrt((XY[1, 1] - XY[2, 1])^2 + (XY[1, 2] - XY[2,
+     2])^2)
[1] 8.446638
```

A *for loop* can be used to produce a 5×5 matrix of pairwise distances between each of the sites:

```
# Create empty object
> DISTANCES <- NULL
```

```
> for (i in 1:5) {
+     X.DIST <- (XY[i, 1] - XY[, 1])^2
+     Y.DIST <- (XY[i, 2] - XY[, 2])^2
+     DISTANCES <- cbind(DISTANCES, sqrt(X.DIST +
+         Y.DIST))
+ }
> colnames(DISTANCES) <- rownames(DISTANCES)
> DISTANCES
          A         B         C        D         E
A  0.000000  8.446638 12.459314 4.088251  7.006069
B  8.446638  0.000000 16.836116 8.571143 12.261472
C 12.459314 16.836116  0.000000 9.049691  5.455868
D  4.088251  8.571143  9.049691 0.000000  3.832075
E  7.006069 12.261472  5.455868 3.832075  0.000000
```

while

A `while` loop executes a set of commands repeatedly while a condition is `TRUE` and exits when the condition evaluates to `FALSE`, and takes the general form:

```
> while (condition) task
```

where `task` is a single expression or *grouped expression* (see section 1.17.1) that performs a specific operation as long as `condition` evaluates to `TRUE`.

To illustrate the use of a `while` loop, consider the situation where a procedure needs to generate a temporary object, but you want to be sure that no existing objects are overwritten. A simple solution is to append the object name with a number. A `while` loop can be used to repeatedly assess whether an object name (`TEMP`) already exists in the current R environment (each time incrementing a suffix) and eventually generate a unique name. The first three commands in the following syntax are included purely to generate a couple of existing names and confirm their existence.

```
> TEMP <- NULL
> TEMP1 <- NULL
> ls()
 [1] "A"          "AUST"          "B"            "C"
 [5] "D"          "DISTANCES"     "EXP"          "EXPERIMENT"
 [9] "i"          "MOTH"          "NEW.OBJECT"   "op"
[13] "QUADRATS"   "SHADE"         "SITE"         "TEMP"
[17] "TEMP1"      "TEMPERATURE"   "X"            "X.DIST"
[21] "XY"         "Y"             "Y.DIST"
#object name suffix, initially empty
> j <- NULL
# proposed temporary object
> NAME <- "TEMP"
# iteratively search for a unique name
```

```
> while (exists(Nm <- paste(NAME, j, sep = ""))) {
+     ifelse(is.null(j), j <- 1, j <- j + 1)
+ }
# assign the unique name to a numeric vector
> assign(Nm, c(1, 3, 3))
# Reexamine list of objects, note the new object, TEMP2
> ls()
 [1] "A"            "AUST"         "B"          "C"
 [5] "D"            "DISTANCES"    "EXP"        "EXPERIMENT"
 [9] "i"            "j"            "MOTH"       "NAME"
[13] "NEW.OBJECT"   "Nm"           "op"         "QUADRATS"
[17] "SHADE"        "SITE"         "TEMP"       "TEMP1"
[21] "TEMP2"        "TEMPERATURE"  "X"          "X.DIST"
[25] "XY"           "Y"            "Y.DIST"
```

The `exists()` *function* assesses whether an object of the given name already exists and `assign()` *function* makes the first argument an object name and assigns it the value of the second argument.

1.17.4 Writing functions

For all but the most trivial cases, lines of R code should be organized into a new *function* which can then be used in the same way as the built in functions. Functions are defined using the `function()` *function*:

```
> name <- function(argument1, argument2, ...) expression
```

The new function (called `name`) will use the arguments (`argument1, argument2, ...`) to evaluate the `expression` (usually *grouped expressions* – see section 1.17.1) and return the result of the evaluated expression. Once defined, the function is called by issuing a statement in the form:

```
> name(argument1, argument2, ...)
```

Functions not only provide a more elegant way to interact with a procedure (as all arguments are provided in one location, and the internal workings are hidden from view), they form a reusable extension of the R environment. As such, there are a couple of general programming conventions that are worth adhering to. Firstly, each function should only perform a single task. If a series of tasks are required, consider writing a number of functions that in turn are called from another function. Secondly, where possible, provide default options, thereby simplifying the use of the function for most regular occasions. Thirdly, user defined functions should be in either upper case or CaMeL case so as to avoid conflicting with functions built into R or one of the many extension packages.

For example, we could extend the functionality of R by writing a function that estimates the standard error of the mean. The standard error of the mean can be estimated using the formula $sd/\sqrt{n-1}$, where sd is the standard deviation of the sample and n is the number of observations.

```
> SEM <- function(x, na.rm = FALSE) {
+     if (na.rm == TRUE)
+         VAR <- x[!is.na(x)]
+     else VAR <- x
+     SD <- sd(VAR)
+     N <- length(VAR)
+     SD/sqrt(N - 1)
+ }
```

The function first assesses whether missing values (values of `'NA'`) should be removed (based on the value of `na.rm` supplied by the function user). If the function is called with `na.rm=TRUE`, the `is.na()` *function* is used to deselect such values, before the standard deviation and length are calculated using the `sd`[k] and `length` *functions*. Finally, the standard error of the mean is calculated and returned. This function could then be used to calculate the standard error of the mean for the `TEMPERATURE` vector:

```
> SEM(TEMPERATURE)
[1] 4.30145
```

1.18 An introduction to the R graphical environment

In addition to providing a highly adaptable statistical environment, R is also a graphical environment in which figures suitable for publication can be generated. The R graphical environment consists of one or more graphical devices along with an extensive library of functions for manipulating objects on these devices. A graphical device is an output stream such as a window, file or printer that is capable of receiving and interpreting graphical/plotting instructions. The exhaustive number of graphical functions can be broadly broken down into three categories:

- **High-level** graphics (plotting) functions are used to generate a new plot on a graphical device, and, unless directed otherwise, accompanying axes, labels and the appropriate (yet basic) points/bars/boxes etc are also automatically generated. When these functions are issued, a graphical device (a window unless otherwise specified) is opened and activated. If the device is already active, the previous plot will be overwritten. Whilst these functions form the basis of all graphics in R, they are rarely used in isolation to produced graphs, as they offer only limited potential for customization.
- **Low-level** graphics functions are used to customize and enhance existing plots by adding more objects and information, such as additional points, lines, words, axes, colors etc.
- **Interactive** graphics functions allow information to be added or extracted interactively from existing plots using the mouse. For example, a label may be added to a plot at the location of the mouse pointer, thereby simplifying the interaction with the graphical device's coordinate system.

[k] The `sd` *function* returns a `'NA'` when a vector containing missing values is encountered.

The R graphical environment also includes a set of graphical parameters that operate over and above these functions to control the settings of the graphical device, such as its dimensions and where a plot is positioned within the device.

As this section aims to provide only an introductory overview of the R graphical environment, documentation will be limited to just some high level graphics functions. Documentation on low level and interactive graphical functions as well as graphical parameters will be reserved until chapter 5.

1.18.1 The `plot()` function

The `plot()` *function* is actually a generic function that produces different types of plots depending on the class of objects upon which it is acting. The `plot()` *function* evaluates the class of the arguments and then passes the objects on to the plotting function most appropriate for those objects. Notice that the first time a plotting statement is issued, a graphical device (window) is opened and a plot generated. Thereafter, the plots on this graphical device are replaced.

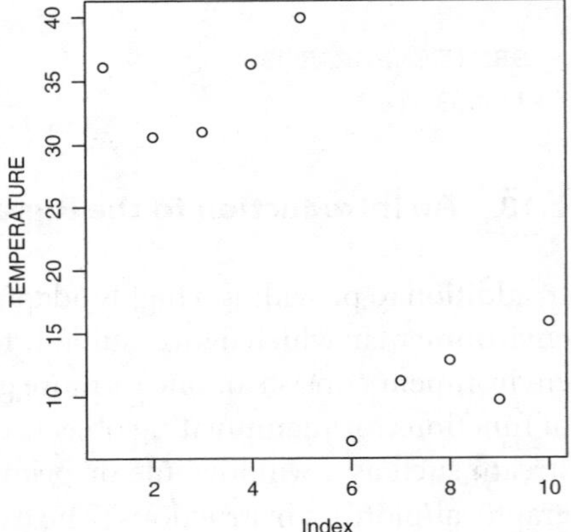

`plot(x)` – if `x` is a *numeric vector* this form of the `plot()` *function* produces a time series plot, a plot of `x` against index numbers.

```
> plot(TEMPERATURE)
```

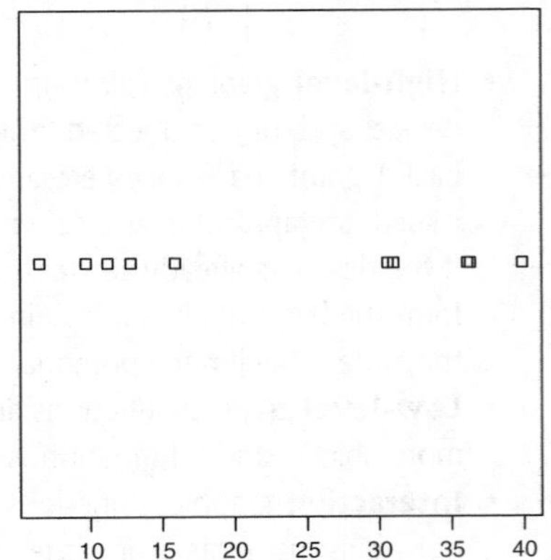

`plot(~x)` – if `x` is a *numeric vector* this form of the `plot()` *function* produces a stripchart for `x`. The same could be achieved with the `stripplot()` *function*. The `~` indicates a formula in which the left side is modeled against the right.

```
> plot(~TEMPERATURE)
```

plot(x,y) – if x and y are *numeric vectors* this form of the plot() *function* produces a scatterplot of y against x.

```
> plot(X, Y)
```

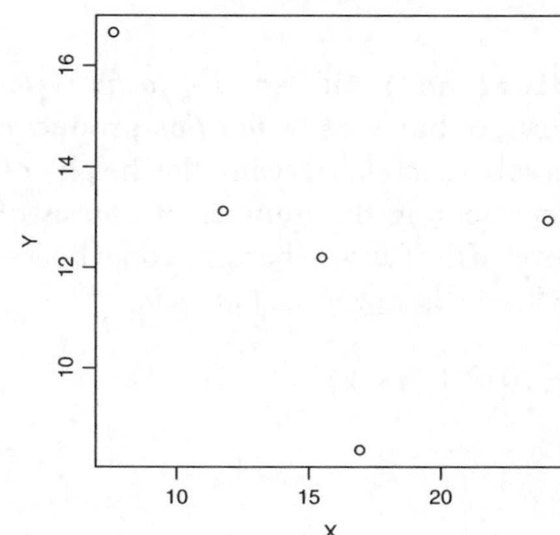

plot(y~expr) – if y is a *numeric vector* and expr is an *expression*, this form of the plot() *function* plots y against each vector in the expression.

```
> plot(Y ~ X)
```

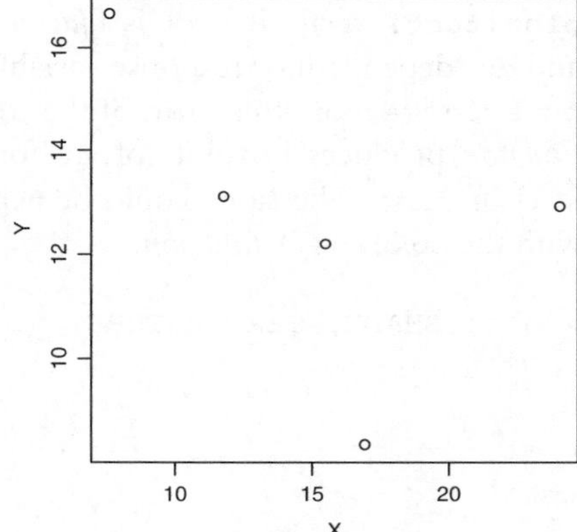

plot(xy) – if xy is a either a two-column *matrix* or a *list* containing the entries x and y, this form of the plot() *function* produces a plot of y (column 2) against x (column 1). If x is *numeric*, this will be a scatterplot, otherwise it will be a boxplot.

```
> plot(XY)
```

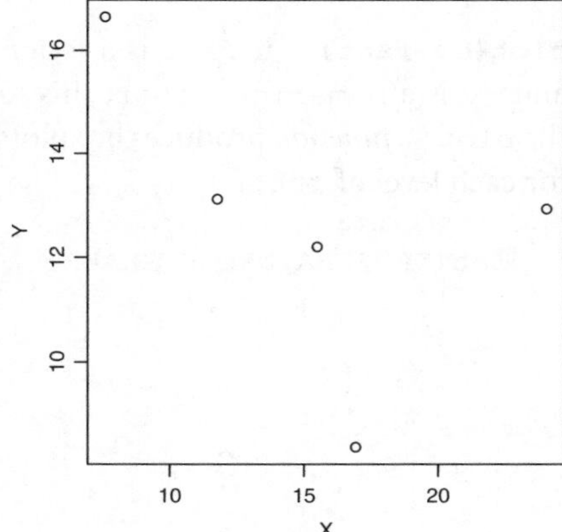

`plot(fact)` – if `fact` is a *factor vector*, this form of the `plot()` *function* produces a bar graph (bar chart) with the height of bars representing the number of entries of each level of the factor. The same could be achieved with the `barplot()` *function*.

```
> plot(SHADE)
```

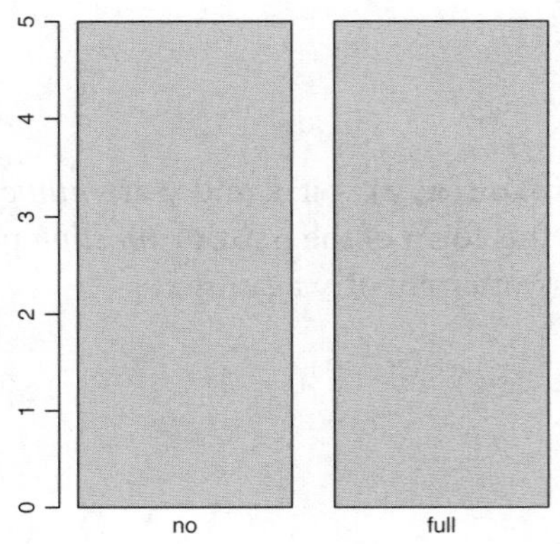

`plot(fact, dv)` – if `fact` is a *factor vector* and `dv` (dependent or response variable) is a `numeric vector`, this form of the `plot()` *function* produces boxplots of `dv` for each level of `fact`. The same could be achieved with the `boxplot()` *function*.

```
> plot(SHADE, TEMPERATURE)
```

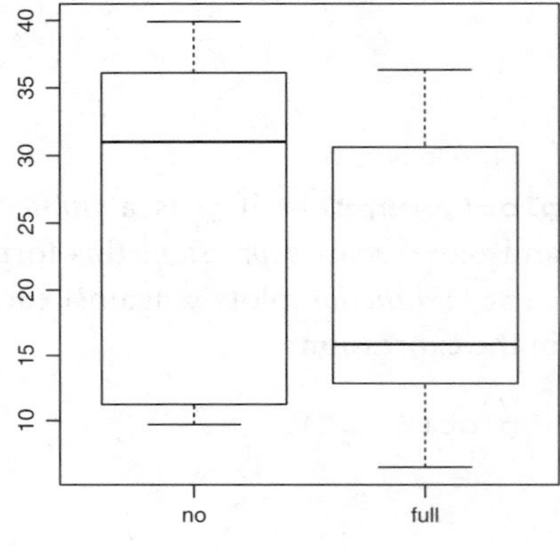

`plot(dv~fact)` – if `fact` is a *factor vector* and `dv` is a `numeric vector`, this form of the `plot()` *function* produces boxplots of `dv` for each level of `fact`.

```
> plot(TEMPERATURE ~ SHADE)
```

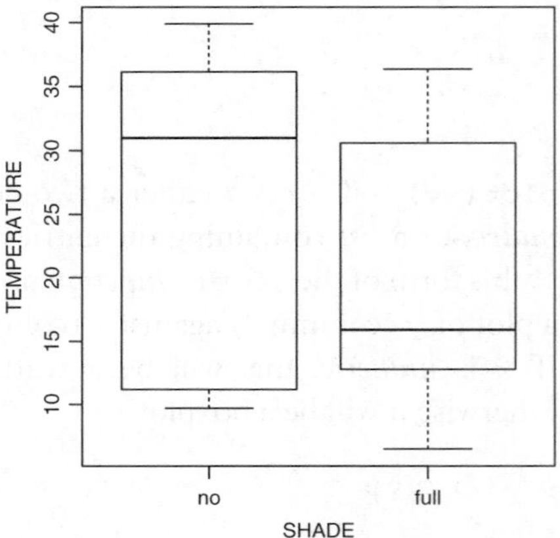

There are a limited number of options available to modify the appearance of these plots. Consider the following example:

ylab= and xlab= – these arguments specify the labels used on the vertical and horizontal axes respectively.

```
> plot(X, Y, ylab = "Y coordinate",
+ xlab = "")
```

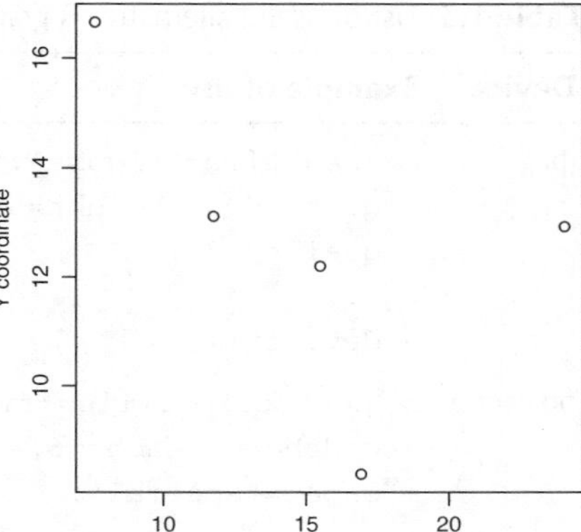

Other useful high-level plotting functions and options will be illustrated in chapter 5.

1.18.2 Graphical devices

By default, R uses the `window()` graphical device in MS Windows, while `X11()` in UNIX/Linux and typically `quartz()` in MacOSX). These provide representations of graphics on the screen within the R application. However, it is often necessary to produce graphics that can be printed or used within other applications. This is achieved by starting an alternative device (such as a graphics file) driver, redirecting graphical commands to this alternative device, and finally completing the process by closing the alternative device driver. The device driver is responsible for converting the graphical command(s) into a format that is appropriate for that sort of device.

Most installations of R come complete with a number of alternative graphics devices, each of which have their own set of options. A list of graphics devices available on your installation can be obtained by examining the `Devices` help file after issuing the following command[l].

```
> ?Devices
```

Table 1.5 lists some of the major alternative graphics devices and illustrates the common options used for each. Note that in all cases, unless full path names are supplied in the filenames, files are written to the current working directory[m].

The `bitmap()` *function* can also be used to provide a consistent interface to a number of device drivers. The `type=` *argument* can be used to select from a large

[l] A function name preceded by a question mark (?) instructs R to bring up the help file on that function. Help files are introduced in section 1.7.

[m] The current working directory is the location in which files user files are read and written. The working directory can be altered to any available directory on your system and is discussed in section 1.6.3.

Table 1.5 List of useful alternative R graphical devices[a].

Device	Example of use	
jpeg	`> jpeg(file="figure1.jpg",`	
	`+ width=500, height=500,`	dimensions of device (pixels)
	`+ quality=75)`	degree of non-compression
	`> ....`	graphical commands
	`> dev.off()`	close the device
postscript	`> postscript(file="figure1.ps",`	
	`+ width=6, height=6,`	dimensions of graphics region (inches)
	`+ paper="special",`	size of the device, if `paper="special"`
	`+ horiz=F,`	portrait orientation
	`+ family="Helvetica")`	font family to use
	`> ....`	graphical commands
	`> dev.off()`	close the device
pdf	`> pdf(file="figure1.pdf",`	
	`+ width=6, height=6,`	dimensions of graphics region (inches)
	`+ paper="special",`	size of the device, if `paper="special"`
	`+ family="Helvetica")`	font family to use
	`> ....`	graphical commands
	`> dev.off()`	close the device

[a]Not all graphical devices are available on all systems.

range of device types including, `"jpeg"`, `"pcx256"`, `"bmp256"` and `"png256"`. This function has a modest set of arguments (options), the most important of which are the device dimensions (width and height) that are specified in inches.

The `dev2bitmap()` *function* converts a screen graphics device into a graphics file device, thereby providing a simple (yet restrictive) way to save a completed graphic to file without the need to reissue the commands. This function takes the same argument set as the `bitmap()` *function*.

1.18.3 Multiple graphics devices

It is also possible to have multiple devices (of the same or different type) open at once, thereby enabling multiple graphics to be viewed and/or modified concurrently. Each opened graphics device is given a number[n] (starting with 2) and the number reflects the order in which it was created.

To create multiple devices, issue the `dev.set(1)` *function* multiple times. Multiple blank windows will be created, the most recently created of which will be the *active*

[n] Graphical device 1 is a null device – an indicator that there are no currently opened devices.

device (the device in which graphical functions will next act). To view the list of currently open devices, issue the following:

```
> dev.set(1)
null device
          1
> dev.list()
pdf pdf
  2   3
```

This indicates that there are currently two `pdf` graphics devices open in my current session. To list the currently active device:

```
> dev.cur()
pdf
  3
```

To make a graphical device *active* and thus ready to accept the next graphical function, specify the device number as an argument to the `dev.set()` *function*. For example, to make graphical device 2 the *active device*:

```
> dev.set(2)
pdf
  2
```

R returns the type and number of the device as confirmation. The active device can be closed by issuing the `dev.off()` *function* without an argument, whereas a specific device can be closed by specifying the device number as the argument.

A graphics device can be copied from one open device to another (or even to a new device) using the `dev.copy()` *function*. To copy the active device to graphics device 3 (assuming that there is a device numbered 3 and that this is not the active device):

```
> dev.copy(which = 3)
pdf
  3
```

To copy the active device to a new display device (e.g. window, X11 or quartz), specify the device type as an argument:

```
> dev.copy(device = X11)
```

The `dev.copy()` *function* can also be used to copy the active device to other device types, such as graphics files. To do so, the `dev.copy()` *function* is able to receive and forward arguments on to the relevant graphics device driver function (see Table 1.5).

```
> dev.copy(device = jpeg, file = "figure1.jpg",
+      height = 600, width = 600)
```

Note that the jpeg graphics file will not be written until the device has been closed by specifying the device number as an argument to the `dev.off()` *function*.

As an alternative, the `dev.print()` *function* can be used. This operates identically to the `dev.copy()` *function* except that it closes the new device once the graphic has been copied to it. In this way, it is similar to the `dev2bitmap()` *function* and is also useful for sending graphics to a printer.

1.19 Packages

The functionality of the core R system is extended through an ever expanding library of add-on *packages*. As new procedures are developed, they can be supported by specific add-on packages rather than necessitating re-writes of the entire application. Packages define a set of functions designed to perform more specific statistical or graphical tasks. Packages also include help files, example data sets and command scripts to provide information about the full use of the functions. All packages that are made available through the official Comprehensive R Archive Network (CRAN) and its many mirror sites, must comply with very specific regulations set and enforced by the R core development team. Authors of packages are also encouraged not to 'reinvent the wheel', but rather make use of the functionality of other packages where possible. These factors help maximize stability, uniformity and consistency across and between R and all of its packages, thereby ensuring that users of R who have attained a reasonable level of proficiency can rapidly master new packages.

The modularized nature of R also means that only the packages that are necessary to perform the current tasks need to be loaded into memory at any one time. This results in a very 'light-weight', fast statistical and graphical system.

As with procedures for installing and running R itself, procedures for installing packages differ between operating systems and are usually best performed with Administrator (super user) privileges[o].

1.19.1 Manual package management

Obtaining packages

The core R system includes only a subset of the available packages – those packages that have been identified by the R core development team as essential for supporting the common and traditional data exploration, analysis and summary procedures. Additional packages can be obtained from the CRAN web site (http://cran.r-project.org) by following the 'packages' hyperlink and locating the specific package(s). Windows users

[o] Installing with Administrator rights ensures that installations take place in the correct locations (with system wide access). Regular users typically do not have write access to these locations and thus installations with lesser privileges result in packages being installed in the users data directories. In Windows, R can be run as an Administrator by right clicking on the RGui.exe file, folder or shortcut and selecting Run As Administrator from the drop-down menu. Linux and MacOSX users usually know how to act as a super user.

should download the .zip versions, Unix/Linux users download the .tar.gz versions and MacOSX users download .tgz versions.

Note that the philosophy of cross-package reliance to reduce the number of replicated procedures, means that many packages depend on other packages. A package's dependencies are listed in the package description. Ensure that when downloading a package, all other packages that are required have either been previously acquired or are also downloaded. The `library()` *function* without any arguments returns a list of installed and currently available packages on your system. This can be useful for checking potential dependency violations.

Installing packages

Windows

To install packages directly from one of the CRAN mirrors or Bioconductor (Bioinformatics packages) repositories, start by selecting the **Packages** menu from within RGui. For CRAN repositories, select the most local CRAN mirror to you from the list that appears after selecting **Set CRAN mirror...** from the **Packages** menu. Anytime thereafter you can install packages from that mirror by selecting the **Install package(s)...** submenu and then selecting the desired package(s) from the list. To install packages from the Bioconductor packages repository, first alter the repository via the **Select repositories...** submenu.

It is also possible to install packages from pre-downloaded package binaries. Select the **Packages** menu, then the **Install from local zip files..** submenu and locate the downloaded .zip file(s) and click the OK button.

Unix/Linux

Typically only root (or a superuser) can install packages. As root, and from the directory containing the compressed package, enter the following command at a terminal prompt:

```
R CMD INSTALL package_name.tar.gz
```

where `package_name` is the name of the package to be installed.

MacOSX

The MacOSX port of R is able to install packages from source packages using the methods outlined for Unix/Linux systems. However, it is also able to install from pre-packaged binary packages. Whilst the latter is sometimes (for some packages) specific to which OS version is in use (typically only the latest), no other additional compiler tools are required for installation. Hence, installation from binary packages is the simplest method.

To install packages directly from one of the CRAN mirrors or Bioconductor (Bioinformatics packages) repositories, after selecting the **Package Installer** submenu, select the appropriate repository and package type (typically CRAN (binaries)) before pressing **Get List**. Select the package(s) you want installed, check the "Install Dependencies" check-box just below the "Install Selected" button to ensure all the necessary dependencies[p] are also retrieved. You are also able to chose where the packages are installed. There are four radio buttons corresponding to the possible locations. The default is "At System Level (in R framework)". For those with Administrator privileges and password, this is recommended. The others are "At User Level", "In Other Location (Will Be Asked Upon Installation)", and "As Defined by .libpaths()" Finally, click the **Install Selected** button.

To install from downloaded binary packages, select the **Package Installer** submenu from the **Packages & Data** menu. Selecting **Local Source Package** and pressing **Install** will bring up a new Finder window form which you should navigate to and select the downloaded package(s).

Package management within R

The R statistical and graphical environment is equipped with a number of tools to help install and update packages on your system. A list of all the currently installed packages can be obtained by issuing:

```
> installed.packages()
```

```
        Package   LibPath                             Version   Priority Bundle Contains
abind   "abind"   "/usr/local/lib/R/site-library" "1.1-0"   NA       NA     NA
akima   "akima"   "/usr/local/lib/R/site-library" "0.5-2"   NA       NA     NA
alr3    "alr3"    "/usr/local/lib/R/site-library" "1.1.7"   NA       NA     NA
Biobase "Biobase" "/usr/local/lib/R/site-library" "2.4.1"   NA       NA     NA
biology "biology" "/usr/local/lib/R/site-library" "1.0"     NA       NA     NA
bitops  "bitops"  "/usr/local/lib/R/site-library" "1.0-4.1" NA       NA     NA
        Depends                          Imports Suggests                   Enhances OS_type Built
abind   "R (>= 1.5.0)"                   NA      NA                         NA       NA      "2.6.2"
akima   NA                               NA      NA                         NA       NA      "2.9.1"
alr3    NA                               NA      NA                         NA       NA      "2.6.2"
Biobase "R (>= 2.7.0), methods, utils" NA      "tools, tkWidgets, ALL"  NA       NA      "2.9.1"
biology "car"                            NA      NA                         NA       NA      "2.9.1"
bitops  NA                               NA      NA                         NA       NA      "2.9.1"
```

Note, I have included only the first six packages to save space. The `installed.packages()` *function* returns the name of the installed packages as well as information about the packages including the version number, dependencies and the version of R on which the package was built.

Packages are often updated in the CRAN repositories. The easiest way to update the installed packages is to use the `update.packages()` *function*

```
> update.packages()
```

[p] In the spirit of modularization, many packages build upon functions contributed by other packages. Consequently, packages that depend on function within other packages list those packages as dependencies. For a given package to install correctly, all its dependencies must already be installed.

You will be prompted for a repository mirror (web locations that provide copies of the official R repositories). You should select the mirror closest to you. The `update.packages()` *function* will then compare your currently installed packages to those on the repositories, download any updated packages and install them on your system. It is also possible to provide a `repos=` *argument* in order to explicitly specify the base URL of the repository you wish to access the package from.

Individual packages can also be installed from a CRAN mirror. The name of the package (without the version codes) is supplied as an argument to the `install.packages()` *function*. As described above, the `repos=` *argument* can be used. The following syntax could be used to install the `car` (Companion to Applied Regression) *package* from the University of Melbourne CRAN mirror.

```
> install.packages(car, repos = "http://cran.ms.unimelb.edu.au")
```

1.19.2 Loading packages

Although packages only need to be installed once, before a package can be used in a session, it needs to be loaded into memory. This ensures that while you may have a very large number of packages installed on your system, only those packages that are actually required to perform the current tasks are taking up valuable resources. A package is loaded by providing the name of the package (without any extensions) as an argument for the `library()` *function*. For example, to load the package `gdata` which provides various data manipulation functions:

```
> library(gdata)
Loading required package: gtools
```

In this case R, informs you that it first loaded a package called `gtools` that `gdata` depends on.

1.20 Working with scripts

One of the advantages of command driven software is that if the commands used to perform certain tasks can be stored, then the tasks can be easily repeated exactly. A collection of one or more commands is called a script. In R, a script is a plain text file with a separate command on each line and can be created and read in any text editor. A script is read into R by providing the full filename (and path if not in the current working directory – see section 1.6.3) of the script file as an argument in the `source()` *function*. By convention, filenames for R scripts end in the extension `.R`. For example:

```
> source("filename.R")
```

A typical script may look like the following:

```
# Temperature.R script
# Written by Murray Logan Aug09
# Sets up temperature and shade variables and calculates mean
# temperature in and out of shade

# Generate a numeric vector called TEMPERATURE
TEMPERATURE <- c(36.1, 30.6, 31.0, 36.3, 39.9, 6.5, 11.2, 12.8,
  9.7, 15.9)
# Define quadrat labels for row names
names(TEMPERATURE) <- paste('Q', 1:10, sep="")

# Generate a factor with the levels 'no' and 'full'
SHADE <- gl(2,5,10,c('no','full'))
# Calculate the mean TEMPERATURE for each level of SHADE
tapply(TEMPERATURE, SHADE, mean)
```

The above script illustrates a couple of important points about R scripts. Firstly, commands within scripts do not begin with a (>) prompt. Expressions can be split over multiple lines (and a '+' prompt is not required) and extra spaces and tabs are completely ignored by R. Finally, the benefits of regular comments throughout a script cannot be overstated. Since scripts are so valuable as a lasting record of analyses, it is of vital importance that each step be thoroughly documented for future reference.

When a script is sourced, each line of the script is parsed[q] (checked for errors), interpreted, and run as if it had been typed directly at the R command prompt. This is an extremely useful feature as it enables complicated and/or lengthy sequences of commands to be stored, modified and reused rapidly as well as acting as a record of data analysis and a repository of analysis techniques. All the commands used in this book are provided as scripts on the accompanying website www.wiley.com/go/logan/r.

1.21 Citing R in publications

The full R citation (and convenient BibTeX entry) is obtained by issuing the following:

```
> citation()
To cite R in publications use:
```

[q] Parsing is a process by which information is first verified before use.

```
  R Development Core Team (2009). R: A language and
  environment for statistical computing. R Foundation
  for Statistical Computing, Vienna, Austria. ISBN
  3-900051-07-0, URL http://www.R-project.org.

A BibTeX entry for LaTeX users is

  @Manual{,
    title = {R: A Language and Environment
             for Statistical Computing},
    author = {{R Development Core Team}},
    organization = {R Foundation for Statistical Computing},
    address = {Vienna, Austria},
    year = {2009},
    note = {{ISBN} 3-900051-07-0},
    url = {http://www.R-project.org},
  }

We have invested a lot of time and effort in creating
R, please cite it when using it for data analysis.
See also 'citation("pkgname")' for citing R packages.
```

1.22 Further reading

Crawley, M. J. (2002). *Statistical computing: an introduction to data analysis using S-PLUS*. John Wiley & Sons, UK.

Crawley, M. J. (2007). *The R Book*. John Wiley, New York.

Dalgaard, P. (2002). *Introductory Statistics with R*. Springer-Verlag, New York.

Fox, J. (2002). *An R and S-PLUS Companion to Applied Regression*. Sage Books.

Ihaka, R., and R. Gentleman. (1996). *R: A Language for Data Analysis and Graphics*. Journal of Computational and Graphical Statistics **5**:299–314.

Maindonald, J. H., and J. Braun. (2003). *Data Analysis and Graphics Using R - An Example-based Approach*. Cambridge University Press, London.

Pinheiro, J. C., and D. M. Bates. (2000). *Mixed effects models in S and S-PLUS*. Springer-Verlag, New York.

R Development Core Team, (2005). R: A Language and Environment for Statistical Computing. R Foundation for Statistical Computing, Vienna, Austria. `http://www.R-project.org`.

Venables, W. N., and B. D. Ripley. (2002). *Modern Applied Statistics with S-PLUS, 4th edn*. Springer-Verlag, New York.

2

Data sets

2.1 Constructing data frames

Data frames are generated by amalgamating vectors of the same length together. To illustrate the translation of a data set (collection of variables) into an R data frame (collection of vectors), a portion of a real data set by Mac Nally (1996) in which the bird communities were investigated from 37 sites across five habitats in southeastern Australia will be used. Although the original data set includes the measured maximum density of 102 bird species from the 37 sites, for simplicity's sake only two bird species (GST: gray shrike thrush, EYR: eastern yellow robin) and the first eight of the sites will be included. The truncated data set, comprises a single factorial (or categorical) variable, two continuous variables, and a set of site (row) names, and is as follows:

Site	HABITAT	GST	EYR
Reedy Lake	Mixed	3.4	0.0
Pearcedale	Gipps.Manna	3.4	9.2
Warneet	Gipps.Manna	8.4	3.8
Cranbourne	Gipps.Manna	3.0	5.0
Lysterfield	Mixed	5.6	5.6
Red Hill	Mixed	8.1	4.1
Devilbend	Mixed	8.3	7.1
Olinda	Mixed	4.6	5.3

Firstly, generate the three variables (excluding the site labels as they are not variables) separately:

```
> HABITAT <- factor(c("Mixed", "Gipps.Manna", "Gipps.Manna",
+     "Gipps.Manna", "Mixed", "Mixed", "Mixed", "Mixed"))
> GST <- c(3.4, 3.4, 8.4, 3, 5.6, 8.1, 8.3, 4.6)
> EYR <- c(0, 9.2, 3.8, 5, 5.6, 4.1, 7.1, 5.3)
```

Biostatistical Design and Analysis Using R: a Practical Guide, 1st edition. By M. Logan.
Published 2010 by Blackwell Publishing.

Next, use the names of the vectors as arguments in the `data.frame()` *function* to amalgamate the three separate variables into a single data frame (data set) which we will call MACNALLY (after the author).

```
> MACNALLY <- data.frame(HABITAT, GST, EYR)
> MACNALLY
      HABITAT GST EYR
1       Mixed 3.4 0.0
2 Gipps.Manna 3.4 9.2
3 Gipps.Manna 8.4 3.8
4 Gipps.Manna 3.0 5.0
5       Mixed 5.6 5.6
6       Mixed 8.1 4.1
7       Mixed 8.3 7.1
8       Mixed 4.6 5.3
```

Notice that each vector (variable) becomes a column in the data frame and that each row represents a single sampling unit (in this case, each row represents a different site). By default, the rows are named using numbers corresponding to the number of rows in the data frame. However, these can be altered to reflect the names of the sampling units by assigning a list of alternative names to the `row.names()` *property* of the data frame.

```
> row.names(MACNALLY) <- c("Reedy Lake", "Pearcedale", "Warneet",
+     "Cranbourne", "Lysterfield", "Red Hill", "Devilbend",
+     "Olinda")
> MACNALLY
                HABITAT GST EYR
Reedy Lake        Mixed 3.4 0.0
Pearcedale  Gipps.Manna 3.4 9.2
Warneet     Gipps.Manna 8.4 3.8
Cranbourne  Gipps.Manna 3.0 5.0
Lysterfield       Mixed 5.6 5.6
Red Hill          Mixed 8.1 4.1
Devilbend         Mixed 8.3 7.1
Olinda            Mixed 4.6 5.3
```

2.2 Reviewing a data frame - `fix()`

As with all other objects, a data frame can be viewed by issuing the name of the data frame. A data frame can also be viewed as a simple spreadsheet in a separate window by using the name of the data frame as an argument in the `fix()` (or `edit()`) *function*. The `fix()` *function* also enables simple editing of the data frame. The arrow keys are used for navigating the spreadsheet and any alterations will be made to the data frame when the window is closed. Try the following:

```
> fix(MACNALLY)
```

Warning - only make alterations to numeric variables, alterations to the entries of factorial variables will not update the factors list of levels and thus the factor will appear to act irrationally in analysis and graphical procedures.

2.3 Importing (reading) data

Generally, statistical systems are not very well suited to tasks of data entry and management. This is the roll of spreadsheets, of which there are many available. Although the functionality of R continues to expand, it is unlikely that R itself will ever duplicate the extensive spreadsheet and database capabilities of other software[a]. R development has roots in the Unix/Linux programming philosophy that dictates that tools should be dedicated to performing specific tasks that they perform very well and rely on other tools to perform other tasks. Consequently, the emphasis of R is, and will continue to be, purely an environment for statistical and graphical procedures. It is expected that other software will be used to generate and maintain data sets.

Unfortunately, data importation into R can be a painful exercise that overshadows the benefits of using R for new users. In part, this is because there are a large number of competing methods that can be used to import data and from a wide variety of sources. This section does not intend to cover all the methods. Rather, it will highlight the simplest and most robust methods of importing data from the most popular sources.

Unless file path names are specified, all data reading functions search for files in the current working directory. Refer to section 1.6.3 for information of reviewing and altering the current working directory.

2.3.1 Import from text file

The easiest form of importation is from a pure text file. Since most software that accepts file input can read plain text files, they can be created in all spreadsheet, database and statistical software packages and are also the default outputs of most data collection devices. In a text file, data are separated or delimited by a specific character, which in turn defines what sort of text file it is. The text file should broadly represent the format of the data frame. That is, variables should be in columns and sampling units in rows. The first row should contain the variable names and if there are row names, these should be in the first column.

[a] However, there are numerous projects in early stages of development that are being designed to offer an interface to R from within major spreadsheet packages.

The following examples illustrate the format of the abbreviated Mac Nally (1996) data set created as both comma delimited (left) and tab delimited (right) files as well as the corresponding `read.table()` commands used to import the files.

Comma delimited text file *.csv

```
HABITAT,GST,EYR
Reedy Lake,Mixed,3.4,0.0
Pearcedale,Gipps.Manna,3.4,9.2
Warneet,Gipps.Manna,8.4,3.8
Cranbourne,Gipps.Manna,3.0,5.0
....
```

```
> MACNALLY <- read.table(
+ 'macnally.csv', header=T,
+ row.names=1, sep=',')
```

Tab delimited text file *.txt

```
             HABITAT        GST   EYR
Reedy Lake   Mixed          3.4   0.0
Pearcedale   Gipps.Manna    3.4   9.2
Warneet      Gipps.Manna    8.4   3.8
Cranbourne   Gipps.Manna    3.0   5.0
....
```

```
> MACNALLY <- read.table(
+ 'macnally.txt', header=T,
+ row.names=1, sep='\t')
```

The first argument to the `read.table()` *function* specifies the name (in quotation marks) of the text file to be imported (and path if not in the current working directory, see section 1.6.3). The `header=T` argument indicates that the first row of the file is a header that defines the variable (vector) names. The `row.names=` argument indicates which column in the data set contains the row names. If there are no row names in the data set, then the `row.names=` argument should be omitted. Finally, the `sep=` *argument* specifies which character is used as the delimiter to separate data entries. The syntax (`'\t'`) indicates a tab character. Field (data) separators are not restricted to commas or tabs, just about any character can be defined as a separator.

2.3.2 Importing from the clipboard

The `read.table()` *function* can also be used to import data (into a data frame) that has been placed on the clipboard[b] by other software, thereby providing a very quick and convenient way of obtaining data from spreadsheets. Simply replace the filename argument with the word `'clipboard'` and indicate a tab field separator (`\t`). For example, to import data placed on the clipboard from Microsoft Excel, use the following syntax;

```
> MACNALLY <- read.table("clipboard", header = T, row.names = 1,
+       sep = "\t")
```

2.3.3 Import from other software

As previously stated, virtually all software packages are able to export data in text file format and usually with a choice of delimiters. However, the `foreign` *package* offers

[b] The clipboard is allocated space in virtual memory from which information can be copied and pasted within and between different applications.

more direct import of native file formats from a range of other popular statistical packages. To illustrate the use of the various relevant functions within the `foreign` *package*, importation of a subset of the Mac Nally (1996) data set from the various formats will be illustrated.

Systat[c]

```
> library(foreign)
> MACNALLY <- read.systat("macnally.syd", to.data.frame = T)
```

Spss

```
> library(foreign)
> MACNALLY <- read.spss("macnally.sav", to.data.frame = T)
```

Minitab

```
> library(foreign)
> MACNALLY <- as.data.frame(read.mtp("macnally.mtp"))
```

Note, the file must be in Minitab Portable Worksheet format.

Sas

```
> library(foreign)
> MACNALLY <- read.xport("macnally")
```

Note, the file must be in the SAS XPORT format. If there is only a single dataset in the XPORT format library, then the `read.xport()` *function* will return a data frame, otherwise it will return a list of data frames.

Excel

Excel is more than just a spreadsheet – it contains macros, formulae, multiple worksheets and formatting. The easiest ways to import data from Excel is either to save the worksheet as a text file (comma or tab delimited) and import the data as a text file (see section 2.3.3), or to copy the data to the clipboard in Excel and import the clipboard data into R (see section 2.3.2).

2.4 Exporting (writing) data

Although plain text files are not the most compact storage formats, they do offer two very important characteristics. Firstly, they can be read by a wide variety of other applications, ensuring that the ability to retrieve the data will continue indefinitely.

[c] Cannot be used to import files produced with the MacOS version of SYSTAT due to incompatible file formats.

Secondly, as they are neither compressed nor encoded, a corruption to one section of the file does not necessarily reduce the ability to correctly read other parts of the file. Hence, this is also an important consideration for the storage of datasets.

The `write.table()` *function* is used to save data frames. Although there are a large number of optional arguments available for controlling the exact format of the output file, typically only a few are required. The following example illustrates the exportation of the Mac Nally (1996) data set as a comma delimited text file.

```
> write.table(MACNALLY, "macnally.csv", quote = F, row.names = T,
+     sep = ",")
```

The first and second arguments specify respectively the name of the data frame and filename (and path if necessary) to be exported. The `quote=F` argument indicates that words and factor entries should not be exported with surrounding double quotation marks. The `row.names=T` argument indicates that the row names in the data frame are also to be exported (they will be the first column in the file). If there are no defined row names in the data frame, alter the argument to `row.names=F`. Finally, specify the field separator for the file (comma specified in above example).

2.5 Saving and loading of R objects

Any object in R (including data frames) can also be saved into a native R workspace image file (*.RData) either individually, or as a collection of objects using the `save()` *function*. For example;

```
> #save just the MACNALLY data frame
> save(MACNALLY, file='macnally.RData')
> #calculate the mean GST
> meanGST <- mean(MACNALLY$GST)
> #display the mean GST
> meanGST
[1] 4.878378
> #save the MACNALLY data frame as well as the mean GST object
> save(MACNALLY, meanGST, file='macnallystats.RData')
```

The saved object(s) can be loaded during subsequent sessions by providing the name of the saved workspace image file as an argument to the `load()` *function*. For example;

```
> load("macnallystats.RData")
```

Similarly, a straight un-encoded text version of an object (including a dataframe) can be saved or added to a text file using the `dump()` *function*.

```
> dump("MACNALLY", file = "macnally")
```

If the file character string is left empty, the text representation of the object will be written to the console. This can then be viewed or copied and pasted into a script file, thereby providing a convenient way to bundle together data sets along with graphical and analysis commands that act on the data sets.

```
> dump("MACNALLY", file = "")
```

Thereafter, the dataset is automatically included when the script is sourced and cannot accidentally become separated from the script.

2.6 Data frame vectors

In generating a data frame from individual vectors (such as above), copies of the original vectors, rather than the actual original vectors themselves are amalgamated. Consequently, while the vectors contained in the data frame contain the same information (entries) as the original vectors, they are completely distinct from the original vectors. So from the examples above, the R workspace will contain the vectors `HABITAT`, `GST` and `EYR` as well as `HABITAT`, `GST` and `EYR` within the `MACNALLY` data frame.

To refer to a vector within a data frame, the name of the vector is proceeded by the name of the data frame and the two names are separated by a $ character. For example, to refer to the `GST` vector of the `MACNALLY` data frame:

```
> MACNALLY$GST
 [1]  3.4  3.4  8.4  3.0  5.6  8.1  8.3  4.6  3.2  4.6  3.7  3.8
[13]  5.4  3.1  3.8  9.6  3.4  5.6  1.7  4.7 14.0  6.0  4.1  6.5
[25]  6.5  1.5  4.7  7.5  3.1  2.7  4.4  3.0  2.1  2.6  3.0  7.1
[37]  4.3
```

Modification made to the original vectors **will not** affect the vectors within a data frame. Therefore, it is important to remember to use the data frame prefix. To avoid confusion, it is generally recommended that following the successful generation of the data frame from individual vectors, the original vectors should be deleted.

```
> rm(HABITAT, GST, EYR)
```

Thereafter, any inadvertent reference to the original vector (`GST`) rather than vector within the data frame (`MACNALLY$GST`) will result in a error informing that the object does not exist.

```
> GST
Error: Object "GST" not found
```

2.6.1 Factor levels

When factors are generated directly using the `factor()` *function* or a data set is imported using one of the above importation methods (which themselves use the `factor()` *function* to convert character vectors into factors), factor levels are automatically arranged alphabetically. For example, examine the levels of the `MACNALLY$HABITAT` factor;

```
> levels(MACNALLY$HABITAT)
[1] "Box-Ironbark"          "Foothills Woodland" "Gipps.Manna"
[4] "Mixed"                 "Montane Forest"     "River Red Gum"
```

Although the order of factor levels has no bearing on most statistical procedures and for many applications, alphabetical ordering is as valid as any other arrangement, for some analyses (particularly those involving contrasts, see section 7.3) it is necessary to know the arrangement of factor levels. Furthermore, for graphical summaries of some data, alphabetical factor levels might not represent the natural trends among groups. Consider a dataset that includes a factorial variable with the levels `'high'`, `'medium'` and `'low'`. Presented alphabetically, the levels of the factor would be `'high'` `'low'` `'medium'`. Those data would probably be more effectively presented in the more natural order of `'high'` `'medium'` `'low'` or `'low'` `'medium'` `'high'`.

When creating a factor, the order of factor levels can be specified as a list of labels. For example, consider a factor with the levels `'low'`,`'medium'` and `'high'`:

```
> FACTOR <- gl(3, 2, 6, c("low", "medium", "high"))
> FACTOR
[1] low    low    medium medium high   high
Levels: low medium high
```

The order of existing factor levels can also be altered by redefining a factor:

```
> # examine the default order of levels
> levels(MACNALLY$HABITAT)
[1] "Box-Ironbark"          "Foothills Woodland" "Gipps.Manna"
[4] "Mixed"                 "Montane Forest"     "River Red Gum"

> # redefine the order of levels
> MACNALLY$HABITAT<-factor(MACNALLY$HABITAT, levels=c(
+ 'Montane Forest', 'Foothills Woodland','Mixed', 'Gipps.Manna',
+ 'Box-Ironbark','River Red Gum'))

> # examine the new order of levels
> levels(MACNALLY$HABITAT)
[1] "Montane Forest"        "Foothills Woodland" "Mixed"
[4] "Gipps.Manna"           "Box-Ironbark"       "River Red Gum"
```

In addition, some analyses perform different operations on factors that are defined as 'ordered' compared to 'unordered' factors. Regardless of whether you have altered the ordering of factor levels or not, by default all factors are implicitly considered 'unordered' until otherwise defined using the `ordered()` *function*[d].

[d] Alternatively, the argument `ordered=TRUE` can be supplied to the `factor` *function* when defining a vector as a factor.

```
> FACTOR <- ordered(FACTOR)
> FACTOR
[1] low    low    medium medium high   high
Levels: low < medium < high
```

2.7 Manipulating data sets

2.7.1 Subsets of data frames – data frame indexing

Indexing of data frames follows the format of `data frame[rows,columns]`, see Table 2.1.

As an alternative to data frame indexing, the `subset()` *function* can be used:

```
> #extract all the bird densities from sites that have GST values
> #greater than 3
> subset(MACNALLY, GST>3)

                   HABITAT  GST EYR
Reedy Lake           Mixed  3.4 0.0
Pearcedale     Gipps.Manna  3.4 9.2
Warneet        Gipps.Manna  8.4 3.8
Lysterfield          Mixed  5.6 5.6
Red Hill             Mixed  8.1 4.1
```

Table 2.1 Data frame indexing.

Action	Example indexing syntax
Indexing by rows (sampling units)	Select the first 5 rows of each of the vectors in the data frame `> MACNALLY[1:5,]`
	Select each of the vectors for the row called 'Pearcedale' from the data frame `> MACNALLY['Pearcedale',]`
Indexing by columns (variables)	Select all rows but just the second and forth vector of the data frame `> MACNALLY[,c(2,4)]`
	Select the GST and EYR vectors for all sites from the dataframe `> MACNALLY[,c('GST','EYR')]`
Indexing by conditions	Select the data for sites that have GST values greater than 3 `> MACNALLY[MACNALLY$GST>3,]`

	Select data for 'Mixed' habitat sites that have GST values greater than 3
	`> MACNALLY[MACNALLY$GST>3 &`
	`+ MACNALLY$HABITAT=='Mixed',]`

```
Devilbend                      Mixed  8.3 7.1
Olinda                         Mixed  4.6 5.3
Fern Tree Gum         Montane Forest  3.2 5.2
Sherwin           Foothills Woodland  4.6 1.2
...

> #extract the GST and EYR densities from sites in which GST
> #is greater than 3
> subset(MACNALLY, GST>3, select=c('GST','EYR'))

               GST EYR
Reedy Lake     3.4 0.0
Pearcedale     3.4 9.2
Warneet        8.4 3.8
Lysterfield    5.6 5.6
Red Hill       8.1 4.1
Devilbend      8.3 7.1
Olinda         4.6 5.3
Fern Tree Gum  3.2 5.2
Sherwin        4.6 1.2
...
```

The `subset()` *function* can be used within many other analysis functions and therefore provides a convenient way of performing data analysis on subsets of larger data sets.

2.7.2 The `%in%` matching operator

It is often desirable to subset according to multiple alternative conditions. The `%in%` *operator* searches through all of the entries in the object on the lefthand side for matches with any of the entries within the vector on the righthand side.

```
> #subset the MACNALLY dataset according to those rows that
> #correspond to HABITAT 'Montane Forest' or 'Foothills Woodland'
> MACNALLY[MACNALLY$HABITAT %in% c("Montane Forest",
+ "Foothills Woodland"),]
                         HABITAT  GST EYR
Fern Tree Gum     Montane Forest  3.2 5.2
Sherwin       Foothills Woodland  4.6 1.2
Heathcote Ju      Montane Forest  3.7 2.5
Warburton         Montane Forest  3.8 6.5
Panton Gap        Montane Forest  3.8 3.8
St Andrews    Foothills Woodland  4.7 3.6
Nepean        Foothills Woodland 14.0 5.6
Tallarook     Foothills Woodland  4.3 2.9
```

Convieniently, the `%in%` *operator* can also be used in the `subset` *function*.

2.7.3 Pivot tables and aggregating datasets

Sometimes it is necessary to calculate summary statistics of a vector separately for different levels of a factor. This is achieved by specifying the numeric vector, the factor (or list of factors) and the summary statistic function (such as mean) as *arguments* in the `tapply()` *function*.

```
> #calculate the mean GST densities per HABITAT
> tapply(MACNALLY$GST, MACNALLY$HABITAT, mean)
   Montane Forest Foothills Woodland              Mixed
         3.625000           6.900000           5.035294
      Gipps.Manna        Box-Ironbark      River Red Gum
         5.325000           4.575000           3.300000
```

When it is necessary to calculate the summary statistic for multiple variables at a time, or to retain the dataset format to facilitate subsequent analyses or graphical summaries, the `aggregate()` *function* is very useful.

```
> #calculate the mean GST and EYR densities per habitat
> aggregate(MACNALLY[c('GST','EYR')],
+ list(Habitat=MACNALLY$HABITAT), mean)
             Habitat      GST      EYR
1     Montane Forest 3.625000 4.500000
2 Foothills Woodland 6.900000 3.325000
3              Mixed 5.035294 4.264706
4        Gipps.Manna 5.325000 6.925000
5       Box-Ironbark 4.575000 1.450000
6      River Red Gum 3.300000 0.000000
```

Alternatively, the `gsummary()` *function* within the `nlme` and `lme4` *packages* performs similarly. The `gsummary()` *function* performs more conveniently than `aggregate()` on grouped data (data containing hierarchical blocking or nesting).

```
> library(nlme)
> gsummary(MACNALLY[c("GST", "EYR")], groups = MACNALLY$HABITAT)
                        GST      EYR
Montane Forest     3.625000 4.500000
Foothills Woodland 6.900000 3.325000
Mixed              5.035294 4.264706
Gipps.Manna        5.325000 6.925000
Box-Ironbark       4.575000 1.450000
River Red Gum      3.300000 0.000000
```

2.7.4 Sorting datasets

Often it is necessary to rearrange or sort datasets according to one or more variables. This is done by using the `order()` *function* to generate the row indices. By default, data are sorted in increasing order, however this can be reversed by supplying the `decreasing=T` *argument* to the `order()` *function*. It is possible to sort according to multiple variables simply by specifying a comma separated list of the vector names (see example below), whereby the data are sorted first by the first supplied vector, then the next and so on. Note however, when multiple vectors are supplied, all are sorted in the same direction.

```
> MACNALLY[order(MACNALLY$HABITAT, MACNALLY$GST), ]

                         HABITAT  GST EYR
Fern Tree Gum     Montane Forest  3.2 5.2
Heathcote Ju      Montane Forest  3.7 2.5
Warburton         Montane Forest  3.8 6.5
Panton Gap        Montane Forest  3.8 3.8
Tallarook      Foothills Woodland  4.3 2.9
Sherwin        Foothills Woodland  4.6 1.2
St Andrews     Foothills Woodland  4.7 3.6
Nepean         Foothills Woodland 14.0 5.6
Donna Buang                 Mixed  1.5 0.0
...
```

To appreciate how this is working, examine just the `order` component

```
> order(MACNALLY$HABITAT, MACNALLY$GST)
 [1]  9 11 12 15 37 10 20 21 26 19 35 14  1 17 23  8 27 13  5 18
[21] 22 28  6  7 16  4  2 24  3 33 34 25 36 30 32 29 31
```

Hence when this sequence is applied as row indices to MACNALLY, it would be interpreted as 'display row 13, then row 27, 29 etc'.

2.7.5 Accessing and evaluating expressions within the context of a dataframe

For times when you find it necessary to repeatedly include the name of the dataframe within functions and expressions, the `with()` *function* is very convenient. This function evaluates an expression (which can include functions) within the context of the dataframe. Hence, the above `order()` illustration could also be performed as:

```
> with(MACNALLY, order(HABITAT, GST))
 [1]  9 11 12 15 37 10 20 21 26 19 35 14  1 17 23  8 27 13  5 18
[21] 22 28  6  7 16  4  2 24  3 33 34 25 36 30 32 29 31
```

2.7.6 Reshaping dataframes

Data sets are typically constructed such that variables (vectors) are in columns and replicates are in rows. This standard format (known as long format) allows a huge variety of graphical and numerical summaries and analyses to be performed with minimal need for data alterations. Nevertheless, there are a small number of analyses (such as paired

t-tests, repeated measures and multivariate analysis of variance (MANOVA)) that can be performed on, or else require data to be arranged in *wide* format. In wide format, the rows represent blocks or individuals and the repeated measurements (responses to treatments within each block) are arranged in columns. Conversion between long and wide data formats is provided by the `reshape()` *function*. To illustrate, we will use the Walter and O'Dowd (1992) randomized block dataset in which the number of mites encountered on leaves with and without domatia blocked within plants were modelled.

```
> walter<-read.table('walter.csv', header=TRUE, sep=',')
> #view first six rows of the walter data set
> head(walter)
  LEAVES BLOCK TREAT MITE
1     a1     1     1    9
2     a2     1     2    1
3     b1     2     1    2
4     b2     2     2    1
5     c1     3     1    0
6     c2     3     2    2
```

Using the `reshape()` *function* to convert the long format into wide format:

```
> walter.wide <- reshape(walter, v.names = "MITE",
+      timevar = "TREAT", idvar = "BLOCK", direction = "wide",
+      drop = "LEAVES")
> walter.wide
   BLOCK MITE.1 MITE.2
1      1      9      1
3      2      2      1
5      3      0      2
7      4     12      4
9      5     15      2
11     6      3      1
13     7     11      0
15     8      6      0
17     9      7      1
19    10      6      0
21    11      5      1
23    12      8      1
25    13      3      1
27    14      6      0
```

In the above, `v.names=` specifies the names of vectors from the long format whose values will fill the repeated measures columns of the wide format, `timevar=` specifies the names of categorical vectors in the long format whose levels will define the separate repeated measures columns, `idvar=` specifies the names of categorical vectors in the long format that define the blocks or individuals. The `direction=` *argument* specifies the format of the resulting dataframe and `drop=` specifies the name of any vectors in the long format that can be removed prior to reshaping. Similarly, the `reshape()` *function* can be used to convert wide to long format. Reshaping from wide to long format is often desirable, since while the long format is necessary for most analysis and summaries, the wide format is typically more compact and suitable for field data collection sheets and spreadsheet entry. For the purpose of an example, the following wide data set represents seal counts from ten sites at three different times of the day (08:00, 12:00 and 16:00). The researcher wishes to reshape it to long format to facilitate analyses.

```
> seals <- data.frame(Seal = paste("Site", 1:10, sep = ""),
+     T8.00 = c(10, 35, 67, 2, 49, 117, 26, 85, 20,
+         15), T12.00 = c(15, 47, 88, 3, 46, 132, 41,
+         101, 36, 18), T16.00 = c(9, 31, 62, 0, 39,
+         86, 11, 3, 14, 7))
> seals.long <- reshape(seals, varying = c("T8.00",
+     "T12.00", "T16.00"), v.names = "Count", timevar = "TIME",
+     times = paste("T", seq(8, 16, by = 4), sep = ""),
+     idvar = "Seal", direction = "long")
> seals.long
             Seal TIME Count
Site1.T8     Site1   T8    10
Site2.T8     Site2   T8    35
Site3.T8     Site3   T8    67
Site4.T8     Site4   T8     2
Site5.T8     Site5   T8    49
Site6.T8     Site6   T8   117
Site7.T8     Site7   T8    26
Site8.T8     Site8   T8    85
Site9.T8     Site9   T8    20
Site10.T8   Site10   T8    15
Site1.T12    Site1  T12    15
Site2.T12    Site2  T12    47
Site3.T12    Site3  T12    88
Site4.T12    Site4  T12     3
Site5.T12    Site5  T12    46
Site6.T12    Site6  T12   132
Site7.T12    Site7  T12    41
Site8.T12    Site8  T12   101
Site9.T12    Site9  T12    36
Site10.T12  Site10  T12    18
Site1.T16    Site1  T16     9
Site2.T16    Site2  T16    31
```

```
Site3.T16   Site3  T16   62
Site4.T16   Site4  T16    0
Site5.T16   Site5  T16   39
Site6.T16   Site6  T16   86
Site7.T16   Site7  T16   11
Site8.T16   Site8  T16    3
Site9.T16   Site9  T16   14
Site10.T16 Site10  T16    7
```

2.8 Dummy data sets - generating random data

Most statisticians strongly recommend that research questions be designed around sets of well defined statistical procedures. This ensures that the eventual data analyses remain possible and relatively straightforward. Furthermore, many would recommend the generation and mock analysis of dummy data sets that approximate the anticipated structure and variability of the anticipated data. This enables many of the common data analysis problems to be anticipated, thereby allowing solutions to be considered prior to data collection. Dummy data sets are usually created by filling the response variable(s) (and continuous predictor variables) with random data.

R uses the Mersenne-Twister Random Number Generator (RNG) with a random number sequence cycle of $2^{19937} - 1$. All random number generators have what is known as a 'seed'. This is a number that uniquely identifies a series of random number sequences. Strictly, computer generated random numbers are 'pseudo-random' as the sequences themselves are predefined. However, with such a large number of possible sequences ($2^{19937} - 1$), for all intents and purposes they are random.

By default, the initial random seed is generated from the computer clock (milliseconds field) and is therefore unbiased. However, it is also possible to specify a random seed. This is often useful for error-checking functions. Additionally, it also facilitates learning how to perform randomizations, as the same outcomes can be repeated.

R has a family of functions (see Table 2.2) that extract random numbers from a range of mathematical distributions that represent the common sampling and statistical distributions encountered in biology.

For example, imagine that you were interested in examining the effect of four different nitrogen treatments (N1, N2, N3, N4) on the growth rate of a particular species of plant. An ANOVA (see chapter 10) appeared suitable for your intended experimental design, and you prudently decided to run a mock analysis prior to data collection. Previous studies had indicated that the growth rate of the plant species was normally distributed with a mean of around 250 mm per year with a standard deviation of about 20 mm, and you had decided (for whatever reason) to have 10 replicates of each treatment. Using these criteria it is possible to generate a dummy data set.

Table 2.2 Random number generation functions for different sampling distributions.

Distribution	Example syntax

Normal	`> # generate 5 random numbers from a normal`
	`> # distribution with a mean of 10 and a standard`
	`> # deviation of 1`
	`> rnorm(5,mean=10,sd=1)`
	`[1] 11.564555  9.732885  8.357070  8.690451 12.272846`

Log-Normal	`> # generate 5 random numbers from a log-normal`
	`> # distribution whose logarithm has a mean of 2 and a`
	`> # standard deviation`
	`> # of 1`
	`> rlnorm(5,mean=2,sd=1)`
	`[1]  8.157636 30.914781 20.175299  5.071559 16.364014`

Uniform	`> # generate 5 random numbers from a uniform`
	`> # distribution with a minimum of 2 and a`
	`> # maximum of 10`
	`> runif(5,min=1,max=10)`
	`[1] 4.710560 8.155589 8.272690 6.898405 4.226496`

Poisson	`> # generate 5 random numbers from a Poisson`
	`> # distribution with a lambda parameter of 4`
	`> rpois(5,min=1,max=10)`
	`[1] 4 4 2 6 1`

Binomial	`> # generate 5 random numbers from a binomial`
	`> # distribution based on 10 Bernoulli trials and`
	`> # a prob. of 0.5`
	`> rbinom(5,size=10,prob=.5)`
	`[1] 4 4 1 4 6`

Negative binomial	`> # generate 5 random numbers from a negative binomial`
	`> # distribution based on 10 Bernoulli trials and`
	`> # an alternative parameterization (mu) of 4`
	`> rnbinom(5,size=10,mu=4)`
	`[1] 5 7 1 4 5`

Exponential	`> # generate 5 random numbers from a exponential`
	`> # distribution with a lambda rate of 2`
	`> rexp(5,rate=2)`
	`[1] 0.3138283 1.1896221 0.2466995 0.4090852 1.1757822`

```
> # create the response variable with four sets of 10 random
> # numbers from a normal distribution
> GROWTH.RATE <- c(rnorm(10, 250,20), rnorm(10, 250,20),
+ rnorm(10, 250,20),rnorm(10, 250,20))
> # create the nitrogen treatment factor with four levels each
> # replicated 10 times
> TREATMENT <- gl(4,10,40,c('N1', 'N2', 'N3', 'N4'))
> # combine the vectors into a dataframe
> NITROGEN <- data.frame(GROWTH.RATE, TREATMENT)
```

For multifactor designs, the `expand.grid()` *function* provides a convenient way to generate dataframes containing all combinations of one or more factors. Following from the previous example, imagine you now wanted to create mock data for a two factor (nitrogen treatment and season) ANOVA design. A dummy data set could be created as follows:

```
> # create the nitrogen treatment factor with four levels
> TREATMENT <- c("N1","N2","N3","N4")
> # create the season factor with two levels
> SEASON <- c("WINTER", "SUMMER")
> # use the expand.grid function to create a dataframe with each
> # combination replicated 5 times
> TS<-expand.grid(TREATMENT=TREATMENT,SEASON=SEASON, reps=1:5)
> # combine a normally distributed response variable to the
> # factor combinations using the data.frame function
> NITROGEN<-data.frame(TS,GROWTH.RATE=rnorm(40,250,20))
```

The data can now be subject to the statistical and graphical procedures. Dummy data sets are also useful for examining the possible impacts of missing data and unbalanced designs.

3

Introductory statistical principles

Statistics is a branch of mathematical sciences that relates to the collection, analysis, presentation and interpretation of data and is therefore central to most scientific pursuits. Fundamental to statistics is the concept that samples are collected and statistics are calculated to *estimate populations* and their *parameters*.

Statistical populations can represent natural biological populations (such as the Victorian koala population), although more typically they reflect somewhat artificial constructs (e.g. Victorian male koalas - a population comprising only males is clearly not a viable biological population). A statistical population strictly refers to all the possible observations from which a sample (a subset) can be drawn and is the entity about which you wish to make conclusions.

The population parameters are the characteristics (such as population mean, variability etc) of the population that we are interested in drawing conclusions about. Since it is usually not possible to observe an entire population, the population parameters must be estimated from corresponding statistics calculated from a subset of the population known as a sample (e.g sample mean, variability etc). Provided the sample adequately represents the population (is sufficiently large and unbiased), the sample statistics should be reliable estimates of the population parameters of interest. It is primarily for this reason that most statistical procedures assume that sample observations have been drawn randomly from populations (to maximize the likelihood that the sample will truly represent the population). Additional terminology fundamental to the study of biometry are listed in Table 3.1.

In addition to estimating population parameters, various statistical functions (or *statistics*) are often calculated to express the relative magnitude of trends within and between populations. For example, the degree of difference between two populations is usually described by a t-statistic (see chapter 6). Another important concept in statistics is the idea of *probability*. The probability of an event or outcome is the proportion of times that the event or outcome is expected to occur in the long-run (after a large number of repeated procedures). For many statistical analyses, probabilities of occurrence are used as the basis for conclusions, inferences and predictions.

Consider the vague research question "How much do Victorian male koalas weigh?". This could be interpreted as:

- How much do each of the Victorian male koalas weigh individually?
- What is the total mass of all Victorian male koalas added together?
- What is the mass of the typical Victorian male koala?

Biostatistical Design and Analysis Using R: a Practical Guide, 1st edition. By M. Logan.
Published 2010 by Blackwell Publishing.

Table 3.1 List of important terms. Examples pertain to a hypothetical research investigation into estimating the protein content of koala milk.

Term	Definition	Example
Measurement	A single piece of recorded information reflecting a characteristic of interest (e.g. length of a leaf, pH of a water aliquot mass of an individual, number of individuals per quadrat etc)	Protein content of the milk of a single female koala
Observation	A single measured sampling or experimental unit (such as an individual, a quadrat, a site etc)	A small quantity of milk from a single koala
Population	All the possible observations that could be measured and the unit of which wish to draw conclusions about (note a statistical population need not be a viable biological population)	The milk of all female koalas
Sample	The (representative) subset of the population that are observed	A small quantity of milk collected from 15 captive female koalas[a]
Variable	A set of measurements of the same type that comprise the sample. The characteristic that differs (varies) from observation to observation	The protein content of koala milk.

[a] Note that such a sample may not actually reflect the defined population. Rather, it could be argued that such a sample reflects captive populations. Nevertheless, such extrapolations are common when field samples are difficult to obtain.

Arguably, it is the last of these questions that is of most interest. We might also be interested in the degree to which these weights differ from individual to individual and the frequency of individuals in different weight classes.

3.1 Distributions

The set of observations in a sample can be represented by a *sampling* or *frequency distribution*. A frequency distribution (or just distribution) represents how often observations in certain ranges occur (see Figure 3.1a). For example, how many male koalas in the sample weigh between 10 and 11 kg, or how many weigh more than 12 kg. Such a sampling distribution can also be expressed in terms of the probability (long-run likelihood or chance) of encountering observations within certain ranges. For example, the probability of encountering a male koala weighing more than 12 kg is equal to the proportion of male koalas in the sample that weighed greater than 12 kg. It is then referred to as a probability distribution. When a frequency distribution can be described by a mathematical function, the probability distribution is a curve. The total area under this curve is defined as 1 and thus, the area under sections of the curve represent the probability of values falling in the associated interval. Note, it is

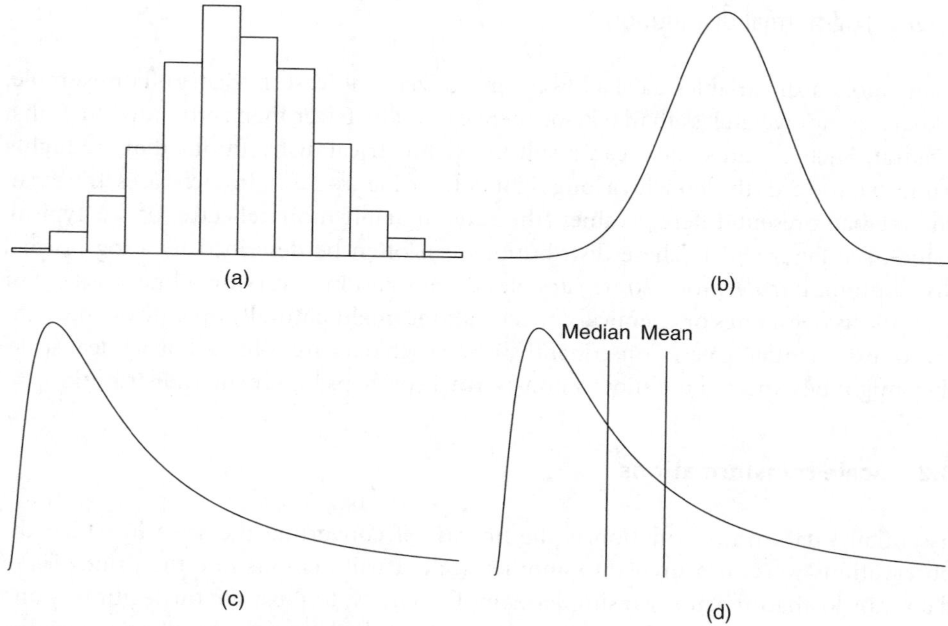

Fig 3.1 Fictitious histogram (a) and (b) normal and (c-d) log-normal probability distributions.

not possible to determine the probability of discrete events (such as the probability of encountering a koala weighing 12.183 kg) only ranges of values (such as larger than 12 kg, or between 8–10 kg).

3.1.1 The normal distribution

It has been a long observed mathematical phenomenon that the accumulation of a set of independent random influences tend to converge upon a central value (**central limit theorem**) and that the distribution of such accumulated values follow a specific 'bell shaped' curve called a *normal* or *Gaussian* distribution (see Figure 3.1b). The normal distribution is a symmetrical distribution in which values close to the center of the distribution are more likely and that progressively larger and smaller values are less commonly encountered.

Many biological measurements (such as the weight of a Victorian male koala) are likewise influenced by an almost infinite number of factors (many of which can be considered independent and random) and thus many biological variables also follow a normal distribution. Since many scientific variables behave according to the central limit theorem, many of the common statistical procedures have been specifically derived for (and thus assume) normally distributed data. In fact, the reliability of inferences based on such procedures is directly related to the degree of conformity to this assumption of normality. Likewise, many other statistical elements rely on normal distributions, and thus the normal distribution (or variants thereof) is one of the most important mathematical distributions.

3.1.2 Log-normal distribution

Many biological variables have a lower limit of zero (at least in theory). For example, a koala cannot weigh less than 0 kg or there cannot be fewer than zero individuals in a quadrat. Such circumstances can result in asymmetrical distributions that are highly truncated towards the left with a long right tail (see Figure 3.1c). In such cases, the mean and median present different values (the latter arguably more reflective of the 'typical' value), see Figure 3.1d. These distributions can often be described by a log-normal distribution. Furthermore, some variables do not naturally vary on a linear scale. For example, growth rates or chemical concentrations might naturally operate on logarithmic or exponential scales. Consequently, when such data are collected on a linear scale, they might be expected to follow a non-normal (perhaps log-normal) distribution.

3.2 Scale transformations

Essentially, data transformation is the process of converting the scale in which the observations were measured into another scale. I will demonstrate the principles of data transformation with two simple examples. Firstly, to illustrate the legitimacy and commonness of data transformations, imagine you had measured water temperature in a large number of streams. Let's assume that you measured the temperature in °C. Supposing later you required the temperatures be in °F. You would not need to re-measure the stream temperatures. Rather, each of the temperatures could be converted from one scale (°C) to the other (°F). Such transformations are very common.

Imagine now that a botanist wanted to examine the leaf size of a particular species. The botanist decides to measure the length of a random selection of leaves using a standard linear, metric ruler and the distribution of sample observations are illustrated in Figure 3.2a. The growth rate of leaves might be expected to be greatest in small leaves and deccelerate with increasing leaf size. That is, the growth rate of leaves might be expected to be logarithmic rather than linear. As a result, the distribution of leaf sizes using a linear scale might also be expected to be non-normal (log-normal). If, instead of using a linear scale, the botanist had used a logarithmic ruler, the distribution of leaf sizes may have been more like that depicted in Figure 3.2b.

If the distribution of observations is determined by the scale used to measure of the observations, and the choice of scale (in this case the ruler) is somewhat arbitrary (a linear scale is commonly used because we find it easier to understand), then it is justifiable to convert the data from one scale to another after the data has been collected and explored. It is not necessary to re-measure the data in a different scale. Therefore, to normalize the data, the botanist can simply convert the data to logarithms.

The important points in the process of transformations are;

(i) The order of the data has not been altered (a large leaf measured on a linear scale is still a large leaf on a logarithmic scale), only the spacing of the data has changed
(ii) Since the spacing of the data is purely dependent on the scale of the measuring device, there is no reason why one scale is more correct than any other scale
(iii) For the purpose of normalization, data can be converted from one scale to another

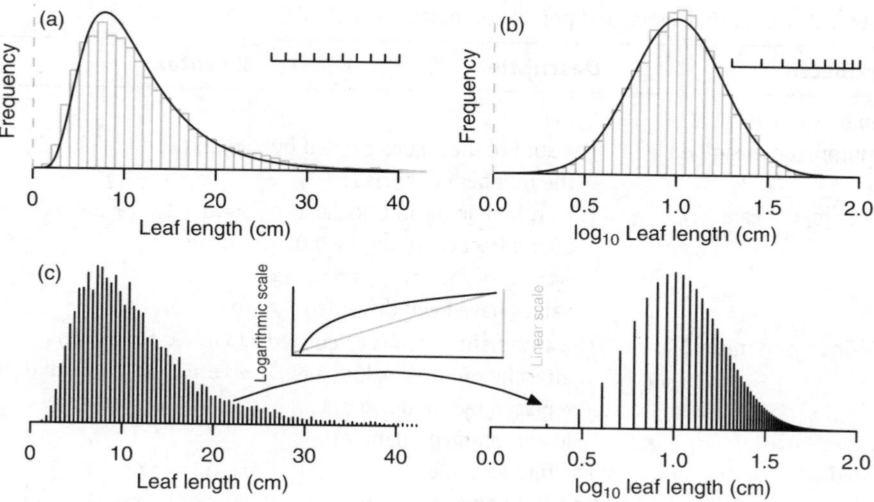

Fig 3.2 Ficticious illustration of scale transformations. Leaf length measurements collected on a linear a) and logarithmic b) scale yielding log-normal and normal sampling distributions respectively. Leaf length measurements collected on a linear scale can be *normalized* by applying a logarithmic function (inset) to each measurement. Such a scale transformation only alters the relative spacing of measurements c). A largest leaf has the largest values on both scales.

Table 3.2 Common data transformations.

Nature of data	Transformation	R syntax
Measurements (lengths, weights, etc)	$\log_e$	`log(x)`
	$\log_{10}$	`log(x, 10)`
	$\log_{10}$	`log10(x)`
	$\log x + 1$	`log(x+1)`
Counts (number of individuals, etc)	$\sqrt{}$	`sqrt(x)`
Percentages (must be proportions)	arcsin square root	`asin(sqrt(x))*180/pi`

where x is the name of the vector (variable) whose values are to be transformed.

The purpose of scale transformation is purely to normalize the data so as to satisfy the underlying assumptions of a statistical analysis. As such, it is possible to apply any function to the data. Nevertheless, certain data types respond more favourably to certain transformations due to characteristics of those data types. Common transformations and R syntax are provided in Table 3.2.

3.3 Measures of location

Measures of location describe the center of a distribution and thus characterize the typical value of a population. There are many different measures of location (see Table 3.3), all of which yield identical values (in the center of the distribution) when

Table 3.3 Commonly estimated population parameters[a].

Parameter	Description	R syntax
Estimates of Location		
Arithmetic mean (μ)	The sum of the values divided by the number of values (n)	`mean(X)`
Trimmed mean	The arithmetic mean calculated after a fraction (typically 0.05 or 5%) of the lower and upper values have been discarded	`mean(X, trim=0.05)`
Winsorized mean	The arithmetic mean is calculated after the trimmed values are replaced by the upper and lower trimmed quantiles	`library(psych)` `winsor(X, trim=0.05)`
Median	The middle value	`median(X)`
Minimum, maximum	Smallest and largest values	`min(X), max(X)`
Estimates of Spread		
Variance (σ^2)	Average deviation of observations from the mean	`var(X)`
Standard deviation (σ)	Square-root of variance	`sd(X)`
Median absolute deviation	The median difference of observations from the median value	`mad(X)`
Inter-quartile range	Difference between the 75% and 25% ranked observations	`IQR(X)`
Precision and confidence		
Standard error of $\bar{y}$ ($s_{\bar{y}}$)	Precision of the estimate $\bar{y}$	`sd(X)/sqrt(length(X))`
95% confidence interval of μ	Interval with a 95% probability of containing the true mean	`library(gmodels)` `ci(X)`

[a]Only L-estimators are provided. L-estimators are linear combinations of weighted statistics on ordered values. M-estimators (of which maximum likelihood is an example) are calculated as the minimum of some function(s).

the population (and sample) follows an exactly symmetrical distribution. Whilst the mean is highly influenced by unusually large or small values (outliers) and skewed distributions, the median is more *robust*. The greater the degree of asymmetry and outliers, the more disparate the different measures of location.

3.4 Measures of dispersion and variability

In addition to having an estimate of the typical value (center of a distribution), it is often desirable to have an estimate of the spread of the values in the population. That is, do all Victorian male koalas weigh the same or do the weights differ substantially?

In its simplest form, the variability, or spread, of a population can be characterized by its range (difference between maximum and minimum values). However, as ranges can only increase with increasing sample size, sample ranges are likely to be a poor estimate of population spread. *Variance* (s^2) describes the typical deviation of values from the typical (mean) value:

$$s^2 = \sum \frac{(y_i - \bar{y})^2}{n-1}$$

Note that by definition, the mean value must be at the center of all the values, and thus the sum of the positive and negative deviations will always be zero. Consequently, the deviances are squared prior to summing. Unfortunately, this results in the units of the spread estimates being different to the units of location. *Standard deviation* (the square-root of the variance) rectifies this issue.

Note also, that population variance (and standard deviation) estimates are calculated with a denominator of $n - 1$ rather than n. The reason for this is that since the sample values are likely to be more similar to the sample mean (which is of course derived from these values) than to the fixed, yet unknown population mean, the sample variance will always underestimate the population variance. That is, the sample variance and standard deviations are biased estimates of the population parameters. Division by n-1 rather than n is an attempt to partly offset these biases.

There are more robust (less sensitive to outliers) measures of spread including the inter-quartile range (difference between 75% and 25% ranked observations) and the median absolute deviation (MAD: the median difference of observations from the median value).

3.5 Measures of the precision of estimates - standard errors and confidence intervals

Since sample statistics are used to estimate population parameters, it is also desirable to have a measure of how good the estimates are likely to be. For example, how well the sample mean is likely to represent the true population mean. The proximity of an estimated value to the true population value is its *accuracy*. Clearly, as the true value of the population parameter is never known (hence the need for statistics), it is not possible to determine the accuracy of an estimate. Instead, we measure the *precision* (repeatability, consistency) of the estimate. Provided an estimate is repeatable (likely to be obtained from repeated samples) and that the sample is a good, unbiased representative of the population, a precise estimate should also be accurate.

Strictly, precision is measured as the degree of spread (standard deviation) in a set of sample statistics (e.g. means) calculated from multiple samples and is called the *standard error*. The standard error can be estimated from a single sample by dividing the sample standard deviation by the square-root of the sample size ($\frac{\sigma}{\sqrt{n}}$). The smaller the standard error of an estimate, the more precise the estimate is and thus the closer it is likely to approximate the true population parameter.

The central limit theorem (which predicates that any set of averaged values drawn from an identical population will always converge towards being normally distributed) suggests that the distribution of repeated sample means should follow a normal distribution and thus can be described by its overall mean and standard deviation (=standard

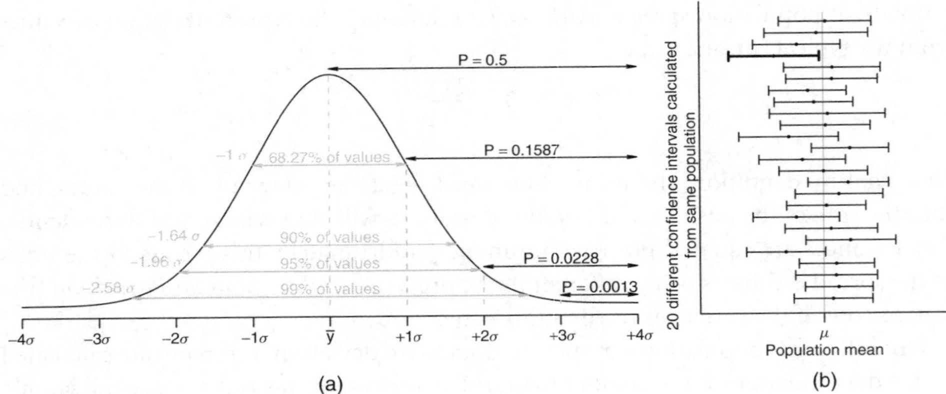

Fig 3.3 (a) Normal distribution displaying percentage quantiles (grey) and probabilities (areas under the curve) associated with a range of standard deviations beyond the mean. (b) 20 possible 95% confidence intervals from 20 samples ($n = 30$) drawn from the one population. Bold intervals are those that do not include the true population mean. In the long run, 5% of such intervals will not include the population mean (μ).

error). In fact, since the standard error of the mean is estimated from the same single sample as the mean, its distribution follows a special type of normal distribution called a t-distribution. In accordance to the properties of a normal distribution (and thus a t-distribution with infinite degrees of freedom), 68.27% of the repeated means fall between the true mean and $\pm$ one sample standard error (see Figure 3.3). Put differently, we are 68.27% percent confident that the interval bound by the sample mean plus and minus one standard error will contain the true population mean. Of course, the smaller the sample size (lower the degrees of freedom), the flatter the t-distribution and thus the smaller the level of confidence for a given span of values (interval).

This concept can be easily extended to produce intervals associated with other degrees of confidence (such as 95%) by determining the percentiles (and thus number of standard errors away from the mean) between which the nominated percentage (e.g. 95%) of the values lie (see Figure 3.3a). The 95% confidence interval is thus defined as:

$$P\left\{\bar{y} - t_{0.05(n-1)}s_{\bar{y}} \leq \mu \leq \bar{y} + t_{0.05(n-1)}s_{\bar{y}}\right\}$$

where $\bar{y}$ is the sample mean, $s_{\bar{y}}$ is the standard error, $t_{0.05(n-1)}$ is the value of the 95% percentile of a t distribution with $n - 1$ degrees of freedom, and μ is the unknown population mean. For a 95% confidence interval, there is a 95% probability that the interval will contain the true mean (see Figure 3.3b). Note, this interpretation is about the interval, not the true population value, which remains fixed (albeit unknown). The smaller the interval, the more confidence is placed in inferences about the estimated parameter.

3.6 Degrees of freedom

The concept of degrees of freedom is sufficiently abstract and foreign to those new to statistical principles that it warrants special attention. The *degrees of freedom* refers to how many observations in a sample are 'free to vary' (theoretically take on any value) when calculating independent estimates of population parameters (such as population variance and standard deviation).

In order for any inferences about a population to be reliable, each population parameter estimate (such as the mean and the variance) must be independent of one another. Yet they are usually all obtained from a single sample and to estimate variance, a prior estimate of the mean is required. Consequently, mean and variance estimated from the same sample cannot strictly be independent of one another.

When estimating the population variance (and thus standard deviation) from sample observations, not all of the observations can be considered independent of the estimate of population mean. The value of at least one of the observations in the sample is constrained (not free to vary). If, for example, there were four observations in a sample with a mean of 5, then the first three of these can theoretically take on any value, yet the forth value must be such that the sum of the values is still 20. The degrees of freedom therefore indicates how many **independent** observations are involved in the estimation of a population parameter. A 'cost' of a single degree of freedom is incurred for each prior estimate required in the calculation of a population parameter.

The shape of the probability distributions of coefficients (such as those in linear models etc) and statistics depend on the number of degrees of freedom associated with the estimates. The greater the degrees of freedom, the narrower the probability distribution and thus the greater the statistical power[a]. Degrees of freedom (and thus power) are positively related to sample size (the greater the number of replicates, the greater the degrees of freedom and power) and negatively related to the number of variables and prior required parameters (the greater the number of parameters and variables, the lower the degrees of freedom and power).

3.7 Methods of estimation

3.7.1 Least squares (LS)

Least squares (LS) parameter estimation is achieved by simply **minimizing** the overall differences between the observed sample values and the estimated parameter(s). For example, the least squares estimate of the population mean is a value that minimizes the differences between the sample values and this estimated mean. Least squares estimation has no inherent basis for testing hypotheses or constructing confidence

[a] Power is the probability of detecting an effect if an effect genuinely occurs.

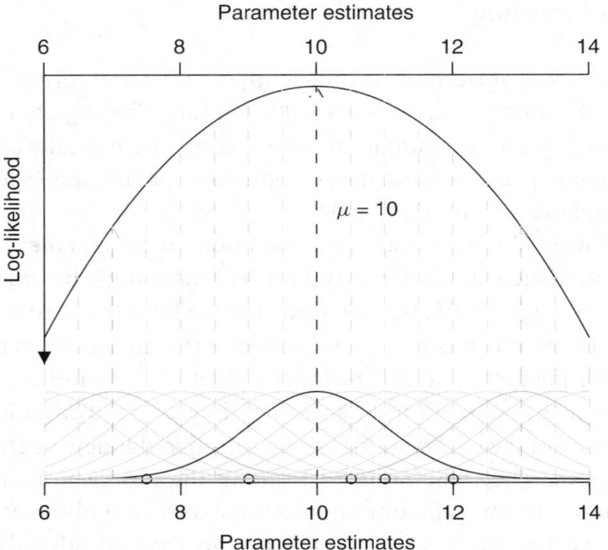

Fig 3.4 Diagrammatic illustration of ML estimation of μ.

intervals and is thus primarily for parameter estimation. Least squares estimation is used extensively in simple model fitting procedures (e.g. regression and analysis of variance) where optimization (minimization) has an exact solution that can be solved via simultaneous equations.

3.7.2 Maximum likelihood (ML)

The maximum likelihood (ML) approach estimates one or more population parameters such that the (log) likelihood of obtaining the observed sample values from such populations is **maximized** for a nominated probability distribution.

Computationally, this involves summing the probabilities of obtaining each observation for a range of possible population parameter estimates, and using integration to determine the parameter value(s) that maximize the likelihood. A simplified example of this process is represented in Figure 3.4.

Probabilities of obtaining observations for any given parameter value(s) are calculated according to a specified exponential probability distribution (such as normal, binomial, Poisson, gamma or negative binomial). When the probability distribution is normal (as in Figure 3.4), ML estimators for linear model parameters have exact computational solutions and are identical to LS solutions (see section 3.7.1). However for other probability distributions (for which LS cannot be used), ML estimators involve complex iterative calculations. Unlike least squares, the maximum likelihood estimation framework also provides standard errors and confidence intervals for estimations and therefore provides a basis for statistical inference. The major draw back of this method is that it typically requires strong assumptions about the underlying distributions of the parameters.

3.8 Outliers

Outliers are extreme or unusual values that do not fall within the normal range of the data. As many of the commonly used statistical procedures are based on means and variances (both of which are highly susceptible to extreme observations), outliers tend to bias statistical outcomes towards these extremes. For a statistical outcome to reliably reflect population trends, it is important that all observed values have an equal influence on the statistical outcomes. Outliers, however, have a greater influence on statistical outcomes than the other observations and thus, the resulting statistical outcomes may no longer represent the population of interest.

There are numerous mathematical methods that can be used to identify outliers. For example, an outlier could be defined as any value that is greater than two standard deviations from the mean[b]. Alternatively, outliers could be defined as values that are greater than two times the inter-quartile range from the inter-quartile range.

Outliers are caused by a variety of reasons including errors in data collection or transcription, contamination or unusual sampling circumstances, or the observation may just be naturally unusual. Dealing with outliers therefore depends on the cause and requires a great deal of discretion.

- If there are no obvious reasons why outlying observations could be considered unrepresentative, they must be retained although it is often worth reporting the results of the analyses with and without these influential observations
- Omitting outliers can be justified if there is reason to suspect that they are not representative (due to sampling errors etc), although their exclusion should always be acknowledged.
- There are many statistical alternatives that are based on more robust (less affected by departures from normality or the presence of outliers) measures that should be employed if outliers are present.

3.9 Further reading

Fowler, J., L. Cohen, and P. Jarvis. (1998). *Practical statistics for field biology*. John Wiley & Sons, England.

Quinn, G. P., and K. J. Keough. (2002). *Experimental design and data analysis for biologists*. Cambridge University Press, London.

Sokal, R., and F. J. Rohlf. (1997). *Biometry, 3rd edition*. W. H. Freeman, San Francisco.

Zar, G. H. (1999). *Biostatistical methods*. Prentice-Hall, New Jersey.

[b] This method clearly assumes that the observations are normally distributed.

4

Sampling and experimental design with R

A fundamental assumption of nearly all statistical procedures is that samples are collected randomly from populations. In order for a sample to truly represent a population, the sample must be collected without bias (intentional or otherwise). R has a rich array of randomization tools to assist researches randomize their sampling and experimental designs.

4.1 Random sampling

Biological surveys involve the collection of observations from naturally existing populations. Ideally, every possible observation should have an equal likelihood of being selected as part of the sample. The `sample()` *function* facilitates the drawing of random samples.

Selecting sampling units from a numbered list

Imagine wanting to perform bird surveys within five forested fragments which are to be randomly selected from a list of 37 fragments:

```
> sample(1:37, 5, replace=F)
[1]  2 16 28 30 20

> MACNALLY <- read.table("macnally.csv", header=T, sep=",")
> sample(row.names(MACNALLY), 5, replace=F)
[1] "Arcadia"      "Undera"       "Warneet"      "Tallarook"
[5] "Donna Buang"
```

Selecting sample times

Consider a mammalogist who is about to conduct spotlighting arboreal mammal surveys at 10 different sites (S1→S10). The mammalogist wants to randomize the time (number of minutes since sundown) that each survey commences so as to restrict any sampling biases or confounding dial effects. Since the surveys are to take exactly

Biostatistical Design and Analysis Using R: a Practical Guide, 1st edition. By M. Logan.
Published 2010 by Blackwell Publishing.

20 minutes and the maximum travel time between sites is 10 minutes, the survey starting times need to be a minimum of 30 minutes apart. One simple way to do this is to generate a sequence of times at 30 minute intervals from 0 to 600 (60×10) and then randomly select 10 of the times using the `sample()` *function*:

```
> sample(seq(0,600, by=30), 10, replace=F)
 [1] 300  90 270 600 480 450  30 510 120 210
```

However, these times are not strictly random, as only a small subset of possible times could have been generated (multiples of 30). Rather, they are a regular sequence of times that could potentially coincide with some natural rhythm, thereby confounding the results. A more statistically sound method is to generate an initial random starting time and then generate a set of subsequent times that are a random time greater than 30 minutes, but no more than (say) 60 minutes after the preceding time. A total of 10 times can then be randomly selected from this set.

```
> # First step is to obtain a random starting (first survey)
> # time. To do this retain the minimum time from a random set of
> # times between 1 (minute) and 60*10 (number of minutes in
> # 10 hours)
> TIMES <- min(runif(20,1,60*10))
> # Next we calculate additional random times each of which is a
> # minimum and maximum of 30 and 60 minutes respectively after
> # the previous
> for(i in 2:20) {
+ TIMES[i] <- runif(1,TIMES[i-1]+30,TIMES[i-1]+60)
+ if(TIMES[i]>9*60) break
+ }
> # Randomly select 10 of these times
> TIMES <- sample(TIMES, 10, replace=F)
> # Generate a Site name for the times
> names(TIMES) <- paste('Site',1:10, sep='')
> # Finally sort the list and put it in a single column
> cbind('Times'=sort(TIMES))
           Times
Site6   53.32663
Site9   89.57309
Site5  137.59397
Site1  180.17486
Site4  223.28241
Site2  312.30799
Site3  346.42314
Site10 457.35221
Site7  513.23244
Site8  554.69444
```

Note, that potentially any times could have been generated, and thus this is a better solution. This relatively simple example could be further extended with the use of some of the Date-Time functions.

```
> # Convert these minutes into hs, mins, seconds
> hrs <- TIMES%/%60
> mins <- trunc(TIMES%%60)
> secs <- trunc(((TIMES%%60)-mins)*60)
> RelTm <- paste(hrs,sprintf("%2.0f",mins),secs, sep=":")
> # We could also express them as real times
> # If sundown occurs at 18:00 (18*60*60 seconds)
> RealTm<-format(strptime(RelTm, "%H:%M:%S")+(18*60*60),
+ "%H:%M:%S")
> # Finally sort the list and put it in a single column
> data.frame('Minutes'=sort(TIMES),
+ 'RelativeTime'=RelTm[order(TIMES)],
+ RealTime=RealTm[order(TIMES)])
         Minutes RelativeTime RealTime
Site6   53.32663      0:53:19 18:53:19
Site9   89.57309      1:29:34 19:29:34
Site5  137.59397      2:17:35 20:17:35
Site1  180.17486      3: 0:10 21:00:10
Site4  223.28241      3:43:16 21:43:16
Site2  312.30799      5:12:18 23:12:18
Site3  346.42314      5:46:25 23:46:25
Site10 457.35221      7:37:21 01:37:21
Site7  513.23244      8:33:13 02:33:13
Site8  554.69444      9:14:41 03:14:41
```

Selecting random coordinates from a rectangular grid

Consider requiring 10 random quadrat locations from a 100 × 200 m grid. This can done by using the `runif()` *function* to generate two sets of random coordinates:

```
> data.frame(X=runif(10,0,100), Y=runif(10,0,200))
           X          Y
1  87.213819 114.947282
2   9.644797  23.992531
3  41.040160 175.342590
4  97.703317  23.101111
5  52.669145   1.731125
6  63.887850  52.981325
7  56.863370  54.875307
8  27.918894  46.495312
9  94.183309 189.389244
10 90.385280 151.110335
```

Random coordinates of an irregular shape

Consider designing an experiment in which a number of point quadrats (lets say five) are to be established in a State Park. These points are to be used for stationary 10 minute bird surveys and you have decided that the location of each of the point quadrats within each site should be determined via random coordinates to minimize sampling bias. As represented in figure to the right, the site is not a regular rectangle and therefore the above technique is not appropriate. This problem is solved by first generating a matrix of site boundary coordinates (GPS latitude and longitude), and then using a specific set of *functions* from the `sp`[a] *package* to generate the five random coordinates.

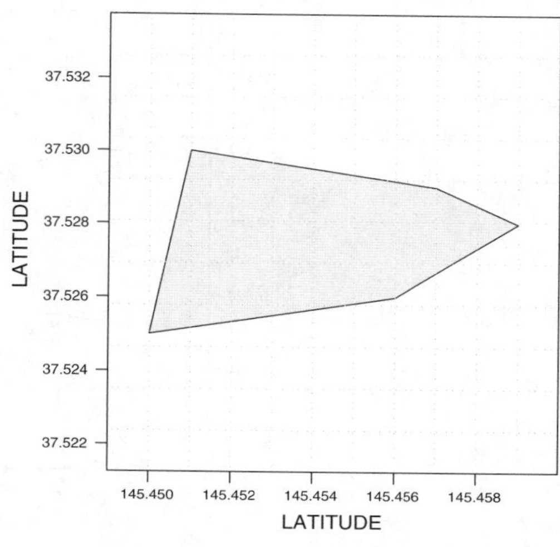


```
> LAT <- c(145.450, 145.456, 145.459, 145.457, 145.451, 145.450)
> LONG <- c(37.525, 37.526, 37.528, 37.529, 37.530,37.525)
> XY <- cbind(LAT,LONG)
> plot(XY, type='l')
> library(sp)
> XY.poly <- Polygon(XY)
> XY.points <- spsample(XY.poly, n=8, type='random')
> XY.points
SpatialPoints:
           r1       r2
[1,] 145.4513 37.52938
[2,] 145.4526 37.52655
[3,] 145.4559 37.52746
[4,] 145.4573 37.52757
[5,] 145.4513 37.52906
[6,] 145.4520 37.52631
[7,] 145.4569 37.52871
[8,] 145.4532 37.52963
Coordinate Reference System (CRS) arguments: NA
```

[a] Note that the *function* responsible for generating the random coordinates (`spsample()`) is only guaranteed to produce approximately the specified number of random coordinates, and will often produce a couple more or less. Furthermore, some locations might prove to be unsuitable (if for example, the coordinates represented a position in the middle of a lake). Consequently, it is usually best to request a 50% more than are actually required and simply ignore any extras.

These points can then be plotted on the map.

```
> points(XY.points[1:5])
```

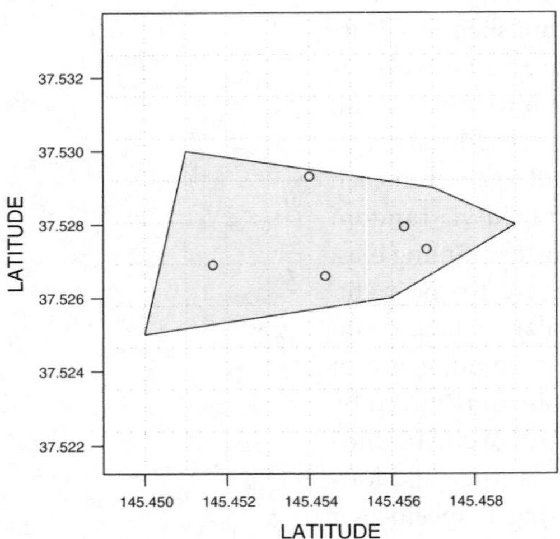

Lets say that the above site consisted of two different habitats (a large heathland and a small swamp) and you wanted to use stratified random sampling rather than pure random sampling so as to sample each habitat proportionally. This is achieved in a similar manner as above, except that multiple spatial rings are defined and joined into a more complex spatial data set.

```
> LAT1 <- c(145.450, 145.456, 145.457, 145.451,145.450)
> LONG1 <- c(37.525, 37.526, 37.529, 37.530, 37.525)
> XY1 <- cbind(LAT1,LONG1)
> LAT2 <- c(145.456,145.459,145.457,145.456)
> LONG2 <- c(37.526, 37.528, 37.529,37.526)
> XY2 <- cbind(LAT2,LONG2)
> library(sp)
> XY1.poly <- Polygon(XY1)
> XY1.polys <- Polygons(list(XY1.poly), "Heathland")
> XY2.poly <- Polygon(XY2)
> XY2.polys <- Polygons(list(XY2.poly), "Swamp")
> XY.Spolys <- SpatialPolygons(list(XY1.polys, XY2.polys))
> XY.Spoints <- spsample(XY.Spolys, n=10, type='stratified')
> XY.Spoints
SpatialPoints:
            x1       x2
 [1,] 145.4504 37.52661
 [2,] 145.4529 37.52649
 [3,] 145.4538 37.52670
 [4,] 145.4554 37.52699
```

```
 [5,] 145.4515 37.52889
 [6,] 145.4530 37.52846
 [7,] 145.4552 37.52861
 [8,] 145.4566 37.52738
 [9,] 145.4578 37.52801
[10,] 145.4510 37.52946
Coordinate Reference System (CRS) arguments: NA
```

The `spsample()` *function* supports random sampling (`'random'`), stratified random sampling (`'stratified'`), systematic sampling (`'regular'`) and non-aligned systematic sampling (`'nonaligned'`). Visual representations of each of these different sampling designs are depicted in Figure 4.1.

Random distance or coordinates along a line

Random locations along simple lines such as linear transects, can be selected by generating sets of random lengths. For example, we may have needed to select a single point along each of ten 100 m transects on four occasions. Since we effectively require $10 \times 4 = 40$ random distances between 0 and 100 m, we generate these distances

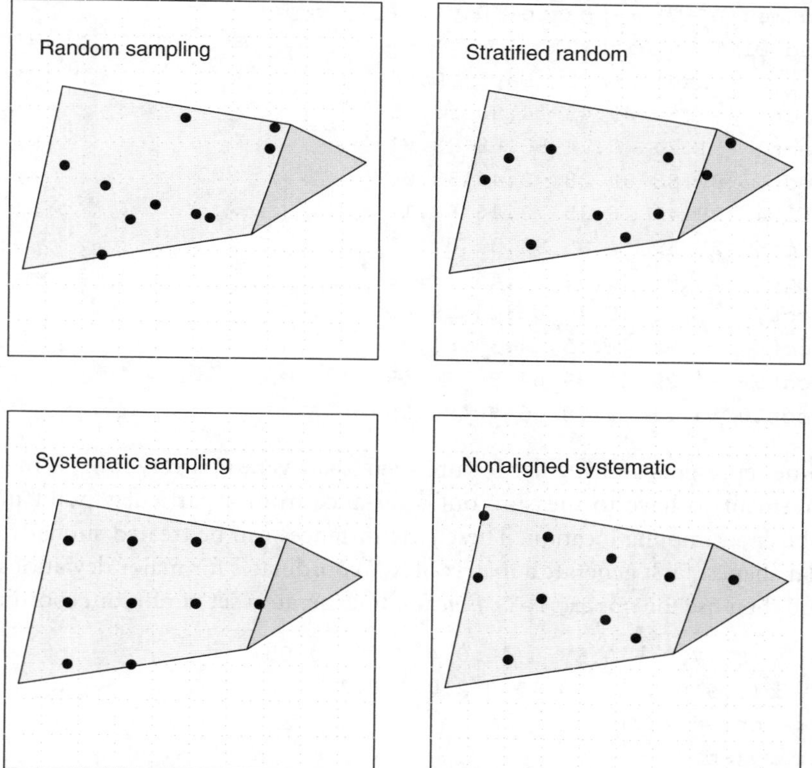

Fig 4.1 Four different sampling designs supported by the `spsample()` *function.*

and arrange them in a 10 × 4 matrix where the rows represent the transects and the columns represent the days:

```
> DIST <- matrix(runif(40,0,100),nrow=10)
> DIST
           [,1]       [,2]      [,3]      [,4]
 [1,]  7.638788 89.4317359 24.796132 24.149444
 [2,] 31.241571  0.7366166 52.682013 38.810297
 [3,] 87.879788 88.2844160  2.437215 32.059111
 [4,] 28.488424  6.3546905 78.463586 60.120835
 [5,] 25.803398  4.8487586 98.311620 87.707566
 [6,] 10.911730 25.5682093 90.443998  9.097557
 [7,] 63.199593 36.7521530 62.775836 29.430201
 [8,] 20.946571 42.7538255  4.389625 81.236970
 [9,] 94.274397 21.9937230 64.892213 70.588414
[10,] 13.114078  9.7766933 43.903295 90.947627
```

To make the information more user friendly, we could put apply row and column names and round the distances to the nearest centimeter:

```
> rownames(DIST) <- paste("Transect", 1:10, sep='')
> colnames(DIST) <- paste("Day", 1:4, sep='')
> round(DIST, digits=2)
            Day1  Day2  Day3  Day4
Transect1   7.64 89.43 24.80 24.15
Transect2  31.24  0.74 52.68 38.81
Transect3  87.88 88.28  2.44 32.06
Transect4  28.49  6.35 78.46 60.12
Transect5  25.80  4.85 98.31 87.71
Transect6  10.91 25.57 90.44  9.10
Transect7  63.20 36.75 62.78 29.43
Transect8  20.95 42.75  4.39 81.24
Transect9  94.27 21.99 64.89 70.59
Transect10 13.11  9.78 43.90 90.95
```

If the line represents an irregular feature such as a river, or is very long, it might not be convenient to have to measure out a distance from a particular point in order to establish a sampling location. These circumstances can be treated similar to other irregular shapes. First generate a matrix of X,Y coordinates for major deviations in the line, and then use the `spsample()` *function* to generate a set of random coordinates.

```
> X <- c(0.77,0.5,0.55,0.45,0.4, 0.2, 0.05)
> Y <- c(0.9,0.9,0.7,0.45,0.2,0.1,0.3)
> XY <- cbind(X,Y)
> library(sp)
> XY.line <- Line(XY)
> XY.points <- spsample(XY.line,n=10,'random')
```

```
> plot(XY, type="l")
> points(XY.points)
```

```
> coordinates(XY.points)
              X         Y
 [1,] 0.5538861 0.9000000
 [2,] 0.4171638 0.2858188
 [3,] 0.3869956 0.1934978
 [4,] 0.4579028 0.4697570
 [5,] 0.3109703 0.1554851
 [6,] 0.1238188 0.2015750
 [7,] 0.5398741 0.6746852
 [8,] 0.4826300 0.5315749
 [9,] 0.1745837 0.1338884
[10,] 0.5248993 0.6372481
```

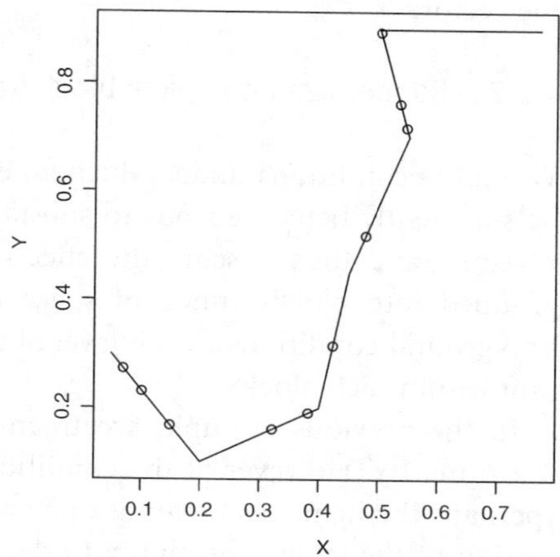

4.2 Experimental design

Randomization is also important in reducing confounding effects. Experimental design incorporates the order in which observations should be collected and/or the physical layout of the manipulation or survey. Good experimental design aims to reduce the risks of bias and confounding effects.

4.2.1 Fully randomized treatment allocation

Lets say that you were designing an experiment in which you intended to investigate the effect of fertilizer on the growth rate of a species of plant. You intended to have four different fertilizer treatments (A, B, C and D) and a total of six replicate plants per treatment. The plant seedlings are all in individual pots housed in a greenhouse and to assist with watering, you want to place all the seedlings on a large table arranged in a 4×6 matrix. To reduce the impacts of any potentially confounding effects (such as variations in water, light, temperature etc), fertilizer treatments should be assigned to seedling positions completely randomly.

This can be done by first generating a factorial vector (containing the levels A, B, C, and D, each repeated six times), using the `sample` *function* to randomize the treatment orders and then arranging it in a 4×6 matrix:

```
> TREATMENTS <- gl(4,6,24,c('A','B','C','D'))
> matrix(sample(TREATMENTS),nrow=4)
     [,1] [,2] [,3] [,4] [,5] [,6]
[1,] "C"  "D"  "A"  "B"  "C"  "A"
[2,] "A"  "B"  "C"  "C"  "C"  "B"
[3,] "A"  "D"  "A"  "B"  "D"  "D"
[4,] "B"  "D"  "C"  "B"  "A"  "D"
```

Note that when the optional size argument (number of random entries to draw) is not supplied, the `sample()` *function* performs a random permutation of the elements of the vector.

4.2.2 Randomized complete block treatment allocation

When the conditions under which an experiment is to be conducted are expected to be sufficiently heterogeneous to substantially increase the variability in the response variable (and thus obscure the effects of the main factor), experimental units are grouped into blocks (units of space or time that are likely to have less variable background conditions). Each level of the treatment factor is then applied to a single unit within each block.

In the previous example, treatments were randomly positioned throughout the 4×6 matrix. However, if the conditions in the greenhouse were not homogeneous (perhaps the light was better at one end and the sprinkler system favoured a certain section of the table), the ability to detect any effects of fertilizer treatment might be impeded. A randomized complete block (in which each level of fertilizer is randomly positioned within each block) design is achieved by repeating the `sample()` *function* six times (one per block) and combining the result into a matrix:

```
> TREATMENTS <- replicate(6,sample(c('A','B','C','D')))
> colnames(TREATMENTS) <- paste('Block',1:6,sep='')
> TREATMENTS
     Block1 Block2 Block3 Block4 Block5 Block6
[1,] "B"    "C"    "B"    "C"    "D"    "A"
[2,] "A"    "D"    "D"    "B"    "A"    "D"
[3,] "C"    "B"    "A"    "A"    "B"    "C"
[4,] "D"    "A"    "C"    "D"    "C"    "B"
```

5

Graphical data presentation

Graphical summaries provide three very important rolls in data analyses. Firstly, they are an important part of the initial exploratory data analyses that should precede any formal statistical analyses. Secondly, they provide visual representations of the patterns and trends revealed in complex statistical analyses. Finally, in some instances (such as regression trees and ordination plots), graphical representations are the primary result of the analyses. R accommodates many of the standard exploratory data analyses via specific plotting functions. Many of these functions require little user input and produce very rudimentary plots – although the quality of such exploratory data analyses is rarely of great importance (as they are typically only for the researcher). Nevertheless, the plotting functionality within R is also highly customizable in order to produce rich, publication quality graphical and analytical summaries.

Typically, a graphic begins with a **high-level** plotting function that defines the coarse structure of the graphic including its dimensions, axes scales, plotting symbol types and titles before creating a new plotting region on the graphics device. The most frequently used high-level plotting function is the `plot()` *function* which is a generic, overloaded[a] function that produces different plots depending on the *class* of object passed as its first argument. A range of the graphics produced by plot were illustrated on page 36. Other commonly used high-level plotting functions include `hist()`, `boxplot()`, `scatterplot()` and `pairs()`. Additional elements (such as text and lines) are added using the rich set of **low-level** graphical functions available. Common low-level plotting functions include `lines()`, `points()`, `text()` and `axis()`. These functions cannot define the dimensions of the plotting region and thus can only be added to existing plots.

It is not the intention of this chapter to produce finalized versions of graphical summaries. Rather, emphasis will be on illustrating the range of the commonly used high and low level plotting functions as well as some of the many graphical options available to help achieve rich and professional graphics. Subsequent chapters will build upon these foundations and illustrate the production of publication quality figures appropriate for the designs and analyses.

[a] A function is overloaded when many separate functions contain the same name (e.g. *plot*), yet differ from each other in the arguments (input) they except and the output they produce. Function overloading provides a common, convenient name to interface a suite of functions (thereby reducing the number of names that need to be learned).

Biostatistical Design and Analysis Using R: a Practical Guide, 1st edition. By M. Logan.
Published 2010 by Blackwell Publishing.

In the plotting system described above, graphics are built up by sequentially adding items (lines, points, text, etc) to a base plot. Each graphical element is evaluated individually. However, for data that can be naturally split into subsets (subjects, blocks), **Trellis** graphics provide an alternative system in which entire sets of graphical elements are applied consistently to multiple subplots within a grid (or trellis). The resulting multipanel displays are produced by a single set of integrated instructions that also handle the otherwise difficult tasks of coordinating the control of axes scales and aspect ratios. Furthermore, the plots represent the underlying data in a manner that closely matches their hierarchical treatment in linear modelling.

All plotting functions are handled via graphics device drivers. When R starts up, it automatically opens a graphics device driver (x11 on linux, windows on Windows and quartz or x11 on Mac OS X) ready to accept plotting commands. These graphics devices are referred to as *display* or screen devices since the output is displayed on the screen. There are also numerous *file* graphics devices (such as postscript, pdf, jpeg, etc) in which the graphical information is stored in standard formats for incorporation into other applications. Importantly, plotting commands can only be sent to a single graphical device at a time and the capabilities of different types of graphical devices vary.

5.1 The `plot()` *function*

The `plot()` *function* is a generic (overloaded) function, the output of which depends on the class of objects passed to it as arguments (see page 36). There are many other parameters that can be used to control various aspects of the `plot()` *function*. Some of these parameters (summarized below) provide convenient ways to control the scaling and overall form of the plot and are specific to the `plot()` high level plotting function (along with many of its derivatives). Others (graphical parameters, see section 5.2) provide even finer control of the overall plot and where relevant, can be applied to most other high and low level plotting functions.

5.1.1 The `type` *parameter*

The `type` *parameter* takes a single character argument and controls how the points should be presented.

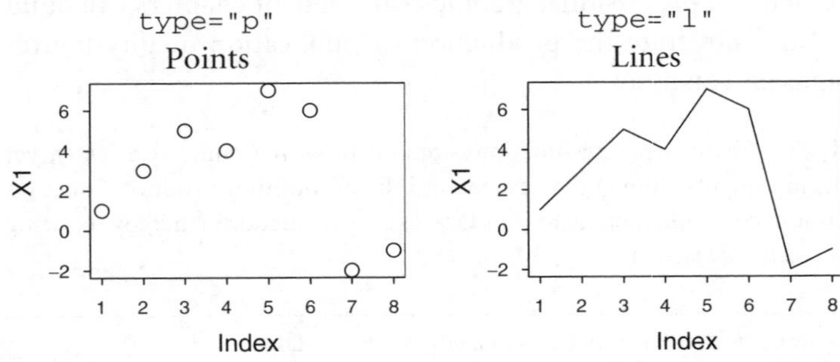

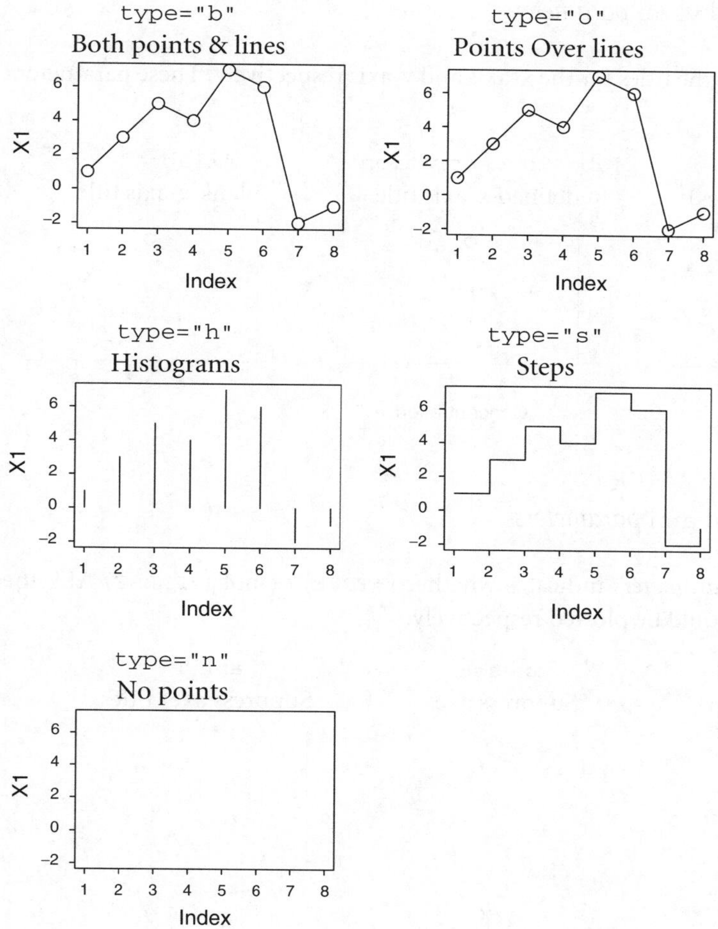

5.1.2 The `xlim` and `ylim` *parameters*

`xlim` and `ylim` control the x-axis and y-axis range respectively. These parameters take a vector with two elements (`c(min,max)`) representing the minimum and maximum scale limits.

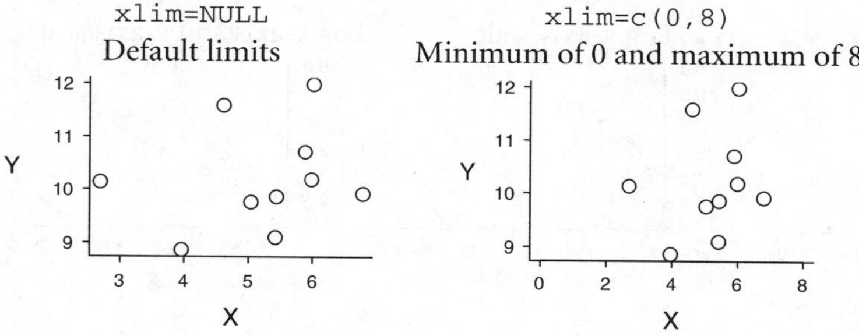

5.1.3 The `xlab` and `ylab` *parameters*

`xlab` and `ylab` define the titles for the x-axis and y-axis respectively. These parameters take a character string.

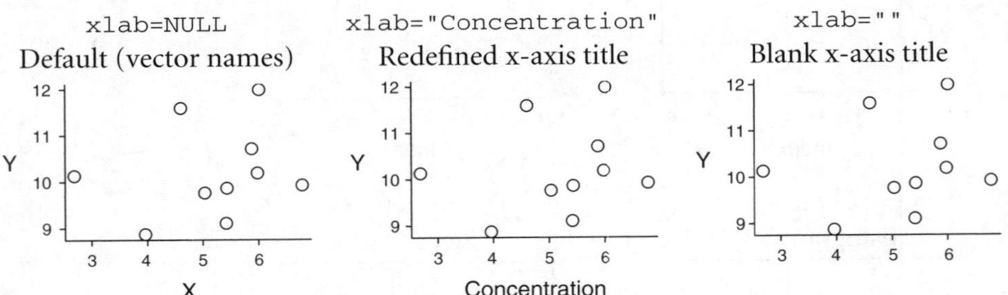

5.1.4 The `axes` and `ann` *parameters*

The `axes` and `ann` *parameters* indicates whether (`=TRUE`) or not (`=FALSE`) ALL the axes and axes titles should be plotted respectively.

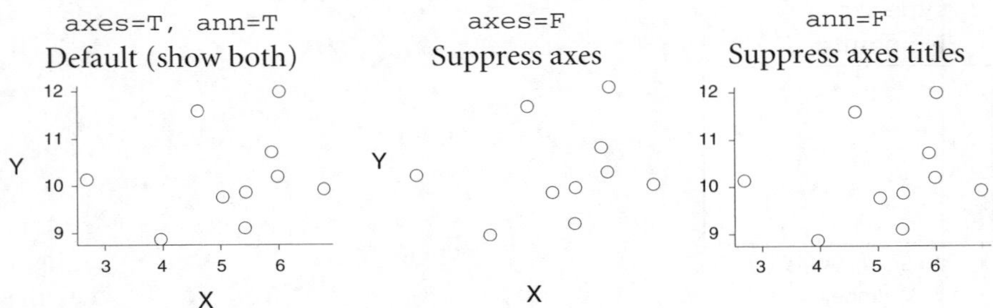

5.1.5 The `log` *parameter*

The `log` *parameter* indicates whether or which axes should be plotted on a logarithmic scale.

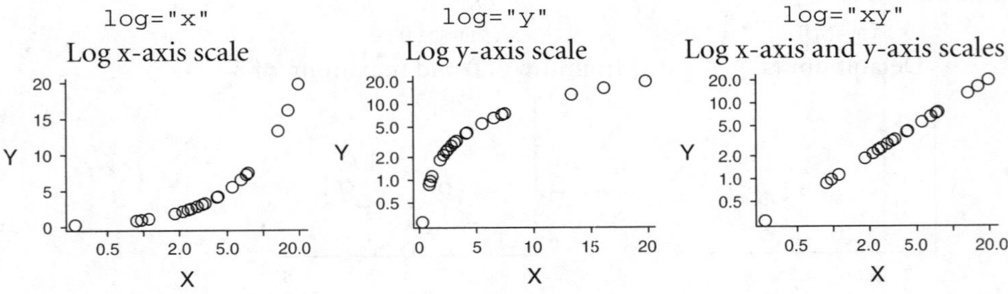

5.2 Graphical Parameters

The graphical parameters provide consistent control over most of the plotting features across a wide range of high and low plotting functions. Any of these parameters can be set by passing them as arguments to the `par()` *function*. Once set via the `par()` *function*, they become global graphical parameters that apply to all subsequent functions that act on the current graphics device.

All of the graphical parameters have default values that are applied when a new graphical device is instantiated. When the `par()` *function* is used to alter a parameter setting, it returns a list containing the previous values of any altered parameters. Applying this list as an argument to the `par()` *function* thereby restores the previous graphical parameters.

```
> opar <- par(mar=c(4,5,1,1)
> # the plot margins of the current or new device are set
> # to be four, five, one and one text lines from the bottom,
> # left, top and right of the figure boundary
> opar

$mar
[1] 5.1 4.1 4.1 2.1

> par(opar)
> # restore plotting margins to be 5.1, 4.1, 4.1 and 2.1 text
> # lines thick.
```

Similarly, calling the `par()` *function* without any arguments returns a list containing ALL the current parameter values (altered or not) in alphabetical order. Whilst it might be tempting to use this list to apply settings to other graphical devices (or even the currently active device at a later date), since the settings will be restored alphabetically, parameters further along the alphabet will overwrite or nullify alternative parameters. For example, both `mai` and `mar` provide alternative ways of altering the plot margin dimensions, however the latter will have the final say. A safer practice for storing current settings for reuse is to call the `par()` *function* with the altered parameters twice. The first time will store the previous settings and the second will store the current altered settings.

```
> # on a new or restored device
> opar <- par(mar=c(4,5,1,1)
> npar <- par(mar=c(4,5,1,1)
> npar

$mar
[1] 4 5 1 1

> par(npar)
```

5.2.1 Plot dimensional and layout parameters

The graphical parameters responsible for controlling the dimensions and layout of graphics can only be set via the `par()` *function* and are itemized in Table 5.1 and represented in Figure 5.1.

Table 5.1 Dimensional and layout graphical parameters.

Parameter tag	Value	Description
`din, fin, pin`	`=c(width,height)`	Dimensions (width and height) of the device, figure and plotting regions (in inches)
`fig`	`=c(left,right,bottom,top)`	Coordinates of the figure region within the device. Coordinates expressed as a fraction of the device region.
`mai, mar`	`=c(bottom,left,top,right)`	Size of each of the four figure margins in inches and lines of text (relative to current font size).
`mfg`	`=c(row,column)`	Position of the currently active figure within a grid of figures defined by either `mfcol` or `mfrow`.
`mfcol, mfrow`	`=c(rows,columns)`	Number of rows and columns in a multi-figure grid.
`new`	`=TRUE` or `=FALSE`	Indicates whether to treat the current figure region as a new frame (and thus begin a new plot over the top of the previous plot (`TRUE`) or to allow a new high level plotting function to clear the figure region first (`FALSE`).
`oma, omd, omi`	`=c(bottom,left,top,right)`	Size of each of the four outer margins in lines of text (relative to current font size), inches and as a fraction of the device region dimensions
`plt`	`=c(left,right,bottom,top)`	Coordinates of the plotting region expressed as a fraction of the device region.
`pty`	`="s"` or `="m"`	Type of plotting region within the figure region. Is the plotting region a square (`="s"`) or is it maximized to fit within the shape of the figure region.
`usr`	`=c(left,right,bottom,top)`	Coordinates of the plotting region corresponding to the axes limits of the plot.

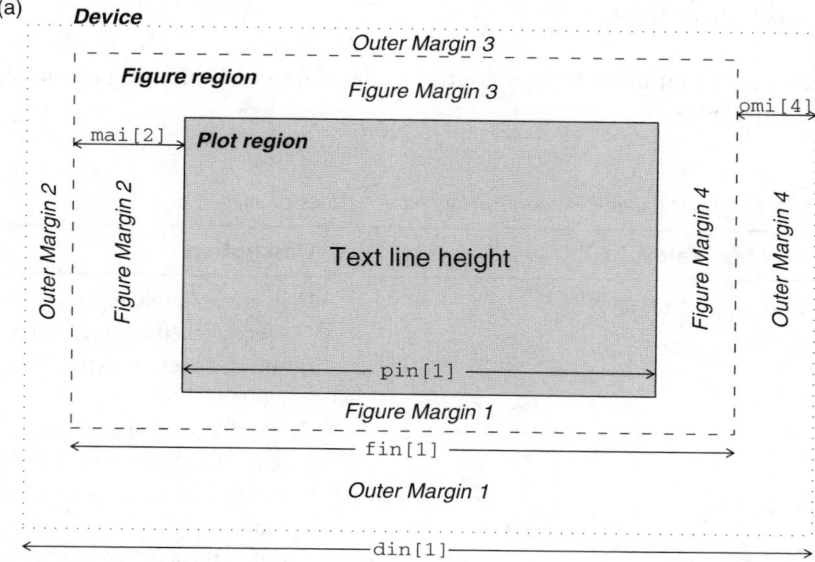

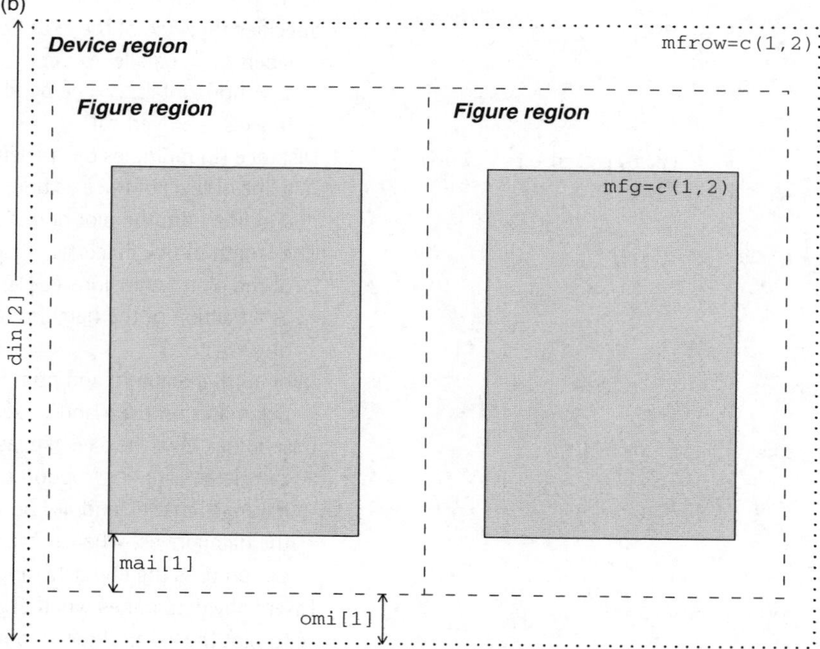

Fig 5.1 Device, figure and plotting regions along with examples of the graphical parameters that control each of the respective dimensions for (a) single figure and (b) multifigure graphics.

5.2.2 Axis characteristics

The parameters that provide finer control of the scale and formatting of the plot axes are listed in Table 5.2.

Table 5.2 Graphical parameters controlling characteristics of axes.

Parameter tag	Value	Description
`ann, axes`	`=T` or `=F`	High level plotting parameters that specify whether or not titles (main, sub and axes) and axes should be plotted.
`bty`	`="o","l","7","c","u" or "]"`	Single character whose upper case letter resembles the sides of the box or axes to be included with the plot.
`lab`	`=c(x,y,length)`	Specifies the length and number of tickmarks on the x and y axes.
`las`	`=0, 1, 2 or 3`	Specifies the style of the axes tick labels. `0` = parallel to axes, `1` = horizontal, `2` = perpendicular to axes, `3` = vertical
`mgp`	`=c(title,labels,line)`	Distance (in multiples of the height of a line of text) of the axis title, labels and line from the plot boundary.
`tck, tcl`	`=length`	The length of tick marks as a fraction of the plot dimensions (`tck`) and as a fraction of the height of a line of text (`tcl`)
`xaxp, yaxp`	`=c(min,max,num)`	Minimum, maximum and number of tick marks on the x and y axes
`xaxs, yaxs`	`="r"` or `="i"`	Determines how the axes ranges are calculated. The `"r"` option results in ranges that extend 4% beyond the data ranges, whereas the `"i"` option uses the raw data ranges.
`xaxt, yaxt`	`="y"`, `="n"` or `="s"`	Essentially determines whether or not to plot the axes. The `"s"` option is for compatibility with S.
`xlog, ylog`	`=FALSE` or `=TRUE`	Specifies whether or not the x and y axes should be plotted on a (natural) logarithmic scale.
`xpd`	`=FALSE`, `=TRUE` or `='NA'`	Specifies whether plotting is clipped to the plotting (`=FALSE`), figure (`=TRUE`) or device (`='NA'`) region

Table 5.3 Character expansion parameters.

Parameter	Applies to
`cex`	All subsequent characters
`cex.axis`	Axes tick labels
`cex.lab`	Axes titles
`cex.main`	Main plot title
`cex.sub`	Plot sub-titles

5.2.3 Character sizes

The base or default character size of text and symbols on a graphic is defined when the graphics device is initiated. Thereafter, the sizes of characters (including symbols) can be controlled by the character expansion (`cex`) *parameter*. The (`cex`) *parameter* determines the amount by which characters should be magnified relative to the base character size and can be set as an argument to the `par()` *function* as well as to individual high and low level plotting functions. In addition to the overall character expansion parameter, there are also separate character expansion parameters that control the sizes of text within each of the major components of a figure (see Table 5.3) relative to `cex`.

```
> set.seed(12)
> plot(rnorm(5,0,1), rnorm(5,0,1),
    xlab="Predictor",
    ylab="Response", cex=2,
    cex.lab=3, cex.axis=1.5,
    bty="l")
```

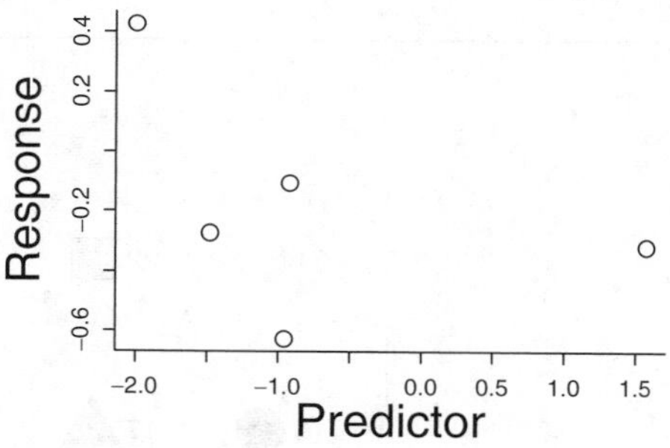

5.2.4 Line characteristics

Many of the characteristics of lines are controlled by arguments to the `par()` *function* or to high and low level plotting functions (see Table 5.4).

5.2.5 Plotting character *parameter* - `pch`

The plotting character (`pch`) *parameter* can be set with the `par()` *function*, and can also be set as arguments within individual high and low level plotting functions.

```
> set.seed(12)
> # plot points as solid circles
> plot(rnorm(5,0,1), rnorm(5,0,1), pch=16, axes=F,
    ann=F, cex=4)
```

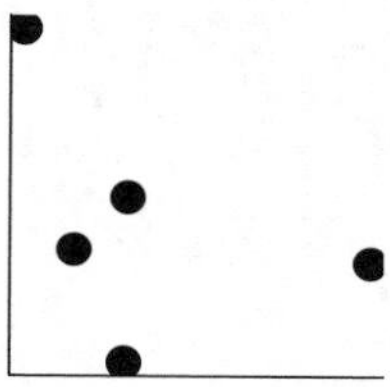

Table 5.4 Line characteristics.

Parameter	Description	Examples
lty	The type of line. Specified as either a single integer in the range of 1 to 6 (for predefined line types) or as a string of 2 or 4 numbers that define the relative lengths of dashes and spaces within a repeated sequence.	lty=1 lty=2 lty=3 lty=4 lty=5 lty=6 lty=7 lwd='1234' lwd='9111'
lwd	The thickness of a line as a multiple of the default thickness (which is device specific)	lwd=0.5 lwd=0.75 lwd=1 lwd=2 lwd=4
lend	The line end style (square, butt or round)	lend=2 lend=1 lend=0
ljoin	The style of the join between lines	ljoin=0 ljoin=1 ljoin=2

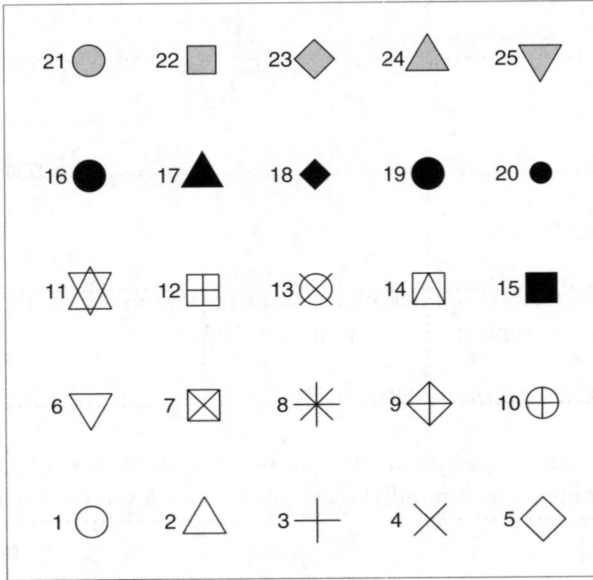

Fig 5.2 Basic pch plotting symbols.

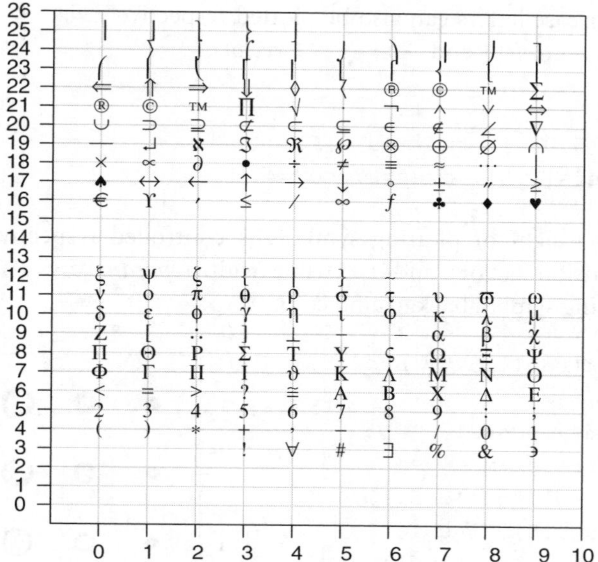

Fig 5.3 Extended `pch` plotting symbols for the symbol font (`font=5`). The plotting character number is determined from the grid by adding the x coordinate to 10 times the y coordinate. Hence, symbol ♣ is character number 167.

There are 25 basic plotting symbols (see Figure 5.2) that can be used to define the point character (`pch`) within many high and low level plotting functions. The numbers to the left of the symbols in the figure indicate the integer value used as the argument.

In addition to these standard plotting characters, when used in conjunction with a *symbol* font face, the `pch` *parameter* can accept any integer between 1:128 and 160:254 to yield an extended point character set (see Figure 5.3).

```
> set.seed(12)
> plot(rnorm(5,0,1), rnorm(5,0,1), pch=167, cex=4,
    font=5)
```

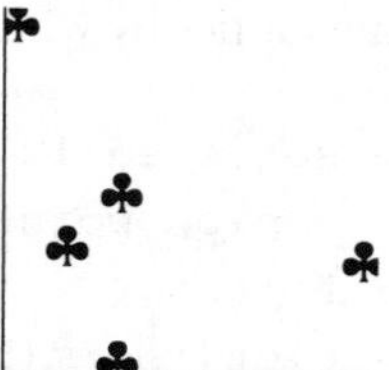

The `pch` *parameter* can also accept any other keyboard printing character (letter, number, punctuation etc) as an argument.

```
> set.seed(12)
> plot(rnorm(5,0,1), rnorm(5,0,1), pch="A",
    axes=F, cex=4)
```

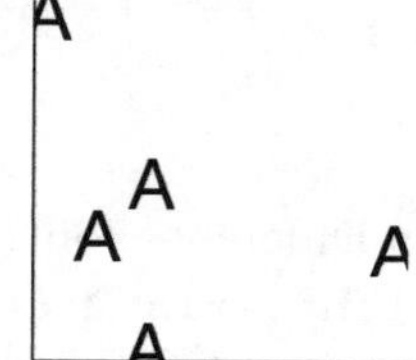

Upper and lower case letters can also be plotted respectively via the predefined `Letters[]` and `letters[]` *vectors.*

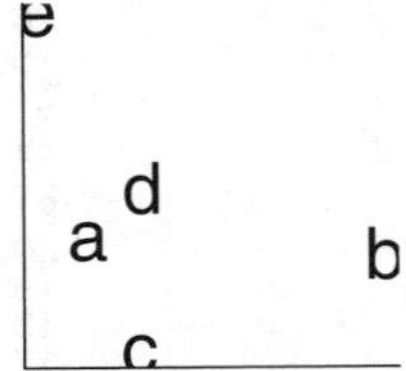


```
> set.seed(12)
> plot(rnorm(5,0,1), rnorm(5,0,1),
    pch=letters[1:5], axes=F, cex=4)
```

The size and weight of plotting symbols is controlled respectively by the `cex` (character expansion factor) and `lwd` (line width) *parameters.* The `bg` *parameter* defines the plotting symbol background color.

```
> m <- matrix(rep(1:5,5),nrow=5,
    byrow=F)
> plot(m, t(m), pch=21,
    bg="grey", cex=m,
    lwd=t(m), xlim=c(.5,5.5),
    ylim=c(.5,5.5), las=1,
    xlab="cex", ylab="lwd")
```

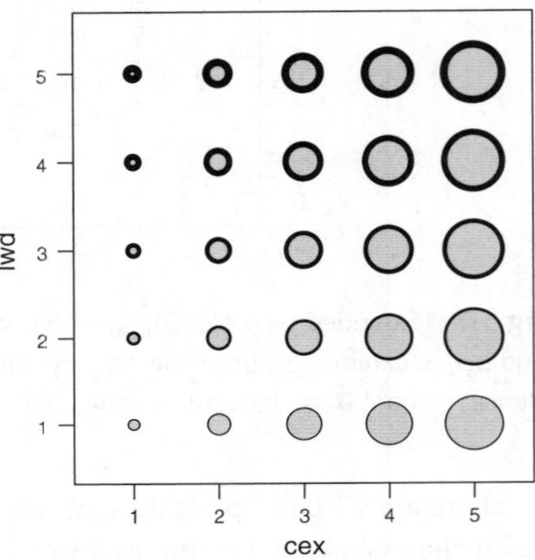

5.2.6 Fonts

The shape of text characters is controlled by the *family* (the overall visual appearance of a group of fonts - otherwise known as the typeface) and the *font* (plain, bold, italics, etc), see Figure 5.4. The font families supported varies for each graphical device as do the names by which they are referred (see Table 5.5).

```
> set.seed(12)
> # plot points with a italic serif
> # font
> plot(rnorm(5,0,1), rnorm(5,0,1),
    pch="A", family="serif", font=4,
    xlab="Predictor", ylab="Response")
```

Different fonts can also be applied to each of the main plotting components (`font.axis`: axes labels, `font.lab`: axes titles, `font.main`: Main plot title and `font.sub`: plot sub-title).

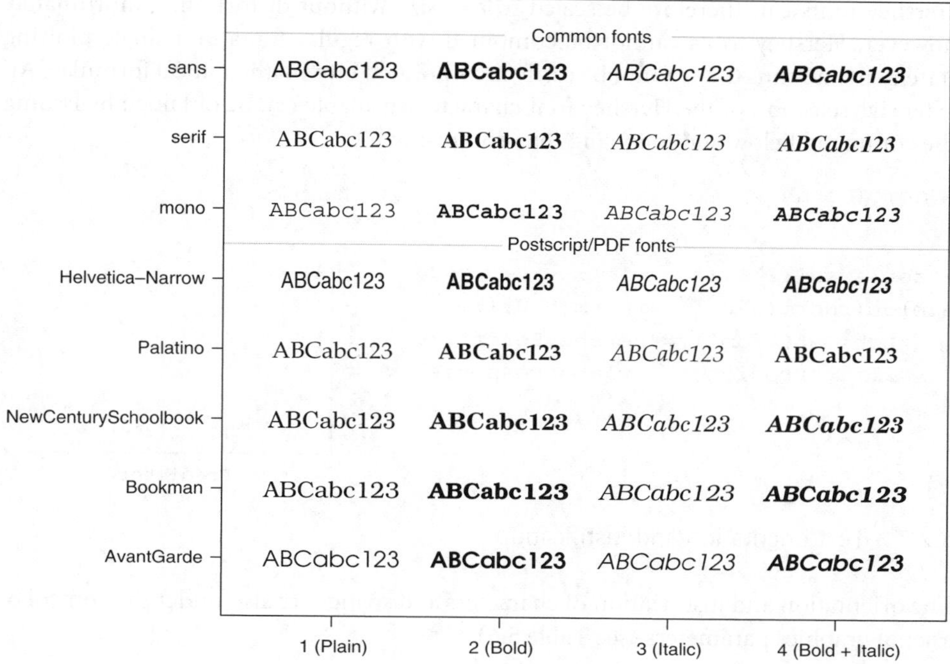

Fig 5.4 Appearance of major family (y-axis) and font (x-axis) sequences.

Table 5.5 Family names appropriate for the most common devices.

Device	Serif	Sans serif	Monospaced
Display devices			
`X11()` (Unix/Linux)	`"serif"`	`"sans"`	`"mono"`
`quartz()` (Mac OS X)	`"serif"`	`"sans"`	`"mono"`
`window()` (Windows)	`"serif"`	`"sans"`	`"mono"`
File devices			
postscript	`"Times"`	`"Helvetica"`	`"Courier"`
pdf	`"Times"`	`"Helvetica"`	`"Courier"`

Hershey fonts

R also supports Hershey (vector) fonts that greatly extend the range of characters and symbols available. In contrast to regular (bitmap) fonts that consist of a set of small images (one for each character of each style and size), vector fonts consist of the coordinates of each of the curves required to create the character. That is, vector fonts store the information on how to draw the character rather than store the character itself.

Hershey fonts can therefore be scaled to any size without distortion. Unfortunately however, Hershey fonts cannot be combined with regular fonts in a single plotting statement and thus they cannot be easily incorporated into mathematical formulae. An extensive selection of the Hershey font characters available can be obtained by issuing the command below and following the prompts:

```
> demo(Hershey)
```

```
> set.seed(12)
> plot(rnorm(5,0,1), rnorm(5,0,1),
   pch="A", family="HersheySerif",
   xlab="Predictor", ylab="Response")
```

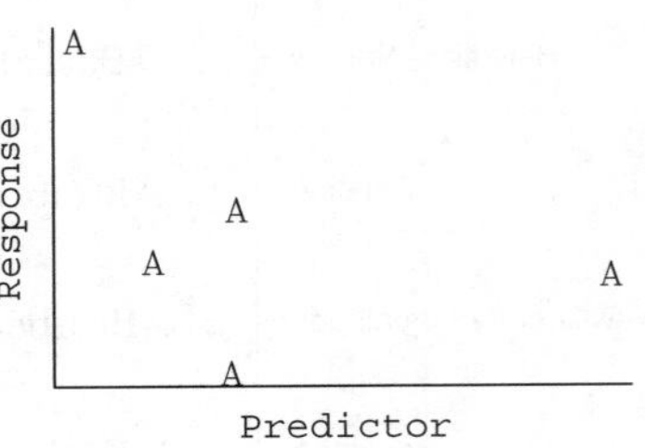

5.2.7 Text orientation and justification

The orientation and justification of characters and strings are also under the control of a set of graphics parameters (see Table 5.6).

5.2.8 Colors

The color of all plotting elements is controlled by a set of parameters. The default color for plotting elements is specified using the `col` *parameter*. There are also separate parameters that control the color of each of the major components of a figure (`col.axis`: the axes tick labels, `col.lab`: the axes titles, `col.main`: the main plot title, `col.sub`: plot sub-titles) and when specified, take precedence over the `col` *parameter*. Two additional parameters, `bg` and `fg` can be used to control the color

Table 5.6 Text orientation and justification characteristics.

Parameter	Description	Examples		
`adj`	Specifies the justification of a text string relative to the coordinates of its origin. A single number between `0` and `1` specifies horizontal justification. A vector of two numbers (`=c(x,y)`) indicates justification in horizontal and vertical directions.	`adj=0` Text `=c(0,1)` Text	`adj=0.5` Text `=c(1,0)` Text	`adj=1` Text `=c(1,-1)` Text
`crt, srt`	Specifies the amount of rotation (in degrees) of single characters (`crt`) and strings (`srt`)	`srt=90` Text	`srt=45` Text	`srt=-45` Text

of the background and foreground (of boxes, symbols and axes) respectively. The color of other elements (such as the axes themselves) is manipulated by using the `col` *parameter* within low-level plotting functions.

```
> set.seed(12)
> plot(rnorm(5,0,1),
    rnorm(5,0,1),
    xlab="Predictor",
    ylab="Response", col=8,
    col.lab="grey50",
    col.axis="grey90", bty="l")
```

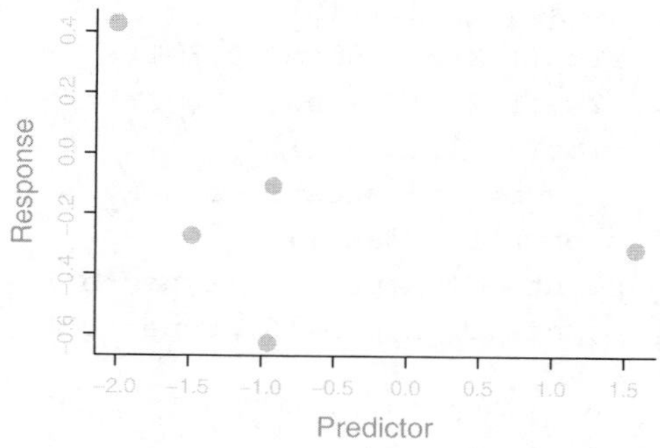

There are numerous ways that colors can be specified:

- by an index (numbers 0-8) to a small palette of eight colors (0 indicates the background color). The colors in this palette can be reviewed with the `palette()` *function*.
- by name. The names of the 657 defined colors can be reviewed with the `colors()` *function*. The `epitools` *package* provides the `colors.plot()` *function* which generates a graphic that displays a matrix of all the colors. When used with the `locator=TRUE` *argument*, a series of left mouse clicks on the color squares, terminated by a right mouse click, will result in a matrix of corresponding color names.
- extract an arbitrary number (`n`) of contiguous colors from built-in color palettes
  - `rainbow(n)` - Red→Violet
  - `heat.colors(n)` - White→Orange→Red
  - `terrain.colors(n)` - White→Brown→Green
  - `topo.colors(n)` - White→Brown→Green→Blue
  - `grey(n)` - White→Black
- by direct specification of the red, green and blue components of the RGB spectrum as a character string in the form `"#RRGGBB"`. This string consists of a `#` followed by a pair of hexadecimal digits in the range `00:FF` for each component.

5.3 Enhancing and customizing plots with low-level plotting functions

In addition to their specific parameters, each of the following functions (e.g. points, text) accept many of the graphical parameters described above. In the function definitions, these capabilities are represented by three consecutive dots (`...`). Technically, `...` indicates that any supplied arguments that are not explicitly part of the definition of a function are passed on to the relevant underlying functions (in this case, `par`).

5.3.1 Adding points - `points()`

Points can be added to a plot using the `points(x, y, pch, ...)` *function*. This function plots a plotting character (specified by the `pch` *parameter*) at the coordinates specified by the vectors x,y. Alternatively, the coordinates can be passed as a formula of the form, y~x.

```
> set.seed(1)
> X<-seq(9,12,l=10)
> Y1<-(1*X+2)+rnorm(10,3,1)
> Y2<-(1.2*X+2)+rnorm(10,3,1)
> plot(c(Y1,Y2)~c(X,X),
   type="n", axes=T, ann=F,
   bty="l", las=1)
> points(Y1~X,pch=21, type="b")
> points(Y2~X,pch=16, type="b")
```


5.3.2 Adding text within a plot - text()

The text() *function* adds text strings (labels *parameter*) to the plot at the supplied coordinates (x,y) and is defined as:

```
> text (x, y = NULL, labels = seq_along(x), adj = NULL,
  pos = NULL, offset = 0.5, vfont = NULL, cex = 1, col = NULL,
  font = NULL, ...)
```

Descriptions and examples of the arguments not previously outlined in the graphical parameters section, are outlined in Table 5.7.

paste()

The paste() *function* concatenates vectors together after converting each of the elements to characters. This is particularly useful for making labels and is equally

Table 5.7 text() arguments.

Parameter	Description	Examples
pos	Simplified text justification that overrides the adj *parameter*. 1=below, 2=left, 3=above and 4=right.	pos=1 Text; pos=2 Text; pos=3 Text; pos=4 Text
offset	Offset used by pos as a fraction of the width of a character.	pos=1,offset=1 Text; pos=1,offset=2 Text
vfont	Provision for Hershey (vector) font specification (vfont=c(typeface, style).	lab='ABCabc123' vfont=c('serif','plain') ABCabc123 lab=c('\VE','\MA','\#H0844') vfont=c('serif','plain') ♀ ♂ ☆

useful in non-graphical applications. Paste has two other optional *parameters* (sep and collapse) which define extra character strings to be placed between strings joined. sep operates on joins between paired vector elements whereas collapse operates on joints of elements within a vector respectively.

```
> cc <- c("H","M","L")
> cc
[1] "H" "M" "L"
> paste(cc,1:3, sep=":")
[1] "H:1" "M:2" "L:3"
> paste(cc, collapse=":")
[1] "H:M:L"
> paste(cc, 1:3,sep="-",collapse=":")
[1] "H-1:M-2:L-3"
```

```
> set.seed(10)
> X<-rnorm(5,10,1)
> Y<-rnorm(5,10,1)
> plot(X,Y, type="n",axes=T,
    ann=F, bty="l", las=1,
    xlim=c(8,11), ylim=c(8,11))
> points(X,Y,col="grey", pch=16)
> text(X,Y,paste("Site",1:5,
    sep="-"), cex=2, pos=4)
```


Non-character arguments

Most other objects[b] passed as a label object are evaluated before being coerced into a string for plotting. In so doing, the output of other functions can be plotted.

```
> plot(c(0,1),c(0,1),type="n",
    axes=T, ann=F, bty="l", las=1)
> text(.5,.75, 5*2+3, cex=2)
> text(.5,.5, mean(c(2,3,4,5)),
    cex=2)
> text(.5,.25, paste("mean=",
    mean(c(2,3,4,5))), cex=2)
```


5.3.3 Adding text to plot margins - mtext()

The mtext() *function* adds text (text) to the plot margins and is typically used to create fancy or additional axes titles. The mtext() *function* is defined as:

```
> mtext(text, side = 3, line = 0, outer = FALSE, at = NA,
  adj = NA, padj = NA, cex = NA, col = NA, font = NA, ...)
```

[b] *Language objects* are treated differently (see section 5.3.5).

Table 5.8 `mtext()` arguments.

Parameter	Description	Examples
`side`	Specifies which margin the title should be plotted in. `1`=bottom, `2`=left, `3`=top and `4`=right.	Response; text='Response',side=2; text='Predictor',side=1; Predictor
`line`	Number of text lines out from the plot region into the margin to plot the marginal text	line=1; Predictor; line=2; Predictor
`outer`	For multi-plot figure, if `outer=TRUE`, put the marginal text in the outer margin (if there is one).	
`at`	Position along the axis (in user coordinates) of the text	at=2; at=8; 0 2 4 6 8 10; Predictor; Predictor
`adj`, `padj`	Adjustment (justification) of the position of the marginal text parallel (`adj`) and perpendicular (`padj`) to the axis. Justification depends on the orientation of the text string and the margin (axis).	adj=0, padj=1; padj=1; adj=1; 0 2 4 6 8 10; Predictor; Predictor; Predictor; A; adj=1; C; adj=0,padj=1; B; padj=1; ACB; (A) las=1,adj=1; (B) las=1,adj=0, padj=1; (C) las=1,padj=1

Descriptions and examples of the arguments not previously outlined in the graphical parameters section, are outlined in Table 5.8.

5.3.4 Adding a legend - `legend()`

The `legend()` *function* brings together a rich collection of plotting functions to produce highly customizable figure legends in a single call. A sense of the rich functionality of the `legend` *function* is reflected in Table 5.9 and the function definition:

```
> legend(x, y = NULL, legend, fill = NULL, col = par("col"),
   lty, lwd, pch, angle = 45, density = NULL, bty = "o",
   bg = par("bg"), box.lwd = par("lwd"), box.lty = par("lty"),
   pt.bg = NA, cex = 1, pt.cex = cex, pt.lwd = lwd,
   xjust = 0, yjust = 1, x.intersp = 1, y.intersp = 1,
   adj = c(0, 0.5), text.width = NULL, text.col = par("col"),
   merge = do.lines && has.pch, trace = FALSE,
   plot = TRUE, ncol = 1, horiz = FALSE, title = NULL,
   inset = 0)
```

Table 5.9 `legend()` arguments. To save space, some parameter descriptions are combined, others are omitted.

Parameter	Description	Examples
`legend`	A vector of strings or expressions to comprise the labels of the legend.	
`title`	A string or expression for a title at the top of the legend	`title='Temperature'` (Temperature / High / Medium / Low)
`bty`, `box.lty`, `box.lwd`	The type (`"o"` or `"n"`), line thickness and line style of box framing the legend.	`box.lwd=1.5, box.lty=2` (High / Medium / Low)
`bg`, `text.col`	The colors used for the legend background and legend labels	`bg='grey', text.col=c('white','grey40','black')` (High / Medium / Low)
`horiz`	Whether or not to produce a horizontal legend instead of a vertical legend	`horiz=TRUE` (High Medium Low)
`ncol`	The number of columns in which to arrange the legend labels	`ncol=2` (High Low / Medium)
`cex`	Character expansion for all elements of the legend relative to the plot `cex` graphical parameter.	
Boxes	If any of the following parameters are set, the legend labels will be accompanied by boxes.	
`fill`	Specifies the fill color of the boxes. A vector of colors will result in different fills.	`fill=c('white','grey','black')` (High / Medium / Low)
`angle`, `density`	Specifies the angle and number of lines that make up the stripy fill of boxes. Negative density values result in solid fills.	`fill=c('white','grey','black')` (High / Medium / Low)
Points		
`pch`	Specifies the type of plotting character.	`col=c('white','grey','black')` (High / Medium / Low)
`pt.cex`, `pt.lwd`	Specifies the character expansion and line width of the plotting characters.	`pch=21,pt.cex=1:3, pt.lwd=2` (High / Medium / Low)
`col`, `pt.bg`	Specifies the foreground and background color of the plotting characters (and lines for `col`).	`pch=16, pt.bg=c('grey80','grey','black'), col=1` (High / Medium / Low)

(continued overleaf)

Table 5.9 *(continued)*

Parameter	Description	Examples	
Lines	If any of the following parameters are set, the legend labels will be accompanied by lines.		
`lwd, lty`	Specifies the width and type of lines.	`lwd=c(1.5), lty=c(1,2,3)`	High / Medium / Low
`merge`	Whether or not to merge points and lines.	`lwd=c(1.5), lty=c(1,2,3)`	High / Medium / Low

In addition to the usual methods for specifying the positioning coordinates, convenient keywords reflecting the four corners (`"bottomleft"`, `"bottomright"`, `"topleft"`, `"topright"`) and boundaries (`"bottom"`, `"left"`, `"top"`, `"right"`) of the plotting region can alternatively be specified.

5.3.5 More advanced text formatting

The text plotting functions described above (`text()`, `mtext()` and `legend()`) can also build plotting text from objects that constitute the R language itself. These are referred to as *language objects* and include:

- **names** - the names of objects
- **expressions** - unevaluated syntactically correct statements that could otherwise be evaluated at the command prompt
- **calls** - these are specific expressions that comprise of an unevaluated named function (complete with arguments)

Any *language object* passed as an argument to one of the text plotting functions described above (`text()`, `mtext()` and `legend()`) will be coerced into an expression and evaluated as a mathematical expression prior to plotting. In so doing, the text plotting functions will also apply TEX-like formatting (the extensive range of which can be sampled by issuing the `demo(plotmath)` command) where appropriate. Hence, advanced text construction, formatting and plotting is thus achieved by skilled use of a variety of functions (described below) that assist in the creation of *language objects* for passing to the text plotting functions.

`expression()`

The `expression` *function* is used to build complex expressions that incorporate TEX-like mathematical formatting. Hence, the `expression` *function* is typically nested within one of the text plotting functions to plot complex combinations of characters and symbols.

The `expression()` *function* is useful for generating axes titles with complex units.

```
> set.seed(10)
> X<-rnorm(5,10,1)
> Y<-rnorm(5,10,1)
> plot(X,Y, type="p", axes=T,
    ann=F, bty="l", las=1)
> mtext(expression(Temperature~
    (degree*C)), side=1, line=3,
    cex=1.5)
> mtext(expression(Respiration~
    (mL~O[2]~h^-1)), side=2,
    line=3.5, cex=1.5)
```

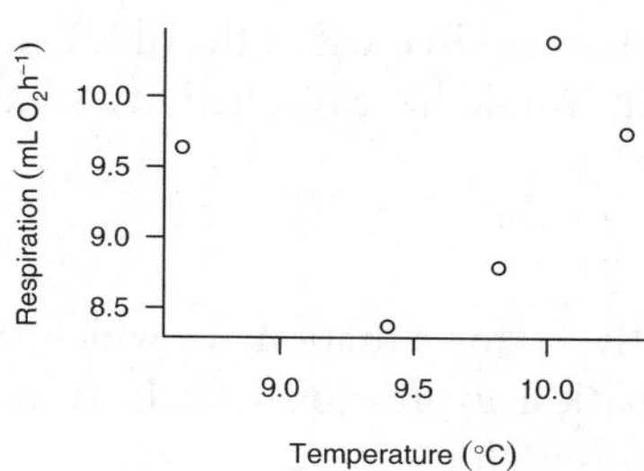

The `expression()` *function* is also useful for plotting complex mathematical formula within the plots.

```
> set.seed(10)
> X<-rnorm(5,10,1)
> Y<-rnorm(5,10,1)
> plot(X,Y,type="p",axes=T, ann=F,
    bty="l", las=1)
> text(9.3,10, expression(f(y) ==
    frac(1,sqrt(2*pi*sigma^2))*
    e^frac(-(y-mu)^2, 2*sigma^2)),
    cex=1.25)
```

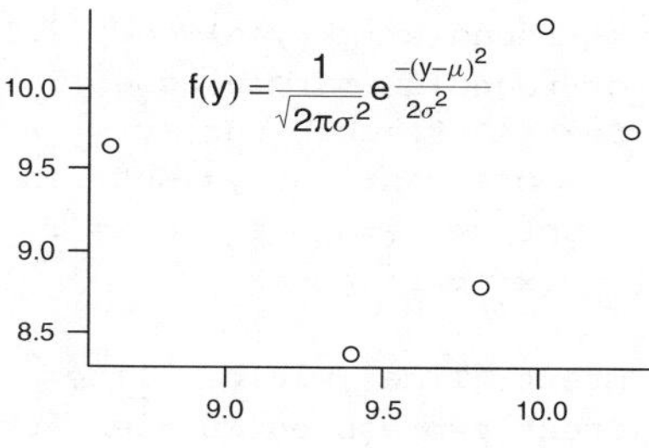

bquote()

The `bquote()` *function* generates a *language object* by converting the argument after first evaluating any objects wrapped in '`.()`'. This provides a way to produce text strings that combine mathematical formatting and the output statistical functions.

```
> set.seed(3)
> X<-rnorm(20,0,1)
> Y<-rnorm(20,0,1)
> # calculate correlation
> # between X and Y
> cc<-cor(X,Y)
> plot(X,Y,type="n",axes=T,
    ann=F, bty="l", las=1)
> points(X,Y,col="grey", pch=16)
> text(0,0,bquote(corr.~coef.==.
    (round(cc,2))), cex=4)
> text(0,0,names(cc))
```

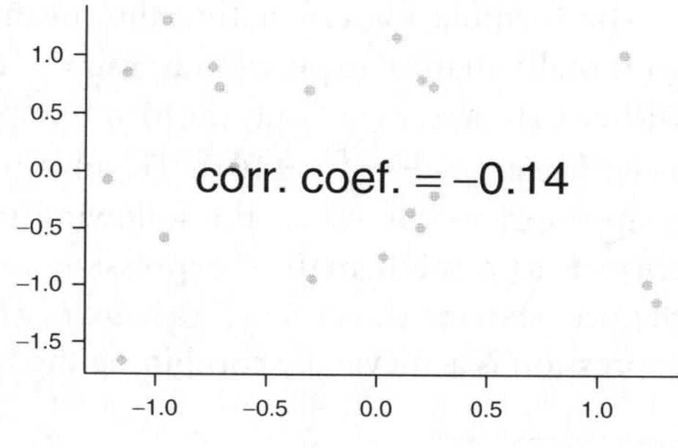

Note the required use of the tilde (~) character to allow spaces[c]. A space character at that point would have resulted in a syntactically incorrect mathematical expression.

substitute()

Alternatively, for situations in which substitutions are required within non-genuine mathematical expressions (such as straight character strings), the `substitute()` function is useful.

```
> X<-c(2,4,6,10,14,18,24,30,36,42)
> Y<-c(5,8,10,11,15,18,16,15,19,16)
> n<-nls(Y~SSasymp(X,a,b,c))
> plot(Y~X, type='p', ann=F)
> lines(1:40, predict(n,
    data.frame(X=1:40)))
> a<-round(summary(n)$coef[1,1],2)
> b<-round(summary(n)$coef[2,1],2)
> c<-round(summary(n)$coef[3,1],2)
> text(40,8,substitute(y == a
    - b*e^c*x,list(y="Nutrient
    uptake",a=a,b=b,c=c,x="Time")),
    cex=1.25, pos=2)
```



```
> mtext("Time (min)",1,line=3)
> mtext(expression(Nutrient~uptake~(mu~mol~g^-1)),
  2, line=3)
```

Combinations of advanced text formatting functions

It is possible to produce virtually any text representation on an R plot, however, some representations require complex combinations of the above functions. Whilst, these functions are able to be nested within one another, the combinations often appear to behave counter-intuitively. Great understanding and consideration of the exact nuances of each of the functions is required in order to successfully master their combined effects. Nevertheless, the following scenarios should provide some appreciation of the value and uses of some of these combinations.

The formula for calculating the mean of a sample ($\mu = \frac{\sum y_i}{n}$) as represented by an R mathematical expression is: `mu == frac(sum(y[i]),n)`. What if however, we wished to represent not only the formula applied to the data, but the result of the formula as well (e.g. ($\mu = \frac{\sum y_i}{n} = 10$))? To substitute the actual result, the `bquote()` function is appropriate. However, the following mathematical expression is not syntactically correct, as a mathematical expression cannot have two relational operators (=) in the one statement. `mu == frac(sum(y[i]),n) == .(meanY)`. Building such an expression is achieved by combining the `bquote()` *function* with a `paste()` *function.*

---

[c] Alternatively, space can be provided by the keyword `phantom(char)`, where `char` is a character whose width is equal to the amount of space required.

```
> set.seed(1)
> Y<-rnorm(100,0,1)
> plot(density(Y),type="l", axes=T,
    ann=F, bty="l", las=1,
    col="grey")
> text(10,0.2,bquote(paste(mu ==
    frac(sum(y[i]),n)) ==
    .(mean(Y))), cex=2)
```

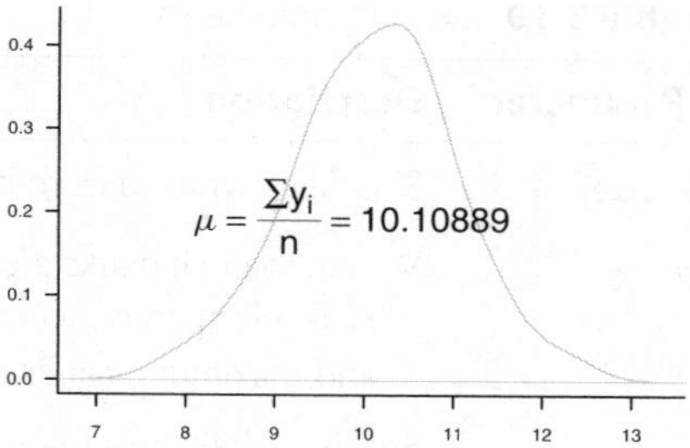

The more observant and discerning reader may have noticed the y-axis label in the `substitute()` example above had a space between the μ and the word 'mol'. Using just the `expression()` *function*, this was unavoidable. A more eligant solution would have been to employ a `expression(paste())` combination.

```
> X<-c(2,4,6,10,14,18,24,30,36,42)
> Y<-c(5,8,10,11,15,18,16,15,19,16)
> n<-nls(Y~SSasymp(X,a,b,c))
> plot(Y~X, type='p', ann=F)
> ...
> mtext(expression(paste("Nutrient
   uptake", " (", mu, "mol.",
   g^-1, ")", sep="")), 2, line=3)
```

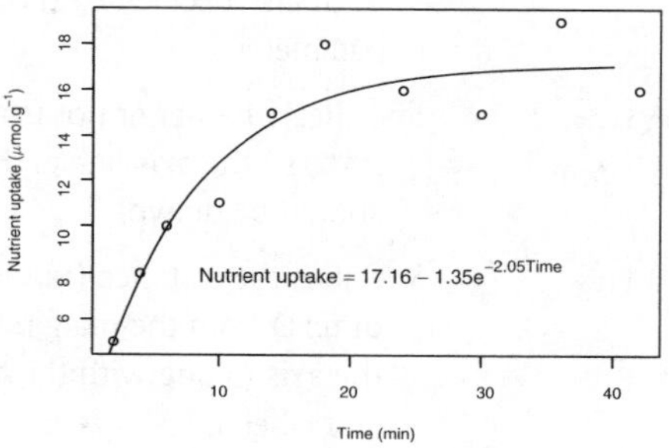

5.3.6 Adding axes - `axis()`

Although most of the high-level plotting functions provide some control over axes construction (typically via graphical parameters), finer control over the individual axes is achieved by constructing each axis separately with the `axis()` *function* (see Table 5.10). The `axis()` *function* is defined as:

```
> axis(side, at = NULL, labels = TRUE, tick = TRUE, line = NA,
   pos = NA, outer = FALSE, font = NA, lty = "solid", lwd = 1,
   col = NULL, hadj = NA, padj = NA, ...)
```

```
> set.seed(1)
> X<-rnorm(200,10,1)
> m<-mean(X)
> s<-sd(X)
> plot(density(X), type="l",
   axes=F, ann=F)
> axis(1, at=c(0, m, m+s, m-s,
   m+2*s, m+2*-s, 100), lab=
   expression(NA, mu, 1*sigma,
   -1*sigma, 2*sigma, -2*sigma,
   NA), pos=0, cex.axis=2)
```

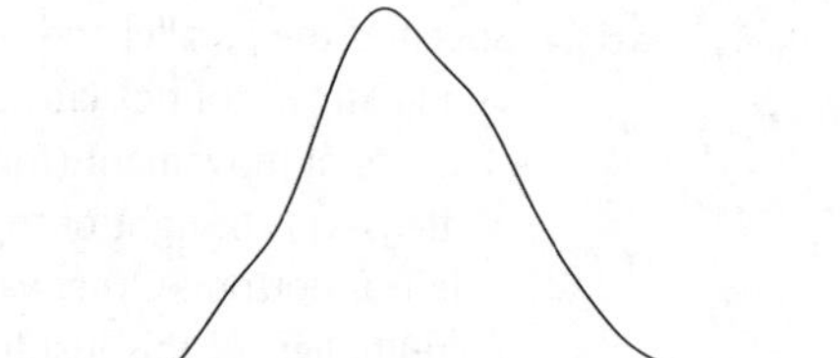

Table 5.10 `axis()` arguments.

Parameter	Description	Examples
`side`	Simplifies which axis to construct. 1=bottom, 2=left, 3=top and 4=right.	
`at`	Where the tick marks are to be drawn. Axis will span between minimum and maximum values supplied.	`at=c(0,.1,.5,.7)` 0.0 0.1 0.5 0.7
`labels`	Specifies the labels to draw at each tickmark. • `TRUE` or `FALSE` - should labels be drawn • a character or expression vector defining the text appear at each tickmark specified by the `at` parameter.	`at=c(0.25,0.5,0.75), labels=c("Low","Medium","High")` Low Medium High
`tick`	Specifies whether or not (`TRUE` or `FALSE`) the axis line and tickmarks should be drawn.	`tick=F` 0.0 0.2 0.4 0.6 0.8 1.0
`line`	Specifies the distance (number of lines of text) from the margin to place the axis (along with the tickmarks and labels).	`line=-1` 0.0 0.2 0.4 0.6 0.8 1.0
`pos`	Specifies where along the perpendicular axis, the current axis should be drawn.	`pos=0.4` 0.0 0.2 0.4 0.6 0.8 1.0
`outer`	Specifies whether or not (`TRUE` or `FALSE`) the axis should be drawn in the outer margin.	
`font`	The font used for the tickmark labels.	
`lwd, lty, col`	Specifies the line width, style and color of the axis line and tickmarks.	`lwd=2.5, lty=1, col="grey60"` 0.0 0.2 0.4 0.6 0.8 1.0
`hadj, padj`	Specifies the parallel and perpendicular adjustment of tick labels to the axis. Units of movement (for example) are `padj=0`: right or top, `padj=1`: left or bottom. Other values are multipliers of this justification.	`hadj=1, padj=-1` 0.0 0.2 0.4 0.6 0.8 1.0

5.3.7 Adding lines and shapes within a plot

There are a number of low-level plotting functions for plotting lines and shapes. Individually and collectively, they provide the tools to construct any custom graphic.

The following demonstrations will utilize a dataset by Christensen et al. (1996) that consists of course woody debris (CWD) measurements as well as a number of human impact/land use characteristics for riparian zones around freshwater lakes in North America.

```
> christ <- read.table("christ.csv", header=T, sep=",")
```

Straight lines - `abline()`

The low-level plotting `abline()` *function* is used to fit straight lines with a given intercept (`a`) and gradient (`b`) or single values for horizontal (`h`) or vertical (`v`) lines. The function can also be passed a fitted linear model (`reg`) or coefficient vector from which it extracts the intercept and slope parameters. The definition of the `abline()` *function* is:

```
> abline(a = NULL, b = NULL, h = NULL, v = NULL, reg = NULL,
    coef = NULL, untf = FALSE, ...)
```

Assessing departures from linearity and homogeneity of variance can be assisted by fitting a linear (least squares regression) line through the data cloud.

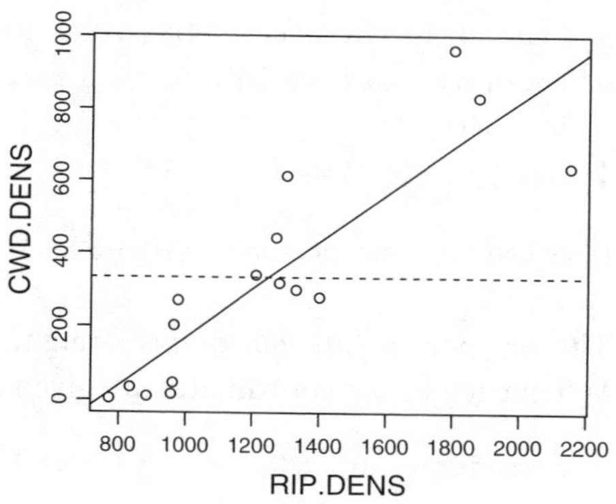


```
> plot(CWD.DENS ~ RIP.DENS,
   data=christ)
> # use abline to add a
> # regression trendline
> abline(lm(CWD.DENS ~ RIP.DENS,
   data=christ))
> # use abline to represent the
> # mean y-value
> abline(h=mean(christ$CWD.DENS),
   lty=2)
```

Lines joining a succession of points - `lines()`

The `lines()` *function* can be used to add lines between points and is particularly useful for adding multiple trends (or non-linear trends, see 'Smoothers') through a data cloud. As with the `points()` *function*, the `lines()` *function* is a generic function whose actions depend on the type of objects passed as arguments. Notably, for simple coordinate vectors, the `points()` and `lines()` *functions* are virtually interchangeable (accept in the type of points they default to). Consequently, a more complex example involving the `predict()` *function* (a function that predicts new values from fitted models) will be used to demonstrate the power of the `lines()` *function*. The model is fitted with the `lm()` *function* (see Chapters 7 and 8).

Assessing departures from linearity and homogeneity of variance can be assisted by fitting a linear (least squares regression) line through the data cloud.

```
> plot(CWD.DENS ~ RIP.DENS,
+  data=christ, type="p")
> # divide the dataset up
> # according to lake size
> area <- cut(christ$AREA,2,
+ lab=c("small", "large"))
> # explore trend for each
> # area separately
> lm.small <- lm(CWD.DENS ~ RIP.DENS, data=christ,
+ subset=area=="small")
> lm.large <- lm(CWD.DENS ~ RIP.DENS, data=christ,
+ subset=area=="large")
> lines(christ$RIP.DENS[area=="small"], predict(lm.small))
> lines(christ$RIP.DENS[area=="large"], predict(lm.large), lty=2)
> legend("bottomright",title="Area",legend=c("small","large"),
+ lty=c(1,2))
```

Lines between pairs of points - `segments()`

The `segments` *function* draws straight lines between points ((`x0`,`y0`) and (`x1`,`y1`)). When each of the coordinates are given as vectors, multiple lines are drawn.

```
> segments(x0, y0, x1, y1, col = par("fg"), lty = par("lty"),
    lwd = par("lwd"), ...)
```

Assessing departures from linearity and homogeneity of variance can also be further assisted by adding lines to represent the residuals (segments that join observed and predicted responses for each predictor). This example also makes use of the `with()` *function* which evaluates any expression or call (in this case the `segments` *function*) in the context of a particular data frame (`christ`) or other environment.

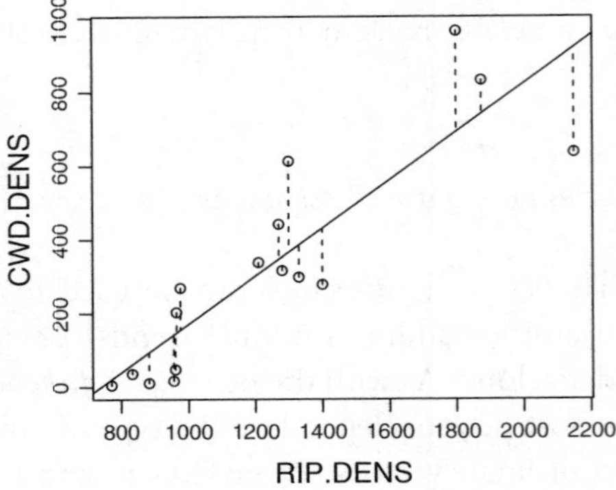


```
> plot(CWD.DENS ~ RIP.DENS,
    data=christ)
```

```
> abline(lm(CWD.DENS ~ RIP.DENS, data=christ))
> # fit the linear model
> christ.lm <- lm(CWD.DENS ~ RIP.DENS, data=christ)
> abline(christ.lm)
> with(christ, segments(RIP.DENS, CWD.DENS, RIP.DENS,
    predict(christ.lm), lty=2))
```

Arrows and connectors - `arrows()`

The `arrows()` *function* builds on the `segments` *function* to add provisions for simple arrow heads. Furthermore, as the length, angle and end to which the arrow head applies are all controllable, the `arrows()` *function* is also particularly useful for annotating figures and creating flow diagrams. The function can also be useful for creating customized error bars (as demonstrated in the following example).

```
> area<-cut(christ$AREA,2,
    lab=c("small","large"))
> library(gmodels)
> s<-tapply(christ$CWD.DENS,
    area,ci)
> plot(christ$CWD.DENS ~ area,
    border="white", ylim=range(s))
> points(1,s$small["Estimate"])
> points(2,s$large["Estimate"])
> with(s, arrows(1,
    small["CI lower"], 1,
    small["CI upper"], length=0.1,
    angle=90, code=3))
> with(s, arrows(2,
    large["CI lower"], 2,
    large["CI upper"], length=0.1,
    angle=90, code=3))
```


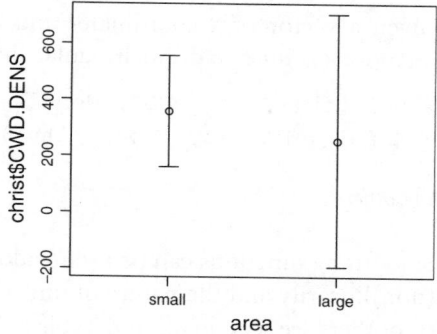

Rectangles - `rect()`

The `rect()` *function* draws rectangles from left-bottom, right-top coordinates that can be filled with solid or striped patterns (according to the line type, width, angle, density and color):

```
> rect(xleft, ybottom, xright, ytop, density = NULL, angle = 45,
    col = NA, border = NULL, lty = par("lty"), lwd = par("lwd"),
    ...)
```

The main use of rectangles is to produce frames for items within plots.

```
> set.seed(1)
> Y<-rnorm(200,10,1)
> plot(density(Y),type="l",axes=T,
    ann=F, bty="l", las=1,
    col="grey")
> rect(7.5,.1,12.5,.3, ang=45,
    density=20, col="grey",
    border="black")
> text(10,0.2,bquote(paste(mu ==
    frac(sum(y[i]),n)) ==
    .(mean(Y))),cex=2)
```

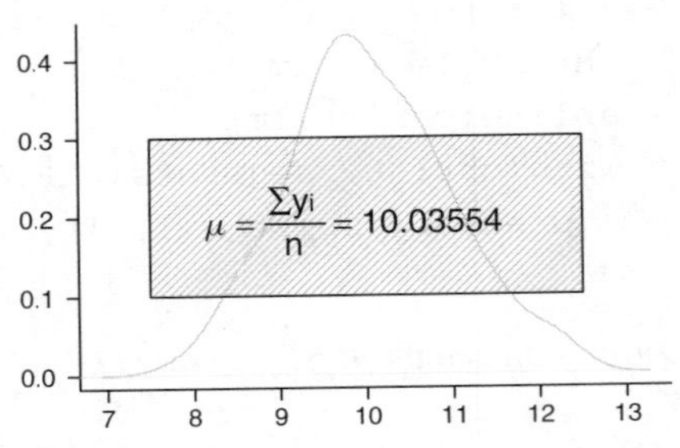

Irregular shapes between a succession of points - `polygon()`

Given a vector of x coordinates and a corresponding vector of y coordinates, the `polygon()` *function* draws irregular shapes:

```
> polygon(x, y = NULL, density = NULL, angle = 45, border = NULL,
    col = NA, lty = par("lty"), ...)
```

Smoothers

Smoothing functions can be useful additions to scatterplots, particularly for assessing (non)linearity and the nature of underlying trends. There are many different types of smoothers see section 8.3 and Table 8.2.

Smoothers are added to a plot by first fitting the smoothing function (e.g. `loess()` or `ksmooth()`) to the data before plotting the values predicted by this function across the span of the data.

```
> plot(CWD.DENS ~ RIP.DENS,
    data=christ)
> # fit the loess smoother
> christ.loess<-loess(CWD.DENS ~
    RIP.DENS, data=christ)
> # created a vector of the sorted
> # X values
> xs<-sort(christ$RIP.DENS)
> lines(xs, predict(christ.loess, data.frame(RIP.DENS=xs)))
> # fit and plot a kernel smoother
> christ.kern <- ksmooth(christ$RIP.DENS, christ$CWD.DENS,
    "norm", bandwidth=200)
> lines(christ.kern, lty=2)
```

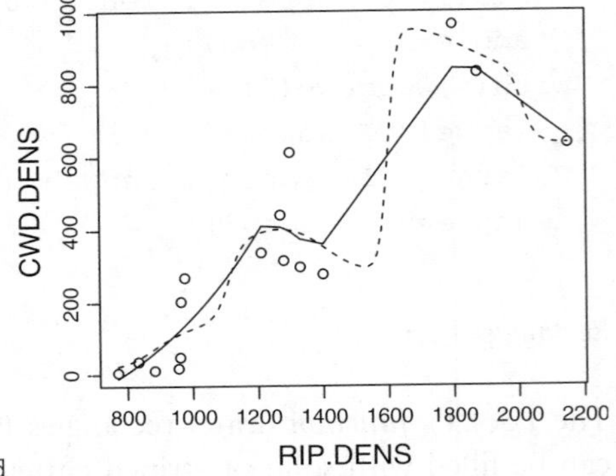

Confidence ellipses - `matlines()`[d]

The `matlines()` *function*, along with the similar `matplot()` and `matpoints()` *functions* provide a convenient method to plot multiple columns of matrices against one another, thereby providing a convenient means to plot predicted trends and confidence intervals in a single statement.

Confidence bands are added by using the value(s) returned by a `predict()` *function* as the second argument to the `matlines()` *function*.

```
> plot(CWD.DENS ~ RIP.DENS,
    data=christ)
> christ.lm<-lm(CWD.DENS ~
    RIP.DENS, data=christ)
> xs<-with(christ,
    seq(min(RIP.DENS),
    max(RIP.DENS), l=1000))
> matlines(xs,
    predict(christ.lm,
    data.frame(RIP.DENS=xs),
    interval="confidence"),
    lty=c(1,2,2), col=1)
```

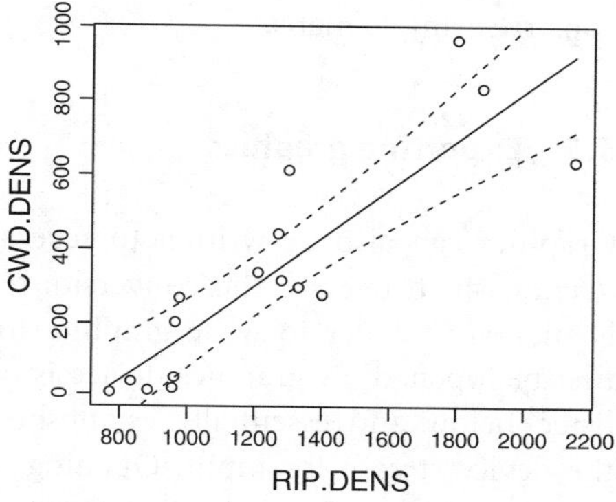

5.4 Interactive graphics

The majority of plotting functions on the majority of graphical devices operate by sending all of the required information to the device at the time of the call - no additional information is required or accepted from the user. The display devices (`X11()`, `windows()` and `quartz()`) however, also support a couple of functions designed to allow interactivity between the user and the current plotting region.

5.4.1 Identifying points - `identify()`

The `identify()` *function* allows the user to label points interactively. After issuing the identify() *function* with arguments corresponding to the x and y axis vectors, R awaits mouse input in the form of left mouse button clicks in the plotting region of the current display device. Each time the left mouse button is clicked on the display device, the coordinates of the mouse pointer are retrieved and the nearest data points (determined by comparing the mouse pointer coordinates to the point coordinates supplied as arguments) are labelled. A right mouse click ('ESC' on MAC OS X) terminates the function which returns a vector of point indices. In its simplest form, `identify()` *function* can be used to identify potentially problematic observations. Additional arguments can be supplied to provide finer control over the relative positioning and text of the labels.

[d] Note, the same could be achieved via three seperate `lines()` calls.

5.4.2 Retrieving coordinates - `locator()`

The `locator()` *function* returns the coordinates of the mouse pointer each time the left mouse button is clicked on the display device. A right mouse click on the display ('ESC' on MacOSX) terminates the function which returns a list of x, y coordinates. Alternatively, the function can be supplied with an argument indicating the number of points to locate (`n`). Furthermore, if the `type=` parameter is set to one of the plotting point types, the points will be echoed onto the current plotting region. The `locator()` *function* provides a convenient way to construct mock data sets, trace objects as well as construct simple maps.

5.5 Exporting graphics

Graphics can also be written to several graphical file formats via specific graphics *devices* which oversee the conversion of graphical commands into actual graphical elements. In order to write graphics to a file, an appropriate graphics device must first be 'opened'. A graphics device is opened by issuing one of the device functions listed below and essentially establishes the devices global parameters and readies the device stream for input. Opening such a device also creates (or overwrites) the nominated file. As graphical commands are issued, the input stream is evaluated and accumulated. The file is only written to disk when the device is closed via the `dev.off()` *function*.

Note that as the capabilities and default global parameters of different devices differ substantially, some graphical elements may appear differently on different devices. This is particularly true of dimensions, locations, fonts and colors.

5.5.1 Postscript - `poscript()` and `pdf()`

Postscript is actually a programming language that defines both the nature of the content and exactly how the content should be displayed or printed on a page. As a result, postscript is device independent and scalable to any size and is therefore the preferred format of most publishers. Whilst there are many other arguments that can be passed to the `postscript()` *function*, common use is as follows:

```
> postscript(file, family, fonts = NULL, width, height,
    horizontal, paper)
```

where `file` is a file name (and path), `font` and `family` declare all the fonts required in the device, `width` and `height` define the dimensions (in inches) of the graphic, `paper` defines the size of the printer paper (or 'special' for graphics in which width and height is defined) and `horizontal` determines the orientation of the graphic relative to the paper type.

Like postscript, pdf (Portable Document Format) files contain information on exactly how the printed page should appear. Pdf documents can also contain a great deal of additional information on how the information should behave in different contexts. Such 'advanced' postscript features are largely designed to enhance the capabilities of documents displayed on screens and are therefore rarely utilized from R. Importantly, unlike R's postscript device, the pdf device does not embed a prologue of font metrics, and thus only fonts that can be assumed to be present on the target devices (printers and other computers) should be used.

5.5.2 Bitmaps - `jpeg()` and `png()`

R also supports a range of bitmap file formats, the range of which depends on the underlying operating system and the availability of external applications.

```
> jpeg(filename, width = 480, height = 480, units = "px",
    pointsize = 12, quality = 75, bg = "white", res = NA, ...)
```

where `filename` defines the name of the file (including path), `width` and `height` define the dimensions of the graphic (in pixels) and quality defines the compression quality (100 indicates no compression). The graphical capabilities of the bitmap devices are largely tied to the default display device.

5.5.3 Copying devices - `dev.copy()`

Alternatively, graphics can be exported to file by copying the contents of one device (such as a display device) to another device (such as a file device) using the `dev.copy()` *function.*

5.6 Working with multiple graphical devices

It is possible to have multiple graphical devices open simultaneously. However, only one device can be active (receptive to plotting commands) at a time. Once a device has been opened (see section 5.5), the device object is given an automatically iterated reference number in the range of 1 to 63. Device 1 will always be a `null` device that cannot accept plotting commands and is essentially just a placeholder for the device counter. The set of functions for managing multiple devices are described in Table 5.11. To appreciate the workings of these functions, first create multiple display devices. To do so, issue one of the commands listed below (the one appropriate for your system) multiple times:

Windows	MacOSX[e]	Linux
`windows()`	`quartz()`	`X11()`

Note that the device title bars will indicate the device reference number as well as whether the device is currently active or inactive. The last one created will be active.

[e] The default graphics device for MacOSX is `X11`, however, many prefer `quartz`.

Table 5.11 Functions for managing multiple graphics devices.

Function	Description	Example
`dev.list()`	Returns the numbers of open devices (with device types as column headings)	`X11 X11` `2 3`
`dev.cur()`	Returns the number (and name) of the currently active device	`X11` `3`
`dev.next()`	Returns the number (and name) of the next available device after the device specified by the `which=` argument (after current if `which=` absent)	`X11` `2`
`dev.prev()`	Returns the number (and name) of the previous available device after the device specified by the `which=` argument (before current if `which=` absent)	`X11` `2`
`dev.set()`	Makes the device specified by the `which=` argument the currently active device and returns the number (and name) of this device. If `which=` argument absent, it is set to the next device.	`X11` `2`
`dev.off()`	Closes the device specified by the `which=` argument (or current device if `which=` argument absent), makes the next device active and returns the number (and name) of this device.	`X11` `3`

5.7 High-level plotting functions for univariate (single variable) data

5.7.1 Histogram

Histograms are useful at representing the distribution of observations for large (> 30) sample sizes.

```
> set.seed(1)
> VAR <- rnorm(100,10,2)
> hist(VAR)
```

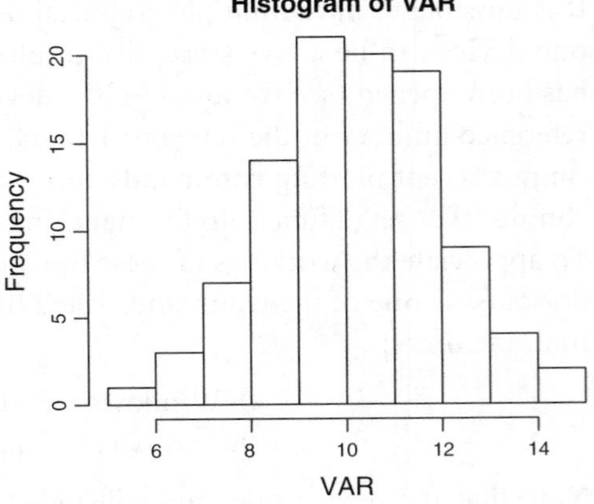

The number or size of the bins can be controlled by passing respectively a single number or vector of bin breakpoints with the `breaks=` argument[f]. Specifying the `probability=T` argument will express the number counts in each bin as a density (probability) rather than as a frequency.

```
> hist(VAR, breaks=18,
    probability=T)
#OR equivalently in this case
> hist(VAR, breaks=seq(5.5,15,
    by=.5), probability=T)
```

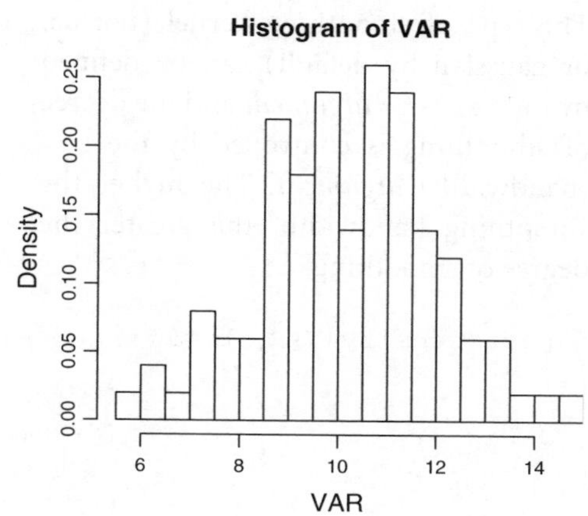

5.7.2 Density functions

Probability density functions are also useful additions or alternatives to histograms as they further assist in describing the patterns of the underlying distribution. Typical kernel density functions fit a series of kernels (symmetric probability functions) to successive subsets (windows) of the ordered dataset from which new estimates of the observations are calculated. The resolution and texture (smoothness) of the density function is controlled by a smoothing parameter which essentially defines the width of the kernel window.

A density function can be plotted using the `density()` *function* as an argument to the high-level overloaded `plot()` *function*.

```
> plot(density(VAR))
```

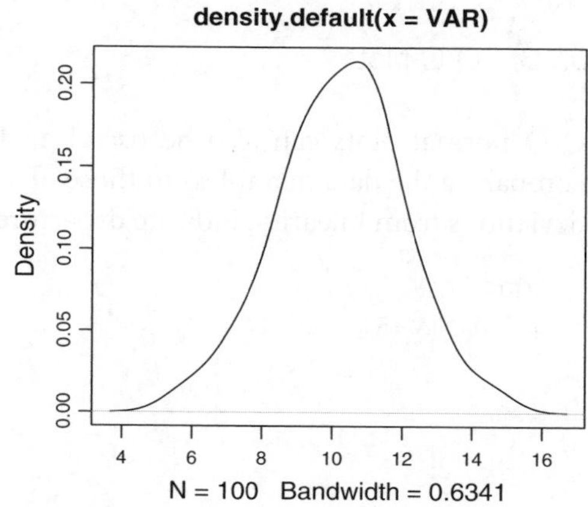

[f] It is also possible to pass a function that computes the number of breaks or the name of a breaking algorithm.

The type of smoothing kernel (normal or gaussian by default) can be defined by the `kernel=` *argument* and the degree of smoothing is controlled by the `bw=` (bandwidth) *argument*. The higher the smoothing bandwidth, the greater the degree of smoothing.

```
> plot(density(VAR, bw=1))
```

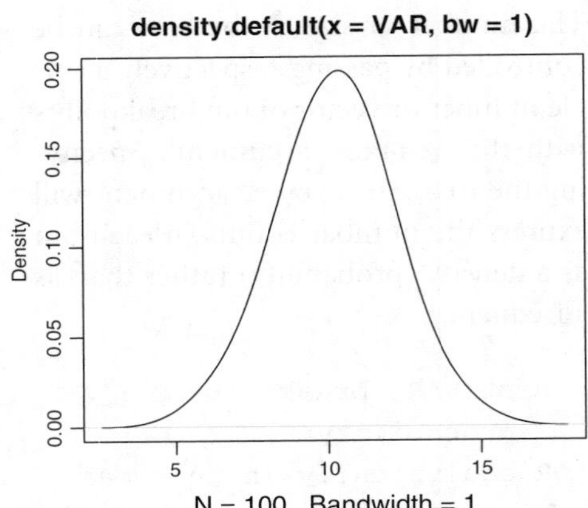

The density function can also be added to a histogram using the `density()` *function* as an argument to a the low-level `lines()` *function*.

```
> set.seed(1)
> VAR1 <- rlnorm(100,2,.5)
> hist(VAR1, prob=T)
> lines(density(VAR1))
```

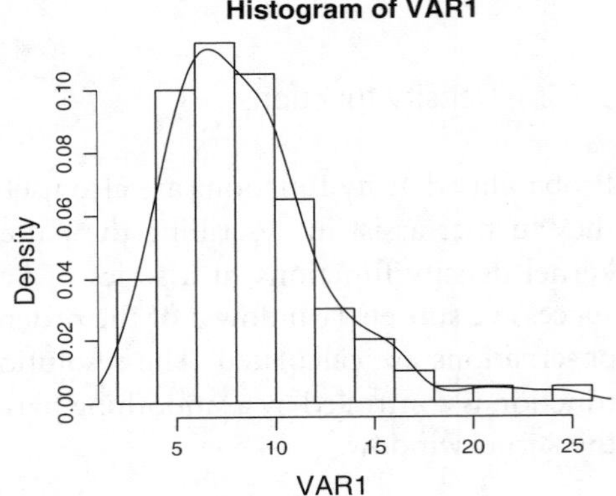

5.7.3 Q-Q plots

Q-Q normal plots can also be useful at diagnosing departures from normality by comparing the data quantiles[g] to those of a standard normal distribution. Substantial deviations from linearity, indicate departures from normality.

```
> qqnorm(VAR1)
> qqline(VAR1)
```

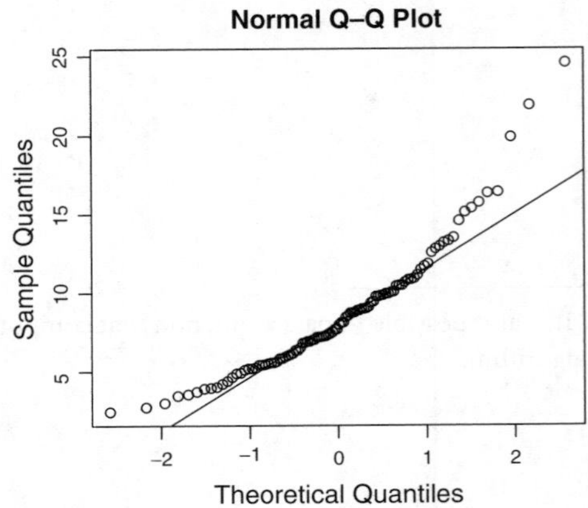

[g] Quantiles are a regular spacing of points throughout an ordered data set.

5.7.4 Boxplots

For smaller sample sizes, histograms and density functions can be difficult to interpret. Boxplots (or box-and-whisker plots) provide an alternative means of depicting the location (median), variability and shape of the distribution of data. The dimensions of a boxplot are defined by the five-number summaries (minimum value, lower quartile (Q1), median (Q2), upper quartile (Q3) and maximum value - each representing 25%) of the data (see Figure 5.5).

Recall that boxplots are typically used to explore the distributions of small samples. The volatility of quantiles from small samples offers little confidence in any single component of a boxplot. Hence, the key characteristic of a boxplot that is indicative of a departure from normality is that *each segment* of the boxplot gets progressively larger (or smaller). Only in such a circumstance, could you be confident that the sample could not have come from a normal distribution of values. The following boxplots provide an illustration of such a departure from normality (log-normal boxplot).

Univariate boxplots are generated by passing a vector to the `boxplot()` *function.*

```
> set.seed(6)
> VAR2<-rlnorm(15,2,.5)
> boxplot(VAR2)
```

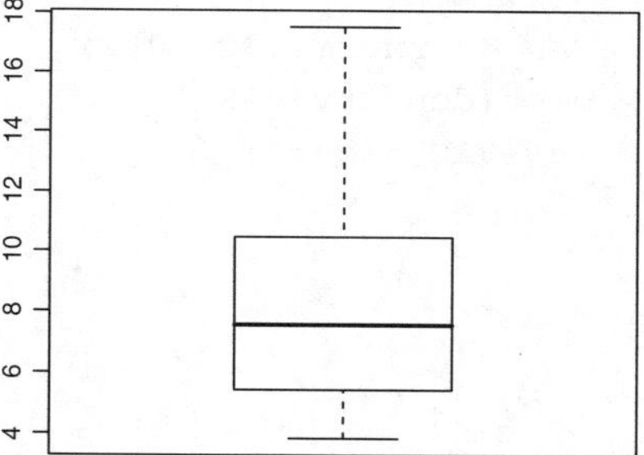

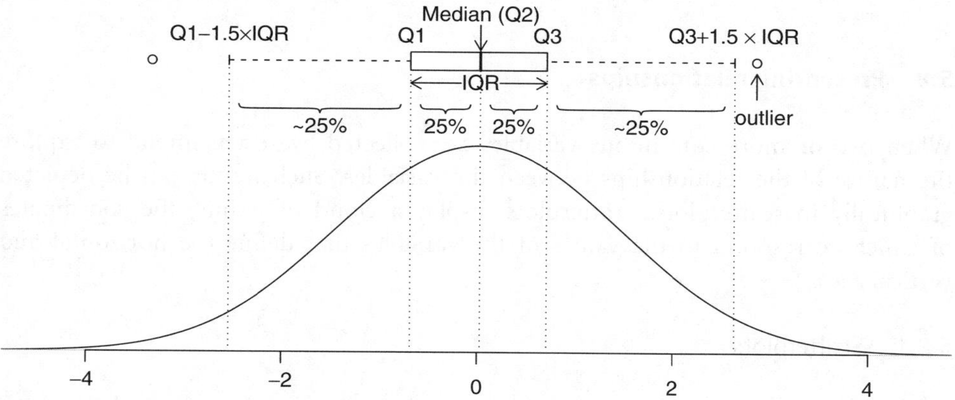

Fig 5.5 Boxplot of a standard normal distribution (mean=0, sd=1). IQR denotes the interquartile range (the range in which 50% of data lay), and percentages reflect proportions of data within the represented regions of the boxplot and distribution.

The `horizontal=T` *argument* is used to produce horizontally aligned boxplots

```
> boxplot(VAR2, horizontal=T)
```

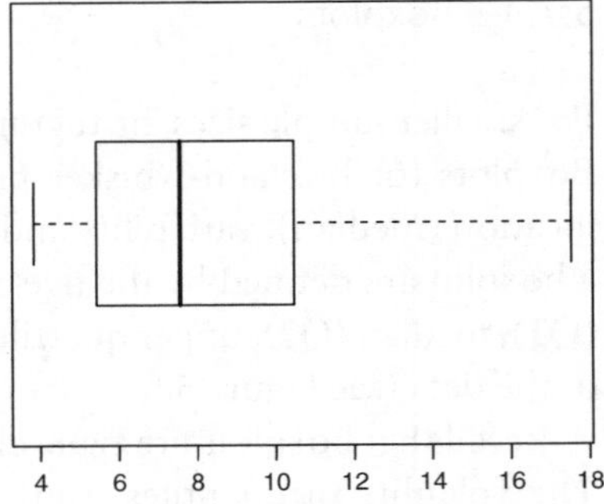

5.7.5 Rug charts

Another representation of the data that can be added to existing plots is a rug chart that displays the values as a series of ticks on the axis. Rug charts can be particularly useful at revealing artifacts in the data that are "smoothed over" by histograms, boxplots and density functions.

```
> set.seed(1)
> VAR <- rnorm(100,10,2)
> plot(density(VAR))
> rug(VAR,side=1)
```

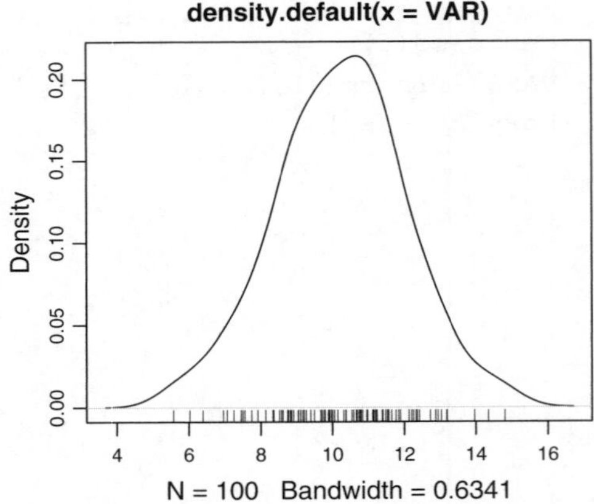

5.8 Presenting relationships

When two or more continuous variables are collected, we often intend to explore the nature of the relationships between the variables. Such trends can be depicted graphically in scatterplots. Scatterplots display a cloud of points, the coordinates of which correspond to the values of the variables that define the horizontal and vertical axes.

5.8.1 Scatterplots

Although scatterplots do not formally distinguish between response (dependent) and predictor (independent) variables, when such distinctions occur, independent variables are conventionally plotted along the horizontal (x) axis.

Scatterplots are used prior to analyses to help assess the suitability of the data to particular analytical procedures. Of particular importance are the insights they provide into the linearity and patterns of variability of trends. They are also presented post analysis as summaries of the trends and analyses.

The following demonstrations will again utilize the course woody debris (CWD) dataset by Christensen et al. (1996). As previously demonstrated, scatterplots can generated with the `plot()` *function*. Additional features (such as trendlines, smoothers and other features that assist in assessing departures from linearity and homogeneity of variance) can then be added with various low-level plotting functions.

To facilitate all of these diagnostic features as well as marginal boxplots, the high-level `scatterplot()` *function* (`car` *package*) is very useful. Note, the `scatterplot()` *function* fits a lowess rather than loess smoother.

```
> library(car)
> scatterplot(CWD.DENS ~
    RIP.DENS, data=christ)
```

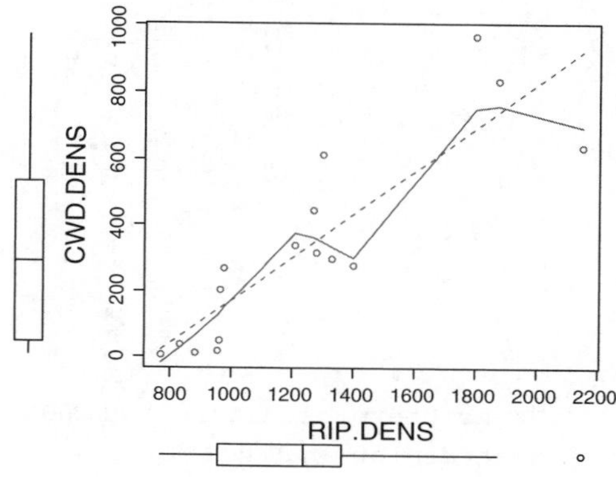

Scatterplot matrices (SPLOMS)

Scatterplot matrices display a panel of scatterplots between each pair of variables when there are three or more continuous variables. A given variable makes up the x-axis of each of the panels up the column and the y-axis of each of the panels along the row. The diagonal panels are often populated with univariate plots such as boxplots, histograms or density functions. The upper right panels are a mirror of the lower left panels. There are a few high-level plotting functions for producing scatterplot matrices:

- the `pairs()` *function* is an extension of the regular `plot()` *function*
  Different functions can be applied to the lower, upper and diagonal panels of the grid. A lowess smoother is supported by the `panel.smooth` *function*. It is also possible to define alternative functions. This example illustrates the application of horizontal boxplots into the diagonal panels. Since, the upper panels are a mirror of the lower panels, the upper panels can be removed with by setting the `upper.panel=` parameter to NULL.

```
> # define a boxplot panel function
> panel.bxp <- function(x, ...)
> \{
> usr <- par("usr"); on.exit(par(usr))
```

```
> par(usr = c(usr[1:2],0,2))
> boxplot(x, add=TRUE, horizontal=T)
> \}
> pairs(~CWD.DENS + RIP.DENS + CABIN + AREA, data=christ,
    lower.panel=panel.smooth, diag.panel=panel.bxp,
    upper.panel=NULL, gap=0)
```

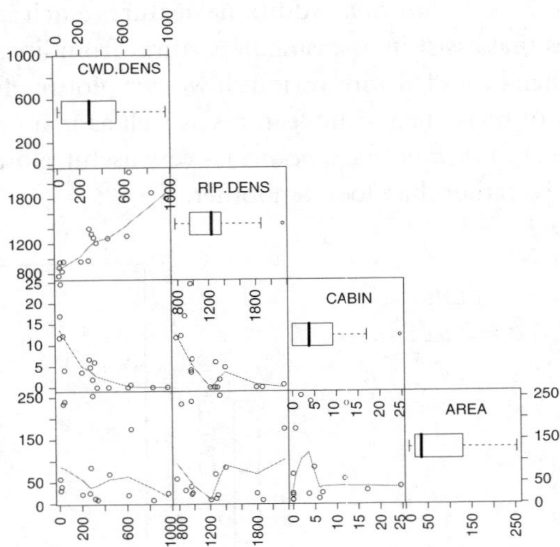

- the `scatterplot.matrix()` *function* (`car` *package*) is an extension of the regular `scatterplot()` *function*.

```
> library(car)
> scatterplot.matrix(~CWD.DENS + RIP.DENS + CABIN + AREA,
    data=christ, diag="boxplot")
```

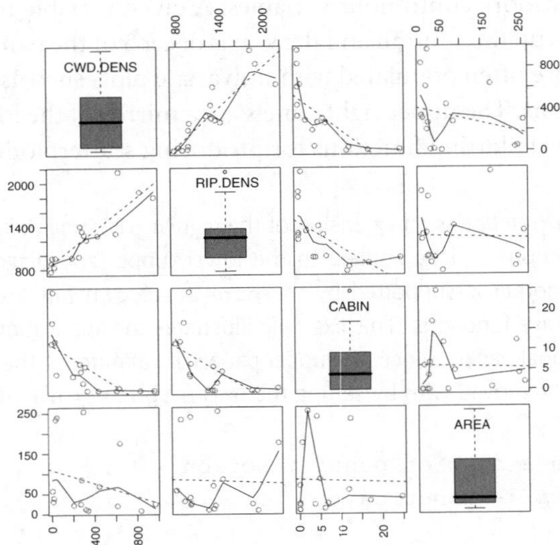

The `scatterplot.matrix()` *function* can differentiate trends for different levels (groups) of a categorical variable. To illustrate, we will use the `cut()` *function* to convert the `AREA` vector into a categorical variable with two levels (small and large).

```
> scatterplot.matrix(~CWD.DENS + RIP.DENS + CABIN,
    groups=cut(christ$AREA,br=2, lab=c("small","large")),
    by.groups=T, data=christ, diag="density")
```

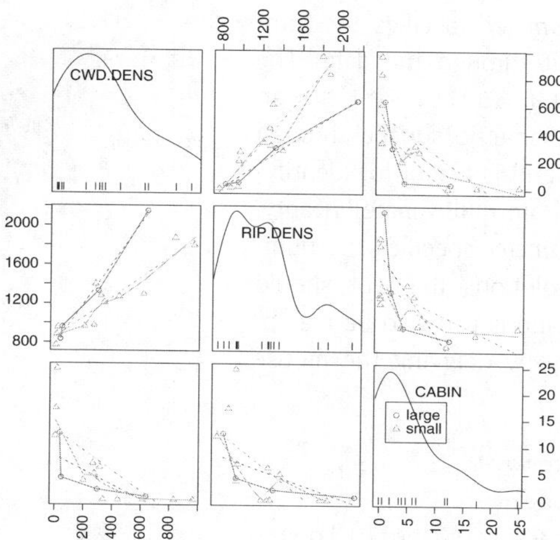

3D scatterplots

Three dimensional scatterplots can be useful for exploring multivariate patterns between combinations of three or more variables. To illustrate 3D scatterplots in R, we will make use of a dataset by Allison and Cicchetti (1976) that compiles sleep, morphology and life history characteristics 62 species of mammal along with predation indices.

```
> allison <- read.table("allison.csv", header=T, sep=",")
```

- the `scatterplot3d` *function* (`scatterplot3d` *package*)

```
> library(scatterplot3d)
> with(allison,
    scatterplot3d(log
    (Gestation), log(BodyWt),
    log(LifeSpan), type="h",
    pch=16))
```

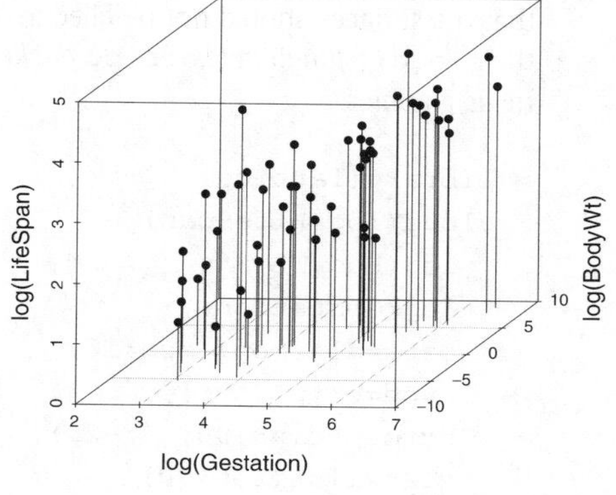

The `type="h"` *parameter* specifies that points should be connected to the base by a line and the `pch=16` *parameter* specifies solid points. All variables were expressed as their natural logarithms using the `log()` *function*.

- the `scatter3d` *function* (`Rcmdr` *package*) displays rotating three dimensional plots.

```
> library(Rcmdr)
> with(allison,
    scatter3d(log(Gestation),
    log(LifeSpan), log(BodyWt),
    fit="additive", rev=1))
```

The `fit=` *parameter* specifies the form of surface to fit through the data. The option selected (`"additive"`) fits an additive non-parametric surface through the data cloud and is useful for identifying departures from multivariate linearity. The `rev=` *parameter* specifies the number of full revolutions the plot should make. Axes rotations can also be manipulated manually by dragging the mouse over the plot.

```
> library(Rcmdr)
> with(allison,
    scatter3d(log(Gestation),
    log(LifeSpan), log(BodyWt),
    fit="linear", parallel=F,
    groups=factor(Predation),
    fill=F))
```

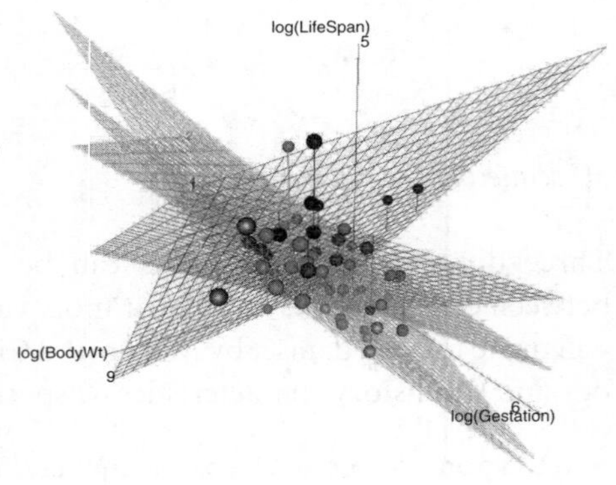

The `parallel=F` *argument* specifies that separate surfaces are generated for each of the levels in the factorial variable specified by the `groups=` *argument*. In this case, the `factor()` *function* was used to convert the numeric predation vector to a factor. The `fill=F` *argument* specifies that the surfaces should not be filled in.

- the `cloud()` *function* (`lattice` *package*). Refer to section 5.11 for more information on trellis graphics.

```
> library(lattice)
> cloud(log(LifeSpan) ~
    log(BodyWt) *
    log(Gestation),
    data=allison, pch=16,
    type=c("p","h"),
    screen=c(x=-90, y=-20),
    zlab=list(rot=90))
```

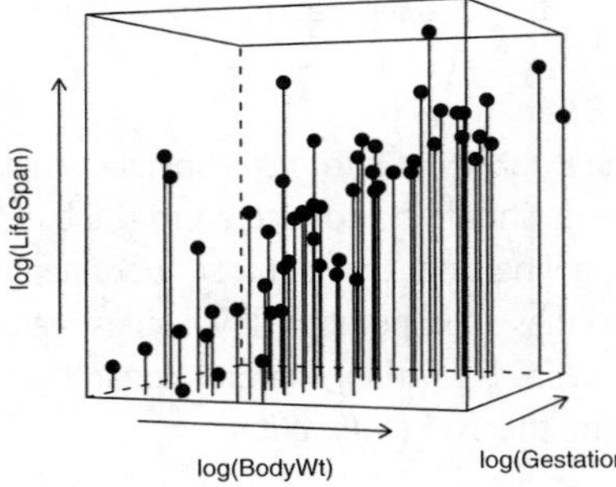

The data are specified as a formula of the format `z~x*y`. The `type=c("p","h")` *argument* specifies that both points and connected lines should be used. The `screen=` *argument* specifies the amount of axes rotation for the x, y and z axes. The `zlab` *list* specifies that the z axis label should be rotated 90 degrees.

5.9 Presenting grouped data

Data for which a response has been measured from two or more groups of sampling units are summarised graphically by estimates of location (such as mean or median) and spread (standard error or standard deviation). As with summaries of relationships, graphical summaries for grouped data serve as both exploratory data analysis tools as well as visual representations of statistical analyses.

5.9.1 Boxplots

Plotting multiple boxplots side by side (one for each level of a factorial variable), provides a useful means of examining homogeneity (equal) of variance assumptions. To illustrate boxplots, we will reproduce Figure 4.5 from Quinn and Keough (2002) using data sets from Ward and Quinn (1988) and Furness and Bryant (1996).

```
> ward<-read.table("ward.csv",
    header=T, sep=",")
> boxplot(EGGS~ZONE, data=ward,
    ylab="Number of eggs per
    capsule", xlab="Zone")
```

```
> furness<-read.table("furness
    .csv", header=T, sep=",")
> boxplot(METRATE~SEX, data=
    furness, ylab="metabolic
    rate", xlab="Sex")
```

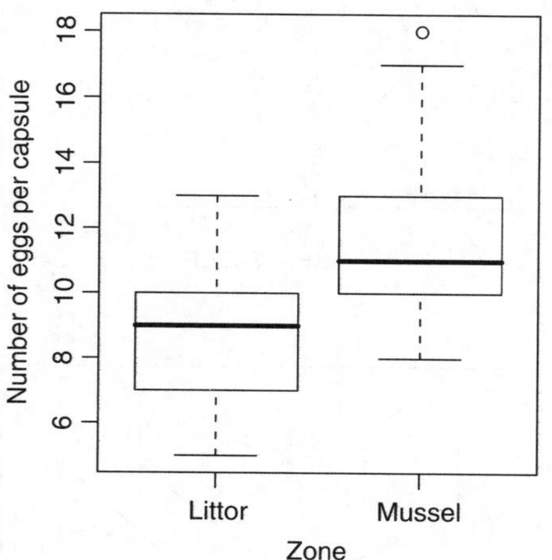

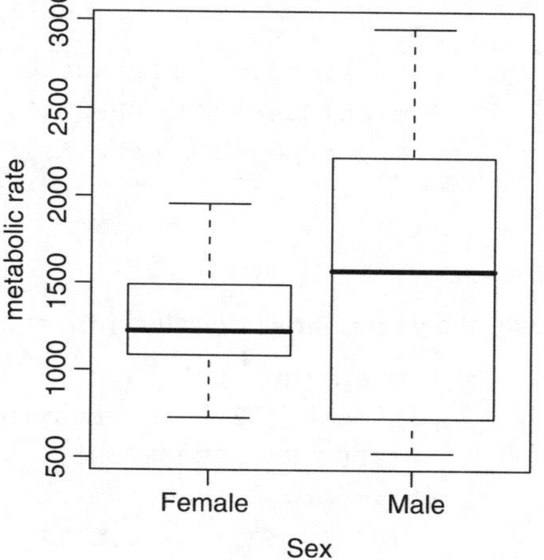

5.9.2 Boxplots for grouped means

Technically, the normality and homogeneity of variance assumptions pertain to the residuals (difference between values observed and those predicted by the proposed model) and thus the model replicates. For multi-factor analysis of variance designs, the appropriate replicates for a hypothesis test are usually the individual observations from each combination of factors. Hence, boxplots should also reflect this level of replication.

To illustrate, a data set introduced in Box 11.2 of Sokal and Rohlf (1997) on the oxygen consumption of two species of limpets under three seawater concentrations will be used.

```
> limpets <-read.table("limpets
    .csv", header=T, sep=",")
> boxplot(O2~SEAWATER*SPECIES,
    limpets)
```

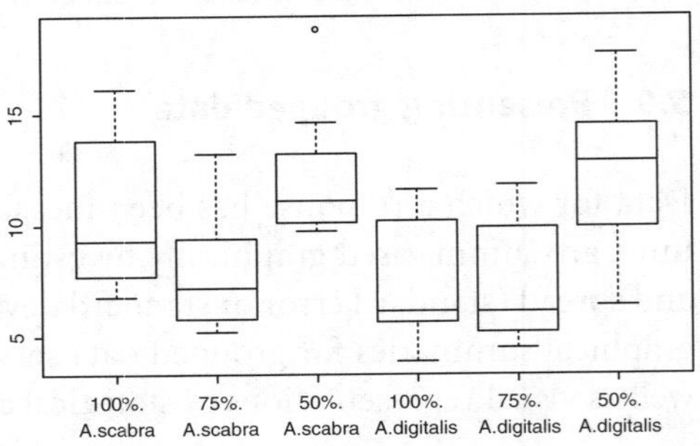

5.9.3 Interaction plots - means plots

Interactions are outcomes in which the effects of one factor are dependent on the levels of other factor(s). That is, the effect of one factor is not consistent across all levels of the other factors. Interaction plots depict the mean response value of each combination of factor levels (groups) and are therefore useful for interpreting interactions.

- the `interaction.plot()` *function* (`car` *package*).

```
> library(car)
> limpets <-read.table
    ("limpets.csv", header=T,
    sep=",")
> with(limpets, interaction.
    plot(SEAWATER, SPECIES,
    O2, type="b", pch=16))
```

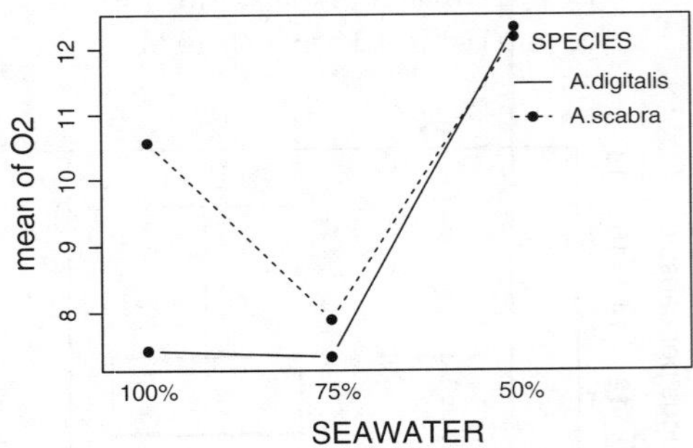

- the `plotmeans()` *function* (`gplots` *package*)

```
> library(gplots)
> plotmeans(O2 ~ interaction
    (SPECIES, SEAWATER),
    limpets, connect=list
    (c(1,3,5), c(2,4,6)))
```

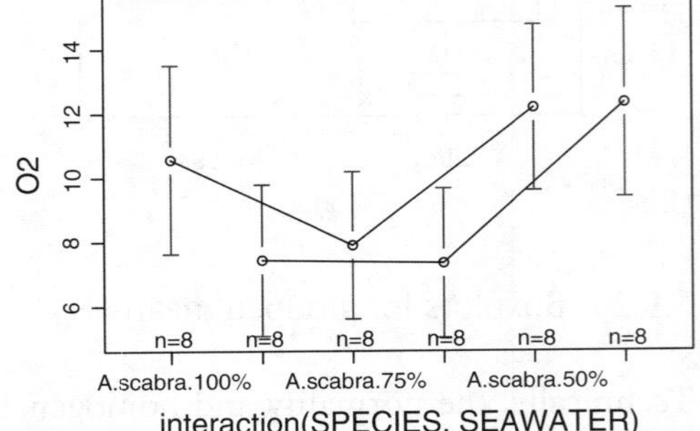

5.9.4 Bargraphs

Bargraphs are plots where group means are represented by the tops of bars or columns. Pure statisticians (who refer to these plots as 'dynamite plots') argue that bars should only be used to represent frequencies (totals) and are not appropriate for representing means (since the body of the bar has no logical interpretation). Furthermore, they implicitly assume parametric assumptions and can misleadingly conceal the true nature of the data. Consequently, there are no high-level bargraph plotting functions (and it is unlikely that the R Core Development Team would ever support such a function). Such professionals prefer boxplots (see section 5.9.2), means plots (means represented by points) and violin plots (see section 5.9.5). Nevertheless, biologist often find bargraph useful graphical summaries and they do provide a greater area for displaying colors and shading to distinguish different treatment combinations. Such is the power of R, they are relatively simple to construct using a series of low-level plotting functions.

```
> means<-with(ward, tapply(EGGS,
    ZONE, mean))
> sds <-with(ward, tapply(EGGS,
    ZONE, sd))
> ns<-with(ward, tapply(EGGS, ZONE,
    length))
> ses <- sds/sqrt(ns)
> b<-barplot(means, ylim=c(min(pretty
    ( means - ses)), max(pretty
    (means+ses))), xpd=F,
    ylab="Number of eggs per capsule")
> arrows(b, means+ses, b, means-ses,
    angle=90, code=3)
> box(bty="l")
```

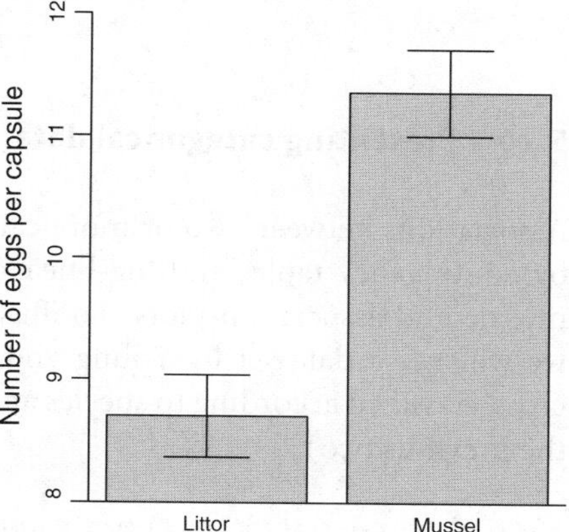

Similarly, multifactor bargraphs can also be constructed from first principles.

```
> means<-with(limpets, tapply(O2,
    list(SPECIES,SEAWATER), mean))
> sds <-with(limpets, tapply(O2,
    list(SPECIES,SEAWATER), sd))
> ns<-with(limpets, tapply(O2,
    list(SPECIES,SEAWATER), length))
> ses <- sds/sqrt(ns)
> b<-barplot(means, ylim=c(min(pretty
    ( means-ses)), max(pretty
    (means+ses))), beside=T, xpd=F,
    ylab="Oxygen consumption",
    legend.text=rownames(means))

> arrows(b,means+ses,b,means-ses,
    angle=90, code=3,length=0.05)
> box(bty="l")
```

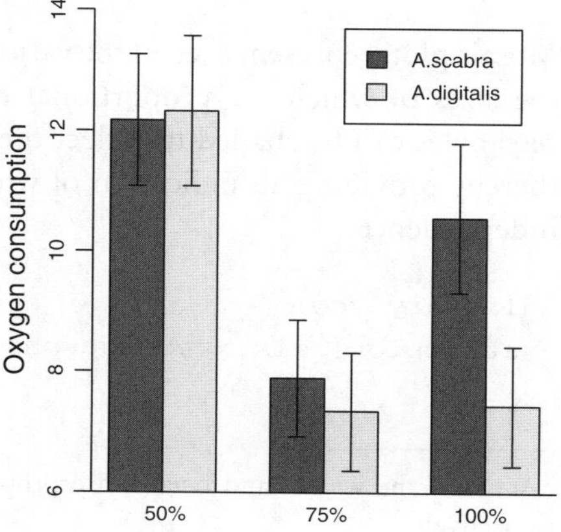

5.9.5 Violin plots

Violin plots are an alternative to boxplots and bargraphs for representing the characteristics of multiple samples.

```
> library(UsingR)
> simple.violinplot(EGGS~ZONE, ward,
+ col="gray", bw="SJ")
> box(bty="l")
```

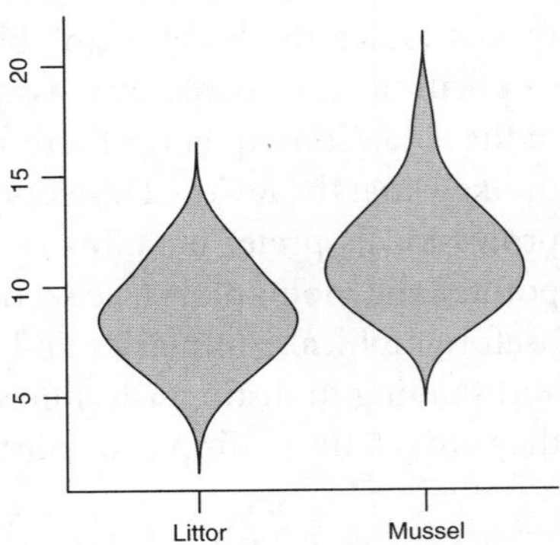

5.10 Presenting categorical data

Associations between two or more categorical variables (such as those data modelled by contingency tables and log-linear modelling) can be summarized graphically by mosaic and association plots. To illustrate graphical summaries for categorical data, we will use a data set by Young and Winn (2003) in which encountered eels were cross-classified according to species and location (grass beds, sand/rubble or bordering the previous two).

```
> eels <-read.table("eels.csv", header=T, sep=",")
> eels.xtab <- xtabs(COUNT ~ LOCATION + SPECIES, eels)
```

5.10.1 Mosaic plots

Mosaic plots represent each of the various cross-classifications as a mosaic of rectangles, the sizes of which are proportional to the observed frequencies[h]. In addition, the rectangles can be shaded to reflect the magnitudes and significance[i] of the residuals, thereby providing an indication of which cross-classifications contribute to a lack of independence.

```
> library(vcd)
> strucplot(eels.xtab, gp=shading_max)
```

[h] Actually, the widths and heights are proportional to the marginal and conditional percentages respectively.

[i] Significance is determined via a permutation test, and thus exact probabilities differ from run to run.

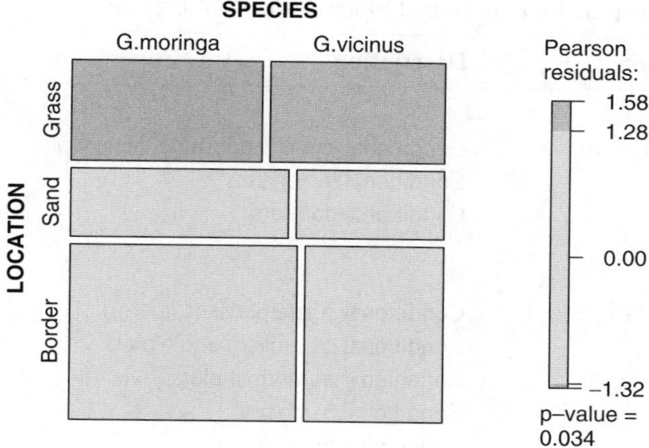

5.10.2 Association plots

Association plots depict cross-classifications as rectangles whose heights reflect the relative sizes and polarity of Pearson residuals and whose areas reflect the raw residuals. As with mosaic plots, shading can be used to reflect the magnitude and significance of residuals.

```
> assoc(eels.xtab, gp=shading_max)
```

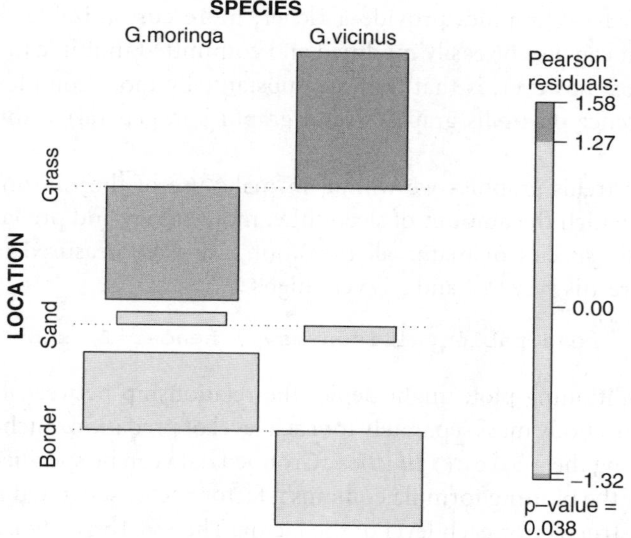

5.11 Trellis graphics

Trellis graphics provide the means of plotting the trends amongst a set of variables separately according to the levels of other variables and can therefore be more

Table 5.12 Incomplete list of high-level lattice (Trellis) plotting functions.

Plotting function	**Description**
Univariate	
`densityplot()`	Conditional kernel smoothing density plot
`histogram()`	Conditional histograms
`dotplot()`	Conditional dotplots
Bivariate	
`xyplot()`	Conditional scatterplots
`qq()`	Conditional quantile-quantile plots
`qqmath()`	Conditional qq-normal plots
`barchart()`	Conditional barcharts
`bwplot()`	Conditional boxplots
Multivariate	
`cloud()`	Conditional 3D scatterplots
`splom()`	Matrix of scatterplots

appropriate for exploring trends within grouped data[j]. The separate trends are presented in multiple panels within a grid and/or as different plotting symbols within plots. Many of the high-level plotting functions described above have trellis equivalents (see Table 5.12), all of which are provided by the `lattice` *package*.

Trellis (`lattice`) graphics provide a richer, more customizable set of graphical procedures that can also be easily modified and committed multiple times to multiple devices. The cost however, is that they are substantially more complex. An excellent source of reference on trellis graphics (and graphics in general) within R is Murrell (2005).

To illustrate trellis graphics we will again make use of the Allison and Cicchetti (1976) data in which the amount of sleep time, morphology and predation risks were compiled for 62 species of mammal. Predation risk was measured on a scale of 1 through 5 where 1 is very low and 5 is very high.

```
> allison <- read.table("allison.csv", header=T, sep=",")
```

A basic conditioning plot, might depict the relationship between the life span of mammals against body mass separately for each level of predation. Such a plot could be constructed using the `xyplot()` *function*. Grouped data can be specified in one of two ways. Firstly, if the plotting formula contains a factor vector separated by a |, separate panels are constructed for each level of the factor. The `xyplot()` *function* introduces the `type="r"` *argument* which specifies regression trendlines.

[j] Such as those data modelled by blocking and repeated measured designs.

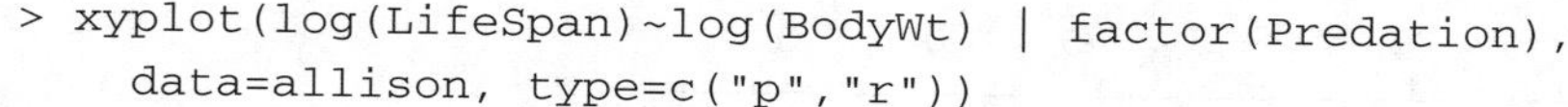

```
> xyplot(log(LifeSpan)~log(BodyWt) | factor(Predation),
    data=allison, type=c("p","r"))
```

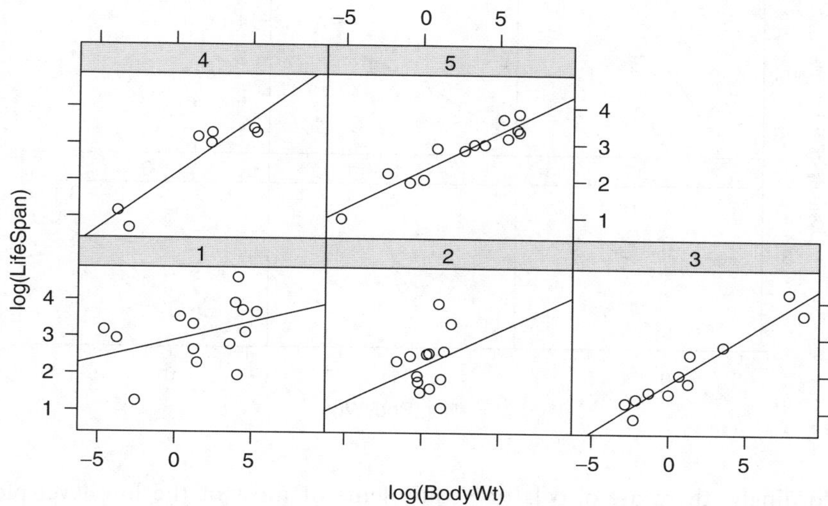

It is clear that the relationship between longevity and body mass is conditional on the level of predation risk.

Alternatively, each of the trends can be included on the one plot by passing the factorial vector as a `group=` *argument.*

```
> xyplot(log(LifeSpan)~
    log(BodyWt), groups=factor
    (Predation), data=allison,
    type=c("p","r"),
    auto.key=list(columns=5))
```

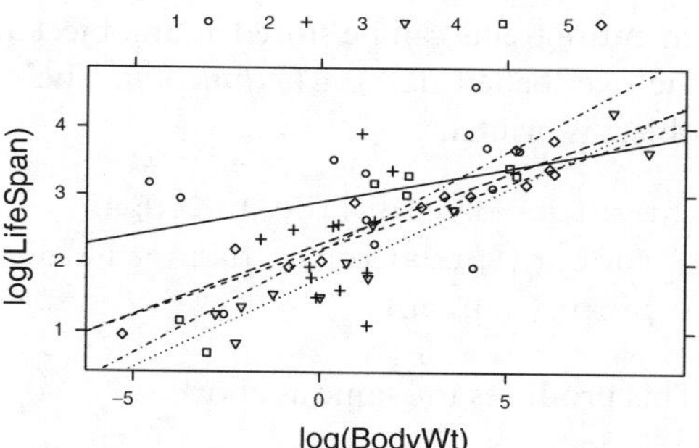

Additional graphical features can be added to the panels using the `panels=` *argument.* This argument accepts a range of predefined functions, as well as user defined functions to achieve specific results and is called by the plotting function for each panel in the lattice.

```
> myFunc<-function(x,y) a<-lm(y~x); panel.points(x,y, pch=16,
    col="grey"); panel.abline(a,col="grey"); panel.loess(x,y)
> xyplot(log(LifeSpan) ~ log(BodyWt) | factor(Predation),
    data=allison, panel=myFunc)
```

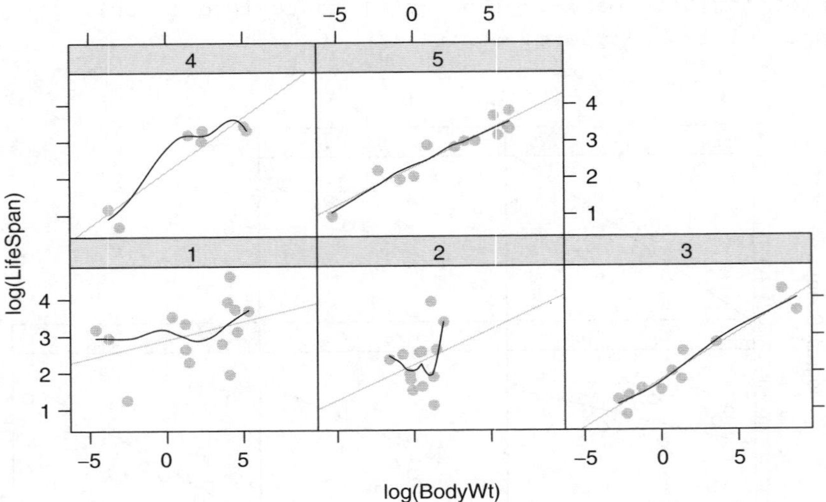

Accordingly, there are also lattice equivalents of most of the low level plotting functions described in section 5.3. Typically, these functions are called by the name of the basic low level function name with a `panel.` prefix.

Unlike the basic plotting system described earlier, lattice plots are not a biproduct of the plotting functions. Instead, the output is returned by the function. Consequently, an entire trellis can be stored as an object and subsequently updated (modified) using the overloaded `update()` *function*. The overall graphic is not committed until the object is printed[k].

```
> myPlot<-xyplot(log(LifeSpan) ~ log(BodyWt) |
  factor(Predation), data=allison, panel=myFunc)
> print(myPlot)
```

This produces the same as above.

5.11.1 `scales()` *parameters*

Many of the elements associated with the panel axes can be customized using the `scales` *parameter*. This parameter accepts a lists of arguments associated with the x and y axes.

```
> update(myPlot,  xlab=expression(paste("Body weight ",
    (log[e]*Kg))), ylab=expression(paste("Lifespan ",
    (log[e]*yrs))), scales=list(x=list(at=seq(-6,6,l=7))))
```

[k] As with most non-plotting functions in R, when a lattice plotting function is called without assigning a name for the output object, the result is automatically passed onto an appropriate print method before being discarded. If the function's output is assigned a name, the object is not "printed", it is stored.

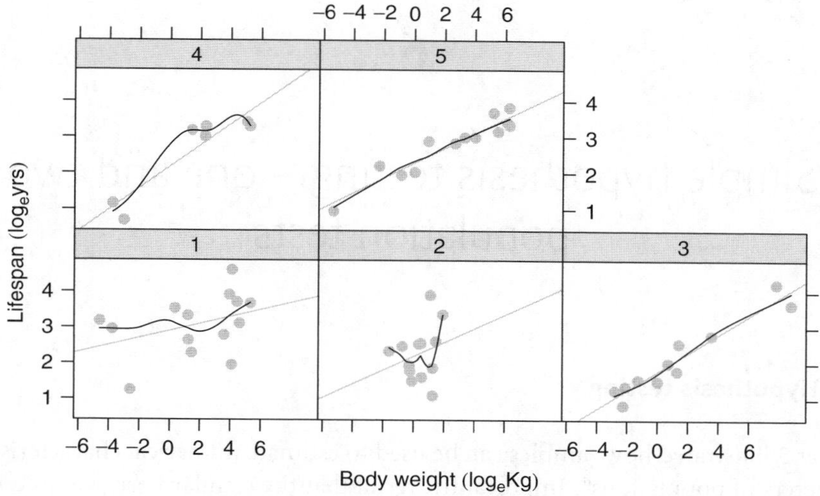

5.12 Further reading

Maindonald, J. H., and J. Braun. (2003). *Data Analysis and Graphics Using R - An Example-based Approach*. Cambridge University Press, London.

Murrell, P. (2005). *R Graphics (Computer Science and Data Analysis)*. Chapman & Hall/CRC.

6

Simple hypothesis testing – one and two population tests

6.1 Hypothesis testing

Chapter 3 illustrated how samples can be used to estimate numerical characteristics or parameters of populations[a]. Importantly, recall that the standard error is an estimate of how variable *repeated* parameter estimates (e.g. population means) are likely to be from repeated (long-run) population re-sampling. Also recall, that the standard error can be estimated from a single collected sample given the degree of variability and size of this sample. Hence, sample means allow us make inferences about the population means, and the strength of these inferences is determined by estimates of how precise (or repeatable) the estimated population means are likely to be (standard error). The concept of precision introduces the value of using the characteristics of a single sample to estimate the likely characteristics of repeated samples from a population.This same philosophy of estimating the characteristics of a large number of possible samples and outcomes forms the basis of frequentist approach to statistics in which samples are used to objectively test specific hypotheses about populations.

A biological or research **hypothesis** is a concise statement about the predicted or theorized nature of a population or populations and usually proposes that there *is* an effect of a treatment (e.g. the means of two populations are different). Logically however, theories (and thus hypothesis) cannot be proved, only disproved (*falsification*) and thus a **null hypothesis** (H_0) is formulated to represent the single logical opposite of the hypothesized prediction. For example, if the hypothesis is that there *is* a difference between (or relationship among) populations, then the null hypothesis is that there is *no* difference or relationship (effect). Evidence against the null hypothesis thereby provides evidence that the hypothesis is likely to be true.

The next step in hypothesis testing is to decide on an appropriate statistic that describes the nature of population estimates in the context of the null hypothesis taking into account the precision of estimates. For example, if the null hypothesis is

[a] Recall that in a statistical context, the term population refers to all the possible observations of a particular condition from which samples are collected, and that this does not necessarily represent a biological population.

Biostatistical Design and Analysis Using R: a Practical Guide, 1st edition. By M. Logan.
Published 2010 by Blackwell Publishing.

that the mean of one population is different to the mean of another population, the null hypothesis is that the population means are equal. The null hypothesis can therefore be represented mathematically as: $H_0 : \mu_1 = \mu_2$ or equivalently: $H_0 : \mu_1 - \mu_2 = 0$.

The appropriate test statistic for such a null hypothesis is a t-statistic:

$$t = \frac{(\bar{y}_1 - \bar{y}_2) - (\mu_1 - \mu_2)}{s_{\bar{y}_1 - \bar{y}_2}} = \frac{(\bar{y}_1 - \bar{y}_2)}{s_{\bar{y}_1 - \bar{y}_2}}$$

where $(\bar{y}_1 - \bar{y}_2)$ is the degree of difference between sample means of population 1 and 2 and $s_{\bar{y}_1 - \bar{y}_2}$ expresses the level of precision in the difference. If the null hypothesis is true and the two populations have identical means, we might expect that the means of samples collected from the two populations would be similar and thus the difference in means would be close to 0, as would the value of the t-statistic. Since populations and thus samples are variable, it is unlikely that two samples will have identical means, even if they are collected from identical populations (or the same population). Therefore, if the two populations were repeatedly sampled (with comparable collection technique and sample size) and t-statistics calculated, it would be expected that 50% of the time, the mean of sample 1 would be greater than that of population 2 and *visa versa*. Hence, 50% of the time, the value of the t-statistic would be greater than 0 and 50% of the time it would be less than 0. Furthermore, samples that are very different from one another (yielding large positive or negative t-values), although possible, would rarely be obtained.

All the possible values of the t-statistic (and thus sample combinations) calculated for a specific sample size for the situation when the null hypothesis is true could be collated and a histogram generated (see Figure 6.1a). From a frequentist perspective, this represents the sampling or probability distribution for the t-statistic calculated from repeated samples of a specific sample size (*degrees of freedom*) collected under the situation when the null hypothesis is true. That is, it represents all the possible expected t-values we might expect when there is no effect. When certain conditions (assumptions) are met, these t-values follow a known distribution called a t-distribution (see Figure 6.1b) for which the exact mathematical formula is known. The area under the entire t-distribution (curve) is one, and thus, areas under regions of the curve

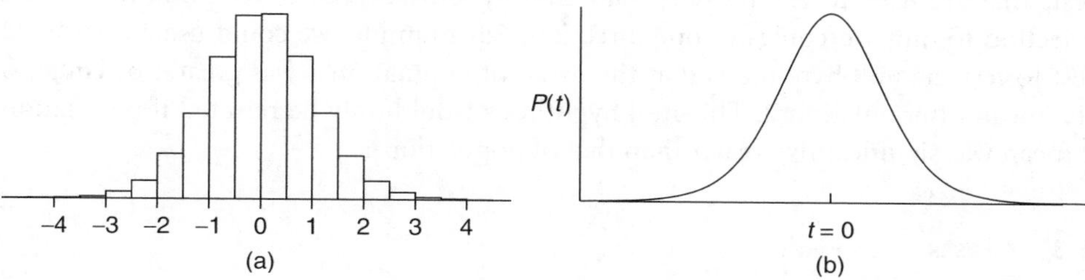

Fig 6.1 Distribution of all possible values of the t-statistic calculated from samples (each comprising of 10 observations) collected from two identical populations (situation when null hypothesis is true) represented as a (a) histogram and (b) t-distribution with 18 degrees of freedom ($df = (n_1 - 1) + (n_2 - 1) = 18$).

can be calculated, which in turn represent the relative frequencies (probabilities) of obtaining t-values in those regions. From the above example, the probability (p-value) of obtaining a t-value of greater than zero when the null hypothesis is true (population means equal) is 0.5 (50%).

When real samples are collected from two populations, the null hypothesis that the two population means are equal is tested by calculating the real value of the t-statistic, and using an appropriate t-distribution to calculate the probability of obtaining the observed (data) t-value or ones more extreme when the null hypothesis is true. If this probability is very low (below a set critical value, typically 0.05 or 5%), it is unlikely that the sample(s) could have come from such population(s) and thus the null hypothesis is unlikely to be true. This then provides evidence that the hypothesis is true.

Similarly, all other forms of hypothesis testing follow the same principle. The value of a test statistic that has been calculated from collected data is compared to the appropriate probability distribution for that statistic. If the probability of obtaining the observed value of the test statistic (or ones more extreme) when the null hypothesis is true is less than a predefined critical value, the null hypothesis is rejected, otherwise it is not rejected.

Note that the probability distributions of test statistics are strictly defined under a specific set of conditions. For example, the t-distribution is calculated for theoretical populations that are exactly normal (see chapter 3) and of identical variability. The further the actual populations (and thus samples) deviate from these ideal conditions, the less reliably the theoretical probability distributions will approximate the actual distribution of possible values of the test statistic, and thus, the less reliable the resulting hypothesis test.

6.2 One- and two-tailed tests

Two-tailed tests are any test used to test a null hypotheses that can be rejected by large deviations from expected in either direction. For example, when testing the null hypothesis that two population means are equal, the null hypothesis could be rejected if either population was greater than the other. By contrast one-tailed tests are those tests that are used to test more specific null hypotheses that restrict null hypothesis rejection to only outcomes in one direction. For example, we could use a one-tailed test to test the null hypothesis that the mean of population 1 was greater or equal to the mean of population 2. This null hypothesis would only be rejected if population 2 mean was significantly greater than that of population 1.

6.3 *t*-tests

Single population (one sample) t-tests

Single population t-tests are used to test null hypotheses that a population parameter is equal to a specific value ($H_0 : \mu = \theta$, where θ is typically 0), and are thus useful for testing coefficients of regression and correlation or for testing whether measured differences are equal to zero.

Two population t-tests

Two population t-tests are used to test null hypotheses that two independent populations are equal with respect to some parameter (typically the mean, e.g. $H_0 : \mu_1 = \mu_2$). The t-test formula presented in section 6.1 above is used in the original student or pooled variances t-test. The separate variances t-test (Welch's test), represents an improvement of the t-test in that more appropriately accomodates samples with modestly unequal variances.

Paired samples t-tests

When observations are collected from a population in pairs such that a single variable is measured twice from each sampling unit, a paired t-test can be used to test the null hypothesis that the population mean difference between paired observations is equal to zero ($H_0 : \mu_d = 0$). Note that this is equivalent to a single population t-test testing a null hypotheses that the population parameter is equal to the specific value of zero.

6.4 Assumptions

The theoretical t-distributions were formulated for samples collected from theoretical populations that are 1) **normally distributed** (see section 3.1.1) and 2) **equally varied**. Consequently, the theoretical t-distribution will only strictly represent the distribution of all possible values of the t-statistic when the populations from which real samples are collected also conform to these conditions. Hypothesis tests that impose distributional assumptions are known as *parametric tests*. Although substantial deviations from normality and/or homogeneity of variance reduce the reliability of the t-distribution and thus p-values and conclusions, t-tests are reasonably robust to violations of normality and to a lesser degree, homogeneity of variance (provided sample sizes are equal).

As with most hypothesis tests, t-tests also assume 3) **that each of the observations are independent** (or that pairs are independent of one another in the case of paired t-tests). If observations are not independent, then a sample may not be an unbiased representation of the entire population, and therefore any resulting analyses could completely misrepresent any biological effects.

6.5 Statistical decision and power

Recall that probability distributions are typically symmetrical, bell-shaped distributions that define the relative frequencies (probabilities) of all possible outcomes and suggest that progressively more extreme outcomes become progressively less frequent or likely. By convention however, the statistical criteria for any given hypothesis test is a watershed value typically set at 0.05 or 5%. Belying the gradational decline in probabilities, outcomes with a probability less than 5% are considered unlikely whereas values equal to or greater are considered likely. However, values less than 5% are of course possible and could be obtained if the samples were by chance not centered similarly in the population(s) – that is, if the sample(s) were atypical of the population(s).

When rejecting a null hypothesis at the 5% level, we are therefore accepting that there is a 5% change that we are making an error (a **Type I error**). We are concluding that there is an effect or trend, yet it is possible that there really there is no trend, we just had unusual samples. Conversely, when a null hypothesis is not rejected (probability of 5% or greater) and a trend or effect really exists in the population, a **Type II error** has been committed. Hence, a Type II error is when you fail to detect an effect that really occurs.

Since rejecting a null hypothesis is considered to be evidence of a hypothesis or theory and therefore scientific advancement, the scientific community projects itself against too many false rejections by keeping the statistical criteria and thus Type I error rate low (5%). However, as Type I and Type II error rates are linked, doing so leaves the Type II error rate (β) relatively large (approximately 20%).

The reciprocal of the Type II error rate, is called *power*. Power is the probability that a test will detect an effect (reject a null hypothesis, not make a Type II error) if one really occurs. Power is proportional to the statistical criteria, and thus lowering the statistical criteria compromises power. The conventional value of $\alpha = 0.05$) represents a compromise between Type I error rate and power.

Power is also affected by other aspects of a research framework and can be described by the following general representation:

$$power(1-\beta) \propto \frac{ES\sqrt{n}\,\alpha}{\sigma}$$

Statistical power is:

- directly proportional to the effect size (*ES*) which is the absolute size or magnitude of the effect or trend in the population. The more subtle the difference or effect, the lower the power
- directly proportional to the sample size (n). The greater the sample size, the greater the power
- directly proportional to the significance level ($\alpha = 0.05$) as previously indicated
- inversely proportional to the population standard deviation (σ). The more variable the population, the lower the power

When designing an experiment or survey, a researcher would usually like to know how many replicates are going to be required. Consequently, the above relationship is often transposed to express it in terms of sample size for a given amount of power:

$$n \propto \frac{(power\ \sigma)^2}{ES\ \alpha}$$

Researchers typically aim for power of at least 0.8 (80% probability of detecting an effect if one exists). Effect size and population standard deviation are derived from either pilot studies, previous research, documented regulations or gut feeling.

6.6 Robust tests

There are a number of more robust (yet less powerful) alternatives to independent samples t-tests and paired t-tests. The **Mann-Whitney-Wilcoxon** test[b] is a non-parametric (rank-based) equivalent of the independent samples t-test that uses the ranks of the observations to calculate test statistics rather than the actual observations and tests the null hypothesis that the two sampled populations have equal distributions. Similarly, the non-parametric **Wilcoxon signed-rank** test uses the sums of positive and negative signed ranked differences between paired observations to test the null hypothesis that the two sets of observations come from the one population. While neither test dictate that sampled populations must follow a specific distribution, the Wilcoxon signed-rank test does assume that the population differences are symmetrically distributed about the median and the Mann-Whitney test assumes that the sampled populations are equally varied (although violations of this assumption apparently have little impact). **Randomization tests** in which the factor levels are repeatedly shuffled so as to yield a probability distribution for the relevant statistic (such as the t-statistic) specific to the sample data do not have any distributional assumptions. Strictly however, randomization tests examine whether the sample patterns could have occurred by chance and do not pertain to the underlying populations. Furthermore, randomization tests do still assume equal variances.

6.7 Further reading

- Theory

  Fowler, J., L. Cohen, and P. Jarvis. (1998). *Practical statistics for field biology.* John Wiley & Sons, England.

  Hollander, M., and D. A. Wolfe. (1999). *Nonparametric statistical methods, 2nd edition.* John Wiley & Sons, New York.

  Manly, B. F. J. (1991). *Randomization and Monte Carlo methods in biology.* Chapman & Hall, London.

  Quinn, G. P., and K. J. Keough. (2002). *Experimental design and data analysis for biologists.* Cambridge University Press, London.

  Sokal, R., and F. J. Rohlf. (1997). *Biometry, 3rd edition.* W. H. Freeman, San Francisco.

  Zar, G. H. (1999). *Biostatistical methods.* Prentice-Hall, New Jersey.

- Practice - R

  Crawley, M. J. (2007). *The R Book.* John Wiley, New York.

  Dalgaard, P. (2002). *Introductory Statistics with R.* Springer-Verlag, New York.

  Maindonald, J. H., and J. Braun. (2003). *Data Analysis and Graphics Using R - An Example-based Approach.* Cambridge University Press, London.

  Wilcox, R. R. (2005). *Introduction to Robust Estimation and Hypothesis Testing.* Elsevier Academic Press.

[b] The Mann-Whitney U-test and the Wilcoxon two-sample test are two computationally different tests that yield identical statistics. Note, that estimating power *after* having performed a hypothesis test is generally considered nonsensical.

6.8 Key for simple hypothesis testing

1 a. Mean of single sample compared to a specific fixed value (such as a predicted population mean) (one-sample t-test) .... Go to 3

b. Two samples used to compare the means of two populations .... Go to 2

2 a. Two completely independent samples (different sampling units used for each replicate of each condition) (independent samples t-test) .... Go to 3

FACTOR	DV
A	.
A	.
..	..
B	.
B	.
..	..

Dataset should be constructed in long format such that the variables are in columns and each replicate is in is own row.

b. Two samples specifically paired (each of the sampling units measured under both conditions) to reduce within-group variation (paired t-test) .... Go to 3

Pair	FACTOR	DV
1	A	.
2	A	.
..	..	..
1	B	.
2	B	.
..	..	

Dataset can be constructed in either long format (left) such that the variables are in columns and each replicate is in is own row or in wide format (right) such that each pair of measurements has its own row.

Pair	DV1	DV2
1	.	.
2	.	.
3	.	.
4	.	.
5	.	.
..	..	..

3 a. Check parametric assumptions

- **Normality of the response variable at both levels (unless one sample t-test) of the categorical variable - boxplots**
  - *one-sample t-test*

```
> boxplot(DV, dataset)
```

  - *two-sample t-test*

```
> boxplot(DV ~ Factor, dataset)
```

  - *paired t-test*

```
> with(dataset, boxplot(DV1 - DV2))
> diffs <- with(dataset, DV[FACTOR == "A"]
+     - DV[FACTOR == "B"])
> boxplot(diffs)
```

where `DV` *and* `Factor` *are response and factor variables respectively in the* `dataset` *data frame.* `DV1` *and* `DV2` *represent the paired responses for group one and two of a paired t-test. Note, paired t-test data is traditionally setup in wide format (see section 2.7.6)*

- **Homogeneity of variance (two-sample t-tests only) - boxplots (as above) and scatterplot of mean vs variance**

```
> boxplot(DV ~ Factor, dataset)
```

where `DV` *and* `FACTOR` *are response and factor variables respectively in the* `dataset` *data frame*

Parametric assumptions met .... Go to 4

b. Parametric assumptions NOT met .... Go to 5

4 a. Perform one-sample t-test

```
> t.test(DV, dataset)
```

b. Perform (separate variances) independent-sample t-test .... See Example 6B

- *one-tailed* ($H_0 : \mu_A > \mu_B$)

```
> t.test(DV ~ FACTOR, dataset, alternative = "greater")
```

- *two-tailed* ($H_0 : \mu_A = \mu_B$)

```
> t.test(DV ~ FACTOR, dataset)
```

for pooled variances t-tests, include the `var.equal=T` *argument (see Example 6A).*

c. Perform (separate variances) paired t-test .... See Example 6C

- *one-tailed* ($H_0 : \mu_A > \mu_B$)

```
> t.test(DV1, DV2, dataset, alternative = "greater")
> t.test(DV ~ FACTOR, dataset, alternative = "greater",
+     paired = T)
```

- *two-tailed* ($H_0 : \mu_A = \mu_B$)

```
> t.test(DV1, DV2, dataset)
> t.test(DV ~ FACTOR, dataset, paired = T)
```

for pooled variances t-tests, include the `var.equal=T` *argument.*

5 a. Attempt a scale transformation (see Table 3.2 for common transformations) .... Go to 3

b. Transformations unsuccessful or inappropriate .... Go to 6

6 a. Underlying distribution of the response variable and residuals is non-normal, yet known .... GLM chapter 17

b. Underlying distribution of the response variable and residuals is non-normal and is NOT known .... Go to 7

7 a. Observations independent or specifically paired, variances not wildly unequal (Wilcoxon rank sum nonparametric test) .... Go to 8

b. Variances not wildly unequal, random sampling not possible (Randomization test) .... See Example 6E

```
> library(boot)
> data.boot <- boot(dataset, stat, R = 999, sim = "parametric",
+     rand.gen = rand.gen)
> plot(data.boot)
> print(data.boot)
```

where `stat` *is the statistic to repeatedly calculate and* `rand.gen` *defines how the data are randomized.*

8 a. Perform one-sample Wilcoxon (rank sum) test

```
> wilcox.test(DV, dataset)
```

b. Perform independent-sample Mann-Whitney Wilcoxon test ..... See Example 6D

- *one-tailed* ($H_0 : \mu_A > \mu_B$)

```
> wilcox.test(DV ~ FACTOR, dataset, alternative = "greater")
```

- *two-tailed* ($H_0 : \mu_A = \mu_B$)

```
> wilcox.test(DV ~ FACTOR, dataset)
```

c. Perform paired Wilcoxon (signed rank) test

- *one-tailed* ($H_0 : \mu_A > \mu_B$)

```
> wilcox.test(DV1,DV2, dataset, alternative="greater")
> #OR for long format
> wilcox.test(DV~FACTOR, dataset, alternative="greater",
+ paired=T)
```

- *two-tailed* ($H_0 : \mu_A = \mu_B$)

```
> wilcox.test(DV1, DV2, dataset)
> wilcox.test(DV ~ FACTOR, dataset, paired = T)
```

6.9 Worked examples of real biological data sets

Example 6A: Pooled variances, student t-test

Ward and Quinn (1988) investigated differences in the fecundity (as measured by egg production) of a predatory intertidal gastropod (*Lepsiella vinosa*) in two different intertidal zones (mussel zone and the higher littorinid zone) (Box 3.2 of Quinn and Keough (2002)).

Step 1 - Import (section 2.3) the Ward and Quinn (1988) data set.

```
> ward <- read.table("ward.csv", header = T, sep = ",")
```

Step 2 (Key 6.3) - Assess assumptions of normality and homogeneity of variance for the null hypothesis that the population mean egg production is the same for both littorinid and mussel zone *Lepsiella*.

```
> boxplot(EGGS ~ ZONE, ward)
```

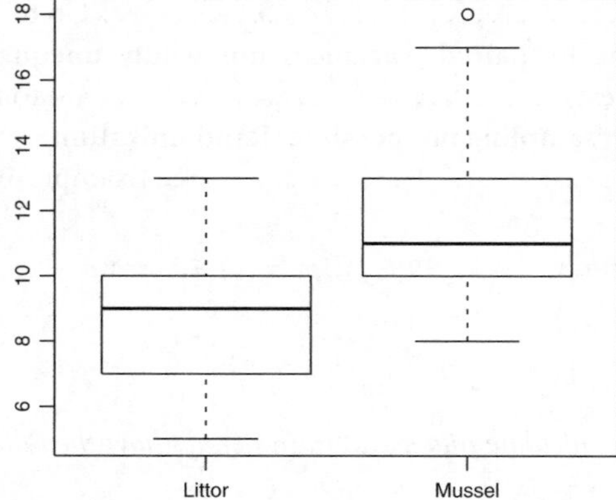

```
> with(ward, rbind(MEAN = tapply(EGGS, ZONE, mean),
+      VAR = tapply(EGGS, ZONE, var)))
       Littor    Mussel
MEAN 8.702703 11.357143
VAR  4.103604  5.357143
```

Conclusions - There was no evidence of non-normality (boxplots not grossly asymmetrical) or unequal variance (boxplots very similar size and variances very similar). Hence, the simple, studentized (pooled variances) *t*-test is likely to be reliable.

Step 3 (Key 6.4b) - Perform a pooled variances *t*-test to test the null hypothesis that the population mean egg production is the same for both littorinid and mussel zone *Lepsiella*.

```
> t.test(EGGS ~ ZONE, ward, var.equal = T)
        Two Sample t-test

data:  EGGS by ZONE
t = -5.3899, df = 77, p-value = 7.457e-07
alternative hypothesis: true difference in means is not equal to 0
95 percent confidence interval:
 -3.635110 -1.673770
sample estimates:
mean in group Littor mean in group Mussel
            8.702703            11.357143
```

Conclusions - Reject the null hypothesis. Egg production by predatory gastropods (*Lepsiella vinosa* was significantly greater ($t_{77} = -5.39, P < 0.001$) in mussel zones than littorinid zones on rocky intertidal shores.

Summarize the trends with a bargraph.

```
> ward.means <- with(ward, tapply(EGGS, ZONE, mean))
> ward.sds <- with(ward, tapply(EGGS, ZONE, sd))
> ward.ns <- with(ward, tapply(EGGS, ZONE, length))
> ward.se <- ward.sds/sqrt(ward.ns)
> xs <- barplot(ward.means, ylim = range(pretty(c(ward.means +
+     ward.se, ward.means - ward.se))), axes = F, xpd = F,
+     axisnames = F, axis.lty = 2, legend.text = F, col = "gray")
> arrows(xs, ward.means + ward.se, xs, ward.means - ward.se,
+     code = 3, angle = 90, len = 0.05)
> axis(2, las = 1)
> axis(1, at = xs, lab = c("Littorinid", "Mussel"), padj = 1,
+     mgp = c(0, 0, 0))
> mtext(2, text = "Mean number of egg capsules per capsule",
+     line = 3, cex = 1)
> mtext(1, text = "Zone", line = 3, cex = 1)
> box(bty = "l")
```

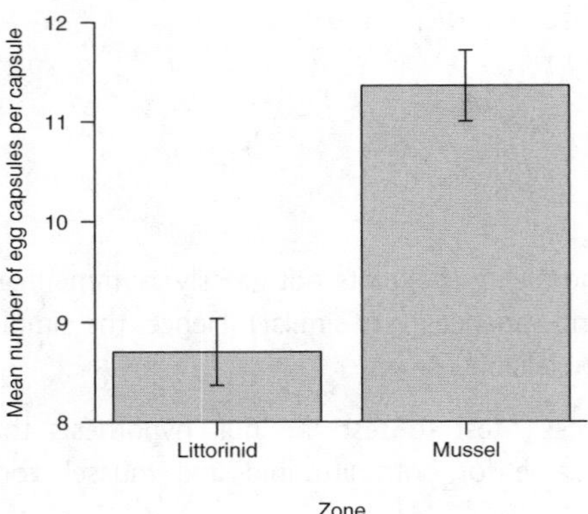

Example 6B: Separate variances, Welch's t-test

Furness and Bryant (1996) measured the metabolic rates of eight male and six female breeding northern fulmars and were interesting in testing the null hypothesis that there was no difference in metabolic rate between the sexes (Box 3.2 of Quinn and Keough (2002)).

Step 1 - Import (section 2.3) the Furness and Bryant (1996) data set.

```
> furness <- read.table("furness.csv", header = T, sep = ",")
```

Step 2 (Key 6.3) - Assess assumptions of normality and homogeneity of variance for the null hypothesis that the population mean metabolic rate is the same for male and female breeding northern fulmars.

```
> boxplot(METRATE ~ SEX, furness)
```

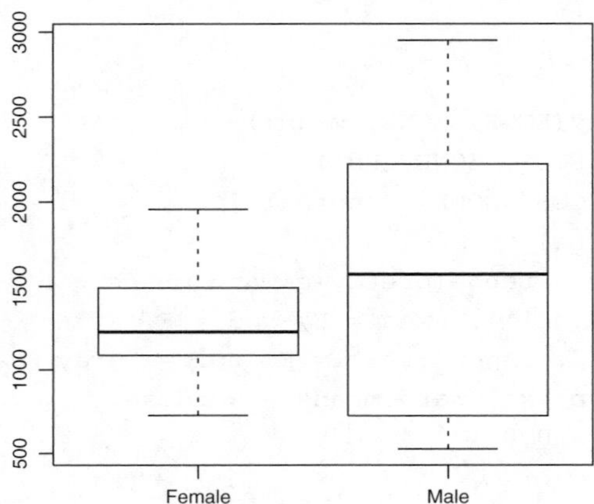


```
> with(furness, rbind(MEAN = tapply(METRATE, SEX, mean),
+      VAR = tapply(METRATE, SEX, var)))
       Female        Male
MEAN     1285.517    1563.775
VAR    177209.418  799902.525
```

Conclusions - Whilst there is no evidence of non-normality (boxplots not grossly asymmetrical), variances are a little unequal (although perhaps not grossly unequal - one of the boxplots is not more than three times smaller than the other). Hence, a separate variances *t*-test is more appropriate than a pooled variances *t*-test.

Step 3 (Key 6.4b) - Perform a separate variances (Welch's) *t*-test to test the null hypothesis that the population mean metabolic rate is the same for both male and female breeding northern fulmars.

```
> t.test(METRATE ~ SEX, furness, var.equal = F)
        Welch Two Sample t-test

data:  METRATE by SEX
t = -0.7732, df = 10.468, p-value = 0.4565
alternative hypothesis: true difference in means is not equal to 0
95 percent confidence interval:
 -1075.3208   518.8042
sample estimates:
mean in group Female       mean in group Male
            1285.517                 1563.775
```

Conclusions - Do not reject the null hypothesis. Metabolic rate of male breeding northern fulmars was not found to differ significantly ($t = -0.773$, $df = 10.468$, $P = 0.457$) from that of females.

Example 6C: Paired t-test

To investigate the effects of lighting conditions on the orb-spinning spider webs Elgar et al. (1996) measured the horizontal (width) and vertical (height) dimensions of the webs made by 17 spiders under light and dim conditions. Accepting that the webs of individual spiders vary considerably, Elgar et al. (1996) employed a paired design in which each individual spider effectively acts as its own control. A paired *t*-test performs a one sample *t*-test on the differences between dimensions under light and dim conditions (Box 3.3 of Quinn and Keough (2002)).

Step 1 - Import (section 2.3) the Elgar et al. (1996) data set.

```
> elgar <- read.table("elgar.csv", header = T, sep = ",")
```

Note the format of this data set. Rather than organizing the data into the usual long format in which variables are represented in columns and rows represent individual replicates, these data have been organized in wide format. Wide format is often used for data containing repeated measures from individual or other sampling units. Whilst, this is not necessary (as paired *t*-tests can be performed on long format data), traditionally it did allow more compact data management as well as making it easier to calculate the differences between repeated measurements on each individual.

Step 2 (Key 6.3) - Assess whether the differences in web width (and height) in light and dim light conditions are normally distributed.

```
> with(elgar, boxplot(HORIZLIG -
+ HORIZDIM))
```

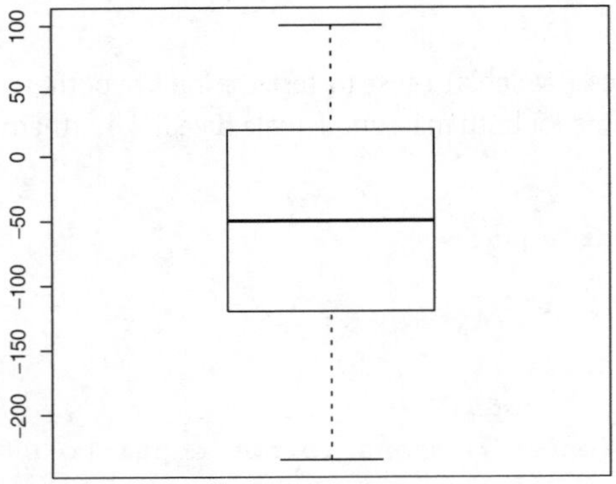

```
> with(elgar, boxplot(VERTLIGH -
+ VERTDIM))
```

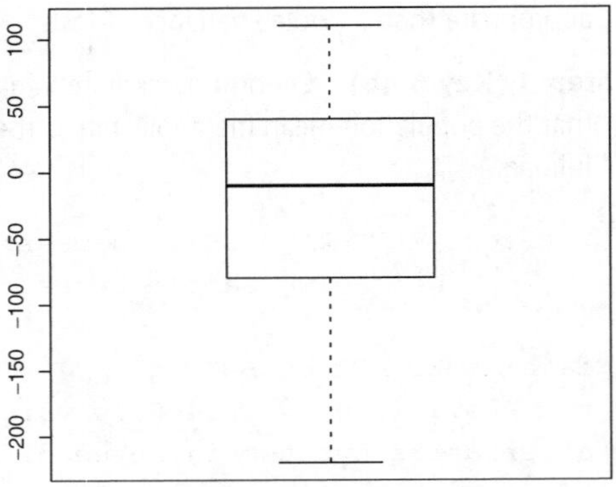

Conclusions - There is no evidence of non-normality for either the difference in widths or heights of webs under light and dim ambient conditions. Therefore paired *t*-tests are likely to be reliable tests of the hypotheses that the mean web dimensional differences are equal to zero.

Step 3 (Key 6.4c) - Perform two separate paired *t*-tests to test the test the respective null hypotheses.

- No effect of lighting on web width

```
> with(elgar, t.test(HORIZLIG, HORIZDIM, paired = T))
        Paired t-test

data:  HORIZLIG and HORIZDIM
t = -2.1482, df = 16, p-value = 0.04735
alternative hypothesis: true difference in means is not
 equal to 0
95 percent confidence interval:
 -91.7443687  -0.6085725
sample estimates:
mean of the differences
              -46.17647
```

- No effect of lighting on web height

```
> with(elgar, t.test(VERTLIGH, VERTDIM, paired = T))
        Paired t-test

data:  VERTLIGH and VERTDIM
t = -0.9654, df = 16, p-value = 0.3487
alternative hypothesis: true difference in means is not
 equal to 0
```

```
95 percent confidence interval:
 -65.79532  24.61885
sample estimates:
mean of the differences
              -20.58824
```

Conclusions - Orb-spinning spider webs were found to be significantly wider ($t = 2.148$, $df = 16$, $P = 0.047$) under dim lighting conditions than light conditions, yet were not found to differ ($t = 0.965$, $df = 16$, $P = 0.349$) in height.

Example 6D: Non-parametric Mann-Whitney-Wilcoxon signed rank test

Sokal and Rohlf (1997) presented a dataset comprising the lengths of cheliceral bases (in μm) from two samples of chigger (*Trombicula lipovskyi*) nymphs. These data were used to illustrate two equivalent tests (Mann-Whitney U-test and Wilcoxon two-sample test) of location equality (Box 13.7 of Sokal and Rohlf (1997)).

Step 1 - Import (section 2.3) the nymph data set.

```
> nymphs <- read.table("nymphs.csv", header = T, sep = ",")
```

Step 2 (Key 6.3) - Assess assumptions of normality and homogeneity of variance for the null hypothesis that the population mean cheliceral base lengths is the same for two samples of female chigger nymphs.

```
> boxplot(LENGTH ~ SAMPLE, nymphs)
```

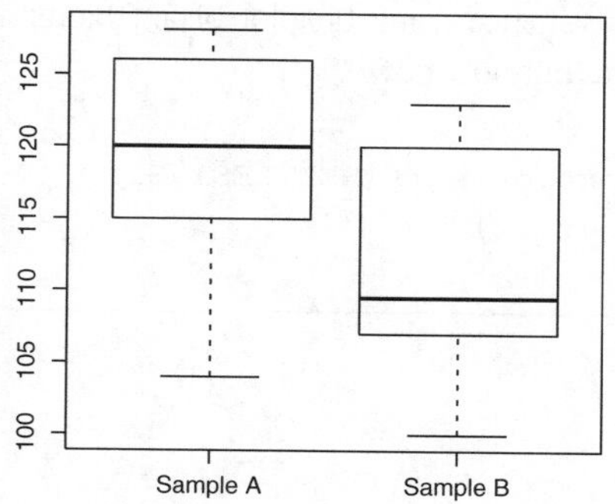


```
> with(nymphs, rbind(MEAN = tapply(LENGTH, SAMPLE, mean),
+      VAR = tapply(LENGTH, SAMPLE, var)))
      Sample A  Sample B
MEAN 119.68750 111.80000
VAR   53.29583  60.17778
```

Conclusions - Whilst there is no evidence of unequal variance, there is some (possible) evidence of non-normality (boxplots slightly asymmetrical). These data will therefore be analysed using a non-parametric Mann-Whitney-Wilcoxon signed rank test.

Step 3 (Key 6.8b) - Perform a Mann-Whitney Wilcoxon test to investigate the null hypothesis that the mean length of cheliceral bases is the same for the two samples of nymphs of chigger (*Trombicular lipovskyi*).

```
> wilcox.test(LENGTH ~ SAMPLE, nymphs)
        Wilcoxon rank sum test with continuity correction

data:  LENGTH by SAMPLE
W = 123.5, p-value = 0.02320
alternative hypothesis: true location shift is not equal to 0
```

Conclusions - Reject the null hypothesis. The length of the cheliceral base is significantly longer in nymphs from sample 1 ($W = 123.5, df = 24, P = 0.023$) than those from sample 2.

Example 6E: Randomization t-test

Powell and Russell (1984, 1985) investigated differences in beetle consumption between two size classes of eastern horned lizard (*Phrynosoma douglassi brevirostre*) represented respectively by adult females in the larger class and adult male and yearling females in the smaller class (Example 4.1 from Manly, 1991).

Step 1 - Import (section 2.3) the Powell and Russell (1984, 1985) beetle data set.

```
> beetles <- read.table("beetle.csv", header = T, sep = ",")
```

Step 2 (Key 6.3) - Assess normality/homogeneity of variance using boxplot of ant biomass against month. Cube root transformation also assessed, but not shown.

```
> boxplot(BEETLES~SIZE,
+ beetles)
```

```
> boxplot(sqrt(BEETLES)~SIZE,
+ beetles)
```

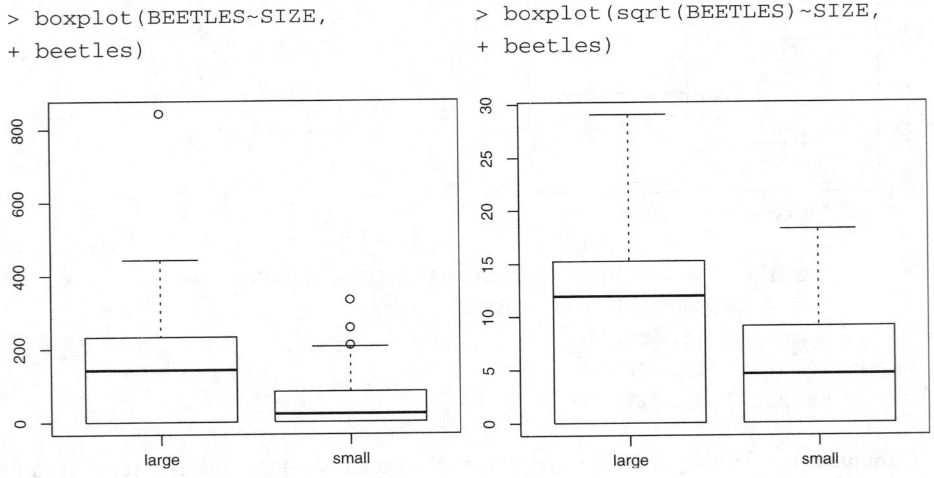

Conclusions - strong evidence of non-normality and lots of zero values. As a result a randomization test in which the *t*-distribution is generated from the samples, might be more robust than a standard *t*-test that assumes each of the populations are normally distributed.

Furthermore, the observations need not be independent, provided we are willing to concede that we are no longer testing hypotheses about populations (rather, we are estimating the probability of obtaining the observed differences in beetle consumption between the size classes just by chance).

Step 3 (Key 6.7b) - define the statistic to use in the randomization test – in this case the *t*-statistic (without replacement).

```
> stat <- function(data, indices) {
+       t.stat <- t.test(BEETLES ~ SIZE, data)$stat
+       t.stat
+ }
```

Step 4 (Key 6.7b) - define how the data should be randomized – randomly reorder the which size class that each observation belonged to.

```
> rand.gen <- function(data, mle) {
+       out <- data
+       out$SIZE <- sample(out$SIZE, replace = F)
+       out
+ }
```

Step 5 (Key 6.7b) - call a bootstrapping procedure to randomize 5000 times (this can take some time).

```
> library(boot)

> beetles.boot <- boot(beetles, stat, R = 5000, sim = "parametric",
+       ran.gen = rand.gen)
```

Step 6 (Key 6.7b) - examine the distribution of *t*-statistics generated from the randomization procedure

```
> print(beetles.boot)
PARAMETRIC BOOTSTRAP


Call:
boot(data = beetles, statistic = stat, R = 5000, sim = "parametric",
    ran.gen = rand.gen)


Bootstrap Statistics :
    original     bias    std. error
t1* 2.190697 -2.237551    1.019904

> plot(beetles.boot)
```

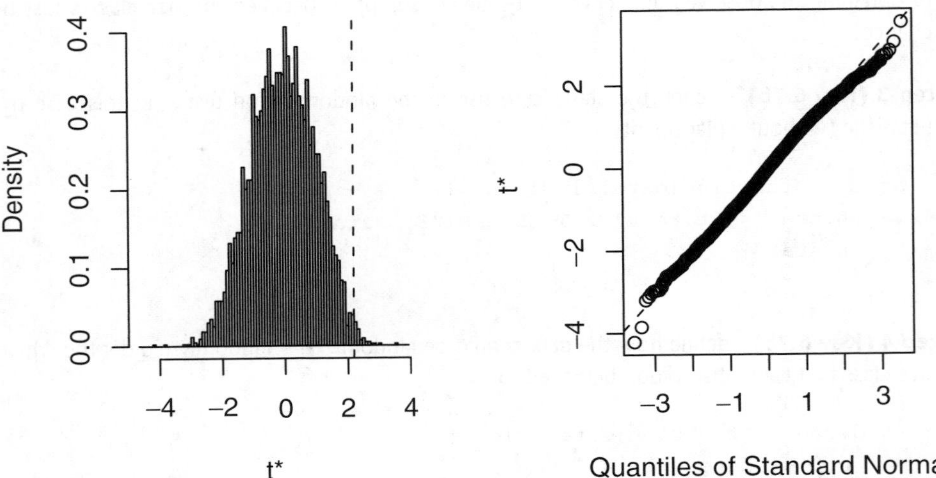

Conclusions - The observed *t*-value was 2.191. Note that the *t*-distribution is centered around zero and thus a *t*-value of 2.191 is equivalent to a *t*-value of −2.191. Only the magnitude of a *t*-value is important, not the sign. Also note that as the procedure is a randomization, the exact shape will vary each time it is run (unless a seed is specified).

Step 7 (Key 6.7b) - calculate the number of possible *t*-values (including the observed *t*-value, which is one possible situation) that were greater or equal to the observed *t*-value and express this as a percentage of the number of randomizations (plus one for the observed situation) performed.

```
> tval <- length(beetles.boot[beetles.boot$t >= abs(beetles.
+       boot$t0)]) + 1
# one-tailed test
> tval/(beetles.boot$R + 1)
[1] 0.00759848
# two-tailed test
> 2*(tval/(beetles.boot$R + 1))
[1] 0.01519696
```

Conclusions - Reject the null hypothesis that the difference in beetle consumption between small and large lizards is purely due to chance. It is likely that beetle consumption is significantly higher in large female eastern horned lizards than the smaller adult males and yearling females ($t = 2.191, R = 5000, P = 0.015$).

7

Introduction to Linear models

A **statistical model** is an expression that attempts to explain patterns in the observed values of a response variable by relating the response variable to a set of predictor variables and parameters. Consider the following familiar statistical model:

$$y = mx + c$$

or equivalently:

$$y = bx + a$$

This simple statistical model relates a response variable (y) to a single predictor variable (x) as a straight line according to the values of two constant parameters:

b – the degree to which y changes per unit of change in x (gradient of line)

a – the value of y when $x = 0$ (y-intercept)

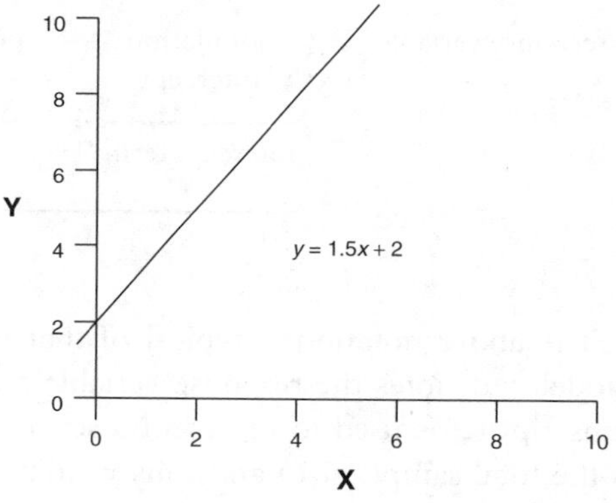

The above line (model) represents a perfect fit, that is, 100% of the change (variation) in y is explained by a change in x. However, rarely would this be the case when modeling biological variables. In complex biological systems, variables are typically the result of many influential and interacting factors and therefore simple models usually fail to fully explain a response variable. Consequently, the statistical model also has an *error* component that represents the portion of the response variable that the model fails to explain. Hence, statistical models are of the form:

$$\text{response variable} = \text{model} + \text{error}$$

where the model component comprises of one or more categorical and/or continuous predictor variable(s) and their parameter(s) that together represent the effect of the

Biostatistical Design and Analysis Using R: a Practical Guide, 1st edition. By M. Logan.
Published 2010 by Blackwell Publishing.

predictors variable(s) on the mean the response variable. A parameter and its associated predictor variable(s) are referred to as a model *term*.

A statistical model is fitted to observed data so as to estimate the model parameters and test hypotheses about these parameters (coefficients).

7.1 Linear models

Linear models are those statistical models in which a series of parameters are arranged as a linear combination. That is, within the model, no parameter appears as either a multiplier, divisor or exponent to any other parameter. Importantly, the term 'linear' in this context does not pertain to the nature of the relationship between the response variable and the predictor variable(s), and thus linear models are not restricted to 'linear' (straight-line) relationships.

An example of a very simple linear model, is the model used to investigate the linear relationship between a continuous response variable (*Y* and a single continuous predictor variable, *X*):

$$\begin{array}{rcccccccc} y_i & = & \beta_0 & + & \beta_1 & \times & x_i & + & \varepsilon_i \\ \text{response variable} & = & \text{population} & + & \text{population} & \times & \text{predictor} & + & \text{error} \\ & = & \text{intercept} & & \text{slope} & & \text{variable} & & \end{array}$$

$$\underbrace{\underbrace{\beta_0}_{\text{intercept term}} + \underbrace{\beta_1 \times x_i}_{\text{slope term}}}_{\text{model}}$$

The above notation is typical of that used to represent the elements of a linear model. *y* denotes the response variable and *x* represents the predictor variable. The subscript (*i*) is used to represent a set of observations (usually from 1 to *n* where *n* is the total sample size) and thus y_i and x_i represent respectively the ith observation of the *Y* and *X* variables. ε_i represents the deviation of the ith observed *Y* from the value of *Y* expected by the model component. The parameters β_0 and β_1 represent population intercept and population slope (effect of *X* on *Y* per unit of *x*) respectively. Population (effect) parameters are usually represented by Greek symbols[a]. The above linear model notation is therefore a condensed representation of a compilation of arithmetic relationships:

$$\begin{array}{ccccccccc} y_1 & = & \beta_0 & + & \beta_1 & \times & x_1 & + & \varepsilon_1 \\ y_2 & = & \beta_0 & + & \beta_1 & \times & x_2 & + & \varepsilon_2 \\ y_3 & = & \beta_0 & + & \beta_1 & \times & x_3 & + & \varepsilon_3 \\ \dots & \dots & \dots & \dots & \dots & \dots & \dots & \dots & \dots \end{array}$$

[a] Typically, effect parameters associated with continuous variables are represented by β and those associated with categorical variables are represented by the symbols $\alpha, \beta, \gamma, \dots$

the first y observation (y_1) is related to the first x observation (x_1) according to the values of the two constants (parameters β_0 and β_1) and ε_1 is the amount that the observed value of Y differs from the value expected according the model (the *residual*).

When there are multiple continuous predictor variables, in addition to the intercept parameter (β_0), the linear model includes a separate slope parameter for each of the predictor variables:

$$y_i = \beta_0 + \beta_1 x1_i + \beta_2 x2_i + ... + \varepsilon_i$$

The model structure for linear models containing a single categorical predictor variable (known as a factor) with two or more treatment levels (groups) is similar in form to the multiple linear regression model (listed immediately above) with the overall mean (μ) replacing the y-intercept (β_0). The factor levels (groups) are represented in the model by binary (contain only of 0s and 1s, see Table 7.1) *indicator* (or 'dummy') variables and associated estimable parameters (β_1, β_2, ...).

For a data set comprising of p groups and n replicates within each group, the linear model is:

$$y_{ij} = \mu + \beta_1(dummy_1)_{ij} + \beta_2(dummy_2)_{ij} + ... + \varepsilon_{ij}$$

where i represents the treatment levels (from 1 to p) and j represents the set of replicates (from 1 to n) within the ith group. Hence, y_{ij} represents the jth observation of the response variable within the ith group and $(dummy_1)_{ij}$ represents the dummy code for the jth replicate within the ith group of the first dummy variable (first treatment level).

The dummy variable for a particular treatment level contains all 0s except in the rows that correspond to observations that received that treatment level. Table 7.1 illustrates

Table 7.1 Fictitious data set (consisting of three replicates for each of three groups:'G1','G1','G2') to illustrate the link between a) single factor dataset, and b) the indicator (dummy) variables.

a)

y	A
2	G1
3	G1
4	G1
6	G2
7	G2
8	G2
10	G3
11	G3
12	G3

b)

y	$dummy_1$	$dummy_2$	$dummy_3$
2	1	0	0
3	1	0	0
4	1	0	0
6	0	1	0
7	0	1	0
8	0	1	0
10	0	0	1
11	0	0	1
12	0	0	1

the dummy coding for a single factor within three levels ('G1', 'G2', 'G3') each with three replicates[b].

More typically however, statistical models that include one or more factors are expressed as *effects models* in which the individual treatment levels (and their parameters) are represented by a single term (e.g. α_i) that denotes the effect of each of the levels of the factor on the overall mean. For a data set comprised of p groups and n replicates within each group, the linear effects model is:

$$y_{ij} = \mu + \alpha_i + \varepsilon_{ij}$$

where i represents the set of treatments (from 1 to p) and j represents the set of replicates (from 1 to n) within the ith group. Hence, y_{ij} represents the jth observation of the response variable within the ith group of the factor. μ is the overall population mean of the response variable (Y) and is equivalent to the intercept. α_i represents the effect of the ith group calculated as the difference between each of the group means and the overall mean ($\alpha_i = \mu_i - \mu$).

7.2 Linear models in R

Statistical models in R are represented by a formula corresponding to the linear model (for continuous variables) or effects model (categorical variables):

```
response~model
```

where the tilde (~) defines a model formula (and is interpreted as "as a function of") and `model` represents a set of terms to include in the model. Terms are included in a model via their variable names and terms preceded by the - (negative sign) operator are explicitly excluded. The intercept term (denoted by a 1) is implicit in the model and need not be specified. Hence the following model formulae all model the effect of the variable `X` on the `Y` variable with the inclusion of the intercept:

```
> Y~X
> Y~1+X
> Y~X+1
```

whereas the following exclude the intercept:

```
> Y~-1+X
> Y~X-1
```

Linear models are fitted by providing the model formula as an argument to the `lm()` *function*. To fit the simple linear regression model relating a fictitious response variable (`Y`) to fictitious continuous predictor variable (`X`):

[b] Note that linear model that this represents ($y_{ij} = \mu + \beta_1(dummy_1)_{ij} + \beta_2(dummy_2)_{ij} + \beta_3(dummy_3)_{ij} + \varepsilon_{ij}$) is over-parameterized, see section 7.3.

```
> Y<-c(0,1,2,4,7,10)
> X<-1:6
> plot(Y~X)
```

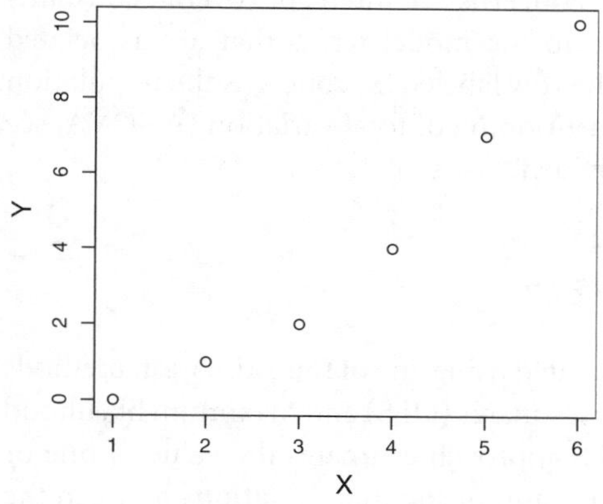

```
> Fictitious.lm <- lm(Y~X)
```

To examine the estimated parameters (and hypothesis tests) from the fitted model, provide the name of the fitted model as an argument to the `summary()` *function*[c].

```
> summary(Fictitious.lm)
Call:
lm(formula = Y ~ X)

Residuals:
        1          2          3          4          5          6
1.000e+00  3.404e-16 -1.000e+00 -1.000e+00  6.280e-17  1.000e+00

Coefficients:
            Estimate Std. Error t value Pr(>|t|)
(Intercept)  -3.0000     0.9309  -3.223  0.03220 *
X             2.0000     0.2390   8.367  0.00112 **
---
Signif. codes:  0 '***' 0.001 '**' 0.01 '*' 0.05 '.' 0.1 ' ' 1

Residual standard error: 1 on 4 degrees of freedom
Multiple R-squared: 0.9459,     Adjusted R-squared: 0.9324
F-statistic:    70 on 1 and 4 DF,  p-value: 0.001116
```

The summary output begins by specifying the nature of the call used to fit the model. Next is a summary of the residuals (differences between observed responses and

[c] Actually, the `summary()` function is an overloaded wrapper that invokes different specific functions depending on the class of object provided as the first argument. In this case, the `summary()` *function* invokes the `summary.lm()` *function*.

expected responses for each value of the predictor variable). The estimated parameters are listed in the coefficients table. Each row of the table lists the value of an estimated parameter from the linear model along with the outcome of a hypothesis test for this parameter. The row labeled '`(Intercept)`' concerns the intercept (overall constant) and subsequent rows are labeled according to the model terms that are associated with the estimated parameter. In this case, the row labeled '`x`' concerns the population slope (β_1). Finally a brief summary of the partitioning of total variation (ANOVA, see section 7.3.2) in the response variable is provided.

7.3 Estimating linear model parameters

During model fitting, parameters can be estimated using any of the estimation methods outlined in section 3.7, although ordinary least squares (OLS) and maximum likelihood (ML or REML) are most common. The OLS approach estimates the value of one or more parameters such that they minimize the sum of squared deviations between the observed values and the parameter (typically the values predicted by the model) and will be illustrated in detail in the following sections. Models that utilize OLS parameter estimates are referred to as 'general' linear models as they accommodate both continuous and categorical predictor variables. Broadly speaking, such models that incorporate purely continuous predictor variables are referred to as 'regression' models (see chapters 8 & 9) whereas models that purely incorporate categorical predictors are called 'ANOVA' models (see chapters 10 – 14). Analysis of covariance (ANCOVA) models incorporate both categorical and continuous predictor variables (see chapter 15).

ML estimators estimate one or more population parameters such that the (log) likelihood of obtaining the observed values from such populations is maximized and these models are useful when there is evidence of a relationship between mean and variance or for models involving correlated data structures. Maximum likelihood parameter estimation is also utilized by 'generalized' linear models, so called as they are not restricted to normally distributed response and residuals. Generalized linear models accommodate any exponential probability distribution (including normal, binomial, Poisson, gamma and negative binomial), see chapter 17.

The parameters estimated during simple linear and multiple linear regression analyses are relatively straightforward to interpret (they simply represent the rates of change in the response variable attributable to each individual predictor variable) and can be used to construct an algebraic representation of the relationship between a response variable and one or more predictor variables. However, this is generally not the case for linear models containing factorial variables.

7.3.1 Linear models with factorial variables

Recall from section 7.1 that linear models comprising of a single factor are expressed as an effects model:

$$y_{ij} = \mu + \alpha_i + \varepsilon_{ij}$$

where α_i estimates the effect of each treatment group on the overall mean of groups ($\alpha_i = \mu_i - \mu$). However, the effects model for a factor with p groups, will have $p + 1$ parameters (the overall mean μ plus the p α parameters), and thus the linear effects model is considered to be 'over-parameterized'[d]. In order to obtain parameter estimates, the model must be reduced to a total of p parameters. Over-parameterization can be resolved either by removing one of the parameters from the effects model (either the overall mean (μ) or one of the treatment effects (α_i) parameters - a procedure rarely used in biology), or by generating a new set ($p - 1$) of effects parameters (α_q^*, where q represents the set of orthogonal parameters from 1 to $p - 1$) each of which represent a linear combination of groups rather than a single group effect. That is, each α^* can include varying contributions from any number of the groups and are not restricted to a single contrast of ($= \mu_i - \mu$). For example, one of the parameters might represent the difference in means between two groups or the difference in means between one group and the average of two other groups. The reduced number of effects parameters are defined through the use of a matrix of 'contrast coefficients'. Note, the new set of effects parameters should incorporate the overall relational effects of each of the groups equally such that each group maintains an equal contribution to the overall model fit.

A number of 'pre-fabricated', contrast matrices exist, each of which estimate a different set of specific comparisons between treatment combinations. The most common contrasts types include:

Treatment contrasts - in which each of the treatment groups means are compared to the mean of a 'control' group. This approach to over-parameterization is computationally identical to fitting $p - 1$ dummy variables via multiple linear regression. However, due to the interpretation of the parameters (groups compared to a control) and the fact that treatment effects are not orthogonal to the intercept, the interpretation of treatment contrasts (and thus dummy regression) is really only meaningful for situations where there is clearly a single group (control) to which the other groups can be compared. For treatment contrasts, the intercept is replaced by α_1^* and thus the remaining α_q^* parameters are numbered starting at 2.

Parameter	Estimates	Null hypothesis
Intercept	mean of 'control' group (μ_1)	$H_0: \mu = \mu_1 = 0$
α_2^*	mean of group 2 minus mean of 'control' group ($\mu_2 - \mu_1$)	$H_0: \alpha_2^* = \mu_2 - \mu_1 = 0$
α_3^*	mean of group 3 minus mean of 'control' group ($\mu_3 - \mu_1$)	$H_0: \alpha_3^* = \mu_3 - \mu_1 = 0$
...		

[d] Given that $\alpha_i = \mu_i - \mu$, it is only possible to estimate $p - 1$ orthogonal (independent) parameters. For example, once μ and $p - 1$ of the effects parameters have been estimated, the final effects parameter is no longer 'free to vary' and therefore cannot be independently estimated. Likewise, if the full linear model contains as many dummy variables as there are treatment groups, then it too is over-parameterized.

```
> Y <- c(2,3,4,6,7,8,10,11,12)
> A <- gl(3,3,9,lab=c("G1","G2","G3"))
> # specify that treatment contrasts should be used
> contrasts(A) <-contr.treatment
> summary(lm(Y~A))
Call:
lm(formula = Y ~ A)

Residuals:
       Min         1Q     Median         3Q        Max
-1.000e+00 -1.000e+00  6.939e-17  1.000e+00  1.000e+00

Coefficients:
            Estimate Std. Error t value Pr(>|t|)
(Intercept)   3.0000     0.5774   5.196  0.00202 **
A2            4.0000     0.8165   4.899  0.00271 **
A3            8.0000     0.8165   9.798  6.5e-05 ***
---
Signif. codes:  0 '***' 0.001 '**' 0.01 '*' 0.05 '.' 0.1 ' ' 1

Residual standard error: 1 on 6 degrees of freedom
Multiple R-squared: 0.9412,     Adjusted R-squared: 0.9216
F-statistic:    48 on 2 and 6 DF,  p-value: 0.0002035
```

Sum to zero contrasts - this technique constrains the sum of the unconstrained treatment effects (α) to zero. In this model, the intercept estimates the average treatment effect and the remaining (α^*) estimate the differences between each of the treatment means and the average treatment mean.

Parameter	Estimates	Null hypothesis
Intercept	mean of group means (μ_{i*}/p)	H_0: $\mu = \mu_q/p = 0$
α_1^*	mean of group 1 minus mean of group means ($\mu_1 - (\mu_q/p)$)	H_0: $\alpha_1 = \mu_1 - (\mu_q/p) = 0$
α_2^*	mean of group 2 minus mean of group means ($\mu_2 - (\mu_q/p)$)	H_0: $\alpha_2 = \mu_2 - (\mu_q/p) = 0$
...		

```
> # specify that sum-to-zero contrast should be used
> contrasts(A) <-contr.sum
> summary(lm(Y~A))
Call:
lm(formula = Y ~ A)

Residuals:
       Min         1Q     Median         3Q        Max
-1.000e+00 -1.000e+00  1.388e-17  1.000e+00  1.000e+00
```

```
Coefficients:
              Estimate Std. Error  t value Pr(>|t|)
(Intercept)  7.000e+00  3.333e-01   21.000  7.6e-07 ***
A1          -4.000e+00  4.714e-01   -8.485 0.000147 ***
A2           1.228e-16  4.714e-01 2.60e-16 1.000000
---
Signif. codes:  0 '***' 0.001 '**' 0.01 '*' 0.05 '.' 0.1 ' ' 1

Residual standard error: 1 on 6 degrees of freedom
Multiple R-squared: 0.9412,     Adjusted R-squared: 0.9216
F-statistic:    48 on 2 and 6 DF,  p-value: 0.0002035
```

Helmert contrasts - the intercept estimates the average treatment effect and the remaining (α^*_q) estimate the differences between each of the treatment means and the mean of the group before it. In reality, parameter estimates from Helmert contrasts have little biological interpretability.

Parameter	Estimates	Null hypothesis
Intercept	mean of group means (μ_q/p)	H_0: $\mu = \mu_q/p = 0$
α^*_1	mean of group 2 minus mean of (group means and mean of group1) ($\mu_2 - (\mu_q/p + \mu_1)/2$)	H_0: $\alpha^*_1 = \mu_2 - (\mu_q/p + \mu_1)/2 = 0$
α^*_2	mean of group 3 minus mean of (group means, mean of group1 and mean of group2) ($\mu_3 - (\mu_q/p + \mu_1 + \mu_2)/3$)	H_0: $\alpha^*_2 = \mu_3 - (\mu_q/p + \mu_1 + \mu_2)/3 = 0$
...		

```
> # specify that Helmert contrasts should be used
> contrasts(A) <-contr.helmert
> summary(lm(Y~A))
Call:
lm(formula = Y ~ A)

Residuals:
       Min         1Q     Median        3Q       Max
-1.000e+00 -1.000e+00 -7.865e-17 1.000e+00 1.000e+00

Coefficients:
            Estimate Std. Error t value Pr(>|t|)
(Intercept)   7.0000     0.3333  21.000  7.6e-07 ***
A1            2.0000     0.4082   4.899 0.002714 **
A2            2.0000     0.2357   8.485 0.000147 ***
---
Signif. codes:  0 '***' 0.001 '**' 0.01 '*' 0.05 '.' 0.1 ' ' 1
```

```
Residual standard error: 1 on 6 degrees of freedom
Multiple R-squared: 0.9412,      Adjusted R-squared: 0.9216
F-statistic:    48 on 2 and 6 DF,  p-value: 0.0002035
```

Polynomial contrasts - generate orthogonal polynomial trends (such as linear, quadratic and cubic). This is equivalent to fitting a multiple linear regression (or polynomial regression) with orthogonal parameters.

Parameter	Estimates	Null hypothesis
Intercept	y-intercept	$H_0: \beta_0^* = 0$
β_1^*	partial slope for linear term	$H_0: \beta_1^* = 0$
β_2^*	partial slope for quadratic term	$H_0: \beta_2^* = 0$
...		

```
> # specify that orthogonal polynomial contrasts should be used
> contrasts(A) <-contr.poly
> summary(lm(Y~A))
Call:
lm(formula = Y ~ A)

Residuals:
       Min         1Q     Median         3Q        Max
-1.000e+00 -1.000e+00 -1.712e-16  1.000e+00  1.000e+00

Coefficients:
              Estimate Std. Error   t value Pr(>|t|)
(Intercept)  7.000e+00  3.333e-01    21.000  7.6e-07 ***
A.L          5.657e+00  5.774e-01     9.798  6.5e-05 ***
A.Q         -9.890e-16  5.774e-01 -1.71e-15        1
---
Signif. codes:  0 '***' 0.001 '**' 0.01 '*' 0.05 '.' 0.1 ' ' 1

Residual standard error: 1 on 6 degrees of freedom
Multiple R-squared: 0.9412,      Adjusted R-squared: 0.9216
F-statistic:    48 on 2 and 6 DF,  p-value: 0.0002035
```

User defined contrasts - In addition to the 'prefabricated' sets of comparisons illustrated above, it is possible to define other contrast combinations that are specifically suited to a particular experimental design and set of research questions. Contrasts are defined by constructing a contrast matrix according to the following rules:

(i) groups to be included and excluded in a specific contrasts (comparison) are represented by non-zero and zero coefficients respectively
(ii) groups to be apposed (contrasted) to one another should have apposing signs

(iii) the number of contrasts must not exceed $p - 1$, where p is the number of groups[e].
(iv) within a given contrast, the sum of positive coefficients (and negative coefficients) should sum to 1 to ensure that the resulting estimates can be sensibly interpreted
(v) all the contrasts must be orthogonal (independent of one another)

```
> # define potential contrast matrix for comparing group G1 with
> # the average of groups G2 and G3
> contrasts(A) <- cbind(c(1, -0.5, -0.5))
> contrasts(A)
   [,1]          [,2]
G1  1.0 -6.407635e-17
G2 -0.5 -7.071068e-01
G3 -0.5  7.071068e-01
> l <- lm(Y~A)
> # summarize the model fitting
> summary(l)
Call:
lm(formula = Y ~ A)

Residuals:
      Min         1Q     Median         3Q        Max
-1.000e+00 -1.000e+00 -4.163e-17  1.000e+00  1.000e+00

Coefficients:
            Estimate Std. Error t value Pr(>|t|)
(Intercept)   7.0000     0.3333  21.000  7.6e-07 ***
A1           -4.0000     0.4714  -8.485 0.000147 ***
A2            2.8284     0.5774   4.899 0.002714 **
---
Signif. codes:  0 '***' 0.001 '**' 0.01 '*' 0.05 '.' 0.1 ' ' 1

Residual standard error: 1 on 6 degrees of freedom
Multiple R-squared: 0.9412,     Adjusted R-squared: 0.9216
F-statistic:    48 on 2 and 6 DF,  p-value: 0.0002035
```

We only defined a single contrast (`A1`), the second contrast (`A2`) is defined by R to satisfy the above requirements and has little, if any, biological meaning. By default, R[f] employs treatment contrasts for unordered factors[g] and orthogonal polynomial contrasts for ordered factors, although this behavior can be altered to an alternative (such as `contr.sum` for unordered factors) using the `options(contrasts =c("contr.sum", "contr.poly"))` *function.*

---

[e] Actually, it must equal $p - 1$ exactly. However, it is usually sufficient to define less than $p - 1$ contrasts and let R generate the remaining constants. These should typically be ignored when interpreting the output.

[f] Note that the default behaviour of S-PLUS is to employ sum to zero contrasts for unordered factors.

[g] Unordered factors are factors that have not specifically defined as 'ordered', see section 2.6.1. The order of groups in an ordered factor is usually important - for example when examining polynomial trends across groups.

Note that while the estimates and interpretations of individual model parameters differ between the alternative approaches, in all but the $\mu = 0$ (set-to-zero) case, the overall effects model is identical ($y_{qj} = \mu + \alpha_q^* + \varepsilon_{qj}$). Hence, the overall null hypothesis tested from the effects model (H_0: $\alpha_1^* = \alpha_2^* = ... = 0$) is the same irrespective of the contrasts chosen.

When the model contains more than one factor, a separate term is assigned for each factor and possibly the interactions between factors (e.g. $\alpha_i + \beta_j + \alpha\beta_{ij}$). Alternatively, statistical models containing factors can be expressed as *cell means models* in which the overall mean and treatment effects ($\mu + \alpha_i$) are replaced by the treatment (cell) means (μ_i). In the cell means model, there are as many cell means as there are unique treatment levels. These differences are thus summarized:

Linear model	$y_{ij} = \mu + \beta_1(dummy_1)_{ij} + \beta_2(dummy_2)_{ij} + ... + \varepsilon_{ij}$
Linear effects model	$y_{ij} = \mu + \alpha_i + \varepsilon_{ij}$
Orthogonal linear effects model	$y_{i^*j} = \mu + \alpha_{i^*}^* + \varepsilon_{i^*j}$
Cell means model	$y_{ij} = \mu_i + \varepsilon_{ij}$

For simple model fitting the choice of model type makes no difference, however for complex factorial models in which entire treatment levels (cells) are missing, full effects models cannot be fitted and therefore cell means models (see section 12.6.2) must be used.

7.3.2 Linear model hypothesis testing

Hypothesis testing is usually concerned with evaluating whether a population parameter is (or set of parameters are) equal to zero, as this signifies no 'relationship' or 'effect'.

Null hypotheses about individual model parameters

In a linear model, there is a null hypothesis associated with each of the individual model parameters (typically that the parameter is equal to zero), although not all the testable null hypotheses are necessarily biologically meaningful. Consider again the simple linear regression model:

$$y_i = \beta_0 + \beta_1 x_i + \varepsilon_i$$

This linear model includes two parameters (β_0 and β_1), and thus there are two individual testable null hypotheses - that the population y-intercept is equal to zero (H_0: $\beta_0 = 0$) and the slope is equal to zero (H_0: $\beta_1 = 0$). While rejecting a null hypothesis that the slope parameter equals zero indicates the presence of a 'relationship', discovering that the value of the response variable when the predictor variable is equal to zero is usually of little biological relevance.

Null hypotheses about individual model parameters are usually tested using a *t*-test (see section 6.3), or equivalently via a single factor ANOVA (see chapter 10) with a single degree of freedom. The latter approach is often employed when user-defined contrasts are involved as it enables the results to be expressed in the context of the overall linear model (see below and section 10.6).

Null hypotheses about the fit of overall model

Recall that in hypothesis testing, a null hypothesis (H_0) is formulated to represent the logical opposite of the hypothesized prediction and that disproving the null hypothesis provides evidence that some alternative hypothesis (H_A) is true. Consequently, there are typically at least two models fitted. The *reduced model*, in which the parameter of interest (and its associated predictor variable) is absent (or equivalently set to zero) represents the model predicted by null hypothesis. The *full model* represents the alternative hypothesis and includes the term of interest. For example, to test the null hypothesis that there is no relationship between populations x and y (and thus that the population slope (β_1)= 0):

$$\begin{aligned} \textit{full model } (H_A) \text{ - } \quad y_i &= \beta_0 + \beta_1 x_i + error_i \\ \textit{reduced model } (H_0) \text{ - } \quad y_i &= \beta_0 + 0x_i + error_i \\ &= \beta_0 + error_i \end{aligned}$$

The degree to which a model 'fits' the observed data is determined by the amount of variation that the model fails to explain, and is measured as the sum of the squared differences (termed *SS* or sums-of-squares) between the observed values of the response variable and the values predicted by the model. A model that fits the observed data perfectly will have a *SS* of 0.

The *reduced model* measures the amount of variation left unexplained by the statistical model when the contribution of the parameter and predictor variable (term) of interest is removed (SS_{Total}). The *full model* measures the amount of variation left unexplained by the statistical model when the contribution of the term is included ($SS_{Residual}$). The difference between the reduced and full models (SS_{Model}) is the amount of explained variation attributed to the term of interest. When the null hypothesis is true, the term of interest should not explain any of the variability in the observed data and thus the full model will not fit the observed data any better than the reduced model. That is, the proposed model would not be expected to explain any more of the total variation than it leaves unexplained. If however, the full model fits the data 'significantly' better (unexplained variability is substantially less in the full model compared to the reduced model) than the reduced model, there is evidence to reject the null hypothesis in favour of the alternative hypothesis.

Hypothesis testing formally evaluates this proposition by comparing the ratio of explained and unexplained variation to a probability distribution representing all possible ratios theoretically obtainable when the null hypothesis is true. The total variability in the observed data ($SS_{Residual}$ – *reduced model*) is partitioned into at least two sources.

(i) the variation that is explained by the model (SS_{Model})
$SS_{Model} = \quad SS_{Total}$ (*reduced model*) – $SS_{Residual}$ (*full model*)
(ii) the variation that is unexplained by the model ($SS_{Residual}$)
$SS_{Residual}$ (*full model*)

The number of degrees of freedom (*d.f.*) associated with estimates of each source of variation reflect the number of observations involved in the estimate minus the

Table 7.2 Analysis of variance (ANOVA) table for a simple linear model. n is the number of observations, f_p is the number of parameters in the full model and r_p is the number of parameters in the reduced model.

Source of variation	SS	df	MS	F-ratio
Model	SS_{Model}	$f_p - 1$	$\frac{SS_{Model}}{df_{Model}}$	$\frac{MS_{Model}}{MS_{Residual}}$
Residual	$SS_{Residual}$	$n - f_p$	$\frac{SS_{Residual}}{df_{Residual}}$	
Total	SS_{Total}	$n - r_p$	$\frac{SS_{Residual}}{df_{Residual}}$	

number of other parameters that must have been estimated previously. Just like *SS*, *df* are additive and therefore:

$$df_{Model} = df_{Total}\ (reduced\ model) - df_{Residual}\ (full\ model)$$

Each of the sources of variation are based on a different number of contributing observations. Therefore more comparable, standardized versions are generated by dividing by the appropriate number of (degrees of freedom). These averaged measures of variation (known as mean squares or *MS*) are thus conservative mean measures of variation and importantly, they have known probability distributions (unlike the SS estimates).

The partitioned sources of variation are tabulated in the form of an analysis of variance (ANOVA) table (see Table 7.2), which also includes the ratio (*F*-ratio) of MS_{Model} to $MS_{Residual}$. When the null hypothesis is true MS_{Model} and $MS_{Residual}$ are expected to be the same, and thus their ratio (*F*-ratio) should be approximately 1. An *F*-ratio based on observed data is thus compared to an appropriate *F*-distribution (theoretical distribution of all possible *F*-ratios for the set of degrees of freedom) when the null hypothesis is true. If the probability of obtaining such an *F*-ratio (or one more extreme) is less than a critical value, the null hypothesis is rejected.

When there are multiple predictor variables, in addition to assessing the fit of the overall model, we usually want to determine the effect of individual factors. This is done by comparing the fit of models with and without the specific term(s) associated with that variable.

7.4 Comments about the importance of understanding the structure and parameterization of linear models

An understanding of how to formulate the correct statistical model from a design and set of null hypotheses is crucial to ensure that the correct R syntax (and thus

Table 7.3 Statistical models in R. Lower case letters denote continuous numeric variables and uppercase letters denote factors. Note that the error term is always implicit and equivalent options are specified for most effects models. `x` and `y` represent continuous variables and `A` and `B` represent categorical (factors).

Effects model	R Model formula	Description
$y_i = \beta_0 + \beta_1 x_i$	`y ~ 1 + x` `y ~ x`	Simple linear regression model of `y` on `x` with intercept term included

$y_i = \beta_1 x_i$	`y ~ 0 + x`
	`y ~ -1 + x`
	`y ~ x - 1`
		Simple linear regression model of `y` on `x` with intercept term excluded

$y_i = \beta_0$	`y ~ 1` `y ~ 1 - x`	Simple linear regression model of `y` against the intercept term
$y_i = \beta_0 + \beta_1 x_{i1} + \beta_2 x_{i2}$	`y ~ x1 + x2`	Multiple linear regression model of `y` on `x1` and `x2` with the intercept term included implicitly
$y_i = \beta_0 + \beta_1 x_{i1} + \beta_2 x_{i1}^2$	`y ~ 1 + x + I(x^2)`	Second order polynomial regression of `y` on `x`
	`y ~ poly(x, 2)`	As above, but using the first two orthogonal polynomials
$y_{ij} = \mu + \alpha_i$	`y ~ A`	Analysis of variance of `y` against a single factor `A`
$y_{ijk} = \mu + \alpha_i + \beta_j + \alpha\beta_{ij}$	`y ~ A + B + A:B` `y ~ A*B`	Fully factorial analysis of variance of `y` against `A` and `B`, including the `A:B` interaction
$y_{ijk} = \mu + \alpha_i + \beta_j$	`y ~ A*B - A:B` `y ~ A+B`	Fully factorial analysis of variance of `y` against `A` and `B` without the interaction term
$y_{ijk} = \mu + \alpha_i + \beta_{j(i)}$	`y ~ B %in% A` `y ~ A/B`	Nested analysis of variance of `y` against `A` and `B` nested within `A`
$y_{ij} = \mu + \alpha_i + \beta(x_{ij} - \overline{x})$	`y ~ A*x` `y ~ A/x`	Analysis of covariance of `y` on `x` at each level of `A`
$y_{ijkl} = \mu + \alpha_i + \beta_{j(i)} + \gamma_k + \alpha\gamma_{ik} + \beta\gamma_{j(i)k}$	`y ~ A + Error(B) + C + A:C + B:C`	Partly nested ANOVA of `y` against a single between block factor (`A`), a single within block factor (`C`) and a single random blocking factor (`B`).

analysis) is employed. This is particularly important for more complex designs which incorporate multiple error strata (such as partly nested ANOVA). Table 7.3 briefly illustrates the ways in which statistical models are represented in R. Moreover, in each of the remaining chapters, the statistical models as well as the appropriate R model formulae for each major form of modeling will be highlighted and demonstrated, thereby providing greater details about use of R in statistical modeling.

8

Correlation and simple linear regression

Correlation and regression are techniques used to examine associations and relationships between continuous variables collected on the same set of sampling or experimental units. Specifically, correlation is used to investigate the degree to which variables change or vary together (covary). In correlation, there is no distinction between dependent (response) and independent (predictor) variables and there is no attempt to prescribe or interpret the causality of the association. For example, there may be an association between arm and leg length in humans, whereby individuals with longer arms generally have longer legs. Neither variable directly causes the change in the other. Rather, they are both influenced by other variables to which they both have similar responses. Hence correlations apply mainly to survey designs where each variable is measured rather than specifically set or manipulated by the investigator.

Regression is used to investigate the nature of a relationship between variables in which the magnitude and changes in one variable (known as the independent or predictor variable) are assumed to be directly responsible for the magnitude and changes in the other variable (dependent or response variable). Regression analyses apply to both survey and experimental designs. Whilst for experimental designs, the direction of causality is established and dictated by the experiment, for surveys the direction of causality is somewhat discretionary and based on prior knowledge. For example, although it is possible that ambient temperature effects the growth rate of a species of plant, the reverse is not logical. As an example of regression, we could experimentally investigate the relationship between algal cover on rocks and molluscan grazer density by directly manipulating the density of snails in different specifically control plots and measuring the cover of algae therein. Any established relationship must be driven by snail density, as this was the manipulated variable. Alternatively the relationship could be investigated via a field survey in which the density of snails and cover of algae could be measured from random locations across a rock platform. In this case, the direction of causality (or indeed the assumption of causality) may be more difficult to defend.

In addition to examining the strength and significance of a relationship (for which correlation and regression are equivalent), regression analysis also explores the functional nature of the relationship. In particular, it estimates the rate at which a change in an independent variable is reflected in a change in a dependent variable

Biostatistical Design and Analysis Using R: a Practical Guide, 1st edition. By M. Logan.
Published 2010 by Blackwell Publishing.

(slope) as well as the expected value of the dependent variable when the independent variable is equal to zero (intercept). These estimates can be used to construct a predictive model (equation) that relates the magnitude of a dependent variable to the magnitude of an independent variable, and thus permit new responses to be predicted from new values of the independent variable.

8.1 Correlation

The simplest measure of association between two variables is the sum product of the deviations of each point from the mean center [*e.g.* $\sum(x - \bar{x})(y - \bar{y})$], see Figure. 8.1f. This method essentially partitions the cloud of points up into four quadrants and weighs up the amount in the positive and negative quadrants. The greater the degree to which points are unevenly distributed across the positive and negative quadrants, the greater the magnitude (either negative or positive) of the measure of association. Clearly however, the greater the number of points, the higher the measure of association. Covariance standardizes for sample size by dividing this measure by the degrees of freedom (number of observation pairs minus 1) and thus represents the average deviations from the mean center. Note that covariance is really the bivariate variance of two variables[a].

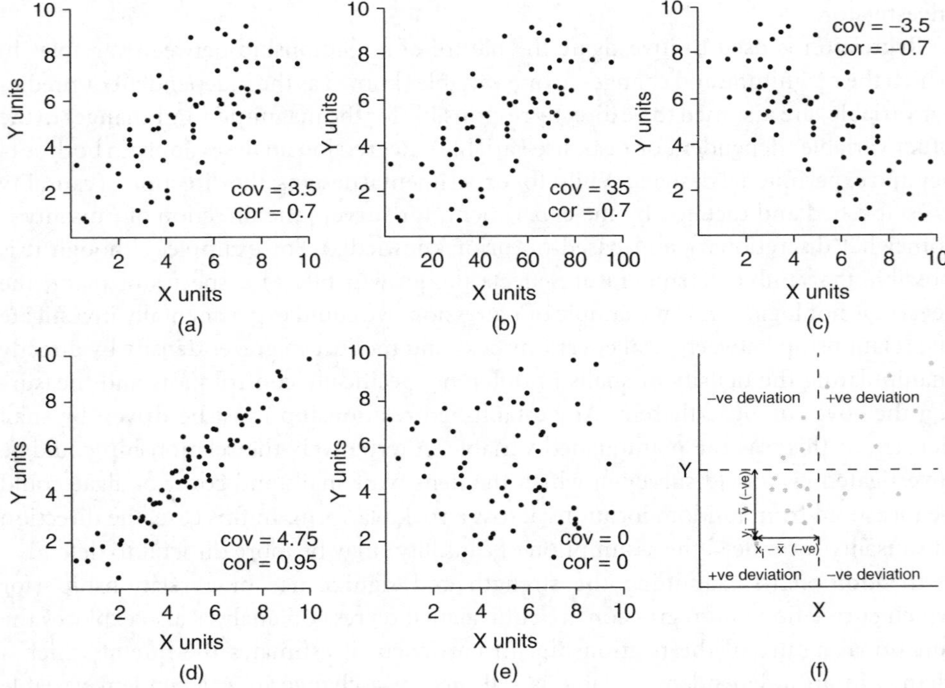

Fig 8.1 Fictitious data illustrating covariance, correlation, strength and polarity.

[a] Covariance of a single variable and itself is the variance of that variable.

8.1.1 Product moment correlation coefficient

Unfortunately, there are no limits on the range of covariance as its magnitude depends on the scale of the units of the variables (see Figure 8.1a-b). The Pearson's (product moment) correlation coefficient further standardizes covariance by dividing it by the standard deviations of x and y, thereby resulting in a standard coefficient (ranging from -1 to $+1$) that represents the strength and polarity of a linear association.

8.1.2 Null hypothesis

Correlation tests the H_0 that the population correlation coefficient (ρ, estimated by the sample correlation coefficient, r) equals zero:

$H_0 : \rho = 0$ (the population correlation coefficient equals zero)

This null hypothesis is tested using a t statistic ($t = \frac{r}{s_r}$), where s_r is the standard error of r. This t statistic is compared to a t distribution with $n - 2$ degrees of freedom.

8.1.3 Assumptions

In order that the calculated t-statistic should reliably represent the population trends, the following assumptions must be met:

(i) linearity - as the Pearson correlation coefficient measures the strength of a linear (straight-line) association, it is important to establish whether or not some other curved relationship represents the trends better. Scatterplots are useful for exploring linearity.
(ii) normality - the calculated t statistic will only reliably follow the theoretical t distribution when the joint XY population distribution is bivariate normal. This situation is only satisfied when both individual populations (X and Y) are themselves normally distributed. Boxplots should be used to explore normality of each variable.

Scale transformations are often useful to improve linearity and non-normality.

8.1.4 Robust correlation

For situations when one or both of the above assumptions are not met and transformations are either unsuccessful or not appropriate (particularly, proportions, indices and counts), monotonic associations (general positive or negative - not polynomial) can be investigated using non-parametric (rank-based) tests. The **Spearman's rank correlation coefficient** (r_s) calculates the product moment correlation coefficient on the ranks of the x and y variables and is suitable for samples with between 7 and 30 observations. For greater sample sizes, an alternative rank based coefficient **Kendall's** (τ) is more suitable. Note that non-parametric tests are more conservative (have less power) than parametric tests.

8.1.5 Confidence ellipses

Confidence ellipses are used to represent the region on a plot within which we have a certain degree of confidence (e.g 95%) the true population mean center is likely to occur. Such ellipses are centered at the sample mean center and oriented according to the covariance matrix[b] of x and y.

8.2 Simple linear regression

Simple linear regression is concerned with generating a mathematical equation (model) that relates the magnitude of dependent (response) variable to the magnitude of the independent (predictor) variable. The general equation for a straight line is $y = bx + a$, where a is the y-intercept (value of y when $x = 0$) and b is the gradient or slope (rate at which y changes per unit change in x).

Figure 8.2 illustrates sets of possible representatives of population trends between two variables. It should be apparent that if the population slope (β_1) is equal to zero there is no relationship between dependent (Y) and independent variables (X). Changes in the independent variable are not reflected by the dependent variable. Conversely, when the population slope is not equal to zero there is a relationship. Note that the population intercept (β_0) has less biological meaning.

The population parameters (β_0 and β_1) are estimated from a line of best fit through the cloud of sample data. There are a number of ways to determine the line of best fit, each of which represent different approach to regression analysis (see Figure 8.4, and section 8.2.5).

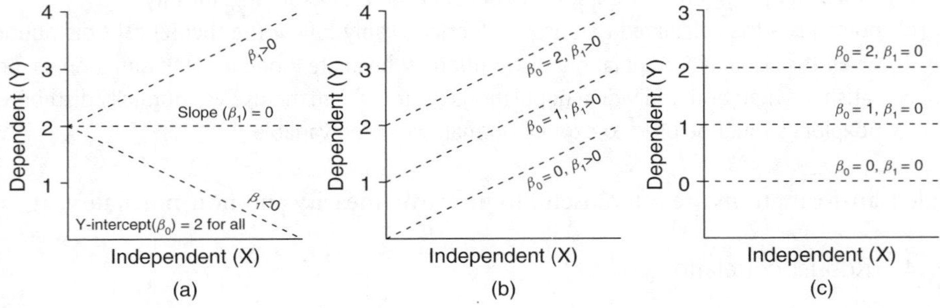

Fig 8.2 Fictitious data contrasting differences in interpretation between slope (β_1) and y-intercept (β_0) parameters.

[b] The covariance matrix of two variables has two rows and two columns. The upper left and lower right entries represent the variances of x and y respectively and the upper right and lower left entries represent the covariance of x and y.

8.2.1 Linear model

The linear model reflects the equation of the line of best fit:

$$y_i = \beta_0 + \beta_1 x_i + \varepsilon_i$$

where β_0 is the population y-intercept, β_1 is the population slope and ε_i is the random unexplained error or residual component.

8.2.2 Null hypotheses

A separate H_0 is tested for each of the estimated model parameters:

$$H_0 : \beta_1 = 0 \qquad \text{(the population slope equals zero)}$$

This test examines whether or not there is likely to be a relationship between the dependent and independent variables in the population. In simple linear regression, this test is identical to the test that the population correlation coefficient equals zero ($\rho = 0$).

$$H_0 : \beta_0 = 0 \qquad \text{(the population y-intercept equals zero)}$$

This test is rarely of interest as it only tests the likelihood that the background level of the response variable is equal to zero (rarely a biologically meaningful comparison) and does not test whether or not there is a relationship (see Figure 8.4b-c).

These H_0's are tested using a t statistic (e.g. $t = \frac{b}{s_b}$), where s_b is the standard error of b. This t statistic is compared to a t distribution with $n - 2$ degrees of freedom.

Along with testing the individual parameters that make up the linear model via t-tests, linear regression typically also tests the $H_0 : \beta_1 = 0$ by partitioning the total variability in the response variable into a component that is explained by the β_1 term in the *full linear model* ($y_i = \beta_0 + \beta_1 x_i + \varepsilon_i$) and a component of the variance that cannot be explained (residual), see Figure 8.3. As it is only possible to directly determine unexplained variation, the amount of variability explained by the full model (and therefore β_1) is calculated as the difference between the amount left unexplained by a *reduced model* ($y_i = \beta_0 + \varepsilon_i$, which represents the situation when $H_0 : \beta_1 = 0$ is true) and the amount left unexplained by the full model ($y_i = \beta_0 + \beta_1 x_i + \varepsilon_i$).

When the null hypothesis is true (no relationship and therefore $\beta_1 = 0$) and the test assumptions are met, the ratio (F-ratio) of explained to unexplained variability follows a F-distribution. Likewise, full and reduced models respectively with and without the y-intercept could be used to test H_0: $\beta_0 = 0$. For simple linear regression, the t-tests and ANOVA's test equivalent null hypotheses[c], however this is not the case for more complex linear models.

---

[c] For simple linear regression the F-statistic is equal to the t-value squared ($F = t^2$).

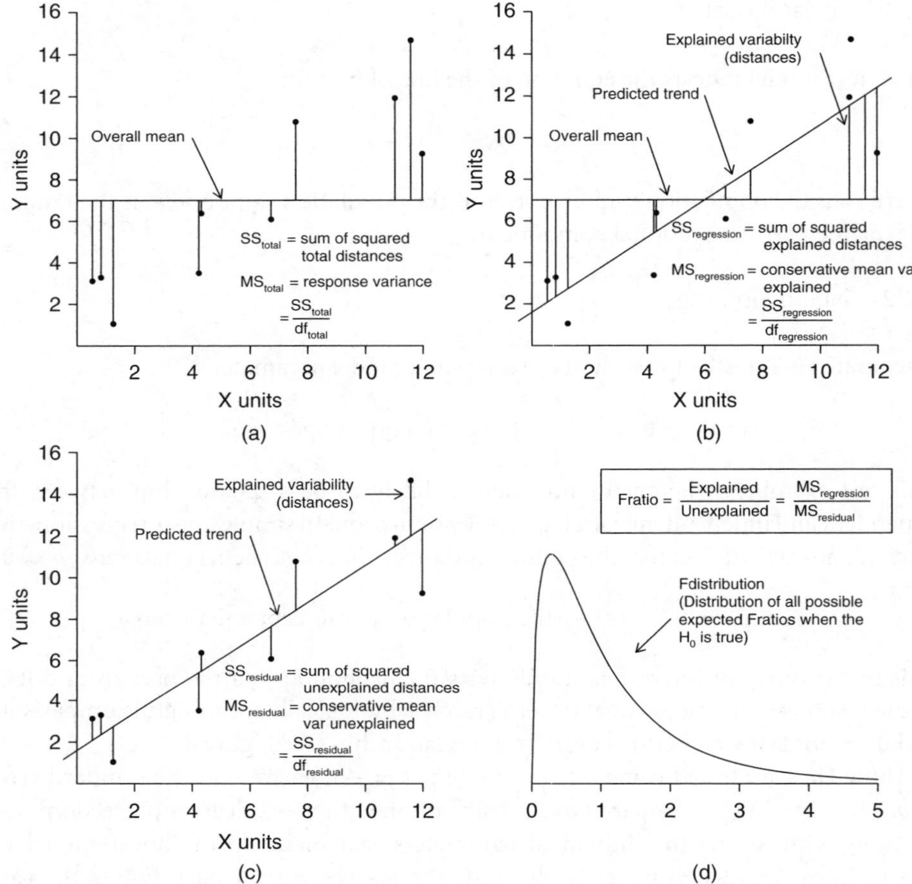

Fig 8.3 Fictitious data illustrating the partitioning of (a) total variation into components (b) explained ($MS_{regression}$) and (c) unexplained ($MS_{residual}$) by the linear trend. The probability of collecting our sample, and thus generating the sample ratio of explained to unexplained variation (or one more extreme), when the null hypothesis is true (and there is no relationship between X and Y) is the area under the F-distribution (d) beyond the sample F-ratio.

8.2.3 Assumptions

To maximize the reliability of null hypotheses tests, the following assumptions apply:

(i) linearity - simple linear regression models a linear (straight-line) relationship and thus it is important to establish whether or not some other curved relationship represents the trends better. Scatterplots are useful for exploring linearity.

(ii) normality - the populations from which the single responses were collected per level of the predictor variable are assumed to be normally distributed. Boxplots of the response variable (and predictor if it was measured rather than set) should be used to explore normality.

(iii) homogeneity of variance - the populations from which the single responses were collected per level of the predictor variable are assumed to be equally varied. With only a single representative of each population per level of the predictor variable, this can only be explored by examining the spread of responses around the fitted regression line. In particular, increasing spread along the regression line would suggest a relationship between population mean and variance (which must be independent to ensure unbiased parameter estimates). This can also be diagnosed with a residual plot.

8.2.4 Multiple responses for each level of the predictor

Simple linear regression assumes linearity and investigates whether there is a relationship between a response and predictor variable. In so doing, it is relying on single response values at each level of the predictor being good representatives of their respective populations. Having multiple independent replicates of each population from which a mean can be calculated thereby provides better data from which to investigate a relationship. Furthermore, the presence of replicates of the populations at each level of the predictor variable enables us to establish whether or not the observed responses differ significantly from their predicted values along a linear regression line and thus to investigate whether the population relationship is linear versus some other curvilinear relationship. Analysis of such data is equivalent to ANOVA with polynomial contrasts (see section 10.6).

8.2.5 Model I and II regression

The **ordinary least squares** (**OLS**, or **model I regression**) fits a line that minimizes the vertical spread of values around the line and is the standard regression procedure. Regression was originally devised to explore the nature of relationship between a measured dependent variable and an independent variable of which the levels where specifically set (and thus controlled) by the researcher to represent a uniform range of possibilities. As the independent variable is set (fixed) rather than measured, there is no uncertainty or error in the *y* values. The coordinates predicted (by the linear model) for any given observation must therefore lie in a vertical plane around the observed coordinates (see Figure 8.4a). The difference between an observed value and its predicted value is called a residual. Hence, OLS regression minimizes the sum of the squared[d] residuals.

Model II regression refers to a family of line fitting procedures that acknowledge and incorporate uncertainty in both response and predictor variables and primarily describe the first major axis through a bivariate normal distribution (see Table 8.1 and Figure 8.4). These techniques generate better parameter estimates (such as population slope) than model I regression when the levels of the predictor variable are measured, however, they are only necessary for situations in which the parameter estimates are the main interest of the analysis. For example, when performing regression analysis

[d] Residuals are squared to remove negatives. Since the regression line is fitted exactly through the middle of the cloud of points, some points will be above this line (+ve residuals) and some points will be below (-ve residuals) and therefore the sum of the residuals will equal exactly zero.

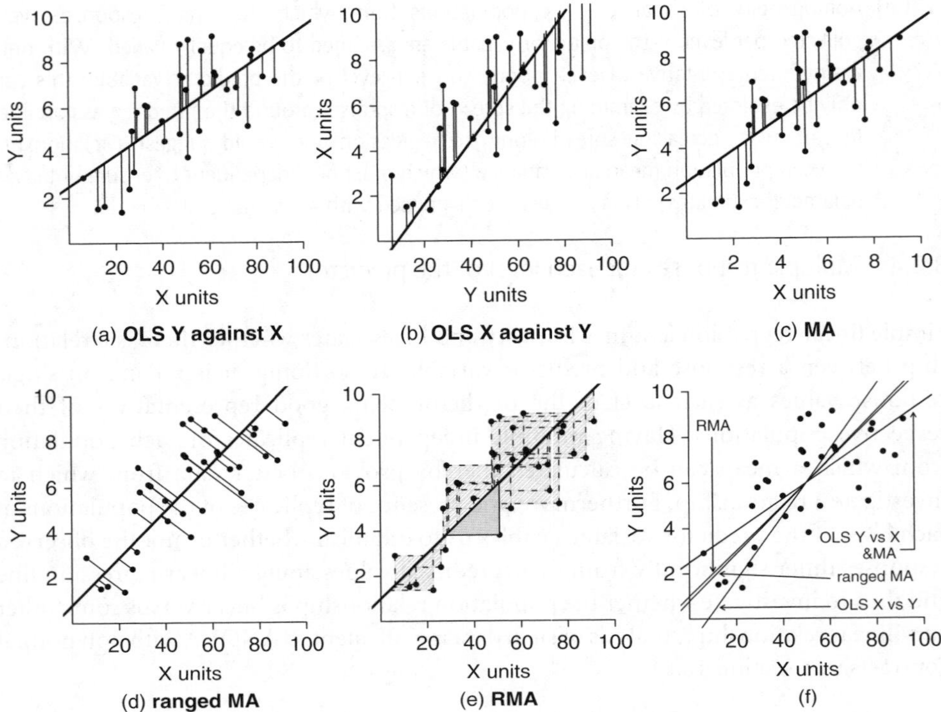

Fig 8.4 Fictitious data illustrating the differences between (a) ordinary least squares, (b) major axis and (c) reduced major axis regression. Each are also contrasted in (d) along with a depiction of ordinary least squares regression for X against *Y*. Note that the fitted line for all techniques passes through the center mean of the data cloud. When the *X* and *Y* are measured on the same scale, MA and RMA are the same.

to estimate the slope in allometric scaling relationships or to compare slopes between models.

Major axis (MA) minimizes the sum square of the perpendicular spread from the regression line (Figure 8.4c) and thus the predicted values line in a perpendicular planes from the regression line. Although this technique incorporates uncertainty in both response and predictor variable, it assumes that the degree of uncertainty is the same on both axes (1:1 ratio) and is therefore only appropriate when both variables are measured on the same scale and with the same units. **Ranged major axis (Ranged MA)** is a modification of major axis regression in which MA regression is performed on variables that are pre-standardized by their ranges (Figure 8.4d) and the resulting parameters are then returned to their original scales. Alternatively, **Reduced major axis (RMA)** minimizes the sum squared triangular areas bounded by the observations and the regression line (Figure 8.4e) thereby incorporating all possible ratios of uncertainty between the response and predictor variables. For this technique, the estimated slope is the average of the slope from a regression of *y* against *x* and the inverse of the slope of *x* against *y*.

Table 8.1 Comparison of the situations in which the different regression methods are suitable.

Method
Ordinary least squares (OLS) • When there is no uncertainty in *IV* (levels set not measured) or uncertainty in *IV* $\ll$ uncertainty in *DV* • When testing $H_0 : \beta_1 = 0$ (no linear relationship between *DV* and *IV*) • When generating predictive models from which new values of *DV* are predicted from given values of *IV*. Since we rarely have estimates of uncertainty in our new predictor values (and thus must assume there is no uncertainty), predictions likewise must be based on predictive models developed with the assumption of no uncertainty. Note, if there is uncertainty in *IV*, standard errors and confidence intervals inappropriate. • When distribution is not bivariate normal `> summary(lm(DV~IV, data))`

Major axis (MA)
• When a good estimate of the population parameters (slope) is required AND
• When distribution is bivariate normal (*IV* levels not set) AND
• When error variance (uncertainty) in *IV* and *DV* equal (typically because variables in same units or dimensionless)
`> library(biology)`
`> summary(lm.II(DV~IV, data, method='MA'))`

Ranged Major axis (Ranged MA)
• When a good estimate of the population parameters (slope) is required AND
• When distribution is bivariate normal (*IV* levels not set) AND
• When error variances are proportional to variable variances AND
• There are no outliers
`> library(biology)`
`> #For variables whose theoretical minimum is arbitrary`
`> summary(lm.II(DV~IV, data, method='rMA'))`
`> #OR for variables whose theoretical minimum must be zero`
`> #such as ratios, scaled variables & abundances`
`> summary(lm.II(DV~IV, data, method='rMA', zero=T))`

Reduced major axis (RMA) or Standard major axis (SMA)
• When a good estimate of the population parameters (slope) is required AND
• When distribution is bivariate normal (*IV* levels not set) AND
• When error variances are proportional to variable variances AND
• When there is a significant correlation *r* between *IV* and *DV*
`> library(biology)`
`> summary(lm.II(DV~IV, data, method='RMA'))`

Modified from Legendre (2001).

8.2.6 Regression diagnostics

As part of linear model fitting, a suite of diagnostic measures can be calculated each of which provide an indication of the appropriateness of the model for the data and the indication of each points influence (and outlyingness) of each point on resulting the model.

Leverage

Leverage is a measure of how much of an outlier each point is in x-space (on x-axis) and thus only applies to the predictor variable. Values greater than $2 * p/n$ (where p=number of model parameters ($p = 2$ for simple linear regression), and n is the number of observations) should be investigated as potential outliers.

Residuals

As the residuals are the differences between the observed and predicted values along a vertical plane, they provide a measure of how much of an outlier each point is in y-space (on y-axis). Outliers are identified by relatively large residual values. Residuals can also standardized and studentized, the latter of which can be compared across different models and follow a t distribution enabling the probability of obtaining a given residual can be determined. The patterns of residuals against predicted y values (residual plot) are also useful diagnostic tools for investigating linearity and homogeneity of variance assumptions (see Figure 8.5).

Cook's D

Cook's D statistic is a measure of the influence of each point on the fitted model (estimated slope) and incorporates both leverage and residuals. Values ≥ 1 (or even approaching 1) correspond to highly influential observations.

8.2.7 Robust regression

There are a range of model fitting procedures that are less sensitive to outliers and underlying error distributions. **Huber M-estimators** fit linear models by minimizing the sum of differentially weighted residuals. Small residuals (weakly influential) are squared and summed as for OLS, whereas residuals over a preselected critical size (more influential) are incorporated as the sum of the absolute residual values. A useful non-parametric test is the **Theil-Sen single median** (**Kendall's robust**) method which estimates the population slope (β_1) as the median of the $n(n-1)/2$ possible slopes (b_1) between each pair of observations and the population intercept (β_0) is estimated as the median of the n intercepts calculated by solving $y - b_1 x$ for each observation. A more robust, yet complex procedure (**Siegel repeated medians**) estimates β_1 and β_0 as the median of the n median of the $n-1$ slopes and intercepts respectively between each point and all others. **Randomization tests** compare the statistic (b_1) to

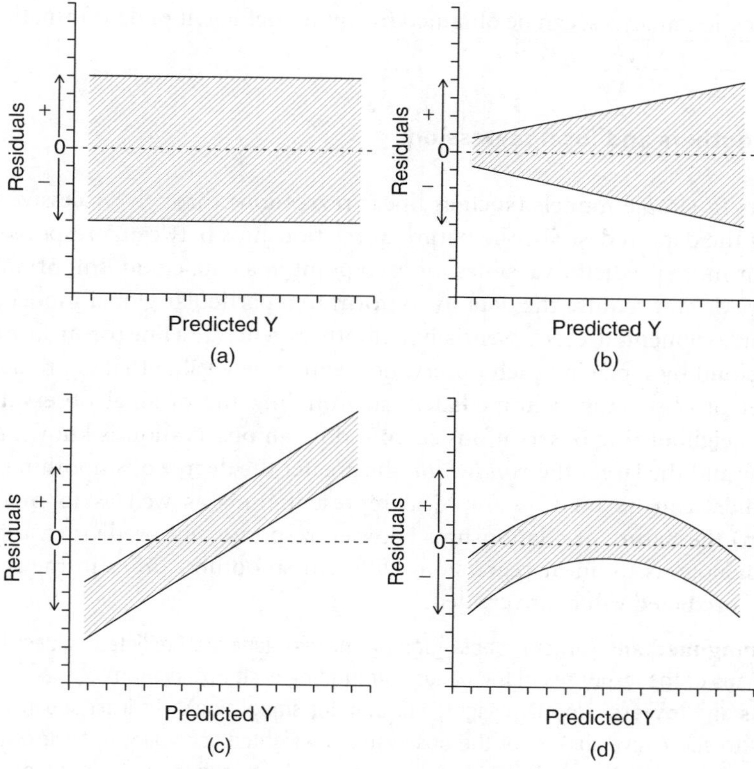

Fig 8.5 Stylised residual plots depicting characteristic patterns of residuals (a) random scatter of points - homogeneity of variance and linearity met (b) "wedge-shaped" - homogeneity of variance not met (c) linear pattern remaining - erroneously calculated residuals or additional variable(s) required and (d) curved pattern remaining - linear function applied to a curvilinear relationship. Modified from Zar (1999).

a unique probability distribution that is generated by repeatedly reshuffling one of the variables and recalculating the test statistic. As a result, they do not impose any distributional requirements on the data. Randomization tests are particularly useful for analysing data that could not be collected randomly or haphazardly as they test whether the patterns in the data could occur by chance rather than specifically testing hypotheses about populations. As a result, technically any conclusions pertain only to the collected observations and not to the populations from which the observations were collected.

8.2.8 Power and sample size determination

Although interpreted differently, the tests $H_0 : \rho = 0$ and $H_0 : \beta_1 = 0$ (population correlation and slope respectively equal zero) are statistically equivalent. Therefore power analyses to determine sample size required for null hypothesis rejection for both correlation and regression are identical and based on r (correlation coefficient), which from regression analyses, can be obtained from the coefficient of determination (r^2) or as $r = b\sqrt{\sum x^2 / \sum y^2}$.

8.3 Smoothers and local regression

Smoothers fit simple models (such as linear regression) through successive localized subsets of the data to describe the nature of relationships between a response variable and one or more predictor variables for each point in a data cloud. Importantly, these techniques do not require the data to conform to a particular global model structure (e.g. linear, exponential, etc). Essentially, smoothers generate a line (or surface) through the data cloud by replacing each observation with a new value that is predicted from the subset of observations immediately surrounding the original observation. The subset of neighbouring observations surrounding an observation is known as a *band* or *window* and the larger the *bandwidth*, the greater the degree of smoothing.

Smoothers can be used as graphical representations as well as to model (local regression) the nature of relationships between response and predictor variables in a manner analogous to linear regression. Different smoothers differ in the manner by which the predicted values are created.

- **running medians** (or less robust running means) generate predicted values that are the medians of the responses in the bands surrounding each observation.
- **loess** and **lowess**[e] (locally weighted scatterplot smoothing) - fit least squares regression lines to successive subsets of the observations weighted according to their distance from the target observation and thus depict changes in the trends throughout the data cloud.
- **kernel smoothers** - new smoothed y-values are computed as the weighted averages of points within a defined window (bandwidth) or neighbourhood of the original x-values. Hence the bandwidth depends on the scale of the x-axis. Weightings are determined by the type of kernel smoother specified, and for. Nevertheless, the larger the window, the greater the degree of smoothing.
- **splines** - join together a series of polynomial fits that have been generated after the entire data cloud is split up into a number of smaller windows, the widths of which determine the smoothness of the resulting piecewise polynomial.

Whilst the above smoothers provide valuable exploratory tools, they also form the basis of the formal model fitting procedures supported via generalized additive models (GAMs, see chapter 17).

8.4 Correlation and regression in R

Simple correlation and regression in R are performed using the `cor.test()` and `lm()` *functions*. The `mblm()` and `rlm()` *functions* offer a range of non-parametric regression

[e] Lowess and loess functions are similar in that they both fit linear models through localizations of the data. They differ in in that loess uses weighted quadratic least squares and lowess uses weighted linear least squares. They also differ in how they determine the data spanning (neighborhood of points regression model fitted to), and in that loess smoothers can fit surfaces and thus accomodate multivariate data.

Table 8.2 Smoothing function within R. For each of the following, `DV` is the response variable within the `data` dataset. Smoothers are plotted on scatterplots by using the smoother function as the response variable in the `points()` function (e.g. `points(runmed(DV)~IV, data, type='l')`).

Smoother[a]	Syntax
Running median	`> runmed(data$DV,k)` *where* `k` *is an odd number that defines the bandwidth of the window and if* `k` *omitted, defaults to either Turlach or Struetzle breaking algorithms depending on data size (Turlack for larger)*
Loess	`> loess(DV~IV1+IV2+..., data, span=0.75)` *where* `IV1, IV2` *represent one or more predictor variables and* `span` *controls the degree of smoothing*
Lowess	`> lowess(data$IV, data$DV, f=2/3)` *where* `IV` *represents the predictor variable and* `f` *controls the degree of smoothing*

Kernel	`> ksmooth(data$IV, data$DV, kernel="normal", bandwidth=0.5)`
	where `IV` *represents the predictor variable,* `kernel` *represents the smoothing kernel (*`box` *or* `normal`*) and* `bandwidth` *is the smoothing bandwidth*
	`> density(data$DV, bw="nrd0", adjust=1)`
	where `IV` *represents the predictor variable and* `bw` *and* `adjust` *"nrd0" the smoothing bandwidth and course bandwidth multiplier respectively. Information on the alternative smoothing bandwidth selectors for gaussian (normal) windows is obtained by typing* `?bw.nrd`

Splines	`> data.spl<-smooth.spline(data$IV, data$DV, spar)`
	`> points(y~x, data.spl, type='l')`
	where `IV` *represents the predictor variable and* `spar` *is the smoothing coeficient, typically between 0 and 1.*

[a]Note, there are many other functions and packages that facilitate alternatives to the smoothing functions listed here.

alternatives. Model II regressions are facilitated via the `lm.II()` *function* and the common smoothing functions available in R are described in Table 8.2.

8.5 Further reading

- Theory

Fowler, J., L. Cohen, and P. Jarvis. (1998). *Practical statistics for field biology*. John Wiley & Sons, England.

Hollander, M., and D. A. Wolfe. (1999). *Nonparametric statistical methods, 2nd edition*. John Wiley & Sons, New York.

Manly, B. F. J. (1991). *Randomization and Monte Carlo methods in biology*. Chapman & Hall, London.

Quinn, G. P., and K. J. Keough. (2002). *Experimental design and data analysis for biologists*. Cambridge University Press, London.

Sokal, R., and F. J. Rohlf. (1997). *Biometry, 3rd edition*. W. H. Freeman, San Francisco.

Zar, G. H. (1999). *Biostatistical methods*. Prentice-Hall, New Jersey.

- Practical - R

Crawley, M. J. (2007). *The R Book*. John Wiley, New York.

Dalgaard, P. (2002). *Introductory Statistics with R*. Springer-Verlag, New York.

Fox, J. (2002). *An R and S-PLUS Companion to Applied Regression*. Sage Books.

Maindonald, J. H., and J. Braun. (2003). *Data Analysis and Graphics Using R - An Example-based Approach*. Cambridge University Press, London.

8.6 Key for correlation and regression

1 a. Neither variable has been set (they are both measured) AND there is no implied causality between the variables (Correlation) . . . . Go to 2

b. Either one of the variables has been specifically set (not measured) OR there is an implied causality between the variables whereby one variable could influence the other but the reverse is unlikely (Regression) . . . . Go to 4

2 a. Check parametric assumptions for correlation analysis

- **Bivariate normality of the response/predictor variables - marginal scatterplot boxplots**

```
> library(car)
> scatterplot(V1 ~ V2, dataset)
```

where `V1` *and* `V2` *are the continuous variables in the* `dataset` *data frame*

- **Linearity of data points on a scatterplot, trendline and lowess smoother useful**

```
> library(car)
> scatterplot(V1 ~ V2, dataset, reg.line = F)
```

where `V1` *and* `V2` *are the continuous variables in the* `dataset` *data frame and* `reg.line=F` *excludes the misleading regression line from the plot*

Parametric assumptions met (Pearson correlation) . . . . See Example 8A

```
> corr.test(~V1 + V2, data = dataset)
```

where `V1` *and* `V2` *are the continuous variables in the* `dataset` *data frame*

For a summary plot . . . . Go to 12

b. Parametric assumptions NOT met or scale transformations (see Table 3.2) not successful or inappropriate . . . . Go to 3

3 a. Sample size between 7 and 30 (Spearman rank correlation) . . . . . . See Example 8B

```
> cor.test(~V1 + V2, data = dataset, method = "spearman")
```

where `V1` *and* `V2` *are the continuous variables in the* `dataset` *data frame*

For a summary plot . . . . Go to 12

b. Sample size > 30 (Kendall's tao correlation)

```
> cor.test(~V1 + V2, data = dataset, method = "kendall")
```

where `V1` *and* `V2` *are the continuous variables in the* `dataset` *data frame*
For a summary plot .... Go to 12

4 a. Check parametric assumptions for regression analysis

- **Normality of the response variable (and predictor variable if measured) - marginal scatterplot boxplots**
- **Homogeneity of variance - spread of data around scatterplot trendline**
- **Linearity of data points on a scatterplot, trendline and lowess smoother useful**

```
> library(car)
> scatterplot(DV ~ IV, dataset)
```

where `DV` *and* `IV` *are response and predictor variables respectively in the* `dataset` *data frame*
Parametric assumptions met .... Go to 5

b. Parametric assumptions NOT met or scale transformations (see Table 3.2) not successful or inappropriate .... Go to 7

5 a. Levels of predictor variable set (not measured) - no uncertainty in predictor variable OR the primary aim of the analysis is:

- **hypothesis testing** ($H_0 : \beta_1 = 0$)
- **generating a predictive model** ($y = \beta_0 + \beta_1 x$)

(Ordinary least squares (OLS) regression) .... Go to 6

b. Levels of predictor variable NOT set (they are measured) AND the main aim of the analysis is to estimate the population slope of the relationship (Model II regression) .... See Example 8F

```
> library(biology)
> data.lm <- lm.II(DV ~ IV, christ, type = "RMA")
> summary(data.lm)
```

where `DV` *and* `IV` *are response and predictor variables respectively in the* `dataset` *data frame.* `type` *can be one of* `"MA"`, `"RMA"`, `"rMA"` *or* `"OLS"`. *For* `type="rMA"`, *it is also possible to force a minimum response of zero* (`zero=T`).
To produce a summary plot.. Go to 12

6 a. Single response value for each level of the predictor variable .... See Examples 8C&8D

```
> dataset.lm <- lm(IV ~ DV, dataset)
> plot(dataset.lm)
> influence.measures(dataset.lm)
> summary(dataset.lm)
```

where `DV` *and* `IV` *are response and predictor variables respectively in the* `dataset` *data frame.*
To get parameter confidence intervals[f] .... Go to 10
To predict new values of the response variable .... Go to 11
To produce a summary plot.. Go to 12

b. Multiple response values for each level of the predictor variable .... See Examples 8E

```
> anova(lm(DV ~ IV + as.factor(IV), dataset))
```

[f] If there is uncertainty in the predictor variable, parameter confidence intervals might be inappropriate.

- Pooled residual term

```
> dataset.lm <- lm(DV ~ IV, dataset)
> summary(dataset.lm)
```

- Non-pooled residual term

```
> dataset.lm <- aov(DV ~ IV + Error(as.factor(IV)), dataset)
> summary(dataset.lm)
> lm(DV ~ IV, dataset)
```

where `DV` *and* `IV` *are response and predictor variables respectively in the* `dataset` *data frame.*

7 a. Observations collected randomly/haphazardly, no reason to suspect non-independence .... Go to 8

b. Random/haphazard sampling not possible, observations not necessarily independent (Randomization test) .... See Example 8H

```
> stat <- function(data, index) {
+     summary(lm(DV ~ IV, data))$coef[2, 3]
+ }
> rand.gen <- function(data, mle) {
+     out <- data
+     out$IV <- sample(out$IV, replace = F)
+     out
+ }
> library(boot)
> dataset.boot <- boot(dataset, stat, R = 5000,
+     sim = "parametric", ran.gen = rand.gen)
> plot(dataset.boot)
> dataset.boot
```

where `DV` *and* `IV` *are response and predictor variables respectively in the* `dataset` *data frame.*

To get parameter confidence intervals[g] .... Go to 10
To predict new values of the response variable .... Go to 11
To produce a summary plot .... Go to 12

8 a. Mild non-normality due mainly to outliers (influential obseravations), data linear (M-regression)

```
> library(MASS)
> data.rlm <- rlm(DV ~ IV, dataset)
```

where `DV` *and* `IV` *are response and predictor variables respectively in the* `dataset` *data frame.*

To get parameter confidence intervals[h] .... Go to 12
To predict new values of the response variable .... Go to 11
To produce a summary plot .... Go to 10

[g] If there is uncertainty in the predictor variable, parameter confidence intervals might be inappropriate.

[h] If there is uncertainty in the predictor variable, parameter confidence intervals might be inappropriate.

b. Data non-normal and/or non-linear .... Go to 9

9 **a. Binary response (e.g. dead/alive, present/absent)** ...... Logistic Regression chapter 17

b. Underlying distribution of response variable and residuals is known ...... GLM chapter 17

c. Data curvilinear .... Non-linear regression chapter 9

d. Data monotonic non-linear (nonparametric regression) .... See Example 8G

- Theil-Sen single median (Kendall's) robust regression

```
> library(mblm)
> data.mblm <- mblm(DV ~ IV, dataset, repeated = F)
> summary(data.mblm)
```

- Siegel repeated medians regression

```
> library(mblm)
> data.mblm <- mblm(DV ~ IV, dataset, repeated = T)
> summary(data.mblm)
```

where `DV` *and* `IV` *are response and predictor variables respectively in the* `dataset` *data frame.*

To get parameter confidence intervals[i] .... Go to 12
To predict new values of the response variable .... Go to 11
To produce a summary plot.. Go to 10

10 **Generating parameter confidence intervals** .... See Example 8C&8G

```
> confint(model, level = 0.95)
```

where `model` *is a fitted model*

To get randomization parameter estimates and their confidence intervals .... See Example 8H

```
> par.boot <- function(dataset, index) {
+     x <- dataset$ALT[index]
+     y <- dataset$HK[index]
+     model <- lm(y ~ x)
+     coef(model)
+ }
> dataset.boot <- boot(dataset, par.boot, R = 5000)
> boot.ci(dataset.boot, index = 2)
```

where `dataset` *is the data.frame. The optional argument* (`R=5000`) *indicates 5000 randomizations and the optional argument* (`index=2`) *indicates which parameter to generate confidence intervals for (y-intercept=1, slope=2). Note the use of the* `lm()` *function for the parameter estimations and could be replaced by robust alternatives such as* `rlm()` *or* `mblm()`.

11 **Generating new response values (and corresponding prediction intervals)** ..... See Example 8C&8D

```
> predict(model, data.frame(IV = c()), interval = "p")
```

[i] If there is uncertainty in the predictor variable, parameter confidence intervals might be inappropriate.

where `model` *is a fitted model and* `IV` *is the predictor variable and* `c()` *is a vector of new predictor values (e.g.* `c(10,13.4)`*)*

To get randomization prediction intervals .... See Example 8H

```
> pred.boot <- function(dataset, index) {
+     dataset.rs <- dataset[index, ]
+     dataset.lm <- lm(HK ~ ALT, dataset.rs)
+     predict(dataset.lm, data.frame(ALT = 1))
+ }
> dataset.boot <- boot(dataset, pred.boot, R = 5000)
> boot.ci(dataset.boot)
```

where `dataset` *is the name of the data frame. Note the use of the* `lm()` *function for the parameter estimations. This could be replaced by robust alternatives such as* `rlm()` *or* `mblm()`.

12 **Base summary plot for correlation or regression**...... See Example 8B&8C&8D&8F

```
> plot(V1 ~ V2, data, pch = 16, axes = F, xlab = "", ylab = "")
> axis(1, cex.axis = 0.8)
> mtext(text = "x-axis title", side = 1, line = 3)
> axis(2, las = 1)
> mtext(text = "y-axis title", side = 2, line = 3)
> box(bty = "l")
```

where `V1` *and* `V2` *are the continuous variables in the* `dataset` *data frame. For regression,* `V1` *represents the response variable and* `V2` *represents the predictor variable.*

Adding confidence ellipse .... See Example 8B

```
> data.ellipse(V2, V1, levels = 0.95, add = T)
```

Adding regression line.. See Example 8C

```
> abline(model)
```

where `model` *represents a fitted regression model*

Adding regression confidence intervals .... See Example 8C&8D

```
> x <- seq(min(IV), max(IV), l = 1000)
> y <- predict(object, data.frame(IV = x), interval = "c")
> matlines(x, y, lty = 1, col = 1)
```

where `IV` *is the name of the predictor variable (including the dataframe)* `model` *represents a fitted regression model*

8.7 Worked examples of real biological data sets

Example 8A: Pearson's product moment correlation

Sokal and Rohlf (1997) present an unpublished data set (L. Miller) in which the correlation between gill weight and body weight of the crab (*Pachygrapsus crassipes*) is investigated.

Step 1 - Import (section 2.3) the crabs data set

```
> crabs <- read.table("crabs.csv", header = T, sep = ",")
```

Step 2 (Key 8.2) - Assess linearity and bivariate normality using a scatterplot with marginal boxplots

```
> library(car)
> scatterplot(GILLWT ~ BODYWT, data = crabs, reg.line = F)
```

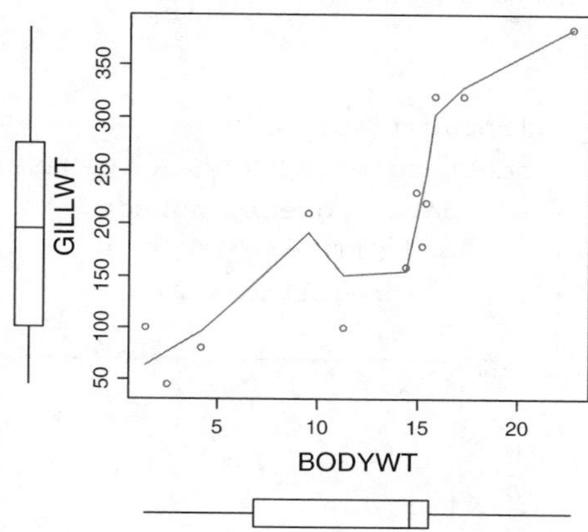

Conclusions - data not obviously nonlinear and no evidence of non-normality (boxplots not asymmetrical)

Step 3 (Key 8.2a) - Calculate the Pearson's correlation coefficient and test $H_0 : \rho = 0$ (that the population correlation coefficient equals zero).

```
> cor.test(~GILLWT + BODYWT, data = crabs)
        Pearson's product-moment correlation

data:  GILLWT and BODYWT
t = 5.4544, df = 10, p-value = 0.0002791
alternative hypothesis: true correlation is not equal to 0
95 percent confidence interval:
 0.5783780 0.9615951
sample estimates:
      cor
0.8651189
```

Conclusions - reject H_0 that population correlation coefficient equals zero, there was a strong positive correlation between crab weight and gill weight ($r = 0.865, t_{10} = 5.45, P < 0.001$).

Example 8B: Spearman rank correlation

Green (1997) investigated the correlation between total biomass of red land crabs (*Gecarcoidea natalis* and the density of their burrows at a number of forested sites (Lower site: LS and Drumsite: DS) on Christmas Island.

Step 1 - Import (section 2.3) the Green (1997) data set

```
> green <- read.table("green.csv", header = T, sep = ",")
```

Step 2 (Key 8.2) - Assess linearity and bivariate normality for the two sites separately using a scatterplots with marginal boxplots

```
> library(car)
> scatterplot(BURROWS ~ TOTMASS,
+       data = green, subset =
+           SITE == "LS",
+           reg.line = F)
```

```
> library(car)
> scatterplot(BURROWS ~ TOTMASS,
+       data = green, subset =
+           SITE == "DS",
+           reg.line = F)
```

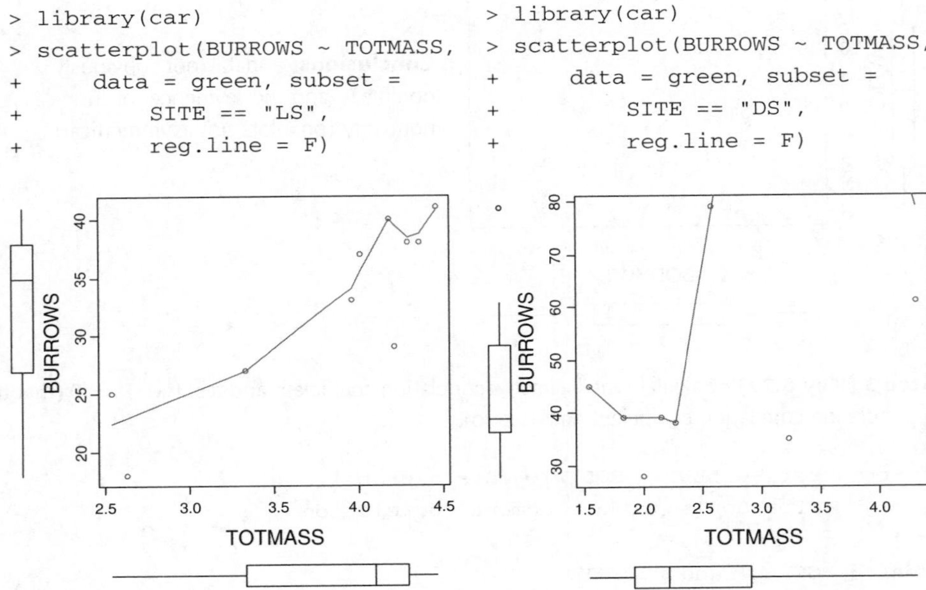

Conclusions - some evidence of non-normality (boxplots not asymmetrical)

Step 3 (Key 8.3a) - Calculate the Spearman's rank correlation coefficient and test $H_0 : \rho = 0$ (that the population correlation coefficient equals zero).

```
> cor.test(~BURROWS + TOTMASS, data = green, subset = SITE ==
+       "LS", method = "spearman")
            Spearman's rank correlation rho

data:  BURROWS and TOTMASS
S = 24.5738, p-value = 0.001791
alternative hypothesis: true rho is not equal to 0
sample estimates:
      rho
0.8510678
```

Conclusions - reject H_0 that population correlation coefficient equals zero, there was a strong positive correlation between crab biomass and burrow density at Low site ($\rho = 0.851, S_{10} = 24.57, P = 0.0018$).

```
> cor.test(~BURROWS + TOTMASS, data = green, subset = SITE ==
+      "DS", method = "spearman")
          Spearman's rank correlation rho

data:  BURROWS and TOTMASS
S = 69.9159, p-value = 0.6915
alternative hypothesis: true rho is not equal to 0
sample estimates:
      rho
0.1676677
```

Conclusions - do not reject H_0 that population correlation coefficient equals zero, there was no detectable correlation between crab weight and gill weight at Drumsite ($\rho = 0.168, S_{10} = 69.92, P = 0.692$).

Step 4 (Key 8.12) - Summarize findings with scatterplots (section 5.8.1), including 95% confidence ellipses for the population bivariate mean center. The following also indicate two alternative ways to specify a subset of a dataframe.

```
> plot(BURROWS ~ TOTMASS,
+     data = green, subset =
+         SITE == "LS",
+         xlim = c(0,
+         8), ylim = c(0,
+         80))
> with(subset(green, SITE ==
+     "LS"), data.ellipse
+     (TOTMASS,
+     BURROWS, levels = 0.95,
+     add = T))
```

```
> plot(BURROWS ~ TOTMASS,
+     data = green, subset =
+         SITE == "DS",
+          xlim = c(0,
+         8), ylim = c(0,
+         150))
> with(subset(green, SITE ==
+     "DS"), data.ellipse
+     (TOTMASS,
+     BURROWS, levels = 0.95,
+     add = T))
```

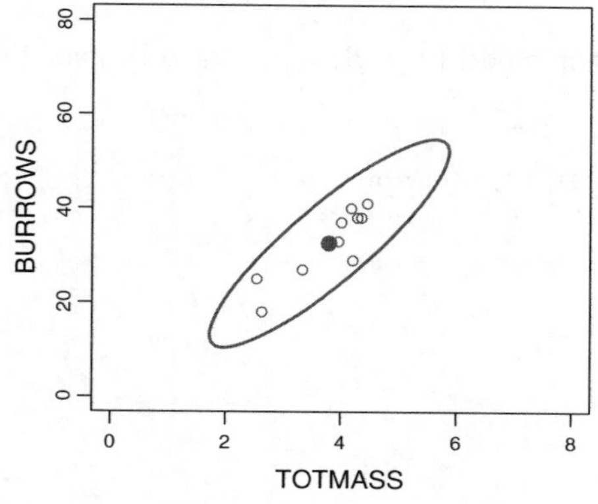

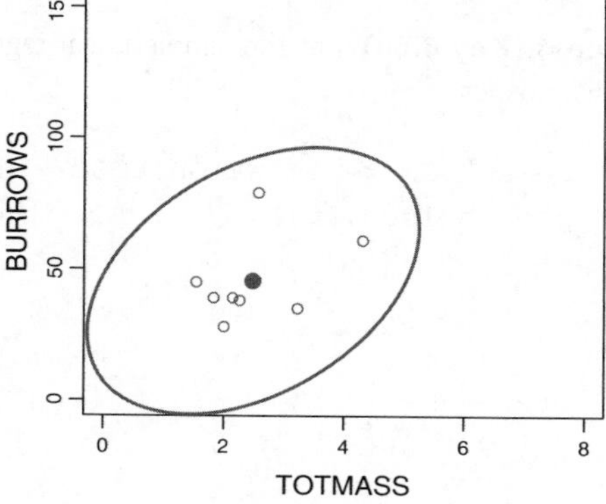

Example 8C: Simple linear regression - fixed X

As part of a Ph.D into the effects of starvation and humidity on water loss in the confused flour beetle (*Tribolium confusum*), Nelson (1964) investigated the linear relationship between humidity and water loss by measuring the amount of water loss (mg) by nine batches of beetles kept at different relative humidities (ranging from 0 to 93%) for a period of six days (Table 14.1 Sokal and Rohlf (1997)).

Step 1 - Import (section 2.3) the Nelson (1964) data set

```
> nelson <- read.table("nelson.csv", header = T, sep = ",")
```

Step 2 (Key 8.4) - Assess linearity, normality and homogeneity of variance using a scatterplot with marginal boxplots and a lowess smoother.

```
> library(car)
> scatterplot(WEIGHTLOSS ~ HUMIDITY, data = nelson)
```

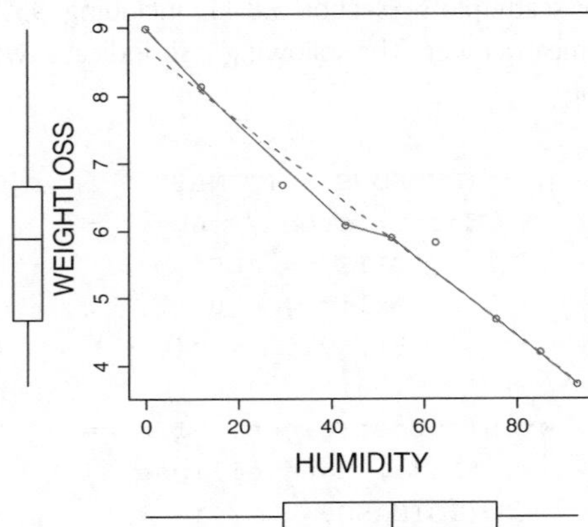

Conclusions - no evidence of non-normality (boxplots not overly asymmetrical), non homogeneity of variance (points do not become progressively more or less spread out along the regression line) or non-linearity.

Step 3 (Key 8.5a) - the ordinary least squares method is considered appropriate as the there is effectively no uncertainty (error) in the predictor variable (relative humidity).

Step 4 (Key 8.6a) - fit the simple linear regression model ($y_i = \beta_0 + \beta_1 x_i$) and examine the diagnostics.

```
> nelson.lm <- lm(WEIGHTLOSS ~ HUMIDITY, nelson)
> plot(nelson.lm)
```

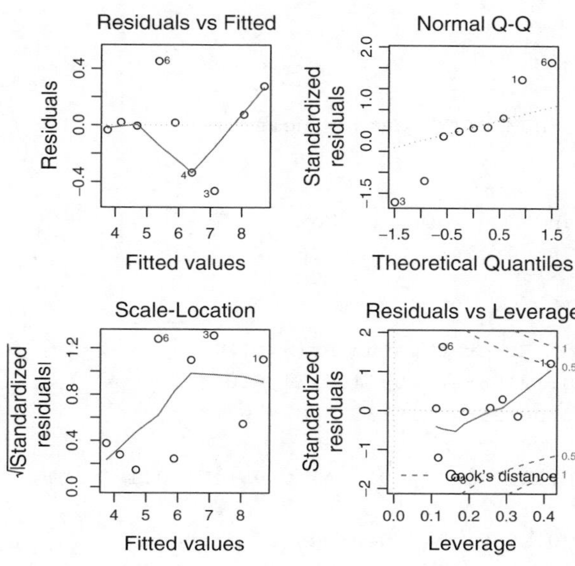

Conclusions - There is no obvious "wedge" pattern evident in the residual plot (confirming that the assumption of homogeneity of variance is likely to be met). Although there is some deviation in the Q-Q normal plot (suggesting that the response variable does deviate from normal), the sample size is rather small and the test is reasonably robust to such deviations. Finally, none of the points approach the high Cook's D contours suggesting that none of the observations are overly influential on the final fitted model.

```
> influence.measures(nelson.lm)
Influence measures of
         lm(formula = WEIGHTLOSS ~ HUMIDITY, data = nelson) :

    dfb.1_ dfb.HUMI    dffit cov.r   cook.d   hat inf
1  1.07457 -0.92033  1.07457 1.449 5.31e-01 0.417   *
2  0.17562 -0.13885  0.17705 1.865 1.81e-02 0.289   *
3 -0.83600  0.52023 -0.91800 0.552 2.86e-01 0.164
4 -0.32184  0.10806 -0.45713 0.970 9.67e-02 0.118
5  0.00868  0.00169  0.01969 1.531 2.26e-04 0.112
6  0.11994  0.27382  0.73924 0.598 1.97e-01 0.129
7  0.00141 -0.00609 -0.00956 1.674 5.33e-05 0.187
8 -0.01276  0.03163  0.04208 1.825 1.03e-03 0.255
9  0.03662 -0.07495 -0.09204 2.019 4.93e-03 0.330   *
```

Conclusions - None of the leverage (hat) values are greater than $2 * p/n = 0.444$ and therefore (none are considered to be outliers in x-space). Furthermore, none of the Cook's D values are ≥ 1 (no point is overly influential). Hence there is no evidence that hypothesis tests will be unreliable.

Step 5 (Key 8.6a) - examine the parameter estimates and hypothesis tests (Boxes 14.1 & 14.3 of Sokal and Rohlf (1997)).

```
> summary(nelson.lm)
Call:
lm(formula = WEIGHTLOSS ~ HUMIDITY, data = nelson)

Residuals:
     Min       1Q   Median       3Q      Max
-0.46397 -0.03437  0.01675  0.07464  0.45236

Coefficients:
             Estimate Std. Error t value Pr(>|t|)
(Intercept)  8.704027   0.191565   45.44 6.54e-10 ***
HUMIDITY    -0.053222   0.003256  -16.35 7.82e-07 ***
---
Signif. codes:  0 '***' 0.001 '**' 0.01 '*' 0.05 '.' 0.1 ' ' 1

Residual standard error: 0.2967 on 7 degrees of freedom
Multiple R-squared: 0.9745,     Adjusted R-squared: 0.9708
F-statistic: 267.2 on 1 and 7 DF,  p-value: 7.816e-07
```

Conclusions - Reject H_0 that the population slope equals zero. An increase in relative humidity was found to be associated with a strong ($r^2 = 0.975$), significant decrease in weight loss ($b = -0.053$, $t_7 = -16.35$, $P < 0.001$) in confused flour beetles.

Step 6 (Key 8.10) - calculate the 95% confidence limits for the regression coefficients (Box 14.3 of Sokal and Rohlf (1997)).

```
> confint(nelson.lm)
                  2.5 %      97.5 %
(Intercept)  8.25104923  9.15700538
HUMIDITY    -0.06092143 -0.04552287
```

Step 7 (Key 8.11) - use the fitted linear model to predict the mean weight loss of flour beetles expected at 50 and 100% relative humidity (Box 14.3 of Sokal and Rohlf (1997)).

```
> predict(nelson.lm, data.frame(HUMIDITY = c(50, 100)),
+      interval = "prediction", se = T)
$fit
       fit      lwr      upr
1 6.042920 5.303471 6.782368
2 3.381812 2.549540 4.214084


$se.fit
        1         2
0.0988958 0.1894001
```

```
$df
[1] 7

$residual.scale
[1] 0.2966631
```

Step 8 (Key 8.12) - summarize the findings of the linear regression analysis with a scatterplot including the regression line, regression equation and r^2.

```
> #create a plot with solid dots (pch=16) and no axis or labels
> plot(WEIGHTLOSS~HUMIDITY, data=nelson, pch=16, axes=F, xlab="",
     ylab="")
> #put the x-axis (axis 1) with smaller label font size
> axis(1, cex.axis=.8)
> #put the x-axis label 3 lines down from the axis
> mtext(text="% Relative humidity", side=1, line=3)
> #put the y-axis (axis 2) with horizontal tick labels
> axis(2, las=1)
> #put the y-axis label 3 lines to the left of the axis
> mtext(text="Weight loss (mg)", side=2, line=3)
> #add the regression line from the fitted model
> abline(nelson.lm)
> #add the regression formula
> text(99,9,"WEIGHTLOSS = -0.053HUMIDITY + 8.704", pos=2)
> #add the r squared value
> text(99,8.6,expression(paste(r^2==0.975)), pos=2)
> #create a sequence of 1000 numbers spanning the range of
    humidities
> x <- seq(min(nelson$HUMIDITY), max(nelson$HUMIDITY),l=1000)
> #for each value of x, calculate the upper and lower 95%
    confidence
> y<-predict(nelson.lm, data.frame(HUMIDITY=x), interval="c")
> #plot the upper and lower 95% confidence limits
> matlines(x,y, lty=1, col=1)
> #put an L-shaped box to complete the axis
> box(bty="l")
```

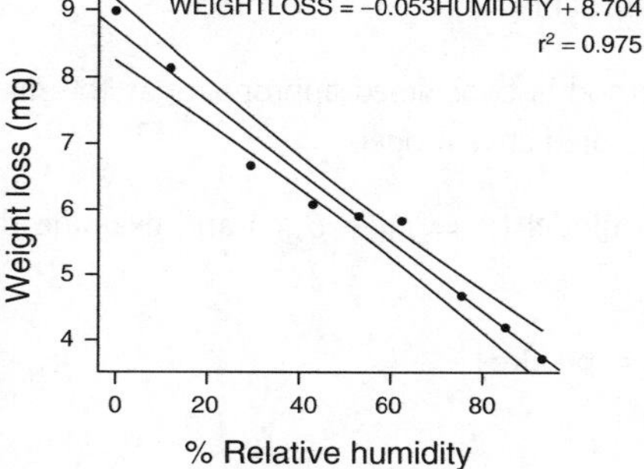

Example 8D: Simple linear regression - random X

To investigated the nature of abundance-area relationships for invertebrates in intertidal mussel clumps, Peake and Quinn (1993) measured area (mm^2) (dependent variable: AREA) and number of non-mussel individuals supported (response variable: INDIV) from a total of 25 intertidal mussel clumps(from Box 5.4 of Quinn and Keough (2002)).

Step 1 - Import (section 2.3) the Peake and Quinn (1993) data set

```
> peake <- read.table("peake.csv", header = T, sep = ",")
```

Step 2 (Key 8.4) - Assess linearity, normality and homogeneity of variance using a scatterplot with marginal boxplots and a lowess smoother.

```
> library(car)
> scatterplot(INDIV ~ AREA,
+       data = peake)
```

```
> library(car)
> scatterplot(log10(INDIV) ~
+       log10(AREA), data = peake)
```

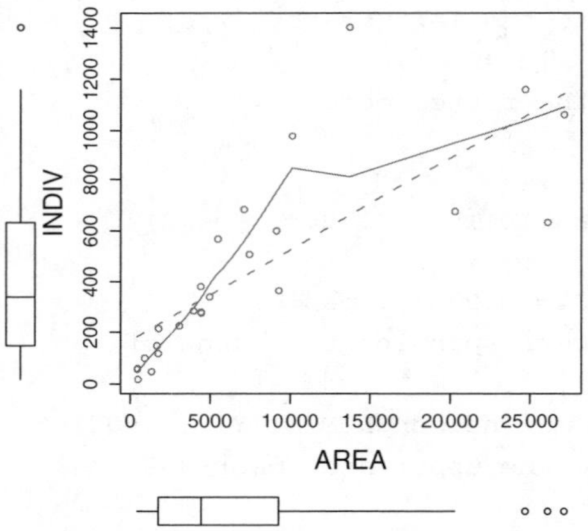

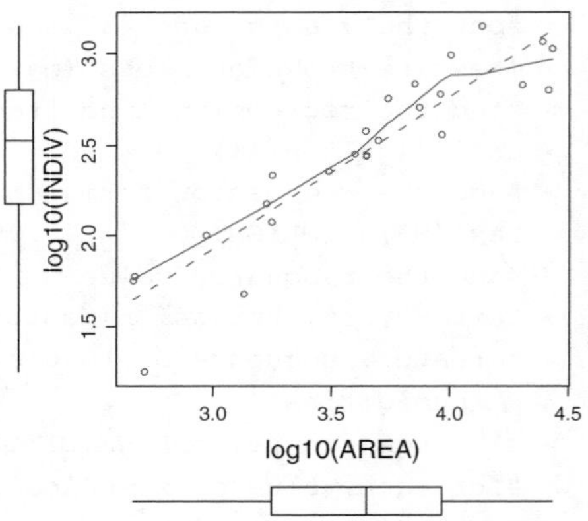

Conclusions - scatterplot of raw data (left figure) indicates evidence of non-normality (boxplots not symmetrical) and evidence that homogeneity of variance my also be violated (points become more spread along the line of the regression line). Data transformed to logarithms (base 10) appear to meet the assumptions of normality and homogeneity of variance better (right figure). Linearity of the log-log relationship also appears reasonable.

Step 3 (Key 8.5a) - the ordinary least squares method is considered appropriate as the main focus will be on hypothesis testing and generating a predictive model.

Step 4 (Key 8.6) - fit the simple linear regression model ($y_i = \beta_0 + \beta_1 x_i$) and examine the diagnostics.

```
> peake.lm <- lm(INDIV ~ AREA, data = peake)
> plot(peake.lm)
```

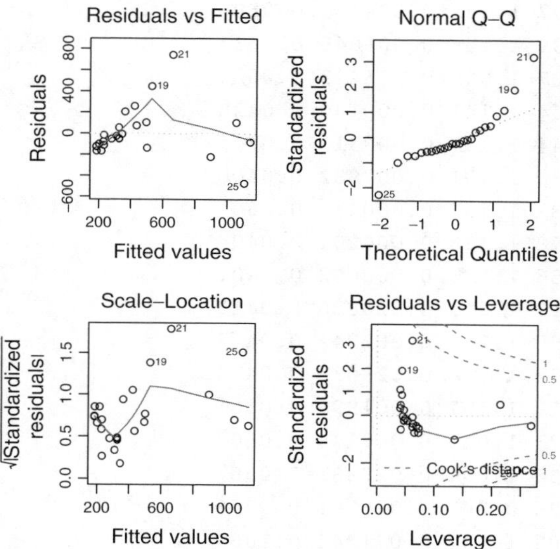

Conclusions - There is a definite "wedge" pattern evident in the residual plot which is indicative of a problem with homogeneity of variance. The Q-Q normal plot confirms that the response variable does deviate from normal. One of the points (observation 25, obscured by the legend) is close to the higher Cook's D contours suggesting that this observation may be overly influential on the final fitted model.

```
> peake.lm <- lm(log10(INDIV) ~ log10(AREA), data = peake)
> plot(peake.lm)
```

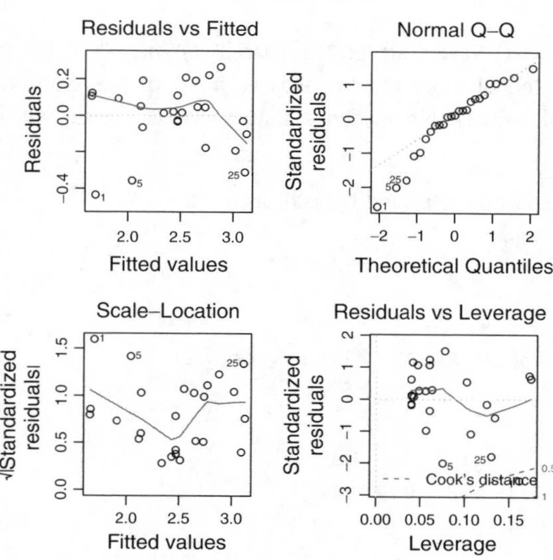

Conclusions - The residual plot resulting from a model based on log transformed data does not depict an obvious "wedge", the Q-Q normal plot indicates a greater degree of normality and non of the points are close to the higher Cook's D contours. This confirms that it is more appropriate to fit the linear model using the log transformed data.

```
> influence.measures(peake.lm)
Influence measures of
         lm(formula = log10(INDIV) ~ log10(AREA), data = peake) :

      dfb.1_ dfb.l10.   dffit cov.r   cook.d    hat inf
1  -1.202012  1.12137 -1.2929 0.670 0.626553 0.1615   *
2   0.310855 -0.29097  0.3319 1.260 0.056245 0.1727
3   0.269684 -0.25255  0.2877 1.278 0.042502 0.1745   *
4   0.153477 -0.13896  0.1781 1.187 0.016366 0.1023
5  -0.484207  0.42414 -0.6182 0.804 0.164749 0.0756
```

```
6  -0.062392  0.05251 -0.0897 1.151 0.004183 0.0608
7   0.052830 -0.04487  0.0739 1.158 0.002846 0.0633
8   0.187514 -0.15760  0.2707 1.052 0.036423 0.0605
9   0.006384 -0.00416  0.0164 1.141 0.000140 0.0428
10  0.004787 -0.00131  0.0244 1.137 0.000311 0.0401
11  0.013583  0.00419  0.1238 1.101 0.007882 0.0400
12 -0.003011 -0.00112 -0.0287 1.137 0.000432 0.0401
13  0.000247  0.00259  0.0198 1.138 0.000204 0.0407
14 -0.003734 -0.00138 -0.0356 1.135 0.000662 0.0401
15 -0.015811  0.05024  0.2419 1.013 0.028826 0.0418
16 -0.017200  0.02518  0.0595 1.142 0.001842 0.0487
17 -0.061445  0.09368  0.2375 1.038 0.028033 0.0474
18 -0.025317  0.03314  0.0619 1.151 0.001995 0.0561
19 -0.146377  0.18521  0.3173 1.015 0.049144 0.0607
20  0.100361 -0.13065 -0.2406 1.064 0.028981 0.0567
21 -0.263549  0.31302  0.4496 0.963 0.095261 0.0776
22  0.263206 -0.29948 -0.3786 1.101 0.071044 0.1069
23  0.043182 -0.04845 -0.0588 1.246 0.001804 0.1248
24  0.167829 -0.18726 -0.2236 1.226 0.025747 0.1341
25  0.545842 -0.61039 -0.7334 0.929 0.241660 0.1302
```

Conclusions - Whilst three leverage (hat) values are greater than $2 * p/n = 0.16$ (observations 1, 2 and 3) and therefore potentially outliers in x-space, none of the Cook's D values are ≥ 1 (no point is overly influential). No evidence that hypothesis tests will be unreliable.

Step 5 (Key 8.6a) - examine the parameter estimates and hypothesis tests.

```
> summary(peake.lm)

Call:
lm(formula = log10(INDIV) ~ log10(AREA), data = peake)

Residuals:
     Min       1Q   Median       3Q      Max
-0.43355 -0.06464  0.02219  0.11178  0.26818

Coefficients:
            Estimate Std. Error t value Pr(>|t|)
(Intercept) -0.57601    0.25904  -2.224   0.0363 *
log10(AREA)  0.83492    0.07066  11.816 3.01e-11 ***
---
Signif. codes:  0 '***' 0.001 '**' 0.01 '*' 0.05 '.' 0.1 ' ' 1

Residual standard error: 0.1856 on 23 degrees of freedom
Multiple R-squared: 0.8586,     Adjusted R-squared: 0.8524
F-statistic: 139.6 on 1 and 23 DF,  p-value: 3.007e-11
```

Conclusions - Reject H_0 that the population slope equals zero. An increase in (log) mussel clump area was found to be associated with a strong ($r^2 = 0.859$), significant increase in the (log) number of supported invertebrate individuals ($b = 0.835$, $t_{23} = 11.816$, $P < 0.001$).

Step 6 (Key 8.12) - summarize the findings of the linear regression analysis with a scatterplot including the regression line, regression equation and r^2.

```
> #create a plot with solid dots (pch=16) and no axis or labels}
> plot(INDIV~AREA, data=peake, pch=16, axes=F, xlab="", ylab="",
      log="xy")
> #put the x-axis (axis 1) with smaller label font size
> axis(1, cex.axis=.8)
> #put the x-axis label 3 lines down from the axis
> mtext(text=expression(paste("Mussel clump area", (mm^2))),
       side=1, line=3)
> #put the y-axis (axis 2) with horizontal tick labels
> axis(2, las=1)
> #put the y-axis label 3 lines to the left of the axis
> mtext(text="Number of individuals", side=2, line=3)
> #add the regression line from the fitted model
> abline(peake.lm)
> #add the regression formula
> text(30000, 30, expression(paste(log[10], "INDIV = 0.835",
+ log[10], "AREA - 0.576")), pos=2)
> #add the r squared value
> text(30000, 22, expression(paste(r^2==0.835)), pos=2)
> #put an L-shaped box to complete the axis
> box(bty="l")
```

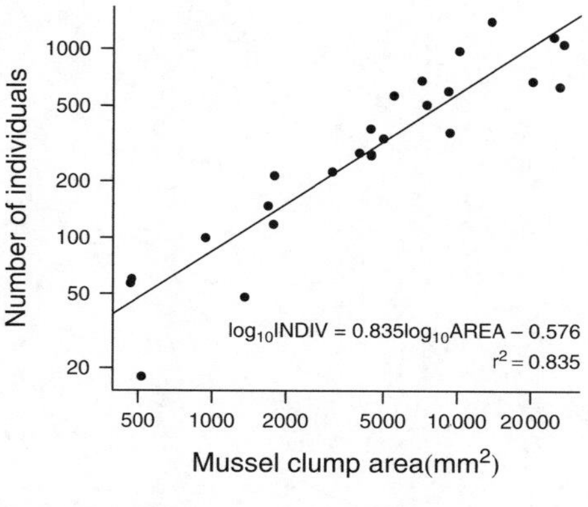

Step 7 (Key 8.11) - use the fitted linear model to predict the number of individuals that would be supported on two new mussel clumps with areas of 8000 and 10000 mm^2.

```
> 10^predict(peake.lm, data.frame(AREA = c(8000, 10000)))
       1        2
481.6561 580.2949
```

Since OLS was used to generate the predictive model, and yet there was likely to have been uncertainty in the original mussel clump area measurements, confidence intervals about these predictions are not valid. Nevertheless, the following illustrates how they would be obtained.

```
> 10^predict(peake.lm, data.frame(AREA = c(8000, 10000)),
           interval = "prediction")
       fit      lwr      upr
1 481.6561 194.5975 1192.167
2 580.2949 233.5345 1441.938
```

Similarly, confidence bands could be incorporated onto the plot to indicate confidence in the population regression line if there was no uncertainty in the predictor variable.

```
> plot(log10(INDIV) ~ log10(AREA), data = peake, pch = 16,
+     axes = F, xlab = "", ylab = "")
> axis(1, cex.axis = 0.8)
> mtext(text = "Log Mussel clump area", side = 1, line = 3)
> axis(2, las = 1)
> mtext(text = "Log number of individuals", side = 2, line = 3)
> abline(peake.lm)
> text(4.5, 1.4, expression(paste(log[10], "INDIV = 0.835",
+     log[10], "AREA - 0.576")), pos = 2)
> text(4.5, 1.3, expression(paste(r^2 == 0.835)), pos = 2)
> x <- seq(min(peake$AREA), max(peake$AREA), l = 1000)
> y <- predict(peake.lm, data.frame(AREA = x), interval = "c")
> matlines(log10(x), y, lty = 1, col = 1)
> box(bty = "l")
```

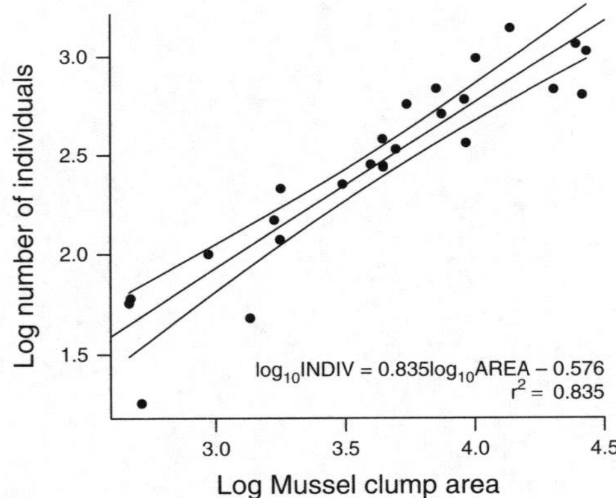

Example 8E: Linear regression - with multiple values of Y per value of X

Sokal and Rohlf (1997) presented data on the (arcsine transformed) percentage survival to adulthood of *Tibolium castaneum* beetles housed at four densities (5, 20, 50 & 100 eggs per gram of flour medium). Each level of the density treatment was replicated (albeit to varying degrees) in a manner similar to single factor classification (ANOVA, see chapter 10).

Step 1 - Import (section 2.3) the beetles data set

```
> beetles <- read.table("beetles.csv", header = T, sep = ",")
```

Step 2 (Key 8.4) - Assess linearity, normality and homogeneity of variance using a scatterplot with marginal boxplots and a lowess smoother. As there are replicates for each level of the predictor, normality and homogeneity of variance can also be assessed with boxplots of each population.

```
> library(car)
> scatterplot(SURVIVAL ~ DENSITY,
+      data = beetles)
```

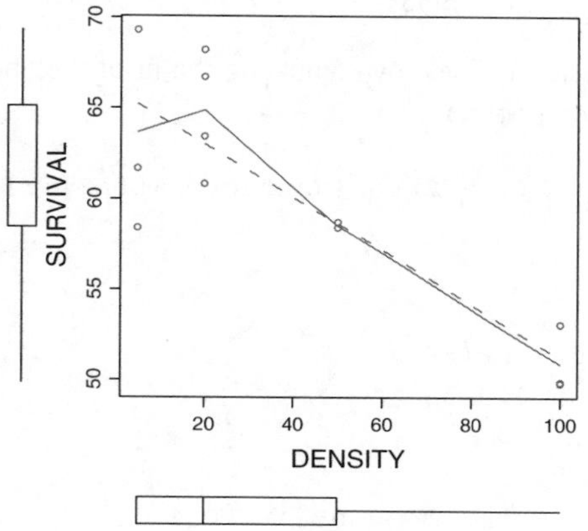

```
> boxplot(SURVIVAL ~ DENSITY,
+      data = beetles)
```

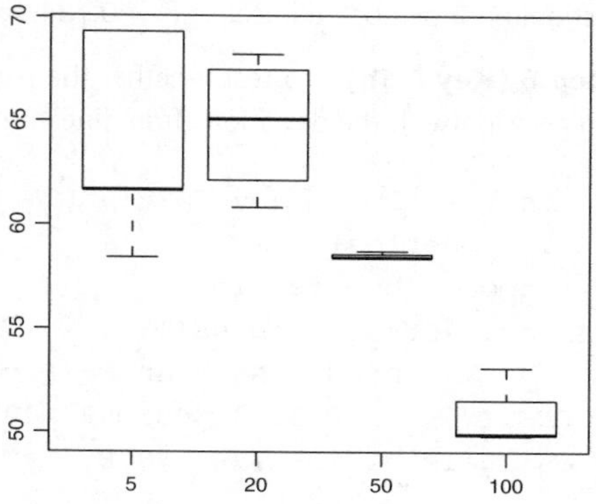

Conclusions - the scatterplot indicates that the assumption of linearity is likely to be ok. Note that the boxplot on the x-margin of the scatterplot only reflects an imbalance in replication. Whilst there is some evidence of non-homogeniety of variance, a consistent relationship between mean and variance cannot be fully established, and thus the data are considered suitable.

Step 3 (Key 8.5a) - the ordinary least squares method is considered appropriate as the there is considered to be no uncertainty (error) in the predictor variable (relative density).

Step 4 (Key 8.5b) - determine the lack of fit to the regression line by comparing deviations of observations from the regression line to deviations of observations from their means per density.

```
> anova(lm(SURVIVAL ~ DENSITY + as.factor(DENSITY), beetles))
Analysis of Variance Table

Response: SURVIVAL
                   Df Sum Sq Mean Sq F value    Pr(>F)
DENSITY             1 403.93  403.93 32.0377 0.0001466 ***
as.factor(DENSITY)  2  19.77    9.89  0.7842 0.4804305
Residuals          11 138.69   12.61
---
Signif. codes:  0 '***' 0.001 '**' 0.01 '*' 0.05 '.' 0.1 ' ' 1
```

Conclusions - deviations from linear not significantly different from zero ($F = 0.7842, P = 0.480$), hence there is no evidence that a straight line is not an adequate representation of these data.

Step 5 (Key 8.5b) - consider whether to pool deviations from the regression line and the deviations from the predictor level means

```
> #calculate critical F for alpha=0.25, df=2,11
> qf(0.25,2,11, lower=T)
[1] 0.2953387
```

Conclusions - Sokal and Rohlf (1997) suggest that while there is no difference between the deviations from the regression line and the deviations from the predictor level means, they should not be pooled because $F = 0.784 > F_{0.75[2,11]} = 0.295$.

Step 6 (Key 8.5b) - to test whether the regression is linear by comparing the fit of the linear regression with the deviations from linearity (non pooled).

```
> beetles.lm <- aov(SURVIVAL ~ DENSITY + Error(as.factor(DENSITY)),
+      beetles)
> summary(beetles.lm)
Error: as.factor(DENSITY)
          Df Sum Sq Mean Sq F value  Pr(>F)
DENSITY    1 403.93  403.93  40.855 0.02361 *
Residuals  2  19.77    9.89
---
Signif. codes:  0 '***' 0.001 '**' 0.01 '*' 0.05 '.' 0.1 ' ' 1

Error: Within
          Df  Sum Sq Mean Sq F value Pr(>F)
Residuals 11 138.687  12.608
```

Conclusions - Reject H_0 that the population is not linear.

```
> #to get the regression coefficients
> lm(SURVIVAL~DENSITY, beetles)
Call:
lm(formula = SURVIVAL ~ DENSITY, data = beetles)

Coefficients:
(Intercept)       DENSITY
     65.960        -0.147
```

If we had decided to pool, the analysis could have been performed as follows:

```
> summary(lm(SURVIVAL ~ DENSITY, beetles))
Call:
lm(formula = SURVIVAL ~ DENSITY, data = beetles)
```

```
Residuals:
    Min      1Q  Median      3Q     Max
-6.8550 -1.8094 -0.2395  2.7856  5.1902

Coefficients:
            Estimate Std. Error t value Pr(>|t|)
(Intercept) 65.96004    1.30593  50.508 2.63e-16 ***
DENSITY     -0.14701    0.02554  -5.757 6.64e-05 ***
---
Signif. codes:  0 '***' 0.001 '**' 0.01 '*' 0.05 '.' 0.1 ' ' 1

Residual standard error: 3.491 on 13 degrees of freedom
Multiple R-squared: 0.7182,     Adjusted R-squared: 0.6966
F-statistic: 33.14 on 1 and 13 DF,  p-value: 6.637e-05
```

Note that these data could also have been analysed as a single factor ANOVA with polynomial contrasts

```
> beetles$DENSITY <- as.factor(beetles$DENSITY)
> contrasts(beetles$DENSITY) <- contr.poly(4, c(5, 20, 50,
+     100))
> beetles.aov <- aov(SURVIVAL ~ DENSITY, beetles)
> summary(beetles.aov, split = list(DENSITY = list(1, c(2,
+     3))))
            Df Sum Sq Mean Sq F value    Pr(>F)
DENSITY      3 423.70  141.23 11.2020 0.0011367 **
  DENSITY: C1  1 403.93  403.93 32.0377 0.0001466 ***
  DENSITY: C2  2  19.77    9.89  0.7842 0.4804305
Residuals   11 138.69   12.61
---
Signif. codes:  0 '***' 0.001 '**' 0.01 '*' 0.05 '.' 0.1 ' ' 1
```

Example 8F: Model II regression

To contrast the parameter estimates resulting from model II regression, Quinn and Keough (2002) used a data set from Christensen et al. (1996) (Box 5.7 Quinn and Keough (2002)). Whilst model II regression is arguably unnecessary for these data (as it is hard to imagine why estimates of the regression parameters would be the sole interest of the Christensen et al. (1996) investigation), we will proceed with the aim of gaining a reliable estimate of the population slope is required.

Step 1 - Import (section 2.3) the Christensen et al. (1996) data set

```
> christ <- read.table("christ.csv", header = T, sep = ",")
```

Step 2 (Key 8.4) - Assess linearity, normality and homogeneity of variance using a scatterplot with marginal boxplots and a lowess smoother.

```
> library(car)
> scatterplot(CWD.BASA ~ RIP.DENS, data = christ)
```

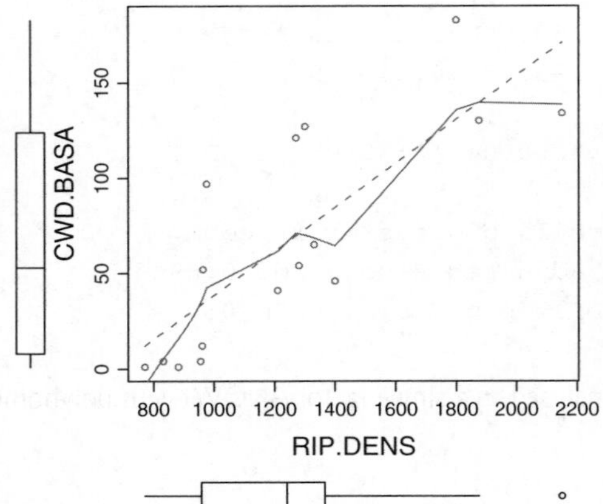

Conclusions - no evidence of non-normality (boxplots not overly asymmetrical), non homogeneity of variance (points do not become progressively more or less spread out along the regression line) or non-linearity.

Step 3 (Key 8.5b) - as there is likely to be uncertainty in the measured levels of the predictor variable and the stated intention of the analysis is to obtain a reliable estimate of the population slope, model II regression is considered appropriate. Furthermore, as the basal area of course woody debris and the density of riparian vegetation are measured on different scales, the degrees of uncertainty in the variables are unlikely to be equal (yet may well be proportionaly to the respective variances of each variable), MA regression is not appropriate. Finally, as there is some evidence that there may be outliers present, RMA is considered the most appropriate method.

Step 4 (Key 8.5b) - fit the RMA linear regression model.

```
> library(biology)
> christ.lm <- lm.II(CWD.BASA ~ RIP.DENS, christ, type = "RMA")
> summary(christ.lm)
$Call
lm.II(formula = CWD.BASA ~ RIP.DENS, data = christ, type = "RMA")

$Coefficients
                Estimate Lower 95% CI Upper 95% CI
(Intercept) -113.9042556 -187.1524427  -61.7666149
RIP.DENS       0.1450207    0.1032249    0.2037396
```

Step 5 (Key 8.12) - summarize the findings of the linear regression analysis with a scatterplot including the regression line, regression equation and r^2.

```
> #create a plot with solid dots (pch=16) and no axis or labels
> plot(CWD.BASA~RIP.DENS, christ, pch=16, axes=F, xlab="",
     ylab="")
> #put the x-axis (axis 1) with smaller label font size
```

```
> axis(1, cex.axis=.8)
> #put the x-axis label 3 lines down from the axis
> mtext(text="Riparian tree density", side=1, line=3)
> #put the y-axis (axis 2) with horizontal tick labels
> axis(2, las=1)
> #put the y-axis label 3 lines to the left of the axis
> mtext(text="Course woody debris basal area", side=2, line=3)
> #add the regression line from the fitted model
> abline(christ.lm)
> #add the regression parameters
> text(1600,50,expression(paste(beta[1]==0.145)), pos=4)
> text(1600,40,expression(paste(beta[0]==-113.904)), pos=4)
> #put an L-shaped box to complete the axis
> box(bty="l")
```

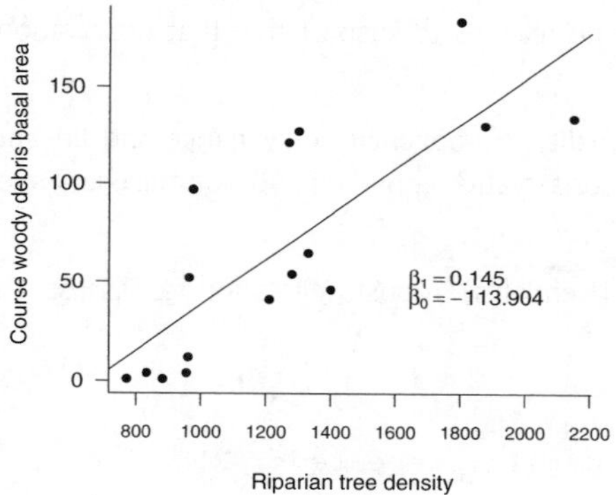

Example 8G: Linear regression - non-parametric regression

Smith (1967) investigated the effects of cloud seeding on rainfall in the Snowy Mountains, Australia. The experiment took place in two areas (the target and control). Within a year a number of periods were randomly allocated for seeding and additional periods for non-seeding. The total rainfall in the target and control areas during each of these periods were recorded. Within a single year, the impact of seeding was assessed via a double ratio (ratio of rainfall in target to control areas for seeding periods versus ratio of target to control areas during non-seeding times) and the experiment was repeated over 5 years (Example 9.2 Hollander and Wolfe (1999)).

Step 1 - Import (section 2.3) the Smith (1967) data set

```
> smith <- read.table("smith.csv", header = T, sep = ",")
```

Step 2 (Key 8.4) - Assess linearity, normality and homogeneity of variance using a scatterplot with marginal boxplots and a lowess smoother.

```
> scatterplot(RATIO ~ YEARS, smith)
```

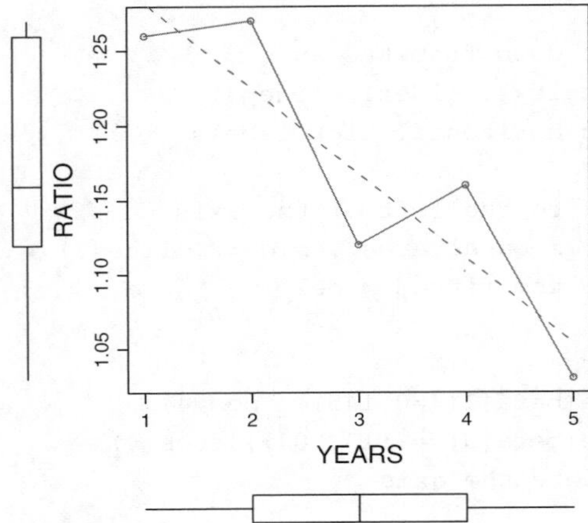

Conclusions - whilst there may not appear to be any evidence of non-normality (boxplots not overly asymmetrical), non homogeneity of variance (points do not become progressively more or less spread out along the regression line) or non-linearity, it could be argued that there are too few observations on which to make meaningful decisions about normality and it might be safer to not make distributional assumptions.

Step 3 (Key 8.7) - as far as we know, there are no reasons to suspect that that observations wont be independent.

Step 4 (Key 8.8b) - it is difficult to assess normality, homogeneity of variance and linearity with such a small sample size. We will take the conservative approach and not make any such assumptions.

Step 5 (Key 8.9d) - perform non-parametric (Kendall's) robust regression to assess the $H_0 : \beta_1 = 0$.

```
> library(mblm)
> smith.mblm <- mblm(RATIO ~ YEARS, smith, repeated = F)
> summary(smith.mblm)
Call:
mblm(formula = RATIO ~ YEARS, dataframe = smith, repeated = F)

Residuals:
       1        2        3        4        5
 0.00000  0.06625 -0.02750  0.06875 -0.00500

Coefficients:
             Estimate      MAD V value Pr(>|V|)
(Intercept)   1.31625  0.04077      15   0.0625 .
YEARS        -0.05625  0.03459       4   0.0137 *
---
Signif. codes:  0 '***' 0.001 '**' 0.01 '*' 0.05 '.' 0.1 ' ' 1

Residual standard error: 0.05744 on 3 degrees of freedom
```

Conclusions - reject H_0. The impact of cloud seeding significantly declines over time (b=-0.056, V=4, P=0.0137).

Step 6 (Key 8.10) - calculate 95% confidence intervals for the parameter estimates.

```
> confint.mblm(smith.mblm, level = 0.95)
                 0.025   0.975
(Intercept)  1.28875  1.385
YEARS       -0.10000 -0.015
```

Example 8H: Linear regression - randomization test

McKechnie et al. (1975) investigated the relationship between altitude and the frequency of hezokinase (HK) 1.00 mobility genes from colonies of *Euphydras editha* butterflies (Example 8.1 Manly (1991)).

Step 1 - Import (section 2.3) the McKechnie et al. (1975) data set

```
> mckechnie <- read.table("mckechnie.csv", header = T, sep = ",")
```

Step 2 (Key 8.4) - Assess linearity, normality and homogeneity of variance using a scatterplot with marginal boxplots and a lowess smoother. For the purpose of this demonstration, lets assume that the assumption of normality could not be met and more importantly, that the observations are not independent, thereby necessitating an alternative regression method.

Step 3 (Key 8.7b) - use randomization to test whether the observed trend could be due to chance.

1. define the statistic[j] to use in the randomization test - in this case the *t*-statistic

```
> stat <- function(data, index) {
+     summary(lm(HK ~ ALT, data))$coef[2, 3]
+ }
```

2. define how the data should be randomized - randomize the pairing of predictor and responses (shuffle without replacement the predictor values amongst observations)

```
> rand.gen <- function(data, mle) {
+     out <- data
+     out$ALT <- sample(out$ALT, replace = F)
+     out
+ }
```

3. call a bootstrapping procedure to randomize 5000 times (this can take some time)

```
> library(boot)
```

[j] Consistent with Manly (1991), I have used OLS to estimate the regression parameters. However, these parameters could alternatively be RMA or non-parametric regression estimates.

```
> mckechnie.boot <- boot(mckechnie, stat, R = 5000,
+      sim = "parametric", ran.gen = rand.gen)
```

4. examine the distribution of *t*-values generated from the randomization procedure

```
> plot(mckechnie.boot)
```

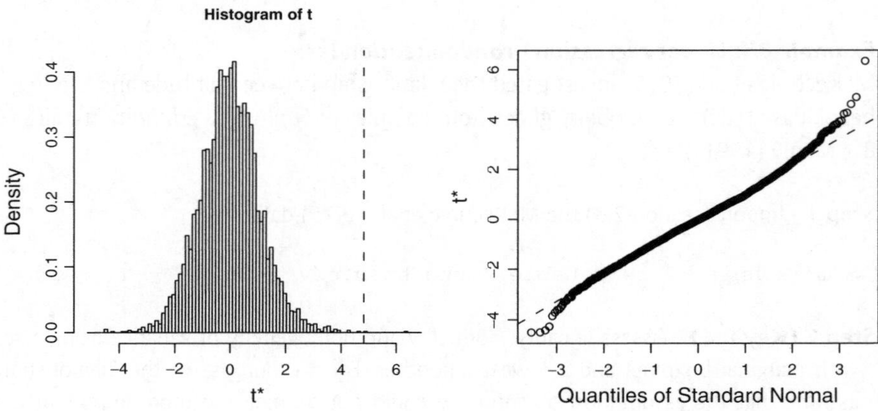

5. examine the bootstrap statistics

```
> mckechnie.boot
PARAMETRIC BOOTSTRAP


Call:
boot(data = mckechnie, statistic = stat, R = 5000,
    sim = "parametric", ran.gen = rand.gen)


Bootstrap Statistics :
    original     bias    std. error
t1* 4.830571 -4.846745     1.084864
```

6. calculate the number of possible *t*-values (including the observed *t*-value, which is one possible outcome) that were greater or equal to the observed *t*-value and express this as a percentage of the number of randomizations (plus one for the observed outcome).

```
> t <- length(mckechnie.boot$t[mckechnie.boot$t >=
+       mckechnie.boot$t0]) + 1
> t/(mckechnie.boot$R + 1)
[1] 0.00059988
```

Conclusions - probability of obtaining a *t*-value of 4.83 or greater when H_0 is true is 0.0006 (0.06%). Note that as this is a randomization procedure, the p-value will vary slightly each time.

Step 4 (Key 8.10) - calculate 95% confidence intervals for the parameter estimates (example 8.2 Manly (1991))

1. define how the parameters (coefficients) are to be calculated (from OLS regression of a random resample with replacement of the observations).

```
> par.boot <- function(mckechnie, index) {
+      x <- mckechnie$ALT[index]
+      y <- mckechnie$HK[index]
+      model <- lm(y ~ x)
+      coef(model)
+ }
```

2. call a bootstrapping procedure to randomize 5000 times (this can take some time)

```
> mckechnie.boot <- boot(mckechnie, par.boot, R = 5000)
> mckechnie.boot
ORDINARY NONPARAMETRIC BOOTSTRAP


Call:
boot(data = mckechnie, statistic = par.boot, R = 5000)


Bootstrap Statistics :
    original      bias    std. error
t1* 10.65409  0.2426368    4.853195
t2* 29.15347 -0.1309074    5.581786
```

3. examine the bootstrap 95% confidence intervals for the second (index=2) parameter (slope)

```
> boot.ci(mckechnie.boot, index = 2)
BOOTSTRAP CONFIDENCE INTERVAL CALCULATIONS
Based on 5000 bootstrap replicates

CALL :
boot.ci(boot.out = mckechnie.boot, index = 2)

Intervals :
Level      Normal              Basic
95%   (18.34, 40.22 )   (18.38, 40.81 )

Level     Percentile            BCa
95%   (17.50, 39.92 )   (16.95, 39.52 )
Calculations and Intervals on Original Scale
```

Conclusions - 95% confidence interval for the true regression coefficients is 15.49 - 39.52

Step 5 (Key 8.11) - predict the percentage of HK genes at an altitude of 1.

1. define the function to predict new values.

```
> pred.boot <- function(mckechnie, index) {
+     mckechnie.rs <- mckechnie[index, ]
+     mckechnie.lm <- lm(HK ~ ALT, mckechnie.rs)
+     predict(mckechnie.lm, data.frame(ALT = 1))
+ }
```

2. call a bootstrapping procedure to randomize 5000 times (this can take some time)

```
> mckechnie.boot <- boot(mckechnie, pred.boot, R = 5000)

> mckechnie.boot
ORDINARY NONPARAMETRIC BOOTSTRAP


Call:
boot(data = mckechnie, statistic = pred.boot, R = 5000)


Bootstrap Statistics :
    original    bias    std. error
t1* 39.80756 0.1235158    4.914043
```

3. examine the bootstrap 95% intervals for this prediction

```
> boot.ci(mckechnie.boot, index = 1)
BOOTSTRAP CONFIDENCE INTERVAL CALCULATIONS
Based on 5000 bootstrap replicates

CALL :
boot.ci(boot.out = mckechnie.boot, index = 1)

Intervals :
Level      Normal              Basic
95%   (30.05, 49.32 )   (30.66, 49.80 )

Level     Percentile            BCa
95%   (29.82, 48.96 )   (27.68, 47.58 )
Calculations and Intervals on Original Scale
```

Conclusions - 95% confidence interval for the true regression coefficients is 27.59 - 47.81

Alternatively, if the levels of the predictor variable were specifically set, then it might be more appropriate to base hypothesis tests, predictions and confidence intervals on randomized residuals rather than randomizing the predictor variable.

Example 8I: Power analysis - sample size determination in testing $H_0 : \rho = 0$

Zar (1999) provided a worked example in which the sample size required to reject the null hypothesis ($H_0 : \rho = 0$) 99% of the time when the correlation coefficient has an absolute magnitude (ignore sign) greater or equal to 0.5 ($|\rho| \geq 0.5$) (Example 19.5 Zar (1999)).

Step 1 - calculate the sample size required to detect a correlation of greater or equal to 0.5 with a power of 0.99

```
> library(pwr)
> pwr.r.test(r = 0.5, power = 0.99)
     approximate correlation power calculation (arctangh
     transformation)

               n = 63.50301
               r = 0.5
       sig.level = 0.05
           power = 0.99
     alternative = two.sided
```

Step 2 - generate a plot that illustrates the relationship between target correlation (from 0.4 to 0.9) and sample size for a range of levels of power (0.75,0.8,0.85,0.9).

```
> library(pwr)
> r <- seq(0.4, 0.9, l = 100)
> plot(sapply(r, function(x) pwr.r.test(r = x, power = 0.8)$n) ~
+     r, type = "l", lwd = 2, xlab = "Correlation coefficient",
+     ylab = "Sample size")
> points(sapply(r, function(x) pwr.r.test(r = x, power = 0.9)$n) ~
+     r, type = "l")
> points(sapply(r, function(x) pwr.r.test(r = x, power = 0.85)$n) ~
+     r, type = "l")
> points(sapply(r, function(x) pwr.r.test(r = x, power = 0.75)$n) ~
+     r, type = "l")
```

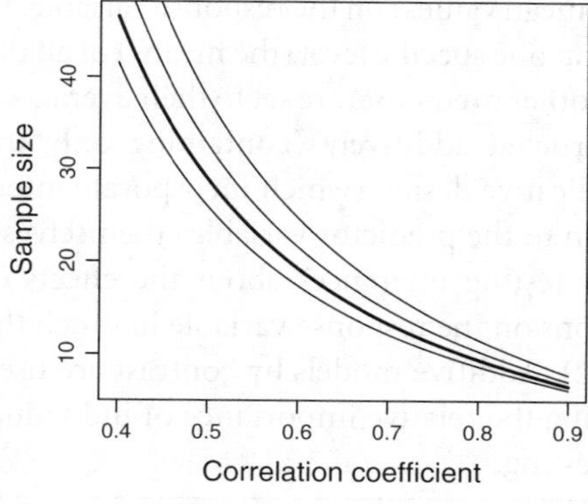

Conclusions - graph provides a means to evaluate the cost-benefit compromises between power and sample size for a range of possible correlations. Informed design decisions can result from such graphs. If the degree of correlation is expected to be high, approximately 10 replicates would be adequate. However, if the degree of correlation is expected to be lower, a greater number of replicates are required. Furthermore, as the degree of correlation declines, the difference in estimated required sample size for different levels of power becomes greater.

9

Multiple and curvilinear regression

Multiple and complex regression analyses can be useful for situations in which patterns in a response variable can not be adequately described by a single straight line resulting from a single predictor and/or a simple linear equation.

9.1 Multiple linear regression

Multiple regression is an extension of simple linear regression whereby a response variable is modeled against a linear combination of two or more simultaneously measured continuous predictor variables. There are two main purposes of multiple linear regression:

(i) To develop a better predictive model (equation) than is possible from models based on single independent variables.
(ii) To investigate the relative individual effects of each of the multiple independent variables above and beyond (standardized across) the effects of the other variables.

Although the relationship between response variable and the additive effect of all the predictor variables is represented overall by a single multidimensional plane (surface), the individual effects of each of the predictor variables on the response variable (standardized across the other variables) can be depicted by single *partial regression* lines. The slope of any single partial regression line (*partial regression slope*) thereby represents the rate of change or effect of that specific predictor variable (holding all the other predictor variables constant to their respective mean values) on the response variable. In essence, it is the effect of one predictor variable at one specific level (the means) of all the other predictor variables (i.e. when each of the other predictors are set to their averages).

Multiple regression models can be constructed additively (containing only the predictor variables themselves) or in a multiplicative design (which incorporate interactions between predictor variables in addition to the predictor variables themselves). Multiplicative models are used primarily for testing inferences about the effects of various predictor variables and their interactions on the response variable in much the same way as factorial ANOVA (see chapter 12). Additive models by contrast are used for generating predictive models and estimating the relative importance of individual predictor variables more so than hypothesis testing.

Biostatistical Design and Analysis Using R: a Practical Guide, 1st edition. By M. Logan.
Published 2010 by Blackwell Publishing.

9.2 Linear models

Additive model

$$y_i = \beta_0 + \beta_1 x_{i1} + \beta_2 x_{i2} + \ldots + \beta_j x_{ij} + \varepsilon_i$$

where β_0 is the population y-intercept (value of y when all partial slopes equal zero), β_1, β_2, etc are the partial population slopes of Y on X_1, X_2, etc respectively holding the other X constant. ε_i is the random unexplained error or residual component. The additive model assumes that the effect of one predictor variable (partial slope) is independent of the levels of the other predictor variables.

Multiplicative model

$$y_i = \beta_0 + \beta_1 x_{i1} + \beta_2 x_{i2} + \beta_3 x_{i1} x_{i2} + \ldots + \varepsilon_i$$

where $\beta_3 x_{i1} x_{i2}$ is the interactive effect of X_1 and X_2 on Y and it examines the degree to which the effect of one of the predictor variables depends on the levels of the other predictor variable(s).

9.3 Null hypotheses

A separate H_0 is tested for each of the estimated model parameters:

H_0: $\beta_0 = 0$ (the population y-intercept equals zero)

This test is rarely of interest as it only tests the likelihood that the background level of the response variable is equal to zero (rarely a biologically meaningful comparison) and does not test whether or not there is a relationship.

H_0: $\beta_1 = 0$ (the partial population slope of X_1 on Y equals zero)
H_0: $\beta_2 = 0$ (the partial population slope of X_2 on Y equals zero)
....

These tests examine respectively whether or not there is likely to be a relationship between the dependent and one of the independent variables (holding the other independent variables constant) in the population.

For an additive model

$H_0 : \beta_3 = 0$ (the partial population slope of the interactive effect of X_1 and X_2 on Y equals zero)

This test examines whether or not the effect of one dependent variable on the independent variable (holding others constant) is dependent on other independent variables.

As with simple linear regression, these individual parameter null hypothesis tests can all be tested using the t-statistic with $n - (p + 1)$ degrees of freedom (where p is the number of parameters in the linear model) or by comparing the lack of fit of a *full model* (model containing all predictor variables) to an appropriate *reduced model* (model containing all but the individual predictor variable or interacting variables) via analysis of variance. In addition, the overall analysis of variance (which tests the $H_0 : \beta_1 = \beta_2 = \ldots = \beta_j = 0$) investigates whether the response variable can be modeled by the particular linear combination of predictor variables.

Interactions

The nature of significant interactions (e.g. X_1 and X_2 on Y) can be further explored by re-fitting the multiple linear model to explore the partial effects of one of the predictor variables (e.g. X_1) for a specific set of levels of the other interacting predictor variable(s) (e.g. the mean of X_2 as well as this mean $\pm$ 1 and or 2 standard deviations). For such subsequent main effects tests, ignore the effect of the interaction, which will be identical to that previously tested, and focus purely on the individual partial slope (β_1).

9.4 Assumptions

To maximize the reliability of hypothesis tests, the following assumptions apply:

(i) linearity - no other curved relationship represents the relationships between each of the predictors and the response variable. Scatterplots and scatterplot matrices are useful for exploring linearity.

(ii) normality - the residuals, and therefore the populations from which each of the responses were collected, are normally distributed. Note that in the majority of multiple linear regression cases, the predictor variables are measured (not specifically set), and therefore the respective populations are also assumed to be normally distributed. Boxplots of each variable (particularly those incorporated within the diagonals of a scatterplot matrix) are useful diagnostics.

(iii) homogeneity of variance - the residuals (populations from which each of the responses were collected) are equally varied. Exploring the spread of points around individual scatterplot trendlines can be useful, as can residual plots. Plots of residuals against each of the predictor variables can also be useful for diagnostic spatial and temporal autocorrelation.

(iv) (multi)collinearity - a predictor variable must not be correlated to the combination of other predictor variables. Multicollinearity has major detrimental effects on model fitting:
- instability of the estimated partial regression slopes (small changes in the data or variable inclusion can cause dramatic changes in parameter estimates).
- inflated standard errors and confidence intervals of model parameters, thereby increasing the type II error rate (reducing power) of parameter hypothesis tests.

Multicollinearity can be diagnosed with the following:
- investigate pairwise correlations between all the predictor variables either by a correlation matrix or a scatterplot matrix.

- calculate **tolerance** ($1 - r^2$ of the relationship between a predictor variable and all the other predictor variables) for each of the predictor variables. Tolerance is a measure of the degree of collinearity and values less < 0.2 should be considered and values < 0.1 given series attention. Variance inflation factor (VIF) are the inverse of tolerance and thus values greater than 5, or worse, 10 indicate collinearity.
- PCA (principle components analysis) eigenvalues (from a correlation matrix for all the predictor variables) close to zero indicate collinearity and component loadings may be useful in determining which predictor variables cause collinearity.

There are several approaches to dealing with collinearity[a]:

- remove the highly correlated predictor variable(s), starting with the least biologically interesting variable(s).
- PCA (principle components analysis) regression - regress the response variable against the principal components resulting from a correlation matrix for all the predictor variables. Each of these principal components by definition are completely independent, but the resulting parameter estimates must be back-calculated in order to have any biological meaning.

Interaction terms in multiplicative models are likely to be correlated to their constituent individual predictors, and thus the partial slopes of these individual predictors are likely to be unstable. However, this problem can be reduced by first centering (subtracting the mean from the predictor values) the individual predictor variables.

(v) the number of predictor variables must be less than the number of observations otherwise the linear model will be over-parameterized (more parameters to estimate than there are independent data from which estimations are calculated).

As with simple linear regression, regression diagnostics (residuals, leverage and Cook's D) should be examined following model fitting.

9.5 Curvilinear models

It is not always appropriate to attempt to model the relationship between a response and predictor variable with a straight line in which it is assumed that the rate of change (slope) remains constant throughout the range of the predictor variable. In such cases, scale transformations may not only be unable to correct linearity, they may be inappropriate when we are trying to describe a model that reflects the true nature of the relationship. To some degree, curvilinear models assume that there is a relationship between the variables and are themselves more concerned with exploring the nature of the relationship. Table 9.1 depicts the general nature and corresponding models and R syntax for some simple or useful non-linear models.

9.5.1 Polynomial regression

Polynomials are linear combinations of predictor variables (no predictor variable is the exponent, multiplier or deviser of any other) in which a predictor variable is represented

[a] Note that all of these are likely to result in biased parameter estimates.

Table 9.1 Illustrative set of useful non-linear functions with corresponding R model fitting syntax. Some examples also illustrate corresponding self-starting functions. Note that this is a non-exhaustive set.

Function	**Preview**

Concave/convex functions

Power ($y = \alpha x^{\beta}$)

Used to describe a large range of physical and biological trends including allometric scaling relationships (e.g. Kleiber's law) and inverse square laws (e.g. Newtonian gravity). α defines the scale of the y-axis and β defines the magnitude and polatity of the rate of change and thus the degree of curvature

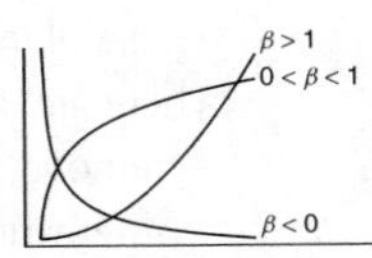


```
> nls(DV~a*IV^b, dataset, start=list(a=1,
    b=0.1))
```

Exponential ($y = \alpha e^{\beta x}$)

Models non-asymptotic growth and decay. α defines the scale of the y-axis and increasing magnitude of β increases the curvature of the curve.

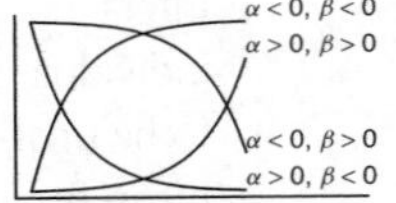


```
> nls(DV~a*exp(b*IV), dataset, start=list(a=1,
    b=0.1))
```

Aymptotic functions

Asymptotic exponential ($y = \alpha + (\beta - \alpha)e^{-e^{\gamma}x}$)

Used to describe general asymptotic relationships.
Equivelent to the more simple $y = a - be^{-cx}$ when $a = \alpha$, $b = \beta - \alpha$ and $c = e^{\gamma}$

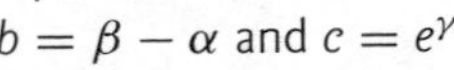

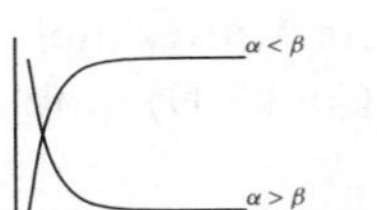

α - y value of horizontal asymptote. β - value of y when $x = 0$.
γ - natural log of rate of curvature

```
> nls(DV~a+b*exp(c*x),dataset,start=list(a=1,
    b=-1,c=-1))
> nls(DV~SSasymp(IV,a,b,c), dataset)
```

Michaelis-Menten ($y = \frac{\alpha x}{\beta + x}$)

Used to relate rates of enzymatic reactions to substrate concentrations

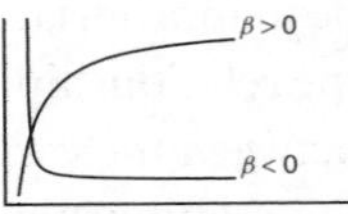

$\alpha - y$ value of horizontal asymptote. β (*Mechaelis parameter*) - value of x at which half the asymptotic response is obtained.

```
> nls(DV~(a*IV)/(b*IV), dataset,
    start=list(a=1, b=1))
> nls(DV~SSmicmen(IV,a,b), dataset)
```

Table 9.1 *(continued)*

Function	Preview
Sigmoidal	

Logistic ($y = \frac{\alpha}{1+e^{(\beta-x)/\gamma}}$)

Used to describe binary responses (presence/absence, alive/dead, etc) relationships.
α - horizontal asymptote (typically 1). β - value of x at which half the asymptotic response is obtained (inflection point).
γ - determines the steepness at inflection.

```
> nls(DV~a/(1+exp((b-IV)/c)), dataset,
     start=list(a=1,b=1,c=.1))
> nls(DV~SSlogis(IV,a,b,c), dataset)
```

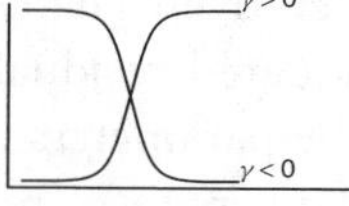

Weibull ($y = \alpha - \beta e^{-(e^{\gamma}x^{\delta})}$)

Describes the kinetics of many enzymes. Used to relate rates of enzymatic reactions to substrate concentrations
α - right side horizontal asymptote. β - rate of vertical change.
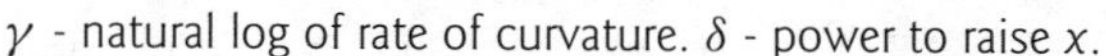
γ - natural log of rate of curvature. δ - power to raise x.

```
> nls(DV~a - b*exp(-exp(c)*IV^d), dataset,
     start=list(a=1, b=1, c=1, d=1))
> nls(DV~SSweibull(IV,a,b,c,d), dataset)
```

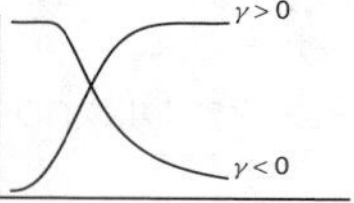

Peaks and/or valleys

Polynomials

Describes the kinetics of many enzymes. Used to relate rates of enzymatic reactions to substrate concentrations

```
> lm(DV~ IV + I(IV^2) + I(IV^3), dataset)
> lm(DV poly(IV, 3), dataset)
```

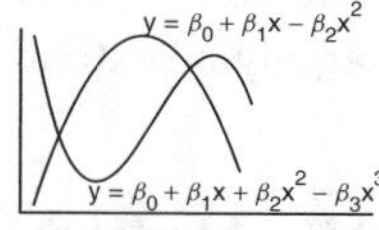

by multiple instances of itself (each of a successively higher order). These higher order terms are quadratic (*2nd* order, x^2), cubic (*3rd* order, x^3), etc terms and are interactions of the predictor variables with itself. The linear model for a second-order (quadratic) regression (parabola) is:

$$y_i = \beta_0 + \beta_1 x_{i1} + \beta_2 x_{i1}^2 + \varepsilon_i$$

Parameters are estimated and tests of the H_0's that $\beta_0 = 0$, $\beta_1 = 0$, $\beta_2 = 0$ and $\beta_0 = \beta_1 = \beta_2 = 0$ are performed as per multiple linear regression. Note that the polynomial regression model contains multiple instances of a predictor variable (including interactions), and that each of these instances will be correlated to one another, thereby violating the assumption of collinearity. Centering the predictor variable first reduces this problem.

Arguably a more biologically meaningful test is whether a higher-order polynomial model (e.g. quadratic) fits the data better than a lower-order model (such as a simple linear regression) and this is tested with a *F-statistic* by comparing the fit of the model with the higher-order term versus a model without this term.

9.5.2 Nonlinear regression

Non-linear regression models enable us to investigate the fit of various predefined functions (such as power, exponential, logarithmic as well as any other non straight line functions) to our collected data. Non-linear model parameters are estimated by iteratively changing the values of the parameters so as to either minimize the sum of squared residuals (OLS) or to maximize the log-likelihood (ML). Starting values of the parameters must be provided, and should be realistic to maximize the chances of convergence (reaching stable parameter estimates). Furthermore, it is advisable that non-linear models be re-fitted with a range of starting values so as to reduce the risks of parameter estimates converging on a 'local minimum' (a set of parameters arrived on through the sequential iteration process that produce a better fit than slightly different values of the parameters, yet still not the estimates that produce the best fit). When using OLS, the typical regression assumptions of residual normality and equal variance apply, whereas, ML can be more robust to these assumptions.

9.5.3 Diagnostics

The same model fitting diagostic issues and measures that were highlighted in section 8.2.6 are relevant to multiple linear regression and non-linear regression.

9.6 Robust regression

The robust alternatives introduced for simple linear regression in section 8.2.7 can largely be extended to multiple linear regression applications.

9.7 Model selection

Not all the predictor variables in a multiple linear model necessarily contribute substantially to explaining variation in the response variable. Those that do not, are unlikely to have much biological impact on the response and therefore could be ommitted from the final regression equation (along with all the other unmeasured variables). Furthermore, we may wish to determine which of a range of linear and non-linear models best fits the collected data. For the purpose of explaining a response variable[b], the 'best' regression model is arguably the model that contains only a subset combination of important predictor variables and is therefore the model that explains the most amount of response variability with the fewest predictor terms[c] (parsimony).

---

[b] Likewise, for the pursuit of developing predictive multiple regression models, the 'best' regression model will contain the fewest predictor variables as greater numbers of predictor variables increases the model complexity and sources of uncertainty and thus decreases the precision of resulting predictions.
[c] Recall that in statistical models, a 'term' denotes an estimable parameter (such as partial slope) and its associated predictor or interaction of predictors.

There are several criteria that can be used to assess the efficiency or fit of a model that are penalized by the number of predictor terms. These criteria are calculated and compared for a set of competing models thereby providing an objective basis on which to select the 'best' regression model.

$MS_{residuals}$ - represents the mean amount of variation unexplained by the model, and therefore the lowest value indicates the best fit.

Adjusted r^2 - (the proportion of mean amount of variation in response variable explained by the model) is calculated as $adj.\ r^2 = \frac{MS_{regression}}{MS_{total}}$ and is therefore adjusted for both sample size and the number of terms. Larger values indicate better fit. Adjusted r^2 and $MS_{residuals}$ should not be used to compare between linear and non-linear models.

Mallow's C_p - is an index resulting from the comparison of the specific model to a model that contain all the possible terms. Models with the lowest value and/or values closest to their respective p (the number of model terms, including the y-intercept) indicate best fit.

Akaike Information Criteria (AIC) - there are several different versions of AIC, each of which adds a different constant (designed to penalize according to the number of parameters and sample size) to a likelihood function to produce a relative measure of the information content of a model. Smaller values indicate more parsimonious models. As a rule of thumb, if the difference between two AIC values (delta AIC) is greater than 2, the lower AIC is a significant improvement in parsimony.

Schwarz Bayesian Information Criteria (BIC or SIC) - is outwardly similar to AIC. The constant added to the likelihood function penalizes models with more predictor terms more heavily (and thus select more simple models) than AIC. It is for this reason that BIC is favored by many workers, however, others argue strongly in favor of AIC claiming that the theoretical basis for BIC may not be relevant for most biological applications[d].

Traditionally, the set of competing linear models were generated by stepwise procedures in which terms were progressively added or dropped from a model on the basis of importance (as assessed via p-values of partial slopes). Whilst such procedures reduce the number of models that are assessed and compared (it is for the associated reductions in computational intensity that such procedures where originally developed), it is possible that the 'best' model is never assessed. Modern computing now allows all combinations to be assessed rapidly thereby voiding the need for such selection procedures.

9.7.1 Model averaging

Typically, there are multiple plausible alternative models that incorporate different combinations of predictor variables and that yield similar degrees of fit (based on AIC, QAIC, BIC, etc). Each alternative model will result in different parameter estimates for the predictor variables. Furthermore, conclusions about the relative importance of each of the predictor variables is likely to be dependent on which model is selected. Model averaging is a technique that calculates weighted averages of the parameter estimates

[d] The original basis for BIC was for situations in which there were either no effects or else there were a mixture of major and no effects with no intermediate or tapering effects. Furthermore, it assumes that the true model (against which all others are compared) is among the set being assessed.

Table 9.2 Comparison of the different model selction criteria. Where n is the number of observations, p is the number of model terms (not including the y-intercept), k is the number of model parameters (including the y-intercept) and c is an additive constant. The value of the additive constant differs under different circumstances (and purposes) and therefore `extractAIC()` and `AIC()` methods can give different values (and do for parametric models). *Model* and *Full* refer to the specific model being assessed and the fully populated model respectively.

Selection criteria	Form	R syntax
$MS_{residuals}$		`> anova(model)["Residuals","Mean Sq"]`
Adjusted r^2	$1 - \frac{SS_{resid}/[n-(p+1)]}{SS_{total}/(n-1)}$	`> summary(model)$adj.r.squared`
Mallow's C_p	$\frac{ModelSS_{resid}}{FullMS_{resid}} - [n - 2(p+1)]$	`> library(biology)`
	$n\left[\ln\left(\frac{SS_{resid}}{n}\right)\right] + 2(p+1) - n$	`> Cp(model, full)`
BIC (Bayesian Information Criterion)		
• for parametric models only	$n\left[\ln\left(\frac{SS_{resid}}{n}\right)\right] + \ln(p+1) + c$	`> extractAIC(model, k=log(nrow(dataset))`
• generic for any fitted model	$n\left[\ln\left(\frac{SS_{resid}}{n}\right)\right] + \ln(p+1) + c$	`> AIC(model, k=log(nrow(dataset))`

AIC (Akaike Information Criterion)		
• for parametric models only	$n\left[\ln\left(\frac{SS_{resid}}{n}\right)\right]+2(p+1)+c$	`> extractAIC(model)`
• generic for any fitted model	$n\left[\ln\left(\frac{SS_{resid}}{n}\right)\right]+2(p+1)+c$	`> AIC(model)`
AIC_c (second order correction) corrected for small sample sizes	$\text{AIC}+\frac{2k(k+1)}{n-k-1}$	`> library(MuMIn)` `> AICc(model)`

QAIC (quasi-AIC) corrected for overdispersion	$n\left[\ln\left(\frac{SS_{resid}}{n}\right)\right]/\hat{c}+2(p+1)+c$	`> library(MuMIn)`
		`> QAIC(model)`
		OR
		`> library(biology)`
		`> qAICc(model)`

[a]The `MuMIn` *package* is not yet part of the official comprehensive R archive network (CRAN). The package can be downloaded from http://mumin.r-forge.r-project.org/ or installed from within R: `> install.packages("MuMIn", repos="http://R-Forge.R-project.org")`.

[b]Only relevant for models in which overdispersion is likely to be an issue, see section 17.1. For such cases, $\hat{c}$ (the quasi-likelihood parameter), is a measure of the degree of overdispersion and can be estimated by dividing the model deviance by its degrees of freedom

for each predictor variable across all the possible models. In so doing, model selection uncertainty can be incorporated into estimates of parameter precision. Furthermore, through model averaging, we are able to obtain an estimate the relative importance of each of the predictor variables on the the response.

9.7.2 Hierarchical partitioning

For applications that are primarily focused on identifying the polarity and relative magnitudes of the effects (importance) of predictor variables, constructing a single 'best' predictive model may be of little value and indeed may not necessarily identify the important causal variables. Similar to model averaging, hierarchical partitioning assesses the independent, joint and total contribution (relative influence) of each predictor variable by averaging a measure of goodness-of-fit[e] over all possible models that include that predictor variable. In so doing, hierarchical partitioning is also less susceptible to multicollinearity problems than are the single-model approaches outlined above. Note that since hierarchical partitioning operates within an entire model set, it is not appropriate for comparing the fit of single models.

In order to evaluate whether the magnitude of a variable's contribution is great enough to warrant retention (or attributed as important), a randomization procedure can be used in which the independent contributions of each predictor variable are compared to distributions of such contributions generated by repeated (e.g. 1000 times) randomizations of the data matrix. Alternatively, the randomized outcomes can be used to calculate Z-scores[f] for each predictor variable, which in turn can be used to test significance ($Z \geq 1.65$ at the 95% level).

9.8 Regression trees

Regression trees are a robust[g] alternative to multiple regression for exploring and describing patterns between a response variable and multiple predictor variables as well as developing predictive models. In addition, as regression trees are rank-based, they accommodate a range and combination of response and predictor data types (including categorical, numerical and rankings) and do not depend on the nature of monotonic relationships (linearity not assumed nor is the arbitrary family of a curvilinear relationship required).

Regression trees are constructed via *binary recursive partitioning*, a process in which the data are progressively split into a dichotomously branching tree. Initially, for each predictor variable, the process iteratively determines the value of that predictor variable that results in the single dichotomous split that minimizes the sum of squared deviations from the split response means. The predictor variable (and split) with the smallest deviations is thereby installed as a *node* at the top of the tree and is interpreted as the most explanatory of the patterns in the response variable. Two

[e] r^2 in multiple linear regression, χ^2 in log-linear models.

[f] calculated as $Z = (I_{obs} - mean\{I_{rand}\})/sd\{I_{rand}\}$.

[g] They are invariant to underlying distributions.

branches descend from this top tree node. The left and right branches represent subsets of the entire dataset for which the values of the top predictor variable are respectively less than and greater than the splitting threshold value. This partitioning process then continues recursively down each branch until either a specific number of branches have been produced or a pre-defined minimum number of observations within the branch has been obtained. Graphical trees can be constructed to illustrate the hierarchy of importance of the predictor variables as well as the nature of interactions between predictor variables.

Each additional split increases the overall explanatory power of the tree (as measured by total deviance). However, greater numbers of branches also increase the degree of *over-fitting*[h] and complexity resulting in models with poor predictive performance. A *cost-complexity measure* can be used to visually assess the compromise between explanatory power and complexity (number of branches) and thus help identify how the tree could be *pruned*.

9.9 Further reading

- Theory

  Hollander, M., and D. A. Wolfe. (1999). *Nonparametric statistical methods, 2nd edition.* John Wiley & Sons, New York.

  Manly, B. F. J. (1991). *Randomization and Monte Carlo methods in biology.* Chapman & Hall, London.

  Quinn, G. P., and K. J. Keough. (2002). *Experimental design and data analysis for biologists.* Cambridge University Press, London.

  Sokal, R., and F. J. Rohlf. (1997). *Biometry, 3rd edition.* W. H. Freeman, San Francisco.

  Zar, G. H. (1999). *Biostatistical methods.* Prentice-Hall, New Jersey.

- Practical - R

  Crawley, M. J. (2007). *The R Book.* John Wiley, New York.

  Faraway, J. J. (2006). *Extending Linear Models with R: generalized linear mixed effects and nonparametric regression models.* Chapman & Hall/CRC.

  Fox, J. (2002). *An R and S-PLUS Companion to Applied Regression.* Sage Books.

  Venables, W. N., and B. D. Ripley. (2002). *Modern Applied Statistics with S-PLUS, 4th edn.* Springer-Verlag, New York.

9.10 Key and analysis sequence for multiple and complex regression

1 a. **Investigating relationships between a single response variable and multiple predictor variables with the expectation that the predictor variables will be linearly related to the response (Multiple linear regression)** . . . . Go to 2

[h] Over-fitting is were additional branches have began to represent and "explain" random aspects of the dataset (such as individual variation) rather than genuine population patterns.

b. Investigating non-linear relationships between a single response variable and a single predictor variable (Non-linear regression) .... Go to 7

c. Develop descriptive and predictive models between a single response variable and multiple predictor variables with few distributional, curvilinear or data type restrictions (Regression trees) .... Go to 13

2 a. Check assumptions for multiple linear regression

Parametric assumptions

- **Normality of the response variable and predictor variables - scatterplot matrix with boxplots in diagonals**
- **Homogeneity of variance - spread of data around scatterplot matrix trendlines**
- **Linearity of data points on a scatterplot, trendline and lowess smoother useful**

```
> library(car)
> scatterplot.matrix(~DV+IV1+IV2+IV3, dataset,
+ diag="boxplot")
```

where `DV` *and* `IV1`, `IV2`,*... are the response and predictor variables respectively in the* `dataset` *data frame*

(Multi)collinearity assumption .... Go to 3

Parametric assumptions met.. Go to 4

b. Parametric assumptions NOT met or scale transformations (see tab. 3.2) not successful or inappropriate .... Go to 7

3 a. Check (multi)collinearity assumption

```
> cor(dataset[, cols])
```

where `cols` *is a set (vector) of numbers representing the column numbers for the predictor variables in the* `dataset` *data frame*

```
> vif(lm(DV ~ IV1 + IV2 + ..., dataset))
> 1/vif(lm(DV ~ IV1 + IV2 + ..., dataset))
```

where `DV` *and* `IV1`, `IV2`, *... are the response and predictor variables respectively in the* `dataset` *data frame.*

(Multi)collinearity assumption met......................... return to previous

b. (Multi)collinearity assumption not met - attempt one of the following:

- **Exclude one or more predictor variables - retain most biologically important on an priori theoretical basis**.............................. See Example 9A
- **(Multi)collinearity due to interactive/polynomial terms - center predictors** See Example 9B

```
> dataset$cIV1 <- scale(dataset$IV1, scale = F)
> dataset$cIV2 <- scale(dataset$IV2, scale = F)
> ...
```

where `IV1` *and* `IV2` *are two of the predictor variables in the* `dataset` *data frame.*

Return .... Return to previous

- **PCA regression** .... see Quinn and Keough (2002) chapter 17.

4 a. The effects of each predictor variable on the response variable are expected to be independent of other measured predictor variables (fit additive model) ..... See Example 9A

```
> data.lm <- lm(DV ~ IV1 + IV2 + .., dataset)
> plot(data.lm)
> summary(data.lm)
```

To summarize the partial relationships graphically .... Go to 12
To select the 'best' model or compare fit to other models .... Go to 8

b. The effects of one or more predictor variables are expected to depend on the level of other measured predictor variables and such interactions are of biological interest (fit multiplicative model) .... See Example 9B

```
> data.lm <- lm(DV ~ IV1 + IV2 + .. + IV1:IV2 + .., dataset)
> plot(data.lm)
> summary(data.lm)
```

where `DV` *and* `IV1, IV2, ...` *are the response and predictor variables respectively in the* `dataset` *data frame.*
To summarize the partial relationships graphically .... Go to 12
Interaction(s) present .... Go to 6
To select the 'best' model or compare fit to other models .... Go to 8

5 a. Random/haphazard sampling not possible, observations not necessarily independent (randomization test) .... See Example 9E

```
> stat <- function(data, indices) {
+     summary(lm(DV ~ IV1 + IV2 + ..., data))$coef[,
+         3]
+ }
> rand.gen <- function(data, mle) {
+     out <- data
+     out$DV <- sample(out$DV, replace = F)
+     out
+ }
> library(boot)
> dataset.boot <- boot(dataset, stat, R = 1000,
+     sim = "parametric", ran.gen = rand.gen)
> t <- apply(apply(abs(dataset.boot$t), 1, ">=",
+     abs(dataset.boot$t0)) * 1, 1, "sum") + 1
> t/(dataset.boot$R + 1)
```

where `DV` *and* `IV1, IV2, ...` *are the response and predictor variables respectively in the* `dataset` *data frame.*
Interaction(s) present .... Go to 6

b. Observations independent however data non-normal with few outliers (robust M-estimator test)

6 **Exploring interactions further** .... See Example 9B

```
> IV1_sd2 <- mean(IV1) - 2 * sd(IV1)
> data.lm2 <- lm(DV ~ IV2 * c(IV1 - IV1_sd2), data = dataset)
> summary(data.lm2)
```

where the effect of one of the predictor variables (`IV2`*) on the dependent variable (*`DV`*) is modeled for a value of another predictor variable (*`IV1`*) equal to its mean minus 1 standard deviation.*

Return .... Return to previous

7 a. **Relationship should theoretically asymptote (reach a plateau) (Nonlinear regression)** .... Go to 7

Power function

```
> dataset.nls <- nls(DV ~ alpha * IV^beta,
+        start = list(alpha = a, beta = b), dataset)
```

Logarithmic function

```
> dataset.nls <- nls(DV ~ alpha * log(IV),
+        start = list(alpha = a), dataset)
```

Exponential function

```
> dataset.nls <- nls(DV ~ alpha * exp(IV * beta),
+       start = list(alpha = a, beta = b), dataset)
```

where `DV` *and* `IV` *are the response and predictor variables respectively in the* `dataset` *data frame. The starting parameters* `a` *and* `b` *are numbers selected to represent the starting configuration (see Table 9.1).*

Examine the parameter estimates

```
> summary(dataset.nls)
```

b. **Relationship does not necessarily plateau (Polynomial regression)** .... see Example 9F

```
> data.lm3 <- lm(DV ~ IV + I(IV^2) + I(IV^3) + ..., dataset)
```

OR

```
> data.lm3 <- lm(DV ~ poly(IV, 3), dataset)
> plot(data.lm3)
```

Compare fit to that of a lower order polynomial

```
> data.lm2 <- lm(DV ~ IV + I(IV ~ 2) + ..., dataset)
> anova(data.lm2, data.lm3)
> summary(data.lm2)
```

To produce a summary plot .... Go to 11

8 Comparing the fit of two or more models (see table 9.2) .... See Example 9G
Additionally, to compare the fit of two or more parametric linear models via ANOVA

```
> anova(model.lm1, model.lm2, ...)
```

where data.lm1 *and* data.lm2, ... *are two or more parametric linear models.*

9 Generating the 'best' predictive model (Model Selection)[i] ...... See Example 9C

```
> library(biology)
> Model.selection(data.lm)
> #OR alternatively
> library(MuMIn)
> model.avg(get.models(dredge(data.glm)))
```

where data.lm *is the full fitted linear model containing all the predictor variable combinations.*

10 Determine the relative influence of each of the predictor variables (Hierarchical partitioning) .... See Example 9D

```
> library(hier.part)
> data.preds <- data.lm$model[, 1]
> hier.part(dataset$DV, data.preds, gof = "Rsqu")
> rand.hp(dataset$DV, data.preds, gof = "Rsqu",
+     num.reps = 100)$Iprobs
```

11 Base summary plot for curvilinear regression .... See Example 9F &9G

```
> plot(V1 ~ V2, data, pch = 16, axes = F, xlab = "", ylab = "")
> axis(1, cex.axis = 0.8)
> mtext(text = "x-axis title", side = 1, line = 3)
> axis(2, las = 1)
> mtext(text = "y-axis title", side = 2, line = 3)
> box(bty = "l")
```

where V1 *and* V2 *are the continuous variables in the* dataset *data frame. For regression,* V1 *represents the response variable and* V2 *represents the predictor variable.*

Adding fitted regression line .... See Example 9F&9G

```
> x <- seq(min(dataset$IV), max(dataset$IV), l = 1000)
> points(x, predict(model, data.frame(IV = x)), type = "l")
```

where IV *represents the predictor variable within the* dataset *data frame and* model *represents a fitted regression model.*

---

[i] The MuMIn *package* is not yet part of the official comprehensive R archive network (CRAN). The package can be downloaded from http://mumin.r-forge.r-project.org/ or installed from within R: > install.packages("MuMIn", repos="http://R-Forge.R-project.org").

12 **Exploring added variable plots to illustrate the relationships between the response variable and each of the predictor terms** .... See Example 9A

```
> av.plots(data.lm, ask = F)
```

where DV *and* IV1, IV2, . . . *are the response and predictor variables respectively in the* dataset *data frame.*

13 **Perform binary recursive partitioning (Regression tree)** .... See Example 9H

```
> library(tree)
> data.tree <- tree(DV ~ IV1 + IV2 + ..., dataset,
+     mindev = 0)
```

where DV *and* IV1, IV2, . . . *are the response and predictor variables respectively in the* dataset *data frame.*

To examine a residual plot

```
> plot(residuals(data.tree) ~ predict(data.tree))
```

To construct the graphical tree

```
> plot(data.tree, type = "uniform")
> text(data.tree, cex = 0.5, all = T)
> text(data.tree, lab = paste("n"), cex = 0.5, adj = c(0,
+     2), splits = F)
```

For tree pruning .... Go to 14

14 **Regression tree pruning** .... See Example 9H

To investigate a const-complexity measure plot

```
> plot(prune.tree(data.tree))
```

To prune the tree to a specific number of branches (e.g. 3)

```
> data.tree.prune <- prune.tree(data.tree, best = 3)
```

9.11 Worked examples of real biological data sets

Example 9A: Multiple linear regression - additive model

To investigate the effects of habitat fragmentation, Loyn (1987) related the abundance of forest birds to a range of variables (including patch area, number of years of isolation, distance to the nearest patch and larger patch, grazing intensity and altitude) collected from a total of 56 forest patches throughout Victoria (Box 6.2 Quinn and Keough (2002)).

Step 1 - Import (section 2.3) the Loyn (1987) data set

```
> loyn <- read.table("loyn.csv", header = T, sep = ",")
```

Step 2 (Key 9.2) - Assess assumptions of linearity, normality and homogeneity of variance.

```
> library(car)
> scatterplot.matrix(~ABUND + AREA + YR.ISOL + DIST +
+     LDIST + GRAZE + ALT, data = loyn, diag = "boxplot")
```

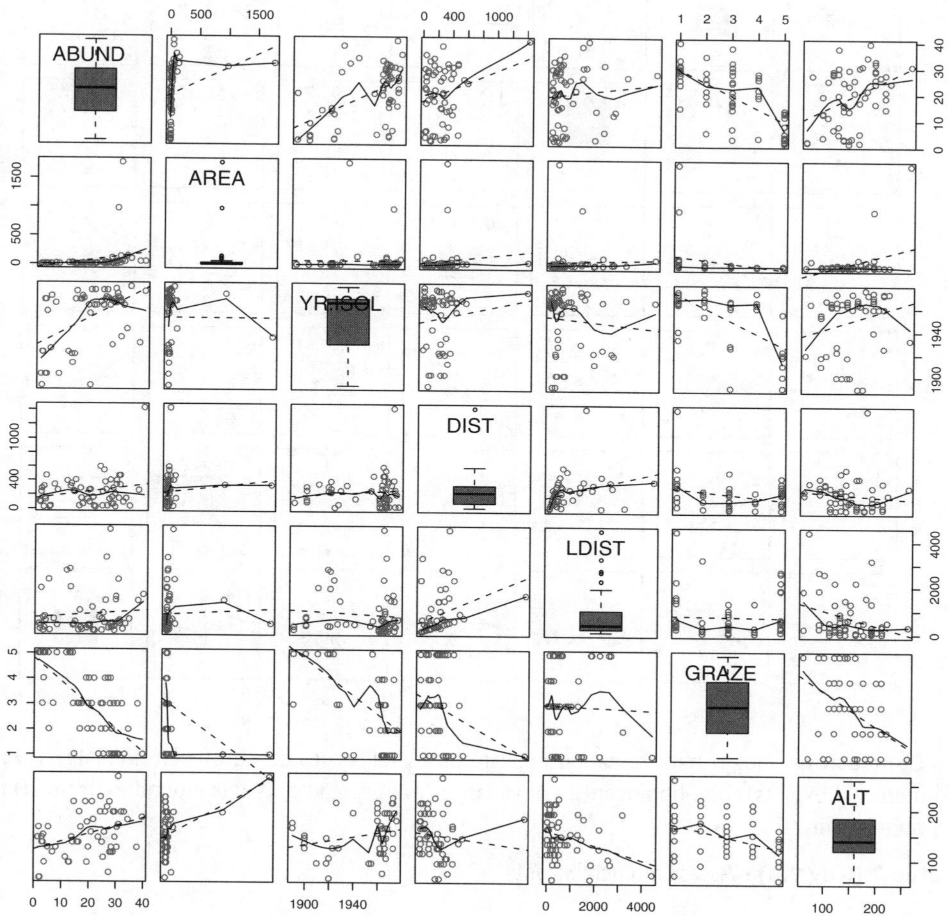

Conclusions - AREA, DIST and LDIST variables obviously non-normal (asymmetrical boxplots) and consequently the relationships between each of these variables and the response variable (ABUND) show non-linearity. In light of the normality problems, homogeneity of variance is difficult to assess. Scale transformations of the non-normal variables should be attempted.

```
> scatterplot.matrix(~ABUND + log10(AREA) + YR.ISOL +
+     log10(DIST) + log10(LDIST) + GRAZE + ALT, data = loyn,
+     diag = "boxplot")
```

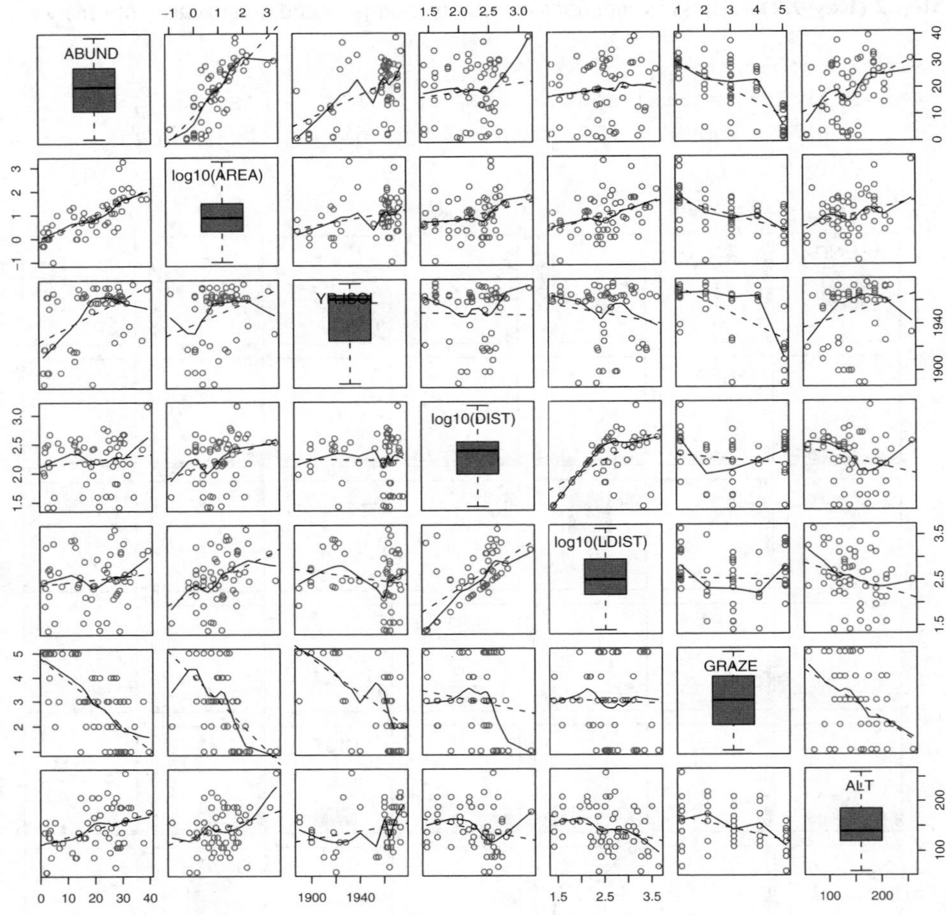

Conclusions - $\log_{10}$ transformation appear successful, no evidence of non-normality (symmetrical boxplots), non-homogeneity of variance (even spread of points around each trend) or non-linearity.

Step 3 (Key 9.3) - Assess multicollinearity.

```
> cor(loyn[, 2:7])
               AREA      YR.ISOL       DIST       LDIST
AREA     1.000000000 -0.001494192  0.1083429  0.03458035
YR.ISOL -0.001494192  1.000000000  0.1132175 -0.08331686
DIST     0.108342870  0.113217524  1.0000000  0.31717234
LDIST    0.034580346 -0.083316857  0.3171723  1.00000000
GRAZE   -0.310402417 -0.635567104 -0.2558418 -0.02800944
ALT      0.387753885  0.232715406 -0.1101125 -0.30602220
              GRAZE        ALT
AREA    -0.31040242  0.3877539
YR.ISOL -0.63556710  0.2327154
DIST    -0.25584182 -0.1101125
```

```
LDIST    -0.02800944 -0.3060222
GRAZE     1.00000000 -0.4071671
ALT      -0.40716705  1.0000000
```

Conclusions - With the exception of GRAZE and YR.ISOL, none of the predictor variables are particularly correlated to one another.

```
> vif(lm(ABUND ~ log10(AREA) + YR.ISOL + log10(DIST) +
+      log10(LDIST) + GRAZE + ALT, data = loyn))
 log10(AREA)       YR.ISOL  log10(DIST) log10(LDIST)        GRAZE
    1.911514      1.804769     1.654553     2.009749     2.524814
         ALT
    1.467937
> 1/vif(lm(ABUND ~ log10(AREA) + YR.ISOL + log10(DIST) +
+      log10(LDIST) + GRAZE + ALT, data = loyn))
 log10(AREA)       YR.ISOL  log10(DIST) log10(LDIST)        GRAZE
   0.5231454     0.5540876    0.6043930    0.4975746    0.3960688
         ALT
   0.6812282
```

Conclusions - Variance inflation and their inverses (tolerances) are less than 5 and greater than 0.2 respectively suggesting that multicollinearity is unlikely to be a problem.

Step 4 (Key 9.4) - fit the additive multiple linear model relating bird abundance to the range of appropriately scaled patch characteristics.

```
> loyn.lm <- lm(ABUND ~ log10(AREA) + YR.ISOL + log10(DIST) +
+      log10(LDIST) + GRAZE + ALT, data = loyn)

> plot(loyn.lm)
```

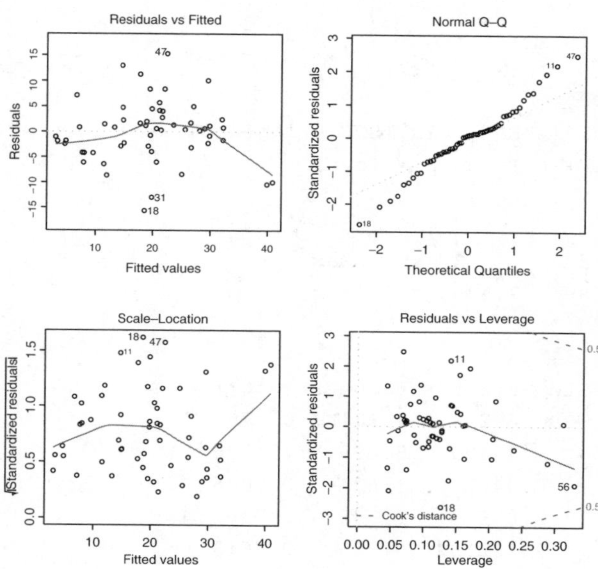

Conclusions - There is no obvious "wedge" pattern evident in the residual plot (confirming that the assumption of homogeneity of variance is likely to be met). The Q-Q normal plot does not deviate greatly from normal. Finally, none of the points approach the high Cook's D contours suggesting that none of the observations are overly influential on the final fitted model.

```
> influence.measures(loyn.lm)

       dfb.1_    dfb.l10(A      dfb.YR.I    dfb.l10(D      dfb.l10(L
1 -0.02454653  0.32534847  0.008468066  0.08370776 -0.022663517
2 -0.01750873  0.01265303  0.016012689 -0.01656030  0.020997123
3 -0.05891170  0.04830884  0.060903999  0.01044557 -0.016320746
4 -0.02464857 -0.04735981  0.028326646 -0.01082504 -0.015503647
5  0.06451364 -0.09167341 -0.078406403  0.17235656 -0.075678399
6 -0.01395526 -0.02707540  0.014184325  0.01153817  0.003907139
      dfb.GRAZ        dfb.ALT       dffit    cov.r        cook.d
1  0.218999564 -0.0055469496 -0.42060699 1.394989 0.0254974592
2  0.003658088  0.0372465169 -0.06571529 1.319078 0.0006293951
3  0.012240659 -0.0219517552 -0.11033159 1.287647 0.0017717789
4 -0.005964993  0.0102469605  0.09983048 1.216839 0.0014493334
5  0.105181168  0.1013851217  0.35751545 1.035693 0.0181201227
6 -0.003666825  0.0009195532  0.03845593 1.243342 0.0002155830
         hat
1 0.23735383
2 0.12793356
3 0.11497013
4 0.06900608
5 0.08492694
6 0.07336138

...
```

Conclusions - Whilst a couple of the leverage (hat) values are greater than $2 \times p/n = 0.286$ and therefore potentially outliers in x-space, none of the Cook's D values are ≥ 1. Hence the hypothesis tests are likely to be reliable.

```
> summary(loyn.lm)

Call:
lm(formula = ABUND ~ log10(AREA) + YR.ISOL + log10(DIST) +
    log10(LDIST) + GRAZE + ALT, data = loyn)

Residuals:
     Min       1Q   Median       3Q      Max
-15.6506  -2.9390   0.5289   2.5353  15.2842

Coefficients:
               Estimate Std. Error t value Pr(>|t|)
(Intercept)  -125.69725   91.69228  -1.371   0.1767
log10(AREA)     7.47023    1.46489   5.099 5.49e-06 ***
YR.ISOL         0.07387    0.04520   1.634   0.1086
log10(DIST)    -0.90696    2.67572  -0.339   0.7361
log10(LDIST)   -0.64842    2.12270  -0.305   0.7613
```

```
GRAZE              -1.66774    0.92993  -1.793    0.0791 .
ALT                 0.01951    0.02396   0.814    0.4195
---
Signif. codes:  0 '***' 0.001 '**' 0.01 '*' 0.05 '.' 0.1 ' ' 1

Residual standard error: 6.384 on 49 degrees of freedom
Multiple R-squared: 0.6849,     Adjusted R-squared: 0.6464
F-statistic: 17.75 on 6 and 49 DF,  p-value: 8.443e-11
```

Conclusions - there was a significant positive partial slope for bird abundance against $\log_{10}$ patch area. The overall model explained 69% of the variability in bird abundances across the 56 patches in Victoria. Bird abundances were found to increase with increasing patch area, but were not found to be significantly effected by grazing, altitude, years of isolation and distance to nearest patch or larger patch.

Step 5 (Key 9.12) - explore plots of the individual partial relationships between the response variable and each of the predictor variables (holding the other predictor variables constant).

```
> av.plots(loyn.lm, ask = F)
```

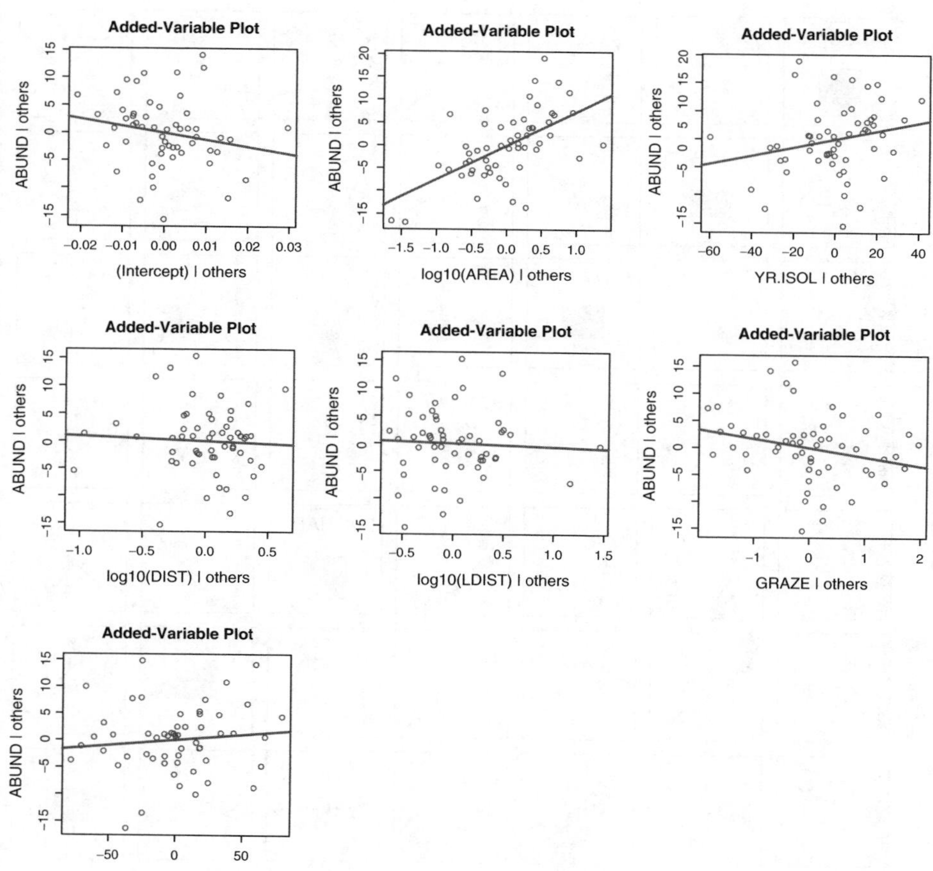

Example 9B: Multiple linear regression - multiplicative model

Paruelo and Lauenroth (1996) investigated the geographic (latitude and longitude) and climatic (mean annual temperature, means annual precipitation and the proportion of the mean annual precipitation that fall in the periods June-August and December-February) patterns in the relative abundance of C_3 plants throughout 73 sites across North America (Box 6.1 Quinn and Keough (2002)).

Step 1 - Import (section 2.3) the Paruelo and Lauenroth (1996) data set

```
> paruelo <- read.table("paruelo.csv", header = T,
+       sep = ",")
```

Step 2 (Key 9.2) - Assess assumptions of linearity, normality and homogeneity of variance.

```
> library(car)
> scatterplot.matrix(~C3 + MAP + MAT + JJAMAP + DJFMAP +
+       LONG + LAT, data = paruelo, diag = "boxplot")
```

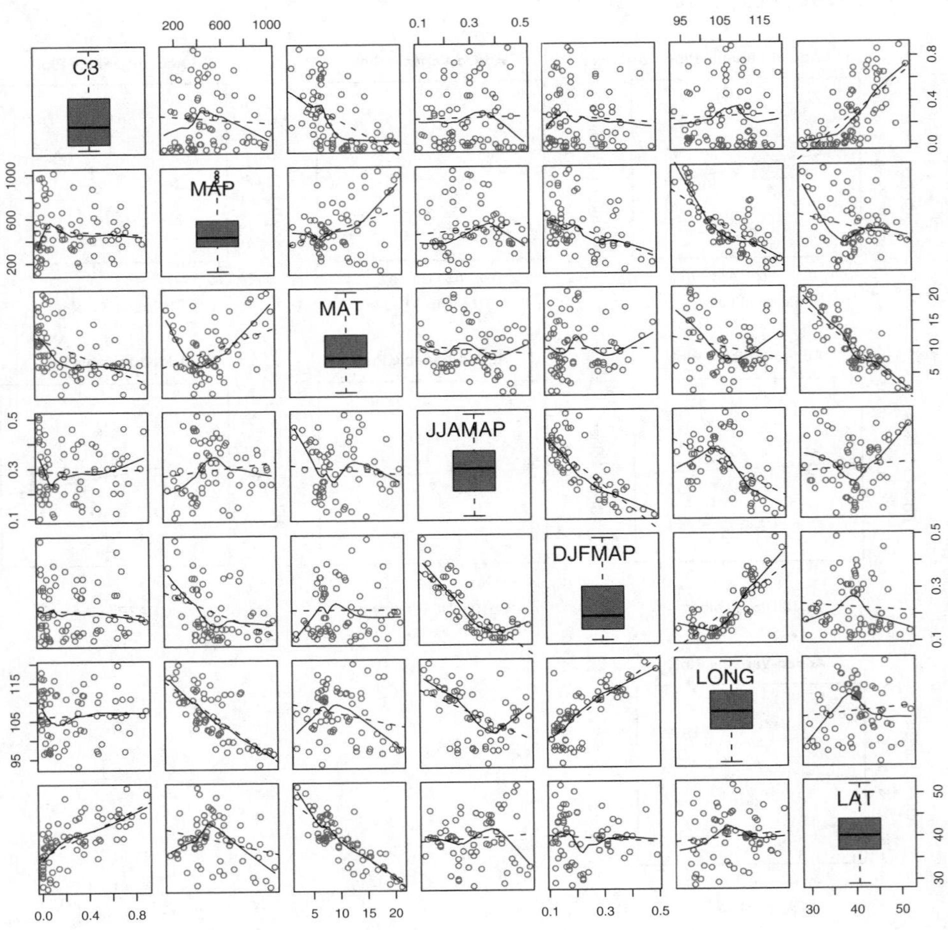

Conclusions - whilst all the predictor variables appear normally distributed (symmetrical boxplots), the response variable (C3) appears to be positively skewed and thus a candidate for scale transformation (either a root transformation or a heavier log transformation). Paruelo and Lauenroth (1996) and therefore Quinn and Keough (2002) used a $\log_{10}(y + 1)$. Note that as there are 0 values present and that log(0) cannot be evaluated, a small constant (such as 0.1[j]) must be added to each count in the response variable prior to the log transformation.

```
> scatterplot.matrix(~log10(C3 + 0.1) + MAP + MAT +
+      JJAMAP + DJFMAP + LONG + LAT, data = paruelo,
+      diag = "boxplot")
```

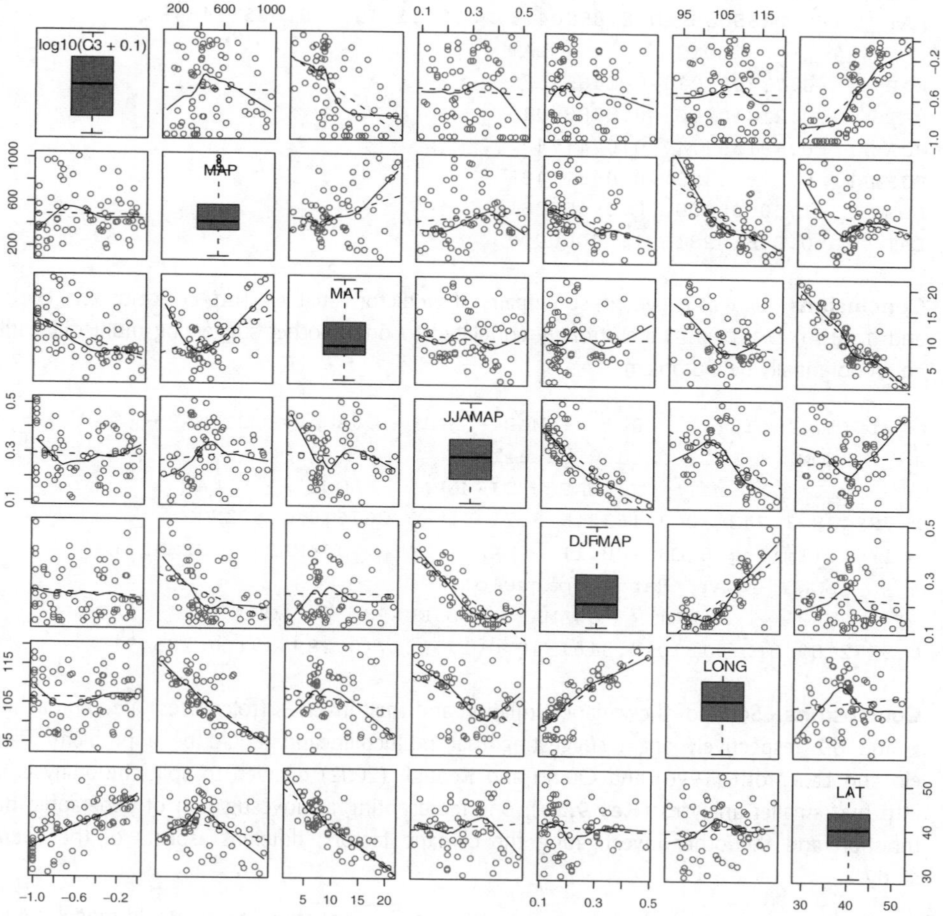

Conclusions - transformation appear successful, now no evidence of non-normality (symmetrical boxplots), non-homogeneity of variance (even spread of points around each trend) or

[j] This constant value should be small relative to the values in the variable so that it does not overshadow the existing values. However, if the value is more than two orders of magnitude smaller than the majority of the values, it will make the zero values outliers (influential points).

non-linearity. However there is some indication that multicollinearity could be an issue (there are some strong trends between pairs of predictor variables).

Step 3 (Key 9.3) - Assess multicollinearity.

```
> cor(paruelo[, 2:7])
              MAP          MAT      JJAMAP       DJFMAP
MAP     1.0000000  0.355090766  0.11225905 -0.404512409
MAT     0.3550908  1.000000000 -0.08077131  0.001478037
JJAMAP  0.1122590 -0.080771307  1.00000000 -0.791540381
DJFMAP -0.4045124  0.001478037 -0.79154038  1.000000000
LONG   -0.7336870 -0.213109100 -0.49155774  0.770743994
LAT    -0.2465058 -0.838590413  0.07417497 -0.065124848
              LONG         LAT
MAP    -0.73368703 -0.24650582
MAT    -0.21310910 -0.83859041
JJAMAP -0.49155774  0.07417497
DJFMAP  0.77074399 -0.06512485
LONG    1.00000000  0.09655281
LAT     0.09655281  1.00000000
```

Conclusions - as was expected, some pairs of predictor variables (MAP & LONG, MAT & LAT and JJAMAP & DJFMAP) are strongly correlated to one another suggesting multicollinearity could potentially be a problem.

```
> vif(lm(log10(C3 + 0.1) ~ MAP + MAT + JJAMAP + DJFMAP +
+      LONG + LAT, data = paruelo))
     MAP      MAT   JJAMAP   DJFMAP     LONG      LAT
2.799428 3.742780 3.163215 5.710315 5.267618 3.502732
> 1/vif(lm(log10(C3 + 0.1) ~ MAP + MAT + JJAMAP + DJFMAP +
+      LONG + LAT, data = paruelo))
      MAP       MAT    JJAMAP    DJFMAP      LONG       LAT
0.3572159 0.2671810 0.3161340 0.1751217 0.1898391 0.2854914
```

Conclusions - Some of the variance inflation and their inverses (tolerances) are approaching 5 and 0.2 respectively again suggesting that multicollinearity could be a problem. Paruelo and Lauenroth (1996) and Quinn and Keough (2002) decided to split the analysis up into two smaller analyses (**Key 9.3b**), one representing an investigation of geographic distribution and the other investigating the climatic factors; different aspects of the overall study.

Step 4 - The investigation of geographic patterns in C_3 plant abundances would model the log transformed abundance of C_3 plants against latitude and longitude. The extent of any latitudinal effects might be expected to depend on longitude and visa versa. For example, perhaps longitudinal effects are only important above or below a certain latitudes. Such possibilities suggest that fitting a more complicated multiplicative model (with interaction effects) might be more informative than an additive model.

Step 5 (Key 9.3) - check multicollinearity by assessing tolerances.

```
> 1/vif(lm(log10(C3 + 0.1) ~ LAT + LONG + LAT:LONG,
+      data = paruelo))
        LAT          LONG     LAT:LONG
0.003249445 0.014973575 0.002494144
```

Conclusions - not surprisingly, there are very low tolerances since each of the individual predictors are going to be correlated to their interaction term. Centering (**Key 9.3b**) the predictor variables before re-fitting the model should address this.

```
> paruelo$cLAT <- paruelo$LAT-mean(paruelo$LAT)
> #OR
> paruelo$cLAT <- scale(paruelo$LAT, scale=F)
> paruelo$cLONG <- scale(paruelo$LONG, scale=F)
> 1/vif(lm(log10(C3+.1)~cLAT+cLONG+cLAT:cLONG, data=paruelo))
      cLAT       cLONG cLAT:cLONG
 0.8268942  0.9799097  0.8195915
```

Conclusions - multicollinearity is no longer likely to be a problem and the parameter estimates and hypothesis tests are likely to be reliable.

Step 6 (Key 9.4b) - fit the multiplicative linear model and test whether each of the partial population slopes are likely to equal zero.

```
> paruelo.lm <- lm(log10(C3 + 0.1) ~ cLAT + cLONG +
+      cLAT:cLONG, data = paruelo)
> plot(paruelo.lm)
```

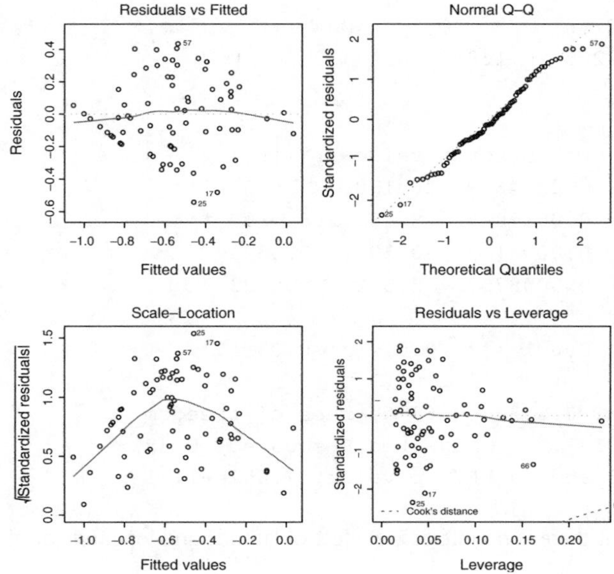

Conclusions - There is no obvious "wedge" pattern evident in the residual plot (confirming that the assumption of homogeneity of variance is likely to be met). The Q-Q normal plot does not deviate greatly from normality. Finally, none of the points approach the high Cook's D contours suggesting that none of the observations are overly influential on the final fitted model.

```
> influence.measures(paruelo.lm)

       dfb.1_     dfb.cLAT     dfb.cLON    dfb.cLAT:        dffit
1 -0.01240897 -0.04291203 -0.04343888 -0.06275532 -0.07869325
2 -0.01232348 -0.03577596 -0.02255957 -0.04094363 -0.05303525
3  0.07696884  0.12765517  0.06321144  0.11087334  0.17912507
4  0.17518366  0.09561479 -0.13875996 -0.06937259  0.25698909
5 -0.05221407 -0.05487872  0.03652972  0.01850913 -0.09147598
6 -0.16175075  0.02214619  0.17475473  0.00759321 -0.24141744
     cov.r       cook.d        hat
1 1.383538 0.0015704573 0.23466106
2 1.229880 0.0007133425 0.13890169
3 1.087217 0.0080746585 0.05557079
4 0.974066 0.0162711273 0.03171179
5 1.098320 0.0021171765 0.04482606
6 0.981941 0.0143925390 0.03048383

...
```

Conclusions - few leverage (hat) values are greater than $2 * p/n = 0.082$, none of the Cook's D values are approaching 1. Hence the hypothesis tests are likely to be reliable.

```
> summary(paruelo.lm)
Call:
lm(formula = log10(C3 + 0.1) ~ cLAT + cLONG + cLAT:cLONG,
  data = paruelo)

Residuals:
     Min       1Q   Median       3Q      Max
-0.54185 -0.13298 -0.02287  0.16807  0.43410

Coefficients:
              Estimate Std. Error t value Pr(>|t|)
(Intercept) -0.5529416  0.0274679 -20.130  < 2e-16 ***
cLAT         0.0483954  0.0057047   8.483 2.61e-12 ***
cLONG       -0.0025787  0.0043182  -0.597   0.5523
cLAT:cLONG   0.0022522  0.0008757   2.572   0.0123 *
---
Signif. codes:  0 '***' 0.001 '**' 0.01 '*' 0.05 '.' 0.1 ' ' 1

Residual standard error: 0.2334 on 69 degrees of freedom
Multiple R-squared: 0.5137,     Adjusted R-squared: 0.4926
F-statistic:  24.3 on 3 and 69 DF,  p-value: 7.657e-11
```

Conclusions - reject the H_0 that there is no interactive effect of latitude and longitude on the (log_{10}) abundance of C_3 plants.

Step 7 (Key 9.6) - to further investigate this interaction, calculate the simple slopes of C_3 plant abundance against longitude for a range of latitudes (e.g. mean $\pm$ 1 standard deviation and $\pm$ 2 standard deviations). Since the partial slopes in the multiplicative model are the simple slopes for the mean values of the other predictor (hence partial effect of one predictor holding the other predictor variables constant), the simple slope of longitude at the mean latitude has already been calculated (−0.0026) and can be extracted from the summarized multiplicative model.

$\overline{x_1} - 2\sigma$ (mean centered longitude - 2 standard deviations)

```
> LAT_sd1 <- mean(paruelo$cLAT) - 2 * sd(paruelo$cLAT)
> paruelo_LONG.lm1 <- lm(log10(C3 + 0.1) ~ cLONG *
+     c(cLAT - LAT_sd1), data = paruelo)
> summary(paruelo_LONG.lm1)
Call:
lm(formula = log10(C3 + 0.1) ~ cLONG * c(cLAT - LAT_sd1),
  data = paruelo)

Residuals:
     Min       1Q   Median       3Q      Max
-0.54185 -0.13298 -0.02287  0.16807  0.43410

Coefficients:
                          Estimate Std. Error t value Pr(>|t|)
(Intercept)             -1.0662239  0.0674922 -15.798  < 2e-16
cLONG                   -0.0264657  0.0098255  -2.694  0.00887
c(cLAT - LAT_sd1)        0.0483954  0.0057047   8.483 2.61e-12
cLONG:c(cLAT - LAT_sd1)  0.0022522  0.0008757   2.572  0.01227

(Intercept)             ***
cLONG                   **
c(cLAT - LAT_sd1)       ***
cLONG:c(cLAT - LAT_sd1) *
---
Signif. codes:  0 '***' 0.001 '**' 0.01 '*' 0.05 '.' 0.1 ' ' 1

Residual standard error: 0.2334 on 69 degrees of freedom
Multiple R-squared: 0.5137,     Adjusted R-squared: 0.4926
F-statistic:  24.3 on 3 and 69 DF,  p-value: 7.657e-11
```

$\overline{x_1} - 1\sigma$ (mean centered longitude - 1 standard deviation)

```
> LAT_sd2 <- mean(paruelo$cLAT) - 1 * sd(paruelo$cLAT)
> paruelo_LONG.lm2 <- lm(log10(C3 + 0.1) ~ cLONG *
+     c(cLAT - LAT_sd2), data = paruelo)
> summary(paruelo_LONG.lm2)
Call:
lm(formula = log10(C3 + 0.1) ~ cLONG * c(cLAT - LAT_sd2),
  data = paruelo)
```

```
Residuals:
     Min       1Q   Median       3Q      Max
-0.54185 -0.13298 -0.02287  0.16807  0.43410

Coefficients:
                         Estimate Std. Error t value Pr(>|t|)
(Intercept)            -0.8095827  0.0417093 -19.410  < 2e-16
cLONG                  -0.0145222  0.0060025  -2.419   0.0182
c(cLAT - LAT_sd2)       0.0483954  0.0057047   8.483 2.61e-12
cLONG:c(cLAT - LAT_sd2)  0.0022522  0.0008757   2.572   0.0123

(Intercept)            ***
cLONG                  *
c(cLAT - LAT_sd2)      ***
cLONG:c(cLAT - LAT_sd2) *
---
Signif. codes:  0 '***' 0.001 '**' 0.01 '*' 0.05 '.' 0.1 ' ' 1

Residual standard error: 0.2334 on 69 degrees of freedom
Multiple R-squared: 0.5137,     Adjusted R-squared: 0.4926
F-statistic:  24.3 on 3 and 69 DF,  p-value: 7.657e-11
```

$\overline{x_1} + 1\sigma$ (mean centered longitude + 1 standard deviation)

```
> LAT_sd4 <- mean(paruelo$cLAT) - 1 * sd(paruelo$cLAT)
> paruelo_LONG.lm4 <- lm(log10(C3 + 0.1) ~ cLONG *
+     c(cLAT - LAT_sd4), data = paruelo)
> summary(paruelo_LONG.lm4)
Call:
lm(formula = log10(C3 + 0.1) ~ cLONG * c(cLAT - LAT_sd4),
  data = paruelo)

Residuals:
     Min       1Q   Median       3Q      Max
-0.54185 -0.13298 -0.02287  0.16807  0.43410

Coefficients:
                         Estimate Std. Error t value Pr(>|t|)
(Intercept)            -0.8095827  0.0417093 -19.410  < 2e-16
cLONG                  -0.0145222  0.0060025  -2.419   0.0182
c(cLAT - LAT_sd4)       0.0483954  0.0057047   8.483 2.61e-12
cLONG:c(cLAT - LAT_sd4)  0.0022522  0.0008757   2.572   0.0123

(Intercept)            ***
cLONG                  *
c(cLAT - LAT_sd4)      ***
cLONG:c(cLAT - LAT_sd4) *
```

```
---
Signif. codes:  0 '***' 0.001 '**' 0.01 '*' 0.05 '.' 0.1 ' ' 1

Residual standard error: 0.2334 on 69 degrees of freedom
Multiple R-squared: 0.5137,     Adjusted R-squared: 0.4926
F-statistic:  24.3 on 3 and 69 DF,  p-value: 7.657e-11
```

$\overline{x_l} + 2\sigma$ (mean centered longitude + 2 standard deviation)

```
> LAT_sd5 <- mean(paruelo$cLAT) - 1 * sd(paruelo$cLAT)
> paruelo_LONG.lm5 <- lm(log10(C3 + 0.1) ~ cLONG *
+     c(cLAT - LAT_sd5), data = paruelo)
> summary(paruelo_LONG.lm5)
Call:
lm(formula = log10(C3 + 0.1) ~ cLONG * c(cLAT - LAT_sd5),
  data = paruelo)

Residuals:
     Min       1Q   Median       3Q      Max
-0.54185 -0.13298 -0.02287  0.16807  0.43410

Coefficients:
                          Estimate Std. Error t value Pr(>|t|)
(Intercept)             -0.8095827  0.0417093 -19.410  < 2e-16
cLONG                   -0.0145222  0.0060025  -2.419   0.0182
c(cLAT - LAT_sd5)        0.0483954  0.0057047   8.483 2.61e-12
cLONG:c(cLAT - LAT_sd5)  0.0022522  0.0008757   2.572   0.0123

(Intercept)             ***
cLONG                   *
c(cLAT - LAT_sd5)       ***
cLONG:c(cLAT - LAT_sd5) *
---
Signif. codes:  0 '***' 0.001 '**' 0.01 '*' 0.05 '.' 0.1 ' ' 1

Residual standard error: 0.2334 on 69 degrees of freedom
Multiple R-squared: 0.5137,     Adjusted R-squared: 0.4926
F-statistic:  24.3 on 3 and 69 DF,  p-value: 7.657e-11
```

Conclusions - the abundance of C_3 plants is negatively related to longitude at low latitudes however this longitudinal effect diminishes with increasing latitude and becomes a positive effect at very high latitudes. Additionally (or alternatively), latitudinal effects could be seen to become more positive with increasing longitude (from east to west).

Example 9C: Selecting the 'best' regression model

Quinn and Keough (2002) used the Loyn (1987) data set (analysed in Example 9A on page 224) demonstrated the use of various criteria as the basis of selecting the 'best' model

(Quinn and Keough (2002) Box 6.8). Continuing on from Example 9A, we will attempt to determine the 'best', most parsimonious regression model for the purpose of either generating a predictive model or simply to determine which predictor variables have the greatest relative influence on the response variable.

Step 1 (Key 9.9b) - Compare the fit of all additive combinations of predictor variables from the full fitted linear model of the Loyn (1987) data set via AIC, BIC, C_p and adjusted r^2.

```
> library(biology)
> Model.selection(loyn.lm)

                                                        Adj.r.sq      AIC     AICc   deltaAIC
1. log10(AREA)                                        0.53927618 224.3964 227.4602 14.2082619
2. YR.ISOL                                            0.23954252 252.4592 255.5230 42.2710623
3. log10(DIST)                                       -0.00216233 267.9149 270.9788 57.7267862
4. log10(LDIST)                                      -0.00430673 268.0346 271.0984 57.8464855
5. GRAZE                                              0.45592959 233.7081 236.7719 23.5199360
6. ALT                                                0.13310788 259.7949 262.8587 49.6067453
7. log10(AREA)+YR.ISOL                                0.63002728 213.0649 216.1288  2.8768100
8. log10(AREA)+log10(DIST)                            0.54130423 225.1026 228.1664 14.9144529
9. log10(AREA)+log10(LDIST)                           0.56364647 222.3063 225.3701 12.1181257
...
24. log10(AREA)+YR.ISOL+GRAZE                         0.65436215 210.1881 213.2520  0.0000000
25. log10(AREA)+YR.ISOL+ALT                           0.64340828 211.9353 214.9992  1.7471955
26. log10(AREA)+log10(DIST)+log10(LDIST)              0.55526607 224.3049 227.3687 14.1167393
27. log10(AREA)+log10(DIST)+GRAZE                     0.64144047 212.2435 215.3073  2.0553756
28. log10(AREA)+log10(DIST)+ALT                       0.56137177 223.5307 226.5946 13.3425950
29. log10(AREA)+log10(LDIST)+GRAZE                    0.64443577 211.7737 214.8376  1.5856031
...
39. log10(DIST)+log10(LDIST)+ALT                      0.16767219 259.4029 262.4667 49.2147489
40. log10(DIST)+GRAZE+ALT                             0.45484515 235.7061 238.7699 25.5179860
41. log10(LDIST)+GRAZE+ALT                            0.47031877 234.0936 237.1575 23.9054939
42. log10(AREA)+YR.ISOL+log10(DIST)+log10(LDIST)      0.62461805 215.7237 218.7875  5.5355253
43. log10(AREA)+YR.ISOL+log10(DIST)+GRAZE             0.65360148 211.2238 214.2877  1.0356946
44. log10(AREA)+YR.ISOL+log10(DIST)+ALT               0.63704328 213.8387 216.9025  3.6505413
...
                Estimate Unconditional_SE   Lower95CI
log10(AREA)   7.54126720       1.43013594  4.73820077
YR.ISOL       0.06204083       0.03729047 -0.01104849
log10(DIST)  -0.51987543       0.87724385 -2.23927338
log10(LDIST) -0.52400077       0.75025473 -1.99450004
GRAZE        -1.73681399       0.83173477 -3.36701413
ALT           0.01065631       0.01150212 -0.01188785
               Upper95CI
log10(AREA)  10.34433364
YR.ISOL       0.13513016
log10(DIST)   1.19952252
log10(LDIST)  0.94649850
GRAZE        -0.10661385
ALT           0.03320047
attr(,"heading")
[1] "Model averaging\n"  "Response: ABUND \n"
```

Note some of the rows and columns have been omitted from the above output to conserve space.
Alternatively, using the `MuMIn` *package*

```
> library(MuMIn)
> model.avg(get.models(dredge(loyn.lm, rank = "AIC")))
Model summary:
            Deviance AIC Delta Weight
2+3+6           2070 371 0.000 0.1330
1+2+3+6         2010 372 0.414 0.1080
2+3+5+6         2030 372 0.962 0.0820
2+3+4+6         2040 372 1.040 0.0790
2+3             2200 373 1.400 0.0657
2+3+5           2130 373 1.590 0.0600
```

```
1+3+6          2140 373 1.750 0.0554
1+2+3          2150 373 2.050 0.0477
2+3+4          2150 373 2.060 0.0475
1+2+3+4+6      2000 373 2.060 0.0473
1+2+3+5+6      2000 373 2.090 0.0467
2+3+4+5+6      2020 374 2.710 0.0343
3+6            2260 374 2.880 0.0315
1+2+3+5        2110 374 3.080 0.0285
2+3+4+5        2120 374 3.340 0.0250
1+2+3+4        2120 374 3.370 0.0246
1+3+5+6        2130 375 3.520 0.0228
3+5+6          2210 375 3.610 0.0218
1+3+4+6        2130 375 3.650 0.0214
1+2+3+4+5+6    2000 375 3.950 0.0184

Variables:
    1          2            3            4            5              6
   ALT       GRAZE  log10(AREA)  log10(DIST) log10(LDIST)      YR.ISOL

Averaged model parameters:
              Coefficient Variance       SE Unconditional SE  Lower CI Upper CI
ALT               0.0107 1.46e-07   0.0177           0.0178   -0.0243   0.0457
GRAZE            -1.7900 1.81e+00   1.1200           1.1300   -4.0000   0.4330
(Intercept)     -99.4000 1.66e+08 111.0000         112.0000 -320.0000 121.0000
log10(AREA)       7.5000 4.07e+00   1.4100           1.4400    4.6700  10.3000
log10(DIST)      -0.4930 5.39e+00   1.1400           1.1600   -2.7600   1.7800
log10(LDIST)     -0.5130 2.95e+00   1.0600           1.0700   -2.6200   1.5900
YR.ISOL           0.0606 9.85e-06   0.0550           0.0556   -0.0485   0.1700

Relative variable importance:
 log10(AREA)        GRAZE      YR.ISOL          ALT log10(LDIST)  log10(DIST)
        1.00         0.85         0.70         0.42         0.34         0.30
```

Conclusions - AIC and C_p (not shown) both select a model with three predictor variables (log_{10}area, grazing intensity and years of isolation). However, it should be noted, that using the rule-of-thumb that delta AIC values less than 2 do not represent significant improvements in fit, it could be argued that the three variable model is not significantly better than the simpler two variable (log_{10}area and grazing intensity) model. Hence log_{10} patch area and grazing intensity are the most important measured influences on bird abundances across the fragmented Victorian landscape.

Step 2 - construct the predictive model

```
> loyn.lm2 <- lm(ABUND ~ log10(AREA) + GRAZE, data = loyn)
> summary(loyn.lm2)
Call:
lm(formula = ABUND ~ log10(AREA) + GRAZE, data = loyn)

Residuals:
     Min       1Q   Median       3Q      Max
-13.4296  -4.3186  -0.6323   4.1273  13.0739

Coefficients:
            Estimate Std. Error t value Pr(>|t|)
(Intercept)  21.6029     3.0917   6.987 4.73e-09 ***
log10(AREA)   6.8901     1.2900   5.341 1.98e-06 ***
GRAZE        -2.8535     0.7125  -4.005 0.000195 ***
---
Signif. codes:  0 '***' 0.001 '**' 0.01 '*' 0.05 '.' 0.1 ' ' 1
```

```
Residual standard error: 6.444 on 53 degrees of freedom
Multiple R-squared: 0.6527,     Adjusted R-squared: 0.6396
F-statistic: 49.81 on 2 and 53 DF,  p-value: 6.723e-13
```

Conclusions - the predictive model (resulting from the 'best' regression model is $abund = 6.89log_{10}area - 2.85graze + 21.60$ and explains approximately 65% of the variation in bird abundance.

Example 9D: Hierarchical partitioning

Quinn and Keough (2002) also used the Loyn (1987) data set (analysed in Example 9A on page 224) to demonstrate the use of hierarchical partitioning to determine the relative contributions of each of the predictor variables (Quinn and Keough (2002) Box 6.8).

Step 1 (Key 9.10) - Perform a hierarchical partitioning on the multiple linear model fitted to the Loyn (1987) data set. As this is a linear model, the goodness-of-fit of the model should be assessed by the r^2 value.

1. determine independent and joint contribution of each predictor variable averaged across all possible model combinations.

```
> library(hier.part)
> loyn.preds <- with(loyn, data.frame(logAREA = log10(AREA),
+     YR.ISOL, logDIST = log10(DIST), logLDIST = log10(LDIST),
+     GRAZE, ALT))
> hier.part(loyn$ABUND, loyn.preds, gof = "Rsqu")

$gfs
 [1] 0.00000000 0.54765298 0.25336902 0.01605880 0.01395339
 [6] 0.46582178 0.14886955 0.64348084 0.55798408 0.57951387
[11] 0.65273437 0.58357693 0.27202894 0.29411677 0.47394321
[16] 0.32970100 0.01878268 0.46670232 0.19573296 0.47484303
[21] 0.20305219 0.47978826 0.64797136 0.65145633 0.67321512
[26] 0.66285874 0.57952428 0.66099826 0.58529695 0.66383018
[31] 0.59521919 0.66105930 0.29441552 0.47580294 0.37071613
[36] 0.48827761 0.40728610 0.48872839 0.47606705 0.21307189
[41] 0.48458087 0.49921047 0.65191856 0.67879410 0.66344013
[46] 0.67921724 0.66420358 0.68234183 0.66529515 0.59537174
[51] 0.66514424 0.66687281 0.48949273 0.40962297 0.49609855
[56] 0.51765498 0.49933677 0.68067311 0.66425545 0.68433597
[61] 0.68419720 0.66776512 0.51772763 0.68493595

$IJ
                   I            J      Total
logAREA  0.315204510 0.2324484698 0.54765298
YR.ISOL  0.101458466 0.1519105495 0.25336902
logDIST  0.007285099 0.0087737041 0.01605880
```

```
logLDIST 0.013677502 0.0002758905 0.01395339
GRAZE    0.190462561 0.2753592211 0.46582178
ALT      0.056847811 0.0920217408 0.14886955

$I.perc
                 I
logAREA  46.019560
YR.ISOL  14.812840
logDIST   1.063618
logLDIST  1.996902
GRAZE    27.807354
ALT       8.299727
```

Conclusions - $\log_{10}$area and grazing intensity contribute most to the explained variance in bird abundance (46.0 and 27.8% respectively), although years of isolation and to a lesser degree, altitude also make some contributions.

2. determine the likelihood that the independent contributions for each predictor variable could be due to change by performing a randomization test and assessing the significance of Z scores at the 95% level. Note that this procedure takes some time.

```
> r.HP <- rand.hp(loyn$ABUND, loyn.preds, gof = "Rsqu",
+      num.reps = 100)$Iprobs

          Obs Z.score sig95
logAREA  0.32   11.86     *
YR.ISOL  0.10    2.67     *
logDIST  0.01   -0.50
logLDIST 0.01   -0.12
GRAZE    0.19    8.99     *
ALT      0.06    1.09
```

Conclusions - the individual contributions of $\log_{10}$area, grazing, and years of isolation were all found to be significantly greater than would be expected by chance and therefore each has some influence on the abundance of forest birds within habitat patches across Victoria.

Example 9E: Randomization and multiple regression

McKechnie et al. (1975) investigated the relationship between the frequency of hezokinase (HK) 1.00 mobility genes and a range of climatic conditions (including altitude, temperature and precipitation) from colonies of *Euphydras editha* butterflies (example 8.3 Manly (1991)).

Step 1 - Import (section 2.3) the McKechnie et al. (1975) data set

```
> mckechnie2 <- read.table("mckechnie2.csv", header = T,
+      sep = ",")
```

Step 2 (Key 9.2) - Assess linearity, normality and homogeneity of variance using a scatterplot with marginal boxplots and a lowess smoother.

For the purpose of this demonstration, lets assume that the assumption of normality could not be met and more importantly, that the observations are not independent, thereby necessitating an alternative regression method.

Step 3 (Key 9.3) - assess (multi)collinearity.

```
> library(car)
> vif(lm(HK ~ PRECIP + MAXTEMP + MINTEMP + ALT, mckechnie2))
  PRECIP  MAXTEMP  MINTEMP      ALT
2.242274 3.375163 6.727932 1.921078
```

Conclusions - there is some indication of a collinearity issue concerning the minimum temperature variable (VIF greater than 5), however this will be overlooked for consistency with Manly (1991).

Step 4 (Key 9.5) - use a randomization test to test whether the observed trends could be due to chance.

1. use conventional multiple regression methods[k] to estimate the regression parameters.

```
> mckechnie2.lm <- lm(HK ~ PRECIP + MAXTEMP + MINTEMP +
+      ALT, mckechnie2)
> summary(mckechnie2.lm)
Call:
lm(formula = HK ~ PRECIP + MAXTEMP + MINTEMP + ALT,
   data = mckechnie2)

Residuals:
    Min      1Q  Median      3Q     Max
-50.995  -5.141   2.656  10.091  29.620

Coefficients:
             Estimate Std. Error t value Pr(>|t|)
(Intercept) -88.5645   101.1793  -0.875  0.39728
PRECIP        0.4720     0.4955   0.952  0.35823
MAXTEMP       0.8668     1.1725   0.739  0.47290
MINTEMP       0.2503     1.0195   0.246  0.80986
ALT          26.1237     8.6450   3.022  0.00982 **
---
Signif. codes:  0 '***' 0.001 '**' 0.01 '*' 0.05 '.' 0.1 ' ' 1

Residual standard error: 20.95 on 13 degrees of freedom
Multiple R-squared: 0.647,      Adjusted R-squared: 0.5384
F-statistic: 5.957 on 4 and 13 DF,  p-value: 0.005984
```

[k] Consistent with Manly (1991), I have used OLS to estimate the regression parameters. However, these parameters could alternatively be RMA or non-parametric regression estimates.

2. define the statistic (again this example uses OLS) to use in the randomization test - in this case the *t*-statistics for each of the estimated parameters.

```
> stat <- function(data, indices) {
+     summary(lm(HK ~ PRECIP + MAXTEMP + MINTEMP +
+         ALT, data))$coef[, 3]
+ }
```

3. define how the data should be randomized - randomize the response-predictor pairings (shuffle the response variable without replacement).

```
> rand.gen <- function(data, mle) {
+     out <- data
+     out$HK <- sample(out$HK, replace = F)
+     out
+ }
```

4. call a bootstrapping procedure to randomize 1000 times (this can take some time)

```
> library(boot)
> mckechnie2.boot <- boot(mckechnie2, stat, R = 1000,
+     sim = "parametric", ran.gen = rand.gen)
```

5. calculate the number of possible *t*-values (including the observed *t*-value, which is one possible outcome) that were greater or equal to the observed *t*-value (for each parameter) and express these as a percentage of the number of randomizations (plus one for the observed outcomes).

```
> t <- apply(apply(abs(mckechnie2.boot$t), 1, ">=",
+     abs(mckechnie2.boot$t0)) * 1, 1, "sum") + 1
> t/(mckechnie2.boot$R + 1)
(Intercept)      PRECIP     MAXTEMP     MINTEMP         ALT
 0.39360639  0.36563437  0.48151848  0.79620380  0.00999001
```

6. perform a similar randomization to investigate the ANOVA *F*-ratio. This requires a couple of minor adjustments of the above procedures.

```
> stat <- function(data, indices) {
+     summary(lm(HK ~ PRECIP + MAXTEMP + MINTEMP +
+         ALT, data))$fstatistic
+ }
> rand.gen <- function(data, mle) {
+     out <- data
+     out$HK <- sample(out$HK, replace = F)
+     out
+ }
> mckechnie2.boot <- boot(mckechnie2, stat, R = 1000,
+     sim = "parametric", ran.gen = rand.gen)
> f <- apply(apply(abs(mckechnie2.boot$t), 1, ">=",
+     abs(mckechnie2.boot$t0)) * 1, 1, "sum") + 1
> f/(mckechnie2.boot$R + 1)
```

```
        value          numdf          dendf
0.006993007 1.000000000 1.000000000
```

Conclusions - in this case, the p-values for both regression parameters and the overall ANOVA are almost identical to those produced via conventional regression analysis.

Example 9F: Polynomial regression

Sokal and Rohlf (1997) present an unpublished data set (R. K. Koehn) in which the nature of the relationship between *Lap*[94] allele frequency in *Mytilus edulis* and distance (in miles) from Southport was investigated (Box 16.5, Sokal and Rohlf (1997)).

Step 1 - Import (section 2.3) the mytilus data set

```
> mytilus <- read.table("mytilus.csv", header = T,
+     sep = ",")
```

As a matter of course, Sokal and Rohlf (1997) transform frequencies using angular transformations (arcsin transformations) and henceforth *Lap*[94] will be transformed in-line using `asin(sqrt(LAP))*180/pi`.

Step 2 (Key 8.2a) - confirm that simple linear regression does not adequately describe the relationship between *Lap*[94] allele frequency and distance by examining a scatterplot and residual plot.

```
> library(car)
> scatterplot(asin(sqrt(LAP)) *
+     180/pi ~ DIST,
+     data = mytilus)
```

```
> plot(lm(asin(sqrt(LAP)) *
+     180/pi ~ DIST,
+     data = mytilus),
+     which = 1)
```

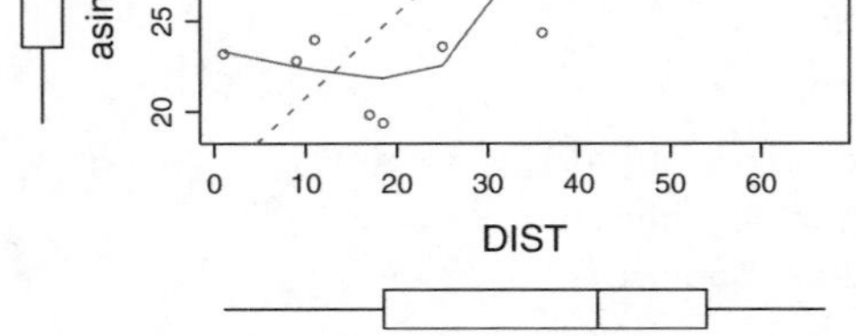

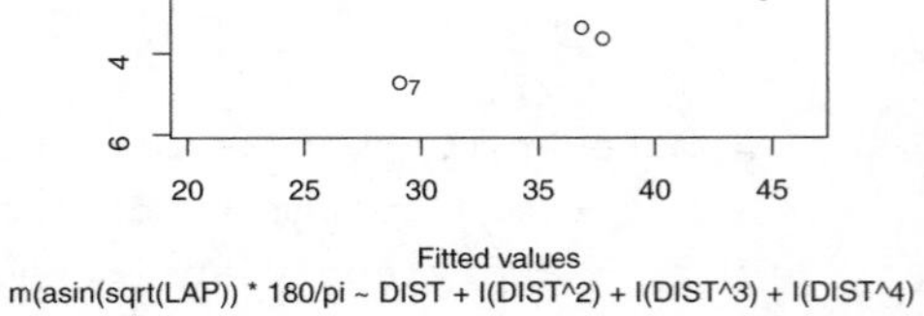

Conclusions - the scatterplot smoother suggests a potentially non-linear relationship and a persisting pattern in the residuals further suggests that the linear model is inadequate for explaining the response variable.

Step 3 (Key 9.7b) - fit a polynomial regression (additive multiple regression) model incorporating up to the fifth power (5th order polynomial)[l].

1. Fit the quintic model

```
> mytilus.lm5 <- lm(asin(sqrt(LAP)) * 180/pi ~ DIST +
+      I(DIST^2) + I(DIST^3) + I(DIST^4) + I(DIST^5),
+      mytilus)
```

2. Examine the diagnostics

```
> plot(mytilus.lm5, which = 1)
```

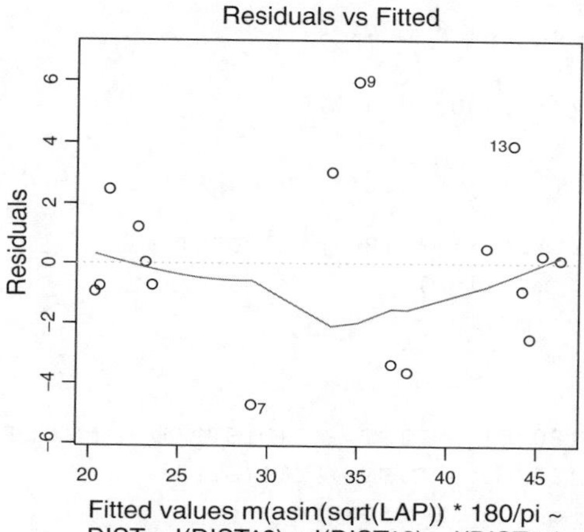

Conclusions - no "wedge" pattern suggesting that homogeneity of variance and there is no persisting pattern suggesting that the fitted model is appropriate for modeling these data.

3. Examine the fit of the model including the contribution of different powers

```
> anova(mytilus.lm5)
Analysis of Variance Table

Response: asin(sqrt(LAP)) * 180/pi
           Df  Sum Sq Mean Sq  F value     Pr(>F)
DIST        1 1418.37 1418.37 125.5532 2.346e-07 ***
I(DIST^2)   1   57.28   57.28   5.0701   0.04575 *
I(DIST^3)   1   85.11   85.11   7.5336   0.01907 *
I(DIST^4)   1   11.85   11.85   1.0493   0.32767
I(DIST^5)   1   15.99   15.99   1.4158   0.25915
Residuals  11  124.27   11.30
---
Signif. codes:  0 '***' 0.001 '**' 0.01 '*' 0.05 '.' 0.1 ' ' 1
```

Conclusions - powers of distance beyond a cubic (3) do not make significant contributions to explaining the variation in arcsin transformed *Lat*^{94} allele frequency.

[l] Note that trends beyond a third order polynomial are unlikely to have much biological basis and are likely to be over-fit.

4. The improved fit (and significance) attributed to an additional power can be evaluated by comparing the fit of the higher order models against models one lower in order.

```
> mytilus.lm1 <- lm(asin(sqrt(LAP)) * 180/pi ~ DIST,
+      mytilus)
> mytilus.lm2 <- lm(asin(sqrt(LAP)) * 180/pi ~ DIST +
+      I(DIST^2), mytilus)
> anova(mytilus.lm2, mytilus.lm1)
Analysis of Variance Table

Model 1: asin(sqrt(LAP)) * 180/pi ~ DIST + I(DIST^2)
Model 2: asin(sqrt(LAP)) * 180/pi ~ DIST
  Res.Df     RSS Df Sum of Sq      F  Pr(>F)
1     14 237.222
2     15 294.500 -1   -57.277 3.3803 0.08729 .
---
Signif. codes:  0 '***' 0.001 '**' 0.01 '*' 0.05 '.' 0.1 ' ' 1
```

```
> mytilus.lm3 <- lm(asin(sqrt(LAP)) * 180/pi ~ DIST +
+      I(DIST^2) + I(DIST^3), mytilus)
> anova(mytilus.lm3, mytilus.lm2)
Analysis of Variance Table

Model 1: asin(sqrt(LAP)) * 180/pi ~ DIST + I(DIST^2) + I(DIST^3)
Model 2: asin(sqrt(LAP)) * 180/pi ~ DIST + I(DIST^2)
  Res.Df     RSS Df Sum of Sq      F Pr(>F)
1     13 152.115
2     14 237.222 -1   -85.108 7.2734 0.0183 *
---
Signif. codes:  0 '***' 0.001 '**' 0.01 '*' 0.05 '.' 0.1 ' ' 1
```

Conclusions - a cubic model fits the data significantly better than a quadratic model ($P = 0.018$), the latter of which does not fit significantly better than a linear model ($P = 0.09$).

5. Estimate the model parameters[m] for the cubic model so as to establish the descriptive or predictive model.

---

[m] Due to the extreme multicollinearity problems (*dist* must be correlated to $dist^2$ and $dist^3$ etc), the parameter estimates are not stable, the standard errors are inflated and the individual parameter hypothesis tests are non informative. As with multiplicative multiple regression, this problem can be greatly alleviated by first centering the predictor variable. However, the value in doing so is limited as the resulting parameters (and associated confidence intervals) would then have to be back transformed into the original scales in order to construct a descriptive or predictive model (main uses of polynomial regression). Since the values of the estimated polynomial parameters do not have any biological meaning, standard errors and hypothesis tests of the parameter estimates should be ignored.

```
> summary(mytilus.lm3)
Call:
lm(formula = asin(sqrt(LAP)) * 180/pi ~ DIST + I(DIST^2) +
+    I(DIST^3), data = mytilus)

Residuals:
    Min      1Q  Median      3Q     Max
-6.1661 -2.1360 -0.3908  1.9016  6.0079

Coefficients:
              Estimate Std. Error t value Pr(>|t|)
(Intercept) 26.2232524  3.4126910   7.684 3.47e-06 ***
DIST        -0.9440845  0.4220118  -2.237  0.04343 *
I(DIST^2)    0.0421452  0.0138001   3.054  0.00923 **
I(DIST^3)   -0.0003502  0.0001299  -2.697  0.01830 *
---
Signif. codes:  0 '***' 0.001 '**' 0.01 '*' 0.05 '.' 0.1 ' ' 1

Residual standard error: 3.421 on 13 degrees of freedom
Multiple R-squared: 0.9112,     Adjusted R-squared: 0.8907
F-statistic: 44.46 on 3 and 13 DF,  p-value: 4.268e-07
```

Conclusions - there was a significant cubic relationship between the frequency of the *Lat*[94] allele in *Mytilus edulis* and distance from Southport ($P < 0.001, r^2 = 0.911$: $arcsin\sqrt{Lat} = 26.2233 - 0.9441dist + 0.0421dist^2 - 0.0003dist^3$).

Step 4 (Key 9.11) - construct a summary figure to summarize the illustrate the proposed nature of the relationship.

```
> plot(asin(sqrt(LAP)) * 180/pi ~ DIST, data = mytilus,
+     pch = 16, axes = F, xlab = "", ylab = "")
> axis(1, cex.axis = 0.8)
> mtext(text = expression(paste("Miles east of Southport,
+      Connecticut")), side = 1, line = 3)
> axis(2, las = 1)
> mtext(text = expression(paste("Arcsin ",
+      sqrt(paste("freq. of allele ", italic("Lap"))^{
+     94
+ }))), side = 2, line = 3)
> x <- seq(0, 80, l = 1000)
> points(x, predict(mytilus.lm3, data.frame(DIST = x)),
+     type = "l")
> box(bty = "l")
```

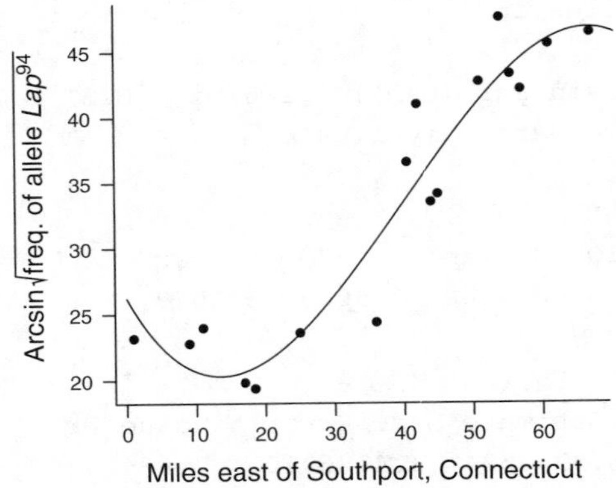

Example 9G: Nonlinear regression

Peake and Quinn (1993) investigated the nature of species-area relationships for invertebrates inhabiting inter-tidal mussel clumps (Box 6.11, Quinn and Keough (2002)).

Step 1 - Import (section 2.3) the peake data set

```
> peake <- read.table("peake.csv", header = T, sep = ",")
```

Step 2 (Key 8.2a) - confirm that simple linear regression does not adequately describe the relationship between the number of species and mussel clump area by examining a scatterplot and residual plot.

```
> library(car)
> scatterplot(SPECIES ~ AREA,
+     data = peake)
```

```
> plot(lm(SPECIES ~ AREA,
+     data = peake), which = 1)
```

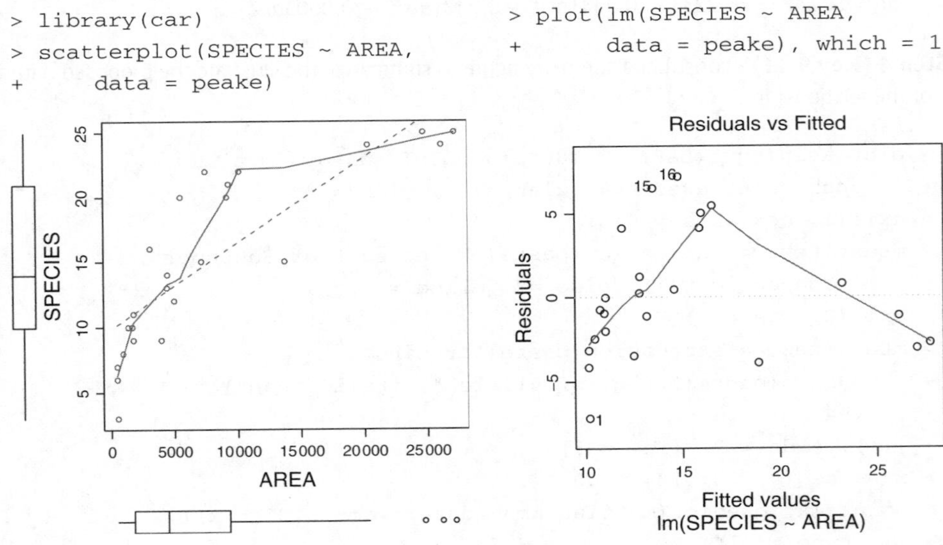

Conclusions - the scatterplot smoother suggests a non-linear relationship and the persisting pattern in the residuals further suggests that the linear model is inadequate for explaining the response variable. Although this could probably be corrected by transforming the scale of the mussel clump area variable, in this case, theory suggests that species-area relationships might be more appropriately modeled with a power function.

Step 3 (Key 9.7) - fit a nonlinear regression (power) model.

1. Fit the model (a power model would seem appropriate, see also Table 9.1)

```
> peake.nls <- nls(SPECIES ~ alpha * AREA^beta,
    start = list(alpha = 0.1,
+      beta = 1), peake)
```

2. Examine the diagnostics

```
> plot(resid(peake.nls) ~ fitted(peake.nls))
```

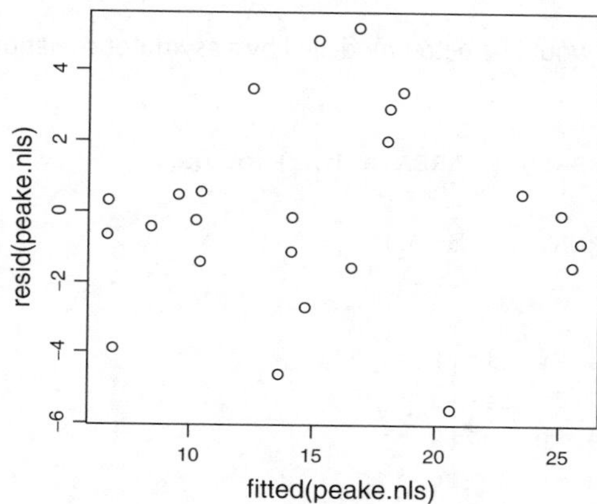

Conclusions - no persisting pattern suggesting that the fitted power model is appropriate for modeling these data. Additionally, there is no "wedge" pattern suggesting that the homogeneity of variance assumption is satisfied.

3. Examine the estimated nonlinear model parameters

```
> summary(peake.nls)
Formula: SPECIES ~ alpha * AREA^beta

Parameters:
      Estimate Std. Error t value Pr(>|t|)
alpha   0.8584     0.2769   3.100  0.00505 **
beta    0.3336     0.0350   9.532 1.87e-09 ***
---
Signif. codes:  0 '***' 0.001 '**' 0.01 '*' 0.05 '.' 0.1 ' ' 1

Residual standard error: 2.733 on 23 degrees of freedom

Number of iterations to convergence: 17
Achieved convergence tolerance: 1.043e-06
```

Step 4 (Key 9.8a) - Examine the fit of the nonlinear model (compared to a linear model).

```
> AIC(peake.nls, k=log(nrow(peake))) #BIC
[1] 128.7878
> AIC(peake.nls) #AIC
[1] 125.1312
> deviance(peake.nls)/df.residual(peake.nls) #MSresid
[1] 7.468933
```

```
> peake.lm<-lm(SPECIES~AREA, data=peake) #linear fit
> AIC(peake.lm, k=log(nrow(peake))) #lm BIC
[1] 144.7322
> AIC(peake.lm) #lm AIC
[1] 141.0756
> deviance(peake.lm)/df.residual(peake.lm) #lm MSresid
[1] 14.13324
```

Conclusions - all fit criterion concur that the nonlinear power model is a better fit to the data than the linear model.

Step 5 (Key 9.8a) - Arguably, these data would be better modelled by a asymptotic relationship. Fit such a relationship.

```
> peake.nls1 <- nls(SPECIES~SSasymp(AREA,a,b,c),peake)
> summary(peake.nls1)
Formula: SPECIES ~ SSasymp(AREA, a, b, c)

Parameters:
  Estimate Std. Error t value Pr(>|t|)
a  24.4114     1.6644  14.667 7.71e-13 ***
b   4.9563     1.4244   3.479  0.00213 **
c  -8.8138     0.2482 -35.512  < 2e-16 ***
---
Signif. codes:  0 '***' 0.001 '**' 0.01 '*' 0.05 '.' 0.1 ' ' 1

Residual standard error: 2.719 on 22 degrees of freedom

Number of iterations to convergence: 0
Achieved convergence tolerance: 7.128e-07
> AIC(peake.nls1) #AIC
[1] 125.7644
> deviance(peake.nls1)/df.residual(peake.nls1) #MSresid
[1] 7.393005
> anova(peake.nls,peake.nls1)

Analysis of Variance Table

Model 1: SPECIES ~ alpha * AREA^beta
Model 2: SPECIES ~ SSasymp(AREA, a, b, c)
  Res.Df Res.Sum Sq Df  Sum Sq F value Pr(>F)
1     23    171.785
2     22    162.646  1   9.139  1.2362 0.2782
```

Conclusions - the asymptotic trend does not fit the data significantly better than the exponential trend.

Step 6 (Key 9.11) - summarize the nonlinear species-area relationship with a scatterplot and exponential (dashed line) and asymptotic (solid) line trends.

```
> plot(SPECIES ~ AREA, peake, pch = 16, axes = F, xlab = "",
+     ylab = "")
> axis(1, cex.axis = 0.8)
> mtext(text = expression(paste("Clump area ", (dm^2))),
+     side = 1, line = 3)
> axis(2, las = 1)
> mtext(text = "Number of species", side = 2, line = 3)
> box(bty = "l")
> x <- seq(0, 30000, l = 1000)
> points(x, predict(peake.nls, data.frame(AREA = x)),
+     type = "l", lty = 2)
> points(x, predict(nls(SPECIES ~ SSasymp(AREA, a,
+     b, c), peake), data.frame(AREA = x)), type = "l",
+     lty = 1)
> box(bty = "l")
```

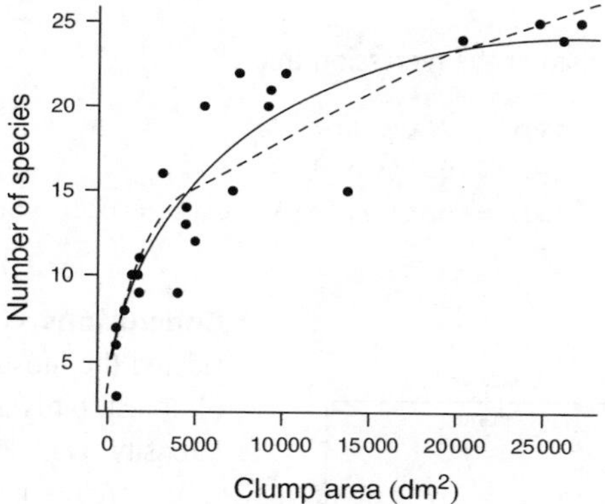

Example 9H: Regression trees

Quinn and Keough (2002) used the Loyn (1987) data set (analysed in Example 9A on page 224) to demonstrate the use of regression trees for producing descriptive and predictive models (Quinn and Keough (2002) Box 6.9). Using the same data from Example 9A, we will illustrate the use of R to produce regression trees.

Step 1 (Key 9.13) - Perform binary recursive partitioning and construct the resulting regression tree.

```
> library(tree)
> loyn.tree <- tree(ABUND ~ AREA + YR.ISOL + DIST +
+     LDIST + GRAZE + ALT, data = loyn, mindev = 0)
```

Note that Quinn and Keough (2002) used log_{10} transformed data for some of the variables. Such transformations have no impact on the construction of the tree nodes or branches, however the split threshold values for transformed predictor variables will be on a log_{10} scale.

Step 2 (Key 9.13) - Examine the residuals for outlying, influential observations.

```
> plot(residuals(loyn.tree) ~ predict(loyn.tree))
```

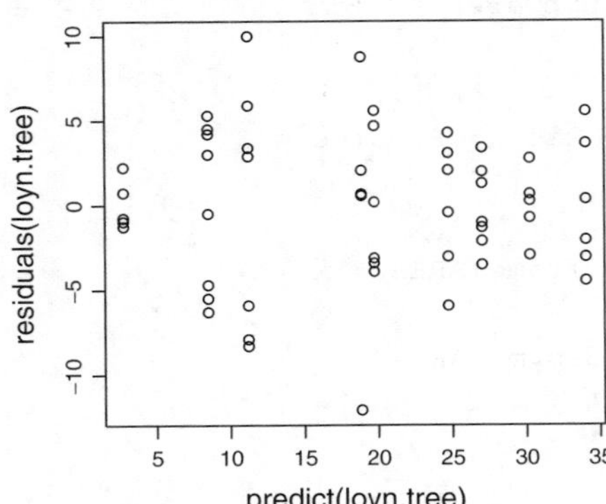

Conclusions - There are an even spread of residuals with no obvious potentially influential observations (no outliers from the patterns within each branches predicted values).

Step 3 (Key 9.13) - Construct the regression tree.

```
> plot(loyn.tree, type = "uniform")
> text(loyn.tree, cex = 0.5, all = T)
> text(loyn.tree, lab = paste("n"), cex = 0.5, adj = c(0,
+      2), splits = F)
```

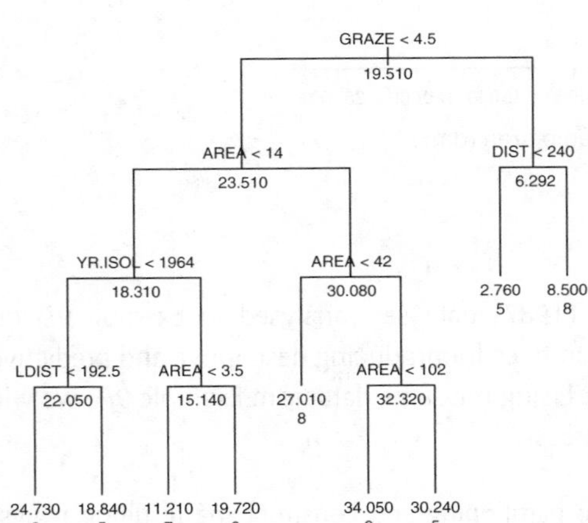

Conclusions - Grazing intensity was considered the most important single predictor of forest bird abundance. When grazing intensity was less than 4.5, patch area is important and when grazing intensity is greater than 4.5, the split in distance to nearest patch produced the greatest deviance (albeit very small suggesting that this entire branch is probably of little importance). Larger patch sizes continue to be split according to patch size suggesting that patch area is an important predictor of bird abundance. Smaller patches however are split by years since isolation and then by distance to the nearest patch and again patch area.

This is in broad agreement with the model selection outcomes demonstrated in examples 9C and 9D, although grazing intensity is of elevated importance in the regression tree. Patch area and years since isolation are considered important within the patches of lower grazing pressure.

Step 4 (Key 9.14) - Examine the cost-complexity measure.

```
> plot(prune.tree(loyn.tree))
```

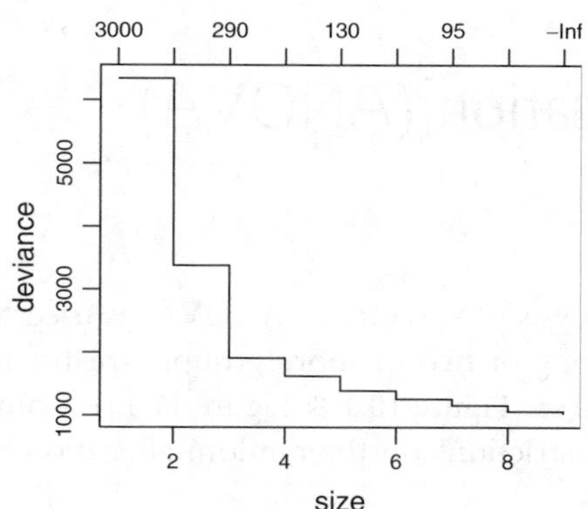

Conclusions - It is clear that the additional deviance (fit) achieved by adding more nodes beyond 3 is very marginal (cost-complexity curve begins to asymptote at this point). This suggests that the tree could potentially be pruned to just three terminal branches without great loss of predictive power to achieve a more genuine predictive model.

Step 5 (Key 9.14) - Prune the tree.

```
> loyn.tree.prune <- prune.tree(loyn.tree, best = 3)
> plot(loyn.tree.prune, type = "uniform")
> text(loyn.tree.prune, cex = 0.5, all = T)
> text(loyn.tree.prune, lab = paste("n"), cex = 0.5,
+     adj = c(0, 2), splits = F)
```

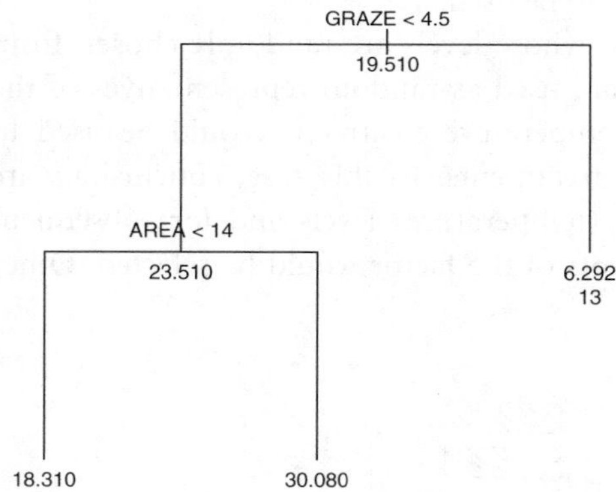

Conclusions - The pruned regression tree suggests a predictive model with two variables (grazing intensity and patch area).

10

Single factor classification (ANOVA)

Single factor classification (also known as analysis of variance of ANOVA) is used to investigate the effect of single factor comprising of two or more groups (treatment levels) from a completely randomized design (see Figure 10.1 & Figure 11.1a). Completely randomized refers to the absence of restrictions on the random allocation of experimental or sampling units to factor levels.

10.0.1 Fixed versus random factors

Fixed factors are factors whose levels represent the specific populations of interest. For example, a factor that comprises 'high', 'medium' and 'low' temperature treatments is a fixed factor – we are only interested in comparing those three populations. Conclusions about the effects of a fixed factor are restricted to the specific treatment levels investigated and for any subsequent experiments to be comparable, the same specific treatments of the factor would need to be used.

By contrast, **Random factors** are factors whose levels are randomly chosen from all the possible levels of populations and are used as random representatives of the populations. For example, five random temperature treatments could be used to represent a full spectrum of temperature treatments. In this case, conclusions are intrapolated to all the possible treatment (temperature) levels and for subsequent experiments, a new random set of treatments of the factor would be selected. Other

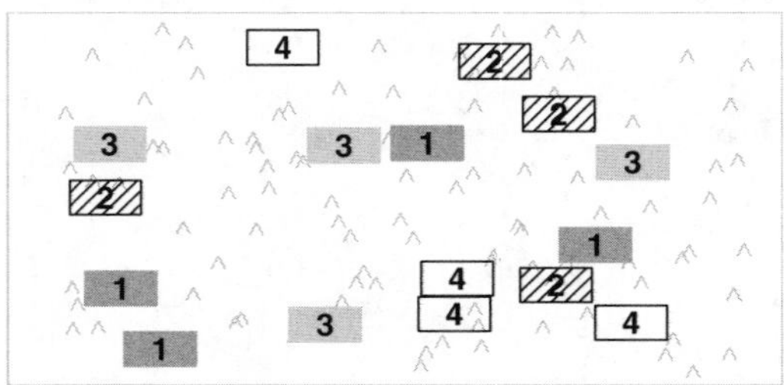

Fig 10.1 A fictitious spatial depiction of sampling units arranged randomly and randomly assigned to one of four treatment levels (n = 4 for each treatment level).

Biostatistical Design and Analysis Using R: a Practical Guide, 1st edition. By M. Logan.
Published 2010 by Blackwell Publishing.

common examples of random factors include sites and subjects - factors for which we are attempting to generalize over. Furthermore, the nature of random factors means that we have no indication of how a new level of that factor (such as another subject or site) are likely to respond and thus it is not possible to predict new observations from random factors.

These differences between fixed and random factors are reflected in the way their respective null hypotheses are formulated and interpreted. Whilst fixed factors contrast the effects of the different levels of the factor, random factors are modelled as the amount of additional variability they introduce.

10.1 Null hypotheses

Fixed factor

A single fixed factor ANOVA tests the H_0 that there are no differences between the population group means

$$H_0 : \mu_1 = \mu_2 = \ldots = \mu_i = \mu \qquad \text{(the population group means are all equal)}$$

That is, that the mean of population 1 is equal to that of population 2 and so on, and thus all population means are equal to an overall mean. If the effect of the ith group is the difference between the ith group mean and the overall mean ($\alpha_i = \mu_i - \mu$) then the H_0 can alternatively be written as:

$$H_0 : \alpha_1 = \alpha_2 = \ldots = \alpha_i = 0 \qquad \text{(the effect of each group equals zero)}$$

If one or more of the α_i are different from zero (the response mean for this treatment differs from the overall response mean), the null hypothesis is not true, indicating that the treatment does affect the response variable.

Random factor

The H_0 for a random factor is that the variance between all possible groups equals zero:

$$H_0 : \sigma^2_\alpha = 0 \qquad \text{(added variance due to this factor equals zero)}$$

10.2 Linear model

The linear model for single factor classification is similar to that of multiple linear regression[a]. There is a separate parameter for each level (group) of the factor and a constant parameter that estimates the overall mean of the response variable:

$$y_{ij} = \mu + \beta_1(level_1)_{ij} + \beta_2(level_2)_{ij} + \ldots + \varepsilon_{ij}$$

[a] Indeed, if the model is fitted with the `lm()` *function* rather than the more specific `aov()` *function*, parameters associated with each level of the treatment are estimated and tested.

where β_1 and β_2 respectively represent the effects of level 1 and 2 on the mean response. When these individual effects are combined into a single term, the linear effects model for single factor classification becomes:

$$y_{ij} = \mu + \alpha_i + \varepsilon_{ij}$$

Term	Fixed/random	Description	Null hypothesis
α_i	fixed	the effect of the ith group	$\alpha_i = 0$ (no effect of factor A)
	random	random variable	$\sigma^2_\alpha = 0$ (variances between all possible levels of A are equal)

Note that whilst the null hypotheses for fixed and random factors are different (fixed: population group means all equal, random: variances between populations all equal zero, the linear model fitted for fixed and random factors in single factor ANOVA models is identical. For more complex multifactor ANOVA models however, the distinction between fixed and random factors has important consequences for statistical models and null hypotheses.

10.3 Analysis of variance

When the null hypothesis is true (and the populations are identical), the amount of variation among observations within groups should be similar to the amount of variation in observations between groups. However, when the null hypothesis is false, the amount of variation among observations might be expected to be less than the amount of variation within groups. Analysis of variance, or ANOVA, partitions the total variance in the response (dependent) variable into a component of the variance that is explained by combinations of one or more categorical predictor variables (called factors) and a component of the variance that cannot be explained (residual), see Figure 10.2. In effect, these are the variances among observations between and within groups respectively. The variance ratio (F-ratio) from this partitioning can then be used to test the null hypothesis (H_0) that the population group or treatment means are all equal.

When the null hypothesis is true (and the test assumptions have not been violated), the ratio (F-ratio) of explained to unexplained variance follows a theoretical probability distribution (F-distribution, see Figure 10.2d). When the null hypothesis is true, and there is no effect of the treatment on the response variable, the ratio of explained variability to unexplained variability is expected to be $\leq 1^b$.

Importantly, the denominator in an F-ratio calculation essentially represents what we would expect the numerator to be in the absence of a treatment effect. For simple analyses, identifying the what these expected values are straight forward (equivalent to the degree of within group variability). However, in more complex designs (particularly involving random factors and hierarchical treatment levels), the logical "groups" can be more difficult (and in some cases impossible) to identify. In such cases, nominating

[b] Since the denominator should represent the expected numerator (i.e. denominator = numerator) in the absence of an effect.

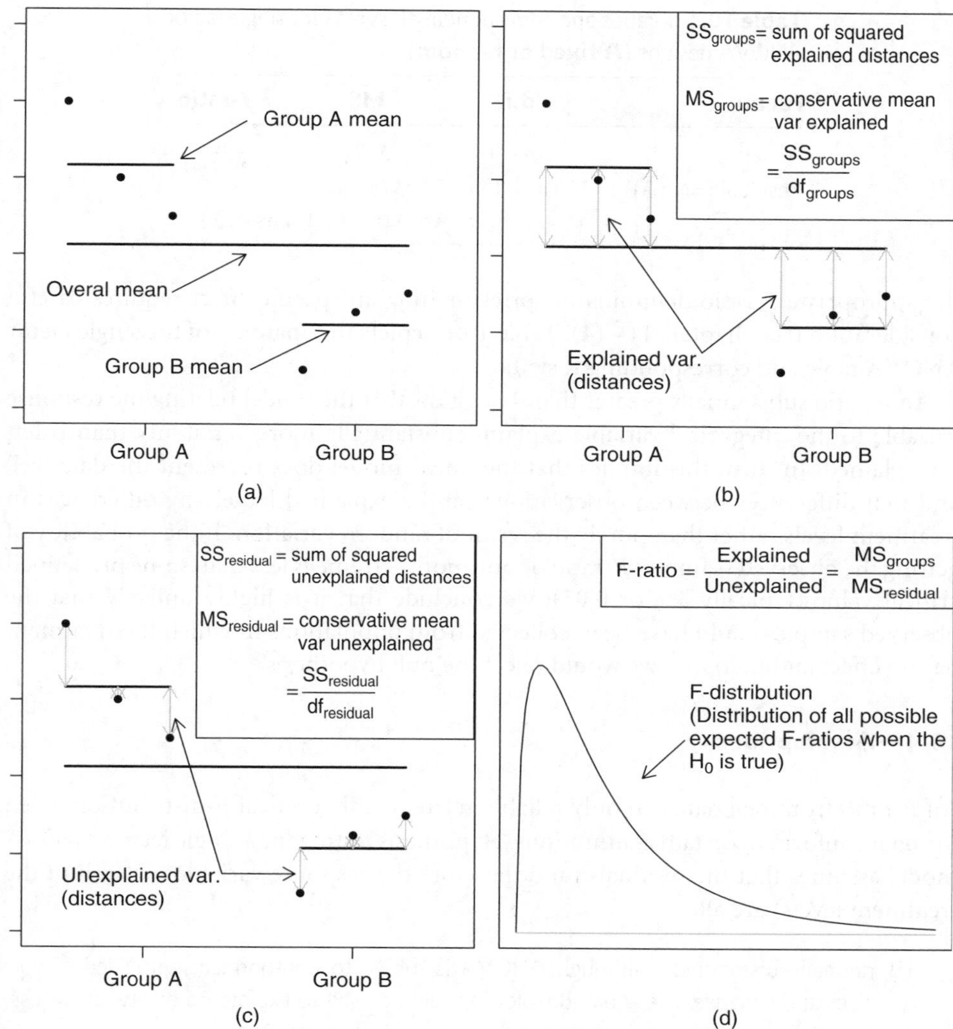

Fig 10.2 Fictitious data illustrating the partitioning of total variation into components explained by the groups (MS_{groups}) and unexplained ($MS_{residual}$) by the groups. The gray arrows in (b) depict the relative amounts explained by the groups. The proposed groupings generally explain why the first few points are higher on the y-axis than the last three points. The gray arrows in (c) depict the relative amounts unexplained (the residuals) by the groups. The proposed groupings fail to explain the differences within the first three points and within the last three points. The probability of collecting our sample, and thus generating the sample ratio of explained to unexplained variation (or one more extreme), when the null hypothesis is true (and population means are equal) is the area under the *F*-distribution (d) beyond our sample *F*-ratio.

Table 10.1 *F*-ratios and corresponding R syntax for single factor ANOVA designs (**A fixed or random**).

Factor	d.f.	MS	F-ratio
A	$a - 1$	MS_A	$\frac{MS_A}{MS_{Resid}}$
Residual (=N′(A))	$(n - 1)a$	MS_{Resid}	
	`> anova(aov(DV A,dataset))`		

the appropriate *F*-ratio deniminator for estimating an specific effect requires careful consideration (see chapters 11–14). Table 10.1 depicts the anatomy of the single factor ANOVA table and corresponding R syntax.

An *F*-ratio substantially greater than 1 suggests that the model relating the response variable to the categorical variable explains substantially more variability than is left unexplained. In turn, this implies that the linear model does represent the data well and that differences between observations can be explained largely by differences in treatment levels rather than purely the result of random variation. If the probability of getting the observed (sample) *F*-ratio or one more extreme is less than some predefined critical value (typically 5% or 0.05), we conclude that it is highly unlikely that the observed samples could have been collected from populations in which the treatment has no effect and therefore we would reject the null hypothesis.

10.4 Assumptions

An *F*-ratio from real data can only reliably relate to a theoretical *F*-distribution when the data conform to certain assumptions. Hypothesis testing for a single factor ANOVA model assumes that the residuals (and therefore the response variable for each of the treatment levels) are all:

(i) normally distributed - although ANOVA is robust to non-normality provided sample sizes and variances are equal. Boxplots should be used to explore normality, skewness, bimodality and outliers. Scale transformations are often useful.
(ii) equally varied - provided sample sizes are equal and the largest to smallest variance ratio does not exceed 3:1 (9:1 for sd), ANOVA is reasonably robust to this assumption, however, relationships between variance and mean and/or sample size are of particular concern as they elevate the Type I error rate. Boxplots and plots of means against variance should be used to explore the spread of values. Residual plots should reveal no patterns (see Figure 8.5). Since unequal variances are often the result of non-normality, transformations that improve normality will also improve variance homogeneity.
(iii) independent of one another - this assumption must be addressed at the design and collection stages and cannot be compensated for later[c].

Violations of these assumptions reduce the reliability of the analysis.

[c] Unless a model is used that specifically accounts for particular types of non-independent data, such as repeated measures ANOVA - see chapter 13.

10.5 Robust classification (ANOVA)

There are a number of alternatives to ANOVA that are more robust (less sensitive) to conditions of either non-normality or unequal variance. **Welch's test** adjusts the degrees of freedom to maintain test reliability in situations where populations are normally distributed but unequally varied. Alternatively, **Randomization tests** repeatedly shuffle the observations randomly, each time calculating a specific test statistic so as to build up a unique probability distribution for the test statistic for the collected data and thus make no assumptions about the distribution of the underlying population. Such tests do not assume observations were collected via random sampling, however they do assume that populations are equally varied.

Non-parametric (rank-based) tests such as the **Kruskal-Wallis test** use ranks of the observations to calculate test statistics rather than the actual observations and thus do not assume that the underlying populations are normally distributed. They test the null hypothesis that population medians are equal and are useful in situations where there are outliers. Although technically these tests still assume that the populations are equally varied, violations of this assumption apparently have little impact.

10.6 Tests of trends and means comparisons

Rejecting the null hypothesis that all of population group means are equal only indicates that at least one of the population group means differs from the others, it does not indicate which groups differ from which other groups. Consequently, researchers often wish to examine patterns of differences among groups. However, this requires multiple comparisons of group means and multiple comparisons lead to two statistical problems. First, multiple significance tests increase the probability of Type I errors (α, the probability of falsely rejecting H_0). If the decision criteria for any single hypothesis test is 0.05 (5%), then we are accepting that there is a 5% chance of committing a Type I error (falsely rejecting the null hypothesis). As a result, if many related hypothesis tests are conducted, then the overall Type I error rate (probability of making at least one Type I error) compounds to unacceptably high levels. For example, testing for differences between 5 groups requires ten pairwise comparisons. If the α for each test is 0.05 (5%), then the probability of at least one Type I error for the family of 10 tests is approximately 0.4 (40%). Second, the outcome of each test might not be independent (orthogonal). For example, if one test reveals that the population mean of group A is significantly different from the population mean of group B (A>B) and B>C then we already know the result of A vs. C.

Post-hoc unplanned pairwise comparisons compare all possible pairs of group means and are useful in an exploratory fashion to reveal differences between groups when it is not possible to justify any specific comparisons over other comparisons prior to the collection and analysis of data. There are a variety of procedures available to control the family-wise Type I error rate (e.g. Bonferroni and Tukey's test), thereby minimizing the probability of making Type I errors. However, these procedures reduce the power of each individual pairwise comparison (increase Type II error), and the reduction in power is directly related to the number of groups (and hence number of comparisons) being compared. For ordered factors (e.g. Temperature: 10, 15, 20, ...), multiple pairwise comparisons are arguably less informative than an investigation of the overall trends across the set of factor levels.

Planned comparisons are specific comparisons that are usually planned during the design stage of the experiment. Most textbooks recommend that multiple comparisons can be made (each at $\alpha = 0.05$) provided each comparison is independent of (orthogonal to) other comparisons and that no more than $p - 1$ (where p is the number of groups) comparisons are made. Among all possible comparisons (both pairwise and combinational), only a select sub-set are performed, while other less meaningful (within the biological context of the investigation) combinations are ignored. Occasionally, the comparisons of greatest interest are not independent (non-orthogonal). In such circumstances, some statisticians recommend performing the each of the individual comparisons separately before applying a Dunn-Sidak p-value correction.

Specific comparisons are defined via a set of contrast coefficients (C) associated with a linear combination of the treatment means ($\bar{y}$) (see section 7.3.1):

$$\bar{y}_1(C_1) + \bar{y}_2(C_2) + \ldots + \bar{y}_p(C_p)$$

where p is the number of groups in the factor. The contrast coefficients for a specific comparison must sum to zero and the groups being contrasted should have opposing signs. In addition to facilitating specific comparisons between individual groups, it is also possible to compare multiple groups to other groups or multiples and investigate polynomial trends. Table 10.2 provides example contrast coefficients for a number of commonly used planned comparison H_0 types. Note that polynomial trends assume that factor levels are ordered according to a natural gradient or progression (eg. low, medium, high) and that the factor levels are evenly spaced along this gradient. If you have reason to suspect that this is not the case, consider either weighting the

Table 10.2 Example contrast coefficients for specific comparisons and the first three order polynomials for a factor with four levels (groups).

H_0:	Group$_1$	Group$_2$	Group$_3$	Group$_4$
$\mu_1 = \mu_2$	1	−1	0	0
$(\mu_1 + \mu_2)/2 = \mu_3$[a]	.5	.5	−1	0
no linear trend	−2	−1	1	2
no quadratic trend	1	−1	−1	1
no cubic trend	−1	3	−3	1

[a] while alternatively, this planned contrast could have been defined as $1, 1, -2, 0$, yielding the same partitioning on $SS_{CONTRAST}$, its estimated parameter value would not reflect the value inferred by the null hypothesis.

contrast coefficients to better represent the increments between treatment levels[d], or else regression analysis (see chapter 8) as an alternative.

10.7 Power and sample size determination

Recall from section 6.5, that power (the probability of detecting an effect if an effect really exists) is proportional to the effect size, sample size and significance level (α) and inversely proportional to the background variability. It is convienient to think about the effect size as the absolute magnitude of the effect. When there are only two groups, the effect size is relatively straight forward to estimate (it is the expected difference between the means of two populations). However, when there are more than two groups, there are numerous ways in which this effect size can manifest. For example, in an investigation into the effect of temperature ('v.high', 'high', 'medium' and 'low') on the growth rate of seedlings, there are numerous ways that an effect size of (for example) 10 units above the expected background mean growth rate of 20 units could be distributed across the four groups (see Table 10.3). Consequently, effect size is expressed in terms of the expected variability both within and between the populations (groups). The smaller the degree of variability between groups, the more difficult it is to detect differences, or the greater the sample size required to detect differences. It is therefore important to anticipate the nature of between group patterns in conducting power analyses and sample size determinations.

Table 10.3 Fictitious illustration of the variety of ways that an effect size of 10 units could be distributed over four groups.

Possible trends		Between group variability
One group different	$\mu_V > \mu_H = \mu_M = \mu_L$	`var(c(30,20,20,20)) = 25.00`
Two groups different	$\mu_V = \mu_H > \mu_M = \mu_L$	`var(c(30,30,20,20)) = 33.33`
Equal increments	$\mu_V > \mu_H > \mu_M > \mu_L$	`var(seq(30,20,l=4)) = 18.52`
Other increments	$\mu_V > \mu_H = \mu_M > \mu_L$	`var(c(30,25,25,20)) = 16.67`

10.8 ANOVA in R

Single factor ANOVA models can be fitted with the either the `lm()` linear modelling *function* or the more specific `aov()` *function*, the latter of which provides a wrapper for the `lm()` *function* that redefines output for standard analysis of variance rather than

[d] For a linear trend, weighted coefficients can be calculated by providing numerical representations of each of the factor levels and then subtracting the mean of these levels from each numeric level.

parameter estimates. ANOVA tables for balanced, fixed factor designs can be viewed using either the `anova()` or `summary()`, the latter of which is used to accommodate planned contrasts with the `split=` *argument*.

10.9 Further reading

- Theory

  Doncaster, C. P., and A. J. H. Davey. (2007). *Analysis of Variance and Covariance. How to Choose and Construct Models for the Life Sciences.* Cambridge University Press, Cambridge.

  Fowler, J., L. Cohen, and P. Jarvis. (1998). *Practical statistics for field biology.* John Wiley & Sons, England.

  Hollander, M., and D. A. Wolfe. (1999). *Nonparametric statistical methods, 2nd edition.* 2 edition. John Wiley & Sons, New York.

  Manly, B. F. J. (1991). *Randomization and Monte Carlo methods in biology.* Chapman & Hall, London.

  Quinn, G. P., and K. J. Keough. (2002). *Experimental design and data analysis for biologists.* Cambridge University Press, London.

  Sokal, R., and F. J. Rohlf. (1997). *Biometry, 3rd edition.* W. H. Freeman, San Francisco.

  Zar, G. H. (1999). *Biostatistical methods.* Prentice-Hall, New Jersey.

- Practical - R

  Crawley, M. J. (2007). *The R Book.* John Wiley, New York.

  Dalgaard, P. (2002). *Introductory Statistics with R.* Springer-Verlag, New York.

  Fox, J. (2002). *An R and S-PLUS Companion to Applied Regression.* Sage Books.

  Maindonald, J. H., and J. Braun. (2003). *Data Analysis and Graphics Using R - An Example-based Approach.* Cambridge University Press, London.

  Venables, W. N., and B. D. Ripley. (2002). *Modern Applied Statistics with S-PLUS,* 4th edn. Springer-Verlag, New York.

  Wilcox, R. R. (2005). *Introduction to Robust Estimation and Hypothesis Testing.* Elsevier Academic Press.

10.10 Key for single factor classification (ANOVA)

1 a. Check parametric assumptions

- **Normality of the response variable at each level of the categorical variable - boxplots**

```
> boxplot(DV ~ Factor, dataset)
```

  where `DV` *and* `Factor` *are response and factor variables respectively in the* `dataset` *data frame*

- **Homogeneity of variance - boxplots (as above) and scatterplot of mean vs variance**

```
> plot(tapply(dataset$DV, dataset$Factor, var),
+       tapply(dataset$DV, dataset$Factor, mean))
```

where `DV` *and* `Factor` *are response and factor variables respectively in the* `dataset` *data frame*

Parametric assumptions met .... Go to 2

b. Parametric assumptions NOT met .... Go to 5

2 a. ANOVA with specific comparisons or trends .... Go to 4

b. ANOVA without specific comparisons or trends .... Go to 3

3 a. Single fixed factor (model I) .... See Example 10A

```
> data.aov <- aov(DV ~ Factor, dataset)
> plot(data.aov)
> anova(data.aov)
```

if Reject H_0 - Significant difference between group means detected .... Go to 9

b. Single random factor (model II) .... See Example 10D

```
> anova(aov(DV ~ Factor, dataset))
```

if Reject H_0 - Significant difference between group means detected - calculate variance components

```
> library(nlme)
> data.lme <- lme(DV ~ 1, random = ~1 | Factor, data = dataset,
+     method = "ML")
> VarCorr(data.lme)
> data.lme <- lme(DV ~ 1, random = ~1 | Factor, data = dataset,
+     method = "REML")
> VarCorr(data.lme)
```

4 a. With planned comparisons of means .... See Example 10B

```
> contrasts(dataset$Factor) <- cbind(c(contrasts), c(contrasts),
+     ...)
> round(crossprod(contrasts(dataset$Factor)), 2)
> data.list <- list(Factor = list(lab = 1, ..), ..)
> data.aov <- aov(DV ~ Factor, data = dataset)
> plot(data.aov)
> summary(data.aov, split = data.list)
```

b. With planned polynomial trends .... See Example 10C

```
> contrasts(dataset$Factor) <- "contr.poly"
> data.list <- list(Factor = list(Linear = 1))
> data.aov <- aov(DV ~ Factor, data = dataset)
> plot(data.aov)
> summary(data.aov, split = data.list)
```

5 a. Attempt a scale transformation (see Table 3.2 for common transformation options) .... Go to 1

b. Transformations unsuccessful or inappropriate .... Go to 6

6 a. Underlying distribution of the response variable is normal but variances are unequal (Welch's test) .... See Example 10F

```
> oneway.test(DV ~ Factor, var.equal = F)
```

If Reject H_0 - Significant difference between group means detected .... Go to 9c
or consider GLM .... GLM chapter 17

b. Underlying distribution of the response variable is NOT normal .... Go to 7

7 a. Underlying distribution of the response variable and residuals is known (yet non-normal) .... GLM chapter 17

b. Underlying distribution of the response variable and residuals is NOT known .... Go to 8

8 a. Variances not wildly unequal, but outliers present (Kruskal-Wallis nonparametric test) .... See Example 10G

```
> kruskal.test(DV ~ Factor, var.equal = F)
```

If Reject H_0 - Significant difference between group means detected ..... Go to 9b/c

b. Variances not wildly unequal, random sampling not possible (Randomization test) .... See Example 10G

```
> library(boot)
> data.boot <- boot(dataset, stat, R = 999, sim = "parametric",
+     rand.gen = rand.gen)
> plot(data.boot)
> print(data.boot)
```

where `stat` *is the statistic to repeatedly calculate and* `rand.gen` *defines how the data are randomized.*

9 a. Parametric simultaneous multiple comparisons - Tukey's test .. See Example 10A

```
> library(multcomp)
> summary(glht(model, linfct = mcp(Factor = "Tukey")))
```

b. Non-parametric simultaneous multiple comparisons - Steel test .... See Example 10E

```
> library(npmc)
> data <- data.frame(var = dataset$DV, class = dataset$Factor)
> summary(npmc(data), type = "steel")
```

c. Multiple comparisons based on p-value adjustments .... See Example 10G

```
> library(multtest)
> mt.rawp2adjp(pvalues, proc = "SidakSD")
> p.adjust(pvalues, method = "holm")
```

where pvalues is a list of pvalues from each pairwise comparison and `'holm'` *and* `'SidakSD'` *are the names of the p-value adjustment procedures. For alternative procedures, see Table 10.4.*

The `p.adjust` function above can also be called from within other pairwise routines
Parametric pairwise tests

```
> pairwise.t.test(DV ~ Factor, pool.sd = F, p.adjust = "holm")
```

Non-parametric pairwise tests

```
> pairwise.wilcox.test(DV ~ Factor, p.adjust = "holm")
```

Table 10.4 Alternative p-value adjustments (`p.adjust`) for use with the `pairwise.wilcoxon.test` and `pairwise.t.test`.

Syntax	Correction	Description
'bonferroni'	Bonferroni single-step correction	p-values multiplied by number of comparisons to control the family-wise error rate
'holm'	sequential step-down Bonferroni correction	More powerful than Bonferroni to control the family-wise error rate
'hochberg'	Hochberg step-up correction	Reverse of Holm procedure and possibly more powerful to control the family-wise error rate
'hommel'	sequential Bonferroni correction	Reportedly more powerful than Hochberg procedure to control the family-wise error rate
'BH'	Benjamini & Hochberg step-up correction	Controls the false discovery rate
'BY'	Benjamini & Yekutieli step-up correction	Controls the false discovery rate
'none'	no correction	Uncorrected p-values
'SidakSS'[a]	Sidak single-step correction	More powerful modification of Bonferroni procedure
'SidakSD'[a]	Sidak step-down correction	More powerful modification of Bonferroni procedure

[a]only available via the `mt.rawp2adjp` function of the `multtest` package, see Example 10F.

10.11 Worked examples of real biological data sets

Example 10A: Single factor ANOVA with Tukey's test

Medley and Clements (1998) investigated the impact of zinc contamination (and other heavy metals) on the diversity of diatom species in the USA Rocky Mountains (from Box 8.1 of Quinn and Keough (2002)). The diversity of diatoms (number of species) and degree of zinc contamination (categorized as either of high, medium, low or natural background level) were recorded from between four and six sampling stations within each of six streams known to be polluted. These data were used to test the null hypothesis that there were no differences the diversity of diatoms between different zinc levels (H_0: $\mu_H = \mu_M = \mu_L = \mu_B = \mu; \ \alpha_i = 0$).

The linear effects model would be:

y_{ij}	=	μ	+	α_i	+	ε_{ij}
diatom species diversity	=	overall mean	+	effect of zinc level	+	error

Step 1 - Import (section 2.3) the Medley and Clements (1998) data set

```
> medley <- read.table("medley.csv", header = T, sep = ",")
```

Step 2 - Reorganize the levels of the categorical factor into a more logical order (section 2.6.1)

```
> medley$ZINC <- factor(medley$ZINC, levels = c("HIGH", "MED",
+     "LOW", "BACK"), ordered = F)
```

Step 3 (Key 10.1) - Assess normality/homogeneity of variance using boxplot of species diversity against zinc group

```
> boxplot(DIVERSITY ~ ZINC, medley)
```

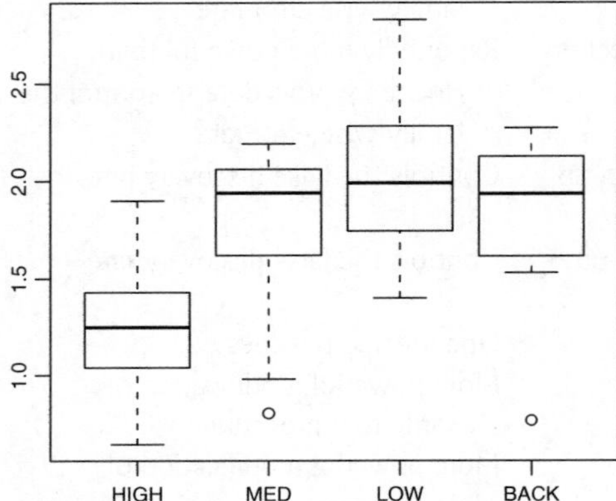

Conclusions - no obvious violations of normality or homogeneity of variance (boxplots not asymmetrical and do not vary greatly in size)

Step 4 (Key 10.1) - Assess homogeneity of variance assumption with a table and/or plot of mean vs variance

```
> plot(tapply(medley$DIVERSITY, medley$ZINC, mean),
+     tapply(medley$DIVERSITY, medley$ZINC, var))
```

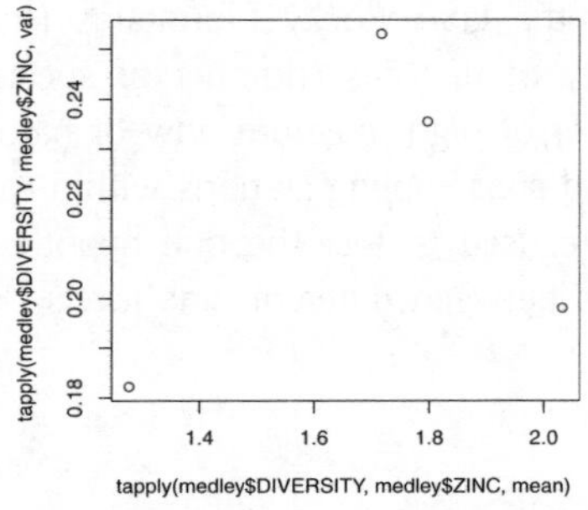

Conclusions - no obvious relationship between group mean and variance

Step 5 (Key 10.3a) - Test H_0 that population group means are all equal - perform analysis of variance (fit the linear model) of species diversity versus zinc-level group and examine the diagnostics (residual plot)

```
> medley.aov <- aov(DIVERSITY ~ ZINC, medley)
> plot(medley.aov)
```

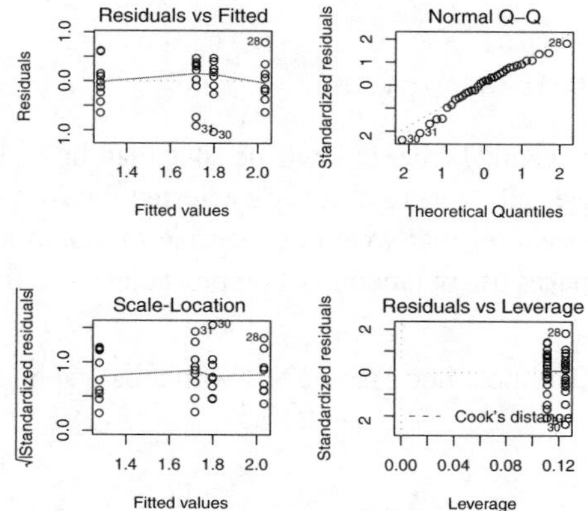

Conclusions - no obvious violations of normality or homogeneity of variance (no obvious wedge shape in residuals, normal Q-Q plot approximately linear). Note that Cook's D values meaningless in ANOVA.

Step 6 (Key 10.3a) - Examine the ANOVA table.

```
> anova(medley.aov)
Analysis of Variance Table

Response: DIVERSITY
          Df Sum Sq Mean Sq F value  Pr(>F)
ZINC       3 2.5666  0.8555  3.9387 0.01756 *
Residuals 30 6.5164  0.2172
---
Signif. codes:  0 '***' 0.001 '**' 0.01 '*' 0.05 '.' 0.1 ' ' 1
```

Conclusions - reject H_0 that population group means are equal, ZINC was found to have a significant impact on the DIVERSITY of diatoms ($F_{3,30} = 3.939, P = 0.018$).

Step 7 (Key 10.9a) - Perform post-hoc Tukey's test to investigate pairwise mean differences between all groups

```
> library(multcomp)
> summary(glht(medley.aov, linfct = mcp(ZINC = "Tukey")))
         Simultaneous Tests for General Linear Hypotheses

Multiple Comparisons of Means: Tukey Contrasts


Fit: aov(formula = DIVERSITY ~ ZINC, data = medley)

Linear Hypotheses:
                 Estimate Std. Error t value Pr(>|t|)
MED - HIGH == 0   0.44000    0.21970   2.003   0.2093
LOW - HIGH == 0   0.75472    0.22647   3.333   0.0114 *
BACK - HIGH == 0  0.51972    0.22647   2.295   0.1219
LOW - MED == 0    0.31472    0.22647   1.390   0.5152
BACK - MED == 0   0.07972    0.22647   0.352   0.9847
BACK - LOW == 0  -0.23500    0.23303  -1.008   0.7457
```

```
---
Signif. codes:  0 '***' 0.001 '**' 0.01 '*' 0.05 '.' 0.1 ' ' 1
(Adjusted p values reported -- single-step method)
```

Conclusions - diatom species diversity is significantly higher in low zinc sites than high zinc sites ($t_{15} = 3.333, P = 0.011$). No other H_0 rejected. Note, the Tukey's adjusted P-values (in the `glht()` *function*) are based on robust procedures that were not available to Quinn and Keough (2002). The more recent Tukey's test makes use of randomization procedures and thus the exact P-values differ from run to run.

Step 8 - Summarize findings of global ANOVA and post-hoc Tukey's test with a bargraph (see also section 5.9.4)

```
> library(biology)
> Mbargraph(medley$DIVERSITY, medley$ZINC, symbols = c("A", "AB",
+     "B", "AB"), ylab = "Mean diatom diversity",
+     xlab = "Zinc concentration")
```

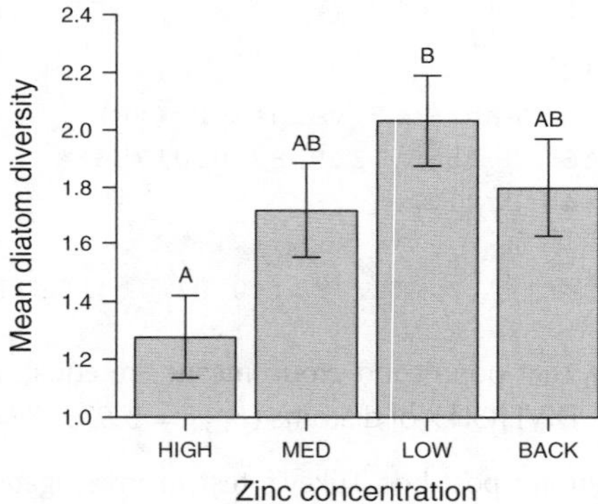

Example 10B: Single factor ANOVA with planned comparisons

Keough and Raimondi (1995) examined the effects of four biofilm types (SL: sterile unfilmed substrate, NL: netted laboratory biofilms, UL: unnetted laboratory biofilms and F: netted field biofilms) on the recruitment of serpulid larvae (from Box8.2 and Box8.4 of Quinn and Keough, 2002). Substrates treated with one of the four biofilm types were left in shallow marine waters for one week after which the number of newly recruited serpulid worms were counted. These data were used to test the null hypothesis that there were no differences in serpulid numbers between the different biofilms (H_0: $\mu_{SL} = \mu_{NL} = \mu_{UL} = \mu_{SL} = \mu_F = \mu; \alpha_i = 0$). The linear effects model would be:

y_{ij}	=	μ	+	α_i	+	ε_{ij}
serpulid number	=	overall mean	+	effect of biofilm type	+	error

Step 1 - Import (section 2.3) the Keough and Raimondi (1995) data set

```
> keough <- read.table("keough.csv", header = T, sep = ",")
```

Step 2 (Keys 10.1 & 10.5) - Check the assumptions and scale data if appropriate

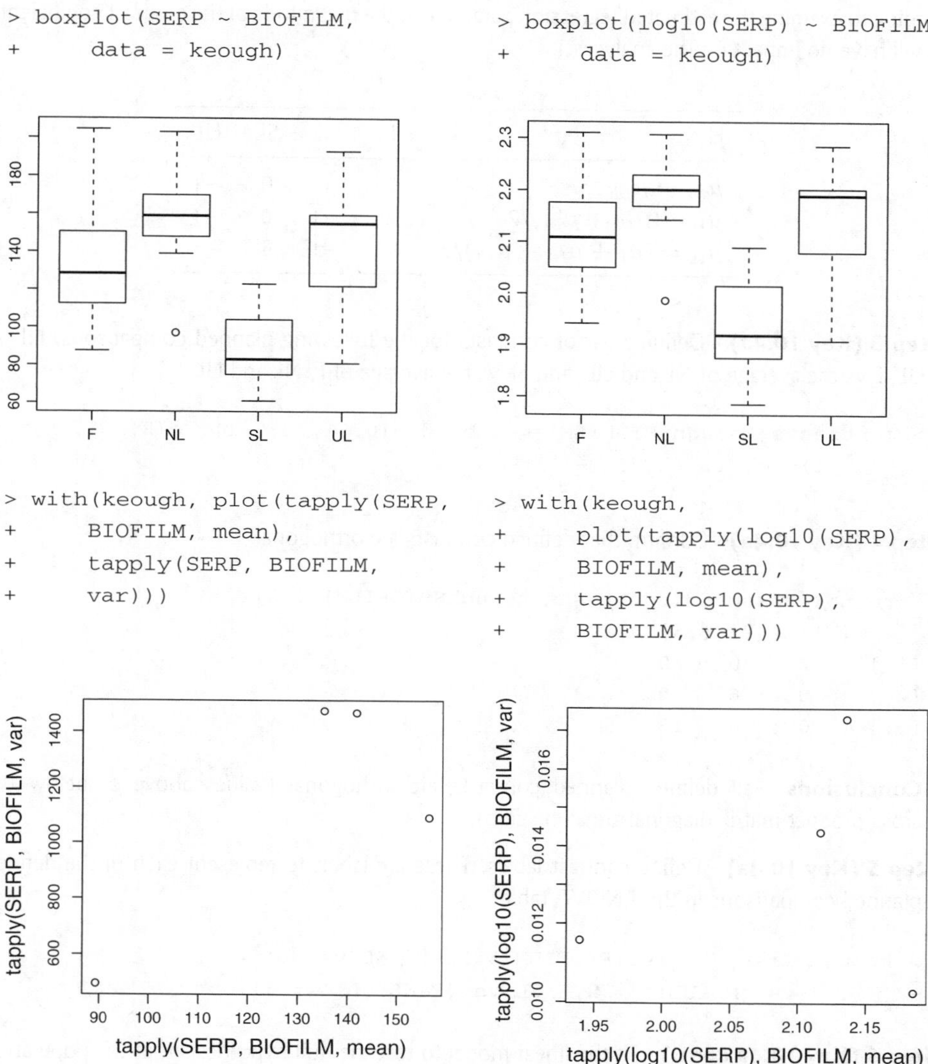

```
> boxplot(SERP ~ BIOFILM,
+     data = keough)
```

```
> boxplot(log10(SERP) ~ BIOFILM,
+     data = keough)
```

```
> with(keough, plot(tapply(SERP,
+     BIOFILM, mean),
+     tapply(SERP, BIOFILM,
+     var)))
```

```
> with(keough,
+     plot(tapply(log10(SERP),
+     BIOFILM, mean),
+     tapply(log10(SERP),
+     BIOFILM, var)))
```


Conclusions - some evidence of a relationship between population mean and population variance from untransformed data, $\log_{10}$ transformed data meets assumptions better, therefore transformation appropriate.

In addition to examining the overall effect of BIOFILM treatments on the number of newly recruited serpulid worms, Keough and Raimondi (1995) were interested in examining a number of other specific null hypotheses. In particular, whether recruitment was effected by the presence of netting in laboratory biofilms (NL vs UL), whether recruitment differed between field and laboratory biofilms (F vs (NL&UL) and finally whether recruitment differed between unfilmed and filmed treatments (SL vs (F&NL&UL)).

There specific null hypotheses and corresponding contrast coefficients are (Note, technically, we should not define contrasts with values greater than 1. However, in this case, as we are not going to examine the estimated regression parameters, the magnitude of the contrast coefficients will have no impact on the analyses.):

H_0:	F	NL	SL	UL
$\mu_{NL} = \mu_{UL}$	0	1	0	−1
$\mu_F = (\mu_{NL} + \mu_{UL})/2$	2	−1	0	−1
$\mu_{SL} = (\mu_F + \mu_{NL} + \mu_{UL})/3$	−1	−1	3	−1

Step 3 (Key 10.4a) - Define a list of contrasts for the following planned comparisons: NL vs UL, F vs the average of NL and UL, and SL vs the average of F, NL and UL.

```
> contrasts(keough$BIOFILM) <- cbind(c(0, 1, 0, -1), c(2, -1, 0,
+     -1), c(-1, -1, 3, -1))
```

Step 4 (Key 10.4a) - Confirm that defined contrasts are orthogonal.

```
> round(crossprod(contrasts(keough$BIOFILM)), 2)
     [,1] [,2] [,3]
[1,]    2    0    0
[2,]    0    6    0
[3,]    0    0   12
```

Conclusions - all defined planned contrasts are orthogonal (values above or below the cross-product matrix diagonal are all be zero).

Step 5 (Key 10.4a) - Define contrast labels. These are labels to represent each of the defined planned comparisons in the ANOVA table

```
> keough.list <- list(BIOFILM = list('NL vs UL' = 1,
+     'F vs (NL&UL)' = 2, 'SL vs (F&NL&UL)' = 3))
```

Step 6 (Key 10.4a cont.) - Fit the linear model to test the null hypothesis that the population group means are all equal as well as the specific null hypotheses that the population means of treatments SL and F are equal, SL and the average of NL and F are equal, and UL and the average of SL, NL and F are equal.

```
> keough.aov <- aov(log10(SERP) ~ BIOFILM, data = keough)
```

Step 7 (Key 10.4a cont.) - Check the diagnostic plots to confirm assumptions are met

```
> plot(keough.aov)
```

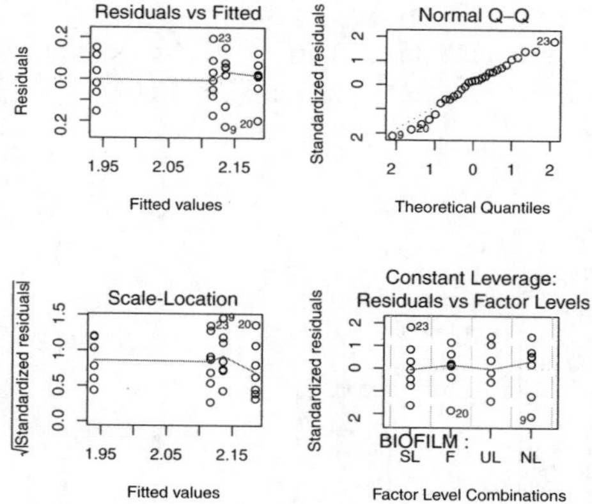

Conclusions - no obvious violations of normality or homogeneity of variance (no obvious wedge shape in residuals, normal Q-Q plot approximately linear). Ignore Cook's D values for ANOVA.

Step 8 (Key 10.4a cont.) - Examine the ANOVA table

```
> summary(keough.aov, split = keough.list)
                               Df  Sum Sq Mean Sq F value     Pr(>F)
BIOFILM                         3 0.24103 0.08034  6.0058 0.0033386 **
  BIOFILM: NL vs UL             1 0.00850 0.00850  0.6352 0.4332635
  BIOFILM: F vs (NL&UL)         1 0.00888 0.00888  0.6635 0.4233267
  BIOFILM: SL vs (F&NL&UL)      1 0.22366 0.22366 16.7188 0.0004208 ***
Residuals                      24 0.32106 0.01338
---
Signif. codes:  0 '***' 0.001 '**' 0.01 '*' 0.05 '.' 0.1 ' ' 1
```

Conclusions - Biofilm treatments were found to have a significant affect on the mean $\log_{10}$ number of serpulid recruits ($F_{3,24} = 6.0058, P = 0.003$). The presence of a net (NL) over the substrate was not found to alter the mean $\log_{10}$ serpulid recruits compared to a surface without (UL) a net ($F_{1,24} = 0.6352, P = 0.4332$). Field biofilms (F) were not found to have different mean $\log_{10}$ serpulid recruits than the laboratory (NL, UL) biofilms ($F_{1,24} = 0.6635, P = 0.4233$). Unfilmed treatments were found to have significantly lower mean $\log_{10}$ serpulid recruits than treatments with biofilms ($F_{1,24} = 16.719, P < 0.001$).

Step 9 - Summarize findings with a bargraph (see section 5.9.4)

```
> means <- with(keough, tapply(SERP, BIOFILM, mean, na.rm = T))
> sds <- with(keough, tapply(SERP, BIOFILM, sd, na.rm = T))
> n <- with(keough, tapply(SERP, BIOFILM, length))
> ses <- sds/sqrt(n)
> ys <- pretty(c(means - ses, means + (2 * ses)))
> xs <- barplot(means, beside = T, axes = F, ann = F,
+      ylim = c(min(ys), max(ys)), xpd = F)
> arrows(xs, means + ses, xs, means - ses, ang = 90, length = 0.1,
+     code = 3)
```

```
> axis(2, las = 1)
> mtext(2, text = "Mean number of serpulids", line = 3, cex = 1.5)
> mtext(1, text = "Biofilm treatment", line = 3, cex = 1.5)
> box(bty = "l")
```

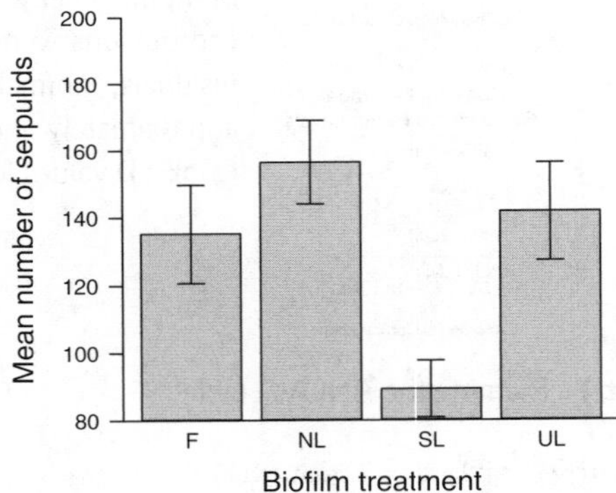

Example 10C: Single factor ANOVA with planned polynomial trends

As an illustration of polynomial trends, Quinn and Keough (2002) suggested a hypothetical situation in which Keough and Raimondi (1995) might have also included an examination of the linear change in settlement across the four treatments (SL, NL, UL & F).

Step 1 - Import the Keough and Raimondi (1995) data set, see Example 10B.

```
> keough <- read.table("keough.csv", header = T, sep = ",")
```

Step 2 (see section 2.6.1) - Reorder the factor levels into a logical order in preparation for the polynomial trends, rather than in alphabetical order.

```
> keough$BIOFILM <- factor(keough$BIOFILM, levels = c("SL", "NL",
+     "UL", "F"))
```

Step 3 (Key 10.4b) - Define the polynomial contrast coefficients. These will be automatically generated and orthogonal.

```
> contrasts(keough$BIOFILM) <- "contr.poly"
```

Step 4 (Key 10.4b) - Define the polynomial contrast labels

```
> keough.list <- list(BIOFILM = list(Linear = 1, Quadratic = 2,
+     Cubic = 3))
```

Step 5 (Key 10.4b) - Fit the ANOVA model and the first, second and third order polynomial trends

```
> keough.aov <- aov(log10(SERP) ~ BIOFILM, data = keough)
```

Step 6 (Key 10.4b) - Examine the ANOVA table including the first three polynomial trends

```
> summary(keough.aov, split = keough.list)
                          Df  Sum Sq Mean Sq F value    Pr(>F)
BIOFILM                    3 0.24103 0.08034  6.0058 0.003339 **
  BIOFILM: Linear          1 0.08155 0.08155  6.0961 0.021054 *
  BIOFILM: Quadratic       1 0.12248 0.12248  9.1555 0.005836 **
  BIOFILM: Cubic           1 0.03700 0.03700  2.7660 0.109294
Residuals                 24 0.32106 0.01338
---
Signif. codes:  0 '***' 0.001 '**' 0.01 '*' 0.05 '.' 0.1 ' ' 1
```

Conclusions - We would reject the null hypothesis of no quadratic trend over and above a linear trend ($F_{1,24} = 9.156, P = 0.006$), suggesting that there is a significant quadratic trend in mean $\log_{10}$ number of serpulid recruits across the ordered BIOFILM treatments (SL, NL, UL, F). Whilst this is a statistically significant outcome, it does not necessarily infer biological significance.

Example 10D: Single random factor ANOVA and variance components

Following on from Example 10A, Medley and Clements (1998) may also have been interested in whether diatom diversity differed across Rocky Mountain streams (Box8.1 from Quinn and Keough, 2002). Hence, streams could be treated as a random factor in testing the null hypothesis that there was no added variance in diatom diversity due to streams.

Step 1 - Import (section 2.3) the Medley and Clements (1998) data set

```
> medley <- read.table("medley.csv", header = T, sep = ",")
```

Step 2 (Key 10.1a & 10.1b) - Assess normality/homogeneity of variance using boxplot of species diversity against stream

```
> boxplot(DIVERSITY ~ STREAM, medley)
```

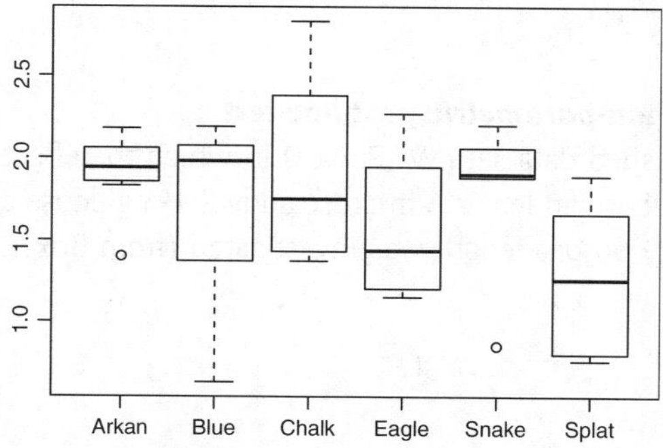

Conclusions - although not ideal, there is no evidence that population diatom diversity is consistently non-normally distributed and drastically unequally varied. Note that small boxplots are accompanied by outliers suggestive of potentially greater variance. Consequently, perform ANOVA and rely on general robustness of the test.

Step 3 (Key 10.3a) - Test H_0 that there is no added variation in diatom diversity due to stream - perform analysis of variance (fit the linear model) of species diversity versus stream and examine the ANOVA table.

```
> medley.aov <- aov(DIVERSITY ~ STREAM, medley)
> anova(medley.aov)
Analysis of Variance Table

Response: DIVERSITY
          Df Sum Sq Mean Sq F value Pr(>F)
STREAM     5 1.8278  0.3656  1.4108 0.2508
Residuals 28 7.2552  0.2591
```

Conclusions - do not reject the null hypothesis that there is no added variance in diatom diversity due to streams.

Step 4 (Key 10.3a) - Calculate ML and REML estimates of variance components (random factor and residuals).

```
> library(nlme)
> print(VarCorr(lme(DIVERSITY ~ 1, random = ~1 | STREAM,
+     method = "ML", data = medley)))
STREAM = pdLogChol(1)
            Variance    StdDev
(Intercept) 0.009927963 0.09963916
Residual    0.257182572 0.50713171
> print(VarCorr(lme(DIVERSITY ~ 1, random = ~1 | STREAM,
+      method = "REML", data = medley)))
STREAM = pdLogChol(1)
            Variance   StdDev
(Intercept) 0.02053683 0.1433068
Residual    0.25755732 0.5075011
```

Conclusions - Most of the variance in diatom diversity is due to differences between sampling stations within the streams (ML: 0.2571, REML: 0.2576), very little variance is added due to differences between streams (ML: 0.0099, REML: 0.0205)

Example 10E: Kruskal-Wallis test with non-parametric post-hoc test

Sokal and Rohlf (1997) present an unpublished data set (W. Purves) in which the effect of different sugar treatments (Control, 2% glucose added, 2% fructose added, 1% glucose and 1% fructose added, and 2% sucrose added) on pea length was investigated (from Box 13.6 of Sokal and Rohlf, 1997).

Step 1 - Import the Purves (unpublished) data set

```
> purves <- read.table("purves.csv", header = T, sep = ",")
```

Step 2 (Keys 10.1a & 10.5) - Check the assumptions of normality and equal variance

```
> boxplot(LENGTH ~ TREAT, data = purves)
```

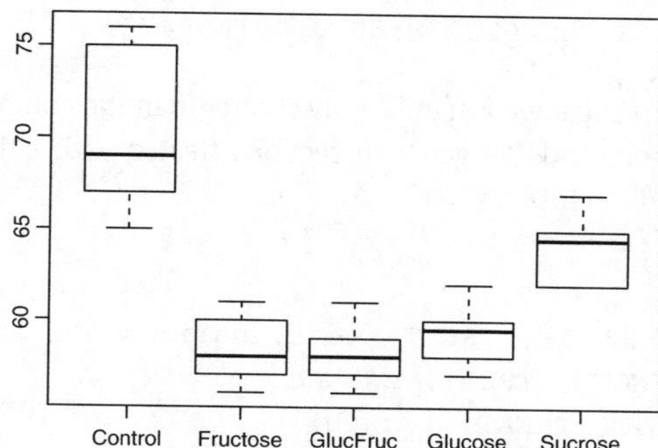

Conclusions - strong evidence of unequal variance. Note that this data set would probably be better suited to a Welch's test, however, for the purpose of providing worked examples that are consistent with popular biometry texts, a Kruskal-Wallis test will be demonstrated.

Step 3 (Key 10.8) - Perform non-parametric Kruskal-Wallis test.

```
> kruskal.test(LENGTH ~ TREAT, data = purves)
        Kruskal-Wallis rank sum test

data:  LENGTH by TREAT
Kruskal-Wallis chi-squared = 38.4368, df = 4, p-value = 9.105e-08
```

Conclusions - reject null hypothesis, sugar treatment has a significant affect on the growth of pea sections.

Step 4 (Key 10.8) - Perform non-parametric post-hoc test.

```
> library(npmc)
> dat <- data.frame(var = purves$LENGTH, class = purves$TREAT)
> summary(npmc(dat), type = "Steel")

$'Data-structure'
         group.index class.level nobs
Control            1     Control   10
Fructose           2    Fructose   10
GlucFruc           3    GlucFruc   10
Glucose            4     Glucose   10
Sucrose            5     Sucrose   10

$'Results of the multiple Steel-Test'
  cmp effect   lower.cl  upper.cl  p.value.1s  p.value.2s
1  1-2  0.000 -0.3599019 0.3599019 1.0000000000 0.001470977
2  1-3  0.000 -0.3596288 0.3596288 1.0000000000 0.001298745
3  1-4  0.000 -0.3600384 0.3600384 1.0000000000 0.001041309
4  1-5  0.050 -0.3081226 0.4081226 1.0000000000 0.005696086
5  2-3  0.495  0.1422692 0.8477308 0.9943192409 1.000000000
```

```
6  2-4  0.670  0.3133899 1.0266101 0.5005921659 0.713955365
7  2-5  1.000  0.6405079 1.3594921 0.0005691443 0.001327216
8  3-4  0.730  0.3746322 1.0853678 0.2525087694 0.407630138
9  3-5  1.000  0.6407814 1.3592186 0.0008494360 0.001372916
10 4-5  0.985  0.6261920 1.3438080 0.0010278350 0.001889472
```

Conclusions - The pea sections treated with sugar were significantly shorter than the controls and sections treated with sucrose were significantly longer than sections treated with either glucose, fructose or a mixture of glucose and fructose.

Step 5 - Summarize findings with a bargraph

```
> means <- with(purves, tapply(LENGTH, TREAT, mean, na.rm = T))
> sds <- with(purves, tapply(LENGTH, TREAT, sd, na.rm = T))
> n <- with(purves, tapply(LENGTH, TREAT, length))
> ses <- sds/sqrt(n)
> ys <- pretty(c(means - ses, means + (2 * ses)))
> xs <- barplot(means, beside = T, axes = F, ann = F,
+      ylim = c(min(ys), max(ys)), xpd = F)
> arrows(xs, means + ses, xs, means - ses, ang = 90, length = 0.05,
+      code = 3)
> axis(2, las = 1)
> mtext(2, text = "Mean pea length", line = 3, cex = 1.5)
> mtext(1, text = "Sugar treatment", line = 3, cex = 1.5)
> text(xs, means + ses, labels = c("A", "B", "B", "B", "C"),
     pos = 3)
> box(bty = "l")
```

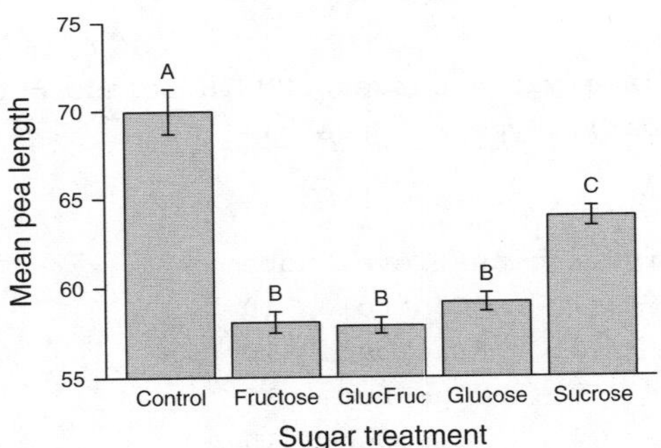

Example 10F: Welch's test

Sánchez-Piñero and Polis (2000) studied the effects of sea birds on tenebrionid beetles on islands in the Gulf of California. These beetles are the dominant consumers on these islands and it was envisaged that sea birds leaving guano and carrion would increase beetle productivity. They had a sample of 25 islands and recorded the beetle density, the type of bird colony (roosting, breeding, no birds), % cover of guano and % plant cover of annuals and perennials.

Step 1 - Import the Sánchez-Piñero and Polis (2000) data set

```
> sanchez <- read.table("sanchez.csv", header = T, sep = ",")
```

Step 2 (Keys 10.1a & 10.5) - Check the assumptions and scale data if necessary

```
> boxplot(GUANO ~ COLTYPE,
+         data = sanchez)
```

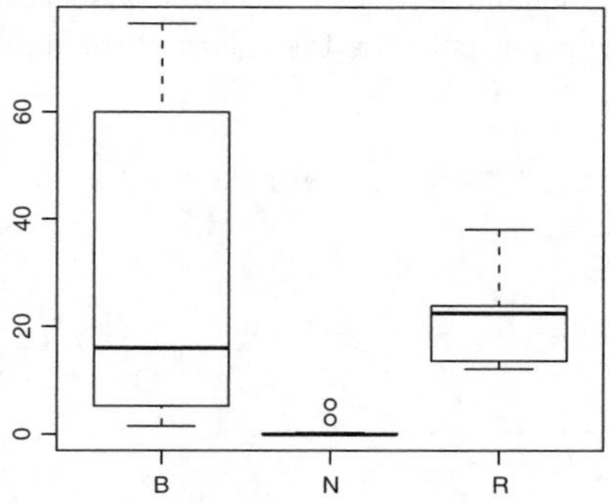

```
> boxplot(sqrt(GUANO) ~ COLTYPE,
+         data = sanchez)
```

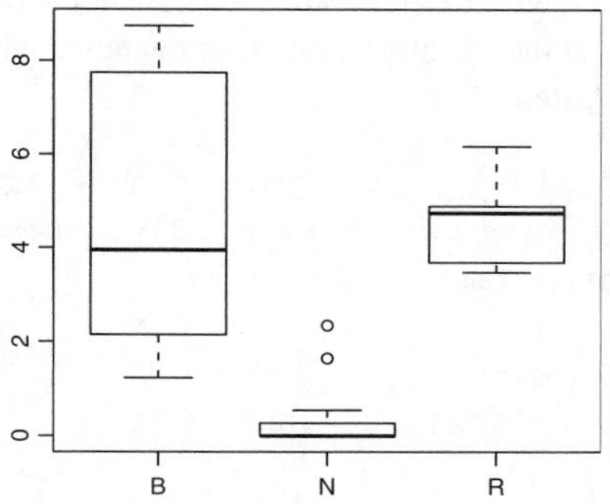

Conclusions - clear evidence that normality and homogeneity of variance assumptions are likely to be violated, square-root transformation improves normality, however, there is still clear evidence that that homogeneity of variance assumption is likely to be violated. Consequently use a Welch's test.

Step 3 (Key 10.6a) - Perform the Welch's test.

```
> oneway.test(sqrt(GUANO) ~ COLTYPE, data = sanchez)
        One-way analysis of means (not assuming equal variances)

data:  sqrt(GUANO) and COLTYPE
F = 42.2862, num df = 2.000, denom df = 10.706, p-value = 8.282e-06
```

Conclusions - Reject the null hypothesis that population means are equal - percentage guano cover differs significantly in different colony types.

Step 4 (Key 10.9c) - Perform post-hoc test.

```
> pairwise.t.test(sqrt(sanchez$GUANO), sanchez$COLTYPE,
+     pool.sd = F, p.adj = "holm")
        Pairwise comparisons using t tests with non-pooled SD

data:  sqrt(sanchez$GUANO) and sanchez$COLTYPE

  B      N
N 0.0091 -
R 0.9390 2.7e-05

P value adjustment method: holm
```

Conclusions - Square root transformed guano cover was significantly higher in breeding colonies than roosting colonies and significantly lower in roosting colonies than the no bird colony.

Alternatively, the Dunn-Sidak procedure of p-value adjustments could be performed. First re-perform each of the pairwise comparisons but without any p-value corrections and keep a copy of the p-values. Examine these unadjusted p-values to determine which p-value is associated with which comparison. Then use the `mt.rawp2adjp` function of the `multtest` package to perform Dunn-Sidak step-down p-value corrections. Note that adjusted p-values are ordered from lowest to largest and labels are not supplied, so to determine which p-values are associated with which comparison, cross reference with the raw p-values or use the values of the index attribute.

```
> pvalues <- pairwise.t.test(sqrt(sanchez$GUANO), sanchez$COLTYPE,
+     pool.sd = F, p.adj = "none")$p.value
> pvalues
           B            N
N 0.00455275           NA
R 0.93900231 8.846058e-06

> library(multtest)
> mt.rawp2adjp(pvalues, proc = "SidakSD")
$adjp
             rawp     SidakSD
[1,] 8.846058e-06 3.538376e-05
[2,] 4.552750e-03 1.359616e-02
[3,] 9.390023e-01 9.962793e-01
[4,]           NA          NA

$index
[1] 4 1 2 3

$h0.ABH
NULL

$h0.TSBH
NULL
```

Conclusions - the square root transformed guano cover of sites without birds was found to be significantly lower than the cover in both breeding ($p < 0.001$) and roosting ($p = 0.0136$) colonies, however the square root transformed guano cover was not found to differ significantly between breeding and roosting colonies ($p = 0.996$).

Step 5 - Summarize findings with a bargraph

```
> library(biology)
> Mbargraph(sanchez$GUANO, sanchez$COLTYPE, symbols = c("A", "B",
+     "A"), ylab = "Mean percentage Guano cover",
+     xlab = "Bird colony type")
```

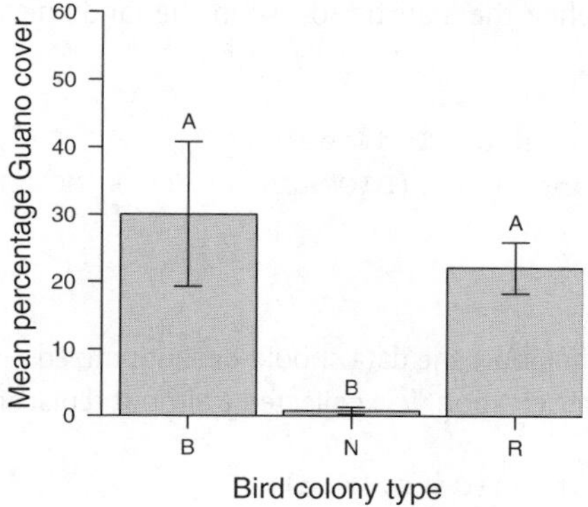

Example 10G: Randomization test

As part of a study into the diets of of eastern horned lizard (*Phrynosoma douglassi brevirostre*), Powell and Russell (1984, 1985) investigated whether the consumption of ants changed over time from June to September (Example 5.1 from Manly, 1991). They measured the dry biomass of ants collected from the stomachs of 24 adult male and yearling females in June, July, August and September of 1980.

Step 1 - Import the Powell and Russell (1984, 1985) data set

```
> ants <- read.table("ants.csv", header = T, sep = ",")
```

Step 2 (Key 10.1a) - Assess normality/homogeneity of variance using boxplot of ant biomass against month. Cube root transformation also assessed.

```
> boxplot(BIOMASS ~ MONTH, ants)
```

```
> boxplot(BIOMASS^(1/3) ~ MONTH,
  ants)
```

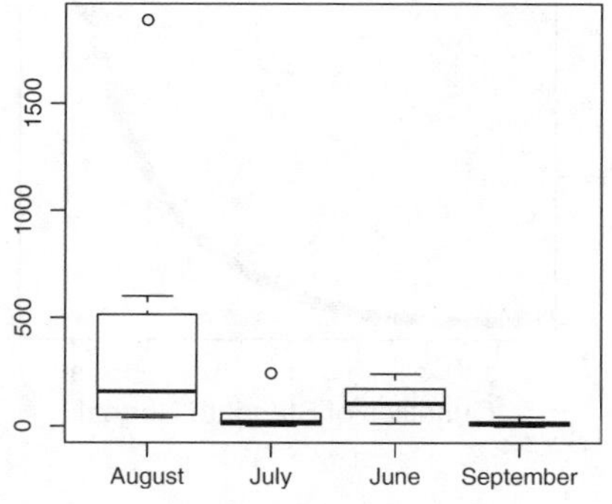

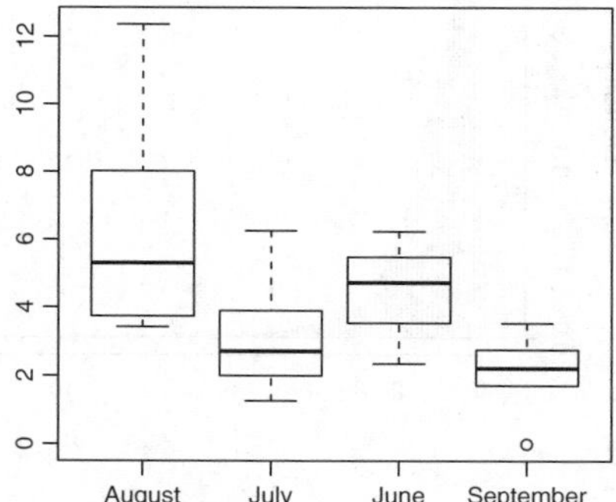

Conclusions - strong evidence of non-normality and unequal variance in raw data. Cube root transformation greatly improved homogeneity of variance, however there is evidence that the populations are not of the same distribution (August appears to be skewed). As a result a randomization test in which the the *F*-distribution is generated from the samples, might be more robust than an ANOVA that assumes each of the populations are normally distributed.

Step 3 (Key 10.8b) - define the statistic to use in the randomization test – in this case the *F*-ratio

```
> stat <- function(data, indices) {
+       f.ratio <- anova(aov(BIOMASS^(1/3) ~ MONTH, data))$"F
+       value"[1] f.ratio
+ }
```

Step 4 (Key 10.8b) - define how the data should be randomized – randomly reorder the month in which each biomass observation was collected (without replacement)

```
> rand.gen <- function(data, mle) {
+       out <- data
+       out$MONTH <- sample(out$MONTH, replace = F)
+       out
+ }
```

Step 5 (Key 10.8b) - call a bootstrapping procedure to randomize 5000 times (this can take some time).

```
> ants.boot <- boot(ants, stat, R = 5000, sim = "parametric",
      ran.gen = rand.gen)
```

Step 6 (Key 10.8b) - examine the distribution of *F*-ratios generated from the randomization procedure

```
> plot(ants.boot)
```

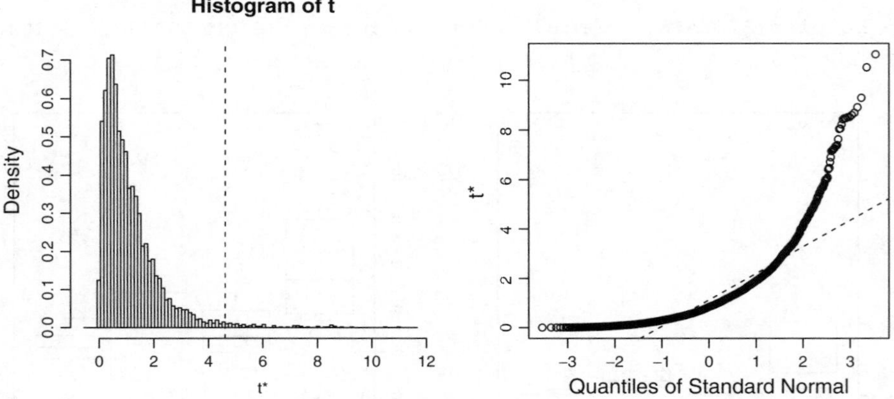

Step 7 (Key 10.8b) - examine the bootstrap statistics

```
> print(ants.boot)
PARAMETRIC BOOTSTRAP
```

```
Call:
boot(data = ants, statistic = stat, R = 5000, sim = "parametric",
    ran.gen = rand.gen)


Bootstrap Statistics :
    original     bias    std. error
t1* 4.618806 -3.491630    1.074420
```

Conclusions - The observed *F*-ratio was 4.619

Step 8 (Key 10.8b) - calculate the number of possible *F*-ratios (including the observed *F*-ratio, which is one possible situation) that were greater or equal to the observed *F*-ratio and express this as a percentage of the number of randomizations (plus one for the observed situation) performed.

```
> f <- length(ants.boot[ants.boot$t >= ants.boot$t0]) + 1
> print(f/(ants.boot$R + 1))
[1] 0.0159968
```

Conclusions - Reject the null hypothesis that the population cubed root ant biomass consumption was equal in each of the four months because the p-value was less than 0.05. The consumption of ants by eastern horned lizard different between the four months.

Step 9 - Perform post-hoc multiple comparisons via randomization and use the Holm correction procedure on the pairwise p-values. For each pairwise comparison, specify which levels of the categorical variable to include in the randomization (`boot`) function and calculate a p-value.

```
> ants.rand1 <- boot(ants[ants$MONTH == "September" | ants$MONTH ==
+     "August", ], stat, R = 1000, sim = "parametric", ran.gen =
+     rand.gen)
> ants.rand2 <- boot(ants[ants$MONTH == "September" | ants$MONTH ==
+     "July", ], stat, R = 1000, sim = "parametric", ran.gen =
+     rand.gen)

> p.S.A <- print(length(ants.rand1[ants.rand1$t >= ants.rand1$t0])/
+     (ants.rand1$R + 1))
[1] 0.000999001
> p.S.Jy <- print(length(ants.rand2[ants.rand2$t >= ants.rand2$t0])/
+     (ants.rand2$R + 1))
[1] 0.2677323
```

Step 10 - Compile a list of all the pairwise p-values and perform Holm correction.

```
> p.values <- c('Sep vs Aug' = p.S.A, 'Sep vs Jul' = p.S.Jy,
+     'Sep vs Jun' = p.S.Jn, 'Aug vs Jul' = p.A.Jy,
+     'Aug vs Jun' = p.A.Jn, 'Jul vs Jun' = p.Jy.Jn)
```

```
> p.adjust(p.values, "holm")
 Sep vs Aug  Sep vs Jul  Sep vs Jun  Aug vs Jul  Aug vs Jun
     Jul vs Jun
0.005994006 0.803196803 0.264735265 0.264735265 0.803196803
     0.803196803
```

Conclusions - The cubed root ant biomass consumption by eastern horned lizards was found to be significantly different between September and August (p=0.006), but was not found to be significantly different between any other month pairs.

Step 11 - Summarize findings with a bargraph

```
> Mbargraph(ants$BIOMASS, ants$MONTH, symbols = c("A", "AB", "AB",
+     "B"), ylab = "Mean ant biomass", xlab = "Month")
```

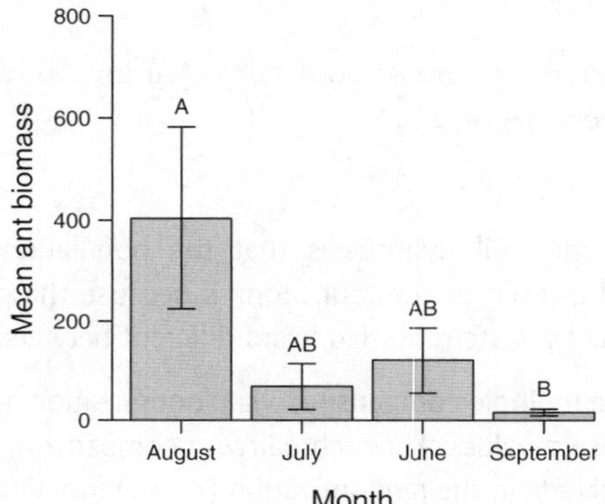

11

Nested ANOVA

When single sampling units are selected amongst highly heterogeneous conditions (as represented in Figure 11.1a), it is unlikely that these single units will adequately represent the populations and repeated sampling is likely to yield very different outcomes. As a result, the amount of variation within the main treatment effect (unexplained variability) remains high, thereby potentially masking any detectable effects due to the measured treatments. Although this problem can be addressed by increased replication, this is not always practical or possible. For example, if we were investigating the impacts of fuel reduction burning across a highly heterogeneous landscape, our ability to replicate adequately might be limited by the number of burn sites available.

Alternatively, sub-replicates within each of the sampling units (e.g. sites) can be collected (and averaged) so as to provided better representatives for each of the units (see Figure 11.1b) and ultimately reduce the unexplained variability of the test of treatments. In essence, the sub-replicates are the replicates of an additional *nested* factor whose levels are nested within the main treatment factor. A nested factor refers to a factor whose levels are unique within each level of the factor it is nested within and each level is only represented once. For example, the fuel reduction burn study design could consist of three burnt sites and three un-burnt (control) sites each containing four quadrats (replicates of site and sub-replicates of the burn treatment). Each site represents a unique level of a random factor (any given site cannot be both burnt and un-burnt) that is nested within the fire treatment (burned or not).

A nested design can be thought of as a hierarchical arrangement of factors (hence the alternative name *hierarchical* designs) whereby a treatment is progressively sub-replicated. As an additional example, imagine an experiment designed to comparing the leaf toughness of a number of tree species. Working down the hierarchy, five individual trees were randomly selected within (nested within) each species, three branches were randomly selected within each tree, two leaves were randomly selected within each branch and the force required to shear the leaf material in half (transversely) was measured in four random locations along the leaf. Clearly any given leaf can only be from a single branch, tree and species. Each level of sub-replication is introduced to further reduce the amount of unexplained variation and thereby increasing the power of the test for the main treatment effect (the effect of species). Additionally, it is possible to investigate which scale of replication has the greatest (or least, etc) degree of variability - the level of the species, individual tree, branch, leaf, leaf region etc.

Biostatistical Design and Analysis Using R: a Practical Guide, 1st edition. By M. Logan.
Published 2010 by Blackwell Publishing.

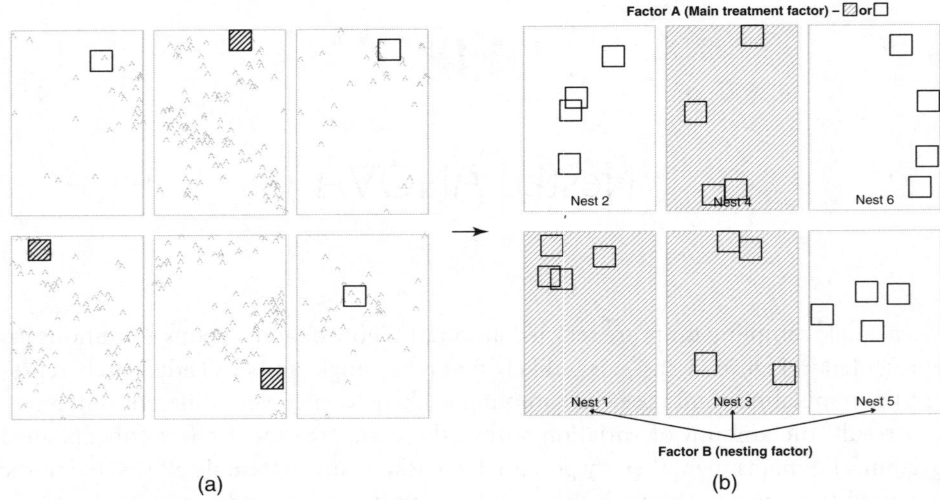

Fig 11.1 Fictitious spatial depictions contrasting (a) single factor and (b) nested ANOVA designs each with three replicate sampling units for each of two treatment levels ($n = 3$ for each treatment level). When single sampling units are selected amongst highly heterogeneous conditions (as represented in (a)), it is unlikely that these single units will adequately represent the populations and repeated sampling is likely to yield very different outcomes. For such situations, this heterogeneity increases the unexplained variation thereby potentially masking any detectable effects due to the measured treatments. Sub-replicates within each of the sampling units can be collected so as to provided a better representative for each unit.

Nested factors are typically random factors (see section 10.0.1), of which the levels are randomly selected to represent all possible levels (e.g. sites). When the main treatment effect (called Factor A) is a fixed factor, such designs are referred to as a *mixed model nested anova*, whereas when Factor A is random, the design is referred to as a *Model II nested anova*. Fixed nested factors are also possible. For example, specific dates (corresponding to particular times during a season) could be nested within season. When all factors are fixed, the design is referred to as a *Model I mixed model*.

Fully nested designs (the topic of this chapter) differ from other multi-factor designs in that all factors within (below) the main treatment factor are nested and thus interactions are un-replicated and cannot be tested[a]. Partly nested designs in which some of the factors within the main treatment effect are not nested (that is, their levels are repeated within each of the levels of the factor(s) above) are dealt with in chapter 14.

11.1 Linear models

The linear models for two and three factor nested design are:

$$\begin{aligned} y_{ijk} &= \mu + \alpha_i + \beta_{j(i)} + \varepsilon_{ijk} \\ y_{ijkl} &= \mu + \alpha_i + \beta_{j(i)} + \gamma_{k(j(i))} + \varepsilon_{ijkl} \end{aligned}$$

[a] Interaction effects are assumed to be zero.

where μ is the overall mean, α is the effect of Factor A, β is the effect of Factor B, γ is the effect of Factor C and ε is the random unexplained or residual component.

11.2 Null hypotheses

Separate null hypotheses are associated with each of the factors, however, nested factors are typically only added to absorb some of the unexplained variability and thus, specific hypotheses tests associated with nested factors are of lesser biological importance.

11.2.1 *Factor A* - the main treatment effect

Fixed

$$H_0(A): \mu_1 = \mu_2 = \ldots = \mu_i = \mu \qquad \text{(the population group means are all equal)}$$

The mean of population 1 is equal to that of population 2 and so on, and thus all population means are equal to an overall mean. If the effect of the ith group is the difference between the ith group mean and the overall mean ($\alpha_i = \mu_i - \mu$) then the H_0 can alternatively be written as:

$$H_0(A): \alpha_1 = \alpha_2 = \ldots = \alpha_i = 0 \qquad \text{(the effect of each group equals zero)}$$

If one or more of the α_i are different from zero (the response mean for this treatment differs from the overall response mean), the null hypothesis is not true indicating that the treatment does affect the response variable.

Random

$$H_0(A): \sigma_\alpha^2 = 0 \qquad \text{(population variance equals zero)}$$

There is no added variance due to all possible levels of A.

11.2.2 *Factor B* - the nested factor

Random (typical case)

$$H_0(B): \sigma_\beta^2 = 0 \qquad \text{(population variance equals zero)}$$

There is no added variance due to all possible levels of B within the (set or all possible) levels of A.

Fixed

$$H_0(B): \mu_{1(1)} = \mu_{2(1)} = \ldots = \mu_{j(i)} = \mu \qquad \text{(the population group means of B (within A) are all equal)}$$

$$H_0(B): \beta_{1(1)} = \beta_{2(1)} = \ldots = \beta_{j(i)} = 0 \qquad \text{(the effect of each chosen B group equals zero)}$$

Table 11.1 *F*-ratios, estimated variance components (for balanced ANOVA only) and corresponding R syntax for two factor nested designs.

			A fixed/random, B random		**A fixed/random, B fixed**	
Factor	**d.f.**	**MS**	***F*-ratio**	**Var. comp.**	***F*-ratio**	**Var. comp.**
A	$a-1$	MS_A	$\frac{MS_A}{MS_{B'(A)}}$	$\frac{MS_A - MS_{B'(A)}}{nb}$	$\frac{MS_A}{MS_{Resid}}$	$\frac{MS_A - MS_{Resid}}{nb}$
B′(A)	$(b-1)a$	$MS_{B'(A)}$	$\frac{MS_{B'(A)}}{MS_{Resid}}$	$\frac{MS_{B'(A)} - MS_{Resid}}{n}$	$\frac{MS_{B'(A)}}{MS_{Resid}}$	$\frac{MS_{B'(A)} - MS_{Resid}}{n}$
Residual (=N′(B′(A)))	$(n-1)ba$	MS_{Resid}				

A fixed/random, B random

```
> summary(aov(DV~A+Error(B), data))
> VarCorr(lme(DV~A,random=~|B,data))
```

Unbalanced
```
> anova(lme(DV~A,random=~|B,data))
```

A fixed/random, B fixed

```
> summary(aov(DV~A+B, data)))
```

Unbalanced
```
> Anova(aov(DV~A/B,data),type="III")
```
[a]

[a] To use Type III sums of squares, Factor B contrasts must first be defined as something other than 'treatment' (such as 'sum' or 'helmert') prior to fitting the model (`> contrasts(data$B)<-contr.helmert`).

The null hypotheses associated with additional factors, are treated similarly to Factor B above.

11.3 Analysis of variance

Analysis of variance sequentially partitions the total variability in the response variable into components explained by each of the factors[b] (starting with the factors lowest down in the hierarchy - the most deeply nested) and the components unexplained by each factor. When the null hypothesis for a factor is true (no effect or added variability), the ratio of explained and unexplained components for that factor (*F*-ratio) should follow a theoretical *F*-distribution with an expected value less than 1.

The appropriate unexplained residuals and therefore the appropriate *F*-ratios for each factor differ according to the different null hypotheses associated with different combinations of fixed and random factors in a nested linear model (see Tables 11.1 & 11.2).

11.4 Variance components

As previously alluded to, it can often be useful to determine the relative contribution (to explaining the unexplained variability) of each of the factors as this provides insights

[b] Explained variability is calculated by subtracting the amount unexplained by the factor from the amount unexplained by a reduced model that does not contain the factor.

Table 11.2 *F*-ratios, estimated variance components (for balanced ANOVA only) and corresponding R syntax for three factor nested designs.

		A fixed/random, B random		A fixed/random, B fixed	
Factor	**d.f.**	***F*-ratio**	**Var. comp.**	***F*-ratio**	**Var. comp.**
C′ random					
A	$a-1$	$\frac{MS_A}{MS_{B'(A)}}$	$\frac{MS_A - MS_{B'(A)}}{ncb}$	$\left[\frac{MS_A}{MS_{C'(B'(A))}}\right]$	$\frac{MS_A - MS_{C'(B'(A))}}{ncb}$
B′(A)	$(b-1)a$	$\frac{MS_{B'(A)}}{MS_{C'(B'(A))}}$	$\frac{MS_{B'(A)} - MS_{C'(B'(A))}}{nc}$	$\left[\frac{MS_{B'(A)}}{MS_{C'(B'(A))}}\right]$	$\frac{MS_{B'(A)} - MS_{C'(B'(A))}}{nc}$
C′(B′(A))	$(c-1)ba$	$\frac{MS_{C'(B'(A))}}{MS_{Resid}}$	$\frac{MS_{C'(B'(A))} - MS_{Resid}}{n}$	$\frac{MS_{C'(B'(A))}}{MS_{Resid}}$	$\frac{MS_{C'(B'(A))} - MS_{Resid}}{n}$
Residual (=N′(C′(B′(A))))	$(n-1)cba$		MS_{Resid}		MS_{Resid}

A fixed/random, B random, C random

```
> summary(aov(DV~A+Error(B/C), data))
> VarCorr(lme(DV~A,random=~1|B/C, data))
```

Unbalanced

```
> anova(lme(DV~A,random=~1|B/C, data))
```

A fixed/random, B fixed, C random

```
> summary(aov(DV~A+B+Error(C), data))
> VarCorr(lme(DV~A+B,random=~1|C, data))
```

Unbalanced

```
> anova(lme(DV~A+B,random=~1|C,data))
```

(*continued overleaf*)

Table 11.2 *(continued)*

Factor	d.f.	A fixed/random, B random		A fixed/random, B fixed	
		F-ratio	Var. comp.	*F*-ratio	Var. comp.
C fixed					
A	$a-1$	$\frac{MS_A}{MS_{B(A)}}$	$\frac{MS_A - MS_{B(A)}}{ncb}$	$\frac{MS_A}{MS_{Resid}}$	$\frac{MS_A - MS_{Resid}}{ncb}$
B′(A)	$(b-1)a$	$\frac{MS_{B'(A)}}{MS_{Resid}}$	$\frac{MS_{B'(A)} - MS_{Resid}}{nc}$	$\frac{MS_{B'(A)}}{MS_{Resid}}$	$\frac{MS_{B'(A)} - MS_{Resid}}{nc}$
C(B′(A))	$(c-1)ba$	$\frac{MS_{C(B'(A))}}{MS_{Resid}}$	$\frac{MS_{C(B'(A))} - MS_{Resid}}{n}$	$\frac{MS_{C(B'(A))}}{MS_{Resid}}$	$\frac{MS_{C(B'(A))} - MS_{Resid}}{n}$
Residual (=N′(C(B′(A))))	$(n-1)cba$		MS_{Resid}		MS_{Resid}
		A fixed/random, B random, C fixed			
		`> summary(aov(DV~A+Error(B), data))`			
		`> VarCorr(lme(DV~A,random=~1|B)`			
	Unbalanced	`> anova(lme(DV~A,random=~1|B), data`			
		A fixed/random, B fixed, C fixed			
		`> summary(aov(DV~A+B, data)))`			
	Unbalanced[a]	`> Anova(aov(DV~A/B,data),type="III")`			

[a]To use Type III sums of squares, Factor B contrasts must first be defined as something other than 'treatment' (such as 'sum' or 'helmert') prior to fitting the model (`> contrasts(data$B)<-contr.helmert`).

into the variability at each different scale. These contributions are known as *variance components* and are estimates of the added variances due to each of the factors. For consistency with other texts, I have included estimated variance components for various balanced nested ANOVA designs in Tables 11.1 & 11.2. However, variance components based on a modified version of the maximum likelihood iterative model fitting (see chapter 3.7.2) procedure (REML) is generally recommended as this accommodates both balanced and unbalanced designs.

While there are no numerical differences in the calculations of variance components for fixed and random factors, fixed factors are interpreted very differently and arguably have little biological meaning (other to infer relative contribution). For fixed factors, variance components estimate the variance between the means of the specific populations that are represented by the selected levels of the factor and therefore represent somewhat arbitrary and artificial populations. For random factors, variance components estimate the variance between means of all possible populations that could have been selected and thus represents the true population variance.

11.5 Assumptions

An F-distribution represents the relative frequencies of all the possible F-ratio's when a given null hypothesis is true and certain assumptions about the residuals (denominator in the F-ratio calculation) hold. Consequently, it is also important that diagnostics associated with a particular hypothesis test reflect the denominator for the appropriate F-ratio. For example, when testing the null hypothesis that there is no effect of Factor A ($H_0(A) : \alpha_i = 0$) in a mixed nested anova, the means of each level of Factor B are used as the replicates of Factor A. As with single factor anova, hypothesis testing for nested ANOVA assumes the residuals are (for greater explanation of each see chapter 10.4):

(i) normally distributed. Factors higher up in the hierarchy of a nested model are based on means (or means of means) of lower factors and thus the Central Limit Theory would predict that normality will usually be satisfied for the higher level factors. Nevertheless, boxplots using the appropriate scale of replication should be used to explore normality. Scale transformations are often useful.

(ii) equally varied. Boxplots and plots of means against variance (using the appropriate scale of replication) should be used to explore the spread of values. Residual plots should reveal no patterns (see Figure 8.5). Scale transformations are often useful.

(iii) independent of one another - this requires special consideration so as to ensure that the scale at which sub-replicates are measured is still great enough to enable observations to be independent.

11.6 Pooling denominator terms

Designs that incorporate fixed and random factors (either nested or factorial), involve F-ratio calculations in which the denominators that are themselves random factors other than the overall residuals. Many statisticians argue that when such denominators are themselves not statistically significant (at the 0.25 level), there are substantial power benefits from pooling together successive non-significant denominator terms. Thus an F-ratio for a particular factor might be recalculated after pooling together its original denominator with its denominators denominator and so on. The conservative 0.25 is used instead of the usual 0.05 to reduce further the likelihood of Type II errors (falsely concluding an effect is non-significant - that might result from insufficient power).

11.7 Unbalanced nested designs

Unbalanced designs are those designs in which sample (subsample) sizes for each level of one or more factors differ. These situations are relatively common in biological research, however such imbalance has some important implications for nested designs. Firstly, hypothesis tests are more robust to the assumptions of normality and equal variance when the design is balanced. Secondly (and arguably, more importantly), the model contrasts are not orthogonal (independent) and the sums of squares component attributed to each of the model terms cannot be calculated by simple additive partitioning of the total sums of squares (see section 12.6). In such situations, exact F-ratios cannot be constructed (at least in theory[c]), variance components calculations are more complicated and significance tests cannot be computed.

The severity of this issue depends on which scale of the sub-sampling hierarchy the unbalance(s) occurs as well whether the unbalance occurs in the replication of a fixed or random factor. For example, whilst unequal levels of the first nesting factor (e.g. unequal number of burn vs un-burnt sites) has no effect on F-ratio construction or hypothesis testing for the top level factor (irrespective of whether either of the factors are fixed or random), unequal sub-sampling (replication) at the level of a random (but not fixed) nesting factor will impact on the ability to construct F-ratios and variance components of all terms above it in the hierarchy.

There are a number of alternative ways of dealing with unbalanced nested designs[d]:

(i) split the analysis up into separate smaller simple ANOVA's each using the means of the nesting factor to reflect the appropriate scale of replication. As the resulting sums of squares components are thereby based on an aggregated dataset the analyses then inherit the procedures and requirements of single (chapter 10) or fully factorial (chapter 12) ANOVA.

(ii) adopt mixed-modelling techniques (see section 11.8)

11.8 Linear mixed effects models

Although the term 'mixed-effects' can be used to refer to any design that incorporates both *fixed* and *random* predictors, its use is more commonly restricted to designs in

[c] The denominator MS in an F-ratio is determined by examining the expected value of the mean squares of each term in a model. Unequal sample sizes result in expected means squares for which there are no obvious logical comparators that enable the impact of an individual model term to be isolated.

[d] All assume that the imbalance is not a direct result of the treatments themselves. Such outcomes are more appropriately analysed by modelling the counts of surviving observations via frequency analysis (see chapters 16&17).

which factors are nested or grouped within other factors. Typically examples include nested, longitudinal[e] data, repeated measures and blocking designs (see chapters 13 & 14). Furthermore, rather than basing parameter estimations on observed and expected mean squares or error strata (as outlined above), mixed-effects models estimate parameters via maximum likelihood (ML) or residual (or restricted) maximum likelihood (REML). In so doing, mixed-effects models more appropriately handle estimation of parameters, effects and variance components of unbalanced designs (particularly for random effects). Resulting fitted (or expected) values of each level of a factor (for example, the expected population site means) are referred to as Best Linear Unbiased Predictors (BLUP's). As an acknowledgement that most estimated site means will be more extreme than the underlying true population means they estimate[f], BLUP's are less spread from the overall mean than are simple site means. In addition, mixed-effects models naturally model the 'within-block' correlation structure that complicates many longitudinal designs (see section 13.4.1). Whilst the basic concepts of mixed-effects models have been around for a long time, recent computing advances and adoptions have greatly boosted the popularity of these procedures.

Linear mixed effects models are currently at the forefront of statistical development, and as such, are very much a work in progress - both in theory and in practice. Recent developments have seen a further shift away from the traditional practices associated with degrees of freedom, probability distribution and p-value calculations.

The traditional approach to inference testing is to compare the fit of an alternative (full) model to a null (reduced) model (via an F-ratio). When assumptions of normality and homogeneity of variance apply, the degrees of freedom are easily computed and the F-ratio has an exact F-distribution to which it can be compared. However, this approach introduces two additional problematic assumptions when estimating fixed effects in a mixed effects model.

Firstly, when estimating the effects of one factor, the parameter estimates associated with other factor(s) are assumed to be the true values of those parameters (not estimates). Whilst this assumption is reasonable when all factors are fixed, as random factors are selected such that they represent one possible set of levels drawn from an entire population of possible levels for the random factor, it is unlikely that the associated parameter estimates accurately reflect the true values. Consequently, there is not necessarily an appropriate F-distribution.

Furthermore, determining the appropriate degrees of freedom (nominally, the number of independent observations on which estimates are based) for models that incorporate a hierarchical structure is only possible under very specific circumstances (such as completely balanced designs). Degrees of freedom is a somewhat arbitrary defined concept used primarily to select a theoretical probability distribution on which a statistic can be compared. Arguably, however, it is a concept that is overly simplistic for complex hierarchical designs.

Most statistical applications continue to provide the 'approximate' solutions (as did earlier versions within R). However, R linear mixed effects development leaders argue

[e] measurements repeated over time.

[f] This is based on the principle that smaller sample sizes result in greater chances of more extreme observations and that nested sub-replicates are also likely to be highly intercorrelated).

strenuously that given the above shortcomings, such approximations are variably inappropriate and are thus omitted.

Markov chain Monte Carlo (MCMC) sampling methods provide a Bayesian-like alternative for inference testing. Markov chains use the mixed model parameter estimates to generate posterior probability distributions of each parameter from which Monte Carlo sampling methods draw a large set of parameter samples. These parameter samples can then be used to calculate highest posterior density (HPD) intervals[g]. Such intervals indicate the interval in which there is a specified probability (typically 95%) that the true population parameter lies. Furthermore, whilst technically against the spirit of the Bayesian philosophy, it is also possible to generate P values on which to base inferences.

11.9 Robust alternatives

There are no formal robust or non-parametric tests specifically formulated for nested analyses. However, since nested designs simply represent a hierarchical set of ANOVA's, it is possible to employ the techniques outlined in chapter 10.5 in a series of simple ANOVA's each using aggregated portions of the full data set (reflecting the appropriate scale of replication of each individual hypothesis test). Likewise, randomization tests (which are useful for situations in which observation independence could be questionable) can be performed by comparing the F-ratios to a large number of sets of F-ratios calculated from repeatedly shuffled data[h].

Note that nested designs are often incompatible with randomization procedures due to the low number of possible randomization combinations possible. For example, if the design consists of three locations nested within two treatments (e.g. burnt and unburnt), there are only $(kn)!/[(n!)^k k!] = 10$ (where n is the number of replicates within each of the k treatments) unique ways in which the sites can be randomized within the treatments, and thus the smallest possible p-value is 0.1 (1/10).

11.10 Power and optimisation of resource allocation

Since nested designs represent a hierarchical set of ANOVA's, it is possible to employ the power analysis techniques outlined in section 10.7 in a series of analyses using aggregated portions of the full data set (reflecting the appropriate scale of replication of each individual hypothesis test).

At the start of this chapter, an example of a leaf toughness investigation was introduced so as to demonstrate the nature of a nested design. In this example, the choice of sample size within each scale of sub-replication (individual tree, branch, leaf) was completely arbitrary, yet such choices are actually of great importance. Since the individual trees are the direct replicates of the species treatment, the power of the test

[g] HPD intervals are also known as Bayesian credible intervals.

[h] Various ways of shuffling the data have been suggested. These include:
(i) Complete shuffling of the data set
(ii) When testing a given factor, constrain (restrict) the shuffling to the scale of the replicates for that factor.

of species is directly affected by the number of replicate trees per species. However, the power of this test will also indirectly benefit from greater replication at the scale with the greatest degree of variability as this will further reduce the unexplained variability.

The optimal degree of replication at each levels of a nested design can be assessed by examining the ratio of the variance components of each of the nested effects with their respective residual variance components. Furthermore, such calculations can incorporate the costs (time and/or money) associated with each level of replication so as to estimate the optimal allocation of resources. For example, in a three factor mixed nested design (fixed A, random B and C), the optimum number of replicates within each level of the random nested factors B and C would be defined by:

$$r = \sqrt{\frac{C_{B(A)}s^2_{C(B(A))}}{C_{C(B(A))}s^2_{B(A)}}} \qquad n = \sqrt{\frac{C_{C(B(A))}s^2}{C_{Reps}s^2_{C(B(A))}}}$$

where C and s^2 are respectively the cost and estimated variances associated with the subscripted effects levels and r and n denote the number of replicates for B (levels of C) and C respectively. Note that for two factor mixed nested model, only the first of these are required (although it is now defining n) and $C(B(A))$ represents the lowest form of replication and therefore the overall residuals (s^2). Costs can be ignored by making them equal to 1. Similarly, for any mixed design with a fixed Factor A, the optimum number of replicates of factor A (levels of factor B) can be estimated by solving for q from either of the following:

$$s^2_A = \frac{ns^2_{B(A)} + s^2_{C(B(A))}}{nq}$$

$$C_A = qC_{B(A)} + nqC_{C(B(A))}$$

where s^2_A represents the expected (or desired) variance amongst group means for the fixed Factor A.

11.11 Nested ANOVA in R

11.11.1 Error strata (aov)

Nested ANOVA can be thought of as a series of ANOVA models, each with a different error (residual term). Each of the separate models and their corresponding error term are referred to as a *strata*. The first error strata corresponds to a linear model that incorporates factor(s) for which the levels first random nesting factor are the appropriate replicates. Likewise, the second error strata corresponds to the next level of error terms (residuals) and so on. For a two factor mixed nested ANOVA, the second error strata will be the overall measurements (residuals). Modelling ANOVA with multiple error strata is accommodated via the aov function. Note however, that this is really only appropriate for balanced designs - particularly if the source of imbalance is at the level of the nesting factor replication.

11.11.2 Linear mixed effects models (`lme` and `lmer`)

The `lme` (`nlme`) and more recent `lmer` (`lme4`) functions facilitate linear mixed-effects and generalized linear mixed-effects modelling respectively. As such these procedures are more suitable for unbalanced and longitudinal designs. Note that recent versions of `lmer` have omitted P value approximations and that inference testing is performed by the `pvals.fnc` (`languageR`) *function* via the presently inconsistent `mcmcsamp` (`lme4`) *function*.

11.12 Further reading

- Theory

  Doncaster, C. P., and A. J. H. Davey. (2007). *Analysis of Variance and Covariance. How to Choose and Construct Models for the Life Sciences.* Cambridge University Press, Cambridge.

  Hollander, M., and D. A. Wolfe. (1999). *Nonparametric statistical methods, 2nd edition.* 2 edition. John Wiley & Sons, New York.

  Quinn, G. P., and K. J. Keough. (2002). *Experimental design and data analysis for biologists.* Cambridge University Press, London.

  Sokal, R., and F. J. Rohlf. (1997). *Biometry, 3rd edition.* W. H. Freeman, San Francisco.

  Zar, G. H. (1999). *Biostatistical methods.* Prentice-Hall, New Jersey.

- Practical - R

  Crawley, M. J. (2007). *The R Book.* John Wiley, New York.

  Fox, J. (2002). *An R and S-PLUS Companion to Applied Regression.* Sage Books.

  Maindonald, J. H., and J. Braun. (2003). *Data Analysis and Graphics Using R - An Example-based Approach.* Cambridge University Press, London.

  Pinheiro, J. C., and D. M. Bates. (2000). *Mixed effects models in S and S-PLUS.* Springer-Verlag, New York.

  Venables, W. N., and B. D. Ripley. (2002). *Modern Applied Statistics with S-PLUS, 4th edn.* Springer-Verlag, New York.

  Zuur, A. F., E. N. Ieno, N. J. Walker, A. A. Saveliev, and G. M. Smith. (2009). *Mixed Effects Models and Extensions in Ecology with R.* Springer.

11.13 Key for nested ANOVA

1 Determine the appropriate model design and hierarchy

- Conceptualise the design into a hierarchy (ladder) of factors
  - Main factor(s) with levels that are applied to complete sets of other (nesting) factors at the top
  - Progressively deeper levels of sub-replication of these main factor(s) considered progressively lower in the hierarchy

- Label random nesting factor levels with unique names for each level across the entire design (within and between main factor(s)). Label fixed nesting factor levels according to the levels they represent (recycled label names within each level of the main factor(s))

Random B			Fixed B		
Fact A	Fact B	DV	Fact A	Fact B	DV
A1	B1	.	A1	B1	.
A1	B2	.	A1	B2	.
A2	B3	.	A2	B1	.
A2	B4	.	A2	B2	.

- Identify the correct error (residual) term for each factor (see Tables 11.1 & 11.2).

.... Go to 2

2 a. Check assumptions for nested ANOVA
As the assumptions of any given hypothesis test relate to residuals, all diagnostics should reflect the appropriate error (residual) terms for the hypothesis. Typically this means generating temporary aggregated data sets.

- **Normality (symmetry) of the response variable at each level of the factor - boxplots of mean values for each level of the next random term in the hierarchy**
  Factor A (with random factor B)

```
> data.B.agg <- with(data, aggregate(data.frame(DV),
+      by = list(A = A, B = B), mean))
> #OR
> library(nlme)
> data.B.agg <- gsummary(data, data$B)
> boxplot(DV ~ A, data.B.agg)
```

where `DV` *is the response variable,* `A` *is the main fixed factor and* `B` *is a random factor nested within* `A` *within the* `data` *dataset.*

Factor B (random)

If Factor C exits and is random

```
> library(nlme)
> data.C.agg <- gsummary(data, data$C)
> boxplot(DV ~ A:B, data.C.agg)
```

If no random Factor C

```
> boxplot(DV ~ A:B, data)
```

where `DV` *is the response variable,* `A` *is the main fixed factor and* `B` *is a random factor nested within* `A` *within the* `data` *dataset.*

- **Homogeneity of variance (relationship between mean and variance) - boxplots (as above) and scatterplot of mean vs variance (fixed factors only)**

```
> with(data.B.agg, plot(tapply(DV, A, var),
      tapply(DV, A, mean)))
```

where `DV` *is the response variable,* `A` *is the main fixed factor and* `B` *is a random factor nested within* `A` *within the* `data.B.agg` *aggregated dataset.*

Parametric assumptions met .... Go to 4

b. Parametric assumptions not met .... Go to 3

3 a. Attempt a scale transformation (see Table 3.2 for transformation options) .... Go to 2

b. Transformations unsuccessful or inappropriate .... Go to 8

4 a. Determine whether the design is balanced and if not, at what scale of replication the imbalance occurs .... See Examples 11A,11C,11D

```
> library(biology)
> is.balanced(DV ~ A + B + C + .., data)
> #OR
> !is.list(replications(DV ~ A + B + C + .., data))
```

value of `TRUE` *indicates design is completely balanced*

```
> replications(DV ~ A + B + C + .., data)
```

where `DV` *is the response variable,* `A` *is the main fixed factor and* `B` *is a random factor nested within* `A` *within the* `data` *dataset.*

Design is balanced with respect to the appropriate sub-replicates of the term of interest .... Go to 5a-d

b. Design is NOT balanced with respect to the appropriate sub-replicates of the term of interest .... Go to 5b-d

5 a. Fit nested model using complete `aov` procedure (for balanced designs only) . See Example 11A

Define planned contrasts if required .... Refer back to Key 10.4

```
> data.aov <- aov(DV ~ A + Error(B), data)
> summary(data.aov)
```

For additional combinations of fixed and random factors see Tables 11.1 & 11.2

Examine residuals .... Go to 6

For variance components.. Go to 7

b. Fit nested model using simple ANOVA of aggregated dataset .... See Example 11C,11D

Factor A (with random factor B)

```
> library(nlme)
> data.B.agg <- gsummary(data, data$B)
```

Define planned contrasts if required .... Refer back to Key 10.4

```
> anova(aov(DV ~ A, data.B.agg))
```

Factor B (with random factor C or no C)

```
> library(nlme)
> data.C.agg <- gsummary(data, data$C)
```

Define planned contrasts if required .... Refer back to Key 10.4

```
> anova(aov(DV ~ A + B, data.C.agg))
```

where `DV` *is the response variable,* `A` *is the main fixed factor,* `B` *is a random factor nested within* `A` *and* `C` *is a random factor nested within* `B(A)` *within the* `data` *dataset. If there is no random Factor C, substitute* `data` *for* `data.C.agg` *in the* `aov()` *function above.*

For additional combinations of fixed and random factors see Table. 11.2

For variance components.. Go to 7

c. Fit nested model using `lme` procedure .... See Example 11D

Define planned contrasts if required .... Refer back to Key 10.4

```
> library(nlme)
> data.lme <- lme(DV ~ A, random = ~1 | B, data)
> summary(data.lme)
> anova(data.lme)
```

OR if three factor mixed-effects (A fixed, B & C random)

```
> data.lme <- lme(DV ~ A, random = ~1 | B/C, data)
> summary(data.lme)
> anova(data.lme)
```

where `DV` *is the response variable,* `A` *is the main fixed factor and* `B` *is a random factor nested within* `A` *and, if present,* `C` *is a random factor nested within* `B(A)` *within the* `data` *dataset. Note that the summary includes variance components for the random factors.*

For additional combinations of fixed and random factors see Table 11.1 & 11.2

Examine residuals .... Go to 6

For variance components.. Go to 7

d. Fit nested model using `lmer` procedure .... See Example 11C,11D

Define planned contrasts if required .... Refer back to Key 10.4

```
> library(lme4)
> data.lmer <- lmer(DV ~ A + (1 | B), data)
> summary(data.lmer)
> anova(data.lmer)
```

OR if three factor mixed-effects (A fixed, B & C random)

```
> data.lmer <- lmer(DV ~ A + (1 | B/C), data)
> summary(data.lmer)
> anova(data.lmer)
```

where `DV` *is the response variable,* `A` *is the main fixed factor and* `B` *is a random factor nested within* `A` *and, if present,*`C` *is a random factor nested within* `B(A)` *within the* `data` *dataset. Note that the summary includes variance components for the random factors.*

Examine residuals .... Go to 6

For model parameter and fixed factor effects confidence intervals via Markov chain Monte Carlo sampling

```
> library(languageR)
> pvals.fnc(data.lmer)
```

For model parameter and fixed factor effects (if more than two groups) significance via Markov chain Monte Carlo sampling

```
> library(languageR)
> pvals <- pvals.fnc(data.lmer, nsim = 10000, withMCMC = T)
> library(biology)
> mcmcpvalue(as.matrix(pvals$mcmc), "A")
```

where `"A"` *is string to indicate the name of the fixed factor (A in this case) to test.*

6 a. Examining a residual plot of the nested models fitted with `aov`. See Example 11A

```
> plot(resid(model[[2]]) ~ fitted(model[[2]]))
```

where `model` *is the name of a model fitted via* `aov` *and* `[[2]]` *refers to the second object in the fitted model (which is the first strata).*

b. Examining a residual plot of the mixed-effects models fitted with `lme` or `lmer` .... See Example 11D

```
> plot(resid(model) ~ fitted(model))
```

where `model` *is the name of a model fitted via* `lme` *or* `lmer`.

7 Calculate variance components of random factors .... See Example 11A

```
> library(nlme)
> VarCorr(lme(DV ~ A, random = ~1 | B, data))
```

For additional combinations of fixed and random factors see Table. 11.1 & 11.2

8 a. Underlying distribution of the response variable is normal for each level of the main fixed factor, but the variances are unequal (Welch's test from aggregated data) .... See Example 11B

```
> data.B.agg <- gsummary(data, data$B)
> oneway.test(DV ~ A, data.B.agg, var.equal = F)
```

or consider GLM .... GLM chapter 17

b. Underlying distributions not normally distributed .... Go to 9

9 a. Underlying distribution of the response variable and residuals is known .... GLM chapter 17

b. Underlying distributions of the response variable and residuals is not known .... Go to 10

10 a. Variances not wildly unequal, outliers present, but data independent (Kruskal-Wallis non-parametric test on aggregated data)

```
> data.B.agg <- gsummary(data, data$B)
> kruskal.test(DV ~ A, data.B.agg, var.equal = F)
```

b. Variances not wildly unequal, random sampling not possible - data might not be independent (Randomization test on aggregated data

```
> data.B.agg <- gsummary(data, data$B)
```

Use this aggregated data set and follow the instructions in Key 10. 8b. **Warning, randomization procedures are only useful when there are a large number of possible randomization combinations (rarely the case in nested designs)**

11.14 Worked examples of real biological data sets

Example 11A: Two factor mixed nested ANOVA

To investigate density-dependent grazing effects of sea urchin Andrew and Underwood (1993) on filamentous algae measured the percentage of filamentous algae within five quadrats randomly positioned within each of four random patches of reef that were in turn nested within four sea urchin density treatments (no urchins, 33% of natural density, 66% natural density and 100% natural density). The sea urchin density treatment was considered a fixed factor and patch within density treatment as well as the individual quadrats were treated as random factors.

Step 1 - Import (section 2.3) the Andrew and Underwood (1993) data set

```
> andrew <- read.table("andrew.csv", header = T, sep = ",")
```

Step 2 - The patch vector (variable) contains numerical representations of the patch identifications, therefore by default R considers this to be a *integer* vector rather than a categorical *factor*. In order to ensure that this variable is treated as a factor we need to redefine its class

```
> class(andrew$PATCH)
[1] "integer"

> andrew$PATCH <- factor(andrew$PATCH)
> class(andrew$PATCH)
[1] "factor"
```

Additionally, all variables that contain strings (alphanumeric characters) are automatically defined as *factor* variables during the data importation stage. In doing so, R by default, orders the levels of all factors in alphabetical order. Consequently, the levels of the density treatment factor are ordered as 0%, 100%, 33%, 66%. Whilst the order of these levels has no impact on the outcome of statistical analyses, defining a more logical order of factor levels can improve graphical summaries and simplify defining contrast matrices. Since 100% density represents the natural density (and thus the control), logically we would order our treatments from 100% down to 0%.

```
> levels(andrew$TREAT)
[1] "0%"   "100%" "33%"  "66%"

> andrew$TREAT <- factor(andrew$TREAT, levels = c("100%", "66%",
+     "33%", "0%"))
```

Step 3 (Key 11.2) - Assess assumptions of normality and homogeneity of variance for each null hypothesis ensuring that the correct scale of replicates are represented for each (they should reflect the appropriate *F*-ratio denominators see Table 11.1).

1. Factor A (density treatment - fixed factor). The patch means are the replicates for the density treatment, and thus an aggregated dataset needs to be created from which the boxplots can be based.

```
> andrew.agg <- with(andrew, aggregate(data.frame(ALGAE),
+     by = list(TREAT = TREAT, PATCH = PATCH), mean))
> #OR alternatively
> library(nlme)
> andrew.agg <- gsummary(andrew, groups = andrew$PATCH)

> boxplot(ALGAE ~ TREAT, andrew.agg)
```

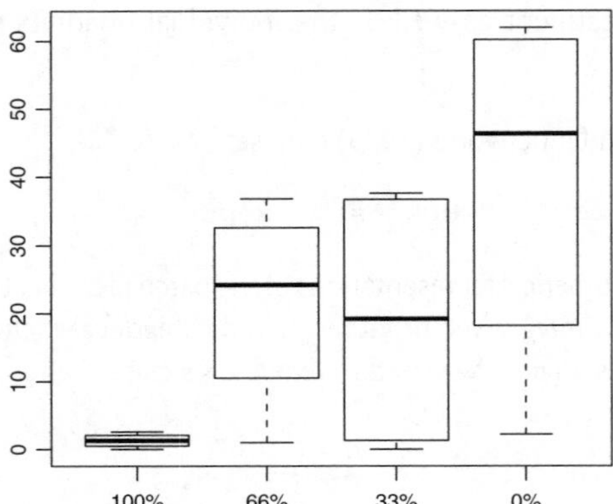

Conclusions - Although there is no evidence of non-normality (boxplots not wildly asymmetrical), there is strong evidence of unequal variance. Of particular concern is the apparent relationship between mean and variance (heights of boxplots increase up the y-axis). Transformations (*arcsin*$\sqrt{}$ and log) are ineffectual. Andrew and Underwood (1993) and therefore Quinn and Keough (2002) decided to proceed and rely on the robustness of the parametric test for balanced designs.

2. Factor B (patches - random factor). As this factor is of little biological interest, checking the assumptions associated with its hypothesis tests are of little value.

Conclusions - For the purpose of demonstrating how to use R to perform the worked examples that appear in the popular biostatistics reference literature, we will proceed with raw data (following Quinn and Keough (2002)). Note, however, as a demonstration of non-parametric or robust alternatives in nested designs, we will reanalyse these data in example 11B.
Although Quinn and Keough (2002) did not include either planned or post-hoc comparisons, in this case, the former would seem appropriate. We will compare each of the reduced urchin density treatments to the control – these are known as treatment contrasts[i].

Step 4 (Key 11.4) - Determine whether or not the design is balanced (at least with respect to sub-replication).

```
> replications(ALGAE ~ TREAT + PATCH, andrew)
TREAT PATCH
   20     5

> library(biology)
> is.balanced(ALGAE ~ TREAT + PATCH, andrew)
[1] TRUE
```

Conclusions - The design is completely balanced. There are two replicate patches within each of the four treatments and there are five replicate quadrats within each patch.

Step 5 - Define treatment contrasts (see sections 10.6 and 7.3.1 for more information on setting contrasts).

```
> contrasts(andrew$TREAT) <- contr.treatment
```

Note that there is no need to check the orthogonality of these contrasts, when using one of the contrasts functions, they will always be constructed correctly in accordance with the relevant contrast definition.

[i] Alternatively, as the levels of the main treatment factor are naturally ordered (according to urchin density), polynomial contrasts might be desirable.

Step 6 (Key 11.5a) - As the design is completely balanced, there are a number of ways to fit the linear model to test the null hypotheses that there is no effect of urchin treatment and no added variance due to patches[j]. The complete `aov()` procedure is the traditional method and arguably the simplest.

```
> andrew.aov <- aov(ALGAE ~ TREAT + Error(PATCH), andrew)
```

Step 7 (Key 11.6a) - Examine the fitted model diagnostics[k]. Note that it is only the first error strata that we are interested in and this is the second object within the `aov` object (hence the `[[2]]`)

```
> plot(resid(andrew.aov[[2]]) ~ fitted(andrew.aov[[2]]))
```

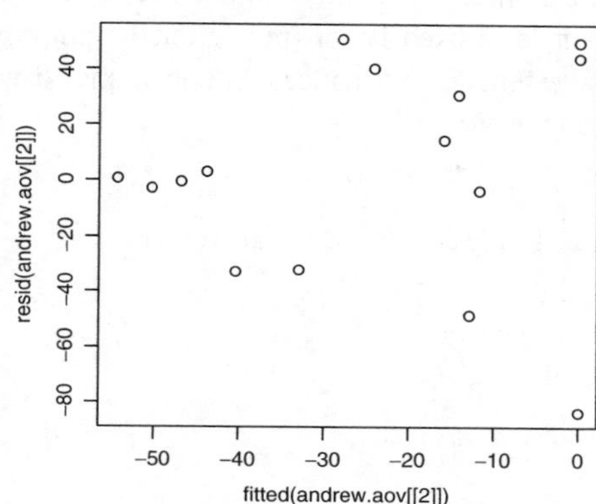

Conclusions - As anticipated, there is an indication of a 'wedge' pattern in the residuals indicative of unequal variance.

Step 8 (Key 11.5a) - Examine the anova tables[l], including the set of defined planned treatment contrasts.

```
> summary(andrew.aov, split = list(TREAT = list('cont vs 66' = 1,
+       'cont vs 33' = 2, 'cont vs 0' = 3)))
Error: PATCH
                        Df   Sum Sq Mean Sq F value Pr(>F)
TREAT                    3 14429.1  4809.7  2.7171 0.09126 .
  TREAT: cont vs 66     1     44.2     44.2  0.0250 0.87707
  TREAT: cont vs 33     1     20.8     20.8  0.0118 0.91540
  TREAT: cont vs 0      1 14364.1 14364.1  8.1146 0.01466 *
Residuals               12 21242.0  1770.2
---
Signif. codes:  0 '***' 0.001 '**' 0.01 '*' 0.05 '.' 0.1 ' ' 1
```

[j] Note that if we were also intending to investigate a set of planned comparisons/contrasts (see chapter 10.6), these should be defined prior to fitting the linear model. In this case, treatment contrasts (with the 100% urchin density as the 'control') would probably be the most logical.

[k] Recall that leverage, and thus Cook's D are not informative for categorical predictor variables.

[l] R does not provide the hypothesis tests associated with the random nesting factors as these are rarely of interest. In order to obtain such tests, re-fit the linear model treating the random nesting factor as a fixed factor. All hypothesis tests in the output above this term in the hierarchy should be ignored as they will be tested against the incorrect error (residual) terms. E.g. `> andrew.aov1<-aov(ALGAE TREAT+PATCH, andrew)`.

```
Error: Within
          Df  Sum Sq Mean Sq F value Pr(>F)
Residuals 64 19110.4   298.6
```

Conclusions - Note that the output has been split into two error strata each reflecting the appropriate error (residual) term to test the corresponding hypothesis against. Do not reject the null hypothesis of no effect of urchin density treatment. Sea urchin density was not found to have an impact on the percentage of filamentous algae. As no overall difference was observed, neither planned or unplanned comparisons are appropriate and therefore ignored.

Step 9 (Key 11.7) - Examine the variance components to determine the relative contribution of each of the random factors. This must be done via a linear mixed effects model. Note further, that to get an estimate of the variance component for a fixed factor (purely for the purpose of comparison to other components, as the actual estimates of variance components for fixed factors are illogical), it must be modelled as a random factor.

```
> library(nlme)
> VarCorr(lme(ALGAE ~ 1, random = ~1 | TREAT/PATCH, andrew))
            Variance     StdDev
TREAT =     pdLogChol(1)
(Intercept) 151.9443     12.32657
PATCH =     pdLogChol(1)
(Intercept) 294.3209     17.15578
Residual    298.6005     17.28006
```

Conclusions - There was a high level of variance between patches within treatment $((294.32 \times 100)/(151.94 + 294.32 + 298.60) = 39.51\%)$ compared to between treatments (20.40%).

Example 11B: Two factor non-parametric mixed nested ANOVA

To demonstrate the hierarchical nature of nested ANOVA designs and how alternative model fitting procedures can be fitted to such designs in R, we will re-analyse the Andrew and Underwood (1993) data (which you may recall from example 11A, did not really satisfy the assumption on equal variance).

Step 1 - Import and prepare the Andrew and Underwood (1993) data set as in Steps 1-2 of example 11A

Step 2- Generate a separate data set for each of the appropriate error strata (consult Table 11.1)

Urchin treatment – for testing the effect of urchin treatment (fixed factor) the patch means are the appropriate replicates. Generate a dataset that is aggregated according to the patch means.

```
> andrew.patch <- with(andrew, aggregate(data.frame(ALGAE),
+     by = list(TREAT = TREAT, PATCH = PATCH), mean))
> library(nlme)
> andrew.patch <- gsummary(andrew, groups = andrew$PATCH)
```

Patch treatment – for testing whether there is any added variance due to patches (random factor) the replicates are the values of the quadrats within the patches that are the appropriate replicates. As the values of the quadrats within each patch are the lowest level of sub-replication represented by the original dataset, the original dataset is appropriate for the error strata for testing the hypothesis about patches.

Step 3 (Key 11.8) - Perform a non-parametric ANOVA on each strata (see also Key 10. 6). Note, it is rarely of interest to test hypotheses about nested factors and thus only the main effect of treatment is tested.

Urchin treatment

```
> oneway.test(ALGAE ~ TREAT, andrew.patch, var.equal = F)
        One-way analysis of means (not assuming equal variances)

data:   ALGAE and TREAT
F = 4.5792, num df = 3.000, denom df = 5.031, p-value = 0.06687
```

Alternatively, we could convert the response variable to ranks and perform the parametric nested ANOVA on these ranks. It should be acknowledged that these methods are not ideal in this example. This approach can be a useful alternative when normality is suspect, yet still assumes similar variances.

```
> summary(aov(rank(ALGAE) ~ TREAT + Error(PATCH), andrew))
Error: PATCH
          Df  Sum Sq Mean Sq F value  Pr(>F)
TREAT      3 10761.7  3587.2  2.8916 0.07929 .
Residuals 12 14886.8  1240.6
---
Signif. codes:  0 '***' 0.001 '**' 0.01 '*' 0.05 '.' 0.1 ' ' 1

Error: Within
          Df  Sum Sq Mean Sq F value Pr(>F)
Residuals 64 13432.9   209.9
```

Conclusions - The conclusions are much the same as they were based on the parametric nested ANOVA, thereby confirming the general robustness of balanced ANOVA.

Example 11C: Two factor model II nested ANOVA with unequal sample sizes

Sokal and Rohlf (1997) present a dataset containing single blood pH readings from the female offspring of 15 dams (females). Each of the offspring were nested within different litters resulting from either two or three sires (males) which were in turn nested within the 15 dams. The dams represent a random factor at the top of the hierarchy (Factor A), sire represents the first random nesting factor (Factor B(A)), and the individual offspring within each litter represent the replicates of the sires.

Step 1 - Import (section 2.3) the blood pH data set

```
> ph <- read.table("ph.csv", header = T, sep = ",")
```

Step 2 (Key 11.2) - Assess assumptions of normality and homogeneity of variance for each null hypothesis ensuring that the correct scale of replicates are represented for each (they should reflect the appropriate *F*-ratio denominators see Table 11.1).

1. Factor A (dams - random factor). The means of mice within each sire litter are the replicates for the dams, and thus an aggregated dataset needs to be created from which the boxplots can be based.

```
> library(nlme)
> ph.agg <- gsummary(ph, groups = ph$SIRE)
> boxplot(PH ~ DAM, ph.agg)
```

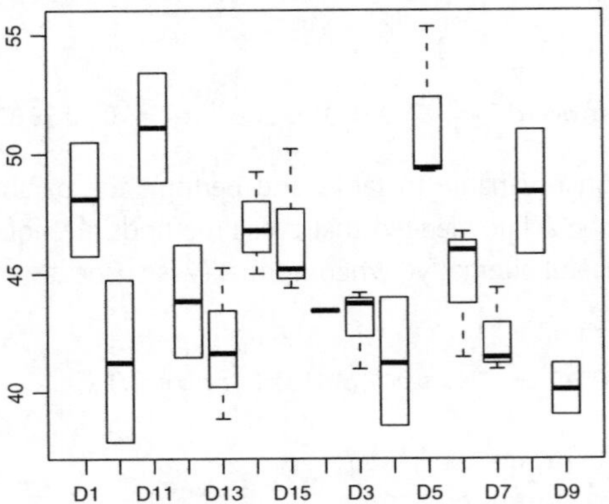

Conclusions - no evidence of consistent non-normality and no evidence of a relationship between mean and variance.

2. Factor B (sires - random factor). The blood pH readings from each mice are the replicates of the sires, therefore boxplots should be based on the entire data set.

```
> boxplot(PH ~ DAM:SIRE, ph)
```

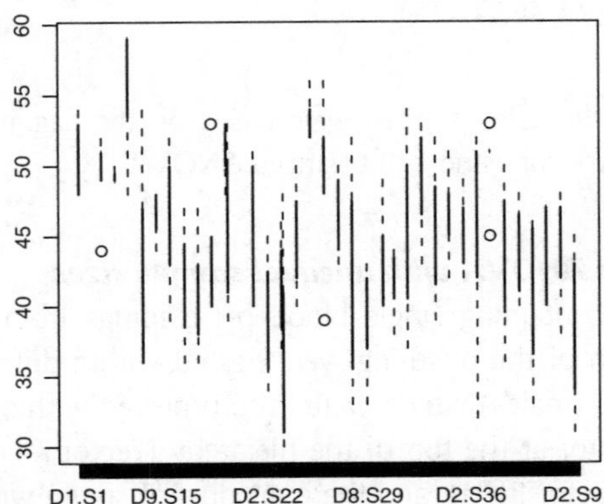

Conclusions - no evidence of consistent non-normality and no evidence of a relationship between mean and variance.

Step 3 (Key 11.4) - Assess whether the design is balanced (are there equal sample sizes in each treatment).

```
> replications(PH ~ DAM + SIRE, data = ph)
$DAM
DAM
 D1 D10 D11 D12 D13 D14 D15  D2  D3  D4  D5  D6  D7  D8  D9
  8   9  10   9  12  13  15   9  13   7  12  13  14   8   8

$SIRE
SIRE
 S1 S10 S11 S12 S13 S14 S15 S16 S17 S18 S19  S2 S20 S21 S22 S23 S24
  4   5   4   3   4   4   5   4   5   5   3   4   5   4   4   5   4
S25 S26 S27 S28 S29  S3 S30 S31 S32 S33 S34 S35 S36 S37  S4  S5  S6
  5   5   5   4   5   5   3   4   4   4   5   5   5   5   4   4   4
 S7  S8  S9
  5   3   4
> library(biology)
> is.balanced(PH ~ DAM + SIRE, data = ph)
[1] FALSE
```

Conclusions - the design is not balanced (there are a different number of sired litters and offspring per dam). The `FALSE` indicates that the design is **not** balanced. This design is therefore best modelled using linear mixed effects (REML) procedures. Note that Sokal and Rohlf (1997) employ an older procedure (which some argue is now outdated and potentially inappropriate) in which the *F*-ratio and variance components calculations are adjusted to account for the degree of imbalance.

Step 4 (Key 11.5b) - fit one or more linear models to test the null hypotheses that there is no added variation due to dams and no added variation due to sires within dams. Note, as this is an unbalanced design, we cannot rely on the usual additive partitioning of SS_{Total}. There are two options (both of which will result in slightly different estimates - yet the conclusions are consistent):

1. (Key 11.5b) use a single factor ANOVA to model the effects of dam against the mean pH values for each sire (use the aggregated dataset from Step 2 above).

```
> ph.aov <- aov(PH ~ DAM, ph.agg)
> anova(ph.aov)
Analysis of Variance Table

Response: PH
          Df Sum Sq Mean Sq F value   Pr(>F)
DAM       14 430.90   30.78  3.5464 0.003963 **
Residuals 22 190.93    8.68
---
Signif. codes:  0 '***' 0.001 '**' 0.01 '*' 0.05 '.' 0.1 ' ' 1
```

Conclusions - There are maternal influences on the blood pH of female offspring in mice ($F_{14,22} = 3.546, P = 0.003$).

Perform simple ANOVA to investigate the effects of sire using the individual pH readings from each of the offspring as the replicates. Note that the hypothesis test for dam that is included in this modelling should be ignored.

```
> ph.aov1 <- aov(PH ~ DAM + SIRE, data = ph)
> anova(ph.aov1)
Analysis of Variance Table

Response: PH
           Df  Sum Sq Mean Sq F value    Pr(>F)
DAM        14 1780.17  127.16  5.1405 1.563e-07 ***
SIRE       22  800.24   36.37  1.4705   0.09662 .
Residuals 123 3042.53   24.74
---
Signif. codes:  0 '***' 0.001 '**' 0.01 '*' 0.05 '.' 0.1 ' ' 1
```

Conclusions - Paternity was not found to have a significant impact on the blood pH of female offspring in mice ($F_{22,123} = 1.470, P = 0.097$).

2. (Key 11.5d) fit the linear mixed effects model using `lmer`.

```
> library(lme4)
> ph.lmer <- lmer(PH ~ 1 + (1 | DAM/SIRE), ph)
> summary(ph.lmer)
Linear mixed model fit by REML
Formula: PH ~ 1 + (1 | DAM/SIRE)
   Data: ph
  AIC  BIC logLik deviance REMLdev
 1006 1019 -499.1    999.9   998.2
Random effects:
 Groups   Name        Variance Std.Dev.
 SIRE:DAM (Intercept)  2.6456  1.6265
 DAM      (Intercept)  8.8957  2.9826
 Residual             24.8079  4.9807
Number of obs: 160, groups: SIRE:DAM, 37; DAM, 15

Fixed effects:
            Estimate Std. Error t value
(Intercept)  44.9179     0.9104   49.34
```

Conclusions - the main interest in this output is the variance components for each of the random effects. It is clear that there is more variation between dams than there is between sires within dams (8.90 *cf* 2.64) suggesting that maternal impacts on female blood pH are stronger than paternal influences. There is however, a large amount of variation between offspring (within sires: 24.81 *cf* 2.64) indicating that blood pH is probably influenced by a number of other factors, some of which may even be more important than the measured maternal and paternal associations.

Step 5 (Key 11.5d) - Calculate the 95% confidence intervals of the random effects (based on Markov chain Monte Carlo sampling).

```
> library(languageR)
> pvals.fnc(ph.lmer)

$fixed
  Estimate MCMCmean HPD95lower HPD95upper  pMCMC Pr(>|t|)
1    44.92    44.91      43.35      46.56 0.0001        0

$random
    Groups        Name Std.Dev.  MCMCmedian MCMCmean HPD95lower HPD95upper
1 SIRE:DAM (Intercept)   1.6265      0.6168   0.7046     0.0000     1.8502
2      DAM (Intercept)   2.9826      2.4766   2.5250     1.3511     3.8754
3 Residual               4.9807      5.2150   5.2319     4.6293     5.8855
```

Conclusions - The 95% confidence interval for the random effect of dam (no added variance due to dams) does not include 0, and therefore we would reject the modified null hypothesis and conclude that there is a maternal influence on offspring blood pH. On the other hand, the interval for the effect of sires does appear to include 0 and thus we would conclude that there is no significant paternal influence on blood pH. It is also evident that the maternal influence on female offspring blood pH is stronger than the paternal influence.

Example 11D: Three factor mixed model nested ANOVA

Sokal and Rohlf (1997) demonstrate the analysis of a balanced three factor nested ANOVA design in which the glycogen levels had been measured from two separate readings from each of three liver preparations from each of two individual rats per one of three different treatments (which they did not elaborate on). In this case, the treatments represent the fixed Factor A, the individual rats represent the first random nesting factor (Factor B and therefore the replicates of the treatment effects) and liver preparations represent an additional random nesting factor (Factor C). The duplicate readings from each liver, are the units of replication for the preparations.

Presumably, the researchers would have been primarily interested in whether there was an effect of treatment on liver glycogen content. The design acknowledges that individual liver preparations and glycogen readings as well as the individual rats are themselves likely to be of substantially great enough variability with respect to glycogen measurements that they could potentially mask the ability to detect an impact of treatment – hence the use of a nested design[m].

Step 1 - Import (section 2.3) the liver glycogen data set

```
> glyco <- read.table("glyco.csv", header = T, sep = ",")
```

Recall that `read.table()` automatically alphabetises the order of factor levels (hence in this case: `Compound217, Compound217Sugar, Control`) and defines treatment contrasts. For treatment contrasts to be meaningful in this case, the order of factor levels should be `Control, Compound217, Compound217Sugar`.

```
> glyco$TREAT <- factor(glyco$TREAT, levels = c("Control",
+      "Compound217", "Compound217Sugar"))
```

[m] Additionally, a nested design substantially reduces the number of rats required for the experiment.

Step 2 (Key 11.2) - Assess assumptions of normality and homogeneity of variance for each null hypotheses ensuring that the correct scale of replicates are represented for each (they should reflect the appropriate *F*-ratio denominators see Table 11.1). Note that for each hypothesis test there are only either two or three replicates, and thus it is virtually impossible to confidently examine the assumptions. Instead, we must rely on the robustness of the test for a balanced design. As a result, I will only illustrate the process of producing the appropriate aggregated data sets for each hypothesis test.

1. Factor A (treatment - fixed factor). The mean glycogen levels per rat are the replicates for the treatment effects, and thus an aggregated dataset needs to be created from which the boxplots can be based.

```
> library(nlme)
> glyco.treat.agg <- gsummary(glyco, groups = glyco$RAT)
```

2. Factor B (rats - random factor). The mean glycogen levels per liver preparation are the replicates for the contributions of rats to added variation.

```
> glyco.rat.agg <- gsummary(glyco, groups = glyco$PREP)
```

3. Factor C (preparations - random factor). The mean glycogen levels per duplicate reading are the replicates for the contributions of the preparations to added variation. Note that in this case, since the individual readings are the lowest level of sub-replication, the aggregated dataset is the same as the original.

```
> glyco.prep.agg <- gsummary(glyco, groups = glyco$READ)
```

Step 3 (Key 11.4) - Assess whether the design is balanced (are there equal sample sizes in each treatment).

```
> library(biology)
> is.balanced(GLYCO ~ TREAT + RAT + PREP, data = glyco)
[1] TRUE
```

Conclusions - the design is balanced.

Step 4 (Key 11.5a) - fit one or more linear models to test the null hypotheses that there are no effects of treatment and no added variation due to rats within treatments and preparations within rats within treatments. As this is a balanced design, all three parametric model fitting procedures (`aov`, ANOVA from aggregated data sets and linear mixed effects models) will yield equivalent outcomes.

1. Factor A (treatment - fixed factor)

```
> glyco.aov <- aov(GLYCO ~ TREAT + Error(RAT/PREP), glyco)
> summary(glyco.aov)
Error: RAT
          Df  Sum Sq Mean Sq F value Pr(>F)
TREAT      2 1557.56  778.78   2.929 0.1971
Residuals  3  797.67  265.89
```

```
Error: RAT:PREP
          Df Sum Sq Mean Sq F value Pr(>F)
Residuals 12  594.0    49.5

Error: Within
          Df Sum Sq Mean Sq F value Pr(>F)
Residuals 18 381.00   21.17
```

2. Factor B (rats - random factor). Ignore the test of treatment from this output.

```
> glyco.rat.aov <- aov(GLYCO ~ TREAT + RAT + Error(PREP),
    glyco.rat.agg)
> summary(glyco.rat.aov)
Error: PREP
          Df Sum Sq Mean Sq F value    Pr(>F)
TREAT      2 778.78  389.39 15.7329 0.0004428 ***
RAT        3 398.83  132.94  5.3715 0.0141091 *
Residuals 12 297.00   24.75
---
Signif. codes:  0 '***' 0.001 '**' 0.01 '*' 0.05 '.' 0.1 ' ' 1
```

3. Factor C (preparations - random factor). Ignore the tests of treatment and rat from this output.

```
> glyco.prep.aov <- aov(GLYCO ~ TREAT + RAT + PREP,
   glyco.prep.agg)
> summary(glyco.prep.aov)
            Df  Sum Sq Mean Sq F value     Pr(>F)
TREAT        2 1557.56  778.78 36.7927 4.375e-07 ***
RAT          3  797.67  265.89 12.5617 0.0001143 ***
PREP        12  594.00   49.50  2.3386 0.0502907 .
Residuals   18  381.00   21.17
---
Signif. codes:  0 '***' 0.001 '**' 0.01 '*' 0.05 '.' 0.1 ' ' 1
```

Conclusions - Treatments were not found to have an impact on the glycogen content of rat livers ($F_{2,3} = 2.929, P = 0.197$). Liver glycogen content varies significantly between rats ($F_{3,12} = 5.372, P = 0.014$), but only marginally between liver preparations $F_{12,18} = 2.339, P = 0.050$). Alternatively, we could use a linear mixed effects model to investigate the effect of treatment and examine the variance components. As the design is balanced, the `lme()` function is perhaps more preferable to many workers (than the `lmer()` function) as it provides an F-ratio and P-value **(Key 11.5c)**

```
> library(nlme)
> glyco.lme <- lme(GLYCO ~ TREAT, random = ~1 | RAT/PREP, glyco)
> summary(glyco.lme)
Linear mixed-effects model fit by REML
 Data: glyco
```

```
      AIC      BIC    logLik
  231.6213 240.6003 -109.8106

Random effects:
 Formula: ~1 | RAT
        (Intercept)
StdDev:    6.005399

 Formula: ~1 | PREP %in% RAT
        (Intercept) Residual
StdDev:    3.763863 4.600725

Fixed effects: GLYCO ~ TREAT
                         Value Std.Error DF   t-value p-value
(Intercept)          140.50000  4.707166 18 29.848111  0.0000
TREATCompound217      10.50000  6.656937  3  1.577302  0.2128
TREATCompound217Sugar -5.33333  6.656937  3 -0.801169  0.4816
 Correlation:
                      (Intr) TREATCm217
TREATCompound217      -0.707
TREATCompound217Sugar -0.707  0.500

Standardized Within-Group Residuals:
        Min          Q1         Med          Q3         Max
-1.48211987 -0.47263005  0.03061539  0.42934293  1.82934636

Number of Observations: 36
Number of Groups:
          RAT PREP %in% RAT
            6            18

> anova(glyco.lme)
            numDF denDF  F-value p-value
(Intercept)     1    18 2738.654  <.0001
TREAT           2     3    2.929  0.1971

> library(nlme)
> VarCorr(glyco.lme)

            Variance     StdDev
RAT =       pdLogChol(1)
(Intercept) 36.06482     6.005399
PREP =      pdLogChol(1)
(Intercept) 14.16667     3.763863
Residual    21.16667     4.600725
```

Conclusions - Again, treatments were not found to have an impact on the glycogen content of rat livers ($F_{2,3} = 2.929, P = 0.197$). The variability in liver glycogen content is greater between the individual rats than it is between preparations within the rats.
Yet another alternative is to employ the newer generalized mixed effects modelling procedure (`lmer`) **(Key 11.5d)**. Although this will not produce *F*-ratios, *P*-values for fixed effects can be determined from a sampling distribution generated via Markov Chain Monte Carlo techniques[n].

```
> library(lme4)
> glyco.lmer <- lmer(GLYCO ~ TREAT + (1 | RAT/PREP), glyco)
```

```
> plot(resid(ph.lmer) ~ fitted(ph.lmer))
```

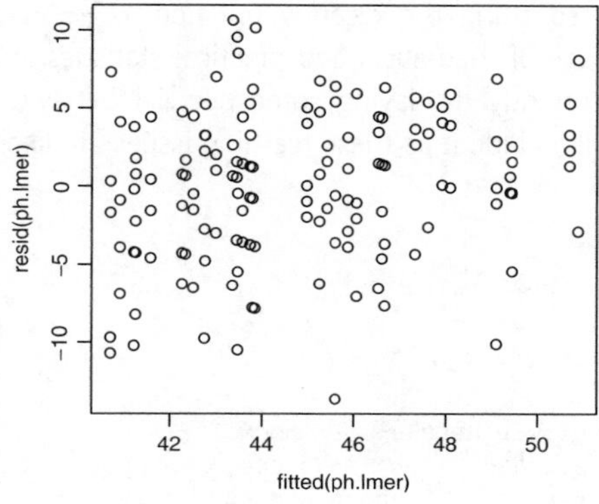

Conclusions - no evidence of a wedge or other pattern in the residuals.

```
> glyco.lmer
Linear mixed model fit by REML
Formula: GLYCO ~ TREAT + (1 | RAT/PREP)
   Data: glyco
   AIC   BIC logLik deviance REMLdev
 231.6 241.1 -109.8    234.3   219.6
Random effects:
 Groups   Name        Variance Std.Dev.
 PREP:RAT (Intercept) 14.167   3.7639
 RAT      (Intercept) 36.065   6.0054
 Residual             21.167   4.6007
Number of obs: 36, groups: PREP:RAT, 18; RAT, 6

Fixed effects:
                      Estimate Std. Error t value
(Intercept)            140.500      4.707  29.850
TREATCompound217        10.500      6.656   1.577
TREATCompound217Sugar   -5.333      6.656  -0.801
```

[n] Markov chain Monte Carlo procedures in this context generate samples of model parameters via randomizations of Markov chains. which themselves represent states or estimates by incorporating previous states or estimates.

```
Correlation of Fixed Effects:
             (Intr) TREATCm217
TREATCmp217 -0.707
TREATCm217S -0.707  0.500
```

Conclusions - The conclusions about the sources of variability are the same as previous (greater variability between rats than between preparations). Note that degrees of freedom and P values are intentionally omitted from the output since (arguably) sensible values are not identifiable by traditional techniques.
Employ Markov chain Monte Carlo (MCMC) sampling methods to generate distributions of each of the parameter estimates from which confidence intervals and P values[o] can be calculated. Markov chain Monte Carlo sampling is performed using the recently updated `mcmcsamp` *function*. These techniques are at the bleeding edge of theoretical and practical statistics and the author of this function stresses that it is currently displaying some peculiar behaviour and should not yet be trusted. Nevertheless, I will include it as these teething issues are likely to be rectified in the near future.

```
> library(languageR)
> glyco.pval <- pvals.fnc(glyco.lmer, nsim = 10000, withMCMC = T)
```

Examine the fixed effects

```
> glyco.pval$fixed
                      Estimate MCMCmean HPD95lower HPD95upper  pMCMC Pr(>|t|)
(Intercept)            140.500  140.501   133.4425     147.54 0.0001   0.0000
TREATCompound217        10.500   10.507     0.3542      20.20 0.0398   0.1242
TREATCompound217Sugar   -5.333   -5.392   -15.2432       4.74 0.2386   0.4287
```

Examine the random effects

```
> glyco.pval$random
    Groups        Name Std.Dev. MCMCmedian MCMCmean HPD95lower HPD95upper
1 PREP:RAT (Intercept)   3.7639     0.8526   1.0771     0.0000     3.1076
2      RAT (Intercept)   6.0054     3.7633   3.9243     0.0000     6.9293
3 Residual               4.6007     6.0172   6.1119     4.4933     7.8493
```

Conclusions - The output would suggest that (based on MCMC P values) whilst there was no evidence that liver glycogen levels associated with the Compound217sugar treatment are not different to those of the control, there is some evidence that the levels are higher when associated with the Compound217 treatment. Note that the significant P value (0.0398) resulting from the MCMC sampling is suspiciously low, particularly when we consider that it is lower than the included anti-conservative P value (0.1242).

Examine the null hypothesis that there is no overall treatment effect (via MCMC sampling).

```
> glyco.mcmc <- glyco.pval$mcmc
> library(biology)
> mcmcpvalue(as.matrix(glyco.mcmc), "TREAT")
[1] 0.017
```

Conclusions - This *P*-value is based on the current implementation of MCMC sampling and thus is presently suspect.

---

[o] Note that the calculation of P values is contrary to the general Bayesian philosophy on which these methods are based and it is therefore an unsupported pursuit.

12

Factorial ANOVA

Factorial designs are an extension of single factor ANOVA designs in which additional factors are added such that each level of one factor is applied to all levels of the other factor(s) and all combinations are replicated (see Figure 12.1). For example, we might design an experiment in which the effects of temperature (high vs low) and fertilizer (added vs not added) on the growth rate of seedlings are investigated by growing seedlings under the different temperature and fertilizer combinations. In addition to investigating the impacts of the main factors, factorial designs allow us to investigate whether the effects of one factor are consistent across levels of another factor. For example, is the effect of temperature on growth rate the same for both fertilized and unfertilized seedlings and similarly, does the impact of fertilizer treatment depend on the temperature under which the seedlings are grown?

To appreciate the interpretation of interactions, consider the following figures that depict fictitious two factor (temperature and fertilizer) designs. For Figure 12.2a, it is clear that whether or not there is an observed effect of adding fertilizer or not depends on whether we are focused on seedlings growth under high or low temperatures. Fertilizer is only important for seedlings grown under high temperatures. In this case it is not possible to simply state that there is an effect of fertilizer, as it depends on the level of temperature. Similarly, the magnitude of the effect of temperature depends on whether fertilizer has been added or not. Such interactions are represented by plots in which lines either intersect or converge. Figure 12.2b-c both depict parallel lines which are indicative of no interaction. That is, the effects of temperature are similar for both fertilizer added and controls and vice versa. Whilst the former displays an effect of both fertilizer and temperature, in the latter, only fertilizer is important. Finally, Figure 12.2d represents a strong interaction that would mask the main effects of temperature and fertilizer (since the nature of the effect of temperature is very different for the different fertilizer treatments and visa versa).

Factorial designs can consist entirely of fixed (see section 10.0.1) factors (**Model I ANOVA**) in which conclusions are restricted to the specific combinations of levels selected for the experiment, entirely of random factors (**Model II ANOVA**) or a mixture of fixed and random factors (**Model III ANOVA**). The latter are useful for investigating the generality of a main treatment effect (fixed) over broad spatial, temporal or biological levels of organization. That is, whether the observed effects of

Biostatistical Design and Analysis Using R: a Practical Guide, 1st edition. By M. Logan.
Published 2010 by Blackwell Publishing.

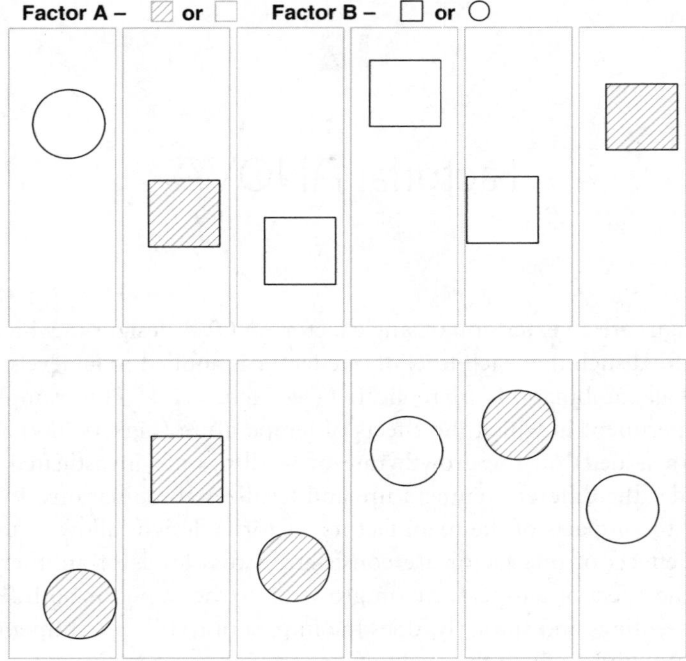

Fig 12.1 Fictitious spatial depictions of a multi (two) factor ANOVA design. There are two levels of factor A (shaded or not) and two levels of factor B (square or circle) and three replicates of each shape/fill combination.

temperature and/or fertilizer (for example) are observed across the entire genera or country.

12.1 Linear models

The linear models for two and three factor designs are:

$$y_{ijk} = \mu + \alpha_i + \beta_j + (\alpha\beta)_{ij} + \varepsilon_{ijk}$$
$$y_{ijkl} = \mu + \alpha_i + \beta_j + \gamma_k + (\alpha\beta)_{ij} + (\alpha\gamma)_{ik} + (\beta\gamma)_{jk} + (\alpha\beta\gamma)_{ijk} + \varepsilon_{ijkl}$$

where μ is the overall mean, α is the effect of Factor A, β is the effect of Factor B, γ is the effect of Factor C and ε is the random unexplained or residual component. Note that although the linear models for Model I, Model II and Model III designs are identical, the interpretation of terms (and thus null hypothesis) differ.

12.2 Null hypotheses

There are separate null hypothesis associated with each of the main effects and the interaction terms.

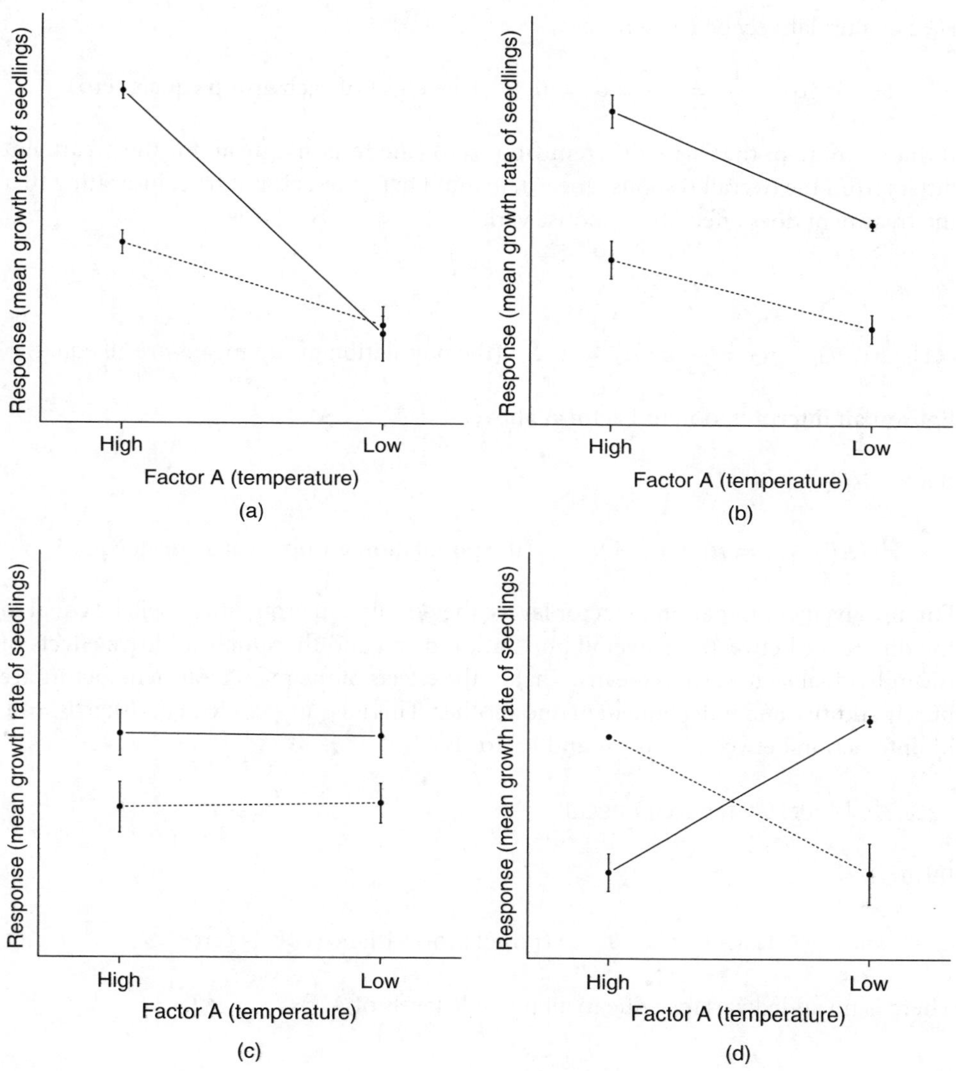

Fig 12.2 Fictitious depictions of two factor ANOVA design. There are two levels of factor A (temperature: High and Low) and two levels of factor B (fertilizer: Added or not added).

12.2.1 Model I - fixed effects

Factor A

$$H_0(A): \mu_1 = \mu_2 = \cdots = \mu_i = \mu \qquad \text{(the population group means are all equal)}$$

The mean of population 1 is equal to that of population 2 and so on, and thus all population means are equal to an overall mean. If the effect of the ith group is the difference between the ith group mean and the overall mean ($\alpha_i = \mu_i - \mu$) then the

H_0 can alternatively be written as:

$$H_0(A)\colon \alpha_1 = \alpha_2 = \cdots = \alpha_i = 0 \qquad \text{(the effect of each group equals zero)}$$

If one or more of the α_i are different from zero (the response mean for this treatment differs from the overall response mean), the null hypothesis is not true, indicating that the treatment does affect the response variable.

Factor B

$$H_0(B)\colon \mu_1 = \mu_2 = \cdots = \mu_i = \mu \qquad \text{(the population group means are all equal)}$$

Equivalent interpretation to Factor A above.

A:B Interaction

$$H_0(AB)\colon \mu_{ij} = \mu_i + \mu_j - \mu \qquad \text{(the population group means are all equal)}$$

For any given combination of factor levels, the population group mean will be equal to the difference between the overall population mean and the simple additive effects of the individual factor group means. That is, the effects of the main treatment factors are purely additive and independent of one another. This is equivalent to $H_0(AB)$: $\alpha\beta_{ij} = 0$, no interaction between Factor A and Factor B.

12.2.2 Model 2 - random effects

Factor A

$$H_0(A)\colon \sigma_\alpha^2 = 0 \qquad \text{(population variance equals zero)}$$

There is no added variance due to all possible levels of A.

Factor B

$$H_0(B)\colon \sigma_\beta^2 = 0 \qquad \text{(population variance equals zero)}$$

There is no added variance due to all possible levels of B.

A:B Interaction

$$H_0(AB)\colon \sigma_{\alpha\beta}^2 = 0 \qquad \text{(population variance equals zero)}$$

There is no added variance due to all possible interactions between all possible levels of A and B.

12.2.3 Model 3 - mixed effects

Fixed factor - e.g. A

$$H_0(A): \mu_1 = \mu_2 = \cdots = \mu_i = \mu \qquad \text{(the population group means are all equal)}$$

The mean of population 1 (pooled over all levels of the random factor) is equal to that of population 2 and so on, and thus all population means are equal to an overall mean pooling over all possible levels of the random factor. If the effect of the ith group is the difference between the ith group mean and the overall mean ($\alpha_i = \mu_i - \mu$) then the H_0 can alternatively be written as:

$$H_0(A): \alpha_1 = \alpha_2 = \cdots = \alpha_i = 0 \qquad \text{(no effect of any level of this factor pooled over all possible levels of the random factor)}$$

Random factor - e.g. B

$$H_0(B): \sigma^2_\beta = 0 \qquad \text{(population variance equals zero)}$$

There is no added variance due to all possible levels of B.

A:B Interaction

The interaction of a fixed and random factor is always considered a random factor.

$$H_0(AB): \sigma^2_{\alpha\beta} = 0 \qquad \text{(population variance equals zero)}$$

There is no added variance due to all possible interactions between all possible levels of A and B.

12.3 Analysis of variance

When fixed factorial designs are balanced, the total variance in the response variable can be sequentially partitioned into what is explained by each of the model terms (factors and their interactions) and what is left unexplained. For each of the specific null hypotheses, the overall unexplained variability is used as the denominator in F-ratio calculations (see Tables 12.1 & 12.2), and when a null hypothesis is true, an F-ratio should follow an F distribution with an expected value less than 1.

Random factors are added to provide greater generality of conclusions. That is, to enable us to make conclusions about the effect of one factor (such as whether or not fertilizer is added) over all possible levels (not just those sampled) of a random factor (such as all possible locations, seasons, varieties etc). In order to expand our conclusions beyond the specific levels used in the design, the hypothesis tests (and thus F-ratios)

Table 12.1 *F*-ratio determination and general R syntax two factor factorial designs.

	Factor	d.f	A&B fixed	A&B random	A fixed, B random	
					Restricted[a]	Unrestricted
1	A	$a-1$	$\frac{MS_A}{MS_{Resid}}$	$\frac{MS_{A'}}{MS_{B'\times A'}}$	$\frac{MS_A}{MS_{B'} \times A}$	$\frac{MS_A}{MS_{B'\times A}}$
2	B	$b-1$	$\frac{MS_B}{MS_{Resid}}$	$\frac{MS_{B'}}{MS_{B'\times A'}}$	$\frac{MS_{B'}}{MS_{Resid}}$	$\frac{MS_{B'}}{MS_{AB'}}$
3	B×A	$(b-1)(a-1)$	$\frac{MS_{B\times A}}{MS_{Resid}}$	$\frac{MS_{B'\times A'}}{MS_{Resid}}$	$\frac{MS_{B'\times A}}{MS_{Resid}}$	$\frac{MS_{B'\times A}}{MS_{Resid}}$
4	Residual (=N′(B×A))	$(n-1)ba$				

R syntax[b]

Type I SS (Balanced)	`> anova(aov(DV~A*B, data))`
Type II SS (Unbalanced)	`> Anova(aov(DV~A*B, data), type="II"))`
Type III SS (Unbalanced)[c]	`> Anova(aov(DV~A*B, data), type="III"))`
Variance components[d]	`> lmer(DV~1+(1|B)+(1|A)+(1|A:B), data)`

[a]Typically only for balanced designs.
[b]Mixed models require manual *F*-ratio and *P*-value calculations.
[c]To use Type III sums of squares, random factors need to be defined as something other than 'treatment' (e.g. 'helmert' or 'sum') contrasts prior to fitting the model.

```
> contrasts(data$B)<-contr.helmert
```

[d]Note this uses the REML method and is therefore valid for balanced and unbalanced designs, but will yield slightly different estimates than simple formulae used for purely balanced designs.

Table 12.2 *F*-ratio determination and general R syntax two and three factor factorial designs.

	Factor	d.f	A,B&C fixed	A,B&C random	A&C fixed, B random: Restricted[a]	A&C fixed, B random: Unrestricted	A fixed, B&C random: Restricted[a]	A fixed, B&C random: Unrestricted
1	A	$a-1$	1/8	1/(3+5-7)	1/3	1/3	1/(3+5-7)	1/(3+5-7)
2	B	$b-1$	2/8	2/(3+6-7)	2/8	?	2/6	?
3	B×A	$(b-1)(a-1)$	3/8	3/7	3/8	3/7	3/7	3/7
4	C	$(c-1)$	4/8	4/(5+6-7)	4/6	4/6	4/6	?
5	C×A	$(c-1)(a-1)$	5/8	5/7	5/7	5/7	5/7	5/7
6	C×B	$(c-1)(b-1)$	6/8	6/7	6/8	6/7	6/8	6/7
7	C×B×A	$(c-1)(b-1)(a-1)$	7/8	7/8	7/8	7/8	7/8	7/7
8	Residual (=N′(C×B×A))	$(n-1)cba$						

R syntax[b]

Type I SS (Balanced)	`> anova(aov(DV~A*B*C, data))`
Type II SS (Unbalanced)	`> Anova(aov(DV~A*B*C, data), type="II")`
Type III SS (Unbalanced)[c]	`> Anova(aov(DV~A*B*C, data), type="III")`
Variance components[d]	`> lmer(DV~1+(1|C)+(1|B)+(1|A)+(1|A:B), data)`

[a] Typically only for balanced designs.

[b] Mixed models require manual *F*-ratio and *P*-value calculations.

[c] To use Type III sums of squares, random factors need to be defined as something other than 'treatment' (e.g. 'helmert' or 'sum') contrasts prior to fitting the model.

```
> contrasts(data$B)<-contr.helmert
```

[d] Note this uses the REML method and is therefore valid for balanced and unbalanced designs, but will yield slightly different estimates than simple formulae used for purely balanced designs.

must reflect this extra generality by being more conservative. The appropriate[a] F-ratios for fixed, random and mixed factorial designs are presented in Tables 12.1 & 12.2. Generally, once the terms (factors and interactions) have been ordered into a hierarchy (single factors at the top, highest level interactions at the bottom and terms of same order given equivalent positions in the hierarchy), the denominator for any term is selected as the next appropriate random term (an interaction that includes the term to be tested) encountered lower in the hierarchy. Interaction terms that contain one or more random factors are considered themselves to be random terms, as is the overall residual term (as all observations are assumed to be random representations of the entire population(s)).

Pooling of non-significant F-ratio denominator terms (see section 11.6), in which lower random terms are added to the denominator (provided $P > 0.25$), may also be useful.

For random factors within mixed models, selecting F-ratio denominators that are appropriate for the intended hypothesis tests is a particularly complex and controversial issue. Traditionally, there are two alternative approaches and whilst the statistical resumes of each are complicated, essentially they differ in whether or not the interaction term is constrained for the test of the random factor. The constrained or restricted method (Model I), stipulates that for the calculation of a random factor F-ratio (which investigates the added variance added due to the random factor), the overall effect of the interaction is treated as zero. Consequently, the random factor is tested against the residual term (see Tables 12.1 & 12.2). The unconstrained or unrestrained method (Model II) however, does not set the interaction effect to zero and therefore the interaction term is used as the random factor F-ratio denominator (see Tables 12.1 & 12.2). This method assumes that the interaction terms for each level of the random factor are completely independent (correlations between the fixed factor must be consistent across all levels of the random factor). Some statisticians maintain that the independence of the interaction term is difficult to assess for biological data and therefore, the restricted approach is more appropriate. However, others have suggested that the restricted method is only appropriate for balanced designs.

12.3.1 Quasi F-ratios

An additional complication for three or more factor models that contain two or more random factors, is that there may not be a single appropriate interaction term to use as the denominator for many of the main effects F-ratios. For example, if Factors A and B are random and C is fixed, then there are two random interaction terms of equivalent level under Factor C ($A' \times C$ and $B' \times C$). As a result, the value of the of the Mean Squares expected when the nul hypothesis is true cannot be easily defined. The solutions for dealing with such situations (quasi F-ratios[b]) involve adding (and subtracting) terms together to create approximate estimates of F-ratio denominators. These solutions are

---

[a] When designs include a mixture of fixed and random crossed effects, exact demoninators for certain F-ratios are undefined and traditional approaches adopt rather inexact estimated approximate or "Quasi" F-ratios.

[b] Alternatively, for random factors, variance components with confidence intervals can be used.

sufficiently unsatisfying as to lead many biostatisticians to recommend that factorial designs with two or more random factors should avoided if possible. Arguably however, **linear mixed effects models** (see section 11.8) offer more appropriate solutions to the above issues as they are more robust for unbalanced designs, accommodate covariates and provide a more comprehensive treatment and overview of all the underlying data structures.

12.3.2 Interactions and main effects tests

Note that for fixed factor models, when null hypotheses of interactions are rejected, the null hypothesis of the individual constituent factors are unlikely to represent the true nature of the effects and thus are of little value. The nature of such interactions are further explored by fitting simpler linear models (containing at least one less factor) separately for each of the levels of the other removed factor(s). Such **Main effects tests** are based on a subset of the data, and therefore estimates of the overall residual (unexplained) variabilty are unlikely to be as precise as the estimates based on the global model. Consequently, F-ratios involving MS_{Resid} should use the estimate of MS_{Resid} from the global model rather than that based on the smaller, theoretically less precise subset of data. For random and mixed models, since the objective is to generalize the effect of one factor *over and above* any interactions with other factors, the main factor effects can be interpreted even in the presence of significant interactions[c].

12.4 Assumptions

Hypothesis tests assume that the residuals are:

(i) normally distributed. Boxplots using the appropriate scale of replication (reflecting the appropriate residuals/F-ratio denominator (see Tables 12.1 & 12.2)) should be used to explore normality. Scale transformations are often useful.
(ii) equally varied. Boxplots and plots of means against variance (using the appropriate scale of replication) should be used to explore the spread of values. Residual plots should reveal no patterns (see Figure 8.5). Scale transformations are often useful.
(iii) independent of one another.

12.5 Planned and unplanned comparisons

As with single factor analysis of variance, planned[d] and unplanned multiple comparisons (such as Tukey's test) can be incorporated into or follow the linear model

[c] Although it should be noted that when a significant interaction is present in a mixed model, the power of the main fixed effects will be reduced (since the amount of variability explained by the interaction term will be relatively high, and this term is used as the denominator for the F-ratio calculation, see Table 12.1).

[d] As with single factor analysis of variance, the contrasts must be defined prior to fitting the linear model, and no more than $p - 1$ (where p is the number of levels of the factor) contrasts can be defined for a factor.

respectively so as to further investigate any patterns or trends within the main factors and/or the interactions (see section 10.6).

12.6 Unbalanced designs

A factorial design can be thought of as a table made up of rows (representing the levels of one factor), columns (levels of another factor) and cells (the individual combinations of the set of factors), see Table 12.3(a). Table 12.3(b) depicts a balanced two factor (3x3) design in which each cell (combination of factor levels) has three replicate observations. Whilst Table 12.3(c) does not have equal sample sizes in each cell, the sample sizes are in proportion and as such, does not present the issues discussed below for unbalanced designs. Tables 12.3(d) & (e), are considered unbalanced.

12.6.1 Missing observations

In addition to impacting on normality and homogeneity of variance, unequal sample sizes in factorial designs have major implications for the partitioning of the total sums of squares into each of the model components.

For balanced designs, the total sums of squares (SS_{Total}) is equal to the additive sums of squares of each of the components (including the residual). For example, in a two factor balanced design, $SS_{Total} = SS_A + SS_B + SS_{AB} + SS_{Resid}$. This can be represented diagrammatically by a Venn Diagram (see Figure 12.3) in which each of the *SS* for the term components butt against one another and are surrounded by the SS_{Resid} (see Figure 12.2a). However, in unbalanced designs, the sums of squares will be nonorthogonal and the sum of the individual components does not add up to the total sums of squares. Diagrammatically, the SS of the terms intersect or are separated (see Figure 12.2b and 12.2g respectively). In regular **sequential sums of squares (Type I SS)**, the sum of the individual sums of squares must be equal to the total sums of squares, the sums of squares of the last factor to be estimated will be calculated as the difference between the total sums of squares and what has already been accounted for by other components. Consequently, the order in which factors are specified in the model (and thus estimated) will alter their sums of squares and therefore their *F*-ratios (see Figure 12.2c-d).

To overcome this problem, traditionally there are two other alternative methods of calculating sums of squares. **Type II (hierarchical) SS** estimate the sums of squares of each term as the improvement it contributes upon the addition of that term to a model of greater complexity and lower in the hierarchy (recall that the hierarchical structure descends from the simplest model down to the fully populated model). The SS for the interaction as well as the first factor to be estimated are the same as for Type I SS. Type II SS estimate the contribution of a factor over and above the contributions of other factors of equal or lower complexity but not above the contributions of the interaction terms or terms nested within the factor (see Figure 12.3e & 12.3k). However, these sums of squares are weighted by the sample sizes of each level and

Table 12.3 Factorial cell means structure (a) for a fictitious two factor design (effect of Temperature: high, medium or low, and Shading: full, partial or control on seedling growth) illustrating (b) balanced, (c) proportionally balanced, (d-e) unbalanced and (f) missing cells designs. For the missing cell example, in which one combination or cell is missing (perhaps seedlings grown under these conditions all died), three alternative sets of that can be used to estimate individual factor effects for factor A and B are listed in subfigures (g) and (h) respectively. Gray coefficients indicate coefficients to be omitted when cell FL is missing (as an example) and coefficients in brackets are replacement coefficients relevant for the missing cell example. Similarly, interaction effects are estimated from one of four alternative contrast sets (i). Note that cell means contrasts are not orthogonal and therefore the individual hypotheses tests should be ignored (SS will differ substantially according to the order in which the contrasts are defined). They are used purely to establish the overall factor and interaction effects.

(a) Cell means structure

	High	Medium	Low
Full shade	μ_{FH}	μ_{FM}	μ_{FL}
Partial shade	μ_{PH}	μ_{PM}	μ_{PL}
Control	μ_{CH}	μ_{CM}	μ_{CL}

(b) Balanced design (3 replicates)

	High	Medium	Low
Full shade	XXX	XXX	XXX
Partial shade	XXX	XXX	XXX
Control	XXX	XXX	XXX

(c) Proportionally balanced design (2-3 replicates)

	High	Medium	Low
Full shade	XXX	XXX	XXX
Partial shade	XX	XX	XX
Control	XXX	XXX	XXX

(d) Unbalanced design (2-3 replicates)

	High	Medium	Low
Full shade	XX	XXX	XXX
Partial shade	XXX	XXX	XXX
Control	XXX	XXX	XXX

(e) Unbalanced design (1-3 replicates)

	High	Medium	Low
Full shade	XX	XXX	XXX
Partial shade	XXX	X	XX
Control	XXX	XXX	XXX

(f) Missing cells design (3 replicates)

	High	Medium	Low
Full shade	XXX	XXX	
Partial shade	XXX	XXX	XXX
Control	XXX	XXX	XXX

(g) Factor A (Shade) contrasts

	FH	FM	FL	PH	PM	PL	CH	CM	CL
Set 1									
$H_0: \mu_F = \mu_P$	1	1	1	−1	−1	−1 (0)	0	0	0
$H_0: \mu_P = \mu_C$	0	0	0	1	1	1	−1	−1	−1
Set 2									
$H_0: \mu_F = \mu_P$	1	1	1	−1	−1	−1 (0)	0	0	0
$H_0: \mu_F = \mu_C$	1	1	1	0	0	0	−1	−1	−1 (0)
Set 3									
$H_0: \mu_F = \mu_C$	1	1	1	0	0	0	−1	−1	−1 (0)
$H_0: \mu_P = \mu_C$	0	0	0	1	1	1	−1	−1	−1

(h) Factor B (Temperature) contrasts

	FH	**FM**	**FL**	**PH**	**PM**	**PL**	**CH**	**CM**	**CL**
Set 1									
$H_0: \mu_H = \mu_M$	**1**	**−1**	0	**1**	**−1**	**0**	**1**	**−1**	**0**
$H_0: \mu_M = \mu_L$	**0**	1 **(0)**	**−1**	**0**	**1**	**−1**	**0**	**1**	**−1**
Set 2									
$H_0: \mu_M = \mu_L$	**0**	1 **(0)**	**−1**	**0**	**1**	**−1**	**0**	**1**	**−1**
$H_0: \mu_H = \mu_L$	1 **(0)**	**0**	**−1**	**1**	**0**	**−1**	**1**	**0**	**−1**
Set 3									
$H_0: \mu_H = \mu_L$	1 **(0)**	**0**	**−1**	**1**	**0**	**−1**	**1**	**0**	**−1**
$H_0: \mu_M = \mu_L$	**0**	1 **(0)**	**−1**	**0**	**1**	**−1**	**0**	**1**	**−1**

Table 12.3 *(continued)*

(i) AB interaction contrasts

Effects of A at each level of B

	FH	FM	FL	PH	PM	PL	CH	CM	CL
Set 1									
$H_0{:}\mu_{FH}+\mu_{PM}=\mu_{PH}+\mu_{FM}$	1	−1	0	−1	1	0	0	0	0
$H_0{:}\mu_{FM}+\mu_{PL}=\mu_{PM}+\mu_{FL}$	0	1	−1	0	−1	1	0	0	0
$H_0{:}\mu_{PH}+\mu_{CM}=\mu_{CH}+\mu_{PM}$	0	0	0	1	−1	0	−1	1	0
$H_0{:}\mu_{PM}+\mu_{CL}=\mu_{CM}+\mu_{PL}$	0	0	0	0	1	−1	0	−1	1
Set 2									
$H_0{:}\mu_{FH}+\mu_{PM}=\mu_{PH}+\mu_{FM}$	1	−1	0	−1	1	0	0	0	0
$H_0{:}\mu_{FH}+\mu_{PL}=\mu_{PH}+\mu_{FL}$	1	0	−1	−1	0	1	0	0	0
$H_0{:}\mu_{FH}+\mu_{CM}=\mu_{CH}+\mu_{FM}$	1	−1	0	0	0	0	−1	1	0
$H_0{:}\mu_{FH}+\mu_{CL}=\mu_{CH}+\mu_{FL}$	1	0	−1	0	0	0	−1	0	1

Effects of B at each level of A

	FH	FM	FL	PH	PM	PL	CH	CM	CL
Set 3									
$H_0{:}\mu_{FH}+\mu_{PM}=\mu_{PH}+\mu_{FM}$	1	−1	0	−1	1	0	0	0	0
$H_0{:}\mu_{PH}+\mu_{CM}=\mu_{PM}+\mu_{CH}$	0	0	0	1	−1	0	1	−1	0
$H_0{:}\mu_{FM}+\mu_{PL}=\mu_{FL}+\mu_{PM}$	0	1	−1	0	−1	1	0	0	0
$H_0{:}\mu_{PM}+\mu_{CL}=\mu_{PL}+\mu_{CM}$	0	0	0	0	1	−1	0	−1	1
Set 4									
$H_0{:}\mu_{FH}+\mu_{PM}=\mu_{FM}+\mu_{PH}$	1	−1	0	−1	1	0	0	0	0
$H_0{:}\mu_{FH}+\mu_{CM}=\mu_{FM}+\mu_{CH}$	1	−1	0	0	0	0	−1	1	0
$H_0{:}\mu_{FH}+\mu_{PL}=\mu_{FL}+\mu_{PH}$	1	0	−1	−1	0	1	0	0	0
$H_0{:}\mu_{FH}+\mu_{CL}=\mu_{FL}+\mu_{CH}$	1	0	−1	0	0	0	−1	0	1

therefore are biased towards the trends produced by the groups (levels) that have higher sample sizes[e].

Type III (marginal or orthogonal) SS estimate the sums of squares of each term as the improvement based on a comparison of models with and without the term and are unweighted by sample sizes. Type III SS essentially measure just the unique contribution of each factor over and above the contributions of the other factors and interactions (see Figure 12.3f & 12.3l). For unbalanced designs,Type III SS essentially test equivalent hypotheses to balanced Type I SS and are therefore arguably more appropriate for unbalanced factorial designs than Type II SS. Importantly, Type III SS are only interpretable if they are based on orthogonal contrasts (such as sum or helmert contrasts and not treatment contrasts).

The choice between Type II and III SS clearly depends on the nature of the question. For example, if we had measured the growth rate of seedlings subjected to two factors (temperature and fertilizer), Type II SS could address whether there was an effect of temperature across the level of fertilizer treatment, whereas Type III SS could assess whether there was an effect of temperature within each level of the fertilizer treatment.

12.6.2 Missing combinations - missing cells

When an entire combination, or cell, is missing (perhaps due to unforeseen circumstances) it is not possible to test all the main effects and/or interactions. Table 12.3(f) depicts such as situation. One solution is to fit a large single factor ANOVA with as many levels as there are cells (this is known as a **cell means model**) and investigate various factor and interaction effects via specific contrasts (see Tables 12.3(g)-(j) and 12.4). Difficulties in establishing appropriate error terms, makes missing cells in random and mixed factor designs substantially more complex.

[e] As a result of the weightings, Type II SS actually test hypotheses about really quite complex combinations of factor levels. Rather than test a hypothesis that $\mu_{High} = \mu_{Medium} = \mu Low$, Type II SS might be testing that $4\mu_{High} = 1\mu_{Medium} = 0.25\mu Low$.

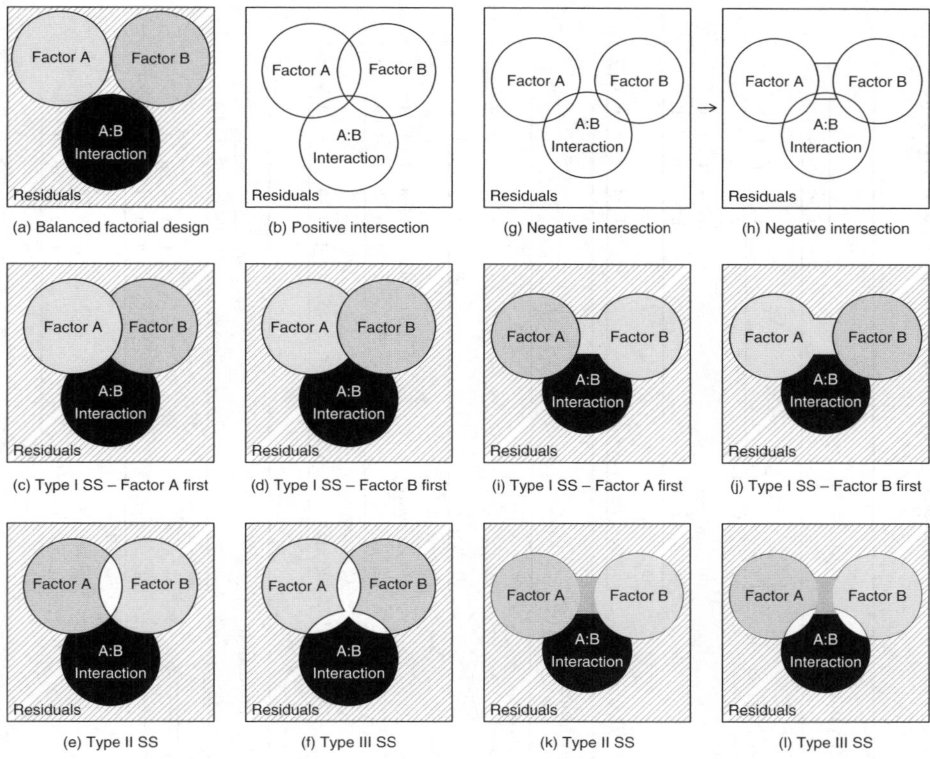

Fig 12.3 Fictitious representations of Type I, II and III Sums of Squares (SS) calculations for balanced and unbalanced two factor designs with positive (b-f) and negative (g-l) intersections. Striped pattern represents *SSresid*, shaded patterns represent SS for the respective terms and the white fill represent ignored areas. For completely balanced designs (a), the terms are all completely orthogonal or independent (no intersections) and thus Type I, II and III SS are identical. The Type I, II and III sums of squares for the interaction term for unbalanced two-factor designs are also identical. Type II SS for the main factors are the same as the Type I SS for the second factor calculated. When there are positive intersections between factors (factors are positively dependent), Type I SS for the first factor will be greater than its Type II estimate which in turn will be greater than its Type III estimate. For negative intersections (in which factors are negatively dependent), Type I SS for the first factor will be less than its Type II and III estimates. For such intersections, factors are joined by a *bridge* which is included in the SS calculations for each of the factors it joins. It is also possible to have bridges between factors and interaction terms, in which case Type III SS estimates can be substantially larger than Type I and II estimates. Note that intersections are not the same as interactions and the two issues are completely separate.

12.7 Robust factorial ANOVA

Factorial designs can be analysed as large single factor designs by arranging each factor combination as a unique level of a new single factor and then incorporating a specific sets of contrasts. Therefore, many of the robust or non-parametric techniques outlined in chapter 10.5 can be used to analyze factorial designs. Alternatively, standard factorial ANOVA can be performed on rank transformed data. This approach can also

Table 12.4 Cell means structure and associated contrasts for fictitious factorial designs (a) 3x2 one cell missing, (b) 3x3 two cells missing and (c) 3x3 three cells missing. Note that contrasts are not orthogonal and that in some cases the set of contrasts presented represents one of multiple possible combinations.

(a)

A \ B	1	2	3
1	μ_{11}	μ_{12}	-
2	μ_{21}	μ_{22}	μ_{23}

Factor A

	1	2	3
1	μ_{11}	μ_{12}	-
2	μ_{21}	μ_{22}	μ_{23}

Factor B

	1	2	3
1	μ_{11}	μ_{12}	-
2	μ_{21}	μ_{22}	μ_{23}

	1	2	3
1	μ_{11}	μ_{12}	-
2	μ_{21}	μ_{22}	μ_{23}

AB interaction

	1	2	3
1	μ_{11}	μ_{12}	-
2	μ_{21}	μ_{22}	μ_{23}

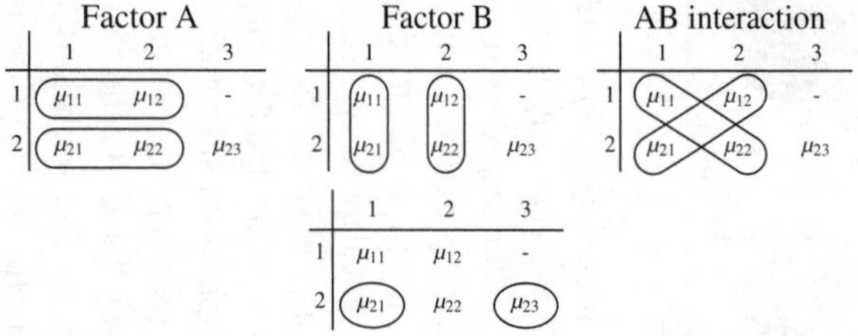

	μ_{11}	μ_{12}	μ_{21}	μ_{22}	μ_{23}
Factor A					
(H_0: $\mu_{A1} = \mu_{A2}$)	1	1	–1	–1	0
Factor B					
(H_0: $\mu_{B1} = \mu_{B2}$)	1	–1	1	–1	0
(H_0: $\mu_{B1} = \mu_{B3}$)	0	0	1	0	–1
AB					
(H_0: $\mu_{A11} + \mu_{22} = \mu_{A21} + \mu_{21}$)	1	–1	–1	1	0

(b)

A \ B	1	2	3
1	μ_{11}	μ_{12}	-
2	μ_{21}	-	μ_{23}
3	μ_{31}	μ_{32}	μ_{33}

Factor A

	1	2	3
1	μ_{11}	μ_{12}	-
2	μ_{21}	-	μ_{23}
3	μ_{31}	μ_{32}	μ_{33}

	1	2	3
1	μ_{11}	μ_{12}	-
2	μ_{21}	-	μ_{23}
3	μ_{31}	μ_{32}	μ_{33}

Factor B

	1	2	3
1	μ_{11}	μ_{12}	-
2	μ_{21}	-	μ_{23}
3	μ_{31}	μ_{32}	μ_{33}

	1	2	3
1	μ_{11}	μ_{12}	-
2	μ_{21}	-	μ_{23}
3	μ_{31}	μ_{32}	μ_{33}

AB interaction

	1	2	3
1	μ_{11}	μ_{12}	-
2	μ_{21}	-	μ_{23}
3	μ_{31}	μ_{32}	μ_{33}

	1	2	3
1	μ_{11}	μ_{12}	-
2	μ_{21}	-	μ_{23}
3	μ_{31}	μ_{32}	μ_{33}

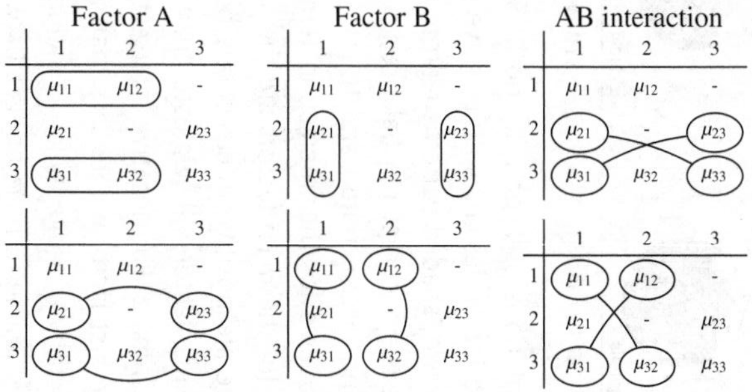

	μ_{11}	μ_{12}	μ_{21}	μ_{23}	μ_{31}	μ_{32}	μ_{33}
Factor A							
(H_0: $\mu_{A1} = \mu_{A3}$)	1	1	0	0	–1	–1	0
(H_0: $\mu_{A2} = \mu_{A3}$)	0	0	1	1	–1	0	–1
Factor B							
(H_0: $\mu_{B2} = \mu_{B3}$)	0	0	1	–1	1	0	–1
(H_0: $\mu_{B1} = \mu_{B2}$)	1	–1	0	0	1	–1	0
AB interaction							
(H_0: $\mu_{A21} + \mu_{33} = \mu_{A23} + \mu_{31}$)	1	–1	0	0	–1	1	0

(c)

A \ B	1	2	3
1	μ_{11}	μ_{12}	μ_{13}
2	μ_{21}	μ_{22}	-
3	-	-	μ_{33}

Factor A

	1	2	3
1	μ_{11}	μ_{12}	μ_{13}
2	μ_{21}	μ_{22}	-
3	-	-	μ_{33}

	1	2	3
1	μ_{11}	μ_{12}	μ_{13}
2	μ_{21}	μ_{22}	-
3	-	-	μ_{33}

Factor B

	1	2	3
1	μ_{11}	μ_{12}	μ_{13}
2	μ_{21}	μ_{22}	-
3	-	-	μ_{33}

	1	2	3
1	μ_{11}	μ_{12}	μ_{13}
2	μ_{21}	μ_{22}	-
3	-	-	μ_{33}

AB interaction

	1	2	3
1	μ_{11}	μ_{12}	μ_{13}
2	μ_{21}	μ_{22}	-
3	-	-	μ_{33}

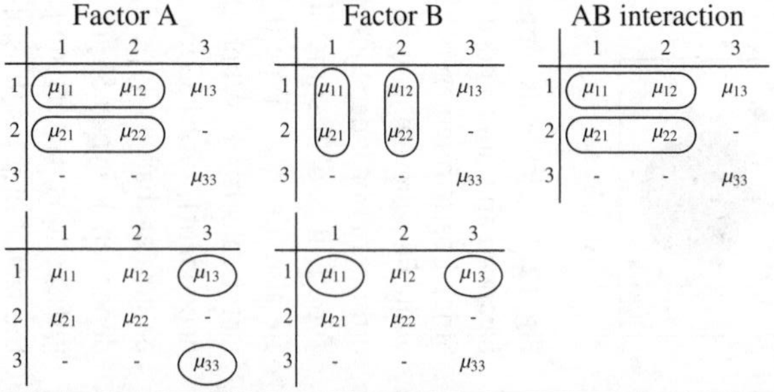

	μ_{11}	μ_{12}	μ_{13}	μ_{21}	μ_{22}	μ_{33}
Factor A						
(H_0: $\mu_{A1} = \mu_{A3}$)	1	1	0	–1	–1	0
(H_0: $\mu_{A2} = \mu_{A3}$)	0	0	1	0	0	–1
Factor B						
(H_0: $\mu_{B2} = \mu_{B3}$)	1	–1	0	1	–1	0
(H_0: $\mu_{B1} = \mu_{B2}$)	1	0	–1	0	0	0
AB interaction						
(H_0: $\mu_{A21} + \mu_{33} = \mu_{A23} + \mu_{31}$)	1	1	0	–1	–1	0

be extended to more complex designs, thereby providing a way to analyse unbalanced and mixed effects designs that display evidence of non-normality. Unfortunately, there is some evidence to suggest that testing interactions on rank transformed data can increase the Type I error rate. Furthermore, in the presence of significant main effects, the power to detect interaction effects is low.

Randomization tests (which are useful for situations in which observation independence could be questionable) can be performed by comparing the *F*-ratios (or mean squares) to a large number of *F*-ratios calculated from repeatedly shuffled data[f]. In so doing, randomization tests can accomodate random, fixed and mixed models as well as Type I, II and III SS and cell means models (for missing cells).

12.8 Power and sample sizes

Although power analyses for main effects within factorial designs follow the same principles as single factor designs, for interactions, it is very difficult to estimate the meaningful effect sizes due to the large number of factor level combinations. That said, the tests of interactions are typically more powerful than main effects (due to greater available degrees of freedom) and for fixed models, efforts to improve the power of any of the main effects will also benefit the corresponding interactions. Power analyses for mixed and random factorial designs should reflect the appropriate residuals (see Tables 12.1 & 12.2).

12.9 Factorial ANOVA in R

Fully factorial linear models are predominantly fitted using the `aov()` *function*. Anova tables for balanced, fixed factor designs can be viewed using either the `anova()` or `summary()`, the latter of which is used to accommodate planned contrasts with the `split=` *argument*. Type II and III sums of squares are estimated for unbalanced designs using either the `Anova()`[g] or `AnovaM()`[h] *functions*, the latter of which also accommodates planned contrasts (with the `split=` *argument*) as well as random and mixed models by enabling the appropriate *F*-ratio denominators to be defined via the `denoms=` *argument*.

12.10 Further reading

- Theory

  Doncaster, C. P., and A. J. H. Davey. (2007). *Analysis of Variance and Covariance. How to Choose and Construct Models for the Life Sciences.* Cambridge University Press, Cambridge.

[f] Although there are various ways in which the data or residuals could be shuffled, simulations suggest that they all yield very similar results.
[g] From the `car` *package*.
[h] From the `biology` *package*.

Hollander, M., and D. A. Wolfe. (1999). *Nonparametric statistical methods, 2nd edition.* 2 edition. John Wiley & Sons, New York.

Quinn, G. P., and K. J. Keough. (2002). *Experimental design and data analysis for biologists.* Cambridge University Press, London.

Sokal, R., and F. J. Rohlf. (1997). *Biometry*, 3rd edition. W. H. Freeman, San Francisco.

Zar, G. H. (1999). *Biostatistical methods.* Prentice-Hall, New Jersey.

- Practical - R

Crawley, M. J. (2007). *The R Book.* John Wiley, New York.

Fox, J. (2002). *An R and S-PLUS Companion to Applied Regression.* Sage Books.

Maindonald, J. H., and J. Braun. (2003). *Data Analysis and Graphics Using R - An Example-based Approach.* Cambridge University Press, London.

Venables, W. N., and B. D. Ripley. (2002). *Modern Applied Statistics with S-PLUS*, 4th edn. Springer-Verlag, New York.

Wilcox, R. R. (2005). *Introduction to Robust Estimation and Hypothesis Testing.* Elsevier Academic Press.

12.11 Key for factorial ANOVA

1 **For each factor (categorical variable), establish whether it is to be considered a fixed or random factor**
- **Conclusions about the factor are restricted to the specific levels selected in the design.** Levels of the factor selected to represent the specific levels of interest (**fixed factor**)
- **Conclusions about the factor to be generalized across all possible levels of the factor.** Levels of the factor used represent a random selection of all the possible levels (**random factor**)

.... Go to 2

2 **Establish what sort of model it is and therefore what the appropriate *F*-ratio denominators apply (see Tables 12.1 & 12.2)**
- **All factors fixed (Model I)**
- **All factors random (Model II)**
- **Mixture of fixed and random factors (Model III)**

.... Go to 3

3 a. **Check assumptions for factorial ANOVA**

As the assumptions of any given hypothesis test relate to residuals, all diagnostics should reflect the appropriate error (residual) terms for the hypothesis. This is particularly important for random and mixed models where interaction terms might be the appropriate denominators (residuals).

- **Normality (symmetry) of the response variable (residuals) at each level of each factor or combination of factors - boxplots of mean values**

Fixed factor model (Model I) - using MS_{Resid} as denominator in each case

```
> boxplot(DV ~ A, data) #factor A
> boxplot(DV ~ B, data) #factor B
> boxplot(DV ~ A * B, data) #A:B interaction
```

Random or mixed model (Model II or III - factor B random) - using MS_{AB} as denominator as example

```
> library(nlme)
> data.AB.agg <- gsummary(data, groups = data$A:data$B)
> boxplot(DV ~ A, data.AB.agg) #factor A
```

where `DV` *is the response variable,* `A` *is a main fixed or random factor within the* `data` *dataset.*

- **Homogeneity (equality) of variance of the response variable (residuals) at each level of each factor or combination of factors - boxplots of mean values**
  As for Normality.

Parametric assumptions met .... Go to 5

b. Parametric assumptions not met .... Go to 4

4 a. Attempt a scale transformation (see Table 3.2 for transformation options) .... Go to 3

b. Transformations unsuccessful or inappropriate .... Go to 15

5 a. All factor combinations (cells) have at least one observation (no missing cells) .... Go to 6

b. One or more factor combinations without any observations (missing cells). Analyze as single factor cell means model. .... Go to 10

6 If incorporating planned contrasts (comparisons) ...... See Examples 12A,12B,12C

```
> contrasts(data$A) <- cbind(c(contrasts), ...)
> round(crossprod(contrasts(data$A)), 2)
```

.... Go to 7

7 a. Determine whether the design is balanced

```
> replications(DV ~ A * B * C + .., data)
> library(biology)
> is.balanced(DV ~ A * B * C + .., data)
```

Design is balanced - sample sizes of all cells are equal (Type I SS) .... Go to 8

b. Design is NOT balanced - sample sizes of cells differ (Type III SS) .... Go to 9

8 a. Balanced Model I (Fixed factors) .... See Examples 12A,12B

```
> data.aov <- aov(DV ~ A * B, data)
```

To check residual plot .... Go to 21

- **With planned contrasts**

```
> library(biology)
> AnovaM(data.aov, split = list(A = list(Name1 = 1, Name2 = 2,
+     ...), B = list()))
> #OR
> summary(data.aov, split = list(A = list(Name1 = 1,
+     Name2 = 2, ...), B = list()))
```

where `DV` *is the response variable,* `A` *and* `B` *are the main fixed factors within the* `data` *dataset.*

- **Without planned contrasts**

```
> AnovaM(data.aov)
> #OR
> summary(data.aov)
> #OR
> anova(data.aov)
```

For post-hoc multiple comparisons .... Go to 20

If significant interation .... Go to 14

For summary plot .... Go to 18

b. Balanced Model II (random factors) or Model III (mixed factors) .... See Example 12C

```
> data.aov <- aov(DV ~ A * B, data)
```

To check residual plot .... Go to 21

- **With planned contrasts**

```
> AnovaM(data.aov, denoms = c("A:B", "Resid", "Resid"),
+     split = list(A = list(Name1 = 1, Name2 = 2, ...),
+         B = list()))
```

This example is a restricted model III where `DV` *is the response variable,* `A` *is a fixed factor and* `B` *is a random factor within the* `data` *dataset.* `denoms=c()` *is used to specify the denominators for each term in the model according to table 12.1*

- **Without planned contrasts**

```
> AnovaM(data.aov, denoms = c("A:B", "Resid", "Resid"))
```

For post-hoc multiple comparisons .... Go to 20

For variance components .... Go to 19

If significant interation .... Go to 14

For summary plot .... Go to 18

9 a. Unbalanced Model I (Fixed factors) .... See Example 12D

```
> data.aov <- aov(DV ~ A * B, data)
```

To check residual plot .... Go to 21

- **With planned contrasts**

```
> AnovaM(data.aov, type = "III", split = list(A = list
+     (Name1 = 1, Name2 = 2, ...), B = list()))
```

where `DV` *is the response variable,* `A` *and* `B` *are the main fixed factors within the* `data` *dataset.*

- **Without planned contrasts** - must define contrasts other than the default (treatment contratsts)

```
> contrasts(data$A) <- contr.helmert
> contrasts(data$B) <- contr.helmert
> data.aov <- aov(DV ~ A * B, data)
> AnovaM(data.aov, type = "III", data)
```

For post-hoc multiple comparisons .... Go to 20

If significant interation .... Go to 14

For summary plot .... Go to 18

b. Unbalanced Model II (random factors) or Model III (mixed factors)

```
> data.aov <- aov(DV ~ A * B, data)
```

To check residual plot .... Go to 21

- **With planned contrasts**

```
> AnovaM(data.aov, denoms = c("A:B", "Resid", "Resid"),
+     type = "III", split = list(A = list(Name1 = 1,
+     Name2 = 2, ...), B = list()))
```

example is a restricted model III where DV *is the response variable,* A *is a fixed factor and* B *is a random factor within the* data *dataset.* denoms=c() *is used to specify the denominators for each term in the model according to table 12.1*

- **Without planned contrasts**

```
> AnovaM(data.aov, denoms = c("A:B", "Resid", "Resid"),
+      type = "III")
```

For post-hoc multiple comparisons .... Go to 20

For variance components .... Go to 19
If significant interation .... Go to 14
For summary plot .... Go to 18

10 Generate a new factorial variable to represent the combinations of factor levels and define sets of contrasts to represent each of the terms (main factors and interactions) in the design .... See Examples 12E,13

```
> data$AB <- factor(paste(data$A, data$B, sep = "A:B"))
> contrasts(data$AB) <- cbind(c(contrasts), c(contrasts), ...)
```

.... Go to 12

11 a. Determine whether the design is otherwise balanced (all present cells have equal sample sizes)

```
> replications(DV ~ A * B * C + .., data)
> library(biology)
> is.balanced(DV ~ A * B * C + .., data)
```

Design is balanced - sample sizes of all cells are equal (Type I SS) .... Go to 12

b. Design is NOT balanced - sample sizes of cells differ (Type III SS) ...... Go to 13

12 a. Balanced missing cells Model I (Fixed factors) .... See Example 12E

```
> data.aov <- aov(DV ~ AB, data)
```

To check residual plot .... Go to 21

```
> AnovaM(data.aov, split = list(AB = list('Factor A' = 1:2)))
```

where in this case, DV *is the response variable and* AB *is the combined factors (*A *and* B*) within the* data *dataset. In this case, the ANOVA table will also include a line titled "Factor A" which represents the combination of the first two contrasts.*

For post-hoc multiple comparisons .... Go to 20

If significant interation .... Go to 14

For summary plot .... Go to 18

b. Balanced missing cells Model II (random factors) or Model III (mixed factors)

```
> data.aov <- aov(DV ~ AB, data)
```

To check residual plot .... Go to 21

```
> AnovaM(data.aov, denoms = c(object), split = list(AB = list
+      ('Factor A' = 1:2)))
```

example is a restricted model III where DV *is the response variable, and* AB *is a random factor representing the combination of factors* A *and* B *within the* data *dataset.* denoms=c(object) *is used to specify the denominators for each term in the model according to table 12.1. The* object *can be either a list of labels that refer to terms in the current model, a single alternative* aov *model from which to extract the* Residual *term, or a list of alternative model terms. Note, interaction terms should be derived prior to main factors.*

For post-hoc multiple comparisons .... Go to 20
For variance components .... Go to 19
If significant interation .... Go to 14
For summary plot .... Go to 18

13 a. Unbalanced missing cells Model I (Fixed factors) .... See Example 12F

```
> data.aov <- aov(DV ~ AB, data)
```

To check residual plot .... Go to 21

```
> AnovaM(data.aov, type = "III", split = list(AB = list
+      ('Factor A' = 1:2)))
```

where DV *is the response variable,* A *and* B *are the main fixed factors within the* data *dataset.*

For post-hoc multiple comparisons .... Go to 20
If significant interation .... Go to 14
For summary plot .... Go to 18

b. Unbalanced missing cells Model II (random factors) or Model III (mixed factors)

```
> data.aov <- aov(DV ~ AB, data)
```

To check residual plot .... Go to 21

```
> AnovaM(data.aov, denoms = c(c(object)), type = "III",
+      split = list(AB = list('Factor A' = 1:2)))
```

example is a restricted model III where DV *is the response variable,* A *is a fixed factor and* B *is a random factor within the* data *dataset.* denoms=c(object) *is used to specify the denominators for each term in the model according to table 12.1. The* object *can be either a list of labels that refer to terms in the current model, a single alternative* aov *model from which to extract the* Residual *term, or a list of alternative model terms.*

For post-hoc multiple comparisons .... Go to 20
For variance components .... Go to 19
If significant interation .... Go to 14
For summary plot .... Go to 18

14 Main effects tests .... See Examples 12B,12D,12E,12F

- **Repeat analysis steps above with on a subset of the data (just one levels of one of the factors) and use the MS_{Resid} from the global model.**

```
> AnovaM(mainEffects(data.aov, at = B == "B1"), split = list
+      (A = list(Name1 = 1, Name2 = 2, ...)))
```

where in this case, `DV` *is the response variable and* `A` *is a fixed factor (*`A` *from a Model I factorial design within the* `data` *dataset.* `denoms=c()` *is used to specify the denominators for each term in the model according to table 12.1*

15 a. Underlying distribution of the response variable is normal for each level of the interaction, but the variances are unequal (Welch's test on combined factors)
Generate a new factorial variable to represent the combinations of factor levels and analyse as a single factor ANOVA using a Welch's test (see Key 10.6)

```
> data$AB <- factor(paste(data$A, data$B, sep = "A:B"))
> oneway.test(DV ~ AB, data, var.equal = F)
```

b. Underlying distributions not normally distributed .... Go to 16
or consider GLM .... GLM chapter 17

16 a. Underlying distribution of the response variable and residuals is known ... GLM chapter 17

b. Underlying distributions of the response variable and residuals is not known .... Go to 17

17 a. Variances not wildly unequal, outliers present, but data independent (Kruskal-Wallis non-parametric test on combined factors)

```
> data$AB <- factor(paste(data$A, data$B, sep = "A:B"))
> kruskal.test(DV ~ AB, data, var.equal = F)
```

b. Variances not wildly unequal, random sampling not possible - data might not be independent (Randomization test)
Follow the instructions in Key 10.8b to randomize the *F*-ratios or *MS* values from ANOVA tables produced using the parametric steps above. **Warning, randomization procedures are only useful when there are a large number of possible randomization combinations (rarely the case in factorial designs)**

18 a. Interaction plot to summarize an ordered trend (line graph) .... See Examples 12A,12B,12E

```
> library(gmodels)
> data.means <- with(data, tapply(DV, list(FACTA, FACTB), mean))
> data.se <- with(data, tapply(DV, list(FACTA, FACTB),
+     function(x) ci(x)[4]))
> with(data, interaction.plot(FACTA, FACTB, DV, las = 1,
+     lwd = 2, ylim = range(pretty(data$DV), na.rm = T),
+     axes = F, xlab = "", ylab = "", pch = c(16, 17),
+     type = "b", legend = F))
> arrows(1:3, data.means - data.se, 1:3, data.means + data.se,
+     code = 3, angle = 90, len = 0.05)
> axis(2, cex.axis = 0.8, las = 1, mgp = c(3, 0.5, 0),
+     tcl = -0.2)
> mtext(text = "Y-label", side = 2, line = 3, cex = 1)
> axis(1, cex.axis = 0.8, at = 1:3, lab = c("Lab1",
+     "Lab2", ...))
> mtext(text = "X-label", 1, line = 3, cex = 1)
> box(bty = "l")
```

```
> legend("topright", leg = c("Lab1", "Lab2", ...), lwd = 2,
+     lty = c(2, 1), bty = "n", pch = c(16, 17), cex = 1)
```

where FACTA *is the factor to placed on the x-axis.*

b. Interaction plot to summarize an unordered categories (bargraph) .... See Examples 12C,12D,12F

```
> library(gmodels)
> data.means <- t(tapply(data$DV, list(data$FACTA, data$FACTB),
+     mean, na.rm = T))
> data.se <- t(tapply(data$DV, list(data$FACTA, data$FACTB),
+     function(x) ci(x, na.rm = T)[4]))
> xs <- barplot(data.means, ylim = range(pretty(data$DV),
+     na.rm = T), beside = T, axes = F, xpd = F, axisnames = F,
+     axis.lty = 2, legend.text = F, col = c(0, 1))
> arrows(xs, data.means, xs, data.means + data.se, code = 2,
+     angle = 90, len = 0.05)
> axis(2, las = 1)
> axis(1, at = apply(xs, 2, median), lab = c("Lab1",
+     "Lab2", ...), padj = 1, mgp = c(0, 0, 0))
> mtext(2, text = "Y-label", line = 3, cex = 1)
> mtext(1, text = "X-label", line = 3, cex = 1)
> box(bty = "l")
> legend("topright", leg = c("Lab1", "Lab2", ...), fill = c(0,
+     1), col = c(0, 1), bty = "n", cex = 1)
```

where FACTA *is the factor to placed on the x-axis.*

19 Estimate variance components .... See Example 12C

```
> library(lme4)
> lmer(DV ~ 1 + (1 | A) + (1 | B) + (1 | A:B) + ..., data)
```

20 a. Perform Tukey's post-hoc multiple comparisons .... See Example 12D

```
> TukeyHSD(mod, which = "Factor")
> #OR alternatively
> library(multcomp)
> summary(glht(mod, linfct = mcp(Factor = "Tukey")))
> confint(glht(mod, linfct = mcp(Factor = "Tukey")))
```

where mod is the name of an aov *model and* ,Factor, *is the name of a factor.*

b. Perform other form of post-hoc multiple comparisons .... Go to Key 10.9

21 Examine a residual plot .... See Examples 12A-12D

```
> plot(data.aov, which = 1)
```

12.12 Worked examples of real biological data sets

Example 12A: Two factor fixed (Model I) ANOVA

Quinn (1988) manipulated the density of adults limpets within enclosures (8, 15, 30 and 45 individuals per enclosure) during two seasons (winter-spring and summer-autumn) so as to investigate the effects of adult density and season on egg mass production by intertidal limpets. Three replicate enclosures per density/season combination were used, and both density and season were considered fixed factors (from Box 9.4 of Quinn and Keough (2002)).

Step 1 - Import (section 2.3) the Quinn (1988) data set

```
> quinn <- read.table("quinn.csv", header = T, sep = ",")
```

Step 2 - The density vector (variable) contains numerical representations of the adult limpet densities, and R will consider this to be a *integer* vector rather than a categorical *factor*. In order to ensure that this variable is treated as a factor we need to redefine its class

```
> class(quinn$DENSITY)
[1] "integer"

> quinn$DENSITY <- factor(quinn$DENSITY)
> class(quinn$DENSITY)
[1] "factor"
```

Step 3 (Key 12.2) Quinn (1988) considered both factors to be fixed factors and thus the data represent a Model I design

Step 4 (Key 12.3) - Assess assumptions of normality and homogeneity of variance for each null hypothesis ensuring that the correct scale of replicates are represented for each (they should reflect the appropriate *F*-ratio denominators see Table 12.1).
According to Table 12.1, the MS_{Resid} (individual enclosures) should be used as the replicates for all hypothesis tests for Model I designs.

Factor A (Fixed)

```
> boxplot(EGGS ~
+       DENSITY, quinn)
```

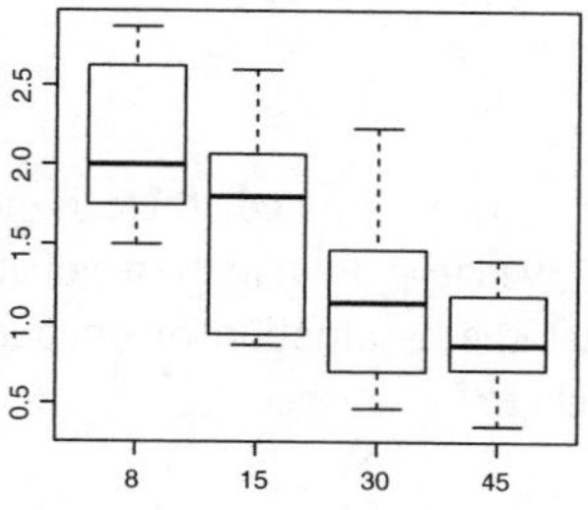

Factor B (Fixed)

```
> boxplot(EGGS ~
+       SEASON, quinn)
```

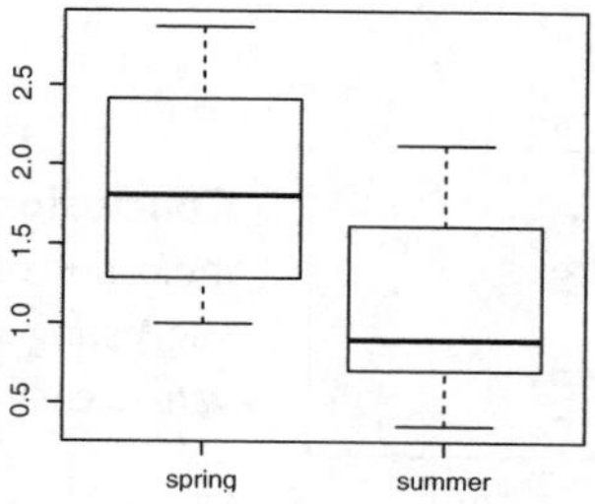

A:B interaction (Fixed)

```
> boxplot(EGGS ~
+       DENSITY * SEASON,
+       quinn)
```

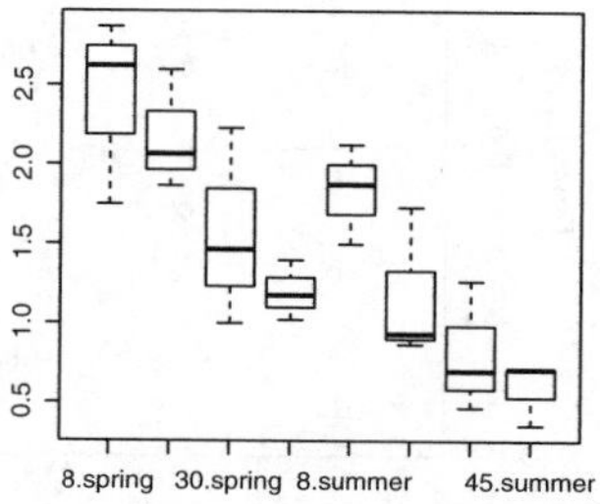

Conclusions - No evidence of non-normality (boxplots not wildly asymmetrical) and no apparent relationship between mean and variance (heights of boxplots increase up the y-axis). No evidence that any of the hypothesis tests will be unreliable.

Step 5 (Key 12.5 & 12.7) - Determine whether or not the design is missing any factor combinations (cells) or is unbalanced (unequal sample sizes).

```
> replications(EGGS ~ DENSITY * SEASON, quinn)
       DENSITY          SEASON DENSITY:SEASON
             6              12              3
```

```
> library(biology)
> is.balanced(EGGS ~ DENSITY * SEASON, quinn)
[1] TRUE
```

Conclusions - The design is completely balanced. There are three replicate enclosures for each of the four densities and two seasons.

Step 6 - (Key 12.6) - Define polynomial contrasts (see sections 10.6 and 7.3.1 for more information on setting contrasts) to further investigate the nature of the effects of density on egg mass production.

```
> contrasts(quinn$DENSITY) <- contr.poly(4, scores = c(8, 15, 30,
+     45))
```

The `scores =` *function* is used to define the levels of the within block effect when they are do not have equal increments. Note that there is no need to check the orthogonality of these contrasts, they will always be constructed to be orthogonal.

Step 7 (Key 12.8) - Fit the factorial linear model[i].

```
> quinn.aov <- aov(EGGS ~ DENSITY + SEASON + DENSITY:SEASON,
+     data = quinn)
> #OR
> quinn.aov <- aov(EGGS ~ DENSITY * SEASON, data = quinn)
```

Step 8 (Key 12.21) - Examine the fitted model diagnostics[j]. Note that this is evaluating the overall residuals and predicted values for the interaction effect.)

```
> plot(quinn.aov, which = 1)
```

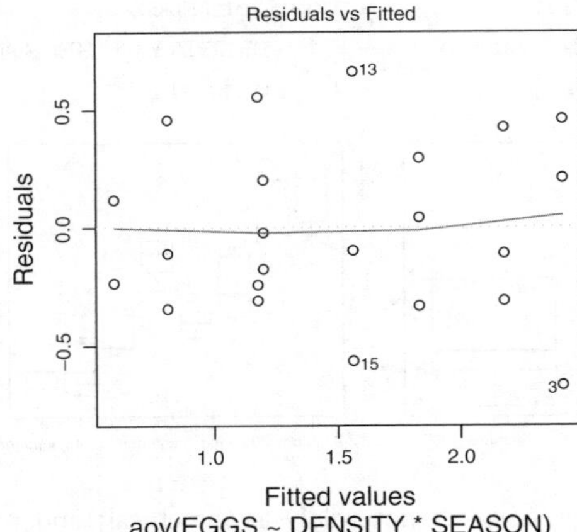

Conclusions - As anticipated, there is no indication of a 'wedge' pattern in the residuals suggesting that the assumption of unequal variance is likely to be satisfied.

Step 9 (Key 12.8) - Examine the balanced model I ANOVA table, including the set of defined planned polynomial contrasts.

```
> summary(quinn.aov, split = list(DENSITY = list(Linear = 1,
+     Quadratic = 2)))
```

[i] Note that if we were also intending to investigate a set of planned comparisons/contrasts (see chapter 10.6), these should be defined prior to fitting the linear model.

[j] Recall that leverage, and thus Cook's D are not informative for categorical predictor variables.

OR

```
> library(biology)
> AnovaM(quinn.aov, type = "I", split = list(DENSITY =
+     list(Linear = 1, Quadratic = 2)))
                              Df Sum Sq Mean Sq F value    Pr(>F)
DENSITY                        3 5.2841  1.7614  9.6691 0.0007041 ***
  DENSITY: Linear              1 5.0241  5.0241 27.5799 7.907e-05 ***
  DENSITY: Quadratic           1 0.2358  0.2358  1.2946 0.2719497
SEASON                         1 3.2502  3.2502 17.8419 0.0006453 ***
DENSITY:SEASON                 3 0.1647  0.0549  0.3014 0.8239545
  DENSITY:SEASON: Linear       1 0.0118  0.0118  0.0649 0.8021605
  DENSITY:SEASON: Quadratic    1 0.0691  0.0691  0.3796 0.5464978
Residuals                     16 2.9146  0.1822
---
Signif. codes:  0 '***' 0.001 '**' 0.01 '*' 0.05 '.' 0.1 ' ' 1
```

Conclusions - There was no evidence of an interaction between density and season (suggesting that the effect of density was consistent across both seasons). Egg production was significantly greater in winter-spring than summer-autumn and declined linearly with increasing adult density.

Step 10 (Key 12.18) - Summarize the trends in a interaction plot.

```
> library(gmodels)
> quinn.means <- tapply(quinn$EGGS, list(quinn$DENSITY,
+     quinn$SEASON), mean)
> quinn.se <- tapply(quinn$EGGS, list(quinn$DENSITY, quinn$SEASON),
+     function(x) ci(x)[4])
> quinn$DENS <- as.numeric(as.character(quinn$DENSITY))
> plot(EGGS ~ DENS, quinn, type = "n", axes = F, xlab = "",
+     ylab = "")
> points(quinn.means[, 1] ~ unique(quinn$DENS), pch = 16,
+     type = "b", lwd = 2)
> arrows(unique(quinn$DENS), quinn.means[, 1] - quinn.se[, 1],
+     unique(quinn$DENS), quinn.means[, 1] + quinn.se[, 1],
+     code = 3, angle = 90, len = 0.1)
> points(quinn.means[, 2] ~ unique(quinn$DENS), pch = 16,
+     type = "b", lwd = 2, lty = 2)
> arrows(unique(quinn$DENS), quinn.means[, 2] - quinn.se[, 2],
+     unique(quinn$DENS), quinn.means[, 2] + quinn.se[, 2],
+     code = 3, angle = 90, len = 0.1)
> axis(1, cex.axis = 0.8)
> mtext(text = "Adult Density", 1, line = 3)
> axis(2, cex.axis = 0.8, las = 1)
> mtext(text = "Egg production", side = 2, line = 3)
> legend("topright", leg = c("Winter-spring", "Summer-autumn"),
+     lwd = 2, lty = c(1, 2), bty = "n")
> box(bty = "l")
```

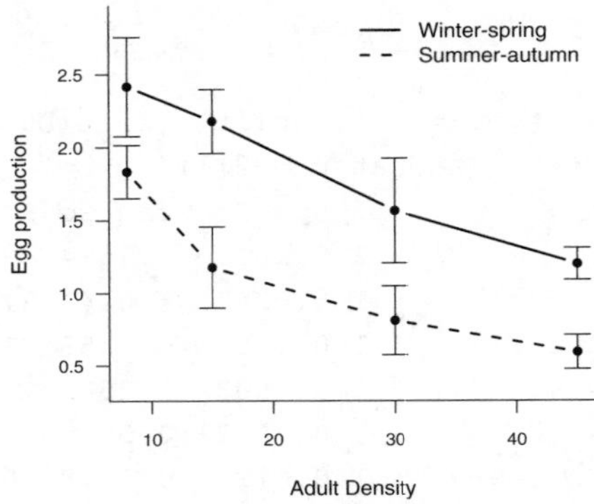

Example 12B: Two factor fixed (Model I) ANOVA

In a similar experiment to that illustrated in Example 12A, Quinn (1988) also manipulated the density of larger adults limpets further down the shoreline within enclosures (6, 12 and 24 individuals per enclosure) during the two seasons (winter-spring and summer-autumn) so as to investigate their effects on egg mass production. Again, three replicate enclosures per density/season combination were used, and both density and season were considered fixed factors (from Box 9.4 of Quinn and Keough (2002)).

Step 1 - Import (section 2.3) the Quinn (1988) data set

```
> quinn1 <- read.table("quinn1.csv", header = T, sep = ",")
```

Step 2 - redefine the density vector as a factor

```
> quinn1$DENSITY <- factor(quinn1$DENSITY)
```

Step 3 (Key 12.2) Quinn (1988) considered both factors to be fixed factors and thus the data represent a Model I design

Step 4 (Key 12.3) - Assess assumptions of normality and homogeneity of variance for each null hypothesis ensuring that the correct scale of replicates are represented for each (they should reflect the appropriate *F*-ratio denominators see Table 12.1).
According to Table 12.1, the MS_{Resid} (individual enclosures) should be used as the replicates for all hypothesis tests for Model I designs.

```
> boxplot(EGGS ~ DENSITY * SEASON, quinn1)
```

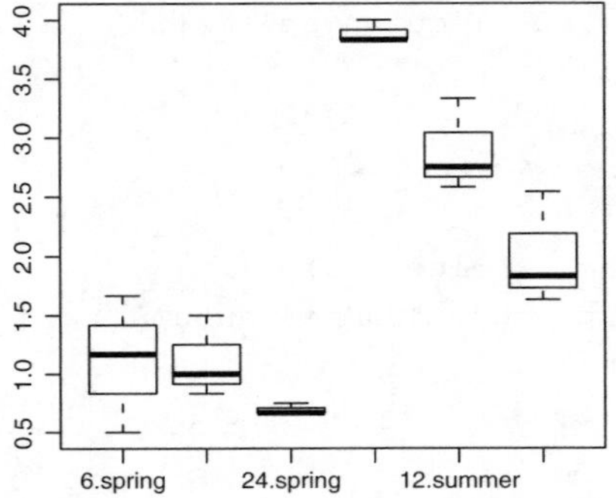

Conclusions - No evidence of non-normality (boxplots not wildly asymmetrical) and no apparent relationship between mean and variance (heights of boxplots increase up the y-axis). No evidence that any of the hypothesis tests will be unreliable.

Step 5 (Key 12.5 & 12.7) - Determine whether or not the design is missing any factor combinations (cells) or is unbalanced (unequal sample sizes).

```
> replications(EGGS ~ DENSITY * SEASON, quinn1)
      DENSITY          SEASON DENSITY:SEASON
            6               9              3
> library(biology)
> is.balanced(EGGS ~ DENSITY * SEASON, quinn1)
[1] TRUE
```

Conclusions - The design is completely balanced. There are three replicate enclosures for each of the three densities and two seasons.

Step 6 - (Key 12.6) - Quinn and Keough (2002) illustrated treatment contrasts to compare the control adult density (6) to the increased densities (12 and 24) and whether this differed between the seasons[k]. To do this we define our own contrasts (see sections 10.6 and 7.3.1 for more information on setting contrasts).

```
> contrasts(quinn1$DENSITY) <- cbind(c(1, -0.5, -0.5))
```

Step 7 (Key 12.8) - Fit the factorial linear model[l].

```
> quinn1.aov <- aov(EGGS ~ DENSITY * SEASON, data = quinn1)
```

Step 8 (Key 12.21) - Examine the fitted model diagnostics[m]. Note that is evaluating the overall residuals and predicted values for the interaction effect.)

```
> plot(quinn1.aov, which = 1)
```

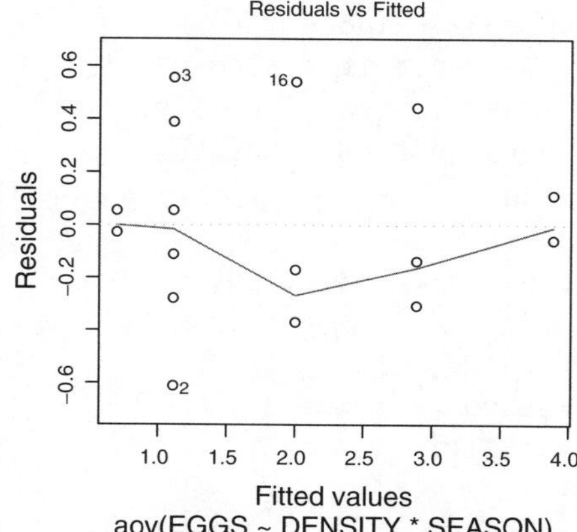

Conclusions - As anticipated, there is no indication of a 'wedge' pattern in the residuals suggesting that the assumption of unequal variance is likely to be satisfied.

Step 9 (Key 12.8) - Examine the model I, balanced anova table, including the set of defined planned contrasts. Store the resulting ANOVA table with a name so that the data therein can later be accessed.

[k] Note that Quinn and Keough (2002) also defined a linear polynomial contrast. However, as this contrast is not orthogonal (independent) of the treatment contrast, it cannot be included in the one linear model.

[l] Note that if we were also intending to investigate a set of planned comparisons/contrasts (see chapter 10.6), these should be defined prior to fitting the linear model.

[m] Recall that leverage, and thus Cook's D are not informative for categorical predictor variables.

```
> library(biology)
> quinn1.anova<-AnovaM(quinn1.aov, type="I", split=list(DENSITY=
+ list('6 vs 12&24'=1)))
> quinn1.anova
                            Df  Sum Sq Mean Sq F value    Pr(>F)
DENSITY                      2  4.0019  2.0010  13.984 0.0007325 ***
  DENSITY: 6 vs 12&24        1  2.7286  2.7286  19.069 0.0009173 ***
SEASON                       1 17.1483 17.1483 119.845 1.336e-07 ***
DENSITY:SEASON               2  1.6907  0.8454   5.908 0.0163632 *
  DENSITY:SEASON: 6 vs 12&24 1  1.5248  1.5248  10.656 0.0067727 **
Residuals                   12  1.7170  0.1431
---
Signif. codes:  0 '***' 0.001 '**' 0.01 '*' 0.05 '.' 0.1 ' ' 1
```

Conclusions - There is strong evidence of a interaction between density and season. Whether or not there is a difference between the egg production of control vs high adult density depends on the season.

Step 10 (Key 12.14) - To further explore the interaction between density and season, Quinn and Keough (2002) investigated the effects of adult density separately for each season using two single factor *ANOVA*'s. For each *ANOVA*, the MS_{Resid} from the global (overall) model was used as the denominator in *F*-ratio calculations.

```
> # effect of density in spring
> library(biology)
> AnovaM(mainEffects(quinn1.aov, at=SEASON=="spring"),
+ split=list(DENSITY=list('6 vs 12&24'=1)))

                     Df  Sum Sq Mean Sq F value    Pr(>F)
INT                   3 22.4940  7.4980 52.4017 3.616e-07 ***
DENSITY               2  0.3469  0.1735  1.2124    0.3315
  DENSITY: 6 vs 12&24 1  0.0869  0.0869  0.6076    0.4508
Residuals            12  1.7170  0.1431
---
Signif. codes:  0 '***' 0.001 '**' 0.01 '*' 0.05 '.' 0.1 ' ' 1

> # effect of density in summer
> AnovaM(mainEffects(quinn1.aov, at=SEASON=="summer"),
+ split=list(DENSITY=list('6 vs 12&24'=1)))

                     Df  Sum Sq Mean Sq F value    Pr(>F)
INT                   3 17.4953  5.8318  40.757 1.436e-06 ***
DENSITY               2  5.3457  2.6728  18.680 0.0002065 ***
  DENSITY: 6 vs 12&24 1  4.1664  4.1664  29.118 0.0001611 ***
Residuals            12  1.7170  0.1431
---
Signif. codes:  0 '***' 0.001 '**' 0.01 '*' 0.05 '.' 0.1 ' ' 1
```

Conclusions - Whilst egg production was found to be significantly lower in higher densities of adult limpets compared to natural densities during the summer-autumn season, such a trend was not observed during the spring-winter season.

Step 11 (Key 12.18) - Summarize the trends in a interaction plot.

```
> library(gmodels)
> quinn1.means <- tapply(quinn1$EGGS, list(quinn1$DENSITY,
+     quinn1$SEASON), mean)
> quinn1.se <- tapply(quinn1$EGGS, list(quinn1$DENSITY,
+     quinn1$SEASON), function(x) ci(x)[4])
> quinn1$DENS <- as.numeric(as.character(quinn1$DENSITY))
> plot(EGGS ~ DENS, quinn1, type = "n", axes = F, xlab = "",
+     ylab = "")
> points(quinn1.means[, 1] ~ unique(quinn1$DENS), pch = 16,
+     type = "b", lwd = 2)
> arrows(unique(quinn1$DENS), quinn1.means[, 1] - quinn1.se[, 1],
+     unique(quinn1$DENS), quinn1.means[, 1] + quinn1.se[, 1],
+     code = 3, angle = 90, len = 0.1)
> points(quinn1.means[, 2] ~ unique(quinn1$DENS), pch = 16,
+     type = "b", lwd = 2, lty = 2)
> arrows(unique(quinn1$DENS), quinn1.means[, 2] - quinn1.se[, 2],
+     unique(quinn1$DENS), quinn1.means[, 2] + quinn1.se[, 2],
+     code = 3, angle = 90, len = 0.1)
> axis(1, cex.axis = 0.8)
> mtext(text = "Adult Density", 1, line = 3)
> axis(2, cex.axis = 0.8, las = 1)
> mtext(text = "Egg production", side = 2, line = 3)
> legend("topright", leg = c("Winter-spring", "Summer-autumn"),
+     lwd = 2, lty = c(1, 2), bty = "n")
> box(bty = "l")
```

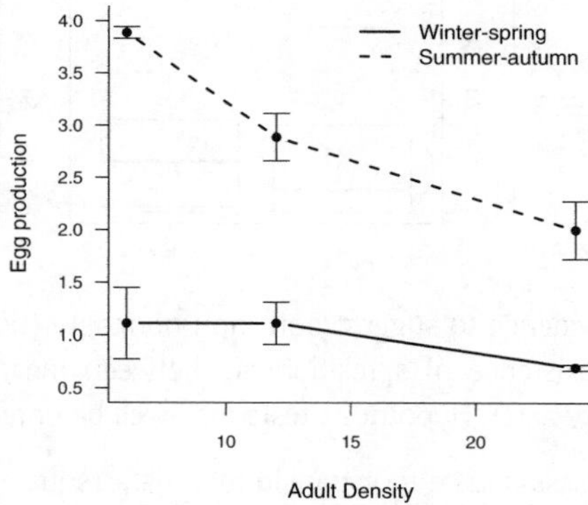

Example 12C: Two factor mixed (Model III) ANOVA

Minchinton and Ross (1999) investigated the distribution of oyster substrates for limpets in four zones alone the shore (the landward zone high on the shore, the mid zone with mangrove trees, the seaward zone with mangrove trees and the seaward zone without trees) by measuring the number of limpets per oyster shell (expressed as the number of limpets per 100 oysters) in five quadrats per zone. Data were collected from two sites (considered a random factor) so as to provide some estimates of the spatial generality of the observed trends (from Box 9.4 of Quinn and Keough (2002)).

Step 1 - Import (section 2.3) the Minchinton and Ross (1999) data set

```
> minch <- read.table("minch.csv", header = T, sep = ",")
```

Step 2 (Key 12.2) Minchinton and Ross (1999) considered the zone factor to be fixed and the site factor to be a random factor and thus the data represent a Model III design

Step 3 (Key 12.3) - Assess assumptions of normality and homogeneity of variance for each null hypothesis ensuring that the correct scale of replicates are represented for each (they should reflect the appropriate *F*-ratio denominators see Table 12.1).
According to Table 12.1, the effect of zone should be tested against the zone by site interaction whereas the effect of site and the interaction should be tested against the overall residual term (MS_{Resid}).

Factor A (Fixed)

```
> library(nlme)
> minch.agg<-gsummary
+ (minch, groups=
+ minch$ZONE:minch$SITE)
> boxplot(LIMPT100~ZONE,
+ minch.agg)
```

Factor B (Random)

```
> boxplot(LIMPT100 ~
+       SITE, minch)
```

A:B interaction (Random)

```
> boxplot(LIMPT100 ~
+       ZONE * SITE,
+       minch)
```

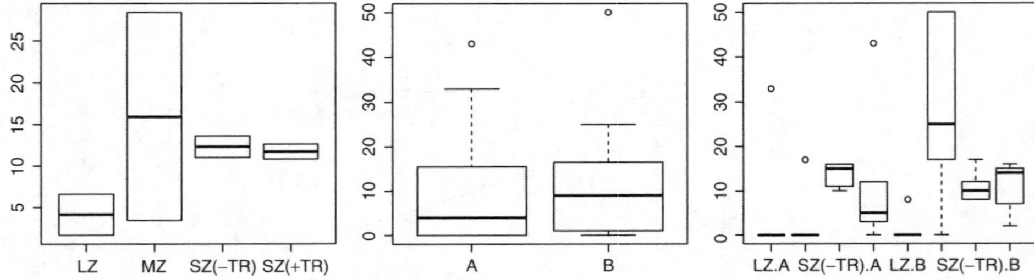

Conclusions - strong evidence to suggest both non-normality (boxplots asymmetrical where enough data) and the existence of a relationship between mean and variance (heights of boxplots increase up the y-axis). Hypothesis tests may well be unreliable.

Step 4 (Key 12.4) - Assess square-root transformed data (square root appropriate given the number of 0 counts).

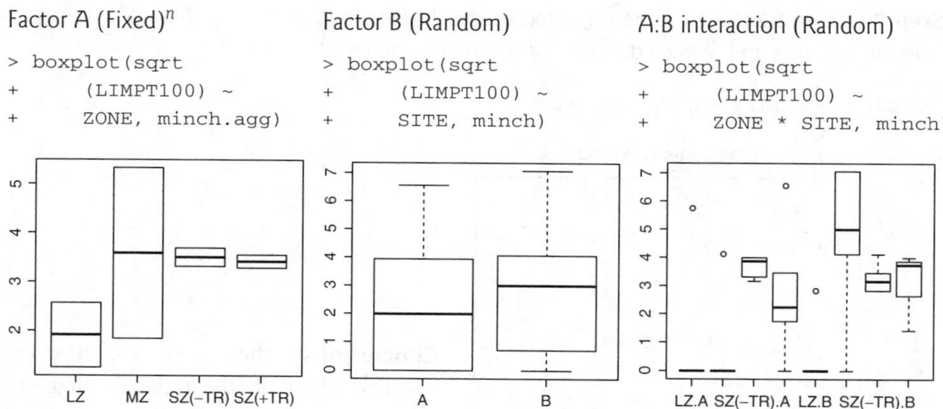
Factor A (Fixed)[n]
> boxplot(sqrt
+ (LIMPT100) ~
+ ZONE, minch.agg)
Factor B (Random)
> boxplot(sqrt
+ (LIMPT100) ~
+ SITE, minch)
A:B interaction (Random)
> boxplot(sqrt
+ (LIMPT100) ~
+ ZONE * SITE, minch)
LZ MZ SZ(−TR) SZ(+TR)
A B
LZ.A SZ(−TR).A LZ.B SZ(−TR).B

Conclusions - although not ideal, the transformation is an improvment and thus hypothesis tests based on the square root transformed data are likely to be more reliable.

Step 5 (Key 12.5 & 12.7) - Determine whether or not the design is missing any factor combinations (cells) or is unbalanced (unequal sample sizes).

```
> replications(sqrt(LIMPT100) ~ ZONE * SITE, minch)
     ZONE       SITE ZONE:SITE
       10         20         5
> library(biology)
> is.balanced(sqrt(LIMPT100) ~ ZONE * SITE, minch)
[1] TRUE
```

Conclusions - The design is completely balanced. There are five replicate quadrats for each of the four zones and two sites.

Step 6 - (Key 12.6) - Quinn and Keough (2002) did not illustrate the use of planned contrasts in Box 9.5 (presumably due to the lack of any main effects). However, prior to analysing these data, a number of sensible planned contrasts are identifiable in the context of investigating the distribution of suitable limpet substrates. We will further propose contrasting the treed zones to the treeless seaward zone by defining our own contrasts (see sections 10.6 and 7.3.1 for more information on setting contrasts).

```
> contrasts(minch$ZONE) <- cbind(c(1/3, 1/3, -1, 1/3))
```

Step 7 (Key 12.8b) - Fit the factorial linear model [o].

```
> minch.aov <- aov(sqrt(LIMPT100) ~ ZONE * SITE, data = minch)
```

[n] Note that the following procedure is mimicking a square root transformation. Ideally, these data should be transformed prior to aggregation rather than transforming the aggregated data (as demonstrated), but for the purpose of assumption checking it is acceptable.

[o] Note that if we were also intending to investigate a set of planned comparisons/contrasts (see chapter 10.6), these should be defined prior to fitting the linear model.

Step 8 (Key 12.21) - Examine the fitted model diagnostics[p]. Note that this is evaluating the overall residuals and predicted values for the interaction effect.

```
> plot(minch.aov, which = 1)
```

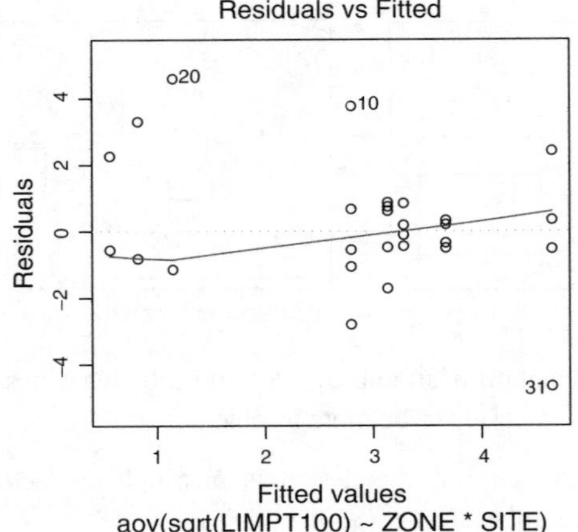

Conclusions - there is no indication of a 'wedge' pattern in the residuals suggesting that the assumption of unequal variance is likely to be satisfied.

Step 9 (Key 12.8b) - Examine the balanced model III ANOVA table, including the set of defined planned contrasts. Store the resulting ANOVA table with a name so that the data therein can later be accessed.

```
> library(biology)
> (minch.anova<-AnovaM(minch.aov, split = list(ZONE =
+ list('Treed vs No trees' = 1)), denoms = c("ZONE:SITE","Resid",
+ "Resid")))
Anova Table (Type III tests)

Response: sqrt(LIMPT100)
                          Df  Sum Sq Mean Sq F value  Pr(>F)
ZONE                       3  39.249  13.083  1.2349 0.43320
  ZONE: Treed vs No trees  1  12.448  12.448  1.1750 0.35772
SITE                       1   6.372   6.372  1.8425 0.18415
ZONE:SITE                  3  31.783  10.594  3.0632 0.04205 *
  ZONE:SITE: Treed vs No trees 1   4.700   4.700  1.3588 0.25236
Residuals                 32 110.673   3.459
---
Signif. codes:  0 '***' 0.001 '**' 0.01 '*' 0.05 '.' 0.1 ' ' 1
```

Conclusions - There is evidence of a interaction between zone and site suggesting that any patterns in limpet numbers between zones are not consistent across sites.

[p] Recall that leverage, and thus Cook's D are not informative for categorical predictor variables.

Step 10 (Key 12.19) - Estimate the variance components of the random (and fixed) terms[q] via the restricted maximum likelihood (REML) method.

```
> library(lme4)
> lmer(sqrt(LIMPT100) ~ 1 + (1 | ZONE) + (1 | SITE) +
+     (1 | ZONE:SITE), minch)
Linear mixed model fit by REML
Formula: sqrt(LIMPT100) ~ 1 + (1 | ZONE) + (1 | SITE) +
             (1 | ZONE:SITE)
   Data: minch
   AIC   BIC logLik deviance REMLdev
 180.8 189.3  -85.4    171.5   170.8
Random effects:
 Groups    Name        Variance   Std.Dev.
 ZONE:SITE (Intercept) 1.2160e+00 1.1027e+00
 ZONE      (Intercept) 3.5443e-01 5.9534e-01
 SITE      (Intercept) 5.0652e-16 2.2506e-08
 Residual              3.4585e+00 1.8597e+00
Number of obs: 40, groups: ZONE:SITE, 8; ZONE, 4; SITE, 2

Fixed effects:
            Estimate Std. Error t value
(Intercept)   2.5096     0.5719   4.388
```

Conclusions - Although the interaction term explained approximately 26% ($1.216/(1.216 + 0 + 3.455)$), most of the variance was unexplained ($(3.455/(1.216 + 0 + 3.455) = 74\%)$). Note that these values differ slightly from those presented by Quinn and Keough (2002) in Box 9.5, because they are estimated by the REML method rather than the ANOVA method which is restricted to balanced designs.

Step 11 (Key 12.18b) - Summarize the trends in a bargraph (from Quinn and Keough (2002)).

```
> library(gmodels)
> minch.means <- t(tapply(sqrt(minch$LIMPT100), list(minch$ZONE,
+     minch$SITE), mean))
> minch.se <- t(tapply(sqrt(minch$LIMPT100), list(minch$ZONE,
+     minch$SITE), function(x) ci(x)[4]))
> xs <- barplot(minch.means, ylim = range(sqrt(minch$LIMPT100)),
+     beside = T, axes = F, xpd = F, axisnames = F, axis.lty = 2,
+     legend.text = F, col = c(0, 1))
```

[q] Note that variance components for fixed terms are interpreted differnently to those of random terms. Whereas for random terms, variance components estimate the variance between all possible population means, for fixed factors they only estimate the variance between the specific populations used.

```
> arrows(xs, minch.means, xs, minch.means + minch.se, code = 3,
+     angle = 90, len = 0.05)
> axis(2, las = 1)
> axis(1, at = apply(xs, 2, median), lab = c("Land", "Mid",
+     "Sea\n(-trees)", "Sea\n(+trees)"), padj = 1,
+     mgp = c(0, 0, 0))
> mtext(2, text = expression(paste(sqrt("number of limpets
+     (x100)"))), line = 3, cex = 1)
> mtext(1, text = "Zone", line = 3, cex = 1)
> legend("topright", leg = c("Site A", "Site B"), fill = c(0, 1),
+     col = c(0, 1), bty = "n", cex = 1)
> box(bty = "l")
```

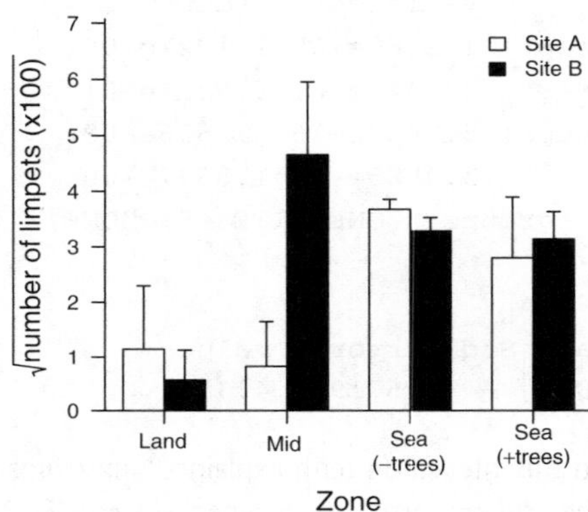

Example 12D: Two factor unbalanced fixed (Model I) ANOVA

Quinn and Keough (2002) present a two factor analysis of variance (Quinn and Keough, 2002; Table 9.15b) of a subset of a dataset by Reich et al. (1999) in which the specific leaf area of a number of plant species were compared from four different biomes (New Mexico woodlands, South Carolina temperate/sub-tropical forests, Venezuela tropical rain forests and Wisconsin temperate forests) and two different functional groups (shrubs and trees). Sample sizes varied for each combination of factors (cells).

Step 1 - Import (section 2.3) the modified Reich et al. (1999) data set

```
> reich <- read.table("reich.csv", header = T, sep = ",")
```

Step 2 (Key 12.2) Reich et al. (1999) considered both location and functional group to be fixed factors and thus the data represent a Model I design

Step 3 (Key 12.3) - Assess assumptions of normality and homogeneity of variance for each null hypothesis ensuring that the correct scale of replicates are represented for each (they should reflect the appropriate *F*-ratio denominators see Table 12.1).
According to Table 12.1, the effect of location, functional group as well as their interaction should all be tested against the overall residual term (MS_{Resid}).

A:B interaction (Fixed)[r]

```
> boxplot(LEAFAREA ~ LOCATION * FUNCTION, na.omit(reich))
```

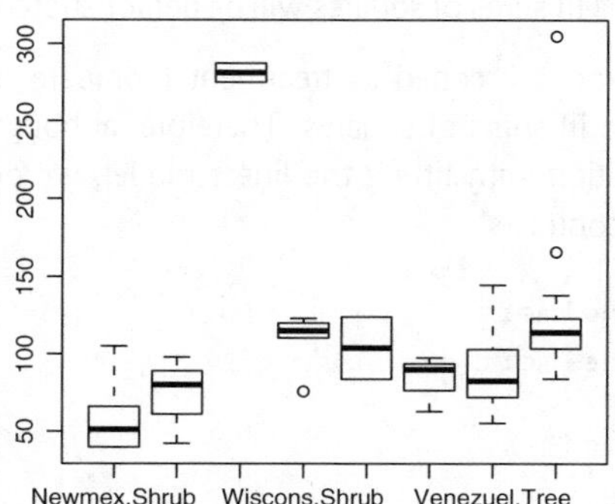

Conclusions - no strong evidence to suggest either consistent non-normality or the presence of a relationship between mean and variance (heights of boxplots increase up the y-axis). Hypothesis tests likely to be reliable.

Step 4 (Key 12.5 & 12.7) - Determine whether or not the design is missing any factor combinations (cells) or is unbalanced (unequal sample sizes).

```
> replications(LEAFAREA ~ LOCATION * FUNCTION, reich)
$LOCATION
LOCATION
  Newmex Scarolin Venezuel  Wiscons
       7        6       23       21

$FUNCTION
FUNCTION
Shrub  Tree
  16    41

$'LOCATION:FUNCTION'
          FUNCTION
LOCATION    Shrub Tree
  Newmex        5    2
  Scarolin      3    3
  Venezuel      2   21
  Wiscons       6   15
> library(biology)
> is.balanced(LEAFAREA ~ LOCATION * FUNCTION, reich)
[1] FALSE
```

[r] Note that there is a missing case (denoted "NA" in the dataset). There are many functions that by default return an error when there are missing cases (so as to reduce the risks that potentially unrepresentative outcomes being blindly accepted by the user). Such functions need to be informed to ignore missing cases. This can be done either with the `na.rm=T` argument or by using the `na.omit()` *function* to create a temporary copy of the original dataset with the entire row of the missing case removed.

Conclusions - The design is unbalanced. The number of samples per location and function combination varies from 2 to 21. Therefore Type II or III sums of squares are appropriate. In this case, as we potentially wish to make conclusions about each of the main effects that are over and above the other main effects and their interaction, Type III sums of squares will be demonstrated.

Step 5 - (Key 12.6) - By default, all unordered factors are coded as treatment (compare to control) contrasts which are not appropriate for Type III sums of squares. Therefore, although we have no planned contrasts to perform in association with fitting the linear model, we do need to code the contrasts of the factors as helmert contrasts[s].

```
> contrasts(reich$LOCATION) <- contr.helmert
> contrasts(reich$FUNCTION) <- contr.helmert
```

Step 6 (Key 12.9) - Fit the factorial linear model.

```
> reich.aov <- aov(LEAFAREA ~ LOCATION * FUNCTION, data = reich)
```

Step 7 (Key 12.21) - Examine the fitted model diagnostics[t]. Note that it is evaluating the overall residuals and predicted values for the interaction effect.)

```
> plot(reich.aov, which = 1)
```

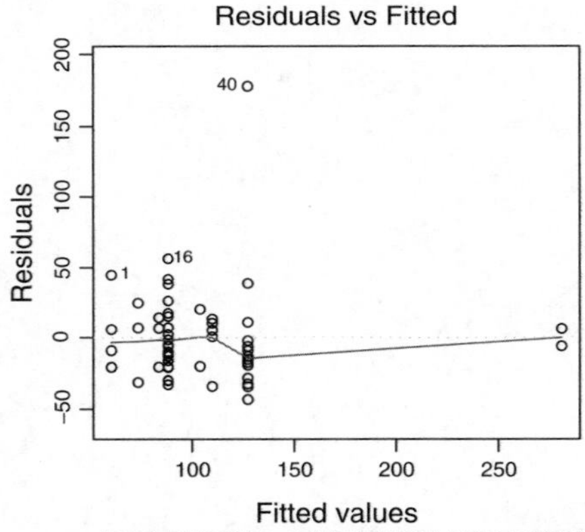

Conclusions - Although there is no indication of a 'wedge' pattern in the residuals, observation 40 has a very large residual (considered an extreme outlier) and is potentially very influential. Caution should be excised for any hypothesis test close to the critical α value (0.05).

Step 8 (Key 12.9) - Examine the unbalanced model I ANOVA table. Store the resulting ANOVA table with a name so that the data therein can later be accessed.

```
> library(biology)
> (reich.anova <- AnovaM(reich.aov, type = "III"))
                   Df Sum Sq Mean Sq F value    Pr(>F)
LOCATION            3  49202   16401 13.6005 1.401e-06 ***
FUNCTION            1   6919    6919  5.7378   0.02047 *
```

[s] Other contrasts (such as polynomial or user defined orthogonal contrasts) would also be equally as valid - just not treatment contrasts.

[t] Recall that leverage, and thus Cook's D are not informative for categorical predictor variables.

```
LOCATION:FUNCTION  3  67783   22594 18.7367 3.120e-08 ***
Residuals         49  59088    1206
---
Signif. codes:  0 '***' 0.001 '**' 0.01 '*' 0.05 '.' 0.1 ' ' 1
1 observation deleted due to missingness
```

Conclusions - There is strong evidence of a interaction between location and functional group suggesting that the patterns between different ecosystems differ according to the functional type of the plants and visa versa.

Step 9 (Key 12.14 & 12.20) - To better appreciate the patterns in specific leaf area between the different ecosystems, simple main effects tests can be performed to investigate the effects of location separately for each functional group. When so doing, recall that it is necessary to use the MS_{Resid} from the original (global) analysis of variance as the residual term. Tukey's post hoc honestly significant difference tests have also been included to investigate the pairwise differences between locations.

Effect of location for the shrub functional group

```
> AnovaM(reich.aov.shrub <- mainEffects(reich.aov, at =
+      FUNCTION == "Shrub"), type = "III")
            Df Sum Sq Mean Sq F value    Pr(>F)
INT          4  14994    3749  3.1086   0.02338 *
LOCATION     3  75012   25004 20.7351 8.199e-09 ***
Residuals   49  59088    1206
---
Signif. codes:  0 '***' 0.001 '**' 0.01 '*' 0.05 '.' 0.1 ' ' 1
1 observation deleted due to missingness
> library(multcomp)
> summary(glht(reich.aov.shrub, linfct = mcp(LOCATION = "Tukey")))
         Simultaneous Tests for General Linear Hypotheses

Multiple Comparisons of Means: Tukey Contrasts


Fit: aov(formula = update(object, ~INT + .), data = dn)

Linear Hypotheses:
                         Estimate Std. Error t value Pr(>|t|)
Scarolin - Newmex == 0      13.07      25.36   0.515   0.9542
Venezuel - Newmex == 0     220.95      29.05   7.605   <0.001 ***
Wiscons - Newmex == 0       49.55      21.03   2.356   0.0973 .
Venezuel - Scarolin == 0   207.88      31.70   6.558   <0.001 ***
Wiscons - Scarolin == 0     36.48      24.55   1.486   0.4485
Wiscons - Venezuel == 0   -171.40      28.35  -6.045   <0.001 ***
---
Signif. codes:  0 '***' 0.001 '**' 0.01 '*' 0.05 '.' 0.1 ' ' 1
(Adjusted p values reported -- single-step method)
```

```
> confint(glht(reich.aov.shrub, linfct = mcp(LOCATION = "Tukey")))
        Simultaneous Confidence Intervals

Multiple Comparisons of Means: Tukey Contrasts


Fit: aov(formula = update(object, ~INT + .), data = dn)

Estimated Quantile = 2.6496
95% family-wise confidence level


Linear Hypotheses:
                         Estimate  lwr       upr
Scarolin - Newmex == 0    13.0667  -54.1263   80.2596
Venezuel - Newmex == 0   220.9500  143.9708  297.9292
Wiscons - Newmex == 0     49.5500   -6.1634  105.2634
Venezuel - Scarolin == 0 207.8833  123.8922  291.8745
Wiscons - Scarolin == 0   36.4833  -28.5760  101.5426
Wiscons - Venezuel == 0 -171.4000 -246.5240  -96.2760
```

Effect of location for the tree functional group

```
> AnovaM(reich.aov.tree <- mainEffects(reich.aov, at = FUNCTION ==
+     "Tree"), type = "III")
            Df Sum Sq Mean Sq F value  Pr(>F)
INT          4  75431   18858 15.6382 2.6e-08 ***
LOCATION     3  14575    4858  4.0289 0.01222 *
Residuals   49  59088    1206
---
Signif. codes:  0 '***' 0.001 '**' 0.01 '*' 0.05 '.' 0.1 ' ' 1
1 observation deleted due to missingness
> library(multcomp)
> summary(glht(reich.aov.tree, linfct = mcp(LOCATION = "Tukey")))
        Simultaneous Tests for General Linear Hypotheses

Multiple Comparisons of Means: Tukey Contrasts


Fit: aov(formula = update(object, ~INT + .), data = dn)

Linear Hypotheses:
                         Estimate Std. Error t value Pr(>|t|)
Scarolin - Newmex == 0     -20.40      31.70  -0.644   0.9108
Venezuel - Newmex == 0     -15.70      25.70  -0.611   0.9224
Wiscons - Newmex == 0       23.37      26.14   0.894   0.7950
Venezuel - Scarolin == 0     4.70      21.43   0.219   0.9959
```

```
Wiscons - Scarolin == 0     43.77       21.96   1.993   0.1895
Wiscons - Venezuel == 0     39.07       11.74   3.328   0.0079 **
---
Signif. codes:  0 '***' 0.001 '**' 0.01 '*' 0.05 '.' 0.1 ' ' 1
(Adjusted p values reported -- single-step method)
> confint(glht(reich.aov.tree, linfct = mcp(LOCATION = "Tukey")))
         Simultaneous Confidence Intervals

Multiple Comparisons of Means: Tukey Contrasts


Fit: aov(formula = update(object, ~INT + .), data = dn)

Estimated Quantile = 2.6156
95% family-wise confidence level


Linear Hypotheses:
                              Estimate  lwr       upr
Scarolin - Newmex == 0     -20.4000 -103.3134   62.5134
Venezuel - Newmex == 0     -15.7000  -82.9132   51.5132
Wiscons - Newmex == 0       23.3667  -45.0055   91.7388
Venezuel - Scarolin == 0     4.7000  -51.3597   60.7597
Wiscons - Scarolin == 0     43.7667  -13.6774  101.2108
Wiscons - Venezuel == 0     39.0667    8.3615   69.7718
```

Conclusions - Specific leaf area differs significantly between locations for both shrub and tree functional groups. However, whilst specific leaf area of trees was only found to differ significantly between Wisconsin cold temperate forests and Venezuela topical forests (the former having greater area), for shrubs, the Venezuela topical forests were found to have significantly greater leaf areas than shrubs in the other ecosystems.

Step 10 (Key 12.18b) - Summarize the trends in a bargraph (from Quinn and Keough (2002)).

```
> library(gmodels)
> reich.means <- t(tapply(reich$LEAFAREA, list(reich$LOCATION,
+     reich$FUNCTION), mean, na.rm = T))
> reich.se <- t(tapply(reich$LEAFAREA, list(reich$LOCATION,
+     reich$FUNCTION), function(x) ci(x, na.rm = T)[4]))
> xs <- barplot(reich.means, ylim = range(reich$LEAFAREA,
+     na.rm = T), beside = T, axes = F, xpd = F, axisnames = F,
+     axis.lty = 2, legend.text = F, col = c(0, 1))
> arrows(xs, reich.means, xs, reich.means + reich.se, code = 2,
+     angle = 90, len = 0.05)
> axis(2, las = 1)
> axis(1, at = apply(xs, 2, median), lab = c("Newmax", "Scarolin",
+     "Venezuel", "Wiscons"), padj = 1, mgp = c(0, 0, 0))
```

```
> mtext(2, text = expression(paste("Mean specific leaf area ",
+       (mm^2))), line = 3, cex = 1)
> mtext(1, text = "Location", line = 3, cex = 1)
> box(bty = "l")
> legend("topright", leg = c("Shrub", "Tree"), fill = c(0, 1),
+       col = c(0, 1), bty = "n", cex = 1)
```

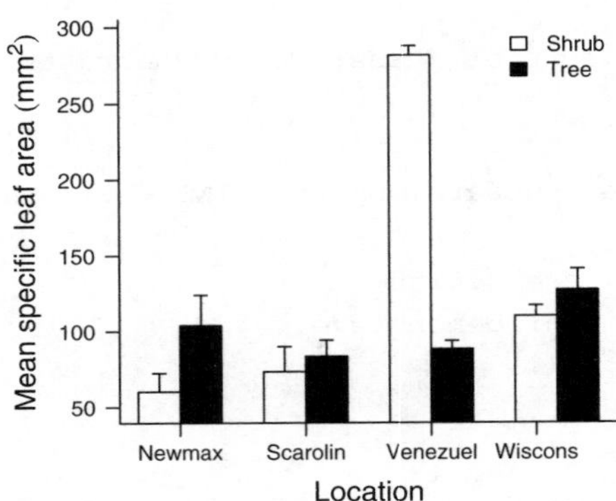

Example 12E: Two factor fixed (Model I) ANOVA with missing cells

Hall et al. (2000) measured the number of macroinvertebrate individuals colonizing small sheets of submerged cloth subjected to one of two treatments (nitrogen and phosphorus nutrients added or control) for either two, four or six months (time factor). Quinn and Keough (2002) present an analysis of a modification of these data in which the control treatments (no nutrients added) for the six month duration are all missing (from Table 9.16 of Quinn and Keough (2002)).

Step 1 - Import (section 2.3) the Hall et al. (2000) data set

```
> hall1 <- read.table("hall1.csv", header = T, sep = ",")
```

Step 2 (Key 12.2) Since the levels of the time factor are purely numbers, R considers this vector as a numeric variable rather than as a factorial variable. In order for the effect of time to be modeled appropriately, the time vector needs to be explicitly defined as a factor.

```
> hall1$TIME <- as.factor(hall1$TIME)
```

Step 3 (Key 12.2) Hall et al. (2000) considered both treatment and time to be fixed factors and thus the data represent a Model I design

Step 4 (Key 12.3) - Assess assumptions of normality and homogeneity of variance for each null hypothesis ensuring that the correct scale of replicates are represented for each (they should reflect the appropriate *F*-ratio denominators see Table 12.1).

According to Table 12.1, the effect of treatment and time as well as their interaction should all be tested against the overall residual term (MS_{Resid}).

```
> boxplot(IND ~ TREAT * TIME,
+    hall1)
```

```
> boxplot(log(IND + 1) ~
+      TREAT * TIME, hall1)
```

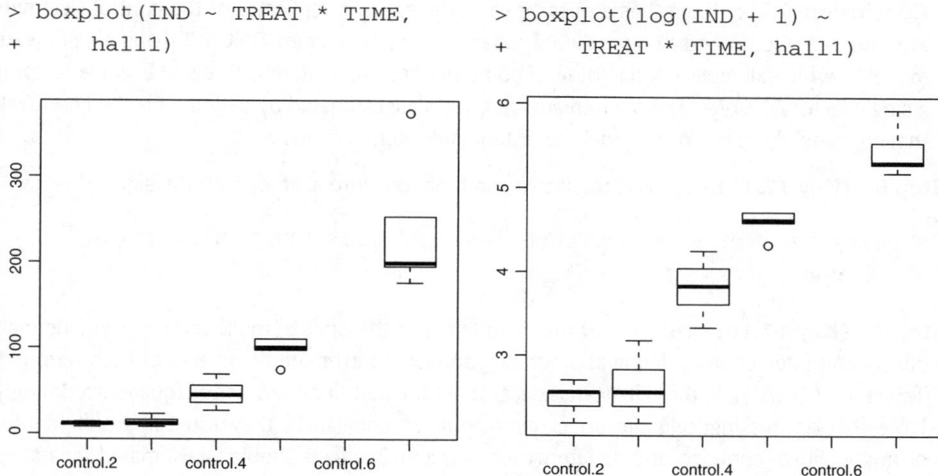

Conclusions - boxplots of the raw data (plot on left) show strong evidence of a relationship between mean and variance (height of boxplots related to their positions on the y-axis). The plot on the right illustrates boxplots of the data transformed to logs[u] and indicates that transforming the data to logs improves its suitability to parametric analysis.

Step 5 (Key 12.5b & 12.11) - Determine whether or not the design is missing any factor combinations (cells) or is unbalanced (unequal sample sizes).

```
> replications(log(IND + 1) ~ TREAT * TIME, hall1)
$TREAT
TREAT
 control nutrient
      10       15

$TIME
TIME
 2  4  6
10 10  5

$'TREAT:TIME'
         TIME
TREAT      2 4 6
  control  5 5 0
  nutrient 5 5 5
> library(biology)
> is.balanced(log(IND + 1) ~ TREAT * TIME, hall1)
[1] FALSE
```

[u] In order to accommodate zero values in the data, a small number (1) is added to each count prior to logarithmic transformation. This is referred to as a log plus one transformation.

Conclusions - The design has a missing cell - there are no replicates of the control treatment at 6 months. Quinn and Keough (2002) analysed this two factor ANOVA using a cell means model in which all replicated factor level combinations are treated as levels of a single factor in a single factor ANOVA. The main treatment effects are estimated by defining planned contrasts that are carefully selected to model the 'estimatable' comparisons.

Step 6 - (Key 12.10) - Convert the factor combinations into a single factor design.

```
> hall1$TREATTIME <- as.factor(paste(hall1$TREAT, hall1$TIME,
+     sep = ""))
```

Step 7 - (Key 12.10) - For each of the main terms in the original multifactor model (the main effects and interactions), define appropriate contrasts to estimate the effects of each term (see Tables 12.3 & 12.4), fit the cell means linear model and partition the sums of squares accordingly. Note that as missing cells are an extreme form of unbalance, they too can result in non-orthogonality of contrasts and therefore each of the main effects should be estimated separately.

Effect of nutrient treatment

```
> contrasts(hall1$TREATTIME) <- cbind(c(1, 1, -1,
+ -1, 0))
> AnovaM(aov(log(IND + 1) ~ TREATTIME, hall1),
+ split = list(TREATTIME = list("treatment" = 1)))
                        Df Sum Sq Mean Sq F value    Pr(>F)
TREATTIME                4 32.013   8.003  93.169 1.232e-12 ***
  TREATTIME: treatment   1  1.063   1.063  12.379  0.002161 **
Residuals               20  1.718   0.086
---
Signif. codes:  0 '***' 0.001 '**' 0.01 '*' 0.05 '.' 0.1 ' ' 1
```

Effect of time

```
> contrasts(hall1$TREATTIME) <- cbind(c(1, -1, 1,
+ -1, 0), c(0, 0, 1, 0, -1))
> AnovaM(aov(log(IND + 1) ~ TREATTIME, hall1),
+ split = list(TREATTIME = list("time" = 1:2,
+ " time 2 vs 4" = 1, " time 2 vs 6" = 2)))
                           Df Sum Sq Mean Sq F value    Pr(>F)
TREATTIME                   4 32.013   8.003  93.169 1.232e-12 ***
  TREATTIME: time           2 24.742  12.371 144.013 1.332e-12 ***
  TREATTIME:  time 2 vs 4   1 13.441  13.441 156.468 6.505e-11 ***
  TREATTIME:  time 2 vs 6   1 11.301  11.301 131.557 3.008e-10 ***
Residuals                  20  1.718   0.086
---
Signif. codes:  0 '***' 0.001 '**' 0.01 '*' 0.05 '.' 0.1 ' ' 1
```

Nutrient treatment by time interaction

```
> contrasts(hall1$TREATTIME) <- cbind(c(1, -1, -1,
+ 1, 0))
```

```
> AnovaM(aov(log(IND + 1) ~ TREATTIME, hall1),
+ split = list(TREATTIME = list("treatment:time" = 1)))
                               Df Sum Sq Mean Sq F value    Pr(>F)
TREATTIME                       4 32.013   8.003 93.1689 1.232e-12 ***
  TREATTIME: treatment:time     1  0.491   0.491  5.7209   0.02670 *
Residuals                      20  1.718   0.086
---
Signif. codes:  0 '***' 0.001 '**' 0.01 '*' 0.05 '.' 0.1 ' ' 1
```

Conclusions - There is strong evidence of a significant interaction between the nutrient treatment and time. The effect of the nutrient treatment on the number of macroinvertebrate individuals colonizing the artificial substrates differs according to the duration for which the substrates have been available. The nature of the interaction could be explored by splitting the data up and analysing the effects of the nutrient treatment separately for each time. Additionally, given the sequential nature of time, polynomial trends could be explored for the nutrient added treatments.

Step 8 (Key 12.18a) - Summarize the trends with an interaction plot.

```
> library(gmodels)
> hall1.means <- with(hall1, tapply(IND, list(TIME, TREAT), mean))
> hall1.se <- with(hall1, tapply(IND, list(TIME, TREAT),
+     function(x) ci(x)[4]))
> with(hall1, interaction.plot(TIME, TREAT, IND, las = 1, lwd = 2,
+     ylim = range(pretty(hall1$IND)), axes = F, xlab = "",
+     ylab = "", pch = c(16, 17), type = "b", legend = F))
> arrows(1:3, hall1.means - hall1.se, 1:3, hall1.means + hall1.se,
+     code = 3, angle = 90, len = 0.05)
> axis(2, cex.axis = 0.8, las = 1, mgp = c(3, 0.5, 0), tcl = -0.2)
> mtext(text = expression(paste("Mean number of macroinvertebrate")),
+     side = 2, line = 3, cex = 1)
> mtext(text = expression(paste("individuals")), side = 2, line = 2,
+     cex = 1)
> axis(1, cex.axis = 0.8, at = 1:3, lab = c("2", "4", "6"))
> mtext(text = "Time (duration)", 1, line = 3, cex = 1)
> box(bty = "l")
> legend("topright", leg = c("Control", "Nutrient added"), lwd = 2,
+     lty = c(2, 1), bty = "n", pch = c(16, 17), cex = 1)
```

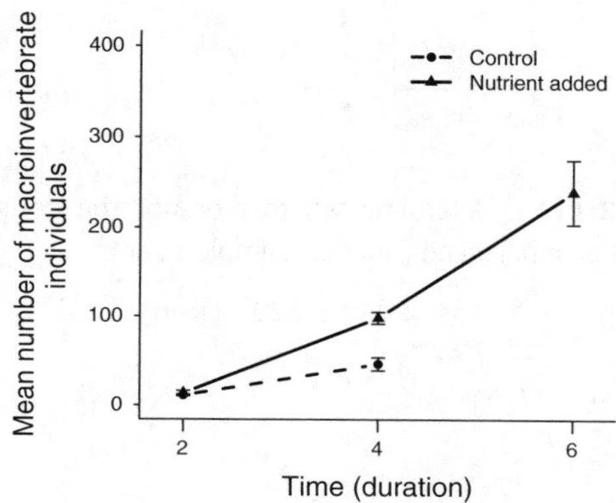

Example 12F: Two factor fixed (Model I) ANOVA with missing cells and unbalanced replication

Milliken and Johnson (1984) present a data set from a fictitious investigation into the effects of different fats and surfactants on the specific volume of baked bread. The 3x3 design was to include four replicates of each of the three fat types and three surfactant types (nine combinations). Unfortunately, many of the replicates were lost due to a defective batch of yeast. The structure of the data a represented below.

	Surf.1	Surf.2	Surf.3
Fat 1	XXX	XXX	
Fat 2	XXX		XXXX
Fat 3	XX	XXXX	XX

Step 1 - Import (section 2.3) the Milliken and Johnson (1984) data set

```
> milliken <- read.table("milliken.csv", header = T, sep = ",")
```

Step 2 (Key 12.2) Milliken and Johnson (1984) considered both treatment and time to be fixed factors and thus the data represent a Model I design

Step 3 (Key 12.3) - Assess assumptions of normality and homogeneity of variance for each null hypothesis ensuring that the correct scale of replicates are represented for each (they should reflect the appropriate *F*-ratio denominators see Table 12.1). According to Table 12.1, the effect of fat and surfactant type as well as their interaction should all be tested against the overall residual term (MS_{Resid}).

```
> boxplot(VOL ~ FAT * SURF, milliken)
```

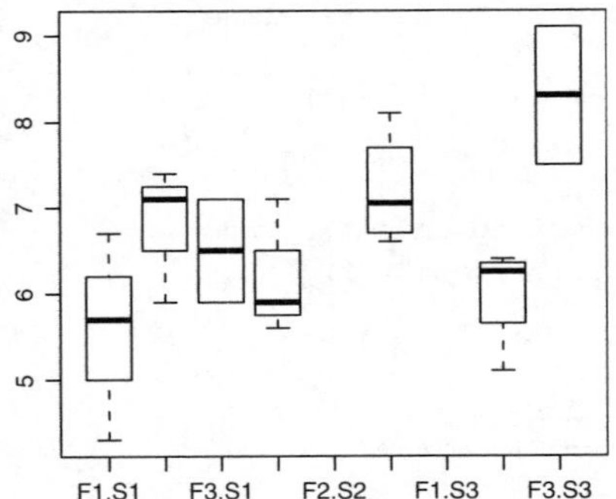

Conclusions - no evidence of either non-normality (boxplots not consistently asymmetrical) or a relationship between mean and variance (height of boxplots related to their positions on the y-axis).

Step 4 (Key 12.5 & 12.11) - Determine whether or not the design is missing any factor combinations (cells) or is unbalanced (unequal sample sizes).

```
> replications(VOL ~ FAT * SURF, milliken)
$FAT
FAT
F1 F2 F3
 6  7  8
```

```
$SURF
SURF
S1 S2 S3
 8  7  6

$'FAT:SURF'
    SURF
FAT  S1 S2 S3
  F1  3  3  0
  F2  3  0  4
  F3  2  4  2
> library(biology)
> is.balanced(VOL ~ FAT * SURF, milliken)
[1] FALSE
```

Conclusions - The design is not balanced - the number of replicates in each fat/surfactant combination differs. Furthermore, there are two missing cells. As with example 12E, this can be analysed with a cell means model in which all replicated factor level combinations are treated as levels of a single factor in a single factor ANOVA. The main treatment effects are estimated by defining planned contrasts that are carefully selected to model the 'estimatable' comparisons.

Step 5 - (Key 12.10) - Convert the factor combinations into a single factor design.

```
> milliken$FS <- as.factor(paste(milliken$FAT, milliken$SURF,
+     sep = ""))
```

Step 6 - (Key 12.12F) - For each of the main terms in the original multifactor model (the main effects and interactions), define appropriate contrasts to estimate the effects of each term (see Tables 12.3 & 12.4), fit the cell means linear model and partition the sums of squares accordingly. Note that Type III sums of squares are used due to unbalanced data. Note also, that additional planned contrasts will also be included to potentially explore any main effects further. In the following example, `FS` represents the intercept.

Effect of the fat type

```
> contrasts(milliken$FS) <- cbind(c(1, 1, 0, 0, -1, -1, 0), c(0,
+     0, 1, 1, -1, 0, -1))
> AnovaM(aov(VOL ~ FS, milliken), split = list(FS = list
+     (fat = 1:2, ' fat: 1 vs 3' = 1, ' fat 2 vs 3' = 2)),
+     type = "III")
                     Df  Sum Sq Mean Sq F value  Pr(>F)
FS                    6 12.4714  2.0786  2.9493 0.04473 *
  FS: fat             2  3.8725  1.9363  2.7474 0.09851 .
  FS:  fat: 1 vs 3    1  1.6233  1.6233  2.3033 0.15135
  FS:  fat 2 vs 3     1  1.6178  1.6178  2.2955 0.15200
Residuals            14  9.8667  0.7048
---
Signif. codes:  0 '***' 0.001 '**' 0.01 '*' 0.05 '.' 0.1 ' ' 1
```

Effect of surfactant type

```
> contrasts(milliken$FS) <- cbind(c(0, 0, 0, 0, 0, 1, -1), c(0,
+     0, 1, -1, 1, 0, -1))
> AnovaM(aov(VOL ~ FS, milliken), split = list(FS = list
+     (surf = 1:2, ' surf: 2 vs 3' = 1, ' surf: 1 vs 3' = 2)),
+     type = "III")
                    Df  Sum Sq Mean Sq F value  Pr(>F)
FS                   6 12.4714  2.0786  2.9493 0.04473 *
  FS: surf           2  1.6702  0.8351  1.1850 0.33464
  FS:  surf: 2 vs 3  1  1.2063  1.2063  1.7116 0.21185
  FS:  surf: 1 vs 3  1  0.1593  0.1593  0.2261 0.64177
Residuals           14  9.8667  0.7048
---
Signif. codes:  0 '***' 0.001 '**' 0.01 '*' 0.05 '.' 0.1 ' ' 1
```

Fat type by surfactant type interaction

```
> contrasts(milliken$FS) <- cbind(c(1, -1, 0, 0, -1, 1, 0), c(0,
+     0, 1, -1, -1, 0, 1))
> AnovaM(aov(VOL ~ FS, milliken), split = list(FS = list
+     ('fat:surf' = 1:2, ' fat:surf1' = 1, ' fat:surf2' = 2)),
+     type = "III")
                Df  Sum Sq Mean Sq F value  Pr(>F)
FS               6 12.4714  2.0786  2.9493 0.04473 *
  FS: fat:surf   2  4.7216  2.3608  3.3498 0.06474 .
  FS:  fat:surf1 1  0.2689  0.2689  0.3815 0.54672
  FS:  fat:surf2 1  4.6935  4.6935  6.6597 0.02178 *
Residuals       14  9.8667  0.7048
---
Signif. codes:  0 '***' 0.001 '**' 0.01 '*' 0.05 '.' 0.1 ' ' 1
```

Conclusions - Neither fat type nor surfactant type were found to significantly affect the specific volume of baked bread and nor was the impact of either found to be dependent on the other.

Step 7 (Key 12.18b) - Summarize the trends with an bar plot.

```
> library(gmodels)
> milliken.means <- with(milliken, tapply(VOL, list(SURF, FAT),
+     mean, na.rm = T))
> milliken.se <- with(milliken, tapply(VOL, list(SURF, FAT),
+     function(x) ci(x, na.rm = T)[4]))
> xs <- barplot(milliken.means, ylim = range(milliken$VOL,
+     na.rm = T), beside = T, axes = F, xpd = F, axisnames = F,
+     axis.lty = 2, legend.text = F, col = c(0, 1, "gray"))
> axis(2, las = 1)
> axis(1, at = apply(xs, 2, median), lab = c("Fat 1", "Fat 2",
+     "Fat 3"), padj = 1, mgp = c(0, 0, 0))
```

```
> mtext(2, text = expression(paste("Mean specific bread volume ")),
+     line = 3, cex = 1)
> box(bty = "l")
> arrows(xs, milliken.means, xs, milliken.means + milliken.se,
+     code = 2, angle = 90, len = 0.05)
> legend("topleft", leg = c("Surfactant 1", "Surfactant 2",
+     "Surfactant 3"), fill = c(0, 1, "gray"), col = c(0, 1,
+     "gray"), bty = "n", cex = 1)
```

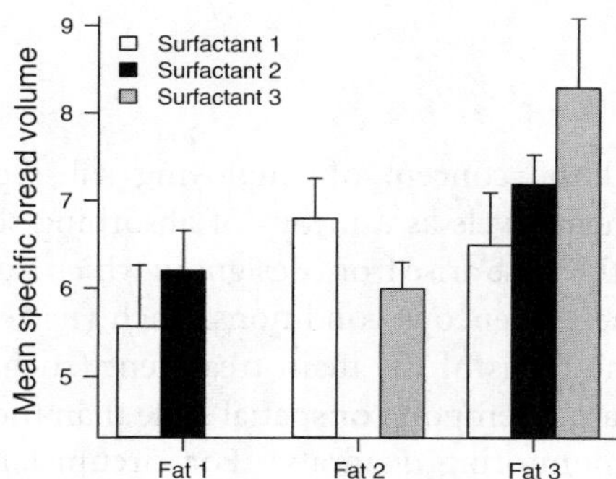

13

Unreplicated factorial designs – randomized block and simple repeated measures

Chapter 11 introduced the concept of employing sub-replicates that are nested within the main treatment levels as a means of absorbing some of the unexplained variability that would otherwise arise from designs in which sampling units are selected from amongst highly heterogeneous conditions. Such (nested) designs are useful in circumstances where the levels of the main treatment (such as burnt and un-burnt sites) occur at a much larger temporal or spatial scale than the experimental/sampling units (e.g. vegetation monitoring quadrats). For circumstances in which the main treatments can be applied (or naturally occur) at the same scale as the sampling units (such as whether a stream rock is enclosed by a fish proof fence or not), an alternative design is available. In this design (*randomized complete block design*), each of the levels of the main treatment factor are grouped (blocked) together (in space and/or time) and therefore, whilst the conditions between the groups (referred to as 'blocks') might vary substantially, the conditions under which each of the levels of the treatment are tested within any given block are far more homogeneous (see Figure 13.1b). If any differences between blocks (due to the heterogeneity) can account for some of the total variability between the sampling units (thereby reducing the amount of variability that the main treatment(s) failed to explain), then the main test of treatment effects will be more powerful/sensitive.

As an simple example of a randomized block, consider an investigation into the roles of different organism scales (microbial, macro invertebrate and vertebrate) on the breakdown of leaf debris packs within streams. An experiment could consist of four treatment levels - leaf packs protected by fish-proof mesh, leaf packs protected by fine macro invertebrate exclusion mesh, leaf packs protected by dissolving antibacterial tablets, and leaf packs relatively unprotected as controls. As an acknowledgement that there are many other unmeasured factors that could influence leaf pack breakdown (such as flow velocity, light levels, etc) and that these are likely to vary substantially throughout a stream, the treatments are to be arranged into groups or 'blocks' (each containing a single control, microbial, macro invertebrate and fish protected leaf pack).

Biostatistical Design and Analysis Using R: a Practical Guide, 1st edition. By M. Logan.
Published 2010 by Blackwell Publishing.

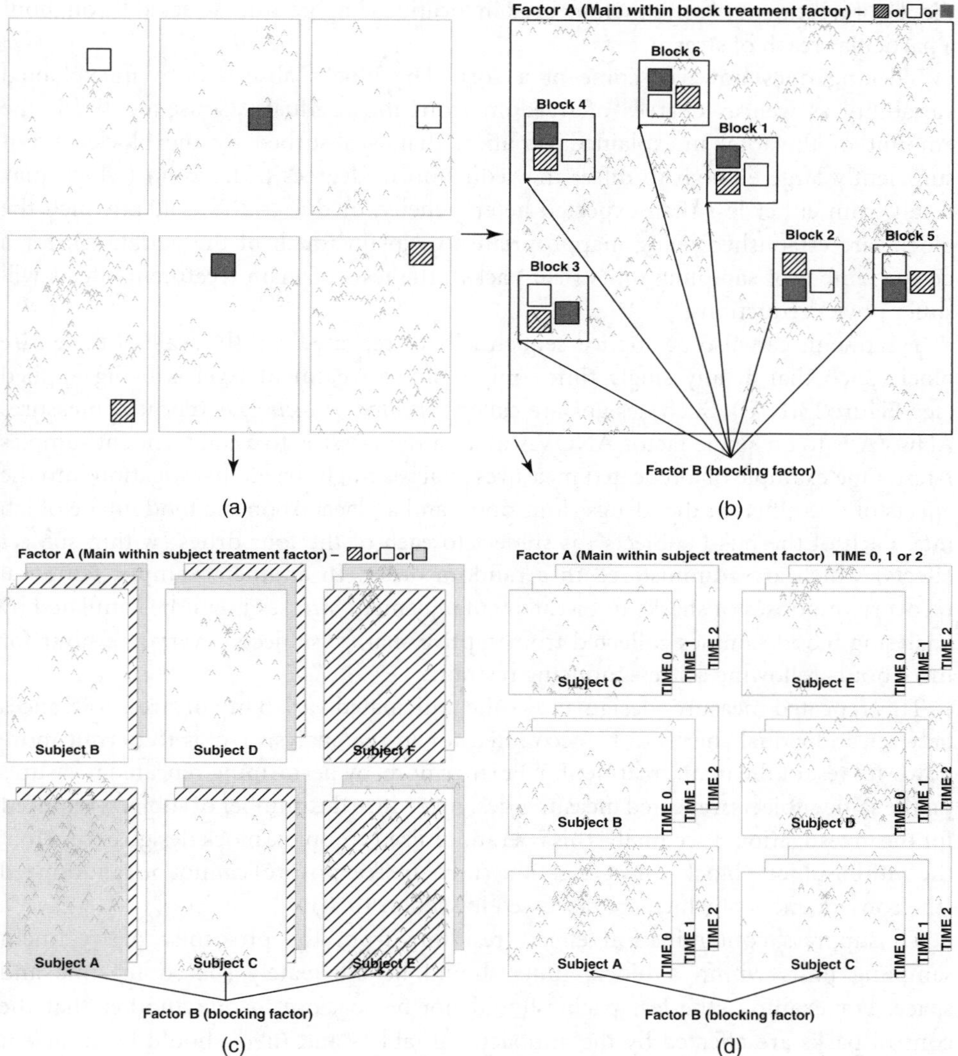

Fig 13.1 Fictitious spatial depictions contrasting (a) single factor (n = 2), (b) randomized complete block (n = 6) and (c-d) repeated measures (n = 6) ANOVA designs each with three treatment levels. When single sampling units are selected amongst highly heterogeneous conditions (as represented in (a)), it is unlikely that these single units will adequately represent the populations and repeated sampling is likely to yield very different outcomes. In such cases, this heterogeneity increases the unexplained variation thereby potentially masking any detectable effects due to the measured treatments. If however, it is possible to group each of the main treatment levels together within a small spatial or temporal scale (in which the conditions are likely to be more homogeneous), the groups (or 'blocks') should account for some of the unexplained variability between replicates thereby reducing the unexplained variability (and thus increasing the power of the main test of treatments).

Blocks of treatment sets are then secured in locations haphazardly selected throughout a particular reach of stream.

Blocking does however come at a cost. The blocks absorb both unexplained variability as well as degrees of freedom from the residuals. Consequently, if the amount of the total unexplained variation that is absorbed by the blocks is not sufficiently large enough to offset the reduction in degrees of freedom (which may result from either less than expected heterogeneity, or due to the scale at which the blocks are established being inappropriate to explain much of the variation), for a given number of sampling units (leaf packs), the tests of main treatment effects will suffer power reductions.

Treatments can also be applied sequentially or repeatedly at the scale of the entire block, such that at any single time, only a single treatment level is being applied (see Figure 13.1c-d). Such designs are called *repeated measures*. A repeated measures ANOVA is to an single factor ANOVA as a paired *t*-test is to a independent samples *t*-test. One example of a repeated measures analysis might be an investigation into the effects of five different diet drugs (four doses and a placebo) on the food intake of lab rats. Each of the rats ('subjects') is subject to each of the four drugs (within subject effects) which are administered in a random order. In another example, temporal recovery responses of sharks to bi-catch entanglement stresses might be simulated by analysing blood samples collected from captive sharks (subjects) every half hour for three hours following a stress inducing restraint.

This repeated measures design allows the anticipated variability in stress tolerances between individual sharks to be accounted for in the analysis (so as to permit more powerful test of the main treatments). Furthermore, by performing repeated measures on the same subjects, repeated measures designs reduce the number of subjects required for the investigation. Essentially, this is a randomized complete block design except that the within subject (block) effect (e.g. time since stress exposure) cannot be randomized (the consequences of which are discussed in section 13.4.1).

To suppress contamination effects resulting from the proximity of treatment sampling units within a block, units should be adequately spaced in time and space. For example, the leaf packs should not be so close to one another that the control packs are effected by the antibacterial tablets and there should be sufficient recovery time between subsequent drug administrations. In addition, the order or arrangement of treatments within the blocks must be randomized so as to prevent both confounding as well as computational complications (see section 13.4.1). Whilst this is relatively straight forward for the classic randomized complete block design (such as the leaf packs in streams), it is logically not possible for repeated measures designs.

Blocking factors are typically random factors (see section 10.0.1) that represent all the possible blocks that could be selected. As such, no individual block can truly be replicated. Randomized complete block and repeated measures designs can therefore also be thought of as un-replicated factorial designs in which there are two or more factors but that the interactions between the blocks and all the within block factors are not replicated.

13.1 Linear models

The linear models[a] for two and three factor un-replicated factorial design are:

$$y_{ij} = \mu + \beta_i + \alpha_j + \varepsilon_{ij} \quad \text{(Model 1 or 2)}$$

$$y_{ijk} = \mu + \beta_i + \alpha_j + \gamma_k + \beta\alpha_{ij} + \beta\gamma_{ik} + \alpha\gamma_{jk} + \gamma\alpha\beta_{ijk} + \varepsilon_{ijk} \quad \text{(Model 1)}$$

$$y_{ijk} = \mu + \beta_i + \alpha_j + \gamma_k + \alpha\gamma_{jk} + \varepsilon_{ijk} \quad \text{(Model 2)}$$

where μ is the overall mean, β is the effect of the Blocking Factor B, α and γ are the effects of withing block Factor A and Factor C respectively and ε is the random unexplained or residual component.

Tests for the effects of blocks as well as effects within blocks assume that there are no interactions between blocks and the within block effects. That is, it is assumed that any effects are of similar nature within each of the blocks. Whilst this assumption may well hold for experiments that are able to consciously set the scale over which the blocking units are arranged, when designs utilize arbitrary or naturally occurring blocking units, the magnitude and even polarity of the main effects are likely to vary substantially between the blocks. The preferred (non-additive or 'Model 1') approach to un-replicated factorial analysis of some bio-statisticians is to include the block by within subject effect interactions (e.g. $\beta\alpha$). Whilst these interaction effects cannot be formally tested, they can be used as the denominators in F-ratio calculations of their respective main effects tests (see Tables 13.1 & 13.2). Opponents argue that since these blocking interactions cannot be formally tested, there is no sound inferential basis for using these error terms separately. Alternatively, models can be fitted additively ('Model 2') whereby all the block by within subject effect interactions are pooled into a single residual term (ε). Although the latter approach is simpler, each of the within subject effects tests do assume that there are no interactions involving the blocks[b] and that perhaps even more restrictively, that sphericity (see section 13.4.1) holds across the entire design.

13.2 Null hypotheses

Separate null hypotheses are associated with each of the factors, however, blocking factors are typically only added to absorb some of the unexplained variability and therefore specific hypothesis tests associated with blocking factors are of lesser biological importance.

[a] Note that whilst the order of the linear model terms is not important as far as software is concerned, the order presented above reflects (most closely) the hierarchy of the design structure. That is, the main factor effect (α) occurs within the blocking factor effect (β) and is thus placed after the blocking effect in the linear model. I say most closely since some of the terms are at the same hierarchical level (e.g. α and γ) and thus their orders are interchangeable.

[b] The presence of such interactions increase the residual variability and thus reduce the power of tests.

13.2.1 *Factor A* - the main within block treatment effect

Fixed (typical case)

$$H_0(A): \mu_1 = \mu_2 = ... = \mu_i = \mu \qquad \text{(the population group means of A (pooling B) are all equal)}$$

The mean of population 1 (pooling blocks) is equal to that of population 2 and so on, and thus all population means are equal to an overall mean. No effect of A within each block (Model 2) or over and above the effect of blocks. If the effect of the ith group is the difference between the ith group mean and the overall mean ($\alpha_i = \mu_i - \mu$) then the H_0 can alternatively be written as:

$$H_0(A): \alpha_1 = \alpha_2 = ... = \alpha_i = 0 \qquad \text{(the effect of each group equals zero)}$$

If one or more of the α_i are different from zero (the response mean for this treatment differs from the overall response mean), the null hypothesis is not true indicating that the treatment does affect the response variable.

Random

$$H_0(A): \sigma_\alpha^2 = 0 \qquad \text{(population variance equals zero)}$$

There is no added variance due to all possible levels of A (pooling B).

13.2.2 *Factor B* - the blocking factor

Random (typical case)

$$H_0(B): \sigma_\beta^2 = 0 \qquad \text{(population variance equals zero)}$$

There is no added variance due to all possible levels of B.

Fixed

$$H_0(B): \mu_1 = \mu_2 = \ldots = \mu_i = \mu \quad \text{(the population group means of B are all equal)}$$

$$H_0(B): \beta_1 = \beta_2 = \ldots = \beta_i = 0 \quad \text{(the effect of each chosen B group equals zero)}$$

The null hypotheses associated with additional within block factors, are treated similarly to Factor A above.

13.3 Analysis of variance

Partitioning of the total variance sequentially into explained and unexplained components and *F*-ratio calculations predominantly follows the rules established in

Table 13.1 *F*-ratios and corresponding R syntax for a range of two un-replicated factorial (randomized complete block and repeated measures) designs.

Factor	d.f.	MS	*F*-ratio Model 1 (non-additive)	*F*-ratio Model 2 (additive)
B′ (block)	$b-1$	$MS_{B'}$	No test[a]	$\frac{MS_{B'}}{MS_{Resid}}$
A	$a-1$	MS_A	$\frac{MS_A}{MS_{Resid}}$	$\frac{MS_A}{MS_{Resid}}$
Residual (=B′A)	$(b-1)(a-1)$	MS_{Resid}		
		`> summary(aov(DV~Error(B)+A))`		
	Unbalanced	`> anova(lme(DV~A, random=~1|B))`		

[a]If A is random (or an unrestricted model), then *F*-ratio is $MS_{B'}/MS_{Resid}$.

chapters 11 and 12. Randomized block and repeated measures designs can essentially be analysed as Model III ANOVAs. The appropriate unexplained residuals and therefore the appropriate *F*-ratios for each factor differ according to the different null hypotheses associated with different combinations of fixed and random factors and what analysis approach (Model 1 or 2) is adopted for the randomized block linear model (see Tables 13.1 & 13.2).

In additively (Model 2) fitted models (in which block interactions are assumed not to exist and are thus pooled into a single residual term), hypothesis tests of the effect of B (blocking factor) are possible. However, since blocking designs are usually employed out of expectation for substantial variability between blocks, such tests are rarely of much biological interest.

13.4 Assumptions

As with other ANOVA designs, the reliability of hypothesis tests is dependent on the residuals being:

(i) normally distributed. Boxplots using the appropriate scale of replication (reflecting the appropriate residuals/*F*-ratio denominator (see Tables 13.1 & 13.2) should be used to explore normality. Scale transformations are often useful.

(ii) equally varied. Boxplots and plots of means against variance (using the appropriate scale of replication) should be used to explore the spread of values. Residual plots should reveal no patterns. Scale transformations are often useful.

(iii) independent of one another. Although the observations within a block may not strictly be independent, provided the treatments are applied or ordered randomly within each block or subject, within block proximity effects on the residuals should be random across all blocks and thus the residuals should still be independent of one another. Nevertheless, it is important that experimental units within blocks are adequately spaced in space and time so as to suppress contamination or carryover effects.

Table 13.2 *F*-ratios and corresponding R syntax for a range of un-replicated three-factor (randomized complete block and repeated measures) designs. *F*-ratio numerators and demoninators are represented by numbers that correspond to the rows from which the appropriate mean square values would be associated.

	Factor	d.f.	*F*-ratio					
			A&C, B random		A fixed,B&C random		A,B&C random	
			Model 1	Model 2	Model 1	Model 2	Model 1	Model 2
1	B′	$b-1$	No test[a]	1/7	$1/6^{b}$	1/7	$1/(5+6-7)^{b\ c}$	1/7
2	A	$a-1$	2/5	2/7	$2/(4+5-7)^{b\ d}$	2/4	$2/(4+5-7)^{b\ c}$	2/4
3	C	$c-1$	3/6	3/7	$3/6^{b}$	$3/7^{e}$	$3/(4+6-7)^{b\ c}$	3/4
4	A×C	$(a-1)(c-1)$	4/7	4/7	4/7	4/7	4/7	4/7
5	B′×A	$(b-1)(a-1)$	No test		No test		5/7	
6	B′×C	$(b-1)(a-1)$	No test		No test		6/7	
7	Residuals (=B′×A×C)	$(b-1)(a-1)(c-1)$						

B random, A&C fixed

Model 1
```
> summary(aov(DV~Error(B/(A*B))+A*C))
```
Model 2
```
> summary(aov(DV~Error(B)+A*C))
```
Unbalanced
```
#sphericity met
> anova(lme(DV~A*C, random=~1|B), type='marginal')
#sphericity not met
> anova(lme(DV~A*C,random=~1|B,corr=corAR1(form=~1|B),
    type='marginal')
```

Other models
```
#F-ratios and P-values must be calculated individually
> AnovaM(aov(DV~B*A*C))
```

[a]If A is random (or an unrestricted model), then *F*-ratio is 1/7 ($MS_{B'}/MS_{Resid}$).
[b]Inexact *F*-ratio for restricted model.
[c]Pooling: higher order interactions with P> 0.25 can be removed to produce more exact denominators.
[d]Pooling: If P>0.25 for AC′ and P<0.25 for B′A, *F*-ratio denominator is $MS_{B'A}$. If P>0.25 for B′A and P<0.25 for AC′, *F*-ratio denominator is $MS_{AC'}$. If P>0.25 for both B′A and AC′, *F*-ratio denominator is $(SS_{AC'}+SS_{B'A}+SS_{B'AC'})/((a-1)(c-1)+(a-1)(c-1)+(a-1)(b-1)(c-1))$.
[e]For unrestricted model *F*-ratio denominator is $MS_{AC'}$.

13.4.1 Sphericity

Un-replicated factorial designs extend the usual equal variance (no relationship between mean and variance) assumption to further assume that the differences between each pair of within block treatments are equally varied across the blocks (see Figure 13.2). To meet this assumption, a matrix of variances (between pairs of observations within treatments) and covariances (between treatment pairs within each block) must display a pattern known as sphericity[c]

Typically, un-replicated factorial designs in which the treatment levels have been randomly arranged (temporally and spatially) within each block (randomized complete

[c] Strictly, the variance-covariance matrix must display a very specific pattern of sphericity in which both variances and covariances are equal (compound symmetry), however an *F*-ratio will still reliably follow an *F* distribution provided basic sphericity holds.

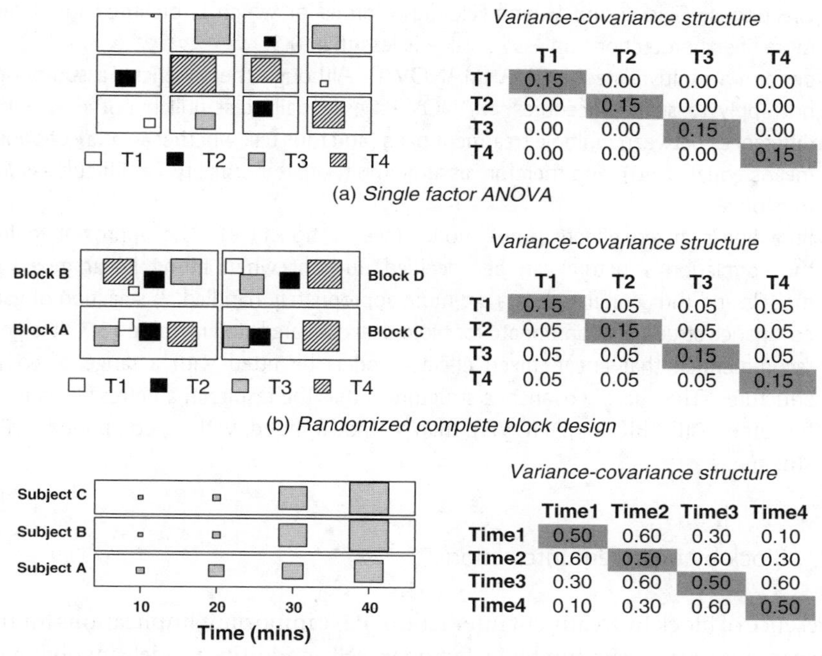

	T1	T2	T3	T4
T1	0.15	0.00	0.00	0.00
T2	0.00	0.15	0.00	0.00
T3	0.00	0.00	0.15	0.00
T4	0.00	0.00	0.00	0.15

(a) *Single factor ANOVA*

	T1	T2	T3	T4
T1	0.15	0.05	0.05	0.05
T2	0.05	0.15	0.05	0.05
T3	0.05	0.05	0.15	0.05
T4	0.05	0.05	0.05	0.15

(b) *Randomized complete block design*

	Time1	Time2	Time3	Time4
Time1	0.50	0.60	0.30	0.10
Time2	0.60	0.50	0.60	0.30
Time3	0.30	0.60	0.50	0.60
Time4	0.10	0.30	0.60	0.50

(c) *Repeated measures design*

Fig 13.2 Fictitious representations of variance-covariance structures associated with examples of (a) Single factor ANOVA, (b) Randomized complete block and (c) Repeated measures designs. The matrix diagonals represent within group variances and the off-diagonals represent the covariances between each group pair. In each of the example designs, homogeneity of variance (between treatment groups) is met. The variance-covariance structure associated with single factor ANOVA designs typically have either zero covariance or at least no pattern in the covariances. Randomized complete block designs (in which the treatment levels are arranged randomly within each block) usually display compound symmetry (equal covariances). By contrast, repeated measures designs often violate this assumption (sphericity) and display a covariance structure that reflects a particular pattern in which progressively closer (temporally or spatially) observations collected from the same sampling units are progressively more similar (autocorrelated).

block) should meet this sphericity assumption. Conversely, repeated measures designs that incorporate factors whose levels cannot be randomized within each block (such as distances from a source or time), are likely to violate this assumption. In such designs, the differences between treatments that are arranged closer together (in either space or time) are likely to be less variable (greater paired covariances) than the differences between treatments that are further apart.

Hypothesis tests are not very robust to substantial deviations from sphericity and consequently would tend to have inflated type I errors. There are three broad techniques for compensating or tackling the issues of sphericity:

(i) reducing the degrees of freedom for *F*-tests according to the degree of departure from sphericity (measured by epsilon (ε)). The two main estimates of epsilon are

Greenhouse-Geisser and Huynh-Feldt, the former of which is preferred (as it provides more liberal protection) unless its value is less than 0.5.

(ii) perform a multivariate ANOVA (MANOVA). Although the sphericity assumption does not apply to such procedures, MANOVA's essentially test null hypotheses about the differences between multiple treatment pairs (and thus test whether an array of population means equals zero), and therefore assume multivariate normality - a difficult assumption to explore.

(iii) fit a linear mixed effects (lme) model (see section 11.8). The approximate form of the correlation structure can be specified up-front when fitting linear mixed effects models and thus correlated data are more appropriately handled. A selection of variance-covariance structures appropriate for biological data are listed in Table 13.3. It is generally recommended that linear mixed effects models be fitted with a range of covariance structures. The "best" covariance structure is that the results in a better fit (as measured by either AIC, BIC or ANOVA) than a model fitted with a compound symmetry structure.

13.4.2 Block by treatment interactions

The presence of block by treatment interactions have important implications for models that incorporate a single within block factor as well as additive models involving two or more within block factors. In both cases, the blocking interactions and overall random errors are pooled into a residual term that is used as the denominator in F-ratio calculations (see Table 13.1). Consequently, block by treatment interactions increase the denominator (MS_{Resid}) resulting in lower F-ratios (lower power). Moreover, the presence of strong blocking interactions would imply that any effects of the main factor are not consistent. Drawing conclusions from such an analysis (particularly in light of non-significant main effects) is difficult. Unless we assume that there are no block by within block interactions, non-significant within block effects could be due to either an absence of a treatment effect, or as a result of opposing effects within different blocks. As these block by within block interactions are unreplicated, they can neither be formally tested nor is it possible to perform main effects tests to diagnose non-significant within block effects.

Block by treatment interactions can be diagnosed by examining;

(i) interaction (cell means) plot. The mean ($n = 1$) response for each level of the main factor is plotted against the block number. Parallel lines infer no block by treatment interaction.

(ii) residual plot. A curvilinear pattern in which the residual values switch from positive to negative and back again (or visa versa) over the range of predicted values implies that the scale (magnitude but not polarity) of the main treatment effects differs substantially across the range of blocks. Scale transformations can be useful in removing such interactions.

(iii) Tukey's test for non-additivity evaluated at $\alpha = 0.10$ or even $\alpha = 0.25$. This (curvilinear test) formally tests for the presence of a quadratic trend in the relationship between residuals and predicted values. As such, it too is only appropriate for simple interactions of scale.

Table 13.3 Standard variance-covariance structures used in `lme`. It is generally recommended that the appropriateness of the various covariance structures be assessed in the order presented (top ones first). The moving average (φ) and autoregressive parameters (ρ) can range from -1 to $+1$ (0 to $+1$ for Continuous time). Note that by default, these parameter estimates vary during model optimization. Alternatively, parameters can be fixed, by providing values for the parameters with the `values=` argument and specifying `fixed=TRUE`.

Description	Structure	R syntax
General (unstructured) structure • Most complex (and least precise) • Separate variance and covariance estimates for all combinations	$\begin{matrix} \sigma_1^2 & \sigma_{21} & \sigma_{31} & \cdots \\ \sigma_{12} & \sigma_2^2 & \sigma_{32} & \cdots \\ \sigma_{13} & \sigma_{23} & \sigma_3^2 & \cdots \\ \cdots & \cdots & \cdots & \cdots \end{matrix}$	`corSymm(form=~ 1|Block)`
Compound symmetry structure • Diagonals equal variance • Off-diagonals equal covariance • Simplest structure	$\begin{matrix} \sigma^2+\sigma_1^2 & \sigma_1^2 & \sigma_1^2 & \cdots \\ \sigma_1^2 & \sigma^2+\sigma_1^2 & \sigma_1^2 & \cdots \\ \sigma_1^2 & \sigma_1^2 & \sigma^2+\sigma_1^2 & \cdots \\ \cdots & \cdots & \cdots & \cdots \end{matrix}$	`corCompSymm(form=~ 1|Block)`
First order autoregressive structure • Diagonals equal variance • Off-diagonal variance multiplied by the autoregressive coefficient (ρ) raised to increasing power • Covariance decreases with increased separation • Assumes equal separation spacing	$\begin{matrix} \sigma^2 & \sigma^2\rho & \sigma_1^2\rho & \cdots \\ \sigma_1^2\rho & \sigma^2 & \sigma_1^2\rho & \cdots \\ \sigma_1^2\rho & \sigma_1^2\rho & \sigma^2 & \cdots \\ \cdots & \cdots & \cdots & \cdots \end{matrix}$	`corAR1(form=~ 1|Block)`
Moving average autoregressive structure • A more general autoregressive structure • Off-diagonal variance multiplied by the moving average (φ) parameter as well as the autoregressive coefficient (ρ) raised to increasing power	$\begin{matrix} \sigma^2 & \sigma^2\varphi\rho & \sigma_1^2\varphi\rho & \cdots \\ \sigma_1^2\varphi\rho & \sigma^2 & \sigma_1^2\varphi\rho & \cdots \\ \sigma_1^2\varphi\rho & \sigma_1^2\varphi\rho & \sigma^2 & \cdots \\ \cdots & \cdots & \cdots & \cdots \end{matrix}$	`corARMA(form=~ 1|Block)`
Continuous time autoregressive structure • Accommodates unequal separation spacing		`corCAR1(form=~ 1|Block)`
Heterogenous variances structures • Each of the above can also be modified to accommodate unequal variances		`weights=varIdent(form=~ 1|Block)`

There are no corrections for other more severe interactions (such as cross-over) - effected conclusions must therefore be made cautiously.

13.5 Specific comparisons

For randomized complete block designs in which the levels of within block factors can be randomly arranged, both planned and unplanned multiple comparisons tests can be performed as per single factor or fully factorial linear models (see chapters 10&12). However, when the assumption of sphericity is likely to be violated (as is typically the case for repeated measures designs), the appropriate compensatory adjustments for each specific comparison are not clearly defined. Therefore, each specific planned comparison should be performed using separately generated denominators (error terms). Unplanned multiple comparisons should be performed as a series of paired *t* tests, subsequently corrected for inflated type I error rates (e.g. Bonferroni corrections) if necessary (see section 10.6).

13.6 Unbalanced unreplicated factorial designs

Since these designs are un-replicated, any missing observation equates to an entire missing combination (cell) and thus an unbalanced design. Unbalanced designs (to reiterate) are less robust to deviations from the assumptions (particularly sphericity) and therefore require special attention. There are a number of approaches for dealing with unbalanced un-replicated designs, the pros and cons of which are described below:

(i) Omit the entire block/subject from which the observation is missing. Clearly, such an approach is only acceptable for designs that have a large number of blocks in the first place as it involves disregarding otherwise good data.
(ii) Fit a cell means model with appropriate contrasts (see section 12.6.2). Defining the appropriate contrasts can be a very difficult process.
(iii) If block interactions are assumed not to exist (additivity)
    (a) perform regular analysis with missing values have been replaced by values predicted by solving equations such as (predicted value = treatment mean + block mean - overall mean) and subtract one degree of freedom for each substituted value.
    (b) compare the fit (residual sums of squares) of appropriate full and reduced models (e.g. full: $y_{ij} = \mu + \beta_i + \alpha_j + \varepsilon_{ij}$ versus reduced: $y_{ij} = \mu + \beta_i + \varepsilon_{ij}$) using ANOVA. Importantly, sphericity corrections should also be incorporated into this approach - a task that is difficult to achieve.
(iv) Fit a linear mixed effects (lme) model (see section 11.8). In contrast to ANOVA, which only produces optimal estimators (estimators that minimize variance) for balanced designs, maximum likelihood (ML and REML) and thus linear mixed effects estimators yield estimators that are 'asymptotically efficient' for both balanced and unbalanced designs. The ability of linear mixed effects models to accommodate balanced and unbalanced, correlated and hierarchical (nested) data makes them the preferred approach to analyzing unbalanced un-replicated factorial designs.

13.7 Robust alternatives

When the data are non-normal (or infected with outliers), rank-based analysis can be useful. Of particular note is the **Friedman test** which generates a test statistic after ranking the observations within each block and compares this statistic to a chi-square distribution. As is the case for other rank based alternatives, this approach is less powerful than the parametric equivalents and is less capable of handling blocking interactions. Moreover, rank based tests do not directly address the issues of sphericity and are therefore inapporpriate for repeated measures designs.

Randomization tests, in which observations are repeatedly shuffled amongst the treatments within each block, are useful (particularly when observational independence is violated).

13.8 Power and blocking efficiency

Power analyses follow single factor and fully factorial power analyses, except that with respect to sample sizes, the blocks become the replicates. The decision of whether or not to block is often a comprimise between reducing unexplained variation and retaining maximum degrees of freedom. For the benifit of future investigations on similar systems, it is often desirable to determine what benifit incorporating a blocking factor offered over a regular completely randomized design. An estimate of the relative effeciency of the blocking can be obtained from:

$$\text{Estimated blocking efficiency} = \frac{(q-1)MS_{Block} + q(p-1)MS_{Resid}}{(pq-1)MS_{Resid}}$$

where p is the number of levels within factor A and q is the number of levels within factor B.

13.9 Unreplicated factorial ANOVA in R

Randomized complete block and repeated measures designs can be analysed using the `aov()` function with blocking factors defined with the `Error=` argument. Anova tables for balanced designs that meet the assumption of sphericity can be viewed using the `summary()` function which can also accommodate planned contrasts with the `split= argument`. Alternatively, `lme` (`nlme`) and the more recent `lmer` (`lme4`) functions facilitate the argubly more appropriate linear mixed effects modelling approach to analysing unreplicated factorial designs. Associated planned comparisons are performed as `estimable()` functions.

13.10 Further reading

- Theory

Doncaster, C. P., and A. J. H. Davey. (2007). *Analysis of Variance and Covariance. How to Choose and Construct Models for the Life Sciences.* Cambridge University Press, Cambridge.

Hollander, M., and D. A. Wolfe. (1999). *Nonparametric statistical methods, 2nd edition*. 2 edition. John Wiley & Sons, New York.

Quinn, G. P., and K. J. Keough. (2002). *Experimental design and data analysis for biologists*. Cambridge University Press, London.

Sokal, R., and F. J. Rohlf. (1997). *Biometry, 3rd edition*. W. H. Freeman, San Francisco.

Zar, G. H. (1999). *Biostatistical methods*. Prentice-Hall, New Jersey.

- Practical - R

Crawley, M. J. (2007). *The R Book*. John Wiley, New York.

Fox, J. (2002). *An R and S-PLUS Companion to Applied Regression*. Sage Books.

Maindonald, J. H., and J. Braun. (2003). *Data Analysis and Graphics Using R - An Example-based Approach*. Cambridge University Press, London.

Pinheiro, J. C., and D. M. Bates. (2000). *Mixed effects models in S and S-PLUS*. Springer-Verlag, New York.

Venables, W. N., and B. D. Ripley. (2002). *Modern Applied Statistics with S-PLUS, 4th edn*. Springer-Verlag, New York.

Zuur, A. F., E. N. Ieno, N. J. Walker, A. A. Saveliev, and G. M. Smith. (2009). *Mixed Effects Models and Extensions in Ecology with R*. Springer.

13.11 Key for randomized block and simple repeated measures ANOVA

1 a. Determine the appropriate model design and hierarchy

- **Conceptualize the design into a hierarchy (ladder) of factors**
  - Blocking factor (factor to which all levels (complete sets) of other factors are applied) at the top
  - Each of the main treatment factors (that are applied within each block) are considered lower in the hierarchy
  - The Block by treatment interactions (which are unreplicated) are next on the heirarchy
  - If there are two or more fixed within block treatment factors, then there are also interactions between these factors to consider
- Label random blocking factor levels (blocks or subjects) with a unique name

Block	Fact A	DV
B1	A1	.
B1	A2	.
B1	A3	.
B2	A1	.

- Identify the correct error (residual) term and thus F-ratio denominator for each factor (see Tables 13.1 & 13.2)

. . . . Go to 2

2 a. Check assumptions for unreplicated factorial ANOVA
As the assumptions of any given hypothesis test relate to residuals, all diagnostics should reflect the appropriate error (residual) terms for the hypothesis. This is particularly important for Model 1 (non-additive) models where interaction terms are used as the appropriate denominators (residuals).

- **No block by within block treatment interactions**

```
> with(data, interaction.plot(B, A, DV))
```

Residual curvature plot and Tukey's test for nonadditivity

```
> library(alr3)
> residual.plots(lm(DV ~ BLOCK + A, data))
> tukey.nonadd.test(lm(DV ~ BLOCK + A, data))
```

- **Normality (symmetry) of the response variable (residuals) at each level of each factor or combination of factors - boxplots of mean values**
Single within block factor or additive model (no interactions - Model 2) using MS_{Resid} as denominator in each case

```
> boxplot(DV ~ A, data)
> boxplot(DV ~ C, data)
> boxplot(DV ~ A * C, data)
```

Two or more within block factor non-additive (Model 1) model using interactions (such as MS_{BA}) as denominator as example

```
> library(lme4)
> data.BA.agg <- gsummary(data, groups = data$B:data$A)
> boxplot(DV ~ A, data.BA.agg)
```

where `DV` *is the response variable,* `A` *is a main fixed or random factor within the* `data` *dataset.*

- **Homogeneity (equality) of variance of the response variable (residuals) at each level of each factor or combination of factors - boxplots of mean values**
As for Normality.
Parametric assumptions (Normality/Homogeneity of variance) met . . Go to 4

b. Parametric assumptions not met . . . . Go to 3

3 a. Attempt a scale transformation (see Table 3.2 for transformation options) Go to 2
b. Transformations unsuccessful or inappropriate . . . . Go to 9

4 a. If incorporating planned contrasts (comparisons) . . . . . . See Examples 13A&13B

```
> contrasts(data$A) <- cbind(c(contrasts), ...)
> round(crossprod(contrasts(data$A)), 2)
```

. . . . Go to 5

5 a. Determine whether the design is balanced

```
> replications(DV ~ Error(Block) + A * C.., data)
> is.balanced(DV ~ Error(Block) + A * C.., data)
```

Design is balanced - sample sizes of all cells are equal . . . . Go to 6
b. Design is NOT balanced - one or more cells (combinations) missing (0 replicates) . . . . Go to 7

c. Design is NOT balanced - sample sizes of cells differ, but all combinations have at least one replicate .... Go to 8

6 a. Balanced single within block factor or additive (no interactions - Model 2) .... See Examples 13A,13B

```
> data.aov <- aov(DV ~ A + Error(Block), data)
> data.aov <- aov(DV ~ A * C + Error(Block), data)
```

Alternatively, consider linear mixed effects (lme) model .... Go to 13
Check for sphericity .... Go to 12

- **Sphericity met**

```
> summary(data.aov)
```

OR

```
> library(biology)
> AnovaM(data.aov)
```

- **Sphericity NOT met**

```
> library(biology)
> AnovaM(data.aov, RM = T)
```

To incorporate planned comparisons, utilize the `split=` argument, see Key 12.6
For post-hoc multiple comparisons .... Go to 12.20a

b. Balanced two or more within block factor non-additive (Model 1) .... See Examples 13A,13B&13D)

```
> data.aov <- aov(DV ~ Error(Block/A + Block/C) + A * C, data)
```

Alternatively, consider linear mixed effects (lme) model .... Go to 13
Check for sphericity .... Go to 12

- **Sphericity met**

```
> summary(data.aov)
```

OR

```
> library(biology)
> AnovaM(data.aov)
```

- **Sphericity NOT met**

```
> library(biology)
> AnovaM(data.aov, RM = T)
```

To incorporate planned comparisons, utilize the `split=` argument, see Key 12.6
For post-hoc multiple comparisons .... Go to Key 12.20a

7 a. Unbalanced (missing cells) single within block or additive (Model 2)

```
> library(nlme)
> data.lme <- lme(DV ~ A, random = ~1 | Block, data)
> data.lme <- lme(DV ~ A * C, random = ~1 | Block, data)
> anova(data.lme)
```

b. Unbalanced (missing cells) two or more within block factor non-additive (Model 1)

```
> data.lme <- lme(DV ~ A * C, random = ~1 | Block/A + 1 |
+     Block/C, data)
> anova(data.lme)
```

8 a. Unbalanced (unequal sample sizes n > 0) additive (Model 2)

```
> contrasts(data$A) <- contr.helmert
> contrasts(data$C) <- contr.helmert
> data.aov <- aov(DV ~ Error(Block) + A * C, data)
> AnovaM(data.aov, type = "III")
```

OR

```
> data.lme <- lme(DV ~ A * C, random = ~1 | Block, data)
```

b. Unbalanced (unequal sample sizes n > 0) non-additive (Model 1)

```
> data.aov <- aov(DV ~ Error(Block/A + Block/C) + A * C, data)
```

OR

```
> data.lme <- lme(DV ~ A, random = ~1 | Block, data)
> data.lme <- lme(DV ~ A * C, random = ~1 | Block, data)
> anova(data.lme)
```

9 a. Underlying distributions not normally distributed .... Go to 10
or consider GLM.. GLM chapter 17
b. Underlying distributions not normally distributed .... Go to 10
10 a. Underlying distribution of the response variable and residuals is known... GLM chapter 17
b. Underlying distributions of the response variable and residuals is not known .... Go to 11
11 a. Variances not wildly unequal, outliers present, but data independent (Friedman non-parametric test).................................... See Examples 13E

```
> friedman.test(DV ~ A | Block, data)
```

b. Variances not wildly unequal, random sampling not possible - data might not be independent (Randomization test

Follow the instructions in Key 10.8b to randomize the *F*-ratios or *MS* values from ANOVA tables produced using the parametric steps above. **Warning, randomization procedures are only useful when there are a large number of possible randomization combinations (rarely the case in blocking designs)**

12 a. Checking sphericity

```
> library(biology)
> epsi.GG.HF(data.aov)
```

13 a. Fitting linear mixed effects models

- Fit a range of models with alternative covariance structures

```
> library(nlme)
> #General (unstructured)
> data.lme <- lme(DV ~ A, random = ~1 | Block, data, corr =
+ corSymm(form = ~1 | Block))
> #Compound symmetry
> data.lme1 <- lme(DV ~ A, random = ~1 | Block, data, corr =
```

```
+ corrCompSymm(form = ~1 | Block))
> #Compound symmetry with heterogenous variances
> data.lme2 <- lme(DV ~ A, random = ~1 | Block, data, corr =
+ corrCompSymm(form = ~1 | Block), weights = varIdent(form =
+ ~1 | Block))
> #First order autoregressive
> data.lme3 <- lme(DV ~ A, random = ~1 | Block, data, corr =
+ corrAR1(form = ~1 | Block))
```

- Compare the fit of each to the model incorporating compound symmetry

```
> anova(data.lme1, data.lme)
```

- Examine the anova table (for fixed effects) for the fitted model with the "best" covariance structure

```
> summary(data.lme)
```

- Examine the parameter estimates for the fitted model with the "best" covariance structure

```
> summary(data.lme)
```

13.12 Worked examples of real biological data sets

Example 13A: Two factor fixed (Model I) ANOVA

To investigate the importance of leaf domatia on the abundance of mites, Walter and O'Dowd (1992) shaved the domatia off the surface of one random leaf from each of 14 leaf pairs. Leaves where blocked into pairs of neighboring leaves in anticipation that different parts of a plant might have different numbers of mites. Their design represents a randomized complete block with leaf pairs as random blocks and the treatment (shaved or not) as the within block effect (from Box 10.1 of Quinn and Keough (2002)).

Step 1 - Import (section 2.3) the Walter and O'Dowd (1992) data set

```
> walter <- read.table("walter.csv", header = T, sep = ",")
```

Step 2 - The block vector (variable) contains a unique identifier of each leaf pair. However, R will consider this to be a *integer* vector rather than a categorical *factor*. In order to ensure that this variable is treated as a factor we need to redefine its class

```
> walter$BLOCK <- factor(walter$BLOCK)
> class(walter$BLOCK)
[1] "factor"
```

Step 3 (Key 13.2) - Assess assumptions of normality and homogeneity of variance for the main null hypothesis that there is no effect of shaving domatia on the number of mites found on leaves.

According to Table 13.1, the MS_{Resid} (individual leaves within leaf pairs) should be used as the replicates for this hypothesis irrespective of whether a blocking interaction (the consistency of the effect of shaving is across leaf pairs) is likely to be present or not.

MITE

```
> boxplot(MITE ~ TREAT, walter)
```

log transformed MITE[d]

```
> boxplot(log(0.5 + (MITE *
          10)) ~ TREAT, walter)
```

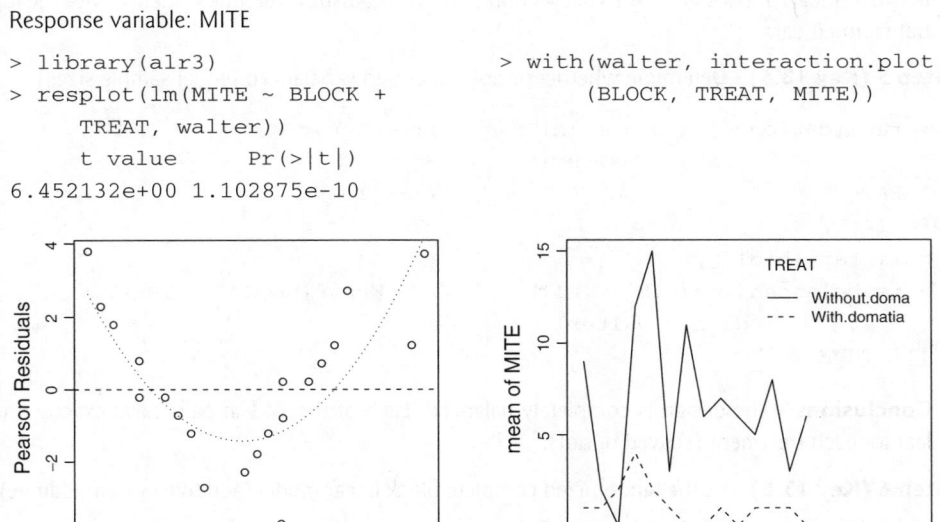

Conclusions - Strong evidence of unequal variance, potentially due to non-normality. Logarithmic transformation to normalize is an improvement.

Step 4 (Key 13.2) - Investigate whether or not there is any evidence of a block by treatment interaction.

Response variable: MITE

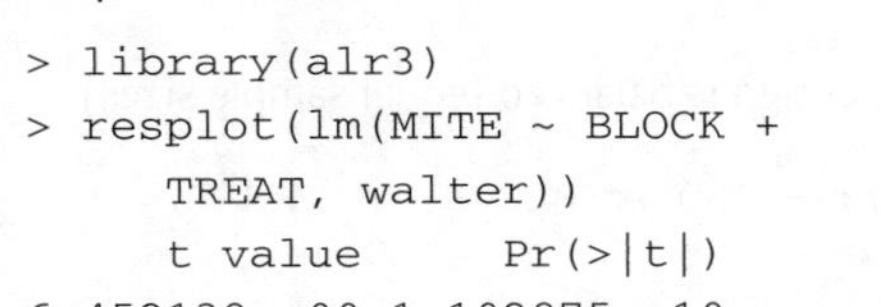

```
> library(alr3)
> resplot(lm(MITE ~ BLOCK +
    TREAT, walter))
    t value      Pr(>|t|)
6.452132e+00 1.102875e-10
```

```
> with(walter, interaction.plot
     (BLOCK, TREAT, MITE))
```

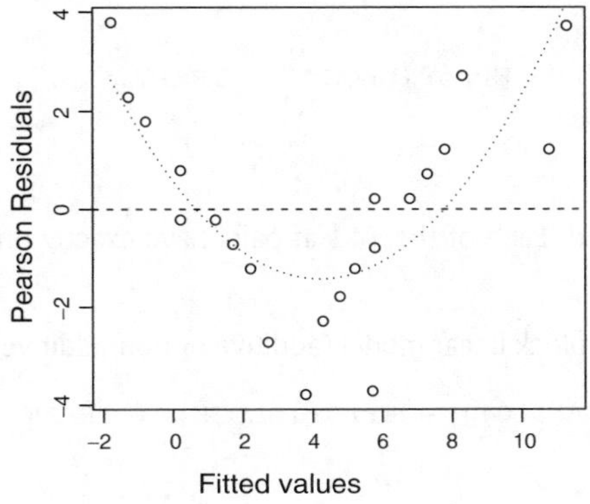

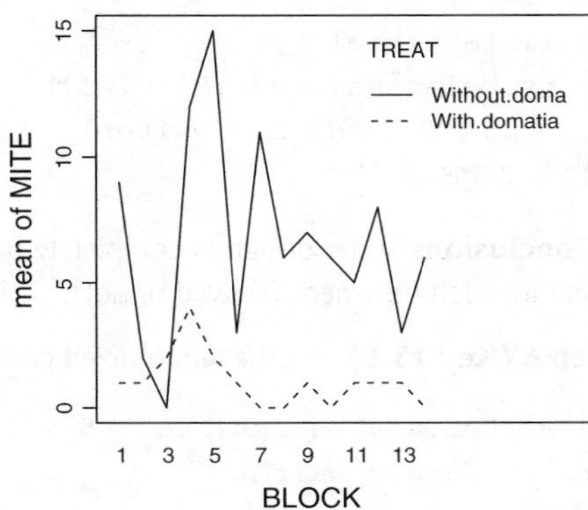

[d] Note that due to the presence of zero values Walter and O'Dowd (1992) added a small constant (0.5) to each of the mite counts prior to logarithmic transformation. They also multiplied the number of mites by 10, although it is not clear why.

Response variable: log transformed MITE

```
> library(alr3)
> resplot(lm(log(0.5 + (MITE *
+     10)) ~ BLOCK + TREAT,
+     walter))
   t value    Pr(>|t|)
-0.4644124  0.6423523
```

```
> with(walter, interaction.plot
+     (BLOCK, TREAT, log(0.5 +
+     (MITE * 10))))
```

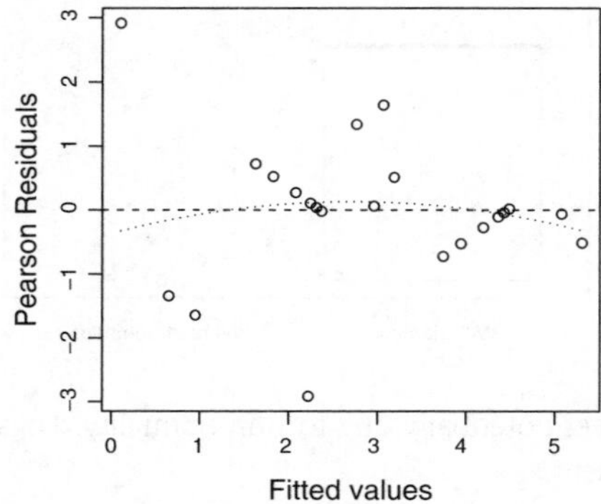

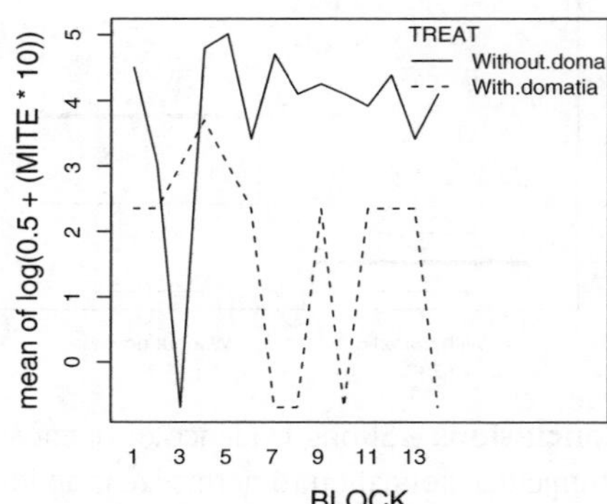

Conclusions - Strong evidence of a blocking interaction with the raw data (curvature pattern in the residuals and a significant Tukey's non-additivity statistic), yet little evidence with the log transformed data.

Step 5 (Key 13.5) - Determine whether or not the design is balanced (equal sample sizes).

```
> replications(log(0.5 + (MITE * 10)) ~ Error(BLOCK) + TREAT,
               data = walter)
TREAT
   14
> library(biology)
> is.balanced(log(0.5 + (MITE * 10)) ~ Error(BLOCK) + TREAT,
             data = walter)
[1] TRUE
```

Conclusions - The design is completely balanced. Each of the 14 leaf pairs have exactly one leaf for each treatment (shaved or not).

Step 6 (Key 13.6) - Fit the randomized complete block linear model (additive or non-additive).

```
> walter.aov <- aov(log(0.5 + (MITE * 10)) ~ Error(BLOCK) + TREAT,
+     data = walter)
```

Step 7 (Key 13.6) - Examine the anova table.

```
> summary(walter.aov)
Error: BLOCK
          Df  Sum Sq Mean Sq F value Pr(>F)
Residuals 13 23.0576  1.7737
```

```
Error: Within
          Df Sum Sq Mean Sq F value   Pr(>F)
TREAT      1 31.341  31.341  11.315 0.005084 **
Residuals 13 36.007   2.770
---
Signif. codes:  0 '***' 0.001 '**' 0.01 '*' 0.05 '.' 0.1 ' ' 1
```

Conclusions - the number of mites were found to be significantly lower on shaved leaves (those without domatia) than unshaved leaves.

Step 8 (Key 12.18) - Summarize the trends in a plot.

```
> op <- par(mar = c(4, 4, 0.1, 0.1))
> plot(MITE ~ as.numeric(BLOCK), data = walter, type = "n",
+      axes = F, xlab = "", ylab = "")
> with(subset(walter, TREAT == "Without.domatia"), points(MITE ~
+      as.numeric(BLOCK), pch = 21, type = "o", lwd = 1))
> with(subset(walter, TREAT == "With.domatia"), points(MITE ~
+      as.numeric(BLOCK), pch = 16, type = "o", lwd = 1, lty = 1))
> axis(1, cex.axis = 0.8)
> mtext(text = "Leaf pair", side = 1, line = 3)
> axis(2, cex.axis = 0.8, las = 1)
> mtext(text = "Number of mites per leaf", side = 2, line = 3)
> legend("topright", leg = c("Without domatia", "With domatia"),
+      lty = 0, pch = c(21, 16), bty = "n", cex = 0.7)
> box(bty = "l")
> par(op)
```

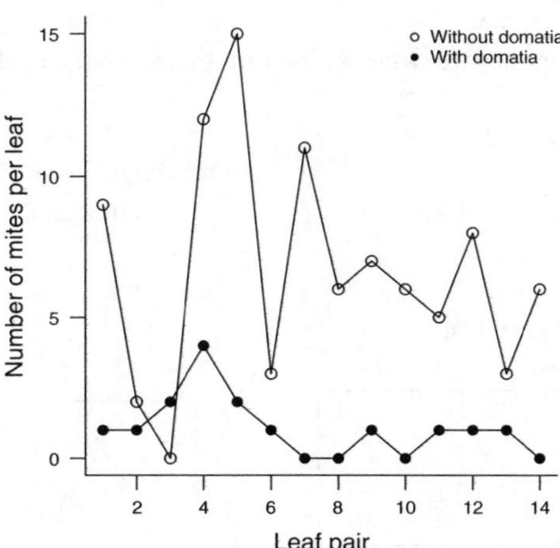

Example 13B: Simple repeated measures ANOVA

Driscoll and Roberts (1997) investigated the impact of fuel-reduction burning on the number of individual male frogs calling. Matched burnt and unburnt sites were blocked within six drainages, and the difference in number of calling male frogs between the sites was recorded for each drainage on three occasions (a 1992 pre-burn and two post burns in 1993 and

1994). They were primarily interested in investigating whether the mean difference in number of calling frogs between burn and control sites differed between years (from Box 10.2 of Quinn and Keough (2002)).

Step 1 - Import (section 2.3) the Driscoll and Roberts (1997) data set

```
> driscoll <- read.table("driscoll.csv", header = T, sep = ",")
```

Step 2 - The year vector is represented by single integer entries, and therefore to ensure that it is treated as a factor, we need to manually define it as such.

```
> driscoll$YEAR <- factor(driscoll$YEAR)
```

Step 3 (Key 13.2) - Assess assumptions of normality and homogeneity of variance for the main null hypothesis that there is no effect of year on the difference in male frogs calling between burnt and unburnt sites (within blocks).
According to Table 13.1, the MS_{Resid} (individual frog call differences) should be used as the replicates for this hypothesis irrespective of whether a blocking interaction is likely to be present or not.

```
> boxplot(CALLS ~ YEAR, driscoll)
```

Conclusions - No evidence of unequal variance, and the hypothesis test should be robust enough to account for any potential non-normality.

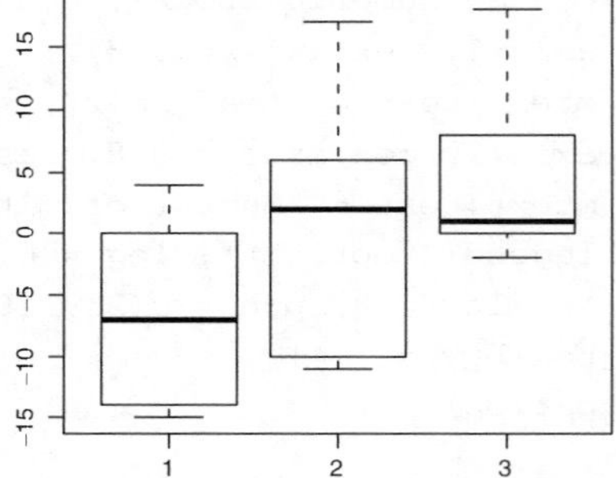

Step 4 (Key 13.2) - Investigate whether or not there is any evidence of a block by year interaction.

```
> library(alr3)
> resplot(lm(CALLS ~ BLOCK +
+     YEAR, driscoll))
    t value     Pr(>|t|)
-0.03404365  0.97284234
```

```
> with(driscoll, interaction.plot
+     (BLOCK, YEAR, CALLS))
```

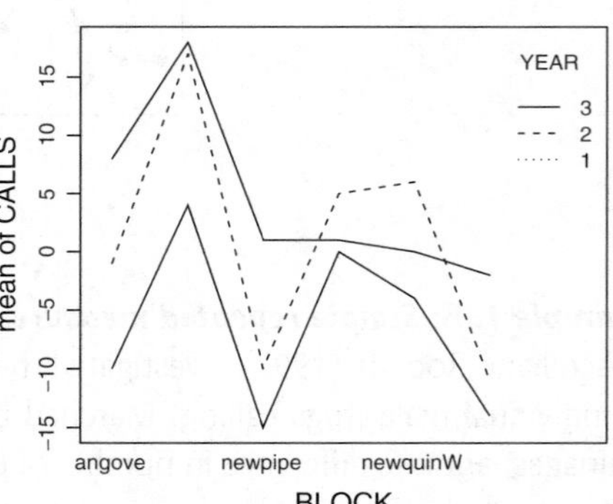

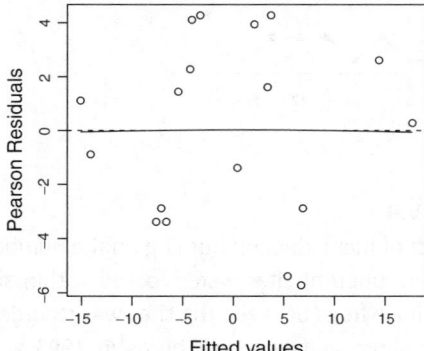

Conclusions - No strong evidence of a blocking interaction.

Step 5 (Key 13.5) - Determine whether or not the design is balanced (equal sample sizes).

```
> replications(CALLS ~ Error(BLOCK) + YEAR, data = driscoll)
YEAR
   6
> library(biology)
> is.balanced(CALLS ~ Error(BLOCK) + YEAR, data = driscoll)
[1] TRUE
```

Conclusions - The design is completely balanced. Each of the three years were represented within each of the 6 drainages (blocks).

Step 6 (Key 13.6) - Fit the repeated measures linear model (either additive or non-additive).

```
> driscoll.aov <- aov(CALLS ~ Error(BLOCK) + YEAR, data = driscoll)
```

Step 7 (Key 13.6) - Examine the anova table. Since the levels of year cannot be randomized within each block (the order must always be 1, 2, 3), we might suspect that sphericity will be an issue. Consequently, we will calculate Greenhouse-Geisser and Huynh-Feldt epsilon values and adjust the hypothesis tests accordingly.

```
> library(biology)
> AnovaM(driscoll.aov, RM = T)
   Sphericity Epsilon Values
-------------------------------
 Greenhouse.Geisser Huynh.Feldt
          0.7121834   0.9153904


Anova Table (Type I tests)
Response: CALLS
Error: BLOCK
          Df Sum Sq Mean Sq F value Pr(>F)
Residuals  5 955.61  191.12

Error: Within
          Df Sum Sq Mean Sq F value   Pr(>F)
YEAR       2 369.44  184.72  9.6601 0.004615 **
Residuals 10 191.22   19.12
---
Signif. codes:  0 '***' 0.001 '**' 0.01 '*' 0.05 '.' 0.1 ' ' 1


Greenhouse-Geisser corrected ANOVA table
Response: CALLS
Error: BLOCK
          Df Sum Sq Mean Sq F value Pr(>F)
Residuals  5 955.61  191.12
```

```
Error: Within
             Df Sum Sq Mean Sq F value  Pr(>F)
YEAR       1.4244 369.44  184.72  9.6601 0.00722 **
Residuals 10.0000 191.22   19.12
---
Signif. codes:  0 '***' 0.001 '**' 0.01 '*' 0.05 '.' 0.1 ' ' 1

Huynh-Feldt corrected ANOVA table
Response: CALLS
Error: BLOCK
          Df Sum Sq Mean Sq F value Pr(>F)
Residuals  5 955.61  191.12

Error: Within
             Df Sum Sq Mean Sq F value   Pr(>F)
YEAR       1.8308 369.44  184.72  9.6601 0.005196 **
Residuals 10.0000 191.22   19.12
---
Signif. codes:  0 '***' 0.001 '**' 0.01 '*' 0.05 '.' 0.1 ' ' 1
```

Conclusions - The Greenhouse-Geisser epsilon (0.712) confirmed a deviation from sphericity and thus the Greenhouse-Geisser adjusted P-value (0.013) should be used. Analysis indicates that there was a significant effect of year (time prior or post fuel reduction burn) on the difference in number of males calling between burnt and unburnt sites.

Step 8 (Key 12.8) - Quinn and Keough (2002) also presented the output of a multivariate analysis of variance (MANOVA) as an alternative.

```
> #convert the data to wide format
> dris.rm <- reshape(driscoll, timevar = "YEAR", v.names = "CALLS",
+ idvar = "BLOCK", direction = "wide")
> #fit the simple MANOVA
> dris.lm <- lm(cbind(CALLS.1, CALLS.2, CALLS.3) ~ 1, dris.rm)
> #create a data frame that defines the intra-block design
> idata <- data.frame(YEAR = as.factor(c(1, 2, 3)))
> #use the Anova (car) function to estimate the MANOVA test
   statistics
> (av.ok <- Anova(dris.lm, idata = idata, idesign = ~YEAR))
Type III Repeated Measures MANOVA Tests: Pillai test statistic
            Df test stat approx F num Df den Df  Pr(>F)
(Intercept)  1    0.0028   0.0142      1      5 0.90965
YEAR         1    0.8725  13.6913      2      4 0.01625 *
---
Signif. codes:  0 '***' 0.001 '**' 0.01 '*' 0.05 '.' 0.1 ' ' 1
> summary(av.ok)      #NOTE the output has been truncated
Type III Repeated Measures MANOVA Tests:

------------------------------------------
```

```
Term: (Intercept)

 Response transformation matrix:
        (Intercept)
CALLS.1           1
CALLS.2           1
CALLS.3           1

Sum of squares and products for the hypothesis:
            (Intercept)
(Intercept)    8.166667

Sum of squares and products for error:
            (Intercept)
(Intercept)    2866.833

Multivariate Tests: (Intercept)
                 Df test stat  approx F num Df den Df  Pr(>F)
Pillai            1 0.0028406 0.0142434      1      5 0.90965
Wilks             1 0.9971594 0.0142434      1      5 0.90965
Hotelling-Lawley  1 0.0028487 0.0142434      1      5 0.90965
Roy               1 0.0028487 0.0142434      1      5 0.90965

------------------------------------------------

Term: YEAR

 Response transformation matrix:
        YEAR1 YEAR2
CALLS.1     1     0
CALLS.2     0     1
CALLS.3    -1    -1

Sum of squares and products for the hypothesis:
         YEAR1     YEAR2
YEAR1 704.1667 216.66667
YEAR2 216.6667  66.66667

Sum of squares and products for error:
         YEAR1    YEAR2
YEAR1 232.8333 215.3333
YEAR2 215.3333 269.3333

Multivariate Tests: YEAR
                 Df test stat  approx F num Df den Df   Pr(>F)
Pillai            1  0.872540 13.691253      2      4 0.016246 *
```

```
Wilks               1  0.127460 13.691253      2        4 0.016246 *
Hotelling-Lawley    1  6.845627 13.691253      2        4 0.016246 *
Roy                 1  6.845627 13.691253      2        4 0.016246 *
---
Signif. codes:  0 '***' 0.001 '**' 0.01 '*' 0.05 '.' 0.1 ' ' 1

Univariate Type III Repeated-Measures ANOVA Assuming Sphericity

                SS num Df Error SS den Df      F   Pr(>F)
(Intercept)   2.72      1   955.61      5 0.0142 0.909649
YEAR        369.44      2   191.22     10 9.6601 0.004615 **
---
Signif. codes:  0 '***' 0.001 '**' 0.01 '*' 0.05 '.' 0.1 ' ' 1


Mauchly Tests for Sphericity

     Test statistic p-value
YEAR        0.59587 0.35506


Greenhouse-Geisser and Huynh-Feldt Corrections
 for Departure from Sphericity

      GG eps Pr(>F[GG])
YEAR 0.71218    0.01252 *
---
Signif. codes:  0 '***' 0.001 '**' 0.01 '*' 0.05 '.' 0.1 ' ' 1

      HF eps Pr(>F[HF])
YEAR 0.91539   0.006175 **
---
Signif. codes:  0 '***' 0.001 '**' 0.01 '*' 0.05 '.' 0.1 ' ' 1
```

Conclusions - Multivariate tests for the within block effects, all concur that there is an effect of YEAR on the differences in number of male frogs calling. Whilst the Mauchly test for sphericity does not indicate a problem with sphericity (P=0.355), Greenhouse-Geisser epsilon suggest substantial departures from sphericity (0.712). Univariate repeated measures ANOVA corrected for sphericity yield the same outcomes as Step 7 above.

Step 9 - Quinn and Keough (2002) suggested a logical planned contrast of year 1 (pre burn) with the year 2 and 3 (post burn). Note that as sphericity was clearly violated, this comparison must be performed using a separately calculated error term.

```
> driscoll.aov2 <- aov(CALLS ~ C(YEAR, c(1, -0.5, -0.5), 1) +
+     BLOCK + Error(BLOCK/C(YEAR, c(1, -0.5, -0.5), 1)),
+     data = driscoll)
> summary(driscoll.aov2)
```

```
Error: BLOCK
      Df Sum Sq Mean Sq
BLOCK  5 955.61  191.12

Error: BLOCK:C(YEAR, c(1, -0.5, -0.5), 1)
                                   Df Sum Sq Mean Sq F value   Pr(>F)
C(YEAR, c(1, -0.5, -0.5), 1)  1 336.11  336.11  29.715 0.002823 **
Residuals                          5  56.56   11.31
---
Signif. codes:  0 '***' 0.001 '**' 0.01 '*' 0.05 '.' 0.1 ' ' 1

Error: Within
          Df Sum Sq Mean Sq F value Pr(>F)
Residuals  6    168      28
```

Conclusions - the burnt-unburnt differences in number of frogs calling was significantly lower prior to the burn than after.
Purely for illustrative purposes, Quinn and Keough (2002) also highlighted the exploration of polynomial trends[e] (specifically a linear trend) across years.

```
> driscoll.aov3 <- aov(CALLS ~ C(YEAR, poly, 1) + BLOCK +
+      Error(BLOCK/C(YEAR, poly, 1)), data = driscoll)
> summary(driscoll.aov3)
Error: BLOCK
      Df Sum Sq Mean Sq
BLOCK  5 955.61  191.12

Error: BLOCK:C(YEAR, poly, 1)
                 Df Sum Sq Mean Sq F value  Pr(>F)
C(YEAR, poly, 1)  1 352.08  352.08  15.122 0.01154 *
Residuals         5 116.42   23.28
---
Signif. codes:  0 '***' 0.001 '**' 0.01 '*' 0.05 '.' 0.1 ' ' 1

Error: Within
          Df Sum Sq Mean Sq F value Pr(>F)
Residuals  6 92.167  15.361
```

Conclusions - there was a significant linear trend in burnt-unburnt differences in number of frogs calling across the years.

Step 10 (Key 13.13) - Finally, rather than attempting a *post-hoc* correction for the *estimated* departures from compound symmetry (sphericity), we could instead fit a linear mixed effects model (lme) in which the within block correlation structure is specified and incorporated.

[e] Note that this contrast is not independent of the previous contrast and is perhaps not of great biological meaning given that the impact occurred mid-way through the years rather than at the start.

- Fit the linear mixed effects model with a range of covariance structures

```
> library(nlme)
> #fit the lme with unstructured covariance structure
> driscoll.lme <- lme(CALLS ~ YEAR, random =~1 | BLOCK,
+ data = driscoll, correlation = corSymm(form = ~1 | BLOCK))
> #fit the lme assuming compound symmetry (sphericity)
> driscoll.lme1 <- update(driscoll.lme, correlation =
+ corCompSymm(form = ~1 | BLOCK))
> #compare the fit of the models
> anova(driscoll.lme, driscoll.lme1)
              Model df      AIC      BIC    logLik   Test  L.Ratio p-value
driscoll.lme      1  8 114.3804 120.0448 -49.19019
driscoll.lme1     2  6 115.7165 119.9648 -51.85826 1 vs 2 5.336127  0.0694

> #fit the lme with a first order autoregressive covariance structure
> driscoll.lme2 <- update(driscoll.lme, correlation = corAR1(form = ~1 |
+ BLOCK))
> driscoll.lme2
Linear mixed-effects model fit by REML
  Data: driscoll
  Log-restricted-likelihood: -51.31218
  Fixed: CALLS ~ YEAR
(Intercept)       YEAR2       YEAR3
   -6.50000     7.50000    10.83333

Random effects:
 Formula: ~1 | BLOCK
        (Intercept) Residual
StdDev: 0.002177376 8.230684

Correlation Structure: AR(1)
 Formula: ~1 | BLOCK
 Parameter estimate(s):
     Phi
0.758245
Number of Observations: 18
Number of Groups: 6
```

Conclusions - ρ (autocorrelation parameter) estimated to be 0.758245.

```
> #compare the fit of the models
> anova(driscoll.lme2, driscoll.lme1)
              Model df      AIC      BIC    logLik
driscoll.lme2     1  6 114.6244 118.8727 -51.31218
driscoll.lme1     2  6 115.7165 119.9648 -51.85826

> #fit the lme with a first order autoregressive covariance and heterogenous
> #variances structure
> driscoll.lme3 <- update(driscoll.lme, correlation = corAR1(form = ~1 |
+ BLOCK), weights = varIdent(form = ~1 | BLOCK))
> #compare the fit of the models
> anova(driscoll.lme3, driscoll.lme1)
              Model df      AIC      BIC    logLik   Test  L.Ratio p-value
driscoll.lme3     1 11 120.1991 127.9876 -49.09953
driscoll.lme1     2  6 115.7165 119.9648 -51.85826 1 vs 2 5.517442   0.356
```

Conclusions - Inferential evidence for a deviation from compound symmetry is not significant (AIC and BIC differentials less than 2 and logLikelihood statistic not significantly for any alternative models).

- Examine the anova table for the "best" lme

```
> anova(driscoll.lme1)
            numDF denDF  F-value p-value
(Intercept)     1    10 0.014243  0.9074
YEAR            2    10 9.660081  0.0046
```

Conclusions - There is a significant effect of year on the difference in number of males calling between burnt and unburnt sites.

- Fit the planned contrast of year 1 (pre burn) versus year 2 and 4 (post burns).

```
> library(gmodels)
> fit.contrast(driscoll.lme1, "YEAR", c(1, -0.5, -0.5))
                          Estimate Std. Error   t-value    Pr(>|t|)
YEAR c=( 1 -0.5 -0.5 ) -9.166667   2.186448 -4.192492 0.001850619
```

- Examine the polynomial trends.

```
> library(gmodels)
> fit.contrast(driscoll.lme1, "YEAR", t(contr.poly(3, c(1, 2, 3))))
        Estimate Std. Error    t-value    Pr(>|t|)
YEAR.L  7.660323   1.785227  4.2909509 0.001583836
YEAR.Q -1.701035   1.785227 -0.9528391 0.363134925
```

Step 11 - Summarize the trends in a plot.

```
> # create a blocking variable (called BLCK) that represents the
> #order of data in rows
> driscoll$BLCK <- as.numeric(factor(driscoll$BLOCK, levels =
+ unique(driscoll$BLOCK)))
> # construct the base plot with different point types for each
> # treatment
> plot(CALLS ~ BLCK, data = driscoll, type = "n", axes = F, xlab = "",
+ ylab = "")
> with(subset(driscoll, YEAR == "1"), points(CALLS ~ BLCK, pch = 21,
+ type = "o", lwd = 1))
> with(subset(driscoll, YEAR == "2"), points(CALLS ~ BLCK, pch = 15,
+ type = "o", lwd = 1, lty = 2))
> with(subset(driscoll, YEAR == "3"), points(CALLS ~ BLCK, pch = 5,
+ type = "o", lwd = 1, lty = 5))
> # create the axes and their labels
> axis(1, cex.axis = 0.8)
> mtext(text = "Block", side = 1, line = 3)
> axis(2, cex.axis = 0.8, las = 1)
> mtext(text = "Difference in calls (burnt - unburnt)", side = 2,
+ line = 3)
> # include a legend
```

```
> legend("topright",leg = c("Year 1", "Year 2", "Year 3"), lty = 0,
+ pch = c(21, 15, 5), bty = "n",
+ cex=0.9)
> box(bty="l")
```

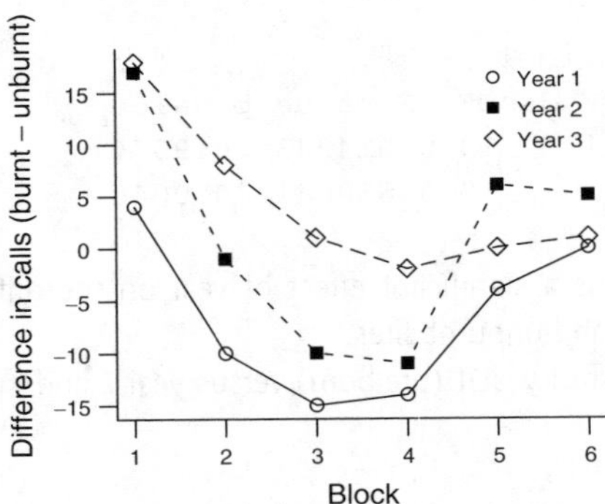

Example 13C: Unreplicated ANOVA with missing observations

Quinn and Keough (2002) presented a modification of the Driscoll and Roberts (1997) data set in which one of the observations (newpipe year 2) was removed - so as to demonstrate and contrast the options for dealing with missing observations (=cells) in unreplicated designs (see Box 10.8 Quinn and Keough (2002)).

Step 1 - Prepare the data (from example 13B).

```
> driscoll1 <- driscoll
> driscoll1[9, 4] <- NA
```

Step 2 - As we have already examined the assumptions associated with the relevant design, we will skip straight to the analysis options

Option 1- Omit the newpipe block

```
> driscoll1.aov <- aov(CALLS ~ Error(BLOCK) + YEAR,
+     data = driscoll1, subset = BLOCK != "newpipe")
> summary(driscoll1.aov)
Error: BLOCK
          Df Sum Sq Mean Sq F value Pr(>F)
Residuals  4 747.07  186.77

Error: Within
          Df  Sum Sq Mean Sq F value  Pr(>F)
YEAR       2 272.133 136.067   7.044 0.01721 *
Residuals  8 154.533  19.317
---
Signif. codes:  0 '***' 0.001 '**' 0.01 '*' 0.05 '.' 0.1 ' ' 1
```

Option 2- Substitute a new value (by solving the equation $\hat{y}_{ij} = \bar{y}_i + \bar{y}_j - \bar{y}$ - that is, the expected value of any given observation within a specific year/block is equal to the sum of the mean of the block, the mean of the year and the negative of the overall mean).

```
> #calculate the mean of the newpipe block
> BM<-with(driscoll1, tapply(CALLS, BLOCK, mean, na.rm=T))
+ ["newpipe"]
> #calculate the mean of year 2
> YM<-with(driscoll1, tapply(CALLS, YEAR, mean, na.rm=T))["2"]
> #calculate the overall mean
> M<-mean(driscoll1$CALLS,na.rm=T)
> #duplicate the data set and work on the duplicate
> driscoll2 <- driscoll1
> #substitute the new value into the data frame
> driscoll2[9,3]<-YM+BM-M
> #fit the linear model
> driscoll2.aov <- aov(CALLS~Error(BLOCK)+YEAR, data=driscoll2)
> summary(driscoll2.aov)
Error: BLOCK
          Df Sum Sq Mean Sq F value Pr(>F)
YEAR       1 116.74  116.74   0.625 0.4734
Residuals  4 747.07  186.77

Error: Within
          Df Sum Sq Mean Sq F value   Pr(>F)
YEAR       2 384.12  192.06  10.135 0.004957 **
Residuals  9 170.55   18.95
---
Signif. codes:  0 '***' 0.001 '**' 0.01 '*' 0.05 '.' 0.1 ' ' 1
> #then make adjustments to the F-ratio and Pvalue (to reflect a
> #reduction) in residual degrees of freedom by one for each
> #substituted value)
> (MSresid <- summary(driscoll2.aov)[[2]][[1]]["Residuals",
  "Sum Sq"]/9)
[1] 18.95

> (Fyear <- summary(driscoll2.aov)[[2]][[1]]["YEAR","Mean Sq"]/
  MSresid)
[1] 10.13500

> (Pvalue <- 1-pf(Fyear, 2,8))
[1] 0.006412925
```

Option 3- Compare appropriate full and reduced models

```
> driscoll1.aovF <- aov(CALLS ~ BLOCK + YEAR, data = driscoll1)
> driscoll1.aovR <- aov(CALLS ~ BLOCK, data = driscoll1)
> anova(driscoll1.aovF, driscoll1.aovR)
Analysis of Variance Table

Model 1: CALLS ~ BLOCK + YEAR
Model 2: CALLS ~ BLOCK
```

```
  Res.Df     RSS Df Sum of Sq      F   Pr(>F)
1      9  170.55
2     11  554.67 -2   -384.12 10.135 0.004957 **
---
Signif. codes:  0 '***' 0.001 '**' 0.01 '*' 0.05 '.' 0.1 ' ' 1
```

OR

```
> anova(driscoll1.aovF)
Analysis of Variance Table

Response: CALLS
          Df Sum Sq Mean Sq F value   Pr(>F)
BLOCK      5 863.80  172.76  9.1167 0.002500 **
YEAR       2 384.12  192.06 10.1350 0.004957 **
Residuals  9 170.55   18.95
---
Signif. codes:  0 '***' 0.001 '**' 0.01 '*' 0.05 '.' 0.1 ' ' 1
```

Note that options 2 and 3 are only valid if we assume that there are no block by year interactions and are both difficult to make reasonable sphericity deviation estimates and corrections.

Option 4- fit some alternative linear mixed effects models (with different covariance structures).

```
> library(nlme)
> #No structure
> driscoll1.lme1 <- lme(CALLS ~ YEAR, random = ~1 | BLOCK, data = driscoll1,
+ subset = !is.na(CALLS))
> #Unstructured
> driscoll1.lme2 <- lme(CALLS ~ YEAR, random = ~1 | BLOCK, data = driscoll1,
+ subset = !is.na(CALLS), correlation = corSymm(form = ~1 | BLOCK))
> #Compound symmetry
> driscoll1.lme3 <- update(driscoll1.lme1, correlation =
+ corCompSymm(form = ~1 | BLOCK))
> #First order autoregressive
> driscoll1.lme4 <- lme(CALLS ~ YEAR, random = ~1 | BLOCK, data = driscoll1,
+ subset = !is.na(CALLS), correlation = corAR1(form = ~1 | BLOCK))
> driscoll1.lme4 <- update(driscoll1.lme1, correlation =
+ corAR1(form = ~1 | BLOCK))
> #Compare each to compound symmetry
> anova(driscoll1.lme3, driscoll1.lme1, driscoll1.lme2, driscoll1.lme4)
               Model df      AIC      BIC    logLik   Test  L.Ratio p-value
driscoll1.lme3     1  6 108.8226 112.6570 -48.41133
driscoll1.lme1     2  5 106.8226 110.0179 -48.41133 1 vs 2 0.000000  1.0000
driscoll1.lme2     3  8 109.2339 114.3464 -46.61695 2 vs 3 3.588753  0.3094
driscoll1.lme4     4  6 107.7288 111.5632 -47.86441 3 vs 4 2.494909  0.2872
> anova(driscoll1.lme3)
            numDF denDF   F-value p-value
(Intercept)     1     9  0.002742  0.9594
YEAR            2     9 10.264400  0.0048
```

Note that the lme method also implicitly incorporates the correlation structure of the data and therefore arguably handles the issues of sphericity (which are exacerbated with missing observations) more appropriately than ANOVA. Nevertheless, none of the alternative covariance structures resulted in significantly better fits (based on AIC values) than a model incorporating compound symmetry (`driscoll1.lme3`). Consistent with other analyses, the impact of burning was found to differ significantly over time.

Example 13D: Two factor randomized block design

To illustrate two factor randomized blocking designs, Doncaster and Davey (2007)[f] introduced a fictitious data set in which all the levels of sowing density (factor A) and fertilizer treatments (Factor B) were randomly allocated within blocks (Factor S) which in turn where arranged across a heterogeneous landscape. The response variable was the yield of crop (Y).

Step 1 - Import (section 2.3) the crop yield data set

```
> crop <- read.table("crop.csv", header = T, sep = ",")
```

Step 2 - Each of the categorical variables are listed as *integer* vectors rather than a categorical *factors*. In order to ensure that this variable is treated as a factor we need to redefine them.

```
> crop$A <- factor(crop$A)
> crop$B <- factor(crop$B)
> crop$S <- factor(crop$S)
```

Step 3 (Key 13.2) - Assess whether there is any evidence of treatment by block interactions

Response variable: Y (yeild)

```
> library(alr3)
> resplot(lm(Y ~ S + A * B,
     crop))
   t value     Pr(>|t|)
-1.3756093   0.1689426
```

```
> with(crop, interaction.plot(S,
+     paste("A", A, ":B", B,
+     sep = ""), Y))
```

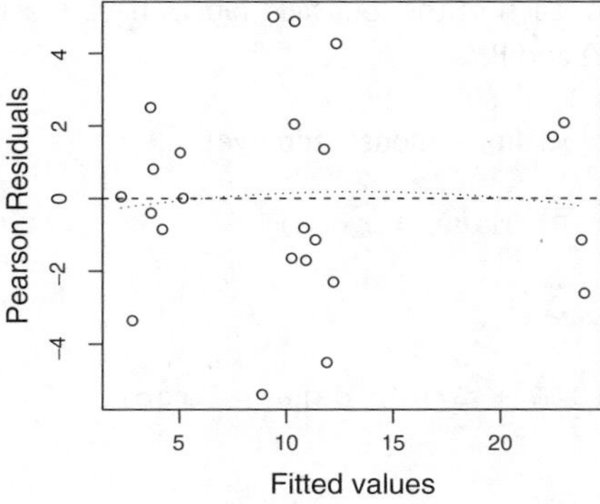

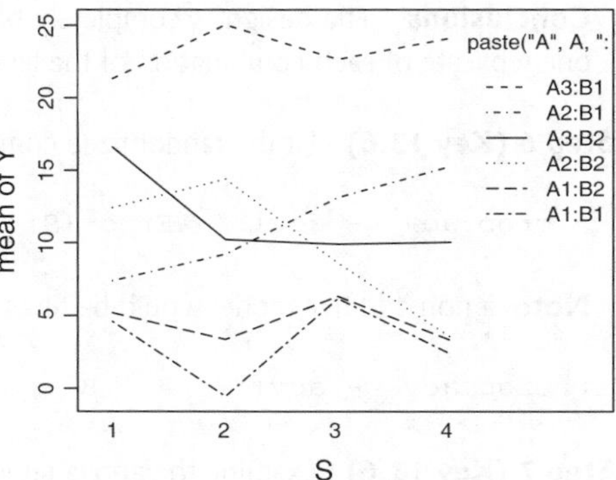

Conclusions - No clear evidence of a blocking interaction (no obvious curvature pattern in the residuals and non-significant Tukey's non-additivity statistic). Hence according to Table 13.2, the MS_{Resid} (individual treatment plots within the blocks) should be used as the replicates for each of the hypotheses.

---

[f] The data and example output can be found on the book's web page http://www.southampton.ac.uk/ cpd/anovas/datasets/.

Step 4 (Key 13.2) - Assess assumptions of normality and homogeneity of variance for the main null hypotheses that there are no effects of sewing density, fertilizer treatment or no interaction between the two on the yield of crop.

```
> boxplot(Y ~ A * B, crop)
```

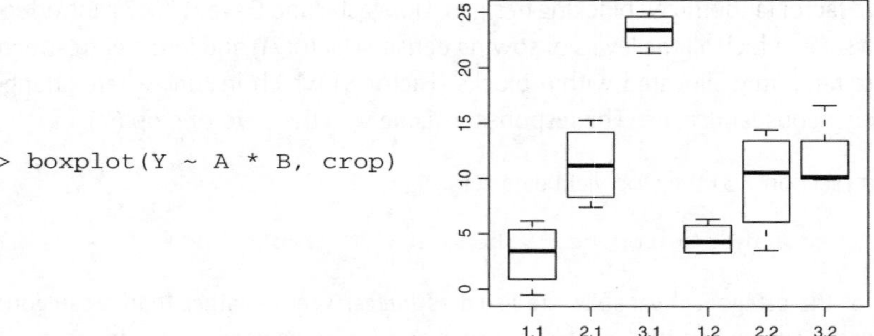

Conclusions - No evidence of unequal variance or non-normality.

Step 5 (Key 13.5) - Determine whether or not the design is balanced (equal sample sizes).

```
> replications(Y ~ Error(S) + A * B, data = crop)
  A    B A:B
  8   12   4

> library(biology)
> is.balanced(Y ~ Error(S) + A * B, data = crop)
[1] TRUE
```

Conclusions - The design is completely balanced. Each of the four field blocks have exactly one replicate of each combination of the levels of *A* and B.

Step 6 (Key 13.6) - Fit the randomized complete block linear model (additive).

```
> crop.aov <- aov(Y ~ Error(S) + A * B, data = crop)
```

Note, a non-additive model would be fit as:

```
> crop.aov <- aov(Y ~ A * B + Error(S/A + S/B), data = crop)
```

Step 7 (Key 13.6) - Examine the anova table.

```
> summary(crop.aov)
Error: S
          Df Sum Sq Mean Sq F value Pr(>F)
Residuals  3 9.0746  3.0249
```

```
Error: Within
          Df Sum Sq Mean Sq F value    Pr(>F)
A          2 745.36  372.68 32.6710 3.417e-06 ***
B          1  91.65   91.65  8.0346  0.012553 *
A:B        2 186.37   93.18  8.1690  0.003983 **
Residuals 15 171.11   11.41
---
Signif. codes:  0 '***' 0.001 '**' 0.01 '*' 0.05 '.' 0.1 ' ' 1
```

Conclusions - there is a significant sewing density by fertilizer treatment interaction.

Step 8 - Examine the main effects

```
> library(biology)
> #Examine the effects of B at A=1
> summary(mainEffects(crop.aov, at = A == "1"))
Error: S
          Df Sum Sq Mean Sq F value Pr(>F)
Residuals  3 9.0746  3.0249

Error: Within
          Df  Sum Sq Mean Sq F value    Pr(>F)
INT        4 1019.46  254.87 22.3429 3.563e-06 ***
B          1    3.91    3.91  0.3432    0.5667
Residuals 15  171.11   11.41
---
Signif. codes:  0 '***' 0.001 '**' 0.01 '*' 0.05 '.' 0.1 ' ' 1
> #Examine the effects of B at A=2
> summary(mainEffects(crop.aov, at = A == "2"))
Error: S
          Df Sum Sq Mean Sq F value Pr(>F)
Residuals  3 9.0746  3.0249

Error: Within
          Df  Sum Sq Mean Sq F value    Pr(>F)
INT        4 1018.78  254.70 22.3280 3.578e-06 ***
B          1    4.59    4.59  0.4028    0.5352
Residuals 15  171.11   11.41
---
Signif. codes:  0 '***' 0.001 '**' 0.01 '*' 0.05 '.' 0.1 ' ' 1
> #Examine the effects of B at A=3
> summary(mainEffects(crop.aov, at = A == "3"))
Error: S
          Df Sum Sq Mean Sq F value Pr(>F)
Residuals  3 9.0746  3.0249
```

```
Error: Within
          Df Sum Sq Mean Sq F value    Pr(>F)
INT        4 753.87  188.47  16.522 2.267e-05 ***
B          1 269.51  269.51  23.627 0.0002077 ***
Residuals 15 171.11   11.41
---
Signi f. codes:  0 '***' 0.001 '**' 0.01 '*' 0.05 '.' 0.1 ' ' 1
```

Conclusions - there is significant effect of fertilizer treatment (B1 vs B2) on crop yield, but only at a sewing density of A3.

Step 9 - Summarize the trends in a plot.

```
> crop.means <- with(crop, t(tapply(Y, list(A, B), mean)))
> library(gmodels)
> crop.se <- with(crop, t(tapply(Y, list(A, B), function(x) ci(x,
+      na.rm = T)[4])))
> ofst <- min(crop$Y)
> xs <- barplot(crop.means, ylim = range(crop$Y, na.rm = T),
+      beside = T, axes = F, xpd = T, axisnames = F,
+      axis.lty = 2, legend.text = F, col = c(0, 1), offset = ofst)
> arrows(xs, crop.means + ofst, xs, crop.means + crop.se + ofst,
+      code = 2, angle = 90, len = 0.05)
> axis(2, las = 1)
> axis(1, at = apply(xs, 2, median), lab = c("A1", "A2", "A3"),
+      padj = 1, mgp = c(0, 0, 0))
> mtext(2, text = expression(paste("Crop yield ", (g.m^2))), line = 3,
+      cex = 1)
> mtext(1, text = "Sewing density", line = 3, cex = 1)
> box(bty = "l", xpd = 1)
> legend("topleft", leg = c("B1", "B2"), fill = c(0, 1), col = c(0,
+      1), bty = "n", cex = 1)
```

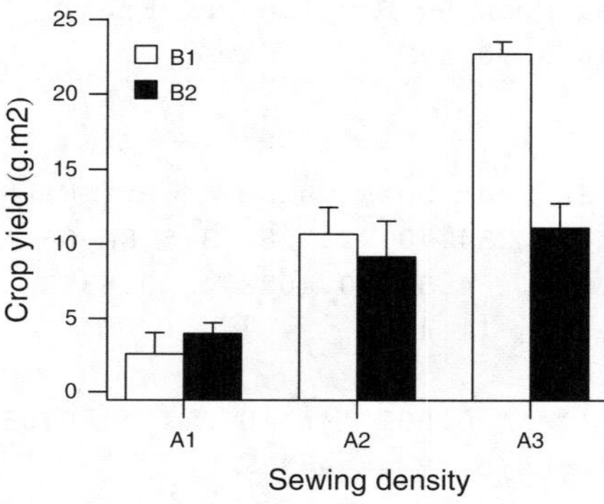

Example 13E: Non-parametric randomized block

Zar (1999) illustrated two approaches (Example 12.6 and Example 12.7) to non-parametric unreplicated factorial designs. Both approaches made use of data collected on the weight gained by guinea pigs maintained on one of four diets. Each guinea pig was individually caged and in an attempt to account for any variability in weight gain resulting from differences in cage position (the holding facility was potentially not homogeneous with respect to lighting, noise, temperature etc), guinea pigs were also blocked into sets of four individuals (one on each diet) whose cages were in close proximity. Within a block, individuals were randomly assigned to one of the four treatment diets. Whilst the data do not show concerning deviations from the parametric assumptions of normality and equal variance, for the purpose of illustration we will assume these assumptions have been violated.

Step 1 - Import (section 2.3) the Zar (1999) guinea pig data set

```
> gp <- read.table("gp.csv", header = T, sep = ",")
```

Step 2 (Key 13.2) - Assess whether there is any evidence of treatment by block interactions
Response variable: GAIN

```
> library(alr3)
> resplot(lm(GAIN ~ BLOCK +
       DIET, gp))
  t value   Pr(>|t|)
0.9315358 0.3515765
```

```
> with(gp, interaction.plot
      (BLOCK, DIET, GAIN))
```

Conclusions - No clear evidence of a blocking interaction (only very slight curvature pattern in the residuals and non-significant Tukey's non-additivity statistic).

Step 3 (Key 13.2) - Assess assumptions of normality and homogeneity of variance for the main null hypotheses that there are no effects of diet within Block on the weight gain of guinea pigs.

```
> boxplot(GAIN ~ DIET, gp)
```

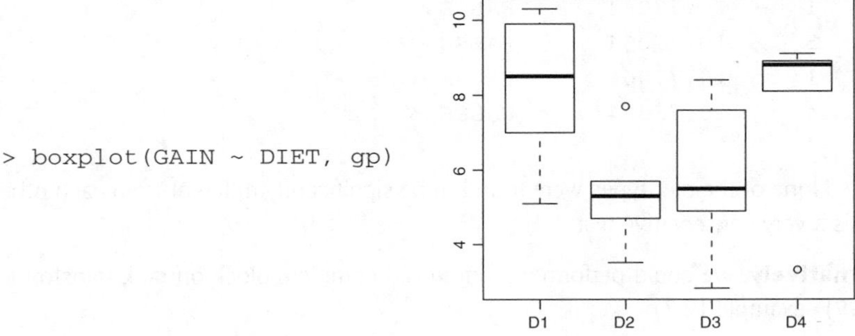

Conclusions - Although the evidence of unequal variance and non-normality is not substantial, outliers are present and some skewness is suggested. **Note, that for the purpose of reproducing the output of one of the major texts in biostatisics, we will proceed as if the parametric assumptions had been violated**.

Step 4 (Key 13.5) - Determine whether or not the design is balanced (equal sample sizes).

```
> replications(GAIN ~ Error(BLOCK) + DIET, data = gp)
DIET
   5
> library(biology)
> is.balanced(GAIN ~ Error(BLOCK) + DIET, data = gp)
[1] TRUE
```

Conclusions - The design is completely balanced. There are exactly one of each diet treatment per block.

Step 5 (Key 13.11) - Perform a Friedman's test (Zar (1999), Example 12.6)

```
> library(pgirmess)
> friedman.test(GAIN ~ DIET | BLOCK, data = gp)
        Friedman rank sum test

data:  GAIN and DIET and BLOCK
Friedman chi-squared = 10.68, df = 3, p-value = 0.01359
```

Conclusions - there is a significant effect of diet on the weight gain of guinea pigs.

Step 6 - Perform a multiple comparisons test following a Friedman's test

```
> library(pgirmess)
> friedmanmc(gp$GAIN, gp$DIET, gp$BLOCK, p = 0.05)
Multiple comparisons between groups after Friedman test
p.value: 0.05
Comparisons
      obs.dif critical.dif difference
D1-D2       0     10.77064      FALSE
D1-D3       5     10.77064      FALSE
D1-D4       1     10.77064      FALSE
D2-D3       5     10.77064      FALSE
D2-D4       1     10.77064      FALSE
D3-D4       4     10.77064      FALSE
```

Conclusions - None of the diet types were found to be significantly different from each other, however, this is a very conservative test.

Step 7 - **Alternatively**, we could perform a randomized complete block on rank transformed data (Zar (1999)–example 12.7)

```
> summary(aov(rank(GAIN) ~ Error(BLOCK) + DIET, gp))
Error: BLOCK
          Df Sum Sq Mean Sq F value Pr(>F)
Residuals  4    400     100

Error: Within
          Df  Sum Sq Mean Sq F value    Pr(>F)
DIET       3 195.400  65.133   11.23 0.0008471 ***
Residuals 12  69.600   5.800
---
Signif. codes:  0 '***' 0.001 '**' 0.01 '*' 0.05 '.' 0.1 ' ' 1
```

Conclusions - there is a significant effect of diet on the weight gain of guinea pigs.

Step 8 - Perform a multiple comparisons test rank based randomized block analysis

```
> library(multcomp)
> summary(glht(aov(rank(GAIN) ~ BLOCK + DIET, gp),
        linfct = mcp(DIET = "Tukey")))
        Simultaneous Tests for General Linear Hypotheses

Multiple Comparisons of Means: Tukey Contrasts


Fit: aov(formula = rank(GAIN) ~ BLOCK + DIET, data = gp)

Linear Hypotheses:
             Estimate Std. Error t value Pr(>|t|)
D2 - D1 == 0   -7.000      1.523  -4.596  0.00279 **
D3 - D1 == 0   -6.200      1.523  -4.070  0.00740 **
D4 - D1 == 0   -0.800      1.523  -0.525  0.95130
D3 - D2 == 0    0.800      1.523   0.525  0.95135
D4 - D2 == 0    6.200      1.523   4.070  0.00712 **
D4 - D3 == 0    5.400      1.523   3.545  0.01827 *
---
Signif. codes:  0 '***' 0.001 '**' 0.01 '*' 0.05 '.' 0.1 ' ' 1
(Adjusted p values reported -- single-step method)
```

Conclusions - The weight gain of guinea pigs on diets one and four was significantly greater than that on either diet two or three.

Step 9 - Summarize the trends in a plot.

```
> gp.means <- with(gp, t(tapply(GAIN, DIET, mean)))
> library(gmodels)
> gp.res <- resid(aov(GAIN ~ BLOCK + DIET, gp))
> gp.se <- with(gp, t(tapply(gp.res, DIET, function(x) ci(x,
+ na.rm = T)[4])))
```

```
> xs <- barplot(gp.means, ylim = range(gp$GAIN), beside = T,
+     axes = F, xpd = F, axisnames = F, axis.lty = 2,
+     legend.text = F, col = c(0,0))
> arrows(xs, gp.means + ofst, xs, gp.means + gp.se, code = 2,
+     angle = 90, len = 0.05)
> axis(2, las = 1)
> axis(1, at = apply(xs, 2, median), lab = c("D1", "D2", "D3",
+     "D4"), padj = 1, mgp = c(0, 0, 0))
> mtext(2, text = expression(paste("Weight gain ", (g))), line = 3,
+     cex = 1)
> mtext(1, text = "Diet", line = 3, cex = 1)
> box(bty = "l", xpd = 1)
> text(gp.means + gp.se + 0.5 ~ xs, lab = c("A", "B", "B", "A"))
```

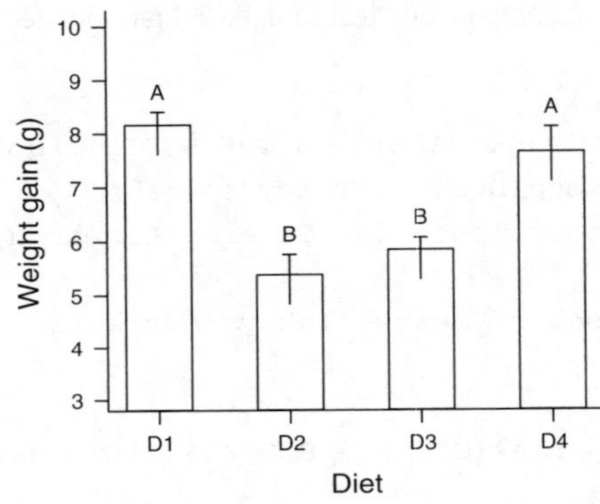

14

Partly nested designs: split plot and complex repeated measures

Split-plot[a] designs extend unreplicated factorial (randomized complete block and simple repeated measures) designs by incorporating an additional factor whose levels are applied to entire blocks. Similarly, complex repeated measures designs are repeated measures designs in which there are different types of subjects. Split-plot and complex repeated measures designs are depicted diagrammatically in Figure 14.1 .

Such designs are often referred to as partly nested designs which reflects the fact that blocks are (partly[b]) nested within the main between blocking factor. These designs include both within and between block (subject) effects and as a result, they are subject to the considerations of both nested (Chapter 11) and unreplicated factorial designs (Chapter 13). Whilst most of the issues have therefore already been covered separately in previous chapters, the popularity and additional accumulated complexity of these designs warrants special treatment.

Consider the example of a randomized complete block presented at the start of Chapter 13. Blocks of four treatments (representing leaf packs subject to different aquatic taxa) were secured in numerous locations throughout a potentially heterogeneous stream. If some of those blocks had been placed in riffles, some in runs and some in pool habitats of the stream, the design becomes a split-plot design incorporating a between block factor (stream region: runs, riffles or pools) and a within block factor (leaf pack exposure type: microbial, macro invertebrate or vertebrate). Furthermore, the design would enable us to investigate whether the roles that different organism scales play on the breakdown of leaf material in stream are consistent across each of the major regions of a stream (interaction between region and exposure type). Alternatively (or in addition), shading could be artificially applied to half of the blocks, thereby introducing a between block effect (whether the block is shaded or not).

Extending the repeated measures examples from Chapter 13, there might have been different populations (such as different species or histories) of rats or sharks. Any single

[a] The term "split-plot" refers to the agricultural field plots for which these designs were originally devised.

[b] It is only partly, since there is only a single block within each level of the main factor.

Biostatistical Design and Analysis Using R: a Practical Guide, 1st edition. By M. Logan.
Published 2010 by Blackwell Publishing.

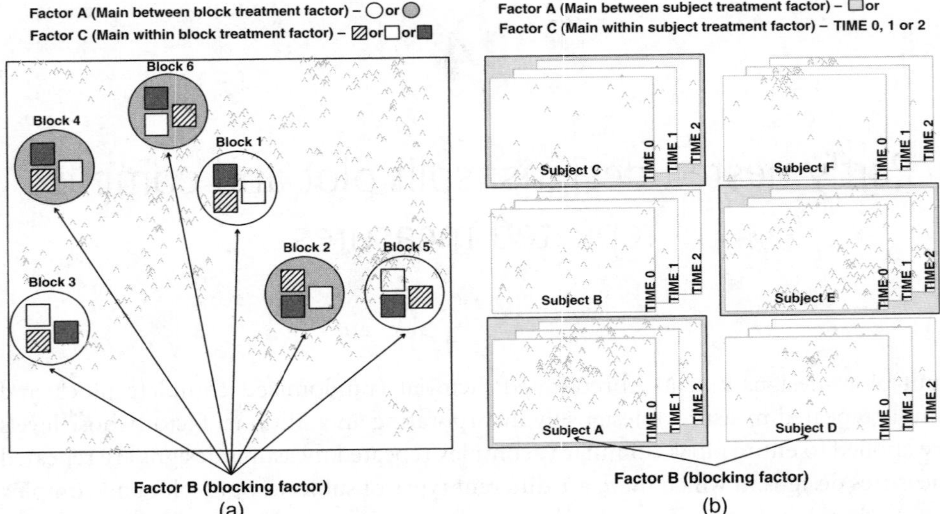

Fig 14.1 Fictitious spatial depictions of (a) split-plot and (b) complex repeated measures designs. The levels of the between block (or subject) effect (Factor A) are applied to the entire block. Note that the appropriate replicates for the effects of the between block effects are the block means. Therefore, for the effect of Factor A, n = 3 and for the effect of Factor C (within block or subject effect), n = 6.

subject (such as an individual shark or rat) can only be of one of the populations types and thus this additional factor represents a between subject effect.

14.1 Null hypotheses

There are separate null hypotheses associated with each of the main factors (and interactions), although typically, null hypotheses associated with the random blocking factors are of little interest.

14.1.1 *Factor A - the main between block treatment effect*

Fixed (typical case)

$H_0(A): \mu_1 = \mu_2 = \ldots = \mu_i = \mu$ (the population group means of A are all equal)

The mean of population 1 is equal to that of population 2 and so on, and thus all population means are equal to an overall mean. No effect of A. If the effect of the ith group is the difference between the ith group mean and the overall mean ($\alpha_i = \mu_i - \mu$) then the H_0 can alternatively be written as:

$H_0(A): \alpha_1 = \alpha_2 = \ldots = \alpha_i = 0$ (the effect of each group equals zero)

If one or more of the α_i are different from zero (the response mean for this treatment differs from the overall response mean), the null hypothesis is not true indicating that the treatment does affect the response variable.

Random

$$H_0(A) : \sigma_\alpha^2 = 0 \quad \text{(population variance equals zero)}$$

There is no added variance due to all possible levels of A.

14.1.2 *Factor B* - the blocking factor

Random (typical case)

$$H_0(B) : \sigma_\beta^2 = 0 \quad \text{(population variance equals zero)}$$

There is no added variance due to all possible levels of B.

Fixed

$$H_0(B) : \mu_1 = \mu_2 = \ldots = \mu_i = \mu \quad \text{(the population group means of B are all equal)}$$
$$H_0(B) : \beta_1 = \beta_2 = \ldots = \beta_i = 0 \quad \text{(the effect of each chosen B group equals zero)}$$

14.1.3 *Factor C* - the main within block treatment effect

Fixed (typical case)

$$H_0(C) : \mu_1 = \mu_2 = \ldots = \mu_k = \mu \quad \text{(the population group means of C (pooling B) are all equal)}$$

The mean of population 1 (pooling blocks) is equal to that of population 2 and so on, and thus all population means are equal to an overall mean. No effect of C within each block (Model 2) or over and above the effect of blocks. If the effect of the kth group is the difference between the kth group mean and the overall mean ($\gamma_k = \mu_k - \mu$) then the H_0 can alternatively be written as:

$$H_0(C) : \gamma_1 = \gamma_2 = \ldots = \gamma_k = 0 \quad \text{(the effect of each group equals zero)}$$

If one or more of the γ_k are different from zero (the response mean for this treatment differs from the overall response mean), the null hypothesis is not true indicating that the treatment does affect the response variable.

Random

$$H_0(C) : \sigma_\gamma^2 = 0 \quad \text{(population variance equals zero)}$$

There is no added variance due to all possible levels of C (pooling B).

14.1.4 *AC interaction* - the within block interaction effect

Fixed (typical case)

$$H_0(A \times C) : \mu_{ijk} - \mu_i - \mu_k + \mu = 0$$ (the population group means of AC combinations (pooling B) are all equal)

There are no effects in addition to the main effects and the overall mean. If the effect of the ik^{th} group is the difference between the ik^{th} group mean and the overall mean ($\gamma_{ik} = \mu_i - \mu$) then the H_0 can alternatively be written as:

$$H_0(AC) : \alpha\gamma_{11} = \alpha\gamma_{12} = \ldots = \alpha\gamma_{ik} = 0$$ (the interaction is equal to zero)

Random

$$H_0(AC) : \sigma^2_{\alpha\gamma} = 0$$ (population variance equals zero)

There is no added variance due to any interaction effects (pooling B).

14.1.5 *BC interaction* - the within block interaction effect

Typically random

$$H_0(BC) : \sigma^2_{\beta\gamma} = 0$$ (population variance equals zero)

There is no added variance due to any block by within block interaction effects. That is, the patterns amongst the levels of C are consistent across all the blocks. Unless each of the levels of Factor C are replicated (occur more than once) within each block, this null hypotheses about this effect cannot be tested.

14.2 Linear models

The linear models for three and four factor partly nested designs are:

14.2.1 One between (α), one within (γ) block effect

$$y_{ijkl} = \mu + \alpha_i + \beta_j + \gamma_k + \alpha\gamma_{ij} + \beta\gamma_{jk} + \varepsilon_{ijkl}$$

14.2.2 Two between (α, γ), one within (δ) block effect

$$y_{ijklm} = \mu + \alpha_i + \gamma_j + \alpha\gamma_{ij} + \beta_k + \delta_l + \alpha\delta_{il} + \gamma\delta_{jl} + \alpha\gamma\delta_{ijl} + \varepsilon_{ijklm}$$ (Model 2 - Additive)

$$y_{ijklm} = \mu + \alpha_i + \gamma_j + \alpha\gamma_{ij} + \beta_k + \delta_l + \alpha\delta_{il} + \gamma\delta_{jl} + \alpha\gamma\delta_{ijl} + \beta\delta_{kl} + \beta\alpha\delta_{kil} + \beta\gamma\delta_{kjl} + \beta\alpha\gamma\delta_{kijl} + \varepsilon_{ijklm}$$ (Model 1 - Non-additive)

14.2.3 One between (α), two within (γ, δ) block effects

$$y_{ijklm} = \mu + \alpha_i + \beta_j + \gamma_k + \delta_l + \gamma\delta_{kl} + \alpha\gamma_{ik} + \alpha\delta_{il} + \alpha\gamma\delta_{ikl} + \varepsilon_{ijk} \quad \text{(Model 2- Additive)}$$

$$y_{ijklm} = \mu + \alpha_i + \beta_j + \gamma_k + \beta\gamma_{jk} + \delta_l + \beta\delta_{jl} + \gamma\delta_{kl} + \beta\gamma\delta_{jkl} + \alpha\gamma_{ik} + \alpha\delta_{il} + \alpha\gamma\delta_{ikl} + \varepsilon_{ijk} \quad \text{(Model 1 - Non-additive)}$$

where μ is the overall mean, β is the effect of the Blocking Factor B and ε is the random unexplained or residual component.

14.3 Analysis of variance

The construction of appropriate F-ratios generally follow the rules and conventions established in Chapters 10-13, albeit with additional complexity. Tables 14.1-14.3 document the appropriate numerator and denominator mean squares and degrees of freedom for each null hypothesis for a range of two and three factor partly nested designs.

14.4 Assumptions

As partly nested designs share elements in common with each of nested, factorial and unreplicated factorial designs, they also share similar assumptions and implications to these other designs. Readers should also consult sections 11.5, 12.4 and 14.4. Specifically, hypothesis tests assume that:

(i) the appropriate residuals are normally distributed. Boxplots using the appropriate scale of replication (reflecting the appropriate residuals/F-ratio denominator (see Tables 14.1-14.3) should be used to explore normality. Scale transformations are often useful.

(ii) the appropriate residuals are equally varied. Boxplots and plots of means against variance (using the appropriate scale of replication) should be used to explore the spread of values. Residual plots should reveal no patterns (see Figure 8.5). Scale transformations are often useful.

(iii) the appropriate residuals are independent of one another. Critically, experimental units within blocks/subjects should be adequately spaced temporally and spatially to restrict contamination or carryover effects.

(iv) that the variance/covariance matrix displays **sphericity**[c] (see section 13.4.1). This assumption is likely to be met only if the treatment levels within each block can be randomly ordered. Violations of this assumption can be managed by either adjusting the sensitivity of the affected F-ratios or employing linear mixed effects (see section 11.8) modelling to the design.

[c] Strictly, the variance-covariance matrix must display a very specific pattern of sphericity in which both variances and covariances are equal (compound symmetry), however an F-ratio will still reliably follow an F distribution provided basic sphericity holds.

Table 14.1 *F*-ratios and corresponding R syntax for partly additive nested designs with one between block and one within block effect. *F*-ratio numerators and demoninators are represented by numbers that correspond to the rows from which the appropriate mean square values would be associated. *F*-ratios denoted '?' indicate inexact denominators.

			***F*-ratio**						
			A&C fixed, B random		**A fixed, B&C random**		**C fixed, A&B random**		**A,B&C random**
	Factor	**d.f.**	**Restricted**	**Unrestricted**	**Restricted**	**Unrestricted**	**Restricted**	**Unrestricted**	
1	A	$a-1$	1/2	1/2	$1/(2+4-5)^a$	$1/(2+4-5)$	1/2	?	$1/(2+4-5)^b$
2	B′(A)	$(b-1)a$	No test	2/5	2/5	2/5	No test	2/5	2/5
3	C	$(c-1)$	3/5	3/5	3/5	3/4	$3/4^a$	3/4	$3/4^b$
4	A×C	$(c-1)(a-1)$	4/5	4/5	4/5	4/5	4/5	4/5	4/5
5	Residuals (=C×B′(A))	$(c-1)(b-1)a$	No test	No test	No test	No test	No test		

R syntax[c]

A&C fixed, B random

```
> summary(aov(DV~A*C+Error(B)))
```

Unbalanced

```
#sphericity met
> anova(lme(DV~A*C, random=~1|B, correlation=corCompSymm(form=~1|B))
#sphericity not met
> anova(lme(DV~A*C, random=~1|B, correlation=corAR1(form=~1|B))
> anova(lme(DV~A*C, random=~1|B, correlation=...)
```

[a] Pooling: higher order interactions with P > 0.25 can be removed to produce more exact denominators.

[b] Inexact *F*-ratio for restricted model.

[c] Mixed models with non-hierarchical random factors require manual *F*-ratio and *P*-value calculations.

Table 14.2 *F*-ratios and corresponding R syntax for partly additive nested designs with one between block and two within block effect. *F*-ratio numerators and demoninators are represented by numbers that correspond to the rows from which the appropriate mean square values would be associated.

		F-ratio						
		A,C&D fixed, B random						
Factor	**d.f.**	**Model 1**	**Model 2**	**A&D fixed B&C random**	**A fixed B,C&D random**	**C&D fixed A&B random**	**D fixed A,B&C random**	**A,B,C&D random**
1 A	$a-1$	1/2	1/2	$1/(2+4-5)^a$	$1/(2+4-5+7-8-10+11)$	$1/2^b$	$1/(2+4-5)^a$	$1/(2+4-5+7-8-10+11)$
2 B′(A)	$(b-1)a$	No test[b c]	No test	$2/(5)^b$	$2/(5+8-11)$	No test[b]	$2/(5)^b$	$2/(5+8-11)^a$
3 C	$(c-1)$	3/5	3/11	$3/5^b$	$3/(5+9-11)$	3/4	$3/4^b$	$3/(4+9-10)^a$
4 C×A	$(c-1)(a-1)$	4/5	4/11	$4/5^b$	$4/(5+10-11)$	$4/5^b$	$4/5^b$	$4/(4+10-11)^a$
5 C×B′(A)	$(c-1)(b-1)a$	No test[b]		No test	5/11	No test	No test	5/11
6 D	$(d-1)$	6/8	6/11	$6/(8+9-11)^a$	$6/(8+9-11)$	6/7	$6/(7+9-10)^b$	$6/(7+9-10)^a$
7 D × A	$(d-1)(a-1)$	7/8	7/11	$7/(8+10-11)^a$	$7/(8+10-11)$	$7/8^b$	$7/(8+10-11)^b$	$7/(8+10-11)^a$
8 D × B′(A)	$(d-1)(b-1)a$	No test[b]		$8/11^a$	8/11	No test	8/11	8/11
9 D×C	$(d-1)(c-1)$	9/11	9/11	$9/11^b$	9/11	9/10	9/10	$9/10^a$
10 D × C × A	$(d-1)(c-1)(a-1)$	10/11	10/11	10/11	10/11	10/10	10/10	10/10
11 Residuals (=D×C×B′(A))	$(d-1)(c-1)(b-1)a$	No test		No test	No test	No test	No test	No test

R syntax

A,C&D fixed, B random

Model 1
```
> summary(aov(DV~A*C*D+Error(B/(C*D))))
```

Unbalanced
```
#sphericity met
> anova(lmer(DV~A*C*D*B+(1|B))) #note, only MS produced
#sphericity not met
> anova(lmer(DV~-1+A*C*D*B+(-1+A|B)+(-1+C|B)+(-1+A:C|B))) #note, only MS produced
```

(*continued overleaf*)

Table 14.2 *(continued)*

Factor	d.f.		*F*-ratio						
			A,C&D fixed, B random		A&D fixed B&C random	A fixed B,C&D random	C&D fixed A&B random	D fixed A,B&C random	A,B,C&D random
			Model 1	Model 2					

Model 2 Unbalanced

```
> summary(aov(DV~A*C*D+Error(B)))
#sphericity met
> anova(lme(DV~A*C*D, random=~1|B))
#sphericity not met
> anova(lme(DV~A*C*D, random=~1|B, correlation=corAR1(form~1|B))
```

Other models

Balanced

```
> AnovaM(aov(DV~A*B*C*D)) #F-ratios and P-values must be calculated individually
```

Unbalanced

```
#sphericity met
> anova(lme(DV~A*C*D, random=~1|B, , correlation=corCompSymm(form~1|B)))
#sphericity not met
> anova(lme(DV~A*C*D, random=~1|B, correlation=corAR1(form~1|B)))
```

[a] Pooling: higher order interactions with $P > 0.25$ can be removed to produce more exact denominators.
[b] Inexact *F*-ratio for restricted model.
[c] Inexact *F*-ratio for restricted model.

Table 14.3 *F*-ratios and corresponding R syntax for partly additive nested designs with two between block and one within block effect. *F*-ratio numerators and demoninators are represented by numbers that correspond to the rows from which the appropriate mean square values would be associated.

	Factor	d.f.	*F*-ratio					
			A,C&D fixed B random	A&C fixed B&D random	A&D fixed B&C random	A fixed C,B&D random	D fixed A,C&B random	A,B,C&D random
1	A	$a-1$	1/4	$1/(4+6-9)^a$	$1/3^a$	$1/(3+6-8)^a$	$1/3^{a\ b}$	$1/(3+6-8)^a$
2	C	$c-1$	2/4	$2/(4+7-9)^a$	$2/4^b$	$2/(4+7-9)^b$	$2/3^a$	$2/(3+7-8)^{a\ b}$
3	C×A	$(c-1)(a-1)$	3/4	$3/(4+8-9)^a$	$3/4^b$	$3/(4+8-9)^a$	$3/4^b$	$3/(3+8-9)^a$
4	B′(C×A)	$(b-1)ca$	No test	4/9	No test	4/9	No test	4/9
5	D	$(d-1)$	5/9	$5/9^b$	$5/7^a$	$5/7^{ab}$	$5/(6+7-8)^a$	$5/(6+7-8)$
6	D×A	$(d-1)(a-1)$	6/9	6/9	$6/8^a$	$6/8^a$	$6/8^a$	$6/8^a$
7	D×C	$(d-1)(c-1)$	7/9	7/9	7/9	7/9	$7/8^a$	$7/8^a$
8	D×C×A	$(d-1)(c-1)(a-1)$	8/9	8/9	8/9	8/9	8/9	8/0
11	Residuals (=D×B′(C×A))	$(d-1)(b-1)ca$	No test	No test	No test	No test	No test	

R syntax[c]

A,C&D fixed, B random

Balanced
```
> summary(aov(DV~A*C*D+Error(B/(C*D))))
```
Unbalanced
```
#sphericity met
> anova(lmer(DV~A*C*D*B+(1|B)))
#sphericity not met
> anova(lmer(DV~A*C*D*B+(1|B)), type='marginal')
```

Other models
```
> AnovaM(aov(DV~(A*C)/B+(D*C*A)/B)) #F-ratios and P-values must be calculated individually
```

[a]Pooling: higher order interactions with P > 0.25 can be removed to produce more exact denominators.
[b]Inexact *F*-ratio for restricted model.
[c]Mixed models with non-hierarchical random factors require manual *F*-ratio and *P*-value calculations.

(v) there are no block by within block interactions. Such interactions render non-significant within block effects difficult to interpret[d].

14.5 Other issues

Issues of *post hoc* and specific comparisons as well design balance and power follow the discussions in sections 10.6, 13.5, 13.6, 11.7, 11.10 and 13.8.

14.5.1 Robust alternatives

As designs increase in complexity, so too do the options for robust alternatives. In particular, rank based procedures can yield highly misleading outcomes. Generalized linear models (GLM: chpt 17) can be useful for modelling alternative (non-normal) residual distributions provided pairs of full and reduced models are chosen carefully and sensibly. Finally, randomizations can also be of use (particularly when observational independence is violated). However, care must be exercised in determining the appropriate scale at which to randomize.

Partly nested designs consist of multiple error or residual terms arranged in hierarchical strata and can therefore be thought of as a series of linear models (one for each strata). For example, a repeated measures design might consist of a linear model representing the between subject effects and one or more linear models representing the within subject effects. As a result, partly nested designs can also be broken down into the individual linear models onto which more the simplified robust alternatives highlighted in previous chapters can be applied.

14.6 Further reading

- Theory

  Doncaster, C. P., and A. J. H. Davey. (2007). *Analysis of Variance and Covariance. How to Choose and Construct Models for the Life Sciences.* Cambridge University Press, Cambridge.

  Quinn, G. P., and K. J. Keough. (2002). *Experimental design and data analysis for biologists.* Cambridge University Press, London.

  Sokal, R., and F. J. Rohlf. (1997). *Biometry, 3rd edition.* W. H. Freeman, San Francisco.

  Zar, G. H. (1999). *Biostatistical methods.* Prentice-Hall, New Jersey.

- Practical - R

  Crawley, M. J. (2007). *The R Book.* John Wiley, New York.

[d] Unless we assume that there are no block by within block interactions, non-significant within block effects could be due to either an absence of a treatment effect, or as a result of opposing effects within different blocks. As these block by within block interactions are unreplicated, they can neither be formally tested nor is it possible to perform main effects tests to diagnose non-significant within block effects.

Faraway, J. J. (2006). *Extending Linear Models with R: generalized linear mixed effects and nonparametric regression models*. Chapman & Hall/CRC.

Fox, J. (2002). *An R and S-PLUS Companion to Applied Regression*. Sage Books.

Maindonald, J. H., and J. Braun. (2003). *Data Analysis and Graphics Using R - An Example-based Approach*. Cambridge University Press, London.

Pinheiro, J. C., and D. M. Bates. (2000). *Mixed effects models in S and S-PLUS*. Springer-Verlag, New York.

Venables, W. N., and B. D. Ripley. (2002). *Modern Applied Statistics with S-PLUS, 4th edn*. Springer-Verlag, New York.

Zuur, A. F., E. N. Ieno, N. J. Walker, A. A. Saveliev, and G. M. Smith. (2009). *Mixed Effects Models and Extensions in Ecology with R*. Springer.

14.7 Key for partly nested ANOVA

1 **Determine the appropriate model design and hierarchy**

- **Conceptualize the design into a hierarchy (ladder) of factors**
  - Between block effects (factors whose levels differ between different blocks)
  - Between block interactions (if there are multiple between block effects)
  - Blocking factor (typically a random factor in which each level of other factors are applied)
  - Within block effects (factors that have all levels applied within each block).
  - Between block by within block interactions
  - Block by within block interactions
  - Within block interactions (if there are multiple within block effects)
- Identify the correct error (residual) term and thus *F*-ratio denominator for each factor (see Tables 14.1-14.3)

.... Go to 2

2 a. **Check assumptions for split-plot and complex randomized block ANOVA** .... see Examples 14A–14C&14E

As the assumptions of any given hypothesis test relate to residuals, all diagnostics should reflect the appropriate error (residual) terms for the hypothesis. This is particularly important for Model 1 (non-additive) models where interaction terms are used as the appropriate denominators (residuals).

- **No block by within block treatment interactions**

```
> with(data, interaction.plot(B, C, DV))
> library(lattice)
> bwplot(DV ~ C, groups = BLOCK, data)
```

Residual curvature plot and Tukey's test for nonadditivity

```
> library(alr3)
> residual.plots(lm(DV ~ B + C, data))
> tukey.nonadd.test(lm(DV ~ B + C, data))
```

- **Normality (symmetry) of the response variable (residuals) at each level of each factor or combination of factors - boxplots of mean values**
  Between block factor using MS_B as denominator in each case

```
> library(nlme)
> data.B.agg <- gsummary(data, groups = data$B)
> boxplot(DV ~ A, data.B.agg)
```

  Single within block factor or additive model (no interactions - Model 2) using MS_{Resid} as denominator in each case

```
> boxplot(DV ~ A, data) #factor A
> boxplot(DV ~ C, data) #factor C
> boxplot(DV ~ A * C, data) #A:C interaction
```

  Two or more within block factor non-additive (Model 1) model using interactions (such as MS_{BC}) as denominator as example

```
> library(nlme)
> data.BC.agg <- gsummary(data, groups = data$B : data$C)
> boxplot(DV ~ C, data.BC.agg) #factor C
```

  where `DV` *is the response variable,* `A` *is a main fixed or random factor within the* `data` *dataset.*

- **Homogeneity (equality) of variance of the response variable (residuals) at each level of each factor or combination of factors - boxplots of mean values**
  As for Normality.

Parametric assumptions (Normality/Homogeneity of variance) met...... Go to 4
b. Parametric assumptions not met.................................... Go to 3
3 a. Attempt a scale transformation (see Table 3.2 for transformation options) Go to 2
b. Transformations unsuccessful or inappropriate................ Go to Key 13.9
4 a. If incorporating planned contrasts (comparisons)....... See Examples 14C,14D

```
> contrasts(data$A) <- cbind(c(contrasts), ...)
> round(crossprod(contrasts(data$A)), 2)
```

.... Go to 5
5 a. Determine whether the design is balanced

```
> replications(DV ~ Error(B) + A * C.., data)
> library(biology)
> is.balanced(DV ~ Error(B) + A * C.., data)
```

Design is balanced - sample sizes of all cells are equal.................. Go to 6
b. Design is NOT balanced - one or more cells (combinations) missing (0 replicates).. Go to 7
c. Design is NOT balanced - sample sizes of cells differ, but all combinations have at least one replicate.. Go to 8b
6 a. Balanced single between and single within block factor or additive (no interactions - Model 2)................................ See Examples 14A,14B

```
> #Single within block factor
> data.aov <- aov(DV ~ A * C + Error(B), data)
> #Multiple within/between block factors
> data.aov <- aov(DV ~ A * C * D + Error(B), data)
```

Alternatively, consider linear mixed effects (lme) model .... See Key 13.13
Check for sphericity .... See Key 13.12

- **Sphericity met**

```
> summary(data.aov)
> library(biology)
> AnovaM(data.aov)
```

- **Sphericity NOT met**

```
> library(biology)
> AnovaM(data.aov, RM = T)
```

To incorporate planned comparisons, utilize the `split=` argument, see Key 12.8
For post-hoc multiple comparisons .... Go to 12.20a
If significant interation .... Go to 12.14

b. Balanced two or more within block factor non-additive (Model 1)

```
> data.aov <- aov(DV ~ A + Error(B/C + B/D) + C * D, data)
```

Alternatively, consider linear mixed effects (lme) model .... See Key 13.13
Check for sphericity .... Go to Key 13.12

- **Sphericity met**

```
> summary(data.aov)
> library(biology)
> AnovaM(data.aov)
```

- **Sphericity NOT met**

```
> library(biology)
> AnovaM(data.aov, RM = T)
```

To incorporate planned comparisons, utilize the `split=` argument, see Key 12.8
For post-hoc multiple comparisons .... Go to Key 12.20a
If significant interation .... Go to Key 12.14

7 a. Unbalanced (missing cells) single within block or additive (Model 2)

- No within block correlation structure

```
> #single within block factor
> data.lme <- lme(DV ~ A, random = ~1 | B, data)
> #multiple within block factors
> data.lme <- lme(DV ~ A * C, random = ~1 | B, data)
```

- Compound symmetry within block correlation structure

```
> #single within block factor
> data.lme <- lme(DV ~ A * C, random = ~1 | B, data,
+ correlation = corCompSymm(form = ~1 | B))
> #multiple within block factor
> data.lme <- lme(DV ~ A * C * D, random = ~1 | B, data,
+ correlation = corCompSymm(form = ~1 | B))
```

- General (unstructured) within block correlation structure

```
> #single within block factor
> data.lme <- lme(DV ~ A * C, random = ~1 | B, data,
```

```
+ correlation = corSymm(form = ~1 | B))
> #multiple within block factor
> data.lme <- lme(DV ~ A * C * D, random = ~1 | B, data,
+ correlation = corSymm(form = ~1 | B))
```

- First order autoregressive within block correlation structure

```
> #single within block factor
> data.lme <- lme(DV ~ A * C, random = ~1 | B, data,
+ correlation = corAR1(form = ~1 | B))
> #multiple within block factor
> data.lme <- lme(DV ~ A * C * D, random = ~1 | B, data,
+ correlation = corAR1(form = ~1 | B))
```

Comparing two models with differing correlation structures

```
> anova(data.lme, data.lme1)
> anova(data.lme)
```

b. Unbalanced (missing cells) two or more within block factor non-additive (Model 1)

```
> data.lme <- lme(Y ~ A * C, random = ~1 | B/A + 1 |
+      B/C, data)
> anova(data.lme)
```

8 a. Unbalanced (unequal sample sizes n > 0) additive (Model 2). . . . . See Examples 14C,14D

```
> data.aov <- aov(DV ~ A * C + Error(B), data)
> AnovaM(data.aov, type = "II")
```

OR

```
> contrasts(data$A) <- contr.helmert
> contrasts(data$C) <- contr.helmert
> data.aov <- aov(DV ~ A * C + Error(B), data)
> AnovaM(data.aov, type = "III")
```

OR

```
> data.lme <- lme(DV ~ A * C, random = ~1 | B, data)
> summary(data.lme, type = "marginal")
```

b. Unbalanced (unequal sample sizes n > 0) non-additive (Model 1)

```
> data.aov <- aov(DV ~ A * C * D + Error(B/C + B/D),
     data)
> AnovaM(data.aov, type = "II")
```

OR

```
> contrasts(data$A) <- contr.helmert
> contrasts(data$C) <- contr.helmert
> contrasts(data$D) <- contr.helmert
> data.aov <- aov(DV ~ A * C * D + Error(B/C + B/D),
     data)
> AnovaM(data.aov, type = "III")
```

OR

```
> data.lme <- lme(Y ~ A * C, random = ~1 | B, data)
> anova(data.lme, type = "marginal")
```

14.8 Worked examples of real biological data sets

Example 14A: Split-plot ANOVA

Kirk (1968) fabricated an experiment in which the effects of mode of signal presentation (Treatment A: 1 = auditory signal, 2 = visual signal), monitoring period throughout experiment (Treatment C[e]: 1 = one hour, 2 = two hours, 3 = three hours and 4 = four hours) on the degree of vigilance displayed (Y: measured as response latency) by a number of subjects was measured. Four of the subjects were randomly assigned to the auditory signal treatment and the another four subjects to the visual signal treatment and the response latency of each subject were repeated every hour for four hours. These data can be analysed as a split-plot or repeated measures design with subjects as the plots, signal type (Treatment A) as the between plot effect and monitoring period (Treatment C) as the within plot effect (from chapter 8 of Kirk (1968)).

Step 1 - Import (section 2.3) the Kirk (1968) spf (split-plot factorial) data set.

```
> spf <- read.table("spf.csv", header = T, sep = ",")
```

Step 2 (Key 14.2) - Assess whether there are likely to be any plot by within plot interactions.

```
> library(alr3)
> resplot(lm(Y ~ A * C + B,
         data = spf))
  t value    Pr(>|t|)
-1.2186824  0.2229648
```

```
> with(spf, interaction.plot
        (spf$B, spf$C, spf$Y))
```

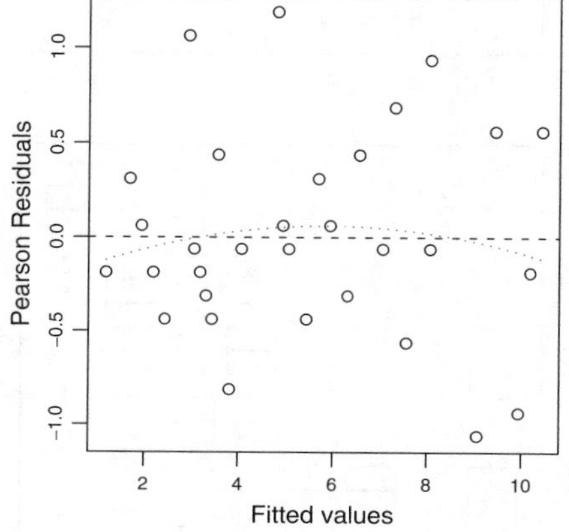

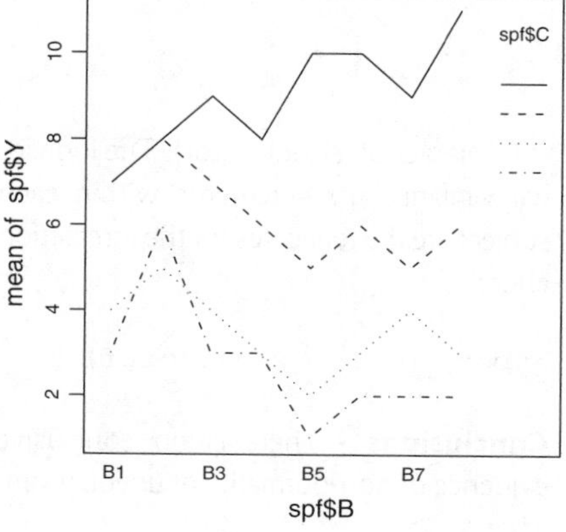

[e] Note, to maintain consistency with the conventions adopted by Quinn and Keough (2002) as well as this book, I have altered Kirk (1968)'s Factor B into Factor C and subjects S into B.

Conclusions - No strong evidence of a blocking interaction, therefore an additive model is appropriate.

Step 3 (Key 14.2) - Assess assumptions of normality and homogeneity of variance for each null hypothesis ensuring that the correct scale of replicates are represented for each (they should reflect the appropriate *F*-ratio denominators).

1. Factor A (signal type treatment - fixed effect). The subject means are the replicates for the signal treatment effect and thus an aggregated dataset needs to be created from which the boxplots can be based.

```
> library(nlme)
> spf.agg <- gsummary(spf,
    groups = spf$B)
> boxplot(Y ~ A, spf.agg)
```

Conclusions - There is no conclusive evidence of non-normality or unequal variance.

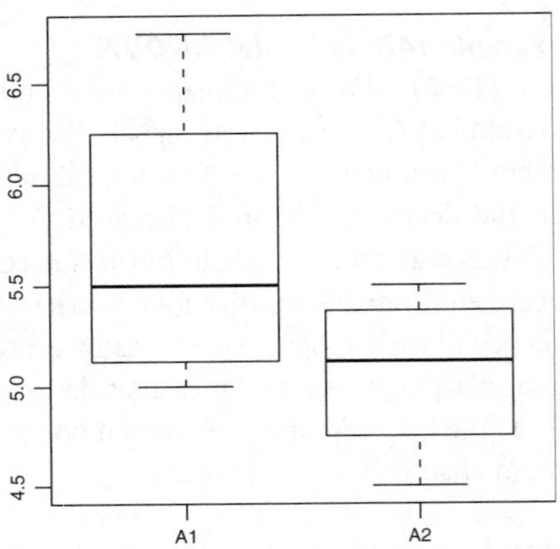

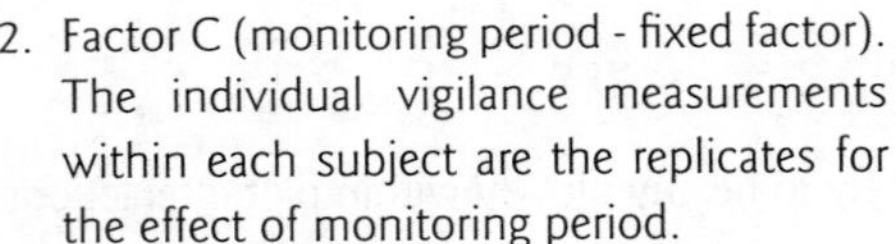

2. Factor C (monitoring period - fixed factor). The individual vigilance measurements within each subject are the replicates for the effect of monitoring period.

```
> boxplot(Y ~ C, spf)
```

Conclusions - There is no conclusive evidence of non-normality or unequal variance.

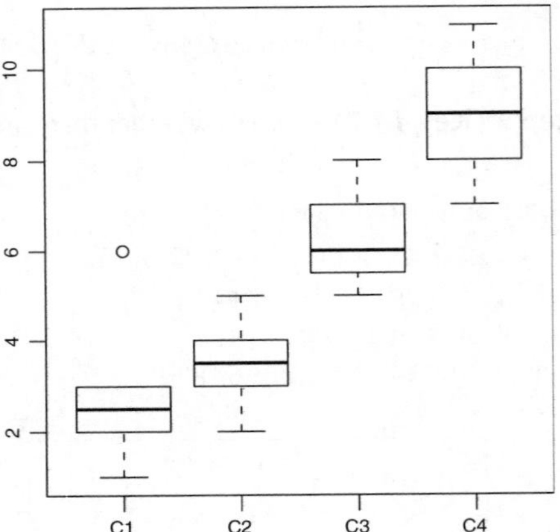

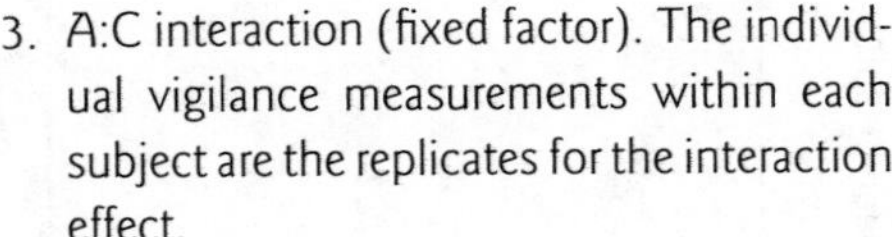

3. A:C interaction (fixed factor). The individual vigilance measurements within each subject are the replicates for the interaction effect.

```
> boxplot(Y ~ A * C, spf)
```

Conclusions - There is no conclusive evidence of non-normality or unequal variance.

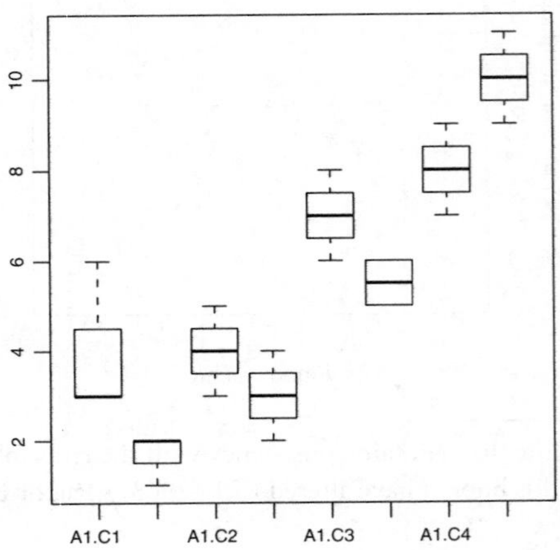

Step 4 (Key 14.5) - Determine whether or not the design is balanced (at least with respect to sub-replication).

```
> replications(Y ~ A * C + Error(B), data = spf)
  A    C A:C
 16    8   4
> library(biology)
> is.balanced(Y ~ A * C + Error(B), data = spf)
[1] TRUE
```

Conclusions - The design is completely balanced. There are exactly one of each of the four monitoring periods per subject within each signal type.

Step 5 (Key 14.6) - fit the linear model and produce an ANOVA table to test the null hypotheses that there no effects of signal type, monitoring time or interaction on vigilance (Table 8.2-2 of Kirk (1968)).

```
> spf.aov <- aov(Y ~ A * C + Error(B), spf)
> summary(spf.aov)
Error: B
          Df Sum Sq Mean Sq F value Pr(>F)
A          1 3.1250  3.1250       2 0.2070
Residuals  6 9.3750  1.5625

Error: Within
          Df  Sum Sq Mean Sq F value    Pr(>F)
C          3 194.500  64.833 127.890 2.516e-12 ***
A:C        3  19.375   6.458  12.740 0.0001051 ***
Residuals 18   9.125   0.507
---
Signif. codes:  0 '***' 0.001 '**' 0.01 '*' 0.05 '.' 0.1 ' ' 1
```

Conclusions - There is a significant signal type by monitoring period interaction ($F_{3,18} = 12.740, P < 0.001$). Note that whilst sphericity might be expected to be an issue for these data (since the order of the monitoring periods could not be randomized), Kirk (1968) concluded that the variance-covariance matrix did not deviate substantially from symmetry and thus considered corrections unnecessary.

Step 6 - Explore the nature of the interaction further by evaluating the simple main effects (Table 8.6-2 of Kirk (1968)).

- Effect of monitoring period (C) at A1 (auditory signal). Note, to reduce inflated family-wise Type I errors, Kirk (1968) advocated testing each of the simple main effects tests at α/p where p is the number of simple main effects tests within a global linear model term such that the main effects family-wise α is the same as the α used to assess the global hypothesis in the original model. In this example, we will perform four (4) simple main effects tests, and thus $\alpha = 0.05/4 = 0.0125$ for each.

```
> library(biology)
> summary(mainEffects(spf.aov, at = A == "A1"))
Error: B
```

```
           Df Sum Sq Mean Sq F value Pr(>F)
INT         1 3.1250  3.1250       2 0.2070
Residuals   6 9.3750  1.5625

Error: Within
          Df  Sum Sq Mean Sq F value    Pr(>F)
INT        3 159.187  53.062 104.671 1.391e-11 ***
C          3  54.688  18.229  35.959 8.223e-08 ***
Residuals 18   9.125   0.507
---
Signif. codes:  0 '***' 0.001 '**' 0.01 '*' 0.05 '.' 0.1 ' ' 1
```

- Effect of monitoring period (C) at A2 (visual signal)

```
> library(biology)
> summary(mainEffects(spf.aov, at = A == "A2"))
Error: B
          Df Sum Sq Mean Sq F value Pr(>F)
INT        1 3.1250  3.1250       2 0.2070
Residuals  6 9.3750  1.5625

Error: Within
          Df  Sum Sq Mean Sq F value    Pr(>F)
INT        3  54.688  18.229  35.959 8.223e-08 ***
C          3 159.188  53.062 104.671 1.391e-11 ***
Residuals 18   9.125   0.507
---
Signif. codes:  0 '***' 0.001 '**' 0.01 '*' 0.05 '.' 0.1 ' ' 1
```

- Effect of signal type (A) at C1 (first hour). Note, when a main effect and an interaction to which it contributes do not have the same error term, main effects should be calculated using a pooled error term so fitting a fully factorial anova will pool error terms

```
> spf.aovA <- aov(Y ~ A * C, spf)
> summary(mainEffects(spf.aovA, at = C == "C1"))
            Df  Sum Sq Mean Sq F value   Pr(>F)
INT          6 209.000  34.833  45.189 6.51e-12 ***
A            1   8.000   8.000  10.378 0.003645 **
Residuals   24  18.500   0.771
---
Signif. codes:  0 '***' 0.001 '**' 0.01 '*' 0.05 '.' 0.1 ' ' 1
```

- Effect of signal type (A) at C2 (second hour).

```
> summary(mainEffects(spf.aovA, at = C == "C2"))
            Df  Sum Sq Mean Sq F value    Pr(>F)
INT          6 215.000  35.833 46.4865 4.783e-12 ***
```

```
A              1    2.000    2.000   2.5946     0.1203
Residuals     24   18.500    0.771
---
Signif. codes:  0 '***' 0.001 '**' 0.01 '*' 0.05 '.' 0.1 ' ' 1
...
```

Conclusions - Whilst the visual signal was more effective (lower response latency) than the auditory signal during the first hour of the experiment ($P < 0.001$), its superiority was not significant during hour two ($P > 0.0125$) and three ($P > 0.0125$) and it was significantly less effective than the auditory signal during the forth hour ($P = 0.004$).

Step 7 - Since factor C (monitoring period) represents a quantitative sequence of the duration of the experiment, we might also be interested in exploring the nature of trends (linear, quadratic, etc) in vigilance over time and whether these trends are consistent for both signal types. Trends should be compared using a separately calculated error term, each of which estimates a different source of variation. Furthermore, family-wise α values should be maintained by dividing the α by three (one for each polynomial trend $\alpha/3 = 0.017$), (Table 8.8-4 of Kirk (1968)).

```
> p1 <- C(spf$C, poly, 1)
> p2 <- C(spf$C, poly, 2)
> p3 <- C(spf$C, poly, 3)
> spf.aov <- aov(Y ~ A * (p1 + p2 + p3) + Error(B/(p1 + p2 + p3)),
+      spf)
> summary(spf.aov)
Error: B
          Df Sum Sq Mean Sq F value Pr(>F)
A          1 3.1250  3.1250       2 0.2070
Residuals  6 9.3750  1.5625

Error: B:p1
          Df   Sum Sq Mean Sq F value     Pr(>F)
p1         1 184.900 184.900 182.617 1.018e-05 ***
A:p1       1  13.225  13.225  13.062   0.01118 *
Residuals  6   6.075   1.012
---
Signif. codes:  0 '***' 0.001 '**' 0.01 '*' 0.05 '.' 0.1 ' ' 1

Error: B:p2
          Df Sum Sq Mean Sq F value   Pr(>F)
p2         1 8.0000  8.0000    25.6 0.002311 **
A:p2       1 3.1250  3.1250    10.0 0.019509 *
Residuals  6 1.8750  0.3125
---
Signif. codes:  0 '***' 0.001 '**' 0.01 '*' 0.05 '.' 0.1 ' ' 1

Error: B:p3
          Df  Sum Sq Mean Sq F value  Pr(>F)
```

```
p3          1 1.60000 1.60000  8.1702 0.02886 *
A:p3        1 3.02500 3.02500 15.4468 0.00771 **
Residuals   6 1.17500 0.19583
---
Signif. codes:  0 '***' 0.001 '**' 0.01 '*' 0.05 '.' 0.1 ' ' 1
```

Conclusions - At $\alpha = 0.017$, it is evident that a substantial component of the global A:C interaction (13.225/19.375 = 63.5%) is due to differences in the nature of the linear decline in vigilance through time between the two signal types ($P = 0.011$).

Step 8 (Key 12.18) - Summarize the trends in a plot.

```
> spf.means <- with(spf, tapply(Y, list(A, C), mean))
> library(gmodels)
> spf.se <- with(spf, tapply(Y, list(A, C), function(x) ci(x)[4]))
> plot(Y ~ as.numeric(C), data = spf, type = "n", axes = F,
+   xlab = "", ylab = "")
> xval <- as.numeric(spf$C)
> points(spf.means["A1", ], pch = 22, type = "b", lwd = 1, lty = 2)
> arrows(xval, spf.means["A1", ] - spf.se["A1", ], xval,
+     spf.means["A1", ] + spf.se["A1", ], code = 3, angle = 90,
+     len = 0.05)
> points(spf.means["A2", ], pch = 19, type = "b", lwd = 1, lty = 1)
> arrows(xval, spf.means["A2", ] - spf.se["A2", ], xval,
+     spf.means["A2", ] + spf.se["A2", ], code = 3, angle = 90,
+     len = 0.05)
> axis(1, at = 1:4, cex.axis = 0.8)
> mtext(text = "Time period (h)", side = 1, line = 3)
> axis(2, cex.axis = 0.8, las = 1)
> mtext(text = "Response latency", side = 2, line = 3)
> legend("topleft", leg = c("Visual", "Auditory"), lty = 0,
+     pch = c(22, 19), bty = "n", cex = 1)
> box(bty = "l")
```

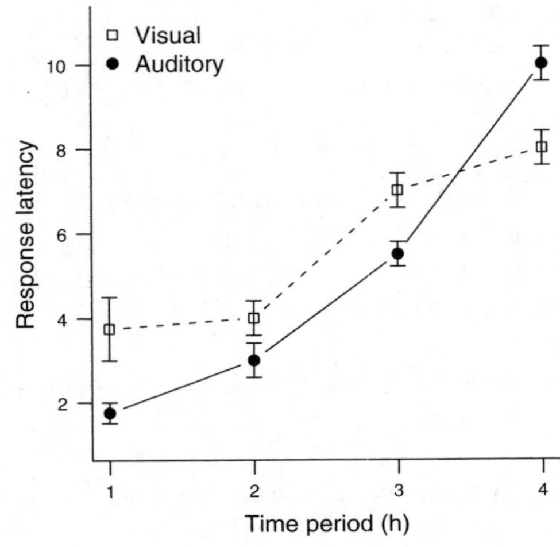

Example 14B: Linear mixed effects split-plot

Alternatively, linear mixed effects modeling could be used to analyze the Kirk (1968) spf (split-plot factorial) data used in Example 14A. Notably, such an approach permits us to attempt to incorporate the nature of the variance-covariance matrix rather than wish it away post-hoc with estimated adjustments.

Step 1 (14.2&14.5) - Refer to Example 14A for importing the data and performing exploratory data analysis.

Step 2 (Key 14.6) - Fit a series of lme models (with and without random slope components as well as alternative correlation structures) and compare them to evaluate the appropriateness of each.

```
> library(nlme)
> spf.lme.1 <- lme(Y ~ A * C, random = ~C | B, spf)
> spf.lme.2 <- update(spf.lme.1, random = ~1 | B)
> anova(spf.lme.1, spf.lme.2)
          Model df      AIC      BIC    logLik   Test  L.Ratio p-value
spf.lme.1     1 19 97.63924 120.0223 -29.81962
spf.lme.2     2 10 89.64876 101.4293 -34.82438 1 vs 2 10.00952  0.3497
```

Conclusions - Random slope not required as the model incorporating the random slope is not a significantly better fit (likelihood ratio not significant).

```
> spf.lme.3 <- update(spf.lme.2, correlation = corAR1(form = ~1 |
+     B))
> anova(spf.lme.2, spf.lme.3)
          Model df      AIC      BIC    logLik   Test  L.Ratio p-value
spf.lme.2     1 10 89.64876 101.4293 -34.82438
spf.lme.3     2 11 88.44767 101.4063 -33.22384 1 vs 2 3.201085  0.0736
> spf.lme.4 <- update(spf.lme.2, correlation = corCompSymm(form = ~1 |
+     B))
> anova(spf.lme.2, spf.lme.4)
          Model df      AIC      BIC    logLik   Test      L.Ratio p-value
spf.lme.2     1 10 89.64876 101.4293 -34.82438
spf.lme.4     2 11 91.64876 104.6073 -34.82438 1 vs 2 1.421086e-14       1
> spf.lme.5 <- update(spf.lme.2, correlation = corSymm(form = ~1 |
+     B))
> anova(spf.lme.2, spf.lme.5)
          Model df      AIC      BIC    logLik   Test  L.Ratio p-value
spf.lme.2     1 10 89.64876 101.4293 -34.82438
spf.lme.5     2 16 94.52970 113.3786 -31.26485 1 vs 2 7.119057    0.31
```

Conclusions - neither first order continuous-time autoregressive, compound symmetry or a general correlation structure yield better fits than a no within-group correlation structure. Examine the fit of the linear mixed effects model.

```
> anova(spf.lme.2)
            numDF denDF  F-value p-value
(Intercept)     1    18 591.6800  <.0001
A               1     6   2.0000  0.2070
C               3    18 127.8904  <.0001
A:C             3    18  12.7397  0.0001
```

Conclusions - There is a significant signal type by monitoring period interaction ($F_{3,18} = 12.740$, $P < 0.001$).

Step 3 - Investigate the simple main effects.

- Effect of monitoring period (C) at A1.

```
> library(biology)
> anova(mainEffects(spf.lme.2, at = A == "A1"))
            numDF denDF  F-value p-value
(Intercept)     1    17 591.6800  <.0001
M1              4    17  79.0034  <.0001
M3              3    17  35.9589  <.0001
```

- Effect of monitoring period (C) at A2.

```
> anova(mainEffects(spf.lme.2, at = A == "A2"))
            numDF denDF  F-value p-value
(Intercept)     1    17 591.6800  <.0001
M1              4    17  27.4692  <.0001
M3              3    17 104.6712  <.0001
```

- Effect of monitoring period (A) at C1.

```
> anova(mainEffects(spf.lme.2, at = C == "C1"))
            numDF denDF  F-value p-value
(Intercept)     1    18 591.6800  <.0001
M1              6    18  68.9187  <.0001
M2              1     6  10.3784  0.0181
```

- Effect of monitoring period (A) at C2.

```
> anova(mainEffects(spf.lme.2, at = C == "C2"))
            numDF denDF  F-value p-value
(Intercept)     1    18 591.6800  <.0001
M1              6    18  70.2160  <.0001
M2              1     6   2.5946  0.1584
```

Step 4 - Similar with `lmer` (`lme4`).

```
> library(lme4)
> spf.lmer <- lmer(Y ~ A * C + (1 | B), spf)
> library(languageR)
> aovlmer.fnc(spf.lmer, noMCMC = T)
Analysis of Variance Table
    Df  Sum Sq Mean Sq  F value        F    Df2         p
A    1   1.014   1.014   1.9997   1.9997 24.000     0.170
C    3 194.500  64.833 127.8904 127.8904 24.000 6.772e-15
A:C  3  19.375   6.458  12.7397  12.7397 24.000 3.508e-05
```

Example 14C: Repeated measures ANOVA

Mullens (1993) investigated the impact of hypoxia (oxygen stress) on the ventilation patterns of cane toads (*Bufo marinus*). In anticipation of variability in ventilation patterns between individual toads, each oxygen concentration level (O2LEVEL: 0, 5, 10, 15, 20, 30, 40 and 50%) was measured from each individual. Hence the individual toads represent the blocks (TOADS) and the oxygen levels represent a within block treatment. Individual toads also categorized according to their typical predominant mode of breathing (BRTH.TYP: buccal or lung) and therefore breathing type represents a between block treatment. Ventilation patterns were measured as the frequency of buccal breathing (Box 11.2 of Quinn and Keough (2002)).

Step 1 - Import (section 2.3) the Mullens (1993) data set.

```
> mullens <- read.table("mullens.csv", header = T, sep = ",")
```

Step 2 - In order to ensure that the oxygen concentration variable is treated as a factor we need to redefine its class

```
> mullens$O2LEVEL <- factor(mullens$O2LEVEL)
```

Step 3 (Key 14.2) - Assess whether there are likely to be any plot by within plot interactions.

Raw data

```
> library(alr3)
> resplot(lm(FREQBUC ~
+       BRTH.TYP * O2LEVEL +
+       TOAD, data = mullens))
       t value      Pr(>|t|)
3.926581e+00 8.616205e-05
```

Square root transformed data

```
> resplot(lm(sqrt(FREQBUC) ~
+       BRTH.TYP * O2LEVEL + TOAD,
+       data = mullens))
  t value   Pr(>|t|)
1.2616950 0.2070586
```

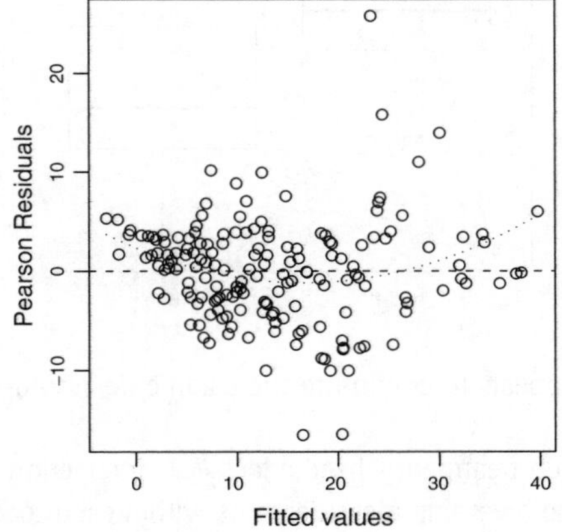

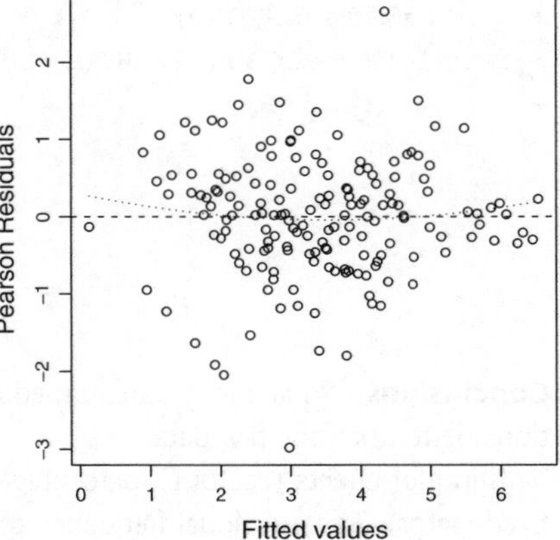

Conclusions - If raw data is appropriate, then there is some evidence of a blocking interaction (thus non-additive model). However, there is no strong evidence of a blocking interaction for square root transformed data (thus additive model).

Step 4 (Key 14.2) - Assess assumptions of normality and homogeneity of variance for each null hypothesis ensuring that the correct scale of replicates are represented for each (they should reflect the appropriate *F*-ratio denominators see Table 14.1).

1. Between plot effect (Factor A: breathing type treatment - fixed effect). The means of each toad are the replicates for the breathing type effect and thus an aggregated dataset needs to be created from which the boxplots can be based.

```
> library(nlme)
> mullens.agg <- gsummary
+     (mullens, groups =
+     mullens$TOAD)
> boxplot(FREQBUC ~ BRTH.TYP,
+     mullens.agg)
```

```
> mullens$SFREQBUC <- sqrt
+       (mullens$FREQBUC)
> mullens.agg <- gsummary
+       (mullens, groups =
+       mullens$TOAD)
> boxplot(SFREQBUC ~ BRTH.TYP,
+     mullens.agg)
```

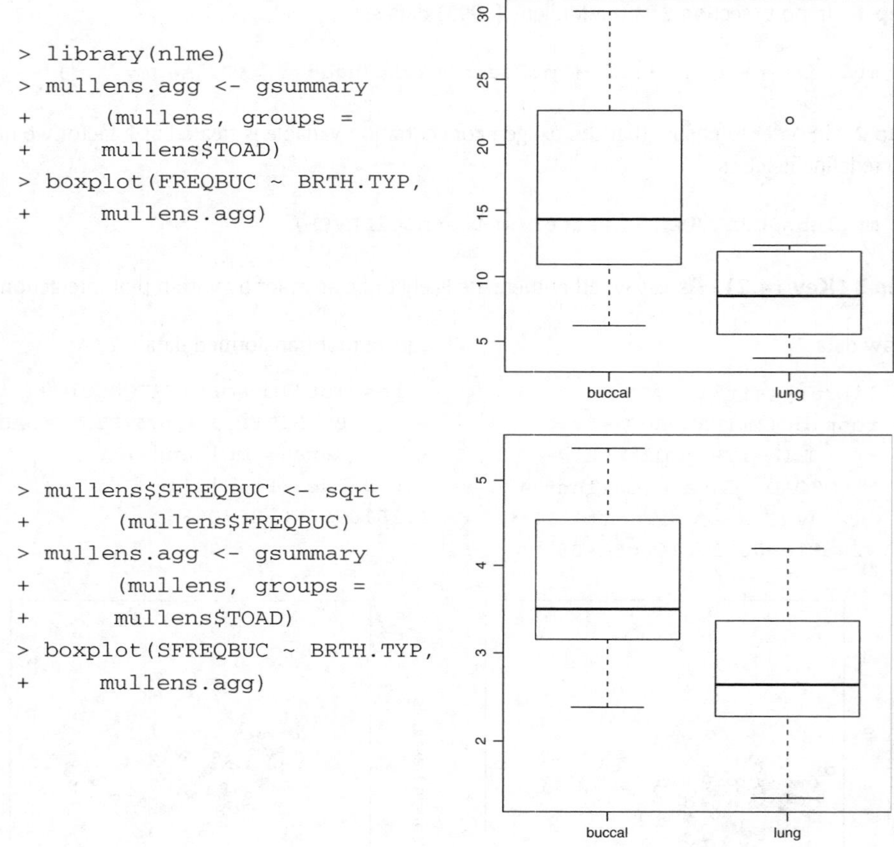

Conclusions - Square root transformed data appears to confirm to the parametric assumptions better than the raw data.

2. Within plot effects (Factor C: percentage oxygen treatment - fixed effect, A:C interaction - fixed factor). The individual frequency of buccal breathing measurements within each toad are the replicates for the effect of oxygen level.

```
> boxplot(FREQBUC ~
+       O2LEVEL, mullens)

> boxplot(FREQBUC ~
+       BRTH.TYP * O2LEVEL,
+       mullens)

> boxplot(sqrt(FREQBUC) ~
+       O2LEVEL, mullens)

> boxplot(sqrt(FREQBUC) ~
+       BRTH.TYP * O2LEVEL,
+       mullens)
```

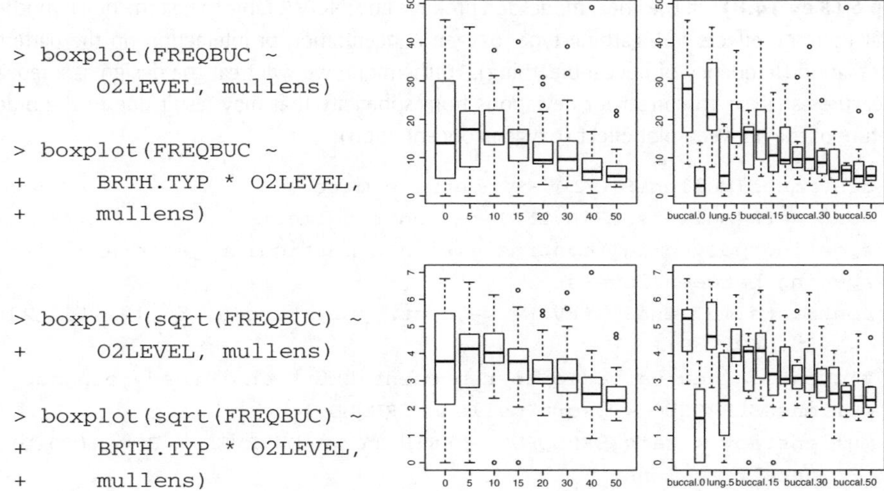

Conclusions - Square root transformed data appears to confirm to the parametric assumptions better than the raw data.

Step 5 (Key 14.5) - Determine whether or not the design is balanced (at least with respect to sub-replication).

```
> replications(sqrt(FREQBUC) ~ BRTH.TYP * O2LEVEL + Error(TOAD),
+       mullens)
$BRTH.TYP
BRTH.TYP
buccal   lung
   104     64

$O2LEVEL
[1] 21

$'BRTH.TYP:O2LEVEL'
       O2LEVEL
BRTH.TYP  0  5 10 15 20 30 40 50
  buccal 13 13 13 13 13 13 13 13
  lung    8  8  8  8  8  8  8  8
> library(biology)
> is.balanced(sqrt(FREQBUC) ~ BRTH.TYP * O2LEVEL + Error(TOAD),
+       mullens)
[1] FALSE
```

Conclusions - The design is not balanced. Of the 21 toads, 13 where buccal breathing and only 8 where lung breathing. Consequently, type I Sums of Squares are not appropriate.

Step 6 (Key 14.8) - fit the linear model and produce an ANOVA table to test the null hypotheses that there no effects of breathing type, oxygen concentration or interaction on the pattern of ventilation (frequency of buccal breathing). Furthermore, we will treat the design as a repeated measures analysis to correct for deviations from sphericity that may result due to the ordered nature of the between plot effect (oxygen concentration).

```
> contrasts(mullens$TOAD) <- contr.helmert
> contrasts(mullens$BRTH.TYP) <- contr.helmert
> # define polynomial contrasts with a particular pattern of
  spacing between levels
> contrasts(mullens$O2LEVEL) <- contr.poly(8, c(0, 5, 10, 15, 20,
+     30, 40, 50))
> # create a new variable to represent the transformed response
> mullens$SFREQBUC <- sqrt(mullens$FREQBUC)
> mullens.aov <- aov(SFREQBUC ~ BRTH.TYP * O2LEVEL + Error(TOAD),
+     data = mullens)
> library(biology)
> AnovaM(mullens.aov, type = "III", RM = T)
   Sphericity Epsilon Values
-------------------------------
 Greenhouse.Geisser Huynh.Feldt
          0.4281775   0.5172755


Anova Table (Type III tests)
Response: SFREQBUC
Error: TOAD
          Df  Sum Sq Mean Sq F value  Pr(>F)
BRTH.TYP   1  39.921  39.921  5.7622 0.02678 *
Residuals 19 131.634   6.928
---
Signif. codes:  0 '***' 0.001 '**' 0.01 '*' 0.05 '.' 0.1 ' ' 1

Error: Within
                  Df  Sum Sq Mean Sq F value    Pr(>F)
O2LEVEL            7  25.748   3.678  4.8841 6.258e-05 ***
BRTH.TYP:O2LEVEL   7  56.372   8.053 10.6928 1.228e-10 ***
Residuals        133 100.166   0.753
---
Signif. codes:  0 '***' 0.001 '**' 0.01 '*' 0.05 '.' 0.1 ' ' 1


Greenhouse-Geisser corrected ANOVA table
Response: SFREQBUC
Error: TOAD
                Df  Sum Sq Mean Sq F value  Pr(>F)
BRTH.TYP   0.42818  39.921  39.921  5.7622 0.04785 *
Residuals 19.00000 131.634   6.928
---
```

```
Signif. codes:  0 '***' 0.001 '**' 0.01 '*' 0.05 '.' 0.1 ' ' 1
Error: Within
                          Df  Sum Sq Mean Sq F value    Pr(>F)
O2LEVEL                2.9972  25.748   3.678  4.8841  0.002981 **
BRTH.TYP:O2LEVEL       2.9972  56.372   8.053 10.6928 2.435e-06 ***
Residuals            133.0000 100.166   0.753
---
Signif. codes:  0 '***' 0.001 '**' 0.01 '*' 0.05 '.' 0.1 ' ' 1

Huynh-Feldt corrected ANOVA table
Response: SFREQBUC
Error: TOAD
                Df  Sum Sq Mean Sq F value  Pr(>F)
BRTH.TYP   0.51728  39.921  39.921  5.7622 0.04393 *
Residuals 19.00000 131.634   6.928
---
Signif. codes:  0 '***' 0.001 '**' 0.01 '*' 0.05 '.' 0.1 ' ' 1

Error: Within
                          Df  Sum Sq Mean Sq F value    Pr(>F)
O2LEVEL                3.6209  25.748   3.678  4.8841  0.001545 **
BRTH.TYP:O2LEVEL       3.6209  56.372   8.053 10.6928 4.223e-07 ***
Residuals            133.0000 100.166   0.753
---
Signif. codes:  0 '***' 0.001 '**' 0.01 '*' 0.05 '.' 0.1 ' ' 1
```

Conclusions - Both Greenhouse-Geisser and Huynh-Feldt epsilon estimates suggest that sphericity was not met (Greenhouse-Geisser preferred as they are both less than 0.75). There is a significant breathing type by oxygen level interaction ($P < 0.001$).

Step 7 - Explore the nature of the interaction further by evaluating the simple main effects.

- Effect of oxygen concentration for buccal breathing toads.

```
> library(biology)
> summary(mainEffects(mullens.aov, at = BRTH.TYP == "buccal"))
Error: TOAD
          Df  Sum Sq Mean Sq F value  Pr(>F)
INT        1  39.921  39.921  5.7622 0.02678 *
Residuals 19 131.634   6.928
---
Signif. codes:  0 '***' 0.001 '**' 0.01 '*' 0.05 '.' 0.1 ' ' 1

Error: Within
           Df  Sum Sq Mean Sq F value    Pr(>F)
INT         7  19.907   2.844  3.7761 0.0009103 ***
O2LEVEL     7  75.433  10.776 14.3085 9.013e-14 ***
Residuals 133 100.166   0.753
---
Signif. codes:  0 '***' 0.001 '**' 0.01 '*' 0.05 '.' 0.1 ' ' 1
```

- Effect of oxygen concentration for lung breathing toads.

```
> summary(mainEffects(mullens.aov, at = BRTH.TYP == "lung"))
Error: TOAD
          Df  Sum Sq Mean Sq F value  Pr(>F)
INT        1  39.921  39.921  5.7622 0.02678 *
Residuals 19 131.634   6.928
---
Signif. codes:  0 '***' 0.001 '**' 0.01 '*' 0.05 '.' 0.1 ' ' 1

Error: Within
           Df  Sum Sq Mean Sq F value    Pr(>F)
INT         7  75.433  10.776 14.3085 9.013e-14 ***
O2LEVEL     7  19.907   2.844  3.7761 0.0009103 ***
Residuals 133 100.166   0.753
---
Signif. codes:  0 '***' 0.001 '**' 0.01 '*' 0.05 '.' 0.1 ' ' 1
```

Step 8 - Quinn and Keough (2002) also illustrated polynomial trends which can be useful for exploring the nature of the within plot treatments(s) in repeated measures designs (when the treatment has an ordered[f] set of levels). Such trends should be compared using a separately calculated error term (to reduce the impacts of deviations from sphericity), each of which estimates a different source of variation.

```
> # begin by defining the appropriate linear, quadratic and cubic terms
> p1 <- C(mullens$O2LEVEL, poly, 1, c(0, 5, 10, 15, 20, 30, 40, 50))
> p2 <- C(mullens$O2LEVEL, poly, 2, c(0, 5, 10, 15, 20, 30, 40, 50))
> p3 <- C(mullens$O2LEVEL, poly, 3, c(0, 5, 10, 15, 20, 30, 40, 50))
> # calculate the Linear trend
> # Note the use of Type III Sums of Squares due to design imbalance
> mullens.aovP1 <- aov(SFREQBUC ~ BRTH.TYP * p1 + Error(TOAD/(p1)),
> # data = mullens)
> AnovaM(mullens.aovP1, type = "III")[[2]]
            Df Sum Sq Mean Sq F value    Pr(>F)
p1           1 17.010  17.010  8.2555 0.0097341 **
BRTH.TYP:p1  1 40.065  40.065 19.4441 0.0003011 ***
Residuals   19 39.149   2.060
---
Signif. codes:  0 '***' 0.001 '**' 0.01 '*' 0.05 '.' 0.1 ' ' 1
> # calculate the Quadratic trend
> mullens.aovP2 <- aov(SFREQBUC ~ BRTH.TYP * (p1 + p2) + Error(TOAD/(p1 +
+ p2)), data = mullens)
> AnovaM(mullens.aovP2, type = "III")[[3]]
            Df  Sum Sq Mean Sq F value   Pr(>F)
p2           1  5.0069  5.0069  6.9667 0.016162 *
BRTH.TYP:p2  1 12.3256 12.3256 17.1498 0.000555 ***
Residuals   19 13.6553  0.7187
---
Signif. codes:  0 '***' 0.001 '**' 0.01 '*' 0.05 '.' 0.1 ' ' 1
```

[f] by ordered, I refer to a set of factor levels that have a natural order such as time, distance, concentration etc.

```
> # calculate the Cubic trend
> mullens.aovP3 <- aov(SFREQBUC ~ BRTH.TYP * (p1 + p2 + p3) +
+ Error(TOAD/(p1 + p2 + p3)), data = mullens)
> AnovaM(mullens.aovP3, type = "III")[[4]]
             Df  Sum Sq Mean Sq F value  Pr(>F)
p3            1  1.7470  1.7470  3.2625 0.08675 .
BRTH.TYP:p3   1  1.7839  1.7839  3.3314 0.08373 .
Residuals    19 10.1742  0.5355
---
Signif. codes:  0 '***' 0.001 '**' 0.01 '*' 0.05 '.' 0.1 ' ' 1
```

Conclusions - There are significant breathing type by oxygen concentration linear and quadratic interactions, suggesting that the nature of the trends in ventilation performance depend upon on the natural breathing type of the toads. We shall therefore explore the nature of the trends separately for each breathing type.

```
> # explore the trends for buccal breathing toads
> library(biology)
> mullens.aovB <- aov(SFREQBUC ~ p1 + p2 + p3 + Error(TOAD/(p1 +
+     p2 + p3)), data = mullens, subset = BRTH.TYP == "buccal")
> AnovaM(mullens.aovB)
Error: TOAD
          Df Sum Sq Mean Sq F value Pr(>F)
Residuals 12 88.286   7.357

Error: TOAD:p1
          Df Sum Sq Mean Sq F value    Pr(>F)
p1         1 71.719  71.719  178.87 1.432e-08 ***
Residuals 12  4.811   0.401
---
Signif. codes:  0 '***' 0.001 '**' 0.01 '*' 0.05 '.' 0.1 ' ' 1

Error: TOAD:p2
          Df  Sum Sq Mean Sq F value  Pr(>F)
p2         1 1.06373 1.06373  5.4981 0.03706 *
Residuals 12 2.32167 0.19347
---
Signif. codes:  0 '***' 0.001 '**' 0.01 '*' 0.05 '.' 0.1 ' ' 1

Error: TOAD:p3
          Df Sum Sq Mean Sq F value Pr(>F)
p3         1 0.0001  0.0001   2e-04 0.9877
Residuals 12 6.1020  0.5085

Error: Within
          Df  Sum Sq Mean Sq F value Pr(>F)
Residuals 52 22.6251  0.4351
> # explore the trends for lung breathing toads
> mullens.aovL <- aov(SFREQBUC ~ p1 + p2 + p3 + Error(TOAD/(p1 +
```

```
+     p2 + p3)), data = mullens, subset = BRTH.TYP == "lung")
> AnovaM(mullens.aovL)
Error: TOAD
          Df Sum Sq Mean Sq F value Pr(>F)
Residuals  7 43.349   6.193

Error: TOAD:p1
          Df Sum Sq Mean Sq F value Pr(>F)
p1         1  1.964   1.964  0.4004  0.547
Residuals  7 34.338   4.905

Error: TOAD:p2
          Df  Sum Sq Mean Sq F value  Pr(>F)
p2         1 13.3447 13.3447  8.2421 0.02396 *
Residuals  7 11.3336  1.6191
---
Signif. codes:  0 '***' 0.001 '**' 0.01 '*' 0.05 '.' 0.1 ' ' 1

Error: TOAD:p3
          Df Sum Sq Mean Sq F value  Pr(>F)
p3         1 2.8518  2.8518  4.9023 0.06242 .
Residuals  7 4.0722  0.5817
---
Signif. codes:  0 '***' 0.001 '**' 0.01 '*' 0.05 '.' 0.1 ' ' 1

Error: Within
          Df  Sum Sq Mean Sq F value Pr(>F)
Residuals 32 18.9595  0.5925
```

Conclusions - Whilst buccal breathing toads respond to increasing hypoxia (reducing oxygen levels) with a significant linear increase in buccal breathing rate ($P < 0.001$), the breathing rates of lung breathing toads displays a quadratic trend ($P = 0.024$), initially rising before declining sharply at oxygen concentrations lower than 10 percent (see figure).

Step 9 - Summarize the trends in a plot.

```
> # calculate the mean and standard error of each group
> mullens.means <- with(mullens, tapply(SFREQBUC, list(BRTH.TYP,
+     O2LEVEL), mean))
> mullens.se <- with(mullens, tapply(SFREQBUC, list(BRTH.TYP,
+     O2LEVEL), function(x) ci(x)[4]))
> mullens$O2 <- as.numeric(as.character(mullens$O2LEVEL))
> # create a numeric version of the oxygen level variable
> xval <- unique(mullens$O2)
> # construct the base plot
> plot(SFREQBUC ~ O2, data = mullens, type = "n", axes = F,
+     xlab = "", ylab = "")
> # create some shortcuts objects
> mB <- mullens.means["buccal", ]
> seB <- mullens.se["buccal", ]
```

```
> # plot the error bars with open circle symbols for buccal breathing toads
> arrows(xval, mB - seB, xval, mB + seB, code = 3, angle = 90,
+     len = 0.01)
> points(mB ~ xval, pch = 16, col = "white", type = "b", lwd = 1,
+     lty = 2)
> points(mB ~ xval, pch = 1, col = "black", type = "b", lwd = 1,
+     lty = 2)
> mL <- mullens.means["lung", ]
> seL <- mullens.se["lung", ]
> points(mL ~ xval, pch = 19, type = "b", lwd = 1, lty = 1)
> arrows(xval, mL - seL, xval, mL + seL, code = 3, angle = 90,
+     len = 0.01)
> axis(1, cex.axis = 0.8)
> mtext(text = expression(paste(O[2], " level (%)")), side = 1,
+     line = 3)
> axis(2, cex.axis = 0.8, las = 1)
> mtext(text = expression(paste("Breathing rate ",
+     (sqrt(breaths.m^{-1
+ })))), side = 2, line = 3)
> legend("topright", leg = c("buccal", "lung"),
+     title = "Breathing type", lty = 0, pch = c(22, 19),
+     bty = "n", cex = 1)
> box(bty = "l")
```

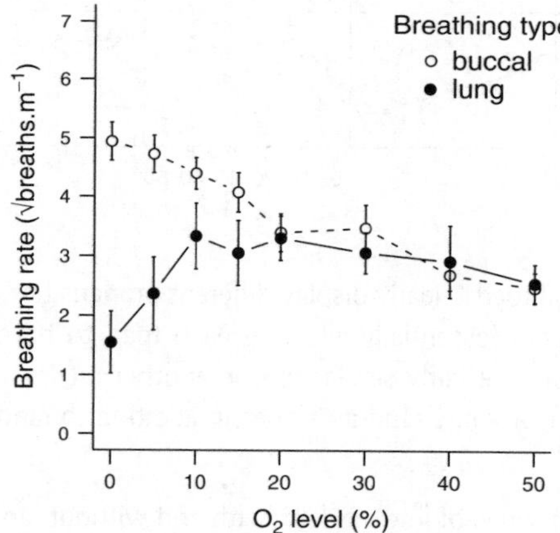

Example 14D: Linear mixed effects - unbalanced and compound symmetry violated

Alternatively, linear mixed effects modeling could be used to analyze the data introduced in Example 14C (Box 11.2 of Quinn and Keough (2002)). Notably, such an approach permits us to attempt to incorporate the nature of the variance-covariance matrix rather than wish it away post-hoc with estimated adjustments.

Step 1 (Key 14.2&14.5) - Refer to Example 14C for importing the data and performing exploratory data analysis.

Step 2 - Examine a lattice (trellis) plot in which the patterns of buccal breathing frequency against oxygen percentage are displayed for each individual toad.

```
> library(lattice)
> mullens$O2 <- as.numeric(as.character(mullens$O2LEVEL))
> xyplot(SFREQBUC ~ O2 | TOAD, groups = BRTH.TYP, mullens,
+      type = c("p", "r"), auto.key = T)
```

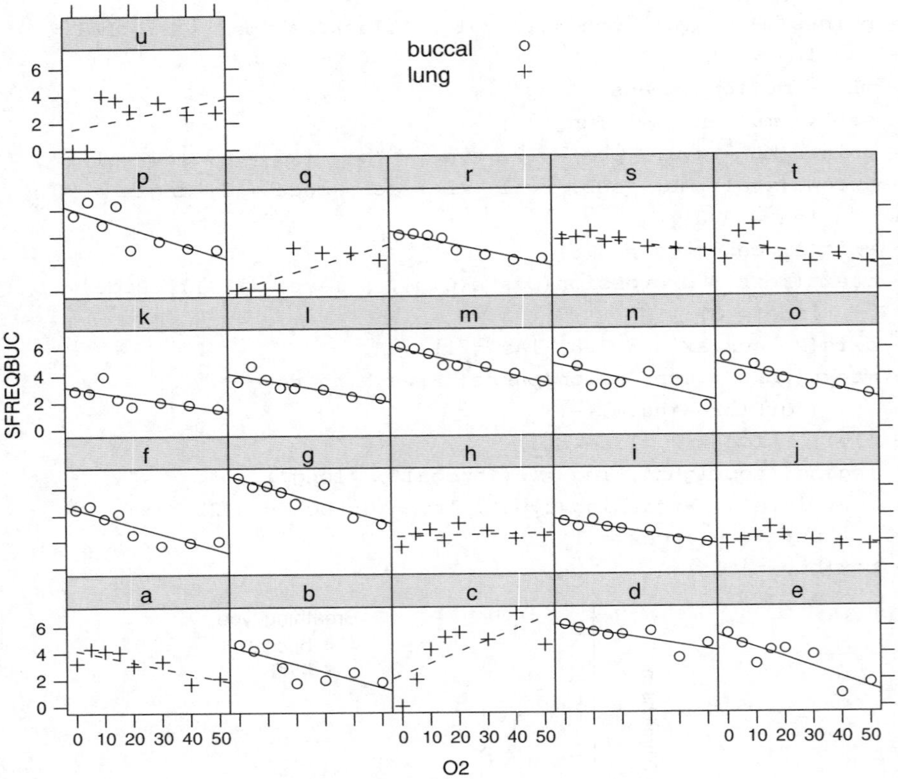

Conclusions - individual toads clearly display different propensities for buccal breathing. Thus a random intercepts model (essentially allowing each toad to have its own intercept) could be very useful. The slopes are fairly similar to one another (at least within a breathing type), and thus, models that incorporate random slopes in addition to random intercepts are perhaps overly complex.

Step 3 (Key 14.8) - Fit a series of lme models (with and without random slope components as well as alternative correlation structures) and compare them to evaluate the appropriateness of each.

```
> library(nlme)
> # model with random intercept and slope
> contrasts(mullens$BRTH.TYP) <- "contr.helmert"
> contrasts(mullens$O2LEVEL) <- contr.poly(8, c(0, 5, 10, 15, 20,
+ 30, 40, 50))
> # fit a model without correlation structure
> mullens.lme.1 <- lme(SFREQBUC ~ BRTH.TYP * O2LEVEL, random = ~1 |
+ TOAD, data = mullens)
> # fit a model with a compound symmetry correlation structure
```

```
> mullens.lme.2 <- lme(SFREQBUC ~ BRTH.TYP * O2LEVEL, random = ~1 |
+ TOAD, data = mullens, corr = corCompSymm(form = ~1 | TOAD))
> # compare the fit of models
> anova(mullens.lme.1, mullens.lme.2)
              Model df      AIC      BIC    logLik   Test
mullens.lme.1     1 18 518.8302 573.2601 -241.4151
mullens.lme.2     2 19 520.8302 578.2839 -241.4151 1 vs 2
                  L.Ratio p-value
mullens.lme.1
mullens.lme.2 1.136868e-13       1
```

Conclusions - Models incorporating either no correlation structure or compound symmetry are essentially equivalent (on the basis of AIC and log-likelihood ratio) to one another.

```
> # fit a model with a continuous first order autoregressive structure
> mullens.lme.3 <- lme(SFREQBUC ~ BRTH.TYP * O2LEVEL, random = ~1 | TOAD,
+ data = mullens, corr = corAR1(form = ~1 | TOAD))
> # compare the fit of models
> anova(mullens.lme.1, mullens.lme.3)
              Model df      AIC      BIC    logLik   Test  L.Ratio p-value
mullens.lme.1     1 18 518.8302 573.2601 -241.4151
mullens.lme.3     2 19 487.8255 545.2793 -224.9128 1 vs 2 33.00467  <.0001
```

Conclusions - A model that incorporates a continuous first order autoregressive correlation structure is a significantly better model that one without any correlation structure. Therefore use the autoregressive model to test the hypotheses about the fixed factors in the model (breathing rate, oxygen concentration and their interaction). Note a continuous time autoregressive structure is more appropriate than a regular first order autoregressive structure as the oxygen levels were not of equal spacing.

Examine the anova table for the model fit. As the design is not balanced, use marginal (Type III) sums of squares.

```
> anova(mullens.lme.3, type = "marginal")
                 numDF denDF   F-value p-value
(Intercept)          1   133 254.69303  <.0001
BRTH.TYP             1    19   5.99813  0.0242
O2LEVEL              7   133   2.96663  0.0064
BRTH.TYP:O2LEVEL     7   133   6.27943  <.0001
```

Conclusions - There is a significant breathing type by oxygen level interaction ($P < 0.001$)[g].

Step 4 - Explore the nature of the interaction further by evaluating the simple main effects.

- Effect of oxygen concentration for buccal breathing toads.

```
> library(biology)
> anova(mainEffects(mullens.lme.3, at = BRTH.TYP == "buccal"))
```

[g] Note, had we used the fitted linear effects model that assumed incorporated compound symmetry (mullens.lme.2), we would have produced the same F-ratios and P-values to a traditional split-plot ANOVA model that assumed compound symmetry (Step 5 of Example 14C).

```
             numDF denDF   F-value p-value
(Intercept)      1   132 283.35264  <.0001
M1               8   132   3.79161   5e-04
M3               7   132   7.02263  <.0001
```

- Effect of oxygen concentration for lung breathing toads.

```
> anova(mainEffects(mullens.lme.3, at = BRTH.TYP == "lung"))
             numDF denDF   F-value p-value
(Intercept)      1   132 283.35264  <.0001
M1               8   132   7.18335  <.0001
M3               7   132   3.14635  0.0042
```

Conclusions - There is a significant effect of oxygen concentration on the rate of breathing in both buccal ($P < 0.001$) and lung breathing toads, although the effect is perhaps stronger in the former ($P = 0.004$).

Step 5 - Quinn and Keough (2002) also illustrated polynomial trends which can be useful for exploring the nature of the within plot treatments(s) in repeated measures designs. Since the oxygen level contrasts were defined as polynomial contrasts prior to fitting the linear mixed effects model, the polynomial trends can be explored by examining their respective contrast estimates.

```
> summary(mullens.lme.3)$tTable
                              Value Std.Error  DF    t-value      p-value
(Intercept)              3.27055552 0.2049335 133 15.9591048 1.072635e-32
BRTH.TYP1               -0.50190423 0.2049335  19 -2.4491075 2.419395e-02
O2LEVEL.L               -0.92665742 0.2960086 133 -3.1305084 2.145655e-03
O2LEVEL.Q               -0.50274699 0.2350434 133 -2.1389536 3.426644e-02
O2LEVEL.C                0.29696969 0.1902856 133  1.5606525 1.209821e-01
O2LEVEL^4               -0.16531509 0.1656535 133 -0.9979572 3.201123e-01
O2LEVEL^5                0.12862277 0.1455696 133  0.8835824 3.785161e-01
O2LEVEL^6                0.21789466 0.1377385 133  1.5819442 1.160375e-01
O2LEVEL^7               -0.09384956 0.1248054 133 -0.7519672 4.533995e-01
BRTH.TYP1:O2LEVEL.L      1.42214172 0.2960086 133  4.8043931 4.125417e-06
BRTH.TYP1:O2LEVEL.Q     -0.78879876 0.2350434 133 -3.3559702 1.031193e-03
BRTH.TYP1:O2LEVEL.C      0.30008904 0.1902856 133  1.5770455 1.171607e-01
BRTH.TYP1:O2LEVEL^4     -0.10039069 0.1656535 133 -0.6060282 5.455289e-01
BRTH.TYP1:O2LEVEL^5     -0.17042006 0.1455696 133 -1.1707115 2.438081e-01
BRTH.TYP1:O2LEVEL^6     -0.07034671 0.1377385 133 -0.5107264 6.103893e-01
BRTH.TYP1:O2LEVEL^7     -0.25859982 0.1248054 133 -2.0720245 4.019500e-02
```

Conclusions - There are significant breathing type by linear and quadratic interactions, suggesting that the nature of the trends in ventilation performance depend upon on the natural breathing type of the toads. We shall therefore explore the nature of the trends separately for each breathing type.

- Explore the polynomial trends for buccal breathing toads. nly terms beginning with `M3` are relevant to the trends of interest.

```
> summary(mainEffects(mullens.lme.3, at = BRTH.TYP == "buccal"))$tTable
                      Value Std.Error  DF     t-value      p-value
(Intercept)     3.772459750 0.2529754 132 14.91235638 4.296929e-30
M1INTlung.0    -3.391410652 0.5469173 132 -6.20095742 6.696311e-09
M1INTlung.5    -2.355189353 0.5469173 132 -4.30629917 3.213505e-05
M1INTlung.10   -1.058672073 0.5469173 132 -1.93570792 5.504132e-02
```

```
M1INTlung.15 -1.018480912 0.5469173 132 -1.86222119 6.479525e-02
M1INTlung.20 -0.092952990 0.5469173 132 -0.16995805 8.653033e-01
M1INTlung.30 -0.414694389 0.5469173 132 -0.75823972 4.496591e-01
M1INTlung.40  0.225424650 0.5469173 132  0.41217322 6.808811e-01
M1INTlung.50  0.075508077 0.5469173 132  0.13806124 8.904024e-01
M3O2LEVEL.L  -2.348799134 0.3654010 132 -6.42800489 2.169510e-09
M3O2LEVEL.Q   0.286051766 0.2901439 132  0.98589614 3.259878e-01
M3O2LEVEL.C  -0.003119349 0.2348936 132 -0.01327984 9.894246e-01
M3O2LEVEL^4  -0.064924399 0.2044871 132 -0.31749874 7.513669e-01
M3O2LEVEL^5   0.299042834 0.1796951 132  1.66416827 9.845096e-02
M3O2LEVEL^6   0.288241366 0.1700281 132  1.69525698 9.238432e-02
M3O2LEVEL^7   0.164750259 0.1540631 132  1.06936865 2.868552e-01
```

- Explore the polynomial trends for lung breathing toads. Only terms beginning with `M3` are relevant to the trends of interest.

```
> summary(mainEffects(mullens.lme.3, at = BRTH.TYP == "lung"))$tTable
                      Value Std.Error  DF    t-value      p-value
(Intercept)      6.16006195 0.4625892 133 13.3164859 3.078255e-26
M1INTlung.0     -3.39141065 0.5469173  19 -6.2009574 5.876085e-06
M1INTbuccal.5   -1.03622130 0.4195306 133 -2.4699543 1.477925e-02
M1INTbuccal.10 -2.33273858 0.5260936 133 -4.4340748 1.918234e-05
M1INTbuccal.15 -2.37292974 0.5783317 133 -4.1030600 7.066792e-05
M1INTbuccal.20 -3.29845766 0.6062166 133 -5.4410546 2.462483e-07
M1INTbuccal.30 -2.97671626 0.6216187 133 -4.7886530 4.410966e-06
M1INTbuccal.40 -3.61683530 0.6302675 133 -5.7385722 6.153507e-08
M1INTbuccal.50 -3.46691873 0.6351661 133 -5.4582867 2.275045e-07
M3O2LEVEL.L      0.49548430 0.4657967 133  1.0637352 2.893762e-01
M3O2LEVEL.Q     -1.29154575 0.3698624 133 -3.4919631 6.512915e-04
M3O2LEVEL.C      0.59705874 0.2994318 133  1.9939723 4.820021e-02
M3O2LEVEL^4     -0.26570578 0.2606709 133 -1.0193149 3.099041e-01
M3O2LEVEL^5     -0.04179729 0.2290672 133 -0.1824674 8.554938e-01
M3O2LEVEL^6      0.14754795 0.2167442 133  0.6807470 4.972150e-01
M3O2LEVEL^7     -0.35244937 0.1963927 133 -1.7946154 7.498631e-02
```

Conclusions - The rows in the above tables that are of interest are those labled `M3O2LEVEL.L`, `M3O2LEVEL.Q` and `M3O2LEVEL.C` representing linear, quadratic and cubic effects respectively. Whilst an increase in hypoxia (reduction in oxygen levels) was associated with a significant linear increase in buccal breathing rate by buccal breathing toads ($P < 0.001$), such as linear trend was not observed in lung breathing toads ($P = 0.289$). Instead, for lung breathing toads, increasing hypoxia was associated with a significant quadratic breathing rate ($P < 0.001$). The breathing rate of lung breathing toads initially increased as the oxygen concentration decreased before displaying a sharp decline after oxygen concentrations lower than 10 percent (see Figure produced in Step 9 of Example 14C).

Example 14E: Repeated measures ANOVA

McGoldrick and Mac Nally (1998) investigated temporal changes in bird abundances in two different eucalypt habitat types (HABITAT: Ironbark and Stringybark) from two different regions (REGION: north and south) across south east Australia. Two sites (random plots) of each habitat/region combination were surveyed once a month for twelve months (MONTH: fixed within plot effect) and thus a partly nested design was employed (Box 11.4 of Quinn and Keough (2002)).

Step 1 - Import (section 2.3) the McGoldrick and Mac Nally (1998) data set.

```
> mcgold <- read.table("mcgold.csv", header = T, sep = ",")
```

Step 2 - To preserve the natural chronological order of the month data (by default R orders all factors alphabetically), specify the logical sequence of months and define the factor as ordered[h]. In so doing, R will also define the contrasts for this factor as polynomials. Note the procedure below relies on the order of data in the data file reflecting the preferred order.

```
> # examine the first six entries in the MONTH vector
> head(mcgold$MONTH)
[1] MAY MAY MAY MAY MAY MAY
12 Levels: APRIL AUGUST DECEMBER FEBRUARY JANUARY JULY JUNE MARCH
    ... SEPTEMBER

> mcgold$MONTH <- ordered(mcgold$MONTH,
      levels = unique(mcgold$MONTH))
> # examine the first six entries in the MONTH vector again
> # note the format of the levels attribute
> head(mcgold$MONTH)
[1] MAY MAY MAY MAY MAY MAY
12 Levels: MAY < JUNE < JULY < AUGUST < SEPTEMBER < OCTOBER < ... <
  APRIL
```

Step 3 (14.2) - Assess whether there are likely to be any plot by within plot interactions.

Raw data

```
> library(alr3)
> resplot(lm(BIRDS ~ HABITAT *
+     REGION * MONTH + SITE,
+     data = mcgold))
    t value      Pr(>|t|)
4.987846e+00 6.105625e-07
```

Log_e + 1 transformed data

```
> resplot(lm(log(BIRDS + 1) ~
+     HABITAT * REGION * MONTH +
+     SITE, data = mcgold))
  t value  Pr(>|t|)
0.7961976 0.4259172
```

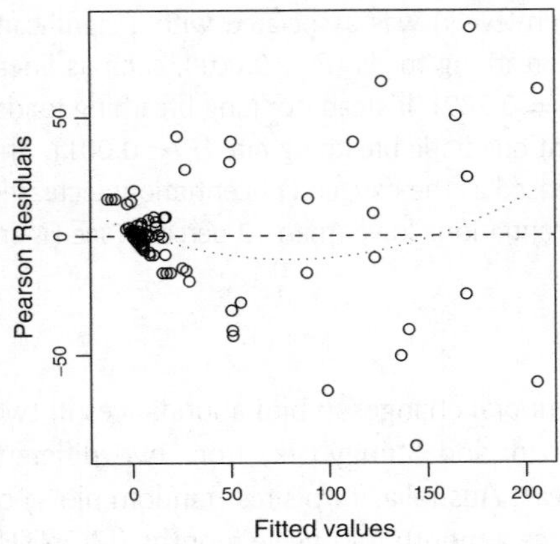

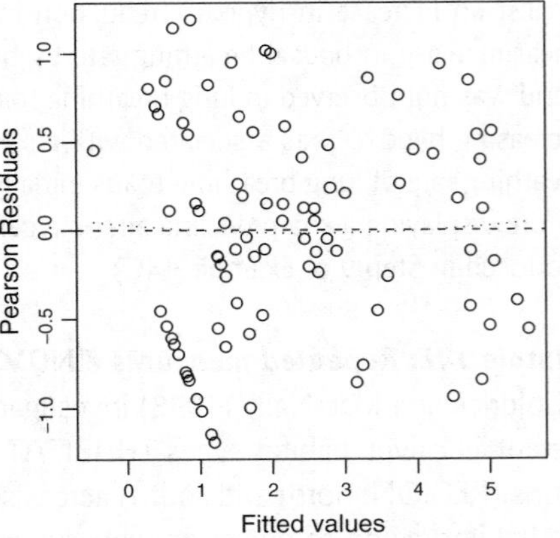

[h] Ordered factors are those in which the trends along the entire sequence of the levels are more interesting than the individual pairwise differences between levels.

Conclusions - The raw data shows a curvilinear trend implying that site by month interactions may be present. Moreover, the plot depicts a definite 'wedge' shape indicating that the assumption of homogeneity of variance is likely to be violated. Model fitting based on $log_e + 1$ transformed data shows no evidence of blocking interactions or non-homogeneity of variance.

Step 4 (14.2) - Assess assumptions of normality and homogeneity of variance for each null hypothesis ensuring that the correct scale of replicates are represented for each (they should reflect the appropriate *F*-ratio denominators see Table 14.3).

1. Between plot effects (Factor A: HABITAT - fixed effect, FACTOR C: REGION - fixed effect, A:C interaction - fixed). The mean bird abundances within each site (pooled over months) are the replicates for the between plot effects and thus an aggregated dataset needs to be created on which exploratory data analysis plots should be based. Prior to aggregating, we need to make a new variable to represent transformed data.

```
> library(nlme)
> mcgold$LBIRDS <- log
+     (mcgold$BIRDS + 1)
> mcgold.agg <- gsummary
+     (mcgold, groups =
+     mcgold$SITE)
> boxplot(BIRDS ~ HABITAT *
+     REGION, mcgold.agg)

> boxplot(LBIRDS ~
+     HABITAT * REGION,
+     mcgold.agg)
```

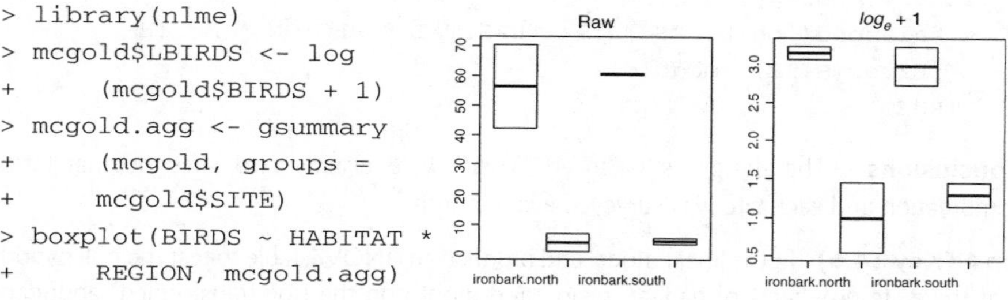

Conclusions - $log_e + 1$ transformed data appears to confirm to the parametric assumptions better than the raw data.

2. Within plot effects (Factor D: MONTH - fixed effect, interactions - fixed factor, interactions involving month). The individual bird abundances within each month of each site are the replicates for the within site effects[i].

```
> boxplot(BIRDS ~
+     MONTH, mcgold)

> boxplot(LBIRDS ~
+     MONTH, mcgold)
```

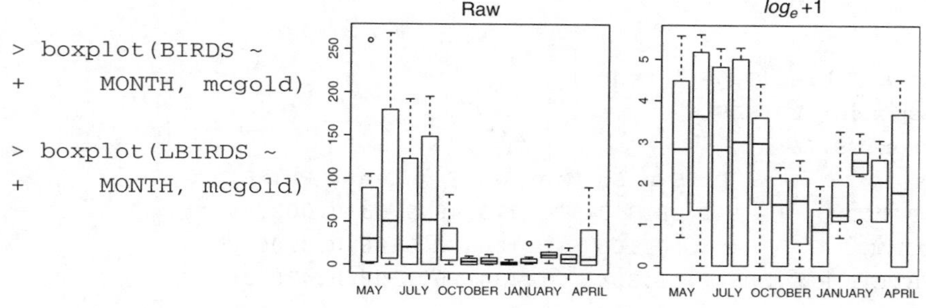

[i] For the transformed data, there was no evidence of interactions involving the sites (blocks) and thus we can use this single pooled residual term. Had there have been strong evidence of blocking interactions, it would be appropriate to generate further appropriately aggregated datasets on which to perform exploratory data analysis.

Conclusions - $log_e + 1$ transformed data appears to confirm to the parametric assumptions better than the raw data.

Step 5 (Key 14.splitPlot-key-notMissing) - Determine whether or not the design is balanced (at least with respect to sub-replication).

```
> replications(log(BIRDS + 1) ~ HABITAT * REGION * MONTH +
+     Error(SITE), mcgold)
          HABITAT                  REGION                 MONTH
               48                      48                     8
   HABITAT:REGION           HABITAT:MONTH          REGION:MONTH
               24                       4                     4
HABITAT:REGION:MONTH
                2
> library(biology)
> is.balanced(log(BIRDS + 1) ~ HABITAT * REGION * MONTH +
+     Error(SITE), mcgold)
[1] TRUE
```

Conclusions - The design is balanced. There were exactly two sites per habitat/region combination and each site was surveyed every month.

Step 6 (Key 14.6) - fit the linear model and produce an ANOVA table to test the null hypotheses that there are no effects of habitat, region and month on the (log transformed) abundance of forest birds. Treat the design as a repeated measures analysis to correct for deviations from sphericity that may result due to the ordered nature of the between plot effect (month).

```
> mcgold.aov <- aov(LBIRDS ~ HABITAT * REGION * MONTH +
+     Error(SITE), data = mcgold)
> library(biology)
> AnovaM(mcgold.aov, RM = T)
  Sphericity Epsilon Values
-------------------------------
 Greenhouse.Geisser Huynh.Feldt
          0.2103946   0.5162103


Anova Table (Type I tests)
Response: LBIRDS
Error: SITE
               Df Sum Sq Mean Sq F value    Pr(>F)
HABITAT         1 88.313  88.313 48.9753 0.002194 **
REGION          1  0.106   0.106  0.0586 0.820678
HABITAT:REGION  1  1.334   1.334  0.7398 0.438236
Residuals       4  7.213   1.803
---
Signif. codes:  0 '***' 0.001 '**' 0.01 '*' 0.05 '.' 0.1 ' ' 1

Error: Within
```

```
                     Df Sum Sq Mean Sq F value    Pr(>F)
MONTH                11 48.676   4.425  5.9408 8.029e-06 ***
HABITAT:MONTH        11 72.152   6.559  8.8061 5.488e-08 ***
REGION:MONTH         11 11.436   1.040  1.3957    0.2089
HABITAT:REGION:MONTH 11  3.858   0.351  0.4709    0.9113
Residuals            44 32.774   0.745
---
Signif. codes:  0 '***' 0.001 '**' 0.01 '*' 0.05 '.' 0.1 ' ' 1

Greenhouse-Geisser corrected ANOVA table
Response: LBIRDS
Error: SITE
                    Df Sum Sq Mean Sq F value   Pr(>F)
HABITAT        0.21039 88.313  88.313 48.9753 0.005497 **
REGION         0.21039  0.106   0.106  0.0586 0.398851
HABITAT:REGION 0.21039  1.334   1.334  0.7398 0.220487
Residuals      4.00000  7.213   1.803
---
Signif. codes:  0 '***' 0.001 '**' 0.01 '*' 0.05 '.' 0.1 ' ' 1

Error: Within
                          Df Sum Sq Mean Sq F value    Pr(>F)
MONTH                 2.3143 48.676   4.425  5.9408 0.0036017 **
HABITAT:MONTH         2.3143 72.152   6.559  8.8061 0.0003426 ***
REGION:MONTH          2.3143 11.436   1.040  1.3957 0.2586627
HABITAT:REGION:MONTH  2.3143  3.858   0.351  0.4709 0.6552869
Residuals            44.0000 32.774   0.745
---
Signif. codes:  0 '***' 0.001 '**' 0.01 '*' 0.05 '.' 0.1 ' ' 1


Huynh-Feldt corrected ANOVA table
Response: LBIRDS
Error: SITE
                    Df Sum Sq Mean Sq F value   Pr(>F)
HABITAT        0.51621 88.313  88.313 48.9753 0.003255 **
REGION         0.51621  0.106   0.106  0.0586 0.644687
HABITAT:REGION 0.51621  1.334   1.334  0.7398 0.341802
Residuals      4.00000  7.213   1.803
---
Signif. codes:  0 '***' 0.001 '**' 0.01 '*' 0.05 '.' 0.1 ' ' 1

Error: Within
                          Df Sum Sq Mean Sq F value    Pr(>F)
MONTH                 5.6783 48.676   4.425  5.9408 0.0001662 ***
HABITAT:MONTH         5.6783 72.152   6.559  8.8061 3.572e-06 ***
```

```
REGION:MONTH             5.6783 11.436    1.040  1.3957 0.2399414
HABITAT:REGION:MONTH     5.6783  3.858    0.351  0.4709 0.8171740
Residuals               44.0000 32.774    0.745
---
Signif. codes:  0 '***' 0.001 '**' 0.01 '*' 0.05 '.' 0.1 ' ' 1
```

Conclusions - Both Greenhouse-Geisser and Huynh-Feldt epsilon estimates suggest that sphericity was not met. There is a significant habitat by month interaction suggesting that the nature of the temporal patterns in bird abundances differ between the two habitats ($P < 0.001$). Similarly, whether or not there are differences in bird abundances in different habitats depends on the focal month.

Step 7 - Quinn and Keough (2002) presented the polynomial output that typically accompanies repeated measures analysis. Such trends should be compared using a separately calculated error term (to reduce the impacts of deviations from sphericity), each of which estimates a different source of variation.

```
> # begin by defining the appropriate linear, quadratic and cubic
> # terms
> MONTH.L <- C(mcgold$MONTH, poly, 1) # linear trend
> MONTH.Q <- C(mcgold$MONTH, poly, 2) # quadratic trend
> MONTH.C <- C(mcgold$MONTH, poly, 3) # cubic trend
> mcgold.aov <- aov(LBIRDS ~ HABITAT * REGION * MONTH + Error(SITE/
+ (MONTH.L + MONTH.Q + MONTH.C)), data = mcgold)
> summary(mcgold.aov)
Error: SITE
               Df Sum Sq Mean Sq F value   Pr(>F)
HABITAT         1 88.313  88.313 48.9753 0.002194 **
REGION          1  0.106   0.106  0.0586 0.820678
HABITAT:REGION  1  1.334   1.334  0.7398 0.438236
Residuals       4  7.213   1.803
---
Signif. codes:  0 '***' 0.001 '**' 0.01 '*' 0.05 '.' 0.1 ' ' 1

Error: SITE:MONTH.L
                     Df  Sum Sq Mean Sq F value  Pr(>F)
MONTH                 1 16.0556 16.0556 12.2311 0.02496 *
HABITAT:MONTH         1 24.5324 24.5324 18.6887 0.01242 *
REGION:MONTH          1  3.0278  3.0278  2.3065 0.20345
HABITAT:REGION:MONTH  1  0.7168  0.7168  0.5460 0.50095
Residuals             4  5.2507  1.3127
---
Signif. codes:  0 '***' 0.001 '**' 0.01 '*' 0.05 '.' 0.1 ' ' 1

Error: SITE:MONTH.Q
                     Df  Sum Sq Mean Sq F value  Pr(>F)
MONTH                 1 13.0991 13.0991  8.8971 0.04063 *
HABITAT:MONTH         1 17.9351 17.9351 12.1818 0.02512 *
```

```
REGION:MONTH            1  1.5739  1.5739  1.0690 0.35958
HABITAT:REGION:MONTH 1  0.8219  0.8219  0.5583 0.49648
Residuals               4  5.8891  1.4723
---
Signif. codes:  0 '***' 0.001 '**' 0.01 '*' 0.05 '.' 0.1 ' ' 1

Error: SITE:MONTH.C
                        Df  Sum Sq Mean Sq F value   Pr(>F)
MONTH                    1  1.6960  1.6960  2.9426 0.161419
HABITAT:MONTH            1 22.6950 22.6950 39.3754 0.003293 **
REGION:MONTH             1  1.4015  1.4015  2.4316 0.193923
HABITAT:REGION:MONTH     1  0.1671  0.1671  0.2900 0.618808
Residuals                4  2.3055  0.5764
---
Signif. codes:  0 '***' 0.001 '**' 0.01 '*' 0.05 '.' 0.1 ' ' 1

Error: Within
                        Df  Sum Sq Mean Sq F value   Pr(>F)
MONTH                    8 17.8249  2.2281  3.6889 0.003745 **
HABITAT:MONTH            8  6.9895  0.8737  1.4465 0.215806
REGION:MONTH             8  5.4324  0.6791  1.1242 0.373928
HABITAT:REGION:MONTH     8  2.1525  0.2691  0.4455 0.884351
Residuals               32 19.3284  0.6040
---
Signif. codes:  0 '***' 0.001 '**' 0.01 '*' 0.05 '.' 0.1 ' ' 1
```

Conclusions - The nature of temporal trends in bird abundances differ between the two habitats.

Step 8 - Although Quinn and Keough (2002) did not show simple main effects tests, in this case, such tests would be useful to formally explore the nature of the habitat by trend interactions further.

- Effects of month in the ironbark region

```
> library(biology)
> summary(mainEffects(mcgold.aov, at = HABITAT == "ironbark"))
Error: SITE
          Df Sum Sq Mean Sq F value   Pr(>F)
INT        2 89.408  44.704  24.791 0.005573 **
REGION     1  0.344   0.344   0.191 0.684633
Residuals  4  7.213   1.803
---
Signif. codes:  0 '***' 0.001 '**' 0.01 '*' 0.05 '.' 0.1 ' ' 1

Error: SITE:MONTH.L
             Df Sum Sq Mean Sq F value   Pr(>F)
INT           2  3.793   1.896  1.4447 0.337090
```

```
MONTH         1 40.140  40.140 30.5789 0.005225 **
REGION:MONTH  1  0.399   0.399  0.3040 0.610719
Residuals     4  5.251   1.313
---
Signif. codes:  0 '***' 0.001 '**' 0.01 '*' 0.05 '.' 0.1 ' ' 1

Error: SITE:MONTH.Q
             Df  Sum Sq Mean Sq F value  Pr(>F)
INT           2  2.5249  1.2624  0.8575 0.48989
MONTH         1 30.8446 30.8446 20.9502 0.01021 *
REGION:MONTH  1  0.0605  0.0605  0.0411 0.84921
Residuals     4  5.8891  1.4723
---
Signif. codes:  0 '***' 0.001 '**' 0.01 '*' 0.05 '.' 0.1 ' ' 1

Error: SITE:MONTH.C
             Df  Sum Sq Mean Sq F value   Pr(>F)
INT           2  7.2597  3.6298  6.2977 0.058096 .
MONTH         1 18.3996 18.3996 31.9230 0.004834 **
REGION:MONTH  1  0.3003  0.3003  0.5211 0.510325
Residuals     4  2.3055  0.5764
---
Signif. codes:  0 '***' 0.001 '**' 0.01 '*' 0.05 '.' 0.1 ' ' 1

Error: Within
             Df  Sum Sq Mean Sq F value   Pr(>F)
INT          16 12.2722  0.7670  1.2699 0.273976
MONTH         8 16.7784  2.0973  3.4723 0.005442 **
REGION:MONTH  8  3.3488  0.4186  0.6930 0.694765
Residuals    32 19.3284  0.6040
---
Signif. codes:  0 '***' 0.001 '**' 0.01 '*' 0.05 '.' 0.1 ' ' 1
```

- Effects of month in the stringybark region

```
> library(biology)
> summary(mainEffects(mcgold.aov, at = HABITAT == "stringybark"))
Error: SITE
          Df Sum Sq Mean Sq F value  Pr(>F)
INT        2 88.657  44.329 24.5832 0.00566 **
REGION     1  1.095   1.095  0.6073 0.47934
Residuals  4  7.213   1.803
---
Signif. codes:  0 '***' 0.001 '**' 0.01 '*' 0.05 '.' 0.1 ' ' 1

Error: SITE:MONTH.L
             Df Sum Sq Mean Sq F value  Pr(>F)
```

```
INT            2 40.540   20.270 15.4415 0.01315 *
MONTH          1  0.448    0.448  0.3409 0.59064
REGION:MONTH   1  3.345    3.345  2.5486 0.18563
Residuals      4  5.251    1.313
---
Signif. codes:  0 '***' 0.001 '**' 0.01 '*' 0.05 '.' 0.1 ' ' 1

Error: SITE:MONTH.Q
              Df  Sum Sq Mean Sq F value  Pr(>F)
INT            2 30.9051 15.4526 10.4956 0.02562 *
MONTH          1  0.1896  0.1896  0.1288 0.73787
REGION:MONTH   1  2.3353  2.3353  1.5862 0.27635
Residuals      4  5.8891  1.4723
---
Signif. codes:  0 '***' 0.001 '**' 0.01 '*' 0.05 '.' 0.1 ' ' 1

Error: SITE:MONTH.C
              Df  Sum Sq Mean Sq F value  Pr(>F)
INT            2 18.7000  9.3500 16.2220 0.01205 *
MONTH          1  5.9914  5.9914 10.3949 0.03215 *
REGION:MONTH   1  1.2683  1.2683  2.2005 0.21212
Residuals      4  2.3055  0.5764
---
Signif. codes:  0 '***' 0.001 '**' 0.01 '*' 0.05 '.' 0.1 ' ' 1

Error: Within
              Df  Sum Sq Mean Sq F value  Pr(>F)
INT           16 20.1272  1.2579  2.0827 0.03784 *
MONTH          8  8.0361  1.0045  1.6631 0.14622
REGION:MONTH   8  4.2361  0.5295  0.8767 0.54617
Residuals     32 19.3284  0.6040
---
Signif. codes:  0 '***' 0.001 '**' 0.01 '*' 0.05 '.' 0.1 ' ' 1
```

Conclusions - Whereas bird abundances in the ironbark habitat increased substantially during the period from May-August (displaying a significant quadratic or even cubic trend through time), no real temporal trend was observed within the stringybark habitat. Bird abundances were not found to differ between the two regions and nor did the nature of the temporal trends.

Step 9 - Summarize the trends in a plot. Note that Quinn and Keough (2002, Fig. 11.5) plotted mean $log_e + 1$ number of birds on a linear scale. The following plot will illustrate plotting the mean number of birds on a log_e scale so as to depict the actual trends analysed, yet allow the actual bird abundances to be appreciated. To do so, slight modifications of the y-axis scale tick marks are necessary.

```
> mcgold.means <- with(mcgold, tapply(BIRDS + 1, list(interaction
+      (HABITAT, REGION), MONTH), mean))
```

```
> library(gmodels)
> mcgold.se <- with(mcgold, tapply(BIRDS + 1, list(interaction
+     (HABITAT, REGION), MONTH), function(x) ci(x)[4]))
> xval <- as.numeric(mcgold$MONTH)
> plot(BIRDS ~ xval, data = mcgold, type = "n", axes = F, xlab = "",
+     ylab = "", log = "y")
> xval <- unique(xval)
> points(mcgold.means["ironbark.north", ] ~ xval, pch = 1,
+     col = "black", type = "b", lwd = 1, lty = 1)
> points(mcgold.means["ironbark.south", ] ~ xval, pch = 16,
+     col = "black", type = "b", lwd = 1, lty = 2)
> points(mcgold.means["stringybark.north", ] ~ xval, pch = 2,
+     col = "black", type = "b", lwd = 1, lty = 1)
> points(mcgold.means["stringybark.south", ] ~ xval, pch = 17,
+     col = "black", type = "b", lwd = 1, lty = 2)
> axis(1, cex.axis = 0.8, at = xval, lab = substr(levels
+     (mcgold$MONTH), 1, 1))
> mtext(text = "Month", side = 1, line = 3)
> yticks <- ifelse(axTicks(2) > 9, axTicks(2), axTicks(2) - 1)
> axis(2, cex.axis = 0.8, las = 1, at = axTicks(2), lab = yticks)
> mtext(text = "Mean number of birds", side = 2, line = 3)
> legend("topright", leg = c("Ironbark north", "Ironbark South",
+     "Stringybark north", "Stringybark south"), lty = 0,
+     pch = c(1, 16, 2, 17), bty = "n", cex = 1)
> box(bty = "l")
```

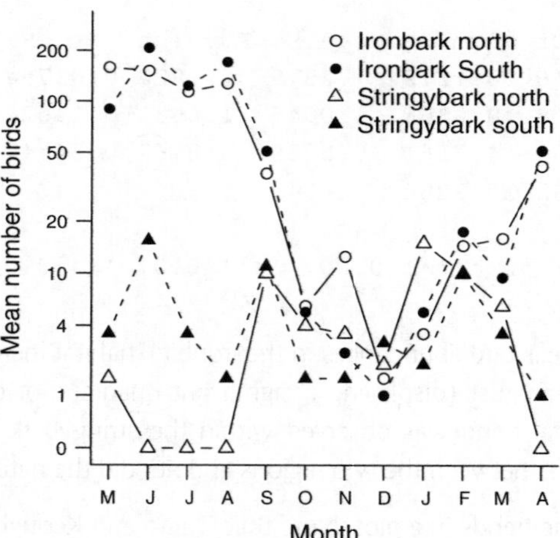

Example 14F: Linear mixed effects - multiple between plot factors

Alternatively, linear mixed effects modeling could be used to analyze the data introduced in Example 14E (Box 11.4 of Quinn and Keough (2002)). Notably, such an approach permits us to attempt to incorporate the nature of the variance-covariance matrix rather than wish it away post-hoc with estimated adjustments.

Step 1 (Key 14.2) - Refer to Example 14E for importing the data and performing exploratory data analysis.

Step 2 (Key 14.6) - Fit a series of lme models (with alternative correlation structures) and compare them to evaluate the appropriateness of each.

```
> library(nlme)
> # fit a model without correlation structure
> mcgold.lme.1 <- lme(LBIRDS ~ HABITAT * REGION * MONTH, random=~1 |
+ SITE, data=mcgold)
> # fit a model with a first order autoregressive correlation structure
> mcgold.lme.2 <- lme(LBIRDS ~ HABITAT * REGION * MONTH, random = ~1 |
+ SITE, data = mcgold, correlation = corAR1(form = ~1 | SITE))
> # compare the fit of models
> anova(mcgold.lme.1, mcgold.lme.2)
             Model df      AIC      BIC    logLik   Test  L.Ratio p-value
mcgold.lme.1     1 50 268.8264 362.3865 -84.41320
mcgold.lme.2     2 51 263.7146 359.1458 -80.85729 1 vs 2 7.111819  0.0077
> # fit a model with compound symmetry structure
> mcgold.lme.3 <- update(mcgold.lme.1, correlation = corCompSymm(form = ~1 |
+ SITE))
> anova(mcgold.lme.2, mcgold.lme.3)
             Model df      AIC      BIC    logLik
mcgold.lme.2     1 51 263.7146 359.1458 -80.85729
mcgold.lme.3     2 51 270.8264 366.2577 -84.41320
```

A model that incorporates a first order autoregressive correlation structure is a significantly better model than either no structure or a compound symmetry model. Therefore use the autoregressive model to test the hypotheses about the fixed factors in the model (habitat type, region, month and their interaction).

```
> anova(mcgold.lme.2)
                     numDF denDF   F-value p-value
(Intercept)              1    44 246.45562  <.0001
HABITAT                  1     4  57.87532  0.0016
REGION                   1     4   0.07888  0.7927
MONTH                   11    44   4.30356  0.0002
HABITAT:REGION           1     4   0.87245  0.4032
HABITAT:MONTH           11    44   5.55797  <.0001
REGION:MONTH            11    44   1.31472  0.2486
HABITAT:REGION:MONTH    11    44   0.48120  0.9050
```

Conclusions - There is a significant habitat type by month interaction ($P < 0.001$). Note that the model assuming compound symmetry (mcgold.lme.3) would have yielded the same F-ratios and P-values to a traditional split-plot ANOVA model that assumed compound symmetry (Step 5 of Example 14E).

Step 3 - Explore the nature of the interaction further by evaluating the simple main effects.

- Effect of month in the ironbark habitat.

```
> library(biology)
> anova(mainEffects(mcgold.lme.2, at = HABITAT == "ironbark"))
```

```
              numDF denDF   F-value p-value
(Intercept)       1    42 246.45562  <.0001
M1               24    42   3.96420  <.0001
M3                1     6   0.21333  0.6604
M4               11    42   7.81231  <.0001
M7               11    42   0.52446  0.8757
```

- Effect of month in the stringybark habitat.

```
> anova(mainEffects(mcgold.lme.2, at = HABITAT == "stringybark"))
              numDF denDF   F-value p-value
(Intercept)       1    42 246.45562  <.0001
M1               24    42   6.24138  <.0001
M3                1     6   0.73800  0.4233
M4               11    42   2.04922  0.0472
M7               11    42   1.27146  0.2739
```

Conclusions - There is a significant effect of month on the abundance of birds rate in both ironbark ($P < 0.001$) and stringybark habitats ($P = 0.0472$), although the effect is perhaps stronger in the former.

Step 4 - Quinn and Keough (2002) also illustrated polynomial trends which can be useful for exploring the nature of the within plot treatments(s) in repeated measures designs.

```
> op <- options(width = 200)
> summary(mcgold.lme.2)$tTable
                                      Value Std.Error DF     t-value      p-value
(Intercept)                      3.14903875 0.2759018 44 11.41362002 9.701113e-15
HABITATstringybark              -2.15401165 0.3901841  4 -5.52050052 5.257047e-03
REGIONsouth                     -0.16942080 0.3901841  4 -0.43420733 6.865331e-01
MONTH.L                         -2.85195444 0.8688652 44 -3.28238987 2.021045e-03
MONTH.Q                          2.65387603 0.7858802 44  3.37694715 1.541953e-03
MONTH.C                          1.87072523 0.7114088 44  2.62960646 1.173306e-02
MONTH^4                         -0.80528671 0.6473149 44 -1.24404167 2.200710e-01
MONTH^5                         -0.57180974 0.5935441 44 -0.96338205 3.406208e-01
MONTH^6                          0.29126582 0.5490521 44  0.53048849 5.984407e-01
MONTH^7                          0.23388559 0.5124500 44  0.45640666 6.503426e-01
MONTH^8                          0.29995662 0.4823553 44  0.62185818 5.372442e-01
MONTH^9                          1.05595693 0.4575438 44  2.30788155 2.576776e-02
MONTH^10                        -0.61026362 0.4369923 44 -1.39650874 1.695666e-01
MONTH^11                        -0.79906329 0.4198714 44 -1.90311424 6.358096e-02
HABITATstringybark:REGIONsouth   0.47151096 0.5518037  4  0.85449042 4.409904e-01
HABITATstringybark:MONTH.L       4.10097201 1.2287610 44  3.33748549 1.727032e-03
HABITATstringybark:MONTH.Q      -3.63565503 1.1114025 44 -3.27123167 2.086112e-03
HABITATstringybark:MONTH.C      -3.65768273 1.0060840 44 -3.63556395 7.228149e-04
HABITATstringybark:MONTH^4       0.69302331 0.9154415 44  0.75703723 4.530626e-01
HABITATstringybark:MONTH^5      -0.32033115 0.8393981 44 -0.38162005 7.045800e-01
HABITATstringybark:MONTH^6      -0.35115544 0.7764769 44 -0.45224196 6.533165e-01
HABITATstringybark:MONTH^7       0.24974620 0.7247138 44  0.34461358 7.320267e-01
HABITATstringybark:MONTH^8      -0.37318162 0.6821535 44 -0.54706402 5.870988e-01
HABITATstringybark:MONTH^9      -1.63946191 0.6470647 44 -2.53369098 1.492385e-02
HABITATstringybark:MONTH^10      0.60736034 0.6180005 44  0.98278294 3.310877e-01
HABITATstringybark:MONTH^11      0.08769159 0.5937879 44  0.14768168 8.832687e-01
REGIONsouth:MONTH.L             -0.63173897 1.2287610 44 -0.51412680 6.097360e-01
REGIONsouth:MONTH.Q              0.24603964 1.1114025 44  0.22137762 8.258226e-01
REGIONsouth:MONTH.C              0.54802968 1.0060840 44  0.54471562 5.886995e-01
REGIONsouth:MONTH^4             -0.96233481 0.9154415 44 -1.05122478 2.988948e-01
REGIONsouth:MONTH^5              0.18744949 0.8393981 44  0.22331416 8.243246e-01
REGIONsouth:MONTH^6              1.02414643 0.7764769 44  1.31896571 1.940041e-01
```

```
REGIONsouth:MONTH^7                      0.69912331 0.7247138 44  0.96468890 3.399730e-01
REGIONsouth:MONTH^8                     -0.49437049 0.6821535 44 -0.72472034 4.724601e-01
REGIONsouth:MONTH^9                     -0.26957160 0.6470647 44 -0.41660690 6.789914e-01
REGIONsouth:MONTH^10                     0.64105415 0.6180005 44  1.03730361 3.052616e-01
REGIONsouth:MONTH^11                     0.34908521 0.5937879 44  0.58789548 5.596079e-01
HABITATstringybark:REGIONsouth:MONTH.L  -1.19732182 1.7377305 44 -0.68901469 4.944315e-01
HABITATstringybark:REGIONsouth:MONTH.Q   1.28213649 1.5717605 44  0.81573274 4.190471e-01
HABITATstringybark:REGIONsouth:MONTH.C   0.57815559 1.4228176 44  0.40634553 6.864584e-01
HABITATstringybark:REGIONsouth:MONTH^4  -0.11272067 1.2946298 44 -0.08706788 9.310126e-01
HABITATstringybark:REGIONsouth:MONTH^5   0.62160040 1.1870882 44  0.52363455 6.031603e-01
HABITATstringybark:REGIONsouth:MONTH^6  -1.59393894 1.0981042 44 -1.45153707 1.537236e-01
HABITATstringybark:REGIONsouth:MONTH^7   0.07801131 1.0249000 44  0.07611602 9.396718e-01
HABITATstringybark:REGIONsouth:MONTH^8   0.31864555 0.9647107 44  0.33030167 7.427396e-01
HABITATstringybark:REGIONsouth:MONTH^9   1.11230331 0.9150876 44  1.21551562 2.306513e-01
HABITATstringybark:REGIONsouth:MONTH^10  0.13738776 0.8739847 44  0.15719699 8.758087e-01
HABITATstringybark:REGIONsouth:MONTH^11  0.03842338 0.8397429 44  0.04575612 9.637117e-01
```

Conclusions - Whereas bird abundances in the ironbark habitat increased substantially during the period from May-August (displaying a significant quadratic or even cubic trend through time), no real temporal trend was observed within the stringybark habitat. Bird abundances were not found to differ between the two regions and nor did the nature of the temporal trends.

Step 5 - Although Quinn and Keough (2002) did not show simple main effects tests, in this case, such tests would be useful to formally explore the nature of the habitat by trend interactions further.

- Explore the polynomial trends for the ironbark habitat. Only terms beginning with `M4` are relevant to the trends of interest.

```
> summary(mainEffects(mcgold.lme.2, at = HABITAT == "ironbark"))$tTable
                                    Value Std.Error DF    t-value      p-value
(Intercept)                     3.1490387 0.2759018 42 11.4136200 1.875333e-14
M1INTstringybark.north.MAY     -3.9079061 0.9070778 42 -4.3082370 9.696800e-05
M1INTstringybark.south.MAY     -2.9858859 0.9070778 42 -3.2917639 2.023752e-03
M1INTstringybark.north.JUNE    -4.9205932 0.9070778 42 -5.4246651 2.656305e-06
M1INTstringybark.south.JUNE    -2.5454031 0.9070778 42 -2.8061575 7.567240e-03
M1INTstringybark.north.JULY    -4.4090191 0.9070778 42 -4.8606847 1.671342e-05
M1INTstringybark.south.JULY    -3.7779198 0.9070778 42 -4.1649348 1.514844e-04
M1INTstringybark.north.AUGUST  -4.8277053 0.9070778 42 -5.3222617 3.718097e-06
M1INTstringybark.south.AUGUST  -4.4377135 0.9070778 42 -4.8923185 1.508977e-05
M1INTstringybark.north.SEPTEMBER -1.7739004 0.9070778 42 -1.9556210 5.718397e-02
M1INTstringybark.south.SEPTEMBER -1.8567860 0.9070778 42 -2.0469975 4.694857e-02
M1INTstringybark.north.OCTOBER -0.7458274 0.9070778 42 -0.8222309 4.155892e-01
M1INTstringybark.south.OCTOBER -0.5058004 0.9070778 42 -0.5576153 5.800672e-01
M1INTstringybark.north.NOVEMBER -1.0797421 0.9070778 42 -1.1903523 2.405928e-01
M1INTstringybark.south.NOVEMBER -0.2027326 0.9070778 42 -0.2235007 8.242294e-01
M1INTstringybark.north.DECEMBER  0.3465736 0.9070778 42  0.3820770 7.043307e-01
M1INTstringybark.south.DECEMBER  0.4236489 0.9070778 42  0.4670480 6.428795e-01
M1INTstringybark.north.JANUARY   0.8770096 0.9070778 42  0.9668515 3.391529e-01
M1INTstringybark.south.JANUARY  -0.3992538 0.9070778 42 -0.4401539 6.620826e-01
M1INTstringybark.north.FEBRUARY -0.7076410 0.9070778 42 -0.7801326 4.396874e-01
M1INTstringybark.south.FEBRUARY -0.4631705 0.9070778 42 -0.5106183 6.122919e-01
M1INTstringybark.north.MARCH    -1.0206102 0.9070778 42 -1.1251628 2.669091e-01
M1INTstringybark.south.MARCH    -0.4904146 0.9070778 42 -0.5406533 5.916025e-01
M1INTstringybark.north.APRIL    -3.6787781 0.9070778 42 -4.0556368 2.121728e-04
M1INTstringybark.south.APRIL    -2.9485769 0.9070778 42 -3.2506329 2.271796e-03
M3                              -0.1694208 0.3901841  6 -0.4342073 6.793175e-01
M4MONTH.L                       -2.8519544 0.8688652 42 -3.2823899 2.077910e-03
M4MONTH.Q                        2.6538760 0.7858802 42  3.3769471 1.589463e-03
M4MONTH.C                        1.8707252 0.7114088 42  2.6296065 1.189480e-02
M4MONTH^4                       -0.8052867 0.6473149 42 -1.2440417 2.203827e-01
M4MONTH^5                       -0.5718097 0.5935441 42 -0.9633821 3.408701e-01
M4MONTH^6                        0.2912658 0.5490521 42  0.5304885 5.985672e-01
M4MONTH^7                        0.2338856 0.5124500 42  0.4564067 6.504491e-01
M4MONTH^8                        0.2999566 0.4823553 42  0.6218582 5.373964e-01
M4MONTH^9                        1.0559569 0.4575438 42  2.3078816 2.600141e-02
```

```
M4MONTH^10                      -0.6102636 0.4369923 42 -1.3965087 1.698983e-01
M4MONTH^11                      -0.7990633 0.4198714 42 -1.9031142 6.389469e-02
M7REGIONsouth:MONTH.L           -0.6317390 1.2287610 42 -0.5141268 6.098580e-01
M7REGIONsouth:MONTH.Q            0.2460396 1.1114025 42  0.2213776 8.258712e-01
M7REGIONsouth:MONTH.C            0.5480297 1.0060840 42  0.5447156 5.888299e-01
M7REGIONsouth:MONTH^4           -0.9623348 0.9154415 42 -1.0512248 2.991664e-01
M7REGIONsouth:MONTH^5            0.1874495 0.8393981 42  0.2233142 8.243736e-01
M7REGIONsouth:MONTH^6            1.0241464 0.7764769 42  1.3189657 1.943270e-01
M7REGIONsouth:MONTH^7            0.6991233 0.7247138 42  0.9646889 3.402226e-01
M7REGIONsouth:MONTH^8           -0.4943705 0.6821535 42 -0.7247203 4.726419e-01
M7REGIONsouth:MONTH^9           -0.2695716 0.6470647 42 -0.4166069 6.790875e-01
M7REGIONsouth:MONTH^10           0.6410541 0.6180005 42  1.0373036 3.055298e-01
M7REGIONsouth:MONTH^11           0.3490852 0.5937879 42  0.5878955 5.597504e-01
```

- Explore the polynomial trends for the stringybark habitat. Only terms beginning with `M4` are relevant to the trends of interest.

```
> summary(mainEffects(mcgold.lme.2, at = HABITAT == "stringybark"))$tTable
                                  Value Std.Error DF     t-value      p-value
(Intercept)                  4.90293320 0.8840529 43  5.545972514 1.666066e-06
M1INTstringybark.north.MAY  -3.90790610 0.9070778  5 -4.308237006 7.655410e-03
M1INTironbark.south.MAY     -0.92202015 1.2828017 43 -0.718755004 4.761797e-01
M1INTironbark.north.JUNE     1.01268715 0.9804901 43  1.032837723 3.074541e-01
M1INTironbark.south.JUNE    -1.36250300 1.2828017 43 -1.062130637 2.941054e-01
M1INTironbark.north.JULY     0.50111305 1.1666564 43  0.429529255 6.696828e-01
M1INTironbark.south.JULY    -0.12998625 1.2828017 43 -0.101329963 9.197596e-01
M1INTironbark.north.AUGUST   0.91979925 1.2358358 43  0.744273003 4.607595e-01
M1INTironbark.south.AUGUST   0.52980735 1.2828017 43  0.413007985 6.816531e-01
M1INTironbark.north.SEPTEMBER -2.13400570 1.2634857 43 -1.688982842 9.846263e-02
M1INTironbark.south.SEPTEMBER -2.05112010 1.2828017 43 -1.598937763 1.171575e-01
M1INTironbark.north.OCTOBER  -3.16207870 1.2748058 43 -2.480439496 1.711415e-02
M1INTironbark.south.OCTOBER  -3.40210565 1.2828017 43 -2.652090045 1.115844e-02
M1INTironbark.north.NOVEMBER -2.82816400 1.2794831 43 -2.210395662 3.244846e-02
M1INTironbark.south.NOVEMBER -3.70517355 1.2828017 43 -2.888344719 6.041419e-03
M1INTironbark.north.DECEMBER -4.25447970 1.2814229 43 -3.320121431 1.840760e-03
M1INTironbark.south.DECEMBER -4.33155500 1.2828017 43 -3.376636435 1.566445e-03
M1INTironbark.north.JANUARY  -4.78491565 1.2822286 43 -3.731718085 5.531570e-04
M1INTironbark.south.JANUARY  -3.50865225 1.2828017 43 -2.735147776 9.022136e-03
M1INTironbark.north.FEBRUARY -3.20026515 1.2825634 43 -2.495210014 1.650603e-02
M1INTironbark.south.FEBRUARY -3.44473560 1.2828017 43 -2.685321954 1.025323e-02
M1INTironbark.north.MARCH    -2.88729595 1.2827026 43 -2.250947218 2.955563e-02
M1INTironbark.south.MARCH    -3.41749150 1.2828017 43 -2.664083987 1.082358e-02
M1INTironbark.north.APRIL    -0.22912800 1.2827605 43 -0.178621026 8.590742e-01
M1INTironbark.south.APRIL    -0.95932920 1.2828017 43 -0.747839039 4.586278e-01
M3                            0.30209015 0.3901841  5  0.774224621 4.737980e-01
M4MONTH.L                     1.24901756 0.8688652 43  1.437527379 1.578060e-01
M4MONTH.Q                    -0.98177900 0.7858802 43 -1.249273045 2.183231e-01
M4MONTH.C                    -1.78695751 0.7114088 43 -2.511857394 1.584424e-02
M4MONTH^4                    -0.11226340 0.6473149 43 -0.173429348 8.631278e-01
M4MONTH^5                    -0.89214089 0.5935441 43 -1.503074297 1.401293e-01
M4MONTH^6                    -0.05988963 0.5490521 43 -0.109078228 9.136479e-01
M4MONTH^7                     0.48363180 0.5124500 43  0.943763856 3.505631e-01
M4MONTH^8                    -0.07322501 0.4823553 43 -0.151807182 8.800490e-01
M4MONTH^9                    -0.58350498 0.4575438 43 -1.275298586 2.090508e-01
M4MONTH^10                   -0.00290328 0.4369923 43 -0.006643778 9.947298e-01
M4MONTH^11                   -0.71137170 0.4198714 43 -1.694260795 9.744800e-02
M7REGIONsouth:MONTH.L        -1.82906078 1.2287610 43 -1.488540721 1.439063e-01
M7REGIONsouth:MONTH.Q         1.52817613 1.1114025 43  1.374997929 1.762546e-01
M7REGIONsouth:MONTH.C         1.12618526 1.0060840 43  1.119374982 2.691941e-01
M7REGIONsouth:MONTH^4        -1.07505548 0.9154415 43 -1.174357359 2.467148e-01
M7REGIONsouth:MONTH^5         0.80904989 0.8393981 43  0.963845241 3.405129e-01
M7REGIONsouth:MONTH^6        -0.56979251 0.7764769 43 -0.733817709 4.670423e-01
M7REGIONsouth:MONTH^7         0.77713462 0.7247138 43  1.072333205 2.895520e-01
M7REGIONsouth:MONTH^8        -0.17572494 0.6821535 43 -0.257603236 7.979420e-01
M7REGIONsouth:MONTH^9         0.84273171 0.6470647 43  1.302391783 1.997153e-01
M7REGIONsouth:MONTH^10        0.77844190 0.6180005 43  1.259613725 2.146029e-01
M7REGIONsouth:MONTH^11        0.38750858 0.5937879 43  0.652604416 5.174852e-01
```

Conclusions - Whereas bird abundances in the ironbark habitat increased substantially during the period from May-August (displaying a significant quadratic or even cubic trend through time), no real temporal trend was observed within the stringybark habitat. Bird abundances were not found to differ between the two regions and nor did the nature of the temporal trends (see figure in Example 14E Step 10).

15

Analysis of covariance (ANCOVA)

Previous chapters have concentrated on designs for either continuous (Regression) or categorical (ANOVA) predictor variables. Analysis of covariance (ANCOVA) models are essentially ANOVA models that incorporate one or more continuous variables (**covariates**). Although the relationship between a response variable and a covariate may itself be of substantial biological interest, typically covariate(s) are incorporated to reduce the amount of unexplained variability in the model (analogous to blocking -see Chapter 13) and thereby increase the power of any treatment effects.

In ANCOVA, a reduction in unexplained variability is achieved by adjusting the response (to each treatment) according to slight differences in the covariate means as well as accounting for any underlying trends between the response and covariate(s), see Figure 15.1. To do so, the extent to which the within treatment group small differences in covariate means between groups and treatment groups are essentially compared via differences in their y-intercepts. The total variation is thereafter partitioned into explained (using the deviations between the overall trend and trends approximated for each of the treatment groups) and unexplained components (using the deviations between the observations and the approximated within group trends). In this way, ANCOVA can be visualized as a regular ANOVA in which the group and overall means are replaced by group and overall trendlines. Importantly, it should be apparent that ANCOVA is only appropriate when each of the within group trends have the same slope and are thus parallel to one another and the overall trend (see Figures 15.1e-f to visualize a situation in which slopes are not parallel). Furthermore, ANCOVA is not appropriate when the resulting adjustments must be extrapolated from a linear relationship outside the measured range of the covariate (see Figures 15.1g-h).

As an example, an experiment might be set up to investigate the energetic impacts of sexual vs parthenogenetic (egg development without fertilization) reproduction on leaf insect food consumption. To do so, researchers could measure the daily food intake of individual adult female leaf insects from female only (parthenogenetic) and mixed (sexual) populations. Unfortunately, the available individual leaf insects vary substantially in body size as this is expected to increase the variability of daily food intake of treatment groups. Consequently, the researchers will also measure the body mass of the individuals as a covariate, thereby providing a means by which daily food consumption can be standardized for body mass.

Although ANCOVA and blocking designs both aim to reduce the sources of unexplained variation by incorporating additional variables, blocking designs do so by

Biostatistical Design and Analysis Using R: a Practical Guide, 1st edition. By M. Logan.
Published 2010 by Blackwell Publishing.

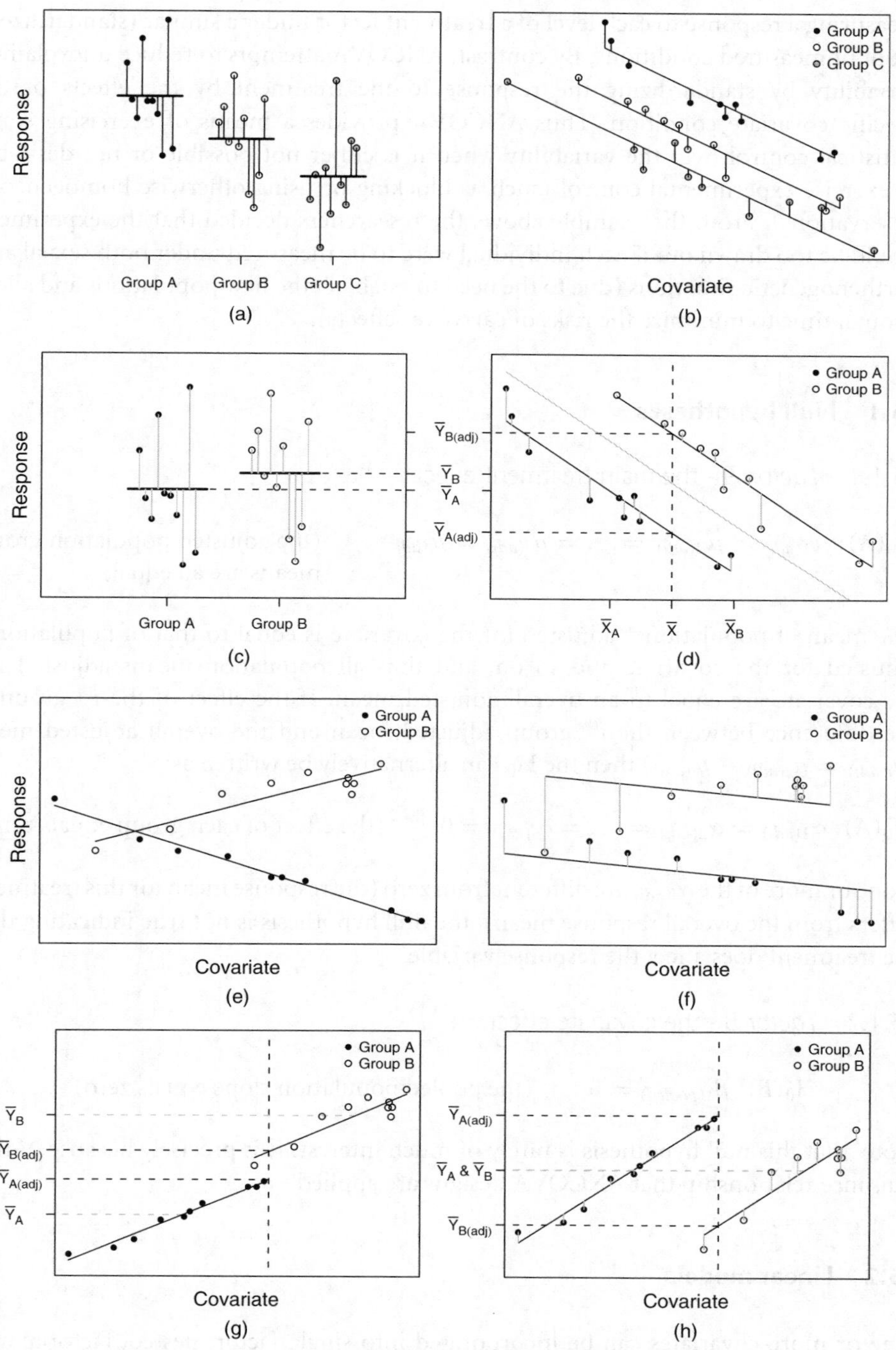

Fig 15.1 Fictitious data to illustrates the principles of analysis of covariance. The degree of unexplained variability (residuals) from single factor ANOVA and ANCOVA are represented in (a) and (b) respectively. (c) and (d) illustrate the use of the covariate in calculating adjusted group means (effects). The consequences of heterogeneous slopes are illustrated in (e) and (f) and the consequences of disparate covariate ranges on adjusted group means are illustrated in (g) and (h).

measuring a response to each level of a treatment factor under a similar (standardized) set of unmeasured conditions. By contrast, ANCOVA attempts to reduce unexplained variability by standardizing the response to the treatment by the effects of the specific covariate condition. Thus ANCOVA provides a means of exercising some statistical control over the variability when it is either not possible or not desirable to exercise experimental control (such as blocking or using otherwise homogeneous observations). From the example above, the researchers decided that the experiment would be too drawn out if each individual were to be measured under both sexual and parthenogenetic situations (due to the need to establish the new populations and allow enough time to minimize the risks of carryover effects).

15.1 Null hypotheses

15.1.1 *Factor A* - the main treatment effect

$H_0(A): \mu_{1(adj)} = \mu_{2(adj)} = \ldots = \mu_{i(adj)} = \mu_{(adj)}$ (the adjusted population group means are all equal)

The mean of population 1 adjusted for the covariate is equal to that of population 2 adjusted for the covariate and so on, and thus all population means adjusted for the covariate are equal to an overall adjusted mean. If the effect of the ith group is the difference between the ith group adjusted mean and the overall adjusted mean ($\alpha_{i(adj)} = \mu_{i(adj)} - \mu_{(adj)}$) then the H_0 can alternatively be written as:

$H_0(A): \alpha_{1(adj)} = \alpha_{2(adj)} = \ldots = \alpha_{i(adj)} = 0$ (the effect of each group equals zero)

If one or more of the $\alpha_{i(adj)}$ are different from zero (the response mean for this treatment differs from the overall response mean), the null hypothesis is not true indicating that the treatment does affect the response variable.

15.1.2 *Factor B* - the covariate effect

$H_0(B): \beta_{1(pooled)} = 0$ (the pooled population slope equals zero)

Note, that this null hypothesis is rarely of much interest. It is precisely because of this nuisance relationship that ANCOVA designs are applied.

15.2 Linear models

One or more covariates can be incorporated into single factor, nested, factorial and partly nested designs in order to reduce the unexplained variation. Fundamentally, the covariate(s) are purely used to adjust the response values prior to the regular analysis. The difficulty is in determining the appropriate adjustments. Following is a list of the appropriate linear models and adjusted response calculations for a range of

ANCOVA designs. Note that these linear models do not include interactions involving the covariates as these are assumed to be zero. The inclusion of these interaction terms is however, a useful means of testing the homogeneity of slopes assumption (see section 15.4.1).

Single categorical and single covariate

$$\text{Linear model: } y_{ij} = \mu + \alpha_i + \beta(x_{ij} - \bar{x}) + \varepsilon_{ij}$$

$$\text{Adjustments: } y_{ij(adj)} = y_{ij} - b(x_{ij} - \bar{x})$$

Single categorical and two covariates (X&Z)

$$\text{Linear model: } y_{ij} = \mu + \alpha_i + \beta_{YX}(x_{ij} - \bar{x}) + \beta_{YZ}(z_{ij} - \bar{z}) + \varepsilon_{ij}$$

$$\text{Adjustments: } y_{ij(adj)} = y_{ij} - b_{YX}(x_{ij} - \bar{x}) - b_{YZ}(z_{ij} - \bar{z})$$

Special attention must be paid to the issues raised for multiple linear regression (see chapter 9).

Factorial designs (A&C categorical) with a single covariate)

$$\text{Linear model: } y_{ijk} = \mu + \alpha_i + \gamma_j + (\alpha\gamma)_{ij} + \beta(x_{ijk} - \bar{x}) + \varepsilon_{ijkl}$$

$$\text{Adjustments: } y_{ijk(adj)} = y_{ijk} - b(x_{ijk} - \bar{x})$$

where β is the population slope between the response and the covariate.

Nested designs (A&C categorical) with a single covariate)

$$\text{Linear model: } y_{ijk} = \mu + \alpha_i + \gamma_{j(i)} + \beta(x_{ijk} - \bar{x}) + \varepsilon_{ijk}$$

$$\text{Adjustments: } y_{ijk(adj)} = y_{ijk} - b(x_{ijk} - \bar{x})$$

Partly nested designs (A&C categorical) with a single covariate)

$$\text{Linear model: } y_{ijkl} = \mu + \alpha_i + \gamma_{j(i)} + \delta_k + (\alpha\delta)_{ik} + \gamma\delta_{j(i)k} + \beta(x_{ijk} - \bar{x}) + \varepsilon_{ijkl}$$

$$\text{Adjustments: } y_{ijk(adj)} = y_{ijk} - b_{between}(x_i - \bar{x}) - b_{within}(x_{ijk} - \bar{x}_i)$$

where $b_{between}$ and b_{within} refer to the between and within block/plot/subject regression slopes respectively.

15.3 Analysis of variance

In ANCOVA, the total variability of the response variable is sequentially partitioned into components explained by each of the model terms, starting with the covariate and is therefore equivalent to performing a regular analysis of variance on the response variables that have been adjusted for the covariate. The appropriate unexplained

Table 15.1 *F*-ratios and corresponding R syntax for simple ANCOVA (B is a covariate).

Factor	d.f.	MS	*F*-ratio A&B fixed	*F*-ratio A random, B fixed
A	$a-1$	MS_A	$\frac{MS_A}{MS_{Resid}}$	$\frac{MS_A}{MS_{Resid}}$
B	1	MS_B	$\frac{MS_B}{MS_{Resid}}$	$\left[\frac{MS_A}{MS_{B\times A'}}\right]^a$
B×A	$a-1$	$MS_{B\times A}$	$\frac{MS_{B\times A}}{MS_{Resid}}$	$\frac{MS_{B\times A'}}{MS_{Resid}}$
Residual (=N′(B×A))	$(n-2)a$	MS_{Resid}		

A&B fixed[b]

```
> Anova(aov(DV~A*B, data), type="III")
```
[c]

[a]If $P > 0.25$ for B×A′, pooled denominator for B could be $(SS_{B\times A'} + SS_{Resid})/((a-1)+(n-2)a)$.
[b]***For mixed models, it is necessary to manually calculate the correct F-ratios and P values.***
[c]To use type III sums of squares, Factor A contrasts must first be defined as something other than 'treatment' (such as 'sum' or 'helmert') prior to fitting the model (`> contrasts(data$A)<-contr.helmert`).

residuals and therefore the appropriate *F*-ratios for each factor differ according to the different null hypotheses associated with different linear models as well as combinations of fixed and random factors in the model (see Tables 15.1 & 15.2). Note that since the covariate levels measured are typically different for each group, ANCOVA designs are inherently non-orthogonal (unbalanced). Consequently, sequential (Type I sums of squares) should not be used[a].

15.4 Assumptions

As ANCOVA designs are essentially regular ANOVA designs that are first adjusted (centered) for the covariate(s), ANCOVA designs inherit all of the underlying assumptions of the appropriate ANOVA design. Readers should also consult sections 11.5, 12.4, 13.4 and 14.4. Specifically, hypothesis tests assume that:

(i) the appropriate residuals are normally distributed. Boxplots using the appropriate scale of replication (reflecting the appropriate residuals/*F*-ratio denominator, see Tables 15.1-15.2) should be used to explore normality. Scale transformations are often useful.
(ii) the appropriate residuals are equally varied. Boxplots and plots of means against variance (using the appropriate scale of replication) should be used to explore the spread of values. Residual plots should reveal no patterns (see Figure 8.5). Scale transformations are often useful.
(iii) the appropriate residuals are independent of one another.

[a] For very simple Ancova designs that incorporate a single categorical and single covariate, Type I sums of squares can be used provided the covariate appears in the linear model first (and thus is partitioned out last).

Table 15.2 *F*-ratios and corresponding R syntax for factorial ANCOVA (C is a covariate).

		F-ratio		
Factor	**d.f.**	**A & B fixed**	**A fixed, B random**	**A & B random**
A	$a-1$	$\frac{MS_A}{MS_{Resid}}$	$\left[\frac{MS_A}{MS_{B'\times A}}\right]^a$	$\left[\frac{MS'_A}{MS_{B'\times A'}}\right]^a$
B	$b-1$	$\frac{MS_B}{MS_{Resid}}$	$\left[\frac{MS_{B'}}{MS_{Resid}}\right]$	$\left[\frac{MS_{B'}}{MS_{B'\times A'}}\right]^a$
B×A	$(b-1)(a-1)$	$\frac{MS_{B\times A}}{MS_{Resid}}$	$\frac{MS_{B'\times A}}{MS_{Resid}}$	$\frac{MS_{B'\times A'}}{MS_{Resid}}$
C	1	$\frac{MS_C}{MS_{Resid}}$	$\left[\frac{MS_C}{MS_{C\times A'}}\right]^a$	$\left[\frac{MS_C}{MS_{C\times A'}+MS_{C\times B'}+MS_{C\times B'\times A'}}\right]^a$
C×A	$(a-1)$	$\frac{MS_{C\times A}}{MS_{Resid}}$	$\frac{MS_{C\times A}}{MS_{C\times B'\times A}}^a$	$\frac{MS_{C\times A}}{MS_{C\times B'\times A'}}^a$
C×B	$(b-1)$	$\frac{MS_{C\times B}}{MS_{Resid}}$	$\frac{MS_{C\times B'}}{MS_{Resid}}$	$\frac{MS_{C\times B'}}{MS_{C\times B'\times A'}}^a$
C×B×A	$(b-1)(a-1)$	$\frac{MS_{C\times B\times A}}{MS_{Resid}}$	$\frac{MS_{C\times B'\times A}}{MS_{Resid}}$	$\frac{MS_{C\times B'\times A'}}{MS_{Resid}}$
Residual (=N′(C×B×A))	$(n-2)ba$	MS_{Resid}		
R syntax				
	A & B fixed[b]			
	`> Anova(aov(DV~A*B*C, data), type="III")`[c]			

[a]Pooling: higher order interactions with $P > 0.25$ can be removed to produce more exact denominators.
[b]***For mixed models, it is necessary to manually calculate the correct F-ratios and P values.***
[c]To use type III sums of squares, Factor A contrasts must first be defined as something other than 'treatment' (such as 'sum' or 'helmert') prior to fitting the model (`contrasts(data$A)<-contr.helmert`).

(iv) the relationship between the response variable and the covariate should be linear. Linearity can be explored using scatterplots and residual plots should reveal no patterns (see fig 8.5).
(v) for repeated measures and other designs in which treatment levels within blocks can not be be randomly ordered, the variance/covariance matrix is assumed to display **sphericity** (see section 13.4.1).
(vi) for designs that utilize blocking, it is assumed that there are no block by within block interactions.

15.4.1 Homogeneity of slopes

In addition to the above assumptions, ANCOVA designs also assume that slopes of relationships between the response variable and the covariate(s) are the same for each treatment level (group). That is, all the trends are parallel. If the individual slopes deviate substantially from each other (and thus the overall slope), then adjustments made to each of the observations are nonsensical (see Figures 15.1e-f). This situation is analogous to an interaction between two or more factors. In ANCOVA, interactions involving the covariate suggest that the nature of the relationship between the response and the covariate differs between the levels of the categorical treatment. More importantly, they also indicate that the strength or presence of an effect of the treatment depends on what range of the covariate you are focussed on. Clearly then, it is not possible to make conclusions about the main effects of treatments in the presence of such interactions. The assumption of homogeneity of slopes can be examined via interaction plots or more formally, by testing hypotheses about the interactions between categorical variables and the covariate(s).

There are three broad approaches for dealing with ANCOVA designs with heterogeneous slopes and selection depends on the primary focus of the study.

(i) When the primary objective of the analysis is to investigate the effects of categorical treatments, it is possible to adopt an approach similar to that taken when exploring interactions in multiple regression. The effect of treatments can be examined at specific values of the covariate (such as the mean and $\pm$ one standard deviation). This approach is really only useful at revealing broad shifts in patterns over the range of the covariate and if the selected values of the covariate do not have some inherent biological meaning (selected arbitrarily), then the outcomes can be of only limited biological interest.
(ii) Alternatively, the Johnson-Neyman technique (or Wilxon modification thereof) procedure indicates the ranges of the covariate over which the individual regression lines of pairs of treatment groups overlap or cross. Although less powerful than the previous approach, the Wilcox(J-N) procedure has the advantage of revealing the important range (ranges for which the groups are different and not different) of the covariate rather than being constrained by specific levels selected.
(iii) Use treatment contrasts to split up the interaction term into its constituent contrasts for each level of the treatment. Essentially this compares each of the treatment level slopes to the slope from the "control" group and is useful if the primary focus is on the relationships between the response and the covariate

15.4.2 Similar covariate ranges

Adjustments made to the response means (in an attempt to statistically account for differences in the covariate) involve predicting mean response values along displaced[b] linear relationships between the overall response and covariate variables (see Figure 15.1d). However, when the ranges of the covariate within each of the groups differ substantially from one another, these adjustments are effectively extrapolations (see Figures 15.1g-h) and therefore of unknown reliability. If a simple ANOVA of the covariate modelled against the categorical factor indicates that the covariate means differ significantly between groups, it may be necessary to either remove extreme observations or reconsider the analysis.

---

[b] The degree of trend displacement for any given group is essentially calculated by multiplying the overall regression slope by the degree of difference between the overall covariate mean and the mean of the covariate for that group.

15.5 Robust ANCOVA

ANCOVA based on rank transformed data can be useful for accommodating data with numerous problematic outliers. Nevertheless, the problems highlighted in section 12.7 about the difficulties of detecting interactions from rank transformed data obviously have implications for inferential tests of homogeneity of slopes. Randomization tests that maintain response-covariate pairs and repeatedly randomize these observations amongst the levels of the treatments can also be useful, particularly when there is doubt over the independence of observations.

15.6 Specific comparisons

Both planned and unplanned comparisons follow those of other ANOVA chapters without any real additional complications. Notably, recent implementations of the Tukey's test (within R) accommodate unbalanced designs and thus negate the need for some of the more complicated and specialized techniques that have been highlighted in past texts.

15.7 Further reading

- Theory

Doncaster, C. P., and A. J. H. Davey. (2007). *Analysis of Variance and Covariance. How to Choose and Construct Models for the Life Sciences.* Cambridge University Press, Cambridge.

Quinn, G. P., and K. J. Keough. (2002). *Experimental design and data analysis for biologists.* Cambridge University Press, London.

Sokal, R., and F. J. Rohlf. (1997). *Biometry*, 3rd edition. W. H. Freeman, San Francisco.

Zar, G. H. (1999). *Biostatistical methods.* Prentice-Hall, New Jersey.

- Practical - R

Crawley, M. J. (2007). *The R Book.* John Wiley, New York.

Fox, J. (2002). *An R and S-PLUS Companion to Applied Regression.* Sage Books.

Maindonald, J. H., and J. Braun. (2003). *Data Analysis and Graphics Using R - An Example-based Approach.* Cambridge University Press, London.

Venables, W. N., and B. D. Ripley. (2002). *Modern Applied Statistics with S-PLUS*, 4th edn. Springer-Verlag, New York.

15.8 Key for ANCOVA

Note, analysis of covariance (ANCOVA) design and analysis elements can be incorporated into more complex regression and ANOVA designs. The key presented here is for simple ANCOVA designs comprising a single categorical and a single covariate. For more complex designs, use the following key in combination with other appropriate keys from their respective chapters.

1 a. Check parametric assumptions

- **Normality of the response variable at each level of the categorical variable - boxplots**

```
> boxplot(DV ~ Factor, dataset)
```

where DV *and* Factor *are response and factor variables respectively in the* dataset *data frame*

- **Homogeneity of variance - residual plots**

```
> plot(aov(DV ~ CV + Factor, dataset), which = 1)
```

where DV, CV *and* Factor *are response, covariate and factor variables respectively in the* dataset *data frame*

Parametric assumptions met .... Go to 2

b. Parametric assumptions NOT met .... Go to 6

2 a. Check assumptions of linearity and homogeneity of slopes See Examples 15A & 15B

```
> library(lattice)
> xyplot(DV ~ CV | FACTOR, dataset, type = c("r", "p"))
> # OR
> library(car)
> scatterplot(DV ~ CV | FACTOR, dataset)
> # inference test for interaction (non-homogenous slopes)
> anova(aov(DV ~ CV * FACTOR, dataset))
```

Homogeneity of slopes assumption met .... Go to 3

b. Homogeneity of slopes assumption NOT met .... Go to 4

3 a. Perform analysis of covariance............................... See Example 15A

```
> data.aov <- aov(DV ~ CV + FACTOR, dataset)
> anova(data.aov)
```

if Reject H_0 - Significant difference between group means detected, consider planned comparisons or post-hoc multiple pairwise comparisons tests ..... Go to Key 10.9a

4 a. Primarily interested in the effect of the categorical variable .... Go to 5

b. Primarily interested in the effect of the continuous covariate

```
> summary(lm(DV ~ CV, dataset, subset = FACTOR == "A"))
```

5 a. Able to sensibly divide the range of the covariate into a small set of meaningful intervals (investigate the effect of the factor in each covariate interval separately using factorial analysis of variance (see chapter 12)

```
> dataset$CV_F <- cut(dataset$CV, 4)
> data.aov1 <- aov(DV ~ CV_F * FACTOR, data = dataset)
```

.... Goto Key 12.11

b. Investigate the effect of the factor at different values of the covariate (nominally, ±1 and ±2 standard deviations around the mean)

```
> CV_sd2 <- mean(CV) - 2 * sd(CV)
> data.aov1 <- aov(DV ~ FACTOR + c(CV - CV_sd2), data = dataset)
> anova(data.lm2)
```

c. **Use the Johnson-Neyman procedure to investigate the range(s) of the covariate for which the Factor levels are not significantly different** . . . . See Example 15B

```
> data.lm <- lm(DV ~ CV * FACTOR, dataset)
> library(biology)
> wilcox.JN(data.lm, type = "H")
```

6 a. **Attempt a scale transformation (see Table 3.2 for common transformation options)** Go to 1

b. **Transformations unsuccessful or inappropriate** - see the range of options available for other analyses.

15.9 Worked examples of real biological data sets

Example 15A: Single factor ANCOVA

To investigate the impacts of sexual activity on male fruitfly longevity, Partridge and Farquhar (1981), measured the longevity of male fruitflies with access to either one virgin female (potential mate), eight virgin females, one pregnant female (not a potential mate), eight pregnant females or no females. The available male fruitflies varied in size and since size is known to impact longevity, the researchers randomly allocated each individual fruitfly to one of the five treatments and also measured thorax length as a covariate (from Box 12.1 of Quinn and Keough (2002)).

Step 1 - Import (section 2.3) the Partridge and Farquhar (1981) data set.

```
> partridge <- read.table("partridge.csv", header = T, sep = ",")
```

Step 2(Key 15.1) - Assess assumptions of normality and homogeneity of variance for each null hypothesis ensuring that the correct scale of replicates are represented for each (they should reflect the appropriate *F*-ratio denominators see Table 15.1).

```
> plot(aov(LONGEV ~
+      THORAX + TREATMENT,
+      partridge), which = 1)
```

```
> plot(aov(log10(LONGEV) ~
+      THORAX + TREATMENT,
+      partridge), which = 1)
```

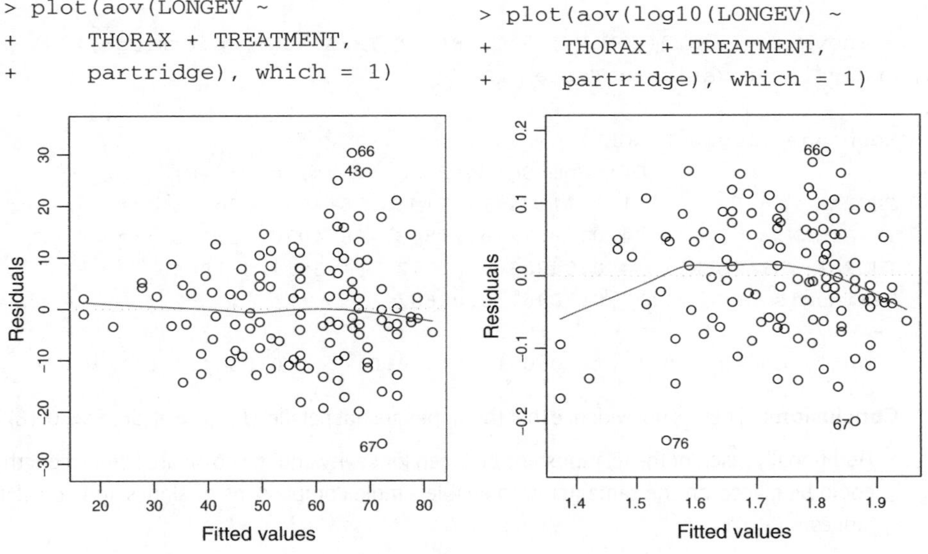

Conclusions - A distinct wedge shape is apparent in the residuals from the model fitted with the raw longevity measurements suggesting homogeneity of variance issues. This issue is less obvious in the residual plot based upon log_{10} transformed data, and thus analyses should be based on the transformed data.

Step 3 (Key 15.2) - Assess assumptions of linearity, homogeneity of slopes and covariate range equality (using log transformed data).

- Plot the relationship between male longevity and thorax length separately for each of the treatment groups in a lattice

```
> library(lattice)
> print(xyplot(log10(LONGEV) ~ THORAX | TREATMENT, partridge,
+      type = c("r","p")))
```

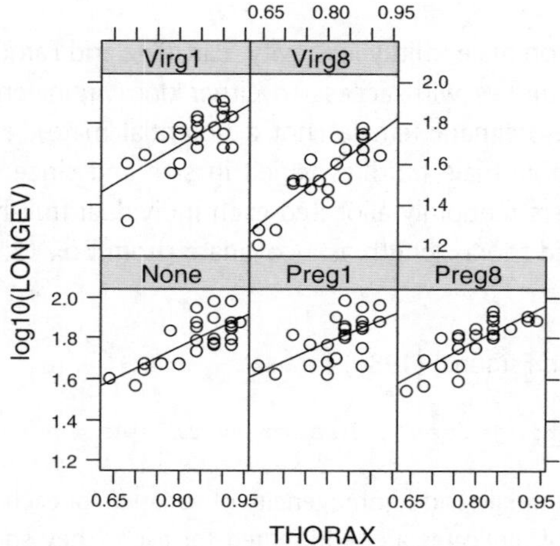

Conclusions - The slopes of each of the relationships between the response (longevity) and the covariate (thorax length) appear similar and there is no evidence of non-linearity.

- The homogeneity of slopes assumption can also be formally tested by fitting the full multiplicative Anova model and examining the interaction term.

```
> anova(aov(log10(LONGEV) ~ THORAX * TREATMENT, partridge))
Analysis of Variance Table

Response: log10(LONGEV)
                  Df  Sum Sq Mean Sq  F value Pr(>F)
THORAX             1 1.21194 1.21194 176.4955 <2e-16 ***
TREATMENT          4 0.78272 0.19568  28.4970 <2e-16 ***
THORAX:TREATMENT   4 0.04288 0.01072   1.5611 0.1894
Residuals        115 0.78967 0.00687
---
Signif. codes:  0 '***' 0.001 '**' 0.01 '*' 0.05 '.' 0.1 ' ' 1
```

Conclusions - There is no evidence that the slopes are not parallel ($F_{4,115} = 1.56, P = 0.182$).

- Additionally, each of the relationships between longevity and the covariate (thorax length), could be placed on the same graph to enable simple comparisons of slopes and covariate ranges.

```
> library(lattice)
> print(with(partridge, xyplot(log10(LONGEV) ~
+     THORAX, groups = TREATMENT, type = c("p",
+     "r"), col = 1, par.settings = list(superpose.symbol =
+     list(pch = 1:5, col = 1), superpose.line = list(lty =
+     1:6)), key = list(space = "right", lty = 1:5,
+         lines = T, points = T, pch = 1:5,
+         col = 1, text = list(levels(TREATMENT))))))
```

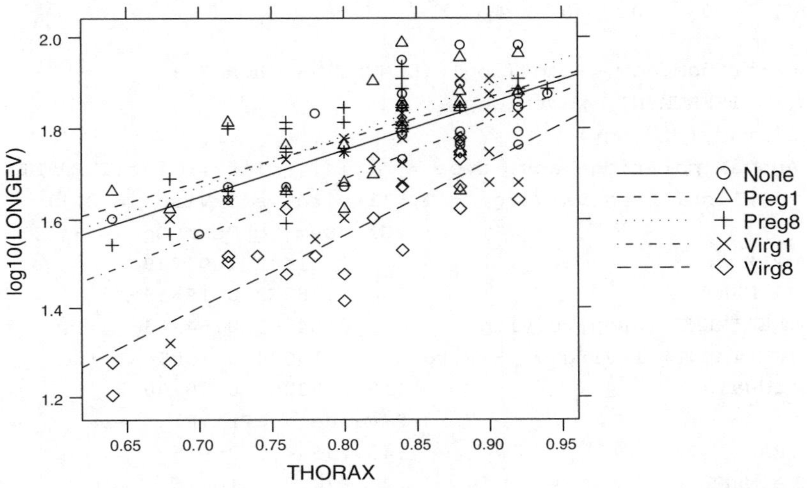

- Formally, the covariate range disparity can be tested by modelling the effect of the treatments on the covariate (thorax length)

```
> anova(aov(THORAX ~ TREATMENT, partridge))
Analysis of Variance Table

Response: THORAX
           Df  Sum Sq Mean Sq F value Pr(>F)
TREATMENT   4 0.03000 0.00750  1.2606 0.2893
Residuals 120 0.71389 0.00595
```

Conclusions - There is no evidence that the treatments affect male fruitfly thorax length and thus that the covariate ranges are not substantially different ($F_{4,120} = 1.26$, $P = 0.289$).

Step 4 (Key 15.3) - fit the linear model and produce an ANOVA table to test the null hypotheses that there are no effects of treatment (female type) on the (log transformed) longevity of male fruitflies adjusted for thorax length. Note that as the design is inherently imbalanced (since there is a different series of thorax lengths within each treatment type), Type I sums of squares are inappropriate. To be consistent with Quinn and Keough (2002) Box 12.1, Type III sums of squares will be used. In addition to the global ANCOVA, the researchers are likely to have been interested in examining a set of specific planned comparisons. Two such contrasts could be pregnant versus virgin partners (to investigate the impacts of any sexual activity) and one virgin versus eight virgin partners (to investigate the impacts of sexual frequency).

```
> # define contrasts
> contrasts(partridge$TREATMENT) <- cbind(c(0, 0.5, 0.5, -0.5,
+ -0.5), c(0, 0, 0, 1, -1))
> # confirm that contrasts orthogonal
> round(crossprod(contrasts(partridge$TREATMENT)), 1)
     [,1] [,2] [,3] [,4]
[1,]    1    0    0    0
[2,]    0    2    0    0
[3,]    0    0    1    0
[4,]    0    0    0    1

> partridge.aov <- aov(log10(LONGEV) ~ THORAX +
+     TREATMENT, partridge)
> library(biology)
> AnovaM(partridge.aov, type = "III", split = list(TREATMENT =
+     list('Preg vs Virg' = 1, '1 Virg vs 8 Virg' = 2)))
                                 Df  Sum Sq Mean Sq
THORAX                            1 1.01749 1.01749
TREATMENT                         4 0.78272 0.19568
  TREATMENT: Preg vs Virg         1 0.54203 0.54203
  TREATMENT: 1 Virg vs 8 Virg     1 0.19934 0.19934
Residuals                       119 0.83255 0.00700
                                F value    Pr(>F)
THORAX                          145.435 < 2.2e-16
TREATMENT                        27.970 2.231e-16
  TREATMENT: Preg vs Virg        77.474 1.269e-14
  TREATMENT: 1 Virg vs 8 Virg    28.492 4.567e-07
Residuals

THORAX                          ***
TREATMENT                       ***
  TREATMENT: Preg vs Virg       ***
  TREATMENT: 1 Virg vs 8 Virg ***
Residuals
---
Signif. codes:  0 '***' 0.001 '**' 0.01 '*' 0.05 '.' 0.1 ' ' 1
```

Conclusions - The reproductive status ($F_{1,119} = 77.47$, $P < 0.001$) and quantity ($F_{1,119} = 28.49$, $P < 0.001$) of female partners that a male fruitfly has access to has a significant affect on male longevity.

Step 5 - Summarize the trends in a plot. Note this is not the same as the plot produced by Quinn and Keough (2002) (Figure 12.3). Whilst Quinn and Keough (2002) logged $\log_{10}$ transformed data on the y-axis, I have elected to plot the raw data on a log-scale y-axis.

```
> # create the base blank plot
> plot(LONGEV ~ THORAX, partridge, type = "n", axes = F, xlab = "",
+ ylab = "", log = "y")
> xs <- seq(min(partridge$THORAX), max(partridge$THORAX), l = 1000)
> # plot the None series
> part.lm <- lm(LONGEV ~ THORAX, partridge, subset = TREATMENT ==
     "None")
> lines(xs, predict(part.lm, data.frame(THORAX = xs)), lty = 1)
> points(LONGEV ~ THORAX, partridge, subset = TREATMENT == "None",
+ type = "p", pch = 1)
> # plot the Preg1 series
> part.lm <- lm(LONGEV ~ THORAX, partridge, subset = TREATMENT ==
     "Preg1")
> lines(xs, predict(part.lm, data.frame(THORAX = xs)), lty = 2)
> points(LONGEV ~ THORAX, partridge, subset = TREATMENT == "Preg1",
+ type = "p", pch = 23, bg = "gray")
> # plot the Preg8 series
> part.lm <- lm(LONGEV ~ THORAX, partridge, subset = TREATMENT ==
     "Preg8")
> lines(xs, predict(part.lm, data.frame(THORAX = xs)), lty = 3)
> points(LONGEV ~ THORAX, partridge, subset = TREATMENT == "Preg8",
+ type = "p", pch = 24, bg = "gray")
> # plot the Virg1 series
> part.lm <- lm(LONGEV ~ THORAX, partridge, subset = TREATMENT ==
     "Virg1")
> lines(xs, predict(part.lm, data.frame(THORAX = xs)), lty = 4)
> points(LONGEV ~ THORAX, partridge, subset = TREATMENT == "Virg1",
+ type = "p", pch = 23, bg = "black")
> # plot the Virg8 series
> part.lm <- lm(LONGEV ~ THORAX, partridge, subset = TREATMENT ==
     "Virg8")
> lines(xs, predict(part.lm, data.frame(THORAX = xs)), lty = 5)
> points(LONGEV ~ THORAX, partridge, subset = TREATMENT == "Virg8",
+ type = "p", pch = 24, bg = "black")
> axis(1)
> mtext("Thorax length (mm)", 1, line = 3)
> axis(2, las = 1)
> mtext(expression(paste("Male fruitfly longevity (days)")), 2,
     line = 3)
> legend("bottomright", legend = c("None", "1 pregnant",
+ "8 pregnant", "1virgin", "8 virgin"), bty = "n", title =
+ "Treatment", lty = 1:6, pch = c(1, 23, 24, 23, 24),
+ pt.bg = c(1, "gray", "gray", 1, 1))
> box(bty = "l")
```

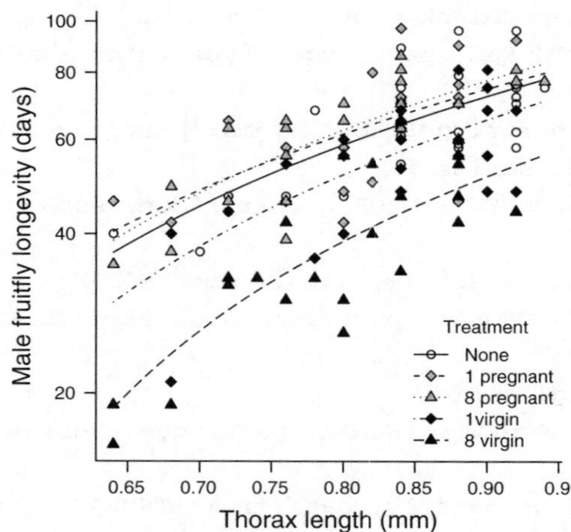

Example 15B: Single factor ANCOVA - nonparallel slopes

Constable (1993) compared the inter-radial suture widths of urchins maintained on one of three food regimes (Initial: no additional food supplied above what was in the initial sample, low: food supplied periodically and high: food supplied *ad libitum*). In an attempt to control for substantial variability in urchin sizes, the initial body volume of each urchin was measured as a covariate (from Box12.2 of Quinn and Keough (2002)).

Step 1 - Import (section 2.3) the Constable (1993) data set.

```
> constable <- read.table("constable.csv", header = T, sep = ",")
```

Step 2 (Key 15.1) - Assess assumptions of linearity and homogeneity of slopes.

```
> library(car)
> scatterplot(SUTW ~
+       IV | TREAT, constable)
```

```
> library(car)
> scatterplot(SUTW ~
+       I(IV^(1/3)) | TREAT,
+       constable)
```

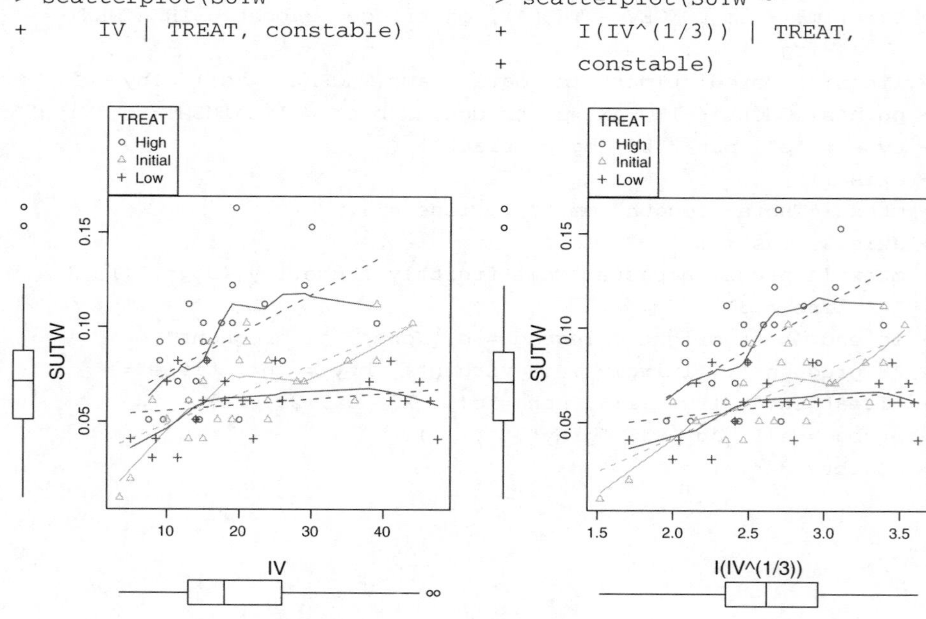

Conclusions - The relationship between suture width and initial volume shows some evidence of being non-linear. Linearity appears to be improved by a cube-root ($\sqrt[3]{}$) transformation, as is initial volume normality.

```
> library(lattice)
> print(with(constable, xyplot(SUTW ~ I(IV^(1/3)),
+     groups = TREAT, type = c("p", "r"), col = 1,
+     par.settings = list(superpose.symbol = list(pch = 1:3,
+         col = 1), superpose.line = list(lty = 1:3)),
+     key = list(space = "right", lty = 1:3, lines = T,
+         points = T, pch = 1:3, col = 1,
+         text = list(levels(TREAT))))))
```

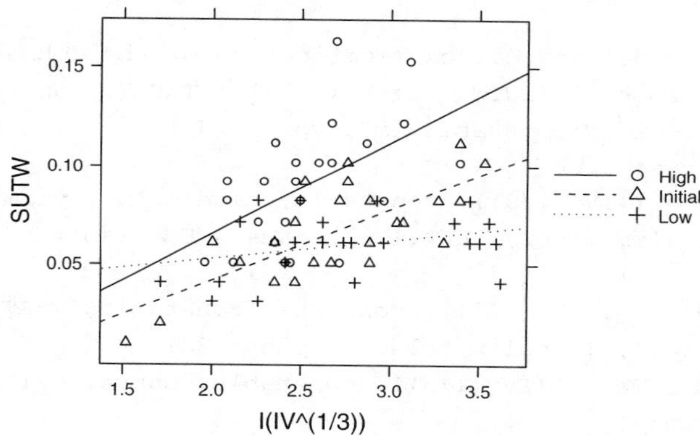


```
> anova(aov(SUTW ~ I(IV^(1/3)) * TREAT, constable))
Analysis of Variance Table

Response: SUTW
                  Df    Sum Sq   Mean Sq F value    Pr(>F)
I(IV^(1/3))        1 0.0065364 0.0065364 15.5799 0.0001945 ***
TREAT              2 0.0167503 0.0083752 19.9626 1.660e-07 ***
I(IV^(1/3)):TREAT  2 0.0039443 0.0019721  4.7007 0.0123436 *
Residuals         66 0.0276899 0.0004195
---
Signif. codes:  0 '***' 0.001 '**' 0.01 '*' 0.05 '.' 0.1 ' ' 1
```

Conclusions - There is clear evidence that the relationships between suture width and initial volume differ between the three food regimes (slopes are not parallel and a significant interaction between food treatment and initial volume). Regular ANCOVA is not appropriate.

Step 3 (Key 12.5cc) - Determine the regions of difference between each of the food regimes pairwise using the Wilcox modification of the Johnson-Newman procedure (with Games-Howell critical value approximation).

```
> library(biology)
> constable.lm <- lm(SUTW ~ I(IV^(1/3)) * TREAT, constable)
> wilcox.JN(constable.lm, type = "H")
```

```
                  df critical value     lower    upper
High vs Initial 37         3.867619  3.260903 2.187197
High vs Low     34         3.885401  6.595600 2.263724
Initial vs Low  43         3.839446 -1.547142 2.938749
```

Conclusions - Suture widths on a high food diet were greater than on initial diet for body volumes greater than 10.5 (2.19^3) ml and greater than a low food diet for body volumes greater than 11.6 (2.26^3), the latter of which was also lower than on initial diet for body volumes greater than 25.4 (2.94^3).

Step 4 (Key 12.18) - Summarize the trends in a plot. Bars at the bottom of the plot indicate Wilcox pairwise simultaneous regions of differences. Regions are capped to the data range. Note this plot also illustrates the use of Hershey fonts for special symbols (in this case a star).

```
> # fit the model and Wilcox modification of the Johnson-Newman
> constable.lm <- lm(SUTW ~ I(IV^(1/3)) * TREAT, constable)
> WJN <- wilcox.JN(constable.lm, type = "H")
> # create base plot
> plot(SUTW ~ I(IV^(1/3)), constable, type = "n", ylim = c(0,
+     0.2), xlim = c(3, 50)^(1/3), axes = F, xlab = "",
+     ylab = "")
> points(SUTW ~ I(IV^(1/3)), constable[constable$TREAT ==
+     "Initial", ], col = "black", pch = 22)
> lm1 <- lm(SUTW ~ I(IV^(1/3)), constable, subset = TREAT ==
+     "Initial")
> abline(lm1, col = "black", lty = 1)
> points(SUTW ~ I(IV^(1/3)), constable[constable$TREAT ==
+     "Low", ], col = "black", pch = 17)
> lm2 <- lm(SUTW ~ I(IV^(1/3)), constable, subset = TREAT ==
+     "Low")
> abline(lm2, col = "black", lty = 4)
> with(constable[constable$TREAT == "High", ], text(SUTW ~
+     I(IV^(1/3)), "\\#H0844", vfont = c("serif", "plain")))
> lm3 <- lm(SUTW ~ I(IV^(1/3)), constable, subset = TREAT ==
+     "High")
> abline(lm3, col = "black", lty = 2)
> axis(1, lab = c(10, 20, 30, 40, 50), at = c(10, 20,
+     30, 40, 50)^(1/3))
> axis(2, las = 1)
> mtext("Initial body volume (ml)", 1, line = 3)
> mtext("Suture width (mm)", 2, line = 3)
> Mpar <- par(family = "HersheySans", font = 2)
> library(biology)
> # the legend.vfont function facilitates Hershey fonts
> legend.vfont("topleft", c("\\#H0841 Initial", "\\#H0844 High",
+     "\\#H0852 Low"), bty = "n", lty = c(1, 2, 3),
+     merge = F, title = "Food regime", vfont = c("serif",
```

```
+         "plain"))
> par(Mpar)
> box(bty = "l")
> mn <- min(constable$IV^(1/3))
> mx <- max(constable$IV^(1/3))
> # since lower<upper (lines cross within the range - two regions
> # of significance (although one is outside data range))
> # region capped to the data range
> arrows(WJN[3, 4], 0, mx, 0, ang = 90, length = 0.05,
+     code = 3)
> text(mean(c(WJN[3, 4], mx)), 0.003, rownames(WJN)[3])
> # since lower>upper (lines cross outside data range
> # region capped to the data range if necessary
> arrows(min(WJN[2, 3], mx), 0.01, max(WJN[2, 4], mn),
+     0.01, ang = 90, length = 0.05, code = 3)
> text(mean(c(min(WJN[2, 3], mx), max(WJN[2, 4], mn))),
+     0.013, rownames(WJN)[2])
> # since lower>upper (lines cross outside data range
> # region capped to the data range if necessary
> arrows(min(WJN[1, 3], mx), 0.02, max(WJN[1, 4], mn),
+     0.02, ang = 90, length = 0.05, code = 3)
> text(mean(c(min(WJN[1, 3], mx), max(WJN[1, 4], mn))),
+     0.023, rownames(WJN)[1])
```

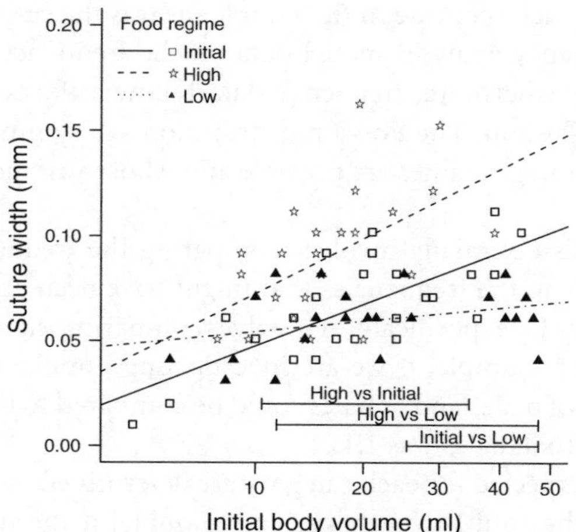

16

Simple Frequency Analysis

The analyses described in previous chapters have all involved response variables that implicitly represent normally distributed and continuous population responses. In this context, continuous indicates that (at least in theory), any value of measurement[a] down to an infinite number of decimal places is possible. Population responses can also be categorical such that the values could be logically or experimentally constrained to a set number of discrete possibilities. For example, individuals in a population can be categorized as either male or female, reaches in a stream could be classified as either riffles, runs or pools and salinity levels of sites might be categorized as either high, medium or low.

Typically, categorical response variables are tallied up to generate the frequency of replicates in each of the possible categories. From above, we would tally up the frequency of males and females, the number of riffles, runs and pools and the high, medium and low salinity sites. Hence, rather than model data in which a response was measured from each replicate in the sample (as was the case for previous analyses in this book), frequency analyses model data on the frequency of replicates in each possible category. Furthermore, frequency data follow a Poisson distribution rather than a normal distribution. The Poisson distribution is a symmetrical distribution in which only discrete integer values are possible and whose variance is equal to its mean (see Figure 16.1).

Frequency analysis essentially involves comparing the frequency of each category observed in a sample to the frequencies that might have been expected according to a particular scenario[b]. More specifically, it involves comparing the observed and expected frequency ratios. For example, if we are investigating population gender parity, the observed frequency of males and females could be compared to the frequency expected if the ratio of males to females was 1:1.

The frequencies expected for each category are determined by the size of the sample and the nature of the (null) hypothesis. For example, if the null hypothesis is that there are three times as many females as males in a population (ratio of 3:1), then a

[a] The term measurement is being used to refer to the characteristic of individual observations or replicates. Therefore a measurement could be a linear measure, a density, a count, etc.
[b] Dictated by the null hypothesis - see sections 16.2.2 and 16.2.2.

Biostatistical Design and Analysis Using R: a Practical Guide, 1st edition. By M. Logan.
Published 2010 by Blackwell Publishing.

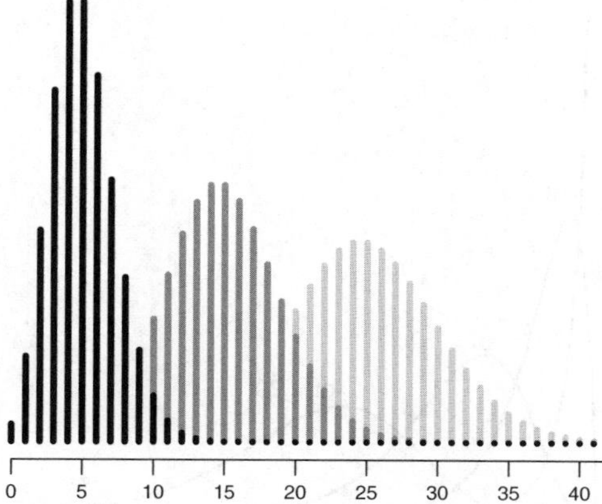

Fig 16.1 Poisson sampling distributions. The mean and variance of a Poisson distribution are equal and thus distributions with higher expected values are shorter and wider than those with smaller means. Note that a Poisson distribution with an expected less than less than 5 will be obviously asymmetrical as a Poisson distribution is bounded to the left by zero. This has important implications for the reliability of frequency analyses when sample sizes are low.

sample of 110 individuals would be expected to yield $0.75 * 110 = 82.5$ females and $0.25 * 110 = 27.5$ males.

16.1 The chi-square statistic

The degree of difference between the observed (o) and expected (e) sample category frequencies is represented by the chi-square (χ^2) statistic.

$$\chi^2 = \sum \frac{(o - e)^2}{e}$$

This is a relative measure that is standardized by the magnitude of the expected frequencies. When the null hypothesis is true (typically this represents the situation when there are no effects or patterns of interest in the population response category frequencies), and we have sampled in an unbiased manner, we might expect the observed category frequencies in the sample to be very similar (if not equal) to the expected frequencies and thus, the chi-square value should be close to zero. Likewise, repeated sampling from such a population is likely to yield chi-square values close to zero and large chi-square values should be relatively rare. As such, the chi-square statistic approximately follows a χ^2 distribution (see Figure 16.2), a mathematical probability distribution representing the frequency (and thus probability) of all possible ranges of chi-square statistics that could result when the null hypothesis is true.

The χ^2 distribution is an asymmetrical distribution bounded by zero and infinity and whose exact shape is determined by the degrees of freedom (calculated as the total

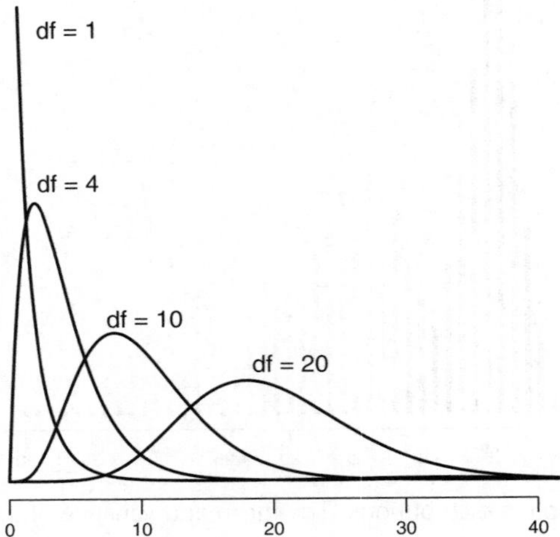

Fig 16.2 χ^2 probability distributions for a range of degrees of freedom. The expected value of the distribution is equal to the degrees of freedom. At low degrees of freedom, the χ^2 distribution is highly asymmetrical and approaches a more symmetrical shape with increasing degrees of freedom.

number of categories minus 1[c]). Note also that the peak of a chi-square distribution is not actually at zero (although it does approach it when the degrees of freedom is equal to zero). Initially, this might seem counter intuitive. We might expect that when a null hypothesis is true, the most common chi-square value will be zero. However, the χ^2 distribution takes into account the expected natural variability in a population as well as the nature of sampling (in which multiple samples should yield slightly different results). The more categories there are, the more likely that the observed and expected values will differ. It could be argued that when there are a large number of categories, samples in which all the observed frequencies are very close to the expected frequencies are a little suspicious and may represent dishonesty on the part of the researcher[d].

By comparing any given sample chi-square statistic to its appropriate χ^2 distribution, the probability that the observed category frequencies could have be collected from a population with a specific ratio of frequencies (for example 3:1) can be estimated. As is the case for most hypothesis tests, probabilities lower than 0.05 (5%) are considered unlikely and suggest that the sample is unlikely to have come from a population characterized by the null hypothesis. Chi-squared tests are typically one-tailed tests focussing on the right-hand tail as we are primarily interested in the probability of obtaining large chi-square values. Nevertheless, it is also possible to focus on the left-hand tail so as to investigate whether the observed values are "too good to be true".

[c] Recall that degrees of freedom is a measure of how many values are free to vary when determining independent estimates of parameters. Since estimations of the expected frequencies require multiplication by the total frequencies (which thereby include each of the category frequencies), not all of the frequencies are free to vary.

[d] Indeed the extraordinary conformity of Gregor Mendel's pea experiments have been subjected to such skepticism.

16.1.1 Assumptions

A chi-square statistic will follow a χ^2 distribution approximately provided;

(i) All observations are classified independently of one another. The classification of one replicate should not be influenced by or related to the classification of other replicates. Random sampling should address this.

(ii) No more than 20% of the expected frequencies are less than five. χ^2 distributions do not reliably approximate the distribution of all possible chi-square values under those circumstances[e]. Since the expected values are a function of sample sizes, meeting this assumption is a matter of ensuring sufficient replication. When sample sizes or other circumstances beyond control lead to a violation of this assumption, numerous options are available (see section 16.5)

16.2 Goodness of fit tests

16.2.1 Homogeneous frequencies tests

Homogeneous frequencies tests (often referred to as goodness of fit tests) are used to test null hypotheses that the category frequencies observed within a single variable could arise from a population displaying a specific ratio of frequencies. The null hypothesis (H_0) is that the observed frequencies come from a population with a specific ratio of frequencies.

16.2.2 Distributional conformity - Kolmogorov-Smirnov tests

Strictly, goodness of fit tests are used to examine whether a frequency/sampling distribution is homogeneous with some declared distribution. For example, we might use a goodness of fit test to formally investigate whether the distribution of a response variable deviates substantially from a normal distribution. In this case, frequencies of responses in a set of pre-defined bin ranges are compared to those frequencies expected according to the mathematical model of a normal distribution. Since calculations of these expected frequencies also involve estimates of population mean and variance (both required to determine the mathematical formula), a two degree of freedom loss is incurred (hence $df = n - 2$).

16.3 Contingency tables

Contingency tables are used to investigate the associations between two or more categorical variables. That is, they test whether the patterns of frequencies in one categorical variable differ between different levels of other categorical variable(s) or

[e] Expected frequencies less than five result in asymmetrical sampling distributions (since they must be truncated at zero) and thus potentially unrepresentative χ^2 distributions.

could the variables be independent of another. In this way, they are analogous to interactions in factorial linear models (such as factorial ANOVA).

Contingency tables test the null hypothesis (H_0) that the categorical variables are independent of (not associated with) one another. Note that analyses of contingency tables do not empirically distinguish between response and predictor variables (analogous to correlation), yet causality can be implied when logical and justified by interpretation. As an example, contingency tables could be used to investigate whether incidences of hair and eye color in a population are associated with one another (is one hair color type more commonly observed with a certain eye color). In this case, neither hair color nor eye color influence one another, their incidences are both controlled by a separate set of unmeasured factors. By contrast, an association between the presence or absence of a species of frog and the level of salinity (high, medium or low) could imply that salinity effects the distribution of that species of frog - but not vice versa.

Sample replicates are cross-classified according to the levels (categories) of multiple categorical variables. The data are conceptualized as a table (hence the name) with the rows representing the levels of one variable and the column the levels of the other variable(s) such that the cells represent the category combinations. The expected frequency of any given cell is calculated as:

$$\frac{(\textit{row total}) \times (\textit{column total})}{\textit{grand total}}$$

Thereafter, the chi-square calculations are calculated as described above and the chi-square value is compared to a χ^2 distribution with $(r-1)(c-1)$ degrees of freedom.

Contingency tables involving more than two variables have multiple interaction levels and thus multiple potential sources of independence. For example, in a three-way contingency table between variables A, B and C, there are four interactions (A:B, A:C, B:C and A:B:C). Such designs are arguably more appropriately analysed using log-linear models (see section 17.3.2).

16.3.1 Odds ratios

The chi-square test provides an indication of whether or not the occurrences in one set of categories are likely to be associated with other sets of categories (an interaction between two or more categorical variables), yet does not provide any indication of how strongly the variables are associated (magnitude of the effect). Furthermore, for variables with more than two categories (e.g. high, medium, low), there is no indication of which category combinations contribute most to the associations. This role is provided by odds ratios which are essentially a measure of effect size.

Odds refer to the likelihood of a specific event or outcome occurring (such as the odds of a species being present) versus the even of it not occurring (and thus the occurrence of an alternative outcome) and are calculated as $\pi_j/(1-\pi_j)$ where π_j refers to the probability of the event occurring. For example we could calculate the odds of frogs being present in highly saline habitats as the probability of frogs being present divided by the probability of them being absent. Similarly, we could calculate the likelihood of frog presence (odds) within low salinity habitats.

The ratio of two of these likelihoods (odds ratio) can then be used to compare whether the likelihood of one outcome (frog presence) is the same for both categories (salinity levels). For example, is the likelihood of frogs being present in highly saline habitats the same as the probability of them being present in habitats with low levels of salinity. Although odds and thus odds ratios (θ) are technically derived from probabilities, they can also be estimated using cell frequencies (n).

$$\theta = \frac{n_{11}n_{22}}{n_{12}n_{21}} \quad \text{or alternatively}$$

$$\theta = \frac{(n_{11} + 0.5)(n_{22} + 0.5)}{(n_{12} + 0.5)(n_{21} + 0.5)}$$

where 0.5 is a small constant added to prevent division by zero. An odds ratio of one indicates that the event or occurance (presence of frogs) is equally likely in both categories (high and low salinity habitats). Odds ratios greater than one signify that the event or occurance is more likely in the first than second category and *vice versa* for odds ratios less than one. For example, when comparing the presence/absence of frogs in low versus high salinity habitats, a odds ratio of 5.8 would suggest that frogs are 5.8 times more likely to be present in low salinity habitats than those that highly saline.

The distribution of odds ratios (which range from 0 to ∞) is not symmetrical around the null possition (1) thereby precluding confidence interval and standard error calculations. Instead, these measures are calculated from log transformed (natural log) odds ratios (the distribution of which is a standard normal distribution centered around 0) and then converted back into a linear scale by anti-logging.

Odds ratios can only be calculated between category pairs from two variables and therefore 2×2 contingency tables (tables with only two rows and two columns). However, tables with more rows and columns can be accommodate by splitting the table up into **partial tables** of specific category pair combinations. Odds ratios (and confidence intervals) are then calculated from each pairing, nothwithstanding their lack of independence. For example, if there were three levels of salinity (high, medium and low), the odds ratios from three partial tables (high vs medium, high vs low, medium vs low) could be calculated.

Multi-way tables

Since odds ratios only explore pairwise patterns within two-way interactions, odds ratios for multi-way (three or more variables) tables are considerably more complex to calculate and interpret. Partial tables between two of the variables (e.g frog presence/absence and high/low salinity) are constructed for each level of a third (season: summer/winter). This essentially removes the effect of the third variable by holding it constant. Associations in partial tables are therefore referred to as *conditional associations*-since the outcomes (associated or independent) from each partial table are explicitly conditional on the level of the third variable at which they were tested.

Interpretation of odds ratios from three-way tables are summarised as:

- The odds ratios of partial tables (between X and Y) are the same for each level of Z and implies that the degree of association between X and Y (or effect of X on Y) is the same at all levels of Z. This is referred to as *homogeneous association* and is indicative of an absence of a three-way interaction.
- The odds ratios of partial tables (between X and Y) are all equal to 1 for each level of Z. This is a special case of homogeneous association referred to as *conditionally independence*. It implies that X and Y are not associated (independent) at all levels of Z.
- The odds ratios of partial tables (between X and Y) differ between the levels of Z implying that the degree of association between X and Y is not consistent across the levels of Z. This is equivalent to a three-way interaction between X, Y and Z.

16.3.2 Residuals

Specific contributions to a lack of independence (significant associations) can also be investigated by exploring the residuals. Recall that residuals are the difference between the observed values (frequencies) and those predicted or expected when the null hypothesis is true (no association between variables). Hence the magnitude of each residual indicates how much each of the cross classification combinations differs from what is expected. The residuals are typically standardized (by dividing by the square of the expected frequencies)[f] to enable individual residuals to be compared relative to one another. Large residuals (in magnitude) indicate large deviations from what is expected when the null hypothesis is true and thus also indicate large influences (contributions) to the overall association. The sign (+ or −) of the residual indicates whether the frequencies were higher or lower than expected.

16.4 G-tests

An alternative to the chi-square test for goodness of fit and contingency table analyses is the G-test. The G-test is based on a log likelihood-ratio test. A log likelihood ratio is a ratio of maximum likelihoods[g] of the alternative and null hypotheses. More simply, a log likelihood ratio test essentially examines how likely (the probability) the alternative hypothesis (representing an effect) is compared to how likely the null hypothesis (no effect) is given the collected data.

The G^2 statistic is calculated as:

$$G^2 = 2\sum o.ln\left(\frac{o}{e}\right)$$

where o and e are the observed and expected sample category frequencies respectively and ln denotes the natural logarithm (base e).

[f] Residuals can also be adjusted by dividing each residual by the square roots of the expected frequency as well as the observed frequency expressed as proportions of row and column totals.

[g] Recall that maximum likelihood refers to the maximum probability of obtaining a particular outcome given the observed data (see section 3.7.2).

When the null hypothesis is true, the G^2 statistic approximately follows a theoretical χ^2 distribution with the same degrees of freedom as the corresponding chi-square statistic. The G^2 statistic (which is twice the value of the log-likelihood ratio) is arguably more appropriate than the chi-square statistic as it is closely aligned with the theoretical basis of the χ^2 distribution (for which the chi-squared statistic is a convenient approximation). For large sample sizes, G^2 and χ^2 statistics are equivalent, however the former is a better approximation of the theoretical χ^2 distribution when the difference between the observed and expected is less than the expected frequencies (ie $|o - e| < e$). Nevertheless, G-tests operate under the same assumptions are the chi-square statistic and thus very small sample sizes (expected values less than 5) are still problematic. G-tests have the additional advantage that they can be used additively with more complex designs and a thus more extensible than the chi-squared statistic.

16.5 Small sample sizes

As discussed previously, both the χ^2 and G^2 statistics are poor approximations of theoretical χ^2 distributions when sample sizes are very small. Under these circumstances a number of alternative options are available:

(i) If the issue has arisen due to a large number of category levels in one or more of the variables, some categories could be combined together.

(ii) Fishers exact test[h] which essentially calculates the probability of obtaining the cell frequencies given the observed marginal totals in 2 × 2 tables. The calculations involved in such tests are extremely tedious as they involve calculating probabilities from hypergeometric distributions (discrete distributions describing the number of successes from sequences of samples drawn without replacement) for all combinations of cell values that result in the given marginal totals.

(iii) Yates' continuity correction calculates the test statistic after adding and subtracting 0.5 from observed values less than and greater than expected values respectively. Yates' correction can only be applied to designs with a single degree of freedom (goodness-of-fit designs with two categories or 2 × 2 tables) and for goodness-of-fit tests provide p-values that are closer to those of an exact binomial. However, they typically yield over inflated p-values in contingency tables.

(iv) Williams' correction is applied by dividing the test statistic by

$$1 + (p^2 - 1)6nv$$

where p is the number of categories, n is the total sample size (total of observed frequencies) and v is the number of degrees of freedom ($p - 1$). Williams' corrections can be applied to designs with greater than one degree of freedom, and are considered marginally more appropriate than Yates' corrections if corrections are insisted.

(v) Randomization tests in which the sample test statistic (either χ^2 or G^2) is compared to a probability distribution generated by repeatedly calculating the test statistic from an

[h] So called because as resulting p-values and assumptions are exact rather than approximated.

equivalent number of observations drawn from a population (sampling with replacement) with the specific ratio of category frequencies defined by the null hypothesis. Significance is thereafter determined by the proportion of the randomized test statistic values that are greater than or equal to the value of the statistic that is based on observed data.

(vi) Log-linear modelling (see section 16.6)

16.6 Alternatives

The χ^2 statistic has many limitations when applied to contingency table analyses (particularly concerning the testing and interpretation of interactions) and these issues are exacerbated with increasing numbers of categories and variables. Log-linear models are considered more appropriate than traditional chi-square statistics for analyzing contingency tables (particularly for multiway tables). Briefly, log-linear models (see section 17.3.2 for more complete treatment) are a form of generalized linear model in which the (natural log) expected frequencies of the category combinations (cells of the contingency table) are modelled against a combination of categorical variables around a Poisson distribution of residuals. This approach is analogous to analysis of variance, and thus, both individual and interaction effects can be estimated[i].

16.7 Power analysis

Power analyses are most usefully performed to provide an estimate of the sample size required to pick up a particular pattern (significant departure of category frequencies from the null hypothesis). Hence, in order to perform a power analysis, it is necessary to first define one or more possible patterns (effect sizes). To do so, we consider what percentage deviation from the null pattern would be considered biologically important and use these deviations to generate possible data sets that represent alternative hypotheses and thus effect sizes.

The overall effect size (w_s) is expressed as a standardized difference between the hypothetical proportions reflecting alternate and null hypotheses:

$$w_s = \sqrt{\sum \frac{(P_A - P_0)^2}{P_0}}$$

where P_A and P_0 represent the proportions expected according to the alternate and null hypotheses respectively. Note that this is just the square root of the χ^2 statistic comparing the alternate hypothesis frequencies to the null hypothesis frequencies. Note also that since mean and variance are related, power analysis calculations do not require estimates of population variation. Although power analysis is only available for χ^2 tests, since χ^2 and G-tests essentially approximate the same thing, the estimates based on χ^2 test should be equally appropriate for G-tests.

[i] Parameters are estimated by maximum likelihood and hypothesis tests are performed by comparing the fit (as measured by log-likelihood) of appropriate sets of full and reduced models.

16.8 Simple frequency analysis in R

Chi-square analysis for both goodness-of-fit and contingency analyses are accommodated by the `chisq.test()` *function.* Kolmogorov-Smirnov tests of distributional conformity are accomodated via the `ks.test()` *function.* G-tests are performed using the `g.test()`[j] *function.*

16.9 Further reading

- Theory

Fowler, J., L. Cohen, and P. Jarvis. (1998). *Practical statistics for field biology.* John Wiley & Sons, England.

Quinn, G. P., and K. J. Keough. (2002). *Experimental design and data analysis for biologists.* Cambridge University Press, London.

Sokal, R., and F. J. Rohlf. (1997). *Biometry, 3rd edition.* W. H. Freeman, San Francisco.

Zar, G. H. (1999). *Biostatistical methods.* Prentice-Hall, New Jersey.

- Practical - R

Crawley, M. J. (2007). *The R Book.* John Wiley, New York.

Dalgaard, P. (2002). *Introductory Statistics with R.* Springer-Verlag, New York.

Venables, W. N., and B. D. Ripley. (2002). *Modern Applied Statistics with S-PLUS,* 4th edn. Springer-Verlag, New York.

16.10 Key for Analysing frequencies

1 a. **Sampling units classified by a single category** .... Go to 2

b. **Sampling units cross classified according to multiple categories - tests of association (Continguency tables)** .... Go to 3

2 a. **Expected frequencies calculated from sample data according to a theoretical ratio (Homogeneous frequencies, chi-square test)** .... See Example 16A

```
> chisq.test(c(C1, C2, ..))
> # OR
> chisq.test(data.xtab)
```

where `C1, C2,..` *are the tabulated counts (frequencies) of each classification and* `data.xtab` *is a table of observed values.*

- To check assumption that no more than 20% of expected frequencies are less than 5, append the above function with `$exp`, e.g. `chisq.test(data.xtab)$exp`
- To specify an alternative ratio of expected values, use the `p=c()` argument
- To perform G-tests, use the `g.test()` function in the `biology` package ..... See Example 16B

[j] Pete Hurd provides R syntax for a version of a `g.test` on his web page http://wwwych.ualberta.ca/phurd/cruft/. I have included his function within the `biology` *package.*

b. Expected frequencies calculated from a mathematical model representing a distribution (Goodness of fit test - Kolmogorov-Smirnov test)

```
> ks.test(DV, DIST, ...)
> # OR
> ks.test(DV, "dist", ...)
> # For example
> ks.test(DV, "pnorm", mean(DV), sd(DV))
```

where DV is the name of the dependent variable. The second argument is either a numeric vector (`DIST`*) representing the distribution to compare the dependent variable to, or else a character string (*`"dist"`*) representing the cummulative distribution function (as illustrated for a normal distribution above). The third and forth arguments in the above example provide parameters to the cummulative distribution function.*

3 a. Two way contingency table .... Go to 4

b. Three or more way contingency table (consider GLM as an alternative) .... Go to Chapter 17

4 a. Check the assumption that no more than 20% of expected frequencies are less than 5. .... See Example 16C

```
> chisq.test(data.xtab, corr = F)$exp
```

Assumption met .... Go to 5a

b. Assumption not met .... Go to 5b

5 a. Analyse contingency table using chi-square test - all expected values greater than 5 .... See Example 16C

```
> chisq.test(data.xtab, corr = F)
```

- To perform G-tests, use the `g.test()` function in the `biology` package ..... See Example 16B

If null hypothesis is rejected

- Examine the residuals .... See Example 16C
  Append the above function with `$res`,
  e.g. `chisq.test(data.xtab,corr=F)$res`
- Examine odds ratios .... Go to 6
- To construct a summary figure .... Go to 7

b. Analyse contingency table using Fishers exact test

```
> fisher.test(data.xtab)
```

If null hypothesis is rejected

- Examine odds ratios .... Go to 6
- To construct a summary figure .... Go to 7

6 Calculate odds ratios .... See Example 16C

```
> library(biology)
> oddsratios(data.xtab)
```

7 a. Structure plot - summary figure .... See Example 16C

```
> library(vcd)
> strucplot(data.xtab, shade = T)
```

16.11 Worked examples of real biological data sets

Example 16A: Goodness of fit test - homogeneous frequencies test

Zar (1999) presented a dataset that depicted the classification of 250 plants into one of four categories on the basis of seed type (yellow smooth, yellow wrinkled, green smooth and green wrinkled). Zar (1999) used these data to test the null hypothesis that the sample came from a population that had a 9:3:3:1 ratio of these seed types (Example 22.2).

Step 1 - Create a dataframe with the Zar (1999) seeds data

```
> COUNT <- c(152, 39, 53, 6)
> TYPE <- gl(4, 1, 4, c("YellowSmooth", "YellowWrinkled",
+      "GreenSmooth", "GreenWrinkled"))
> seeds <- data.frame(TYPE, COUNT)
```

Step 2 - Convert the seeds dataframe into a table. Whilst this step is not strictly necessary, it does ensure that columns in various tabular outputs have meaningful names.

```
> seeds.xtab <- xtabs(COUNT ~ TYPE, seeds)
```

Step 3 (Key 16.2) - Assess the assumption of sufficient sample size ($\leq$ 20% of expected values $<$ 5) for the specified null hypothesis.

```
> chisq.test(seeds.xtab, p = c(9/16, 3/16, 3/16, 1/16),
      correct = F)$exp
 YellowSmooth YellowWrinkled    GreenSmooth  GreenWrinkled
      140.625         46.875         46.875         15.625
```

Conclusions - all expected values are greater than 5, therefore the chi-squared statistic is likely to be a reliable approximation of the χ^2 distribution.

Step 4 (Key 16.2) - Test the null hypothesis that the sample could have come from a population with a 9:3:3:1 seed type ratio. Yates' continuity correction is not required (`correct=F`).

```
> chisq.test(seeds.xtab, p = c(9/16, 3/16, 3/16, 1/16),
      correct = F)
       Chi-squared test for given probabilities

data:  seeds.xtab
X-squared = 8.9724, df = 3, p-value = 0.02966
```

Conclusions - reject the H_0. The samples are unlikely to have come from a population with a 9:3:3:1 ratio

Example 16B: G-test for goodness of fit test - homogeneous frequencies test

Smith (1939) crossed a complex combination of two varieties of beans yielding a total of 241 progeny across eight phenotypes. Mendelian theory should have resulted in phenotypic ratios of 18:6:6:2:12:4:12:4. Sokal and Rohlf (1997) used these data to test the null hypothesis that the observed frequencies could have come from a population with a 18:6:6:2:12:4:12:4 phenotypic ratio (Box 11.1).

Step 1 - Create a dataframe with the Smith (1939) beans data

```
> COUNT <- c(63, 31, 28, 12, 39, 16, 40, 12)
> PHENOTYPE <- gl(8, 1, 8, c("Pt", "Pt", "Rb", "Rt", "P", "O",
+     "B", "T"))
> beans <- data.frame(PHENOTYPE, COUNT)
```

Step 2 - Convert the beens dataframe into a table so as to allow for more meaningful output.

```
> beans.xtab <- xtabs(COUNT ~ PHENOTYPE, beans)
```

Step 3 - Define the expected probabilities based on the null hypothesis

```
> H0 <- c(18, 6, 6, 2, 12, 4, 12, 4)
> H0.prob <- H0/sum(H0)
```

Step 4 (Key 16.2) - Assess the assumption of sufficient sample size ($\leq$ 20% of expected values $<$ 5) for the specified null hypothesis.

```
> library(biology)
> g.test(beans.xtab, p = H0.prob)$exp
      Pt       Pt       Rb       Rt        P        O        B        T
67.78125 22.59375 22.59375  7.53125 45.18750 15.06250 45.18750 15.06250
```

Conclusions - all expected values are greater than 5, therefore the chi-squared and G-statistics are likely to be a reliable approximation of the χ^2 distribution. As one of the expected frequencies is close to 5 it could be argued that the G-statistic will more closely approximate the χ^2 distribution.

Step 5 (Key 16.2) - Test the null hypothesis that the sample could have come from a population with a 18:6:6:2:12:4:12:4 seed type ratio. As one of the expected values is close to 5, we will apply a Williams' correction - although this is unlikely to make much of a difference.

```
> g.test(beans.xtab, p = H0.prob, correct = "williams")
        Log likelihood ratio (G-test) goodness of fit test

data:  beans.xtab
Log likelihood ratio statistic (G) = 8.7694, X-squared df = 7,
p-value = 0.2696
```

Conclusions - do not reject the H_0. There is no evidence to suggest that the samples didn't come from a population with a 18:6:6:2:12:4:12:4 phenotypic ratio.

Example 16C: Two-way contingency table

In order to investigate the mortality of coolibah (*Eucalyptus coolibah*) trees across riparian dunes, Roberts (1993) counted the number of quadrats in which dead trees were present and the number in which they were absent in three positions (top, middle and bottom) along transects from the lakeshore up to the top of dunes. In this case, the classification of quadrats according to the presence/absence of dead coolibah trees will be interpreted as a response variable and the position along transect as a predictor variable (see Box 14.3 of Quinn and Keough (2002)).

Step 1 - Import (section 2.3) the Roberts (1993) data set[k].

```
> roberts <- read.table("roberts.csv", header = T, sep = ",")
```

Note that this data set contains the uncollated raw data (cross-classification of each quadrat).

Step 2 - Convert the dataframe into a collated table in preparation for contingency table analysis

```
> roberts.xtab <- table(roberts$POSITION, roberts$DEAD)
> #OR alternatively
> roberts.xtab <- with(roberts, table(POSITION, DEAD))
> roberts.xtab
         DEAD
POSITION With Without
  Bottom   15      13
  Middle    4       8
  Top       0      17
```

Step 3 (Key 16.4b) - Assess the assumption of sufficient sample size ($\leq$ 20% of expected values $<$ 5) for the specified null hypothesis.

```
> chisq.test(roberts.xtab, corr = F)$exp
         DEAD
POSITION      With  Without
  Bottom 9.333333 18.66667
  Middle 4.000000  8.00000
  Top    5.666667 11.33333
```

Conclusions - only one (1/6 = 16.67%) of the expected values are less than 5, therefore the χ^2 statistic should be a reasonably reliable approximation of the χ^2 distribution. Nevertheless, G-test will also be performed to confirm the outcome.

Step 4 (Key 16.5) - Test the null hypothesis that there is no association between the presence/absence of dead coolibah trees and position along transect.

```
> chisq.test(roberts.xtab, corr = F)
        Pearson's Chi-squared test

data:  roberts.xtab
X-squared = 13.6607, df = 2, p-value = 0.001080
> library(biology)
> g.test(roberts.xtab, corr = "williams")
```

[k] Note that for such a small dataset, it is also possible to tally the data up and enter it directly into a dataframe, however, in the interests of illustrating computer tallying, we will import the full data set containing the classification of each replicate.

```
        Log likelihood ratio (G-test) test of independence with
        Williams' correction

data:  roberts.xtab
Log likelihood ratio statistic (G) = 17.7815, X-squared df = 2,
p-value = 0.0001377
```

Conclusions - the null hypothesis of no association would be rejected via both the χ^2 test and the G-test. The mortality of coolibah trees was found to be significantly associated to position along lakeside-dune transects ($\chi^2 = 13.67$, $df = 2$, $P = 0.001$).

Step 5 (Key 16.5) - Explore the pattern of standardized residuals to reveal which cross classifications deviate greatest from the expected values and thus contribute greatest to the lack of independence between coolibah mortality and transect position.

```
> chisq.test(roberts.xtab, corr = F)$res
        DEAD
POSITION        With    Without
  Bottom   1.854852 -1.311578
  Middle   0.000000  0.000000
  Top     -2.380476  1.683251
```

Conclusions - clearly there were fewer quadrats at the bottom of the transects with dead coolibah trees (and more at the top of the transects) than would be expected if there was no association. This implies that coolibah mortality is greatest further up the dunes.

Step 6 (Key 16.6) - Explore the odds ratios to statistically compare the death of coolibah trees between each pairing of the transect positions. Note, we will use the modified Wald's odds ratio calculations that correct (by adding 0.5) for the impacts of observed frequencies of zero. Note also that since odds ratios can only be calculated for 2 × 2 tables, odds ratios must be calculated in a number of steps.

```
> library(biology)
> oddsratios(roberts.xtab + 0.5)
         Comparison  estimate     lower      upper   midp.exact
1 Bottom vs Middle  2.168724 0.5590128   8.413699 2.675536e-01
2    Bottom vs Top 40.185185 2.2016841 733.460860 6.449331e-05
3    Middle vs Top 18.529412 0.8912652 385.226628 1.806240e-02
  fisher.exact   chi.square
1 0.3147544186 0.2585776014
2 0.0000805218 0.0003656938
3 0.0180623974 0.0173950255
```

Conclusions - the odds of having dead coolibah trees is significantly higher at the top of the transect than the bottom (95% CI 2.2-733.5) or to a lesser degree, the middle (95% CI 0.9-385.2) of the transect.

Step 7 (Key 16.7) - Summarize the findings with a mosaic plot[l].

---

[l] Note an association plot can be produced with the `assoc()` *function* using similar syntax.

```
> library(vcd)
> strucplot(roberts.xtab, shade=T, labeling_args=list(
+ set_varnames=c(POSITION="Transect position",
+ DEAD="Dead coolibah trees"), offset_varnames = c(left = 1.5,
+ top=1.5)), margins=c(5,2,2,5))
```

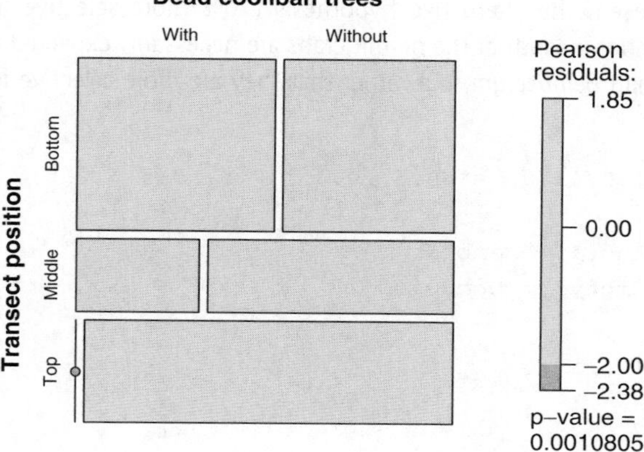

Example 16D: Power analysis for contingency tables

In the absence of a good biological example of a power analysis for contingency tables in any of the main biostatistics texts, a fictitious example will be presented. A marine ecologist was interested in investigating whether North Stradbroke Island hermit crabs were selective in the shells they occupied (what a wet ecologist does on holidays I guess!). He intended to conduct a survey in which shells were cross-classified according to whether or not they were occupied and what type of gastropod they were from (*Austrocochlea* or *Bembicium*). Shells with living gastropods were to be ignored. Essentially, the nerd wanted to know whether or not hermit crabs occupy shells in the proportions that they are available (null hypothesis). A quick count of shells on the rocky shore revealed that approximately 30% of available gastropod shells were occupied and that there were less *Austrocochlea* shells available than *Bembicium* shells (40:60%). The ecologist scratches his sparsely haired scalp, raises one eyebrow and contemplates performing a quick power analysis to determine how many observation would be required to have an 80% chance of detecting a 20% preference for *Austrocochlea* shells.

Step 1 - Using the marginal proportions (0.7 and 0.3 for absent and occupied; 0.4 and 0.6 for *Austrocochlea* and *Bembicium*), calculate the proportions of each cross-classification for the null hypothesis (no association or selection).

```
> H0.tab <- matrix(c(0.7 * 0.4, 0.7 * 0.6, 0.3 * 0.4, 0.3 * 0.6),
+     nrow = 2)
> rownames(H0.tab) <- c("Aust", "Bemb")
> colnames(H0.tab) <- c("Empty", "Occupied")
> library(epitools)
```

```
> table.margins(H0.tab)
      Empty Occupied Total
Aust   0.28     0.12   0.4
Bemb   0.42     0.18   0.6
Total  0.70     0.30   1.0
```

Step 2 - Create proportions to represent the alternative hypothesis (20% more selective for *Austrocochlea*). Note that this does not mean that the hermit crabs are necessarily expected to occupy *Austrocochlea* 20% more than *Bembecium*, but rather that they are more selective for them.

```
> HA.tab <- matrix(c(0.7 * 0.4, 0.7 * 0.6, 0.3 * 0.5, 0.3 * 0.5),
+     nrow = 2)
> rownames(HA.tab) <- c("Aust", "Bemb")
> colnames(HA.tab) <- c("Empty", "Occupied")
> table.margins(HA.tab)
      Empty Occupied Total
Aust   0.28     0.15  0.43
Bemb   0.42     0.15  0.57
Total  0.70     0.30  1.00
```

Note from this alternate hypothesis, we expect to see hermit crabs occupying the different shells in equal proportion, despite *Austrocochlea* shells being less available.

Step 3 - Calculate the effect size corresponding to hermit crabs being 20% more selective for *Austrocochlea* shells.

```
> ws <- sqrt(chisq.test(as.vector(HA.tab),
  p = as.vector(H0.tab))$stat[[1]])
```

Step 4 - Calculate the approximate sample size required to have an 80% change of detecting such an association between shell type and occupancy.

```
> library(pwr)
> pwr.chisq.test(df = 1, w = ws, power = 0.8)
     Chi squared power calculation

              w = 0.1118034
              N = 627.9088
             df = 1
      sig.level = 0.05
          power = 0.8

NOTE: N is the number of observations
```

Conclusions - The ecologist would need to contemplate sampling at least 628 shells in order to be confident of detecting a 20% greater selectivity of hermit crabs for *Austrocochlea* shells. Holidays don't get any better than that!

17

Generalized linear models (GLM)

General linear models (Chapters 8-15) provide a set of well adopted and recognised procedures for relating response variables to a linear combination of one or more predictors. Nevertheless, the reliability and applicability of such models are restricted by the degree to which the residuals conform to normality and the mean and variance are independent of one another. There are many real situations for which those assumptions are unlikely to be satisfied. For example, if the measured response to a predictor treatment (such as nest parasite load) can only be binary (such as abandoned or not), then the differences between the observed and expected values (residuals) are unlikely to follow a normal distribution. Instead, in this case, they will follow a binomial distribution. Furthermore, the variance will likely be tied to the mean in that the higher the expected probability of an event, the greater the variability in this probability.

Transformations to normalize the residuals and stabilize variances are useful in many instances (as demonstrated in numerous examples in previous chapters). However, the biological interpretations of models and parameters can be greatly complicated by scale alterations and scale transformations are not always successful. For example, response variables that represent counts (e.g. the number of individuals of a species per quadrat), are often highly skewed and contain an abundance of zeros. Thus, linear models based on transformed data in such situations can be unsuitable.

Generalized linear models (GLM's) extend the application range of linear modelling by accommodating non-stable variances as well as alternative exponential[a] residual distributions (such as the binomial and Poisson distributions). Generalized linear models have three components:

(i) The random component that specifies the conditional distribution of the response variable. Such distributions are characterised by some function of the mean (canonical or location parameter) and a function of the variance (dispersion parameter). Note that for binomial and Poisson distributions, the dispersion parameter is 1, whereas for the

[a] The exponential distributions are a class of continuous distribution which can be characterized by two parameters. One of these parameters (the location parameter) is a function of the mean and the other (the *dispersion* parameter) is a function of the variance of the distribution. Note that recent developments have further extended generalized linear models to accommodate other non-exponential residual distributions.

Biostatistical Design and Analysis Using R: a Practical Guide, 1st edition. By M. Logan.
Published 2010 by Blackwell Publishing.

Table 17.1 Common generalized linear models and associated canonical link-distribution pairs.

Model	Response variable	Predictor variable(s)	Residual distribution	Link
Linear regression[a]	Continuous	Continuous/ Categorical	Gaussian (normal)	Identity $g(\mu) = \mu$
Logistic regression	Binary	Continuous/ Categorical	Binomial	Logit $g(\mu) = log_e \frac{\mu}{1-\mu}$
Log-linear models	Counts	Categorical	Poisson	Log $g(\mu) = log_e \mu$

[a]Includes the standard ANOVA and ANCOVA designs.

Guassian (normal) distribution the dispersion parameter is the error variance and is assumed to be independent of the mean.

(ii) The systematic component that represents the linear combination of predictors (which can be categorical, continuous, polynomial or other contrasts). This is identical to that of general linear models.

(iii) The link function which links the expected values of the response (random component) to the linear combination of predictors (systematic component). The generalized linear model can thus be represented as:

$$g(\mu) = \beta_0 + \beta_1 X_1 + \beta_2 X_2 + \ldots$$

where $g(\mu)$ represents the link function and β_0, β_1 and β_2 represent parameters broadly analogous to those of general linear models. Although there are many commonly employed link functions, typically the exact form of the link function depends on the nature of the random response distribution. Some of the canonical (natural) link function and distribution pairings that are suitable for different forms of generalized linear models are listed in Table 17.1.

The *generalized* nature of GLM's makes them incompatible with ordinary least squares model fitting procedures. Instead, parameter estimates and model fitting are typically achieved by maximum likelihood[b] methods based on an iterative re-weighting algorithm (such as the Newton-Raphson algorithm). Essentially, the Newton-Raphson algorithm (also known as a scoring algorithm) fits a linear model to an adjusted response variable (transformed via the link function) using a set of weights and then iteratively re-fits the model with new sets of weights recalculated according to the fit of the previous iteration. For canonical link-distribution pairs (see Table 17.1), the Newton-Raphson algorithm usually converges (arrives at a common outcome or equilibrium) very efficiently and reliably.

The Newton-Raphson algorithm facilitates a unifying model fitting procedure across the family of exponential probability distributions thereby providing a means by which binary and count data can be incorporated into the suit of linear model designs

[b] Recall that maximum likelihood estimates are those maximize the likelihood of obtaining the actual observations for the chosen model.

described in chapters 8-15. In fact, linear regression (including ANOVA, ANCOVA and other general linear models) can be considered a special form of GLM that features a normal distribution and identity link function and for which the maximum likelihood procedure has an exact solution. Notably, when variance is stable, both maximum likelihood and ordinary least squares yield very similar parameter estimates.

17.1 Dispersion (over or under)

The variance of binomial or Poisson distributions is assumed to be related to the sample size and mean respectively, and thus, there is not a variance parameter in their definitions. In fact, the variance (or dispersion) parameter is fixed to 1. As a result, logistic regression and log-linear modelling assume that sample variances conform to the respective distribution definitions. However, it is common for individual sampling units (e.g. individuals) to co-vary such that other, unmeasured influences, increase (or less commonly, decrease) variability. For example, although a population sex ratio might be 1:1, male to female ratios within a clutch might be highly skewed towards one or other sex. Positive correlations cause greater variance (overdispersion) and result in deflated standard errors (and thus exaggerated levels of precision and higher Type I errors). Methods of diagnosing and modelling over-dispersed data are described in section 17.4.

17.2 Binary data - logistic (logit) regression

Logistic regression is a form of GLM that employs the logit-binomial link distribution canonical pairing to model the effects of one or more continuous or categorical (with dummy coding) predictor variables on a binary (dead/alive, presence/absence, etc) response variable. For example, we could investigate the relationship between salinity levels (salt concentration) and mortality of frogs. Similarly, we could model the presence of a species of bird as a function of habitat patch size, or nest predation (predated or not) as a function of the distance from vegetative cover.

17.2.1 Logistic model

Consider the fictitious data presented in Figure 17.1a&b. Clearly, a regular simple linear model (straight line, Figure 17.1a) is inappropriate for modelling the probability of presence. Note that at very low and high levels of X, the predicted probabilities (probabilities or proportions of the population) are less than zero and greater than one respectively - logically impossible outcomes.

The logistic model (Figure 17.1c) relating the probability ($\pi(x)$) that the response (y_i) equals one (present) for a given level of x_i (patch size) is defined as:

$$\pi(x) = \frac{e^{\beta_0+\beta_1 x}}{1 + e^{\beta_0+\beta_1 x}}$$

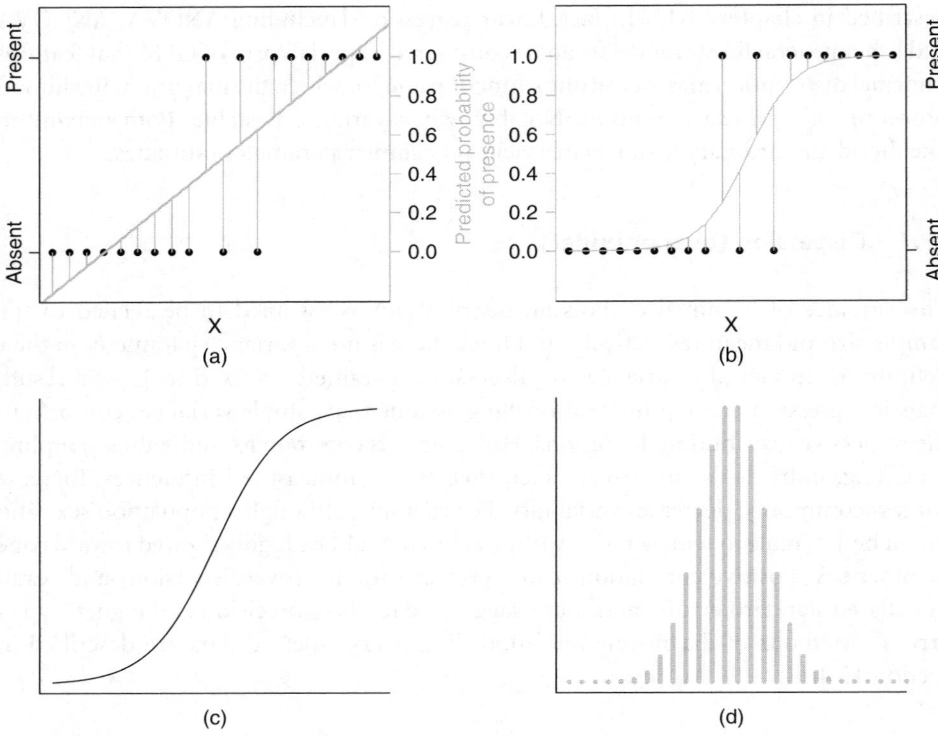

Fig 17.1 Fictitious data illustrating a binary response variable modelled with (a) a linear model and (b) an equivalent logistic regression model. Not only does the linear model violate linearity and normality, the predicted values are not bounded by the logical probability limits of 0 and 1. Accordingly, the inappropriately fitted linear model (a) implies that at very low levels of X, individuals are expected to be less than absent! Subfigures (c) and (d) represent the general logistic model and binomial probability distribution respectively.

Appropriately, since $e^{\beta_0+\beta_1 x}$ (the "natural constant" raised to a simple linear model) must evaluate to between 0 and infinity, the logistic model must asymptote towards (and is thus bounded by) zero and one. Alternatively, the logit link function:

$$\ln\left(\frac{\pi(x)}{1-\pi(x)}\right)$$

can be used to transform $\pi(x)$ such that the logistic model is expressed as the log odds (probability of one state relative to the alternative) against a familiar linear combination of the explanatory variables (as is linear regression).

$$\ln\left(\frac{\pi(x)}{1-\pi(x)}\right) = \beta_0 + \beta_1 x_i$$

Although the β_0 (y-intercept) parameter is interpreted similar to that of linear regression (albeit of little biological interest), this is not the case for the slope parameter (β_1).

Rather than representing the rate of change in the response for a given change in the predictor, in logistic regression, β_1 represents the rate of change in the odds ratio (ratio of odds of an event at two different levels of a predictor) for a given unit change in the predictor. The exponentiated slope represents the odds ratio, the proportional rate at which the predicted odds change for a given unit change of the predictor.

$$odds\ ratio = e^{\beta_1}$$

17.2.2 Null hypotheses

As with linear regression, a separate H_0 is tested for each of the estimated model parameters:

$$H_0: \beta_1 = 0 \qquad \text{(the population slope equals zero)}$$

This test examines whether the log odds of an occurrence are independent of the predictor variable and thus whether or not there is likely to be a relationship between the response and predictor.

$$H_0: \beta_0 = 0 \qquad \text{(the population y-intercept equals zero)}$$

As stated previously, this is typically of little biological interest.

Similar to linear regression, there are two ways of testing the main null hypotheses[c]

(i) Parameter estimation approach. Maximum likelihood estimates of the parameters and their asymptotic[d] standard errors (S_{b_1}) are used to calculate the Wald t (or t ratio) statistic:

$$W = \frac{b_1}{S_{b_1}}$$

which approximately follows a standard z distribution when the null hypothesis is true. The reliability of Wald tests deminishes substantially with small sample sizes. For such cases, the second option is therefore more appropriate.

(ii) (log)-likelihood ratio tests approach. This approach essentially involves comparing the fit of models with (full) and without (reduced) the term of interest:

$$logit(\pi) = \beta_0 + \beta_1 X_1 \ \ \text{(Full model)}$$

$$logit(\pi) = \beta_0 \ \ \text{(Reduced model)}$$

The fit of any given model is measured via log-likelihood and the differences between the fit of two models is described by a likelihood ratio statistic (G^2 = 2(log-likelihood reduced

[c] Note, that whilst in simple regression, the parameter and model comparison approaches yield identical outcomes, this is not the case here and that the degree of correspondence depends on sample sizes. For small sample sizes, the model comparisons approach is considered more reliable.

[d] A parameter is refered to as an assyptotic estimate if their reliability is sample size dependent - they become progressively more accurate with increasing sample size, albeit with diminishing returns.

model - log-likelihood full model)). The G^2 quantity is also known as deviance and is analygous to the residual sums of squares in a linear model. When the null hypothesis is true, the G^2 statistic approximately follows a χ^2 distribution with one degree of freedom. An analogue of the linear model r^2 measure can be calculated as:

$$r^2 = 1 - \frac{G_0^2}{G_1^2}$$

where G_0^2 and G_1^2 represent the deviances due to the intercept and slope terms respectively.

17.2.3 Analysis of deviance

Analogous to the ANOVA table that partitions the total variation into components explained by each of the model terms (and the unexplained error), it is possible to construct a analysis of deviance table that partitions the deviance into components explained by each of the model terms.

17.2.4 Multiple logistic regression

Multiple logistic regression is an extension of logistic regression in the same way that multiple linear regression is an extension of simple linear regression.

$$logit(\pi) = \beta_0 + \beta_1 x_1 + \beta_2 x_2 + \ldots$$

Each of the parameters can be estimated either via Wald statistics or via a sequence of log-likelihood (G^2) tests comparing models with and without each predictor term. These estimatated parameters are partial logistic regression parameters. That is, they are the effect of one predictor on the odds of an occurance holding all other predictors constant.

Since the systematic component of GLM's is identical to that of linear models, multiple logistic regression shares the issues and diagnoses concerning (multi)collinearity[e] with multiple linear regression.

Model selection and model averaging

Selecting the best (most parsimonious) model as well as assessing the relative importance of each of the predictor variables follows similar procedures to those outlined in sections 9.7 & 9.7.1 and can be based on the following measures (see Table 9.2 for more formula and R syntax):

- Differences in deviance (G^2) between model pairs
- r^2 - analogous to multiple linear regression
- *AIC* (preferred). The Akaike Information Criterion (AIC) for generalized linear models is the deviance (G^2) penalized for the number of predictors (p) and either the number of

[e] Recall from chapter 9 that the assumption of multicollinearity concerns the issues that arise when two or more of the predictor variables are correlated to one another.

observations (n) or unique category combinations (D):

$$AIC = G^2 - n + 2p$$

$$AIC = G^2 - D + 2p$$

When comparing two possible models from a family of models, this is reduced to:

$$AIC = G^2 - 2df$$

where df is the difference in degrees of freedom of the two models. Models with the smallest AIC are the most parsimonious.

- *QAIC*. The Quasi Akaike Information Criterion is adjusted for the degree of overdispersion of lack of fit
- *AICc* and *QAICc*. Both *AIC* and *QAIC* also have versions that correct for small ($n < 30$) sample sizes. Model selection should be based upon models fitted using maximum likelihood (ML) rather than restricted maximum likelihood (REML) as the former is more appropriate for comparing models with different fixed and random effects structures. The resulting 'best' model should then be refit using REML.

17.3 Count data - Poisson generalized linear models

Another form of data for which scale transformations are often unsuitable or unsuccessful are count data. Count data tend to follow a Poisson distribution (see Figure 16.1) and consequently, the mean and variance are usually related. Generalized linear models provide appropriate means to model count data according to two design contexts:

(i) as an alternative to linear regression for modeling count data against a linear combination of continuous and/or categorical predictor variables (**Poisson regresssion**)
(ii) as an alternative to contingency tables in which the associations between categorical variables are explored (**log-linear modelling**)

17.3.1 Poisson regression

The Poisson regression model is:

$$log(\mu) = \beta_0 + \beta_1 x_1$$

where $log(\mu)$ is the link function used to link the mean of the Poisson response variable to the linear combination of predictor variables. Poisson regression otherwise shares null hypotheses, parameter estimation, model fitting and selection with logistic regression (see section 17.2).

17.3.2 Log-linear Modelling

Contingency tables were introduced in section 16.3 along with caveats regarding the reliability and interoperability of such analyses (particularly when expected proportions are small or for multiway tables). In contrast to logistic and Poisson regression, a log-linear model does not empirically distinguish between response and predictor variables. Nevertheless, as in contingency tables, causality can be implied when logical and justified by interpretation.

Log-linear models

The saturated (or full) log-linear model resembles a multiway ANOVA model (see chapter 12). The full and reduced log-linear models for a two factor design are:

$$log(f_{ij}) = \mu + \lambda_i^A + \lambda_j^B + \lambda_{ij}^{AB} \text{ (full)}$$
$$log(f_{ij}) = \mu + \lambda_i^A + \lambda_j^B \text{ (reduced)}$$

where $log(f_{ij})$ is the log link function, μ is the mean of the (log) of expected frequencies (f_{ij}) and λ_i^A is the effect of the ith category of the variable (A), λ_j^B is the effect of the jth category of B and λ_{ij}^{AB} is the interactive effect of each category combination on the (log) expected frequencies.

Reduced models differ from full models in the absence of all higher order[f] interaction terms. Comparing the fit of full and reduced models therefore provides a means of assessing the effect of the interaction. Whilst two-way tables contain only a single interaction term (and thus a single full and reduced model), multiway tables have multiple interactions. For example, a three-way table has a three way interaction (ABC) as well as three two-way interactions (AB, AC, BC). Consequently, there can be numerous pairs of full and reduced models, each appropriate for different interaction terms (see Table 17.2).

Null hypotheses

Consistent with contingency table analysis, log-linear models test the null hypothesis ($\mathbf{H}_0$) that the categorical variables are independent of (not associated with) one another. Such null hypotheses are tested by comparing the fit (deviance, G^2, see section 17.2.2) of full and reduced models. The G^2 is compared to a χ^2 distribution with degrees of freedom equal to the difference in degrees of freedom of the full and reduced models. Thereafter, odds ratios are useful for interpreting any lack of independence.

For multi-way tables, there are multiple full and reduced models.

Complete dependence:

H_0: $A{:}B{:}C = 0$. No three way interaction. Either no association (conditional independence) between each pair of variables, or else the patterns of associations (conditional dependencies) are the same for each level of the third. If this null hypothesis is rejected ($A{:}B{:}C \neq 0$), the causes of lack of independence can be explored by examining the residuals or odds ratios. Alternatively, main effects tests (testing the effects of two-way interactions separately

[f] In this context, higher order refers to interaction terms containing the term of interest as well as other factors/interactions.

Table 17.2 Full and reduced log-linear models for three-way tables in hierarchical order.

H_0	Log-linear model	df	G^2 (reduced-full)
Saturated model			
1	$A+B+C+AB+$ $AC+BC+ABC$	0	
Complete dependence			
2 $ABC=0$	$A+B+C+$ $AB+AC+BC$	$(I-1)(J-1)$ $(K-1)$	2-1
Conditional independence			
3 $AB=0$	$A+B+C+AC+BC$	$K(I-1)(J-1)$	3-2
4 $AC=0$	$A+B+C+AB+BC$	$J(I-1)(K-1)$	4-2
5 $BC=0$	$A+B+C+AB+AC$	$I(J-1)(K-1)$	5-2
Conditional independence			
6 $AB=0$	$A+B$	(I-1)(J-1)	6-$(A+B+AB)$
7 $AC=0$	$A+C$	(I-1)(K-1)	7-$(A+C+AC)$
8 $BC=0$	$B+C$	(J-1)(K-1)	8-$(B+C+BC)$
Complete independence			
9 $AB=AC=BC=0$	$A+B+C$		9-2

at each level of the third) can be performed. If the three-way interaction is not rejected (no three-way association), lower order interactions can be explored.

Conditional independence/dependence:
If the three-way interaction is not rejected (no three-way association), lower order interactions can be explored.

H_0: $AB = 0$. A and B conditionally independent (not associated) within each level of C.

H_0: $AC = 0$. A and C conditionally independent (not associated) within each level of B.

H_0: $BC = 0$. B and C conditionally independent (not associated) within each level of A.

Marginal independence:

H_0: $AB = 0$. No association between A and B pooling over C

H_0: $AC = 0$. No association between A and C pooling over B

H_0: $BC = 0$. No association between B and C pooling over A

Complete independence:
If none of the two-way interactions are present (no two-way associations), complete independence (all two-way interactions equal zero) can be explored.

H_0: $AB = AC = BC = 0$. Each of the variables are completely independent of all the other variables.

Analysis of designs with more than three factors proceed similarly, starting with tests of higher order interactions and progressing to lower order interactions only in the absence of higher order interactions. Selection of the "best" (most parsimonious) model is on the basis of the smallest G^2 or AIC where:

$$AIC = G^2 - 2df$$

17.4 Assumptions

Compared to general linear models, the requirements of generalized linear models are less stringent. In particular, neither normality nor homoscedasticity (homogeneity of variance) are assumed. Nevertheless, to maximize the reliability of null hypotheses tests, the following assumptions do apply:

(i) all observations should be **independent** to ensure that the samples provide an unbiased estimate of the intended population.

(ii) it is important to establish that no observations are overly influential. Most linear model **influence** (and outlier) diagnostics extend to generalized linear models and are taken from the final iteration of the weighted least squares algorithm. Useful diagnoses include:
   (a) Residuals - there are numerous forms of residuals that have been defined for generalized linear models, each essentially being a variant on the difference between observed and predicted (influence in y-space) theme. Note that the residuals from logistic regression are difficult to interpret.
   (b) Leverage - a measure of outlyingness and influence in x-space.
   (c) *Dfbeta* - an analogue of Cook's D statisic which provides a standardized measure of the overall influence of observations on the parameter estimates and model fit.

(iii) although **linearity** between the response and predictors is not assumed, the relationship between each of the predictors and the link function is assumed to be linear. This linearity can be examined via the following:
   (a) goodness-of-fit. For log-linear models, χ^2 contingency tables (see chapter 16) can be performed[g], however due to the low reliability of such tests with small sample sizes, this is not an option for logistic regression with continuous predictor(s) (since each combination is typically unique and thus the expected values are always 1).
   (b) Hosmer-Lemeshow ($\hat{C}$). Data are aggregated into 10 groups or bins (either by cutting the data according to the predictor range or equal frequencies in each group) such that goodness-of-fit test is more reliable. Nevertheless, the Hosmer-Lemeshow statistic has low power and relies on the somewhat arbitrary bin sizes.
   (c) le Cessie-van Houwelingen-Copas omnibus test. This is a goodness-of-fit test for binary data based on the smoothing of residuals.
   (d) component+residual (partial residual) plots. Non-linearity is diagnosed as a substantial deviation from a linear trend.

   Non-linearity can be dealt with either by transformation or generalized additive modelling (GAM, see section 17.5) depending on the degree and nature of the non-linearity.

(iv) **(over or under) dispersion (see section 17.1)**. The dispersion parameter (degree of variance inflation or over-dispersion) can be estimated[h] by dividing the Pearsons

[g] This is really examining whether the data could have come from a population that displays that specific fitted logistic model

[h] Overdispersion can also be diagnosed graphically from deviations on a q-q plot.

χ^2 by the degrees of freedom ($n - p$, where n is the number of observations in p parameters). As a general rule, dispersion parameters approaching 2 (or 0.5) indicate possible violations of this assumption. Where over (or under) dispersion is suspected to be an issue, **quasibinomial** and **quasipoisson** families can be used as alternatives to model the dispersion. These *quasi-likelihood* models derive the dispersion parameter (function of the variance) from the observed data. Test statistics from such models should be based on *F*-tests rather than chi-squared tests.

17.5 Generalized additive models (GAM's) - non-parametric GLM

Generalized additive models[i] are non-parametric alternatives to generalized linear models and are useful when the relationships are expected to be complex (not simple linear trends). In generalized additive models, the slope coefficients are replaced by smoothing functions;

$$g(\mu) = \beta_0 + f_1 x_{i1} + f_2 x_{i2} + \dots$$

where f_1 and f_2 are non-parametric smoothing functions. The weighted smoothing functions permit trends to deviate at critical regions throughout the data cloud (see Figure 17.2) and thus the resulting smoother estimates tend to be less variable (or smoother) than the corresponding regression coefficients. Generalized additive models are fitted using a modification of the Newton-Raphson scoring algorithm in which the partial residuals are iteratively smoothed in a process known as backfitting.

Common smoothers include cubic splines and Loess smoothers (as well as running means, running medians, running lines, and kernel smoothers). Selection of the appropriate smoother(s) and smoothing coefficients usually follows scatterplot examination. Note that it is possible to apply different smoothers and smoothing coefficients for each of the predictor variables.

GAM's potentially model the nature of the data trends more "truly" and yield better fits in the presence of non-linear trends. However, they are substantially more complex to fit than GLM's, requiring consideration of not only the appropriate distribution and linkage function, but also the appropriate smoothers and smoothing coefficients. GAM's must also be fitted judiciously to avoid over-fitting[j]. GAM's can also be more difficult to interpret than GLM's, particularly with respect predictions. The principles of parsimony should be applied by verifying the fit of the GAM against the equivalent GLM.

Early methodologies extended the application of smoothing and local regression (as described in section 8.3) to generalized linear models. More recent developments in

[i] GAM's are a form of additive model. Additive models fit each of the model terms additively. That is, there are no interactions in the model.

[j] Over-fitting occurs when overly complex models are fitted to data. This is analogous to fitting a very high order polynomial to a data cloud. Whilst the model fits the observed data well, it does not reflect the true nature of the relationship (i.e. its explanatory power is low).

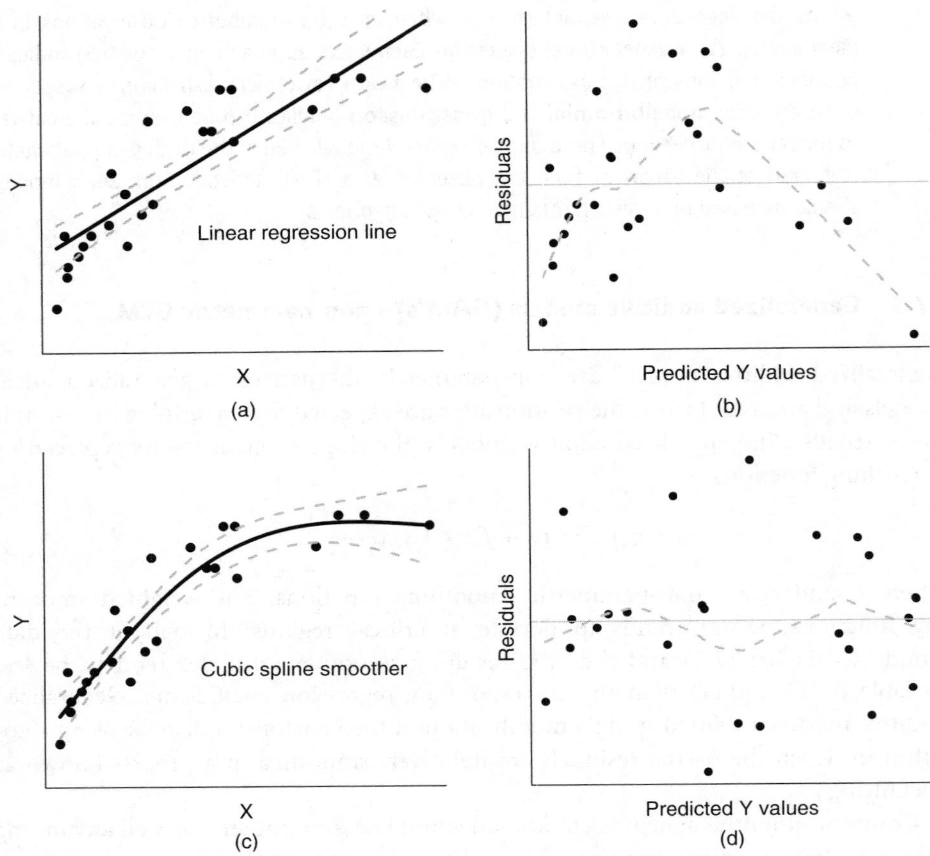

Fig 17.2 Fictitious relationship between Y and X contrasting the fit of (a) linear and (c) loess smoothers as well as the corresponding residual plots (b) and (d) respectively. The cubic spline fits the data substantially better than the fitted linear regression line.

the field of GAM's have expanded their capabilities to provide more sophisticated optimization of smoothing as well as accommodating mixed effects modelling approaches to hierarchical designs and correlations structures.

Clearly this has been a very brief and non-technical description of GAM's and is intended as an introduction to the existence of additional non-parametric alternatives.

17.6 GLM and R

Generalized linear models can be fit using the `glm()` *function* with the *family* parameter to specify the random component. The optional `link` parameter can be used to specify non-canonical link functions, otherwise the link function will be determined as appropriate for the specified `family`. Full and reduced models can be compared using the `anova`[k] *function*. GAM's are supported by two packages, `gam` and `mgcv`, reflecting the simple and more modern generalized additive modelling techniques respectively.

17.7 Further reading

- Theory

  Hastie, T. J., and R. J. Tibshirani. (1990). *Generalized Additive Models.* Chapman & Hall.

  Quinn, G. P., and K. J. Keough. (2002). *Experimental design and data analysis for biologists.* Cambridge University Press, London.

  Wood, S. N. (2006). *Generalized Additive Models: An Introduction with R.* Chapman & Hall/CRC.

- Practical - R

  Crawley, M. J. (2007). *The R Book.* John Wiley, New York.

  Faraway, J. J. (2006). *Extending Linear Models with R: generalized linear mixed effects and nonparametric regression models.* Chapman & Hall/CRC.

  Venables, W. N., and B. D. Ripley. (2002). *Modern Applied Statistics with S-PLUS,* 4th edn. Springer-Verlag, New York.

  Zuur, A. F., E. N. Ieno, N. J. Walker, A. A. Saveliev, and G. M. Smith. (2009). *Mixed Effects Models and Extensions in Ecology with R.* Springer.

17.8 Key for GLM

1 a. Binary response variable (logistic regression) .... Go to 2

b. Count (frequency) data (Poisson generalized linear models) .... Go to 5

2 a. Logistic regression - single predictor variable .... See Example 17A

```
> data.glm <- glm(DV ~ IV, dataset, family = "Poisson")
```

- **Check that the model adheres to the assumptions** .... Go to 3
- **To examine (over) dispersion** .... Go to 4
- **To get the model parameter estimates**

  ```
  > summary(data.glm)
  ```

- **To get the deviance table**

  ```
  > anova(data.glm, test = "Chisq")
  ```

- **Examine the odds ratios** .... Go to 6

[k] Alternatively, the `Anova` *function* can be used to support Type II and Type III analogues when designs are not balanced.

b. Multiple predictor variables - multiple logistic regression .... See Examples 17B & 17C

```
> data.glm <- glm(DV ~ IV1 + IV2 + ..., dataset,
+     family = "Poisson")
```

- **Check for issues with (multi) collinearity** .... See Chapter 9
- **Check that the model adheres to the assumptions** .... Go to 3
- **To examine (over) dispersion** .... Go to 4
- **To get the model parameter estimates**

  ```
  > summary(data.glm)
  ```

  OR

  ```
  > anova(data.glm, data.glmR, test = "Chisq")
  ```

  where `data.glmR` *is a reduced model containing constructed by ommitting the term of interest.*
- **Examine the odds ratios** .... Go to 6
- **Perform model selection and model averaging** .... Go to 8

3 a. Check the assumptions .... See Examples 17A–17C.
In the following, `data.glm` *is the fitted generalized linear model.*

- **Lack of fit**
  - le Cessie-van Houwelingen normal test statistic

    ```
    > library(Design)
    > data.lrm <- lrm(formula, dataset, y = T, x = T)
    > resid(data.lrm)
    ```

    where `formula` *is a formula relating the response variable to the linear combination of predictor variables*
  - *Pearson* χ^2

    ```
    > pp <- sum(resid(data.lrm, type = "pearson")^2)
    > 1 - pchisq(pp, data.glm$df.resid)
    ```
  - *Deviance* (G^2)

    ```
    > 1 - pchisq(data.glm, data.glm$df.resid)
    ```
- **Linear relationship between predictors and link function (component+residual plot)**

  ```
  > library(car)
  > cr.plots(data.glm, ask = F)
  ```
- **Influence**

  ```
  > influence.measures(data.glm)
  ```

Assumptions met .... Go back

b. Assumptions not met - Transformations of the predictor variable scale can be useful in improving linearity, otherwise consider GAM's (Go to 7)

4 a. Examine (over) dispersion .... See Examples 17A – 17C

- **Pearson's residuals**

```
> sum(resid(data.glm, type = "pearson")^2)/data.glm$df.resid
```

- **Deviance**

```
> data.glm$deviance/data.glm$df.resid
```

Dispersion does not deviate substantially from 1 .... Go back

b. Model is over dispersed

- **Refit model with "quasi" distribution**

```
> data.glm <- glm(DV ~ IV, dataset, family = "quasibinomial")
> anova(data.glm, test = "F")
```

- **Consider a negative binomial**

```
> data.glm <- glm.nb(DV ~ IV, dataset)
> anova(data.glm, test = "F")
```

5 a. Continuous predictor variable(s) (Poisson regression)

```
> data.glm <- glm(DV ~ IV1 + ..., dataset, family = "poisson")
```

- **Check that the model adheres to the assumptions** .... Go to 3
- **To examine (over) dispersion** .... Go to 4
- **To get the model parameter estimates**

```
> summary(data.glm)
```

OR

```
> anova(data.glm, data.glmR, test = "Chisq")
```

where `data.glmR` *is a reduced model containing constructed by ommitting the term of interest.*

- ***To calculate the odds ratios*** .... *Go to 6*
- ***To perform model selection and model averaging*** .... *Go to 8*

b. Categorical variables only (log-linear modelling) .... See Examples 17D & 17E

```
> data.glm <- glm(DV ~ CAT1 * CAT2 * ..., dataset,
+     family = "poisson")
```

- **To examine conditional independence**

```
> data.glm1 <- update(data.glm, ~. - CAT1:CAT2, dataset)
> anova(data.glm, data.glm1, test = "Chisq")
```

See Table 17.2 for appropriate full and reduced log-linear models for examining complete and conditional dependence and independence

- **To calculate odds ratios** .... Go to 6
- **To perform model selection** .... Go to 8

6 a. Calculate odds ratios .... See Examples 17A – 17E

```
> library(biology)
> odds.ratio(data.glm)
```

7 a. Generalized additive models .... See Example 17F

```
> library(gam)
> data.gam <- gam(DV ~ lo(CAT1) + lo(CAT2) + ...,
+     family = "gaussian", dataset)
```

- **The `family=` parameter can be used to specify the appropriate error distribution**
- **To check that the model adheres to the assumptions**
- **To examine the parameter estimates**

```
> sumamry(data.gam)
```

- **To perform model selection** .... Go to 8

8 a. Perform model selection .... See Examples 17B, 17C & 17F

In the following model *is the fitted model from either glm or gam*

```
> library(MuMIn)
> dredge(model)
> model.avg(get.models(dredge(model)))
```

OR

```
> library(biology)
> Model.selection.glm(model)
```

17.9 Worked examples of real biological data sets

Example 17A: Logistic regression

As part of an investigation into the factors controlling island spider populations, Polis et al. (1998) recorded the physical and biotic characteristics of the islands in the Gulf of California. Quinn and Keough (2002) subsequently modelled the presence/absence (PA) of a potential spider predator (*Uta* lizards) against the perimeter to area ratio (RATIO) of the islands to illustrate logistic regression (from Box 13.1 of Quinn and Keough (2002)).

Step 1 - Import (section 2.3) the Polis et al. (1998) data set

```
> polis <- read.table("polis.csv", header = T, sep = ",")
```

Step 2 (Key 17.2) - Fit the logistic regression model relating the log odds of *Uta* presence against perimeter to area ratio $\left(ln\left(\frac{\pi(\mu)}{1-\pi(\mu)}\right) = \beta_0 + \beta_1(P/A\ ratio)\right)$

```
> polis.glm <- glm(PA ~ RATIO, family = binomial, data = polis)
```

Step 3 (Key 17.3) - Check the (lack of) fit and appropriateness of the model with goodness-of-fit tests

- le Cessie-van Houwelingen normal test statistic

```
> library(Design)

> polis.lrm <- lrm(PA ~ RATIO, data = polis, y = T, x = T)
> resid(polis.lrm, type = "gof")
```

```
Sum of squared errors      Expected value|H0                SD
          2.2784683              2.2633569          0.1462507
                  Z                      P
          0.1033257              0.9177045
```

- Pearson χ^2 p-value

```
> pp <- sum(resid(polis.lrm, type = "pearson")^2)
> 1 - pchisq(pp, polis.glm$df.resid)
[1] 0.5715331
```

- Deviance (G^2) significance

```
> 1 - pchisq(polis.glm$deviance, polis.glm$df.resid)
[1] 0.6514215
```

- Estimated dispersion parameter **(Key 17.4)**

```
> pp/polis.glm$df.resid
[1] 0.901922
```

Conclusions - no evidence for a lack of fit or over-dispersion (G^2 and dispersion values not approaching 2) in the model.

Step 4 (Key 17.3) - Confirm linearity between the log odds ratio of lizard presence and perimeter to area ratio with a component+residual plot

```
> library(car)
> cr.plots(polis.glm, ask = F)
```

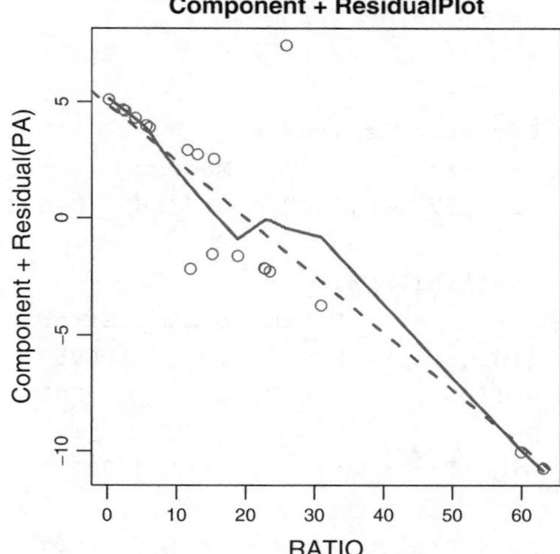

Conclusions - no evidence of non-linearity. Thus no evidence to suggest that data did not come from population that follows the logistic regression- not evidence for a lack of fit of the model

Step 5 (Key 17.3) - Examine the influence measures

```
> influence.measures(polis.glm)
Influence measures of
         glm(formula = PA ~ RATIO, family = binomial, data = polis) :
```

```
     dfb.1_   dfb.RATI      dffit cov.r   cook.d        hat inf
1   0.182077 -0.007083  0.447814 1.043 5.50e-02 0.109124
2   0.167005 -0.141263  0.169959 1.235 6.62e-03 0.111730
3  -0.723849  1.079157  1.278634 0.537 8.43e-01 0.151047    *
4  -0.239967  0.028419 -0.546081 0.953 9.01e-02 0.108681
5   0.248270 -0.126175  0.359999 1.117 3.30e-02 0.110025
6   0.028088 -0.196986 -0.437403 1.110 5.00e-02 0.129177
7   0.077131 -0.102575 -0.111591 1.250 2.81e-03 0.108288
8   0.140334 -0.247315 -0.332565 1.242 2.65e-02 0.155414
9  -0.562402  0.338850 -0.723598 0.805 1.89e-01 0.112842
10  0.257651 -0.162838  0.319655 1.157 2.52e-02 0.114067
11  0.176591 -0.147771  0.180516 1.234 7.49e-03 0.113765
12  0.104228 -0.093408  0.104419 1.225 2.46e-03 0.090774
13  0.135395 -0.118138  0.136380 1.233 4.23e-03 0.102909
14  0.000410 -0.000476 -0.000481 1.131 5.14e-08 0.001445
15  0.000218 -0.000251 -0.000254 1.130 1.43e-08 0.000817
16  0.139447 -0.248090 -0.335881 1.239 2.70e-02 0.155114
17  0.143708 -0.240774 -0.311977 1.255 2.31e-02 0.156543
18  0.074831 -0.068694  0.074832 1.211 1.26e-03 0.075520
19  0.108633 -0.097001  0.108890 1.226 2.68e-03 0.092718
```

Conclusions - Although the Dfbeta (Cook's D equivalent) values of islands 3 (Cerraja) and 9 (Mitlan) where elevated relative to the other islands, no observations are considered overly influential, as none of the values approached 1.

Step 6 (Key 17.2) - Examine the parameter estimates from the fitted logistic regression model.

```
> summary(polis.glm)
Call:
glm(formula = PA ~ RATIO, family = binomial, data = polis)

Deviance Residuals:
    Min       1Q   Median       3Q      Max
-1.6067  -0.6382   0.2368   0.4332   2.0986

Coefficients:
            Estimate Std. Error z value Pr(>|z|)
(Intercept)   3.6061     1.6953   2.127   0.0334 *
RATIO        -0.2196     0.1005  -2.184   0.0289 *
---
Signif. codes:  0 '***' 0.001 '**' 0.01 '*' 0.05 '.' 0.1 ' ' 1

(Dispersion parameter for binomial family taken to be 1)

    Null deviance: 26.287  on 18  degrees of freedom
Residual deviance: 14.221  on 17  degrees of freedom
AIC: 18.221

Number of Fisher Scoring iterations: 6
```

Conclusions - reject the null hypothesis. An increase in perimeter to area ratio was associated with a significant decline in the chances of *Uta* lizard presence on Gulf of California islands ($b = -0.202, z = -2.184, P = 0.029$).

Step 7 (Key 17.2) - Compare the fit of full and reduced models (G^2) as an alternative (potentially more reliable given the relatively small sample size) to the individual parameter based approach

```
> anova(polis.glm, test = "Chisq")
Analysis of Deviance Table

Model: binomial, link: logit

Response: PA

Terms added sequentially (first to last)


      Df Deviance Resid. Df Resid. Dev P(>|Chi|)
NULL                     18    26.2869
RATIO  1  12.0662        17    14.2207    0.0005
```

Conclusions - reject the null hypothesis. An increase in perimeter to area ratio was associated with a significant decline in the chances of *Uta* lizard presence on Gulf of California islands ($G^2 = 12.066, df = 1, P < 0.001$).

Step 8 (Key 17.6) - Examine the odds ratio for the occurrence of *Uta* lizards.

```
> library(biology)
> odds.ratio(polis.glm)
      Odds ratio Lower 95
RATIO  0.8028734     0.659303     0.9777077
```

Conclusions - the chances of *Uta* lizards being present on an island decline by 0.803 (20%) for every unit increase in perimeter to area ratio.

Step 9 - Estimate the strength (r^2) of the association

```
> 1 - (polis.glm$dev/polis.glm$null)
[1] 0.4590197
```

Conclusions - 46% of the uncertainty in *Uta* lizard occurrence is explained by the perimeter to area ratio of the islands.

Step 10 - Calculate the LD50 (perimeter to area ratio at which there is a 50% chance of *Uta* lizard occurrence).

```
> -polis.glm$coef[1]/polis.glm$coef[2]
(Intercept)
   16.42420
```

Step 11 - Summarize the association between *Uta* lizard occurrence and island perimeter to area ratio.

```
> # Calculate predicted values based on fitted model
> xs <- seq(0, 70, l = 1000)
> polis.predict <- predict(polis.glm, type = "response", se = T,
+     newdata = data.frame(RATIO = xs))
> # construct base plot
> plot(PA ~ RATIO, data = polis, xlab = "", ylab = "", axes = F,
+     pch = 16)
> # Plot fitted model and 95% CI bands
> points(polis.predict$fit ~ xs, type = "l", col = "gray")
> lines(polis.predict$fit + polis.predict$se.fit ~ xs,
+     col = "gray", type = "l", lty = 2)
> lines(polis.predict$fit - polis.predict$se.fit ~ xs,
+     col = "gray", type = "l", lty = 2)
> mtext(expression(paste(italic(Uta), "presence/absence")), 2,
+     line = 3)
> axis(2, las = 1)
> mtext("Permenter to area ratio", 1, line = 3)
> axis(1)
> box(bty = "l")
```

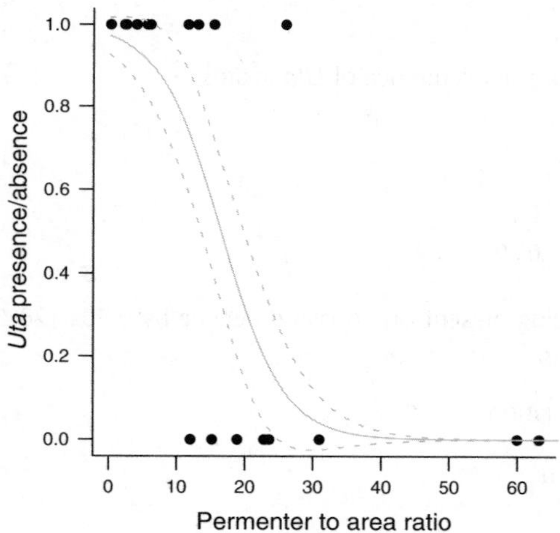

Example 17B: Multiple logistic regression

Bolger et al. (1997) investigated the impacts of habitat fragmentation on the occurrence of native rodents. Quinn and Keough (2002) subsequently modelled the presence/absence native rodents against some of the Bolger et al. (1997)'s biogeographic variables (area of the canyon fragment, percent shrub cover and distance to the nearest canyon fragment) (from Box 13.2 of Quinn and Keough (2002)).

Step 1 - Import (section 2.3) the Bolger et al. (1997) data set

```
> bolger <- read.table("bolger.csv", header = T, sep = ",")
```

Step 2 (Key 9.3 & 17.2b) - Investigate the assumption of (multi)collinearity

```
> library(car)
> scatterplot.matrix(~RODENTSP + DISTX + AGE + PERSHRUB,
      data = bolger)
```

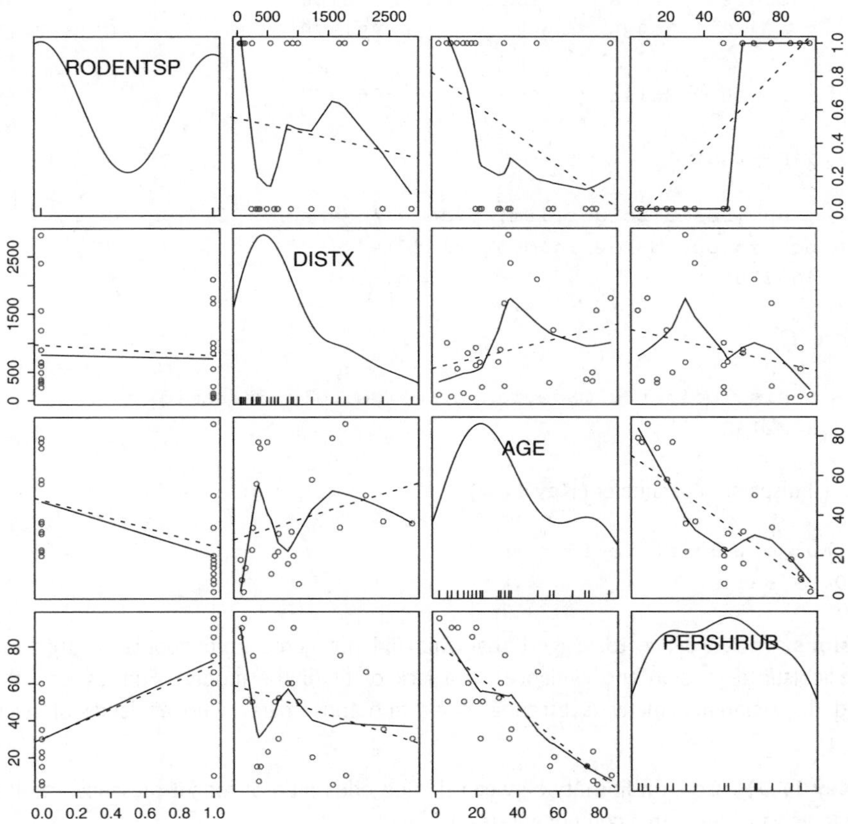


```
> bolger.glm <- glm(RODENTSP ~ DISTX + AGE + PERSHRUB, family =
+     binomial, data = bolger)
> vif(bolger.glm)
   DISTX      AGE PERSHRUB
1.117702 1.971138 2.049398
```

Conclusions - Although there is clearly a relationship between fragment age and percent shrub cover, variance inflation values do not indicate a major collinearity issue (values less than 5).

Step 3 (Key 17.3) - Check the (lack of) fit and appropriateness of the model with goodness-of-fit tests

- le Cessie-van Houwelingen normal test statistic

```
> library(Design)
> bolger.lrm <- lrm(RODENTSP ~ DISTX + AGE + PERSHRUB, data =
+     bolger, y = T, x = T)
> resid(bolger.lrm, type = "gof")
Sum of squared errors     Expected value|H0                    SD
            3.1538988             3.0291378             0.1382219
                    Z                     P
            0.9026142             0.3667307
```

- Pearson $\chi^2 p - value$

```
> pp <- sum(resid(bolger.lrm, type = "pearson")^2)
> 1 - pchisq(pp, bolger.glm$df.resid)
[1] 0.4697808
```

- Deviance (G^2)

```
> 1 - pchisq(bolger.glm$deviance, bolger.glm$df.resid)
[1] 0.5622132
```

- Estimated dispersion parameter **(Key 17.4)**

```
> pp/bolger.glm$df.resid
[1] 0.991585
```

Conclusions - no evidence to suggest that data did not come from population that follows the logistic regression (no evidence for a lack of fit of the model). Furthermore, the estimated dispersion parameter is essentially one and thus there is no evidence of overdispersion.

Step 4 (Key 17.3) - Confirm linearity between the log odds ratio of rodent presence and the biogeographic variables with a component+residual plot

```
> library(car)
> cr.plots(bolger.glm, ask = F)
```

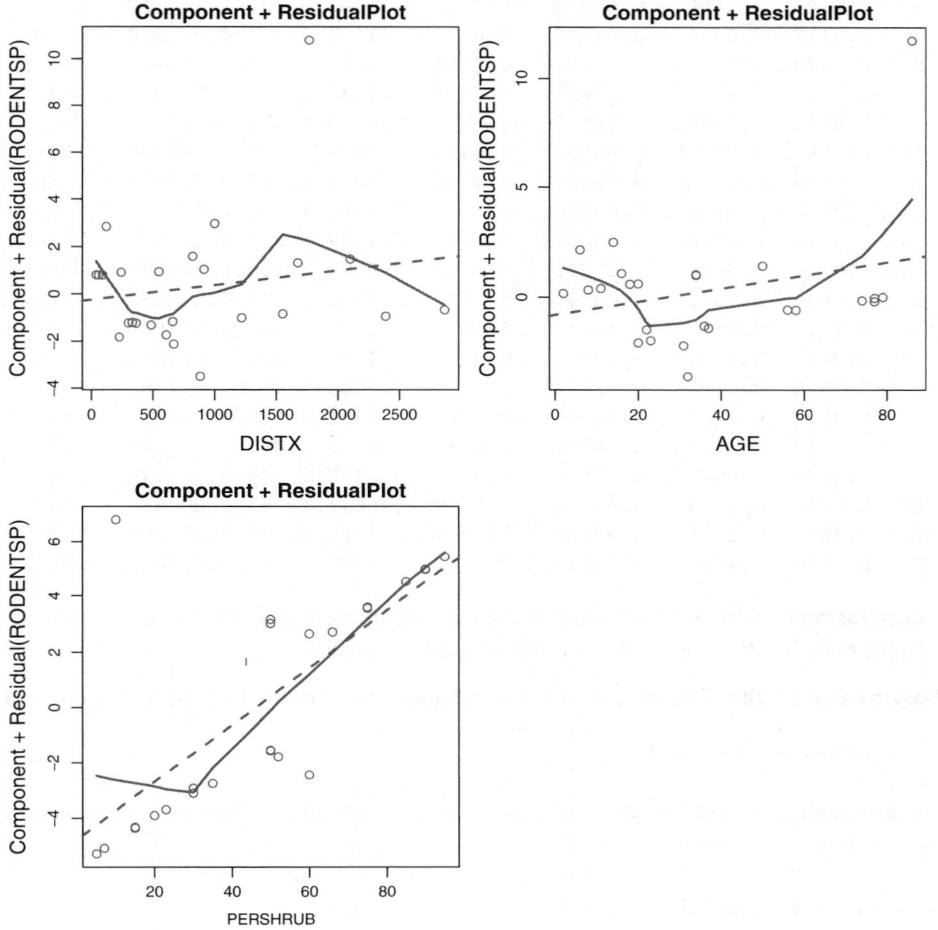

Conclusions - no substantial evidence of non-linearity.

Step 5 (Key 17.3) - Examine the influence measures

```
> influence.measures(bolger.glm)

     dfb.1_  dfb.DIST  dfb.AGE dfb.PERS   dffit cov.r   cook.d    hat inf
1  -0.2416  0.17167  0.19092   0.2339  0.2945 1.536 0.010863 0.2486
2  -0.0507  0.01588  0.03176   0.0635  0.0702 1.289 0.000603 0.0693
3  -0.1286  0.08647  0.08633   0.1393  0.1640 1.367 0.003342 0.1397
4  -0.1331 -0.05235  0.14044   0.1744  0.2180 1.366 0.005983 0.1551
5   0.0853  0.02470 -0.14900   0.0436  0.4100 1.101 0.024581 0.1239
```

```
6    0.7766 -0.58021 -0.58883  -0.4920  1.0292 0.822 0.200988 0.2300
7   -0.0112 -0.00293 -0.04378   0.0337 -0.1114 1.317 0.001530 0.0976
8   -0.0474  0.00919 -0.03268   0.0664 -0.1578 1.272 0.003141 0.0906
9   -0.0806 -0.72577  0.22425   0.1696 -0.8547 1.773 0.095918 0.4319   *
10  -0.0302  0.11865 -0.06183  -0.0776 -0.4350 0.952 0.030802 0.0952
11  -0.0291  0.09988 -0.08901   0.0438 -0.1893 1.386 0.004468 0.1563
12  -0.0476  0.00555  0.02388   0.0705  0.0872 1.291 0.000936 0.0756
13  -0.0650 -0.03614  0.05294   0.1024  0.1365 1.324 0.002310 0.1093
14  -0.0592  0.06048 -0.00219   0.0613 -0.1017 1.298 0.001276 0.0841
15  -0.0316 -0.57390  0.12542   0.0908 -0.6971 1.426 0.066536 0.3097
16  -0.2834  0.30568  0.14991   0.1456 -0.4906 1.131 0.035237 0.1595
17  -0.1710  0.05037  0.12748   0.1513 -0.1798 1.322 0.004060 0.1223
18  -0.0429 -0.02244  0.02273   0.0769  0.1100 1.309 0.001494 0.0928
19  -0.3040  0.22753  0.95111  -0.0251  1.5502 0.352 0.813906 0.2120   *
20   0.8191  0.12450 -0.96546  -0.5818  1.1426 0.860 0.240598 0.2675
21  -0.2730  0.12393  0.22277   0.1531 -0.4288 1.090 0.027170 0.1271
22  -0.0278  0.05457 -0.03695   0.0370 -0.1020 1.329 0.001279 0.1022
23  -0.0315 -0.01174  0.01115   0.0580  0.0841 1.297 0.000868 0.0781
24   0.3076 -0.05357 -0.29988  -0.4401 -0.6763 0.731 0.094200 0.1175
25   0.0636  0.20880 -0.33862  -0.0242 -0.4887 1.568 0.030804 0.3042
```

Conclusions - Although the Cook's D value of one of the fragments (19) was substantially higher than the others, it was not considered overly influential[l].

Step 6 (Key 17.2b) - Examine the parameter estimates from the fitted logistic regression model.

```
> summary(bolger.glm)
Call:
glm(formula = RODENTSP ~ DISTX + AGE + PERSHRUB, family = binomial,
    data = bolger)

Deviance Residuals:
    Min        1Q    Median        3Q       Max
-1.5823   -0.5985   -0.2813    0.3699    2.1702

Coefficients:
               Estimate Std. Error z value Pr(>|z|)
(Intercept) -5.9099159  3.1125426  -1.899   0.0576 .
DISTX        0.0003087  0.0007741   0.399   0.6900
AGE          0.0250077  0.0376618   0.664   0.5067
PERSHRUB     0.0958695  0.0406119   2.361   0.0182 *
---
Signif. codes:  0 '***' 0.001 '**' 0.01 '*' 0.05 '.' 0.1 ' ' 1

(Dispersion parameter for binomial family taken to be 1)
```

[l] Note that as indicated by Quinn and Keough (2002), the model would not converge in the absence of this observation and thus its lack of influence on the fit of the model could not be varified.

```
    Null deviance: 34.617  on 24  degrees of freedom
Residual deviance: 19.358  on 21  degrees of freedom
AIC: 27.358

Number of Fisher Scoring iterations: 5
```

Conclusions - The chances of native rodent occurence increases significantly with increasing shrub cover ($b = 0.096, z = 2.361, P = 0.0182$), yet were not found to be affected by fragment isolation age or distance.

Step 7 (Key 17.2b) - Compare the fit of full and reduced models (G^2) as an alternative (potentially more reliable given the relatively small sample size) to the individual parameter based approach.

```
> # saturated model
> bolger.glmS <- glm(RODENTSP ~ DISTX + AGE + PERSHRUB,
+ family = binomial, data = bolger)
> # Reduced model for distance
> bolger.glm.Dist <- glm(RODENTSP ~ AGE + PERSHRUB,
+ family = binomial, data = bolger)
> #OR
> bolger.glm.Dist <- update(bolger.glmS, "~.-DISTX")
> anova(bolger.glmS, bolger.glm.Dist, test = "Chisq")
Analysis of Deviance Table

Model 1: RODENTSP ~ DISTX + AGE + PERSHRUB
Model 2: RODENTSP ~ AGE + PERSHRUB
  Resid. Df Resid. Dev Df Deviance P(>|Chi|)
1        21    19.3576
2        22    19.5135 -1  -0.1559    0.6929

> # Reduced model for age
> bolger.glm.Age <- update(bolger.glmS, "~.-AGE")
> anova(bolger.glmS, bolger.glm.Age, test = "Chisq")
Analysis of Deviance Table

Model 1: RODENTSP ~ DISTX + AGE + PERSHRUB
Model 2: RODENTSP ~ DISTX + PERSHRUB
  Resid. Df Resid. Dev Df Deviance P(>|Chi|)
1        21    19.3576
2        22    19.8022 -1  -0.4446    0.5049

> # Reduced model for shrub cover
> bolger.glm.Shrub <- update(bolger.glmS, "~.-PERSHRUB")
> anova(bolger.glmS, bolger.glm.Shrub, test = "Chisq")
Analysis of Deviance Table
```

```
Model 1: RODENTSP ~ DISTX + AGE + PERSHRUB
Model 2: RODENTSP ~ DISTX + AGE
  Resid. Df Resid. Dev Df Deviance P(>|Chi|)
1        21    19.3576
2        22    28.9152 -1   -9.5577     0.0020
```

Step 8 (Key 17.6) - Examine the odds ratio for the occurrence of native rodents.

```
> library(biology)
> odds.ratio(bolger.glm)
         Odds ratio Lower 95
DISTX      1.000309    0.9987922     1.001828
AGE        1.025323    0.9523639     1.103871
PERSHRUB   1.100615    1.0164046     1.191803
```

Conclusions - the chances of native rodents being present in fragments increases slightly (10%) for every 1% increase in shrub cover.

Step 9 (Key 17.8) - Compare the fit of all additive combinations of predictor variables to select the most parsimonious model and perform model averaging to estimate the relative contribution of each of the predictor variables (based on AIC_c).

```
> library(biology)
> Model.selection.glm(bolger.glm)
Model selection
Response: RODENTSP
            Deviance      AIC      AICc  deltaAIC         wAIC qAIC
1. DI       34.24479 38.24479 38.79024 14.195496 0.000466208 15.5
2. AG       28.92306 32.92306 33.46852  8.873775 0.006670784 15.5
3. PE       20.04929 24.04929 24.59474  0.000000 0.563757818 15.5
4. DI+AG    28.91524 34.91524 36.05810 11.463358 0.001827494 17.0
5. DI+PE    19.80219 25.80219 26.94505  2.350306 0.174072445 17.0
6. AG+PE    19.51350 25.51350 26.65636  2.061614 0.201103152 17.0
7. DI+AG+PE 19.35758 27.35758 29.35758  4.762839 0.052102098 18.5
               qAICc Select
1. DI       16.04545
2. AG       16.04545
3. PE       16.04545      *
4. DI+AG    18.14286
5. DI+PE    18.14286
6. AG+PE    18.14286
7. DI+AG+PE 20.50000      *


Model averaging
Response: RODENTSP
                Sum     Estimate Unconditional_SE      Lower95CI
DISTX     0.2284682 8.008503e-05     6.688235e-05 -5.100437e-05
```

```
AGE      0.2617035 6.202364e-03    5.591199e-03 -4.756386e-03
PERSHRUB 0.9910355 8.106718e-02    6.891972e-03  6.755891e-02
            Upper95CI
DISTX    0.0002111744
AGE      0.0171611152
PERSHRUB 0.0945754434
attr(,"heading")
[1] "Model averaging\n"      "Response: RODENTSP \n"
```

Conclusions - The most parsimonious model relates the presence of native rodents to percentage shrub cover only (on the basis of AIC_c). Model averaging indicated that the percentage of shrub cover was substantially more influential than the other predictors.

Step 10 - construct the predictive model

```
> bolger.glm <- glm(RODENTSP ~ PERSHRUB, family = binomial,
      data = bolger)
> summary(bolger.glm)
Call:
glm(formula = RODENTSP ~ PERSHRUB, family = binomial, data = bolger)

Deviance Residuals:
    Min       1Q   Median       3Q      Max
-1.4827  -0.6052  -0.2415   0.5421   2.5218

Coefficients:
            Estimate Std. Error z value Pr(>|z|)
(Intercept) -3.90342    1.55775  -2.506  0.01222 *
PERSHRUB     0.07662    0.02878   2.663  0.00775 **
---
Signif. codes:  0 '***' 0.001 '**' 0.01 '*' 0.05 '.' 0.1 ' ' 1

(Dispersion parameter for binomial family taken to be 1)

    Null deviance: 34.617  on 24  degrees of freedom
Residual deviance: 20.049  on 23  degrees of freedom
AIC: 24.049

Number of Fisher Scoring iterations: 5
```

Conclusions - The predictive model is: $g(PArodents) = (0.08 \times Shrubcover) - 3.90$. Expressing this in terms of likelihood of rodents being present, the predictive model becomes:

$$presence = \frac{1}{(1 + \exp^{-(0.08 \times Perc\ Shrub) - 3.9)})}$$

Step 11 - Summarize the association between native rodent occurrence and percentage shrub cover.

```
> xs <- seq(0, 100, l = 1000)
> bolger.predict <- with(bolger, (predict(bolger.glm, type =
+     "response", se = T, newdata = data.frame(DISTX = mean(DISTX),
+         AGE = mean(AGE), PERSHRUB = xs))))
> plot(RODENTSP ~ PERSHRUB, data = bolger, xlab = "", ylab = "",
+     axes = F, pch = 16)
> points(bolger.predict$fit ~ xs, type = "l", col = "gray")
> lines(bolger.predict$fit + bolger.predict$se.fit ~ xs, col =
+     "gray", type = "l", lty = 2)
> lines(bolger.predict$fit - bolger.predict$se.fit ~ xs, col =
+     "gray", type = "l", lty = 2)
> mtext("Native rodent presence/absence", 2, line = 3)
> axis(2, las = 1)
> mtext("Percentage shrub cover", 1, line = 3)
> axis(1)
> box(bty = "l")
```


Example 17C: Multiple logistic regression

Gotelli and Ellison (2002) investigated the biogeographical determinants of ant species richness at a regional scale. Ellison (2004) then used an excerpt of those data to contrast inferential and Bayesian approaches. Specifically, ant species richness was modelled against latitude, elevation and habitat type (bog or forest) using Poisson regression.

Step 1 - Import (section 2.3) the Gotelli and Ellison (2002) data set

```
> gotelli <- read.table("gotelli.csv", header = T, sep = ",")
```

Step 2 (Key 9.3b & 17.2b) - In anticipation of fitting a multiplicative poisson regression model, the continuous predictor variables should be centered to avoid obvious collinearity issues.

```
> gotelli$cLatitude <- scale(gotelli$Latitude, scale = F)
> gotelli$cElevation <- scale(gotelli$Elevation, scale = F)
```

Step 3 (Key 9.3 & 17.2b) - Investigate the assumption of (multi)collinearity

```
> library(car)
> scatterplot.matrix(~Srich + Habitat * cLatitude * cElevation,
+     data = gotelli)
```

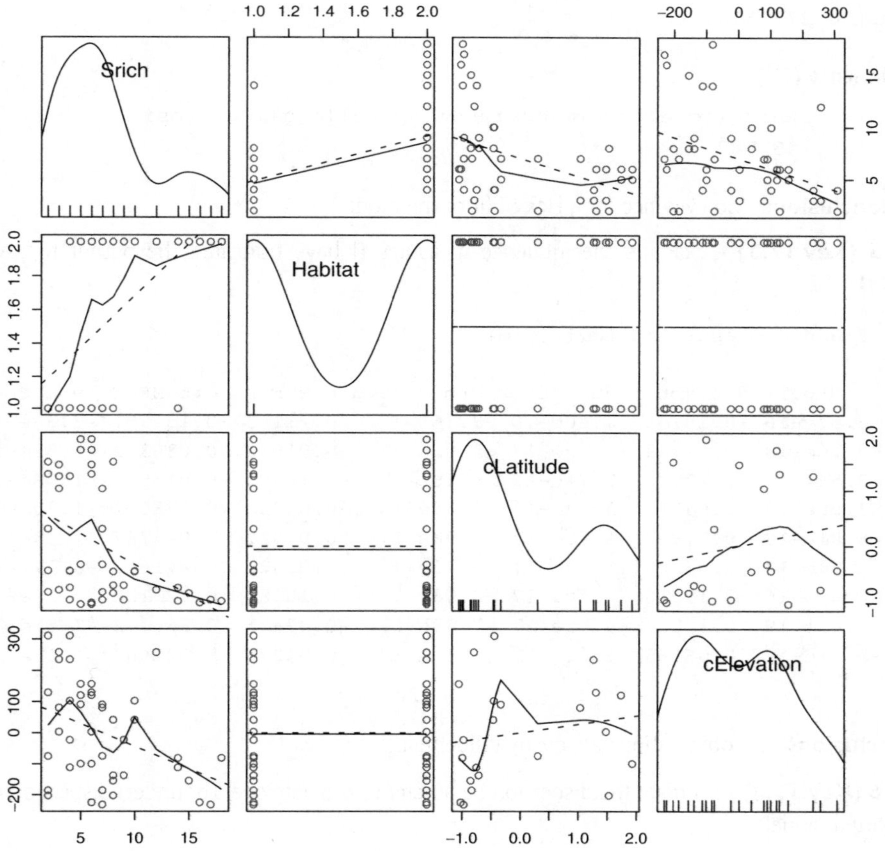


```
> gotelli.glm <- glm(Srich ~ Habitat * cLatitude * cElevation,
+     family = poisson, data = gotelli)
> vif(gotelli.glm)
                    Habitat                    cLatitude
                   1.167807                     3.113812
                 cElevation            Habitat:cLatitude
                   3.563564                     3.220434
         Habitat:cElevation         cLatitude:cElevation
                   3.609016                     3.477485
Habitat:cLatitude:cElevation
                   3.644151
```

Conclusions - no evidence of collinearity for the centered predictor variables.

Step 4 (Key 17.3) - Check the (lack of) fit and appropriateness of the model with goodness-of-fit tests

- Pearson χ^2

```
> pp <- sum(resid(gotelli.glm, type = "pearson")^2)
> 1 - pchisq(pp, gotelli.glm$df.resid)
[1] 0.2722314
```

- Deviance (G^2)

```
> 1 - pchisq(gotelli.glm$deviance, gotelli.glm$df.resid)
[1] 0.3057782
```

Conclusions - no evidence for a lack of fit of the model).

Step 5 (Key 17.3) - Examine the influence measures (I have truncated the output to save space).

```
> influence.measures(gotelli.glm)

      dfb.1_  dfb.HbtF   dfb.cLtt   dfb.cElv dfb.HbF.L  dfb.HF.E  dfb.cL.E
1   2.57e-16 -0.18734  2.40e-16 -9.36e-17   0.21122 -0.151987 -7.36e-17
2  -9.16e-18  0.01983 -1.62e-17  2.03e-17  -0.01912 -0.035302 -3.52e-17
3   9.54e-17  0.17021  2.74e-16  6.18e-17  -0.16883 -0.016553  1.08e-16
4   3.98e-17  0.04115  1.93e-17 -1.34e-16  -0.03238 -0.078512 -1.30e-16
5   8.01e-18 -0.07957 -4.75e-17  2.98e-17   0.07837 -0.017767 -1.23e-17
6   1.84e-17  0.05225 -1.49e-17  2.78e-17  -0.03326 -0.041660 -8.27e-18
7   2.63e-16 -0.19210  7.70e-17 -3.16e-16   0.10281  0.223120 -7.27e-16
8  -1.45e-19  0.32864  4.13e-17 -7.36e-17  -0.29425  0.368322 -1.51e-16
9  -2.71e-17  0.06155 -1.61e-17  1.35e-17  -0.03276 -0.027660  1.35e-17
...
```

Conclusions - no observations are overly influential.

Step 6 (Key 17.4) - Estimate the dispersion parameter to evaluate over (or under) dispersion in the fitted model

```
> # via Pearson residuals
> pp/gotelli.glm$df.resid
[1] 1.129723
> # OR via deviance
> gotelli.glm$deviance/gotelli.glm$df.resid
[1] 1.104765
```

Conclusions - the dispersion parameter is not substantially greater than 1 (not approaching 2 or 0.5), overdispersion is unlikely to be an issue.

Step 7 (Key 17.2b) - Examine the parameter estimates and associated null hypothesis tests.

```
> summary(gotelli.glm)
Call:
glm(formula = Srich ~ Habitat * cLatitude * cElevation, family =
    poisson, data = gotelli)
```

```
Deviance Residuals:
    Min       1Q   Median       3Q      Max
-2.1448  -0.7473  -0.0856   0.5426   2.6453

Coefficients:
                                  Estimate Std. Error z value Pr(>|z|)
(Intercept)                      1.5237266  0.1044276  14.591  < 2e-16 ***
HabitatForest                    0.6284757  0.1292095   4.864 1.15e-06 ***
cLatitude                       -0.2257304  0.1059277  -2.131   0.0331 *
cElevation                      -0.0006575  0.0006878  -0.956   0.3391
HabitatForest:cLatitude         -0.0089115  0.1314652  -0.068   0.9460
HabitatForest:cElevation        -0.0006053  0.0008531  -0.710   0.4780
cLatitude:cElevation             0.0004718  0.0007208   0.655   0.5127
HabitatForest:cLatitude:cElevation -0.0003348  0.0008941  -0.375   0.7080
---
Signif. codes:  0 '***' 0.001 '**' 0.01 '*' 0.05 '.' 0.1 ' ' 1

(Dispersion parameter for poisson family taken to be 1)

    Null deviance: 102.763  on 43  degrees of freedom
Residual deviance:  39.772  on 36  degrees of freedom
AIC: 216.13

Number of Fisher Scoring iterations: 4
```

Conclusions - Species richness of native rodents was found to be significantly greater in forest than bog habitats ($P < 0.001$) and was found to decline significantly with increasing latitude ($b = -0.226, z = -2.131, P = 0.0331$)

Step 8 (Key 17.8) - Select the most parsimonious[m] model on the basis of AIC_c.

```
> library(MuMIn)
> model.avg(get.models(dredge(gotelli.glm)))
Model summary:
         Deviance AICc Delta Weight
1+2+3        40.7  210  0.00  0.510
1+2+3+5      40.3  212  2.14  0.175
1+2+3+4      40.3  212  2.19  0.170
1+2+3+6      40.7  213  2.51  0.145

Variables:
                   1                    2                 3
          cElevation            cLatitude           Habitat
                   4                    5                 6
cElevation:cLatitude   cElevation:Habitat  cLatitude:Habitat

Averaged model parameters:
                     Coefficient Variance       SE Unconditional SE
cElevation             -1.07e-03 4.05e-14 0.000436         0.000449
cLatitude              -2.33e-01 2.32e-05 0.067900         0.070000
HabitatForest           6.31e-01 2.14e-04 0.121000         0.125000
(Intercept)             1.53e+00 9.72e-05 0.099300         0.102000
cElevation:cLatitude    4.35e-05 1.61e-15 0.000117         0.000119
```

[m] model with greatest fit considering the number of predictor terms (including interactions).

```
cElevation:HabitatForest    -8.65e-05 1.88e-14 0.000223          0.000227
cLatitude:HabitatForest     -3.66e-03 5.60e-06 0.021600          0.022200
                           Lower CI  Upper CI
cElevation                 -0.00195 -0.000190
cLatitude                  -0.37000 -0.095300
HabitatForest               0.38700  0.876000
(Intercept)                 1.33000  1.730000
cElevation:cLatitude       -0.00019  0.000277
cElevation:HabitatForest   -0.00053  0.000357
cLatitude:HabitatForest    -0.04710  0.039800

Relative variable importance:
          cElevation             cLatitude               Habitat
                1.00                  1.00                  1.00
  cElevation:Habitat cElevation:cLatitude     cLatitude:Habitat
                0.18                  0.17                  0.15
```

Conclusions - the most parsimonious model includes only the three main factors (elevation, habitat and latitude), which are of roughly equivalent relative importance.

Step 9 - Examine the parameter estimates from the best fitting model. Note , there is no need for these variables to be centered as there are no interactions.

```
> gotelli.glm <- glm(Srich ~ Habitat + Latitude + Elevation,
+     family = poisson, data = gotelli)
> summary(gotelli.glm)
Call:
glm(formula = Srich ~ Habitat + Latitude + Elevation, family =
    poisson, data = gotelli)

Deviance Residuals:
     Min         1Q     Median         3Q        Max
-2.20939  -0.72643  -0.05933    0.51571    2.60147

Coefficients:
                Estimate Std. Error z value Pr(>|z|)
(Intercept)   11.9368121  2.6214970   4.553 5.28e-06 ***
HabitatForest  0.6354389  0.1195664   5.315 1.07e-07 ***
Latitude      -0.2357930  0.0616638  -3.824 0.000131 ***
Elevation     -0.0011411  0.0003749  -3.044 0.002337 **
---
Signif. codes:  0 '***' 0.001 '**' 0.01 '*' 0.05 '.' 0.1 ' ' 1

(Dispersion parameter for poisson family taken to be 1)

    Null deviance: 102.763  on 43  degrees of freedom
Residual deviance:  40.690  on 40  degrees of freedom
AIC: 209.04

Number of Fisher Scoring iterations: 4
```

Step 10 - Produce a summary figure relating the species richness of ants to latitudinal variation for forests and bog habitats.

```
> # Produce base plot
> xs <- seq(40, 45, l = 1000)
> plot(Srich ~ Latitude, data = gotelli, type = "n", axes = F,
+ xlab = "", ylab = "")
> # Plot the points and predicted trends
> points(Srich ~ Latitude, data = gotelli, subset = Habitat ==
+ "Forest", pch = 16)
> pred <- predict(gotelli.glm, type = "response", se = T, newdata
+ = data.frame(Latitude = xs, Habitat = "Forest", Elevation =
+ mean(gotelli$Elevation)))
> lines(pred$fit ~ xs)
> points(Srich ~ Latitude, data = gotelli, subset = Habitat ==
+ "Bog", pch = 21)
> pred <- predict(gotelli.glm, type = "response", se = T, newdata
+ = data.frame(Latitude = xs, Habitat = "Bog", Elevation =
+ mean(gotelli$Elevation)))
> lines(pred$fit ~ xs)
> # Axes titles
> mtext("Ant species richness", 2, line = 3)
> axis(2, las=1)
> mtext(expression(paste("Latitude (", degree*N, ")")), 1,
+ line = 3)
> axis(1)
> legend("topright", legend = c("Forest", "Bog"), pch = c(16, 21),
+ title = "Habitat", bty = "n")
> box(bty = "l")
```


Example 17D: Log-linear modelling

Sinclair and Arcese (1995) investigated the association between predation, sex and health (via marrow type) in Serengeti wildebeest. Quinn and Keough (2002) used these data to illustrate log-linear modelling (Box 14.5 of Quinn and Keough (2002)).

Step 1 - Import (section 2.3) the Sinclair and Arcese (1995) data set

```
> sinclair <- read.table("sinclair.csv", header = T, sep = ",")
```

Step 2 (Key 17.5b & 17.8) - Fit the various combinations of log-linear models heirarchically (starting with the highest order, or saturated, model).

- Fit the full saturated model

```
> sinclair.glm <- glm(COUNT ~ SEX * MARROW * DEATH, family =
+      poisson, data = sinclair)
```

- Perform model selection to identify the most parsimonious model (on the basis of *AIC*)

```
> library(MuMIn)
> dredge(sinclair.glm, rank = "AIC")
Model selection table
   (Intr) DEATH MARROW SEX DEATH:MARROW DEATH:SEX MARROW:SEX
19  3.258     1      1   1            1         1          1
9   2.944     1      1                1
16  2.971     1      1   1            1                    1
18  3.072     1      1   1            1         1          1
12  2.953     1      1   1            1
15  2.976     1      1   1            1         1
5   3.146     1      1
14  3.173     1      1   1                                 1
8   3.155     1      1   1
17  3.195     1      1   1                      1          1
13  3.178     1      1   1                      1
3   3.341            1
11  3.367            1   1                                 1
7   3.350            1   1
2   2.741     1
6   2.750     1          1
10  2.773     1          1                      1
1   2.936
4   2.944                1
   DEATH:MARROW:SEX  k        Dev.   AIC  delta weight
19                1 12 -1.776e-15 24.00  0.000  0.435
9                    6  1.326e+01 25.26  1.260  0.231
16                   9  8.465e+00 26.46  2.465  0.127
18                  10  7.188e+00 27.19  3.188  0.088
12                   7  1.324e+01 27.24  3.243  0.086
15                   8  1.316e+01 29.16  5.156  0.033
5                    4  4.278e+01 50.78 26.780  0.000
14                   7  3.798e+01 51.98 27.980  0.000
8                    5  4.276e+01 52.76 28.760  0.000
17                   8  3.790e+01 53.90 29.900  0.000
13                   6  4.268e+01 54.68 30.680  0.000
```

```
3                     3  4.990e+01 55.90 31.900  0.000
11                    6  4.510e+01 57.10 33.100  0.000
7                     4  4.988e+01 57.88 33.880  0.000
2                     2  6.983e+01 73.83 49.830  0.000
6                     3  6.982e+01 75.82 51.820  0.000
10                    4  6.973e+01 77.73 53.730  0.000
1                     1  7.695e+01 78.95 54.950  0.000
4                     2  7.693e+01 80.93 56.930  0.000
```

Conclusions - On the basis of AIC, model 19 (the full saturated model) is the best fit (lowest AIC). However, model 9 (`~DEATH+MARROW+DEATH:MARROW`) is not a significantly poorer fit (its delta[n] is less than 2) than the model with the smallest AIC. Note, this is a slightly different conclusion to that drawn by Quinn and Keough (2002). The model selection procedure used by Quinn and Keough (2002) used a hierarchical step function to generate the set of possible model fits, whereas the function above assesses the fit of all possible model combinations. Furthermore, the AIC values reported by Quinn and Keough (2002) are AIC delta values.

Step 3 (Key 17.5b) - Fit a range of full and reduced models (according to Table 17.2) to examine conditional dependence.

- Full saturated model

```
> sinclair.glm <- glm(COUNT ~ SEX * MARROW * DEATH, family =
+     poisson, data = sinclair)
```

- Complete dependence (`SEX:MARROW:DEATH`= 0)

```
> sinclair.glm1 <- update(sinclair.glm, ~. - SEX:MARROW:DEATH,
+     data = sinclair)
> anova(sinclair.glm, sinclair.glm1, test = "Chisq")
Analysis of Deviance Table

Model 1: COUNT ~ SEX * MARROW * DEATH
Model 2: COUNT ~ SEX + MARROW + DEATH + SEX:MARROW + SEX:DEATH
           + MARROW:DEATH
  Resid. Df Resid. Dev Df Deviance P(>|Chi|)
1         0 -6.883e-15
2         2     7.1883 -2  -7.1883     0.0275
```

- Conditional independence (`SEX:DEATH`= 0)

```
> sinclair.glm2 <- update(sinclair.glm1, ~. - SEX:DEATH, data =
      sinclair)
> anova(sinclair.glm1, sinclair.glm2, test = "Chisq")
Analysis of Deviance Table

Model 1: COUNT ~ SEX + MARROW + DEATH + SEX:MARROW + SEX:DEATH
           + MARROW:DEATH
Model 2: COUNT ~ SEX + MARROW + DEATH + SEX:MARROW + MARROW:DEATH
```

[n] Delta is the difference between a models' AIC and the smallest AIC.

```
  Resid. Df Resid. Dev Df Deviance P(>|Chi|)
1         2     7.1883
2         3     8.4647 -1  -1.2763    0.2586
```

- Conditional independence (SEX:MARROW= 0)

```
> sinclair.glm4 <- update(sinclair.glm1, ~. - SEX:MARROW, data =
      sinclair)
> anova(sinclair.glm1, sinclair.glm4, test = "Chisq")
Analysis of Deviance Table

Model 1: COUNT ~ SEX + MARROW + DEATH + SEX:MARROW + SEX:DEATH
             + MARROW:DEATH
Model 2: COUNT ~ SEX + MARROW + DEATH + SEX:DEATH + MARROW:DEATH
  Resid. Df Resid. Dev Df Deviance P(>|Chi|)
1         2     7.1883
2         4    13.1560 -2  -5.9677    0.0506
```

- Conditional independence (DEATH:MARROW= 0)

```
> sinclair.glm3 <- update(sinclair.glm1, ~. - DEATH:MARROW,
      data = sinclair)
> anova(sinclair.glm1, sinclair.glm3, test = "Chisq")
Analysis of Deviance Table

Model 1: COUNT ~ SEX + MARROW + DEATH + SEX:MARROW + SEX:DEATH
             + MARROW:DEATH
Model 2: COUNT ~ SEX + MARROW + DEATH + SEX:MARROW + SEX:DEATH
  Resid. Df Resid. Dev Df Deviance P(>|Chi|)
1         2      7.188
2         4     37.898 -2  -30.710 2.145e-07
```

Conclusions - reject the null hypothesis of no three-way interaction. There is an association between cause of death, sex and marrow type (health condition) in Serengeti wildebeest ($G^2 = 7.19, df = 2, P = 0.028$).

Step 4 - Investigate the patterns of association further

- Pearson residuals

```
> xtabs(resid(sinclair.glm1, type = "pearson") ~ SEX + MARROW +
+     DEATH, sinclair)
, , DEATH = NPRED

        MARROW
SEX             OG        SWF         TG
  FEMALE 0.9479718 -0.8907547 -0.4245814
  MALE  -1.0876228  1.2484046  0.3639733

, , DEATH = PRED
```

```
        MARROW
SEX                OG         SWF          TG
  FEMALE -0.7301089  0.5406249  0.7186928
  MALE    0.7090967 -0.6413988 -0.5215390
```

Conclusions - there were more healthy males (SWF marrow type) and fewer undernourished (OG marrow type) that died of non-predation causes than expected, whereas the reverse was the case for females.

- Split the analysis up and investigate the associations between cause of death and marrow type for each sex separately.

```
> # females
> sinclair.glmR <- glm(COUNT ~ DEATH + MARROW, family = poisson,
+ data = sinclair, subset = SEX == "FEMALE")
> sinclair.glmF <- glm(COUNT ~ DEATH * MARROW, family = poisson,
+ data = sinclair, subset = SEX == "FEMALE")
> anova(sinclair.glmR, sinclair.glmF, test = "Chisq")
Analysis of Deviance Table

Model 1: COUNT ~ DEATH + MARROW
Model 2: COUNT ~ DEATH * MARROW
  Resid. Df Resid. Dev Df Deviance P(>|Chi|)
1         2    13.9626
2         0 -2.220e-15  2  13.9626    0.0009

> # males
> sinclair.glmR <- glm(COUNT ~ DEATH + MARROW, family = poisson,
+ data = sinclair, subset = SEX == "MALE")
> sinclair.glmF <- glm(COUNT ~ DEATH * MARROW, family = poisson,
+ data = sinclair, subset = SEX == "MALE")
> anova(sinclair.glmR, sinclair.glmF, test = "Chisq")
Analysis of Deviance Table

Model 1: COUNT ~ DEATH + MARROW
Model 2: COUNT ~ DEATH * MARROW
  Resid. Df Resid. Dev Df Deviance P(>|Chi|)
1         2     23.935
2         0  3.331e-15  2   23.935 6.346e-06
```

Conclusions - an association exists between cause of death and marrow type for both males and females, although it is perhaps strongest for the latter.

- Odds ratios of being killed by predation vs non-predation for each sex and marrow type combination (**Key 17.6**)

```
> # Males
> library(biology)
> male.tab <- xtabs(COUNT ~ DEATH + MARROW, data=sinclair,
+ subset=SEX == "MALE")
```

```
> # transpose to express in the context of cause of death
> male.tab <- t(male.tab)
> oddsratios(male.tab)
  Comparison  estimate      lower     upper   midp.exact
1  OG vs SWF 0.5581395 0.18389618 1.6939979 3.199869e-01
2   OG vs TG 0.1073345 0.04067922 0.2832085 2.247925e-06
3  SWF vs TG 0.1923077 0.06004081 0.6159519 5.465174e-03
  fisher.exact   chi.square
1 3.762577e-01 2.998756e-01
2 2.928685e-06 1.865442e-06
3 5.794237e-03 4.123680e-03

> # Females
> female.tab <- xtabs(COUNT ~ DEATH + MARROW, data=sinclair,
+ subset=SEX == "FEMALE")
> female.tab <- t(female.tab)
> oddsratios(female.tab)
  Comparison  estimate      lower     upper   midp.exact
1  OG vs SWF 3.5208333 1.26009037 9.8376018 0.0137649202
2   OG vs TG 0.4062500 0.15034804 1.0977134 0.0788761506
3  SWF vs TG 0.1153846 0.03378972 0.3940136 0.0003808416
  fisher.exact   chi.square
1 0.0206121992 0.0133633241
2 0.0914047377 0.0718385552
3 0.0003765135 0.0002797362
```

Conclusions - the odds of being killed by predation for males with TG marrow type are less than that for either OG or SWF marrow types, whereas female wildebeest with SWF marrow type were less and more likely to be killed by predation than females with OG and TG marrow type respectively.

Step 5 (Key 17.6) - Summarize the predation odds ratios for bone marrow type pairs according to sex.

```
> # make a table for females
> female.tab <- xtabs(COUNT ~ DEATH + MARROW, data = sinclair,
+     subset = SEX == "FEMALE")
> library(biology)
> # calculate the odds ratios for females
> # the table should be transposed such that cause of death
# #     are in columns
> sinclair.or <- oddsratios(t(female.tab))
> plot(estimate ~ as.numeric(Comparison), data = sinclair.or,
+     log = "y", type = "n", axes = F, xlab = "", ylab = "", ylim =
+         range(c(upper, lower)), xlim = c(0.5, 3.5))
> # plot the female data displaced to the right slightly
> with(sinclair.or, points(as.numeric(Comparison) + 0.1, estimate,
+     type = "b"))
```

```
> with(sinclair.or, arrows(as.numeric(Comparison) + 0.1, upper,
+     as.numeric(Comparison) + 0.1, lower, ang = 90, length = 0.1,
+     code = 3))
> # make the male table
> male.tab <- xtabs(COUNT ~ DEATH + MARROW, data = sinclair,
+     subset = SEX == "MALE")
> sinclair.or <- oddsratios(t(male.tab))
> # plot the male odds ratios
> points(estimate ~ Comparison, data = sinclair.or, type = "b",
+     pch = 16)
> with(sinclair.or, arrows(as.numeric(Comparison), upper,
+     as.numeric(Comparison), lower, ang = 90, length = 0.1,
+     code = 3))
> abline(h = 1, lty = 2)
> with(sinclair.or, axis(1, at = as.numeric(Comparison),
      lab = Comparison))
> axis(2, las = 1, cex.axis = 0.75)
> mtext("Marrow type", 1, line = 3)
> mtext("Odds ratio of death by predation", 2, line = 3)
> legend("topright", legend = c("Male", "Female"), pch = c(16,
+     21), bty = "n", title = "Sex")
> box(bty = "l")
```

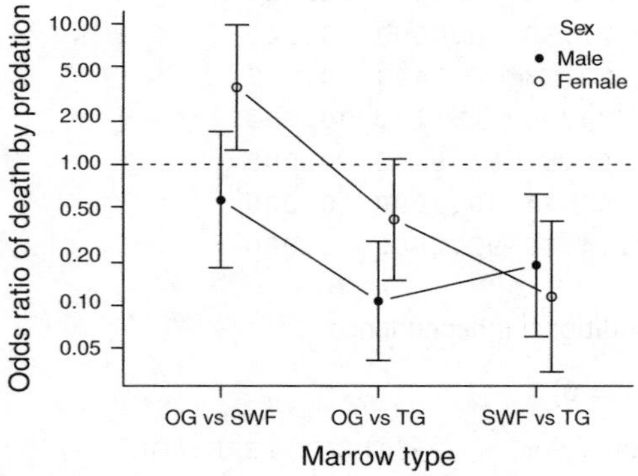

Example 17E: Log-linear modelling

To investigate the effects of logging (treatment) on the demographics of southern flying squirrels, Taulman et al. (1998) recorded the age and sex of squirrels captured over three years in experimentally logged and unlogged sites. Quinn and Keough (2002) used these data to illustrate log-linear modelling in which squirrel age has considered and interpreted as a response variable (Box 14.6 of Quinn and Keough (2002)).

Step 1 - Import (section 2.3) the Taulman et al. (1998) data set

```
> taulman <- read.table("taulman.csv", header = T, sep = ",")
```

Step 2 - Define year of capture as a categorical, factor vector

```
> taulman$YEAR <- as.factor(taulman$YEAR)
```

Step 3 (Key 17.5b & 17.8) - Fit the various combinations of log-linear models heirarchically (starting with the highest order (saturated) model). As the investigators were primarily interested in demographic (age) patterns, age (juvenile or adult) was considered a response and the investigators were primarily interested in the conditional independence of year by treatment interactions. Consequently, when examining the selection of possible fitted models, it is logical to include this interaction in all the possible models.

- Full saturated model

```
> taulman.glm <- glm(COUNT ~ TREAT * YEAR * AGE, family = poisson,
+       data = taulman)
```

- Note, as age is considered to be a response variable, all fitted models should include the treatment by year interaction term.

```
> dredge(taulman.glm, rank = "AIC", fixed = ~TREAT:YEAR)
Model selection table
  (Intr) AGE TREAT YEAR AGE:TREAT TREAT:YEAR AGE:YEAR
5  3.843  1     1    1         1          1        1
4  3.813  1     1    1                    1        1
6  3.829  1     1    1         1          1        1
2  3.654  1     1    1                    1
3  3.676  1     1    1         1          1
1  3.332        1    1                    1
  AGE:TREAT:YEAR  k       Dev.    AIC   delta weight
5                10 1.882e+00  21.88  0.0000  0.448
4                 9 4.126e+00  22.13  0.2443  0.397
6              1 12 4.122e-10  24.00  2.1180  0.155
2                 7 4.651e+01  60.51 38.6300  0.000
3                 8 4.627e+01  62.27 40.3900  0.000
1                 6 1.021e+02 114.10 92.2600  0.000
```

Step 4 (Key 17.5b) - Examine patterns of conditional independence.

- Complete dependence (`TREAT:YEAR:AGE`= 0)

```
> taulman.glm1 <- update(taulman.glm, ~. - TREAT:YEAR:AGE,
      data = taulman)
> anova(taulman.glm, taulman.glm1, test = "Chisq")
Analysis of Deviance Table

Model 1: COUNT ~ TREAT * YEAR * AGE
Model 2: COUNT ~ TREAT + YEAR + AGE + TREAT:YEAR + TREAT:AGE
    + YEAR:AGE
  Resid. Df Resid. Dev Df Deviance P(>|Chi|)
1         0  4.122e-10
2         2    1.88187 -2 -1.88187   0.39026
> AIC(taulman.glm1) - AIC(taulman.glm)
[1] -2.118125
```

- Conditional independence
  - H_0: AGE:YEAR=0

```
> taulman.glm2 <- update(taulman.glm, ~. - YEAR:AGE -
+     TREAT:YEAR:AGE, data = taulman)
> anova(taulman.glm, taulman.glm2, test = "Chisq")
Analysis of Deviance Table

Model 1: COUNT ~ TREAT * YEAR * AGE
Model 2: COUNT ~ TREAT + YEAR + AGE + TREAT:YEAR + TREAT:AGE
  Resid. Df Resid. Dev Df Deviance P(>|Chi|)
1         0  4.122e-10
2         4      46.27 -4    -46.27 2.163e-09
> AIC(taulman.glm2) - AIC(taulman.glm)
[1] 38.27045
```

  - H_0: TREAT:AGE=0

```
> taulman.glm3 <- update(taulman.glm, ~. - TREAT:AGE -
+     TREAT:YEAR:AGE, data = taulman)
> anova(taulman.glm, taulman.glm3, test = "Chisq")
Analysis of Deviance Table

Model 1: COUNT ~ TREAT * YEAR * AGE
Model 2: COUNT ~ TREAT + YEAR + AGE + TREAT:YEAR + YEAR:AGE
  Resid. Df Resid. Dev Df Deviance P(>|Chi|)
1         0  4.122e-10
2         3     4.1262 -3  -4.1262    0.2482
> AIC(taulman.glm3) - AIC(taulman.glm)
[1] -1.873847
> dredge(taulman.glm, rank = "AIC", fixed = ~TREAT:YEAR)
Model selection table
  (Intr) AGE TREAT YEAR AGE:TREAT TREAT:YEAR AGE:YEAR
5  3.843   1     1    1         1          1        1
4  3.813   1     1    1                    1        1
6  3.829   1     1    1         1          1        1
2  3.654   1     1    1                    1
3  3.676   1     1    1         1          1
1  3.332         1    1                    1
  AGE:TREAT:YEAR  k       Dev.    AIC   delta weight
5                10 1.882e+00  21.88  0.0000  0.448
4                 9 4.126e+00  22.13  0.2443  0.397
6              1 12 4.122e-10  24.00  2.1180  0.155
2                 7 4.651e+01  60.51 38.6300  0.000
3                 8 4.627e+01  62.27 40.3900  0.000
1                 6 1.021e+02 114.10 92.2600  0.000
```

Conclusions - Whilst, squirrel age was not found to be dependent on the logging treatment in any year ($G^2 = 4.13, df = 3, P = 0.248$), squirrel age was found to be dependent on year within both logging and control treatment sites ($G^2 = 46.27, df = 4, P < 0.001$). The relative abundance of adult squirrels declined between 1994 and 1995 in both logging and control sites, however, this demography was restored by 1996 (see figure below).

Step 5 - Summarize the adult odds ratios for year pairs according to the logging treatment.

```
> control.tab <- xtabs(COUNT ~ AGE + YEAR, data = taulman, subset =
+      TREAT == "CONTROL")
> library(biology)
> taulman.or <- oddsratios(t(control.tab), corr = T)
> plot(estimate ~ as.numeric(Comparison), data = taulman.or,
+      log = "y", type = "n", axes = F, xlab = "", ylab = "", ylim =
+          range(c(upper, lower)), xlim = c(0.5, 3.5))
> with(taulman.or, points(as.numeric(Comparison) + 0.1, estimate,
+      type = "b", pch = 21))
> with(taulman.or, arrows(as.numeric(Comparison) + 0.1, upper,
+      as.numeric(Comparison) + 0.1, lower, ang = 90, length = 0.1,
+      code = 3))
> harvest.tab <- xtabs(COUNT ~ AGE + YEAR, data = taulman, subset =
+      TREAT == "HARVEST")
> taulman.or <- oddsratios(t(harvest.tab), corr = T)
> points(estimate ~ Comparison, data = taulman.or, type = "b",
+      pch = 16)
> with(taulman.or, arrows(as.numeric(Comparison), upper,
+      as.numeric(Comparison), lower, ang = 90, length = 0.1,
           code = 3))
> abline(h = 1, lty = 2)
> axis(1, at = as.numeric(taulman.or$Comparison),
        lab = taulman.or$Comparison)
> axis(2, las = 1, cex.axis = 0.75)
> mtext("Year", 1, line = 3)
> mtext("Odds ratio of adults", 2, line = 3)
> legend("topright", legend = c("Logging", "Control"), pch = c(16,
+      21), bty = "n", title = "Sex")
> box(bty = "l")
```

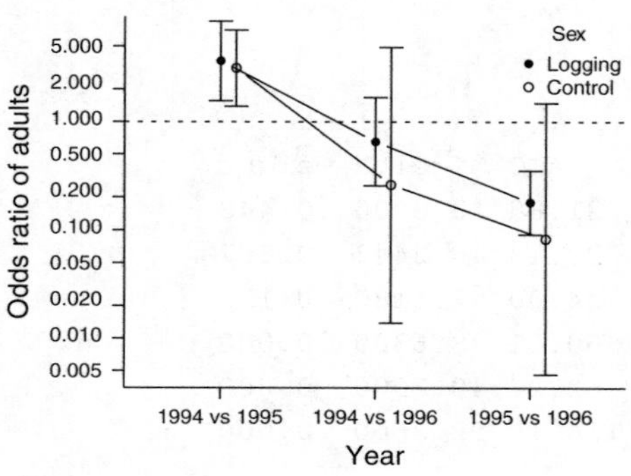

Example 17F: Generalized additive models

Quinn and Keough (2002) used a subset of the Loyn (1987) bird abundances across fragmented landscapes data to illustrate generalized additive models. Whilst this example is suboptimal in that the fitting of a generalized additive model cannot be entirely justified over a simpler multiple linear regression, there are no more suitable examples throughout the common biostatistics literature (Box 13.3 of Quinn and Keough (2002))[o]

Step 1 - Import (section 2.3) the Loyn (1987) data set

```
> loyn <- read.table("loyn.csv", header = T, sep = ",")
```

Step 2 (Key 9.3) - Investigate the assumptions of normality, predictor linearity (multi)collinearity using a scatterplot matrix.

```
> scatterplot.matrix(~ABUND + AREA + I(1987 - YR.ISOL) + DIST,
+       data = loyn, diag = "boxplot")
```

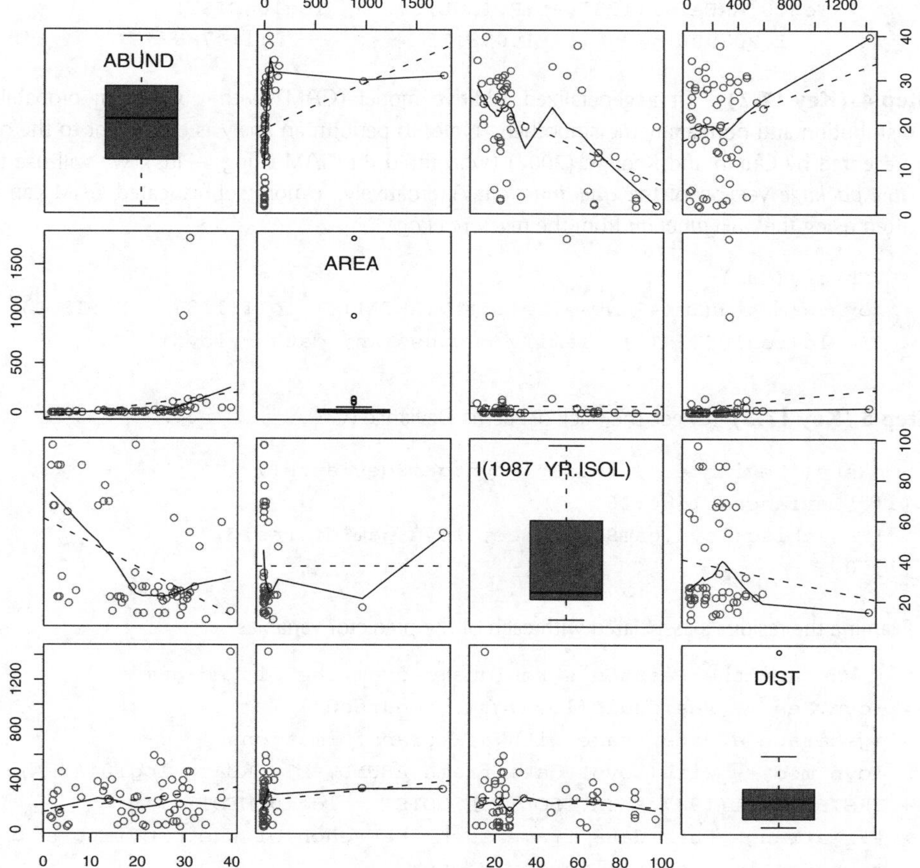

[o] Note that in Example 9A, years of isolation was effectively treated as the date (year) that patches became isolated, whereas in this example it will be treated as the number of years that fragments have been isolated up to 1987.

Conclusions - there is no evidence of non-normality in the response variable (bird abundance) and therefore a Gaussian probability distribution (and identity link function) is appropriate. Consistent with Quinn and Keough (2002), $\log_{10}$ transformations of fragment area and distance to the nearest patch were applied and improve normality of those variables. As previously indicated, linear conformity would normally mean that a generalized additive model approach is not necessary (or even appropriate) for these data. Nevertheless, concordant with Quinn and Keough (2002), the additive model incorporating Loess smoothing functions for each variable will be fit to the data.

Step 3 (Key 9.3) - Confirm the assumptions of (multi)collinearity for the form of model using variance inflation. Note, (multi)collinearity is investigated as if for a regular linear or generalized linear model.

```
> library(car)
> vif(glm(ABUND ~ log10(AREA) + I(1987 - YR.ISOL) + log10(DIST),
+     family = gaussian, data = loyn))
    log10(AREA) I(1987 - YR.ISOL)       log10(DIST)
       1.207990          1.098115          1.114780
```

Step 4 (Key 17.7) - Fit a generalized additive model (GAM) with a Gaussian probability distribution and nonparametric smoothers. Note, to perform an analysis equivalent to the one presented by Quinn and Keough (2002) (who fitted the GAM using S-Plus), we will use the `gam` *package* version of the `gam` *function*. Alternatively, a more sophisticated GAM can be fitted using the `gam` *function* from the mgcv *package*[p].

```
> library(gam)
> loyn.gam <- gam(ABUND ~ lo(log10(AREA)) + lo(I(1987 - YR.ISOL)) +
+     lo(log10(DIST)), family = gaussian, data = loyn)
```

Step 5 (Key 17.3) - Check the (lack of) fit via Deviance (G^2)

```
> paste("Deviance:", format(loyn.gam$deviance))
[1] "Deviance: 1454.26"
> 1 - pchisq(loyn.gam$deviance, loyn.gam$df.resid)
[1] 0
```

Examine the residuals associated with each of the predictor variables.

```
> # extract the Pearson's residuals from the fitted gam
> loyn.Res <- residuals(loyn.gam, "pearson")
> #generate a data frame with all transformations
> loyn.mod <- with(loyn, data.frame(ABUND, L10AREA = log10(AREA),
+ YRSISOL = I(1987 - YR.ISOL), L10DIST = log10(DIST)))
> # rearrange this data frame such that each of the predictors
> # become levels of a factor vector
```

[p]
```
> library(mgcv)
> loyn.gam <- gam(ABUND ~ s(log10(AREA)) + s(I(1987 - YR.ISOL)) + s(log10(DIST)),
    family = gaussian, data = loyn).
```

```
> loyn.L <- reshape(loyn.mod, direction = "long", varying =
+ list(c(2, 3, 4)), timevar = "Predictor", v.names = "Var", times =
+ names(loyn.mod[, c(2, 3, 4)]))
> # add the residuals to this data frame
> loyn.L$Res <- rep(loyn.Res, 3)
> # construct a lattice graphic
> library(lattice)
> print(xyplot(Res ~ Var | Predictor, data = loyn.L, scales = list(
+ alternating = TRUE, x = list(relation = "free")), xlab=
+ "Predictor variables", panel = function(x,y) {
+  panel.points(x, y, col = 1, pch = 16)
+  panel.loess(x, y, lwd = 2, col = 1)
+  }
+  ))
```

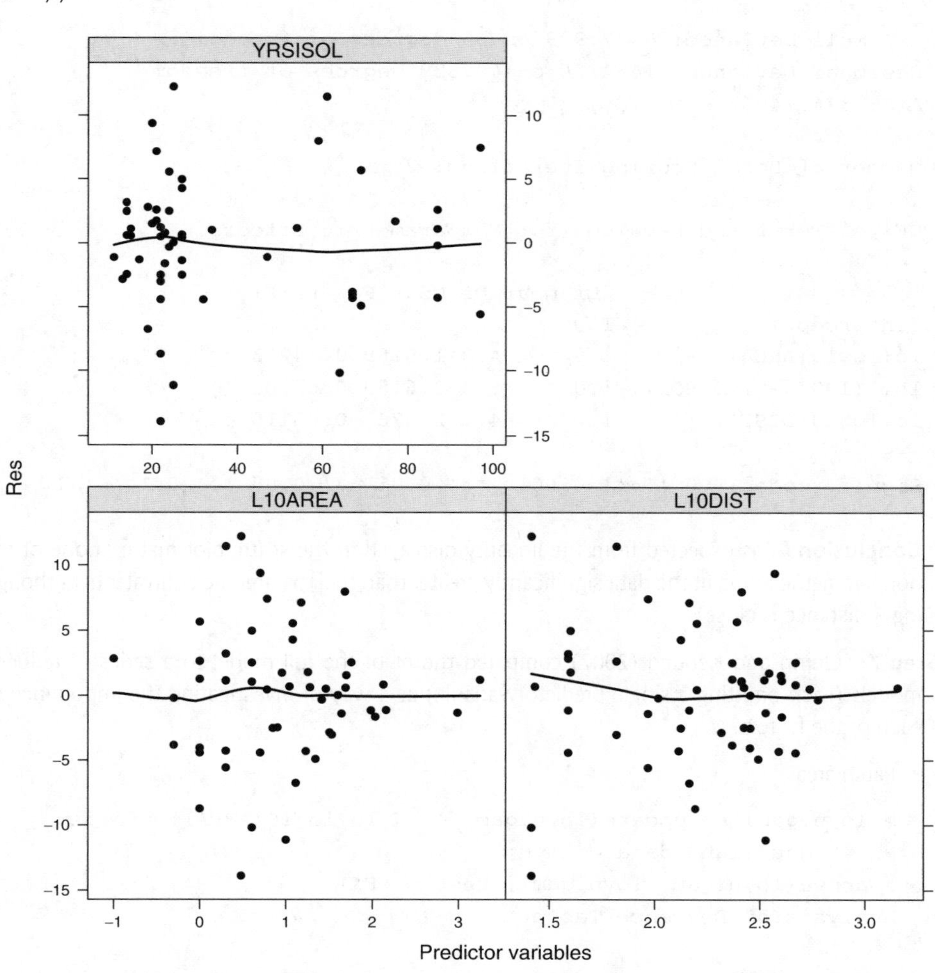

Conclusions - no evidence to suggest that the model did not fit. Note, it is not necessary to investigate overdispersion as this is not an issue for models fitted with a gaussian distribution. the data.

Step 6 (Key 17.7) - Examine the parameter estimates from the fitted GAM.

```
> summary(loyn.gam)
Call: gam(formula = ABUND ~ lo(log10(AREA)) + lo(I(1987 - YR.ISOL))
   + lo(log10(DIST)), family = gaussian, data = loyn)
Deviance Residuals:
     Min        1Q    Median       3Q      Max
-13.8785   -2.8945   0.5522   2.5558  12.1815

(Dispersion Parameter for gaussian family taken to be 35.882)

    Null Deviance: 6337.929 on 55 degrees of freedom
Residual Deviance: 1454.26 on 40.529 degrees of freedom
AIC: 374.2495

Number of Local Scoring Iterations: 2

DF for Terms and F-values for Nonparametric Effects

                       Df Npar Df Npar F   Pr(F)
(Intercept)           1.0
lo(log10(AREA))       1.0     4.2 1.8169 0.14213
lo(I(1987 - YR.ISOL)) 1.0     3.3 0.6189 0.62008
lo(log10(DIST))       1.0     4.1 2.5767 0.05115 .
---
Signif. codes:  0 '***' 0.001 '**' 0.01 '*' 0.05 '.' 0.1 ' ' 1
```

Conclusions - as expected from the linearity displayed in the scatterplot matrix, none of the nonparametric terms fit the data significantly greater than their parametric equivalents (although log_{10} distance is close).

Step 7 - Quinn and Keough (2002) compared the fit of the full model to a series of reduced models (each omitting a single predictor variable) as a way of investigating the importance of each of the factors.

- Patch area

```
> loyn.gam1 <- update(loyn.gam, ~. - lo(log10(AREA)), family =
+      gaussian, data = loyn)
> anova(loyn.gam, loyn.gam1, test = "F")
Analysis of Deviance Table

Model 1: ABUND ~ lo(log10(AREA)) + lo(I(1987 - YR.ISOL))
      + lo(log10(DIST))
Model 2: ABUND ~ lo(I(1987 - YR.ISOL)) + lo(log10(DIST))
```

```
  Resid. Df Resid. Dev       Df Deviance       F    Pr(>F)
1   40.5290     1454.3
2   45.6833     3542.6 -5.1543  -2088.3 11.291 6.021e-07 ***
---
Signif. codes:  0 '***' 0.001 '**' 0.01 '*' 0.05 '.' 0.1 ' ' 1
```

- Years of isolation

```
> loyn.gam2 <- update(loyn.gam, ~. - lo(I(1987 - YR.ISOL)),
+      family = gaussian, data = loyn)
> anova(loyn.gam, loyn.gam2, test = "F")
Analysis of Deviance Table

Model 1: ABUND ~ lo(log10(AREA)) + lo(I(1987 - YR.ISOL))
      + lo(log10(DIST))
Model 2: ABUND ~ lo(log10(AREA)) + lo(log10(DIST))
  Resid. Df Resid. Dev      Df Deviance      F  Pr(>F)
1   40.5290    1454.26
2   44.7957    1872.38 -4.2666  -418.12 2.7311 0.03912 *
---
Signif. codes:  0 '***' 0.001 '**' 0.01 '*' 0.05 '.' 0.1 ' ' 1
```

- Distance to the nearest patch

```
> loyn.gam3 <- update(loyn.gam, ~. - lo(log10(DIST)), family =
+      gaussian, data = loyn)
> anova(loyn.gam, loyn.gam3, test = "F")
Analysis of Deviance Table

Model 1: ABUND ~ lo(log10(AREA)) + lo(I(1987 - YR.ISOL))
      + lo(log10(DIST))
Model 2: ABUND ~ lo(log10(AREA)) + lo(I(1987 - YR.ISOL))
  Resid. Df Resid. Dev      Df Deviance      F Pr(>F)
1   40.5290    1454.26
2   45.5791    1795.78 -5.0501  -341.52 1.8847 0.1177
```

Conclusions - bird abundance in fragmented landscapes is significantly effected by the size and duration of isolation of the habitat patches, but not the distance between patches.

Step 8 (Key 17.8) - Select the most parsimonious model relating bird abundances to the landscape variables.

```
> library(MuMIn)
> dredge(loyn.gam)
Model selection table
  (Intr)  l(I(-Y l(10(A l(10(D k Dev.   AIC  AICc  delta weight
8  20.62 -0.1223  9.107 -2.271 5 1454 374.2 375.4  0.000  0.614
5  16.41 -0.1224  8.221        4 1796 376.0 376.7  1.297  0.321
7  16.23         10.720 -3.026 4 1872 379.9 380.7  5.203  0.046
```

```
3  10.40           9.778          3 2326 381.9 382.4  6.923  0.019
2  27.38 -0.2112                  3 4087 411.7 412.2 36.710  0.000
6  20.57 -0.2178           3.188 4 3543 413.8 414.6 39.140  0.000
1  19.51                          2 6338 427.7 428.0 52.520  0.000
4  12.23                   3.287 3 5779 432.7 433.1 57.680  0.000
```

Conclusions - the model with all three predictor variables has the lowest AIC (and AIC_C). However, the delta for the model with patch area and years of isolation is less than two units, indicating that this latter model is not significantly less parsimonious than the former model.

Bibliography

Allison, T., and D. V. Cicchetti. (1976). Sleep in mammals: ecological and constitutional correlates. *Science* **194**, 732–734.

Andrew, N. L., and A. J. Underwood. (1993). Density-dependent foraging in the sea urchin *Centrostephanus rodgersii* on shallow subtidal reefs in New South Wales, Australia. *Marine Ecology Progress Series* **99**, 89–98.

Bolger, D. T., A. C. A., R. M. Sauvajot, P. Potenza, C. McCalvin, D. Tran, S. Mazzoni, and M. E. Soule. (1997). Response of Rodents to Habitat Fragmentation in Coastal Southern California. *Ecological Applications* **7**, 552–563.

Christensen, D. L., B. R. Herwig, D. E. Schindler, and S. R. Carpenter. (1996). Impacts of lakeshore residential development on couarse woody debris in north temperature lakes. *Ecological Applications* **64**, 1143–1149.

Constable, A. J. (1993). The role of sutures in shrinking of the test in *Heliocidaris erythrogramma* (Echinoidea: Echiniometridae). *Marine Biology* **117**, 423–430.

Crawley, M. J. (2002). *Statistical computing: an introduction to data analysis using S-PLUS*. John Wiley & Sons, New York.

Crawley, M. J. (2007). *The R Book*. John Wiley & Sons, New York.

Dalgaard, P. (2002). *Introductory Statistics with R*. Springer-Verlag, New York.

Doncaster, C. P., and A. J. H. Davey. (2007). *Analysis of Variance and Covariance. How to Choose and Construct Models for the Life Sciences*. Cambridge University Press, Cambridge.

Driscoll, D. A., and J. D. Roberts. (1997). Impact of fuel-reduction burning on the frog *Geocrinia lutea* in southwest Western Australia. *Australian Journal of Zoology* **22**, 334–339.

Elgar, M. A., R. A. Allan, and T. A. Evans. (1996). Foraging strategies in orb-spinning spiders: ambient light and silk decorations in *Argiope aetherea Walckenaer* (Araeneae: Araneoidea). *Australian Journal of Ecology* **21**, 464–467.

Ellison, A. M. (2004). Bayesian inference in ecology. *Ecology Letters* **7**, 509–520.

Everitt, B. S. (1994). *A handbook of statistical analyses using S-Plus*. Chapman & Hall, Boca Raton, FL.

Faraway, J. J. (2006). *Extending Linear Models with R: generalized linear mixed effects and nonparametric regression models*. Chapman & Hall/CRC, Boca Raton, FL.

Fowler, J., L. Cohen, and P. Jarvis. (1998). *Practical statistics for field biology*. John Wiley & Sons, New York.

Fox, J. (2002). *An R and S-PLUS Companion to Applied Regression*. Sage Books, Thousand Oaks, CA.

Furness, R. W., and D. M. Bryant. (1996). Effect of wind on field metabolic rates of breeding Northern Fulmars. *Ecology* **77**, 1181–1188.

Gotelli, N. J., and A. M. Ellison. (2002). Biogeography at a regional scale: determinants of ant species density in bogs and forests of New England. *Ecology* **83**, 1604–1609.

Green, P. T. (1997). Red crabs in rain forest on Christmas Island, Indian Ocean: activity patterns, density and biomass. *Journal of Tropical Ecology* **13**, 17–38.

Hall, S. J., S. A. Gray, and Z. L. Hammett. (2000). Biodiversity-productivity relations: an experimental evaluation of mechanisms. *Oecologia* **122**, 545–555.

Hastie, T. J. and Tibshirani, R. J. (1990). *Generalized Additive Models.* Chapman & Hall, Boca Raton, FL.

Hollander, M., and D. A. Wolfe. (1999). *Nonparametric statistical methods, 2nd edition.* 2 edition. John Wiley & Sons, New York.

Ihaka, R., and R. Gentleman. (1996). R: A Language for Data Analysis and Graphics. *Journal of Computational and Graphical Statistics* **5**, 299–314.

Keough, M. J., and P. T. Raimondi. (1995). Responses of settling invertebrate larvae to bioorganic films: effects of different types of films. *Journal of Experimental Marine Biology and Ecology* **185**, 235–253.

Kirk, R. E. (1968). *Experimental design: procedures for the behavioral sciences.* Brooks/Cole, Monterey, CA.

Legendre, P., (2001). Model II regression - User's guide. Départment de sciences biologiques, Université de Montréal.

Loyn, R. H., (1987). *Nature Conservation: the Role of Remnants of Native Vegetation*, Chapter effects of patch area and habitat on bird abundances, species numbers and tree health in fragmented victorian forests. Surrey Beatty & Sons, Chipping Norton, NSW.

Mac Nally, R. M. (1996). Hierarchical partitioning as an interpretative tool in multivariate inference. *Australian Journal of Ecology* **21**, 224–228.

Maindonald, J. H., and J. Braun. (2003). *Data Analysis and Graphics Using R – An Example-based Approach.* Cambridge University Press, London.

Manly, B. F. J. (1991). *Randomization and Monte Carlo methods in biology.* Chapman & Hall, London.

McGoldrick, J. M., and R. C. Mac Nally. (1998). Impact of flowering on bird community dynamics in some central Victorian eucalypt forests. *Ecological Research* **13**.

McKechnie, S. W., P. R. Ehrlich, and R. R. White. (1975). Population genetics of *Euphdryas* butterflies. I. Genetic variation and the neutrality hypothesis. *Genetics* **81**, 571–594.

Medley, C. N., and W. H. Clements. (1998). Responses of diaton communities to heavy metals in streams: the influence of longitudinal variation. *Ecological Applications* **8**, 663–644.

Milliken, G. A., and D. E. Johnson. (1984). *Analysis of messy data. Volume I: Designed Experiments.* Van Nostrand Reinhold, New York.

Minchinton, T. E., and P. M. Ross. (1999). Oysters as habitat for limpets in a temerate mangrove forest. *Australian Journal of Ecology* **24**, 157–170.

Mullens, A., (1993). The effects of inspired oxygen on the pattern of ventilation in the Can Toad (*Bufo marinus*) and the Salt Water Crocodile (*Crocodylus porosus*). Honours thesis, University of Melbourne, Australia.

Murrell, P. (2005). *R Graphics (Computer Science and Data Analysis).* Chapman & Hall/CRC.

Nelson, V. E., (1964). The effects of starvation and humidity on water content in *Tribolium confusum* Duval (Coleoptera). Ph.D. thesis, University of Colorado.

Partridge, L., and M. Farquhar. (1981). Sexual activity and the lifespan of male fruitflies. *Nature* **294**, 580–581.

Paruelo, J. M., and W. K. Lauenroth. (1996). Relative abundance of plant functional types in grasslands and shrublands of North America. *Ecological Applications,* pp. 1212–1224.

Peake, A. J., and G. P. Quinn. (1993). Temporal variation in species-area curves for invertebrates in clumps of an intertidal mussel. *Ecography* **16**, 269–277.

Pinheiro, J. C., and D. M. Bates. (2000). *Mixed effects models in S and S-PLUS.* Springer-Verlag, New York.

Polis, G. A., S. D. Hurd, C. D. Jackson, and F. Sanchez-Piñero. (1998). Multifactor population limitation: variable spatial and temporal control of spiders on Gulf of California islands. *Ecology* **79**, 490–502.

Powell, G. L., and A. P. Russell. (1984). The diet of the eastern short-horned lizard (*Phrynosoma douglassi brevirostre*) in Alberta and its relationship to sexual size dimorphism. *Canadian Journal of Zoology* **62**, 428–440.

Powell, G. L., and A. P. Russell. (1985). Growth and sexual size dimorphism in Alberta populations of the eastern short-horned lizard *Phrynosoma douglassi brevirostre*. *Canadian Journal of Zoology* **63**, 139–154.

Quinn, G. P. (1988). Ecology of the intertidal pulmonate limpet *Siphonaria diemenensis* Quoy et Gaimard. II Reproductive patterns and energetics. *Journal of Experimental Marine Biology and Ecology* **117**, 137–156.

Quinn, G. P., and K. J. Keough. (2002). *Experimental design and data analysis for biologists.* Cambridge University Press, London.

R Development Core Team, (2005). R: A Language and Environment for Statistical Computing. R Foundation for Statistical Computing, Vienna, Austria. URL http://www.R-project.org.

Reich, P. B., D. S. Ellsworth, M. B. Walters, J. M. Vose, C. Gresham, J. C. Volin, and W. D. Bowman. (1999). Generality of leaf trait relationships: a test across six biomes. *Ecology* **80**, 1955–1969.

Roberts, J. (1993). Regeneration and growth of coolibah, *Eucalyptus coolibah* subsp. *arida*, a riparian tree, in the Cooper Creek region of South Australia. *Australian Journal of Ecology* **18**, 345–350.

Sánchez-Piñero, F., and G. A. Polis. (2000). Bottom-up dynamics of allochthonous input: direct and indirect effects of seabirds on islands. *Ecology* **81**, 3117–3132.

Sinclair, A. R. E., and P. Arcese. (1995). Population consequences of predation-sensitive foraging: the Serengeti wildebeest. *Ecology* **76**, 882–891.

Smith, E. J. (1967). Cloud seeding experiments in Australia. *Procedings of the 5th Berkley Symposium* **5**, 161–176.

Smith, F. (1939). A genetic analysis of red-seed coat color in *Phaseolus vulgaris*. *Hilgardia* **12**, 553–621.

Sokal, R., and F. J. Rohlf. (1997). *Biometry, 3rd edition.* W. H. Freeman, San Francisco.

Taulman, J. F., K. G. Smith, and R. E. Thill. (1998). Demographic and behavioral responses of southern flying squirrels to experimental logging in Arkansas. *Ecological Applications* **8**, 1144–1155.

Venables, W. N., and B. D. Ripley. (2002). *Modern Applied Statistics with S-PLUS, 4th edn.* Springer-Verlag, New York.

Walter, D. E., and D. J. O'Dowd. (1992). Leaves with domatia have more mites. *Ecology* **73**, 1514–1518.

Ward, S., and G. P. Quinn. (1988). Preliminary investigations of the ecology of the predatory gastropod *Lepsiella vinosa* (Lemarck) (Gastropoda Muricidae). *Journal of Molluscan Studies* **73**, 109–117.

Wilcox, R. R. (2005). *Introduction to Robust Estimation and Hypothesis Testing.* Elsevier Academic Press, New York.

Wood, S. N. (2006). *Generalized Additive Models: An Introduction with R.* Chapman & Hall/CRC, Boca Raton, FL.

Young, R. F., and H. E. Winn. (2003). Activity patterns, diet, and shelter site use for two species of moray eels, *Gymnothorax moringa* and *Gymnothorax vicinus*, in Belize. *Copeia* **2003**, 44–55.

Zar, G. H. (1999). *Biostatistical methods.* Prentice-Hall, New Jersey.

Zuur, A. F., E. N. Ieno, N. J. Walker, A. A. Saveliev, and G. M. Smith. (2009). *Mixed Effects Models and Extensions in Ecology with R.* Springer, New York.

R Index

Statistics Index